D1538855

CARBONATE SEDIMENTATION AND DIAGENESIS IN THE EVOLVING PRECAMBRIAN WORLD

Edited by

John P. Grotzinger, Massachusetts Institute of Technology, Cambridge, MA

and

Noel P. James, Queen's University, Kingston, Ontario, Canada

Tulsa, Oklahoma, U.S.A.

May, 2000

SEPM greatly acknowledges the following for their generous contributions to
Carbonate Sedimentation and Diagenesis in the Evolving Precambrian World

Natural Sciences and Engineering Research Council of Canada

Colorado College

Massachusetts Institute of Technology

Division of Geological and Geophysical Surveys,
State of Alaska Department of Natural Resources

DEPOSITIONAL δ^{18}O SIGNATURES IN PROTEROZOIC DOLOSTONES: CONSTRAINTS ON SEAWATER CHEMISTRY AND EARLY DIAGENESIS

LINDA C. KAH

Department of Geological Sciences, University of Tennessee, Knoxville, Tennessee 37996, U.S.A.

ERRATA

In Table 1 on page 350, the column heading δ^{18}O should end with a superscript b.

In table footnote a, "Primry" should be "Primary."

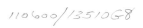

CONTENTS

INTRODUCTION

I. TECHNIQUES

II. STROMATOLITES AND PRECIPITATES

III. REEFS

IV. FACIES DYNAMICS

V. DIAGENESIS AND GEOCHEMISTRY

PREFACE

Precambrian carbonates are usually regarded as the simple cousins of the sedimentary realm, composed of stromatolites and dolostones, texturally not challenging and commonly altered beyond recognition by the vagaries of time, diagenesis and metamorphism. The last 20 years of research has clearly demonstrated that it is the view that is simple, not the rocks! These carbonates that formed in deep time are commonly exquisitely preserved, contain within them a record of the evolving young earth, if we can read it, and like Phanerozoic carbonates, changed dramatically through geologic time. As the interest of the scientific community about the early earth continues to grow, it becomes increasingly important to understand these rocks which, because they formed from seawater in the marine realm, contain within them a record of the early ocean, atmosphere and biosphere.

This compilation of papers, on all aspects of Archean and Proterozoic carbonate rocks, is an outgrowth of a symposium entitled "Precambrian Carbonates" that was organized by the editors and held at the SEPM/CSPG Joint Congress in Calgary, Alberta on June 02, 1997. The core of the volume comprises papers presented orally at the meeting. They are augmented by solicited and volunteered contributions from numerous other authors working on these very ancient rocks.

The fabric of the book is a series of interwoven themes that are always present in the recurring pattern of Precambrian carbonates. The impressive advances in understanding these ancient carbonates that have taken place over the last decade or more are first highlighted in an overview paper (Grotzinger and James). Such progress has been aided by the development of new analytical methods. Two particularly new techniques illustrated here are integrated field gamma-ray and U/Pb-zircon geochronology (Jackson et al.) used to reinterpret extensive successions in tectonically complex regions, and forward modeling (Myrow and Grotzinger) used to evaluate the effects of varying accommodation space and the importance of sampling intervals for assessing chemostratigraphic curves.

The building blocks of Archean and Proterozoic carbonate platforms are highly variable and as in modern environments they vary from organic to abiotic carbonate precipitates. Seafloor 'cements' were clearly extensive across the spectrum of late Archean paleoenvironments (Sumner and Grotzinger), but also tend to recur in late Paleoproterozoic settings (Winefield) and as Neoproterozoic cap carbonates. While these are dominantly inorganic precipitates, the nature of the quintessant elements of Precambrian carbonates, stromatolites, are the subject of much recent thinking. Field studies and modeling indicate that some late Paleoproterozoic (Pope and Grotzinger) and Mesoproterozoic (Seong-Joo and Golubic), (Bartley et al.) stromatolites are mixtures of biotic and abiotic precipitation. In most of these examples silicification is early and preserves microbial fossils. Disturbingly, the shapes of many biologically-induced mineral textures and shapes of primitive microfossils can be emulated by precipitation of carbonate into alkaline solutions, reminiscent of many environments on the young earth (Garcia-Ruiz).

Reefs, amongst the most complex of marine ecosystems, are preserved throughout the Archean and Proterozoic. Neoproterozoic buildups are especially interesting because they grew just before the appearance of skeletel metazoans. Such buildups from Arctic Canada are found as patch reefs in shallow-water settings (Narbonne et al.) and as immense structures in deepwater basin paleoenvironments (Turner et al.). Macro- and microfabrics from some of these reefs have the attributes of early Paleozoic reefs, but without the metazoans.

There is a clear gradual temporal transition from Archean rimmed, flat-topped platforms to Mesoproterozoic—Neoproterozoic carbonate ramps. Such ramps exhibit stratigraphic sequences and stacking patterns identical to those defined from Phanerozoic rocks. Carbonate ramps from the Mesoproterozoic of northern Australia (Sami et al.) are defined by storm-dominated and reworked sediments, a signature of many Phanerozoic ramps. In contrast, younger Mesoproterozoic ramps from Arctic Canada (Sherman et al.) contain few stromatolites and are mud-dominated, with most clastic sediment derived from the reworking of molar tooth structure calcite spar. Neoproterozoic ramps from Alaska (Clough and Goldhammer) also illustrate strong grainy subtidal and tufa/tepee/karst-capped peritidal *m*-scale cyclicity.

Some of the most critical information about Precambrian carbonatesis preserved in the geochemical and diagenetic signatures of the rocks themselves, often amazingly preserved given their antiquity. In most instances a wide array of techniques, including carbon, oxygen, sulphur, strontium isotopes and biomarkers are utilized to resolve palenvironmental problems (Hill et al.). In other cases oxygen isotopes seem somehow to variably preserve a signature of paleoenvironmental differences (Kah), that can also be seen in minor element distributions (Frank and Lyons). Finally, every geochemical paradigm must be continuously tested, as illustrated by the interpretation of C-isotope variations in Sr-rich Neoproterozoic carbonates as being due to coeval paleoenvironmental rather than secular differences in ocean chemistry (Fairchild et al.).

The rich store of information and interpretation in these papers has been honed for publication through careful review by many of our colleagues. We would especially like to thank the following people who gave up their precious spare time to make sure the manuscripts were scientifically and scholarly the best possible; Pierre-Andre Bourque, Roger Buick, Sherry Cady, Jim Clough, Mario Coniglio, Bob Demicco, Ian Fairchild, Peter Flemings, Paul Gammon, Steve Golubic, Hans Hofmann, Jim Jackson, Brian Jones, Andy Knoll, Kurt Kyser, Tim Lowenstein, Isabel Montanez, Eric Mountjoy, Maria Mutti, Bill Myers, Dave Osleger, Brian Pratt, Rob Rainbird, Gerry Ross, Rick Sarg, Martin Savard, Bev Saylor, Charlotte Schreiber, Bruce Simonson, Peter Southgate, Dawn Sumner, Maurice Tucker, Malcolm Walter, Don Winston, Grant Young. The final volume also owes much to the skillful copyediting of John Southard and the help of David Pettyjohn.

John P. Grotzinger
Cambridge, Massachusetts

Noel P. James
Kingston, Ontario

INTRODUCTION

PRECAMBRIAN CARBONATES: EVOLUTION OF UNDERSTANDING

JOHN P. GROTZINGER

Department of Earth, Atmospheric, and Planetary Sciences, Massachusetts Institute of Technology, Cambridge, MA 02139, U.S.A.

AND

NOEL P. JAMES

Department of Geological Sciences, Queen's University Kingston, Ontario, K7L 3N6, Canada

ABSTRACT: In the Precambrian world, devoid of higher organisms except near its end, carbonate sediments formed by a variety of abiotic and microbial processes, with patterns of deposition determined by tectonic, eustatic, and climatic processes. These ancient rocks demonstrate that the fundamental tenets of carbonate production and accumulation were initiated early in earth history, with the basic attributes of carbonate sedimentation well established by Neoproterozoic time.

The broad temporal patterns of Precambrian carbonate facies composition and disposition parallel the long-term evolution of the earth's oceans and atmosphere. Archean and Paleoproterozoic carbonates commonly contain abundant sea-floor precipitates, whereas the Neoproterozoic record is dominated by clastic-textured facies and abundant carbonate mudstones; Mesoproterozoic carbonates are transitional. Mesoproterozoic and early Neoproterozoic carbonates also contain abundant quantitites of the enigmatic molar-tooth structure. Grainstones, dominated by giant ooids with centimeter-scale diameters, are characteristic of many Neoproterozoic carbonates. Texturally unusual carbonates, featuring a reprise of Archean-style sea-floor precipitates, often cap glacial deposits of middle Neoproterozoic age.

The influence of biology on sediment texture is best expressed in the history of Precambrian reefs. Archean through Mesoproterozoic reefs are dominantly stromatolite-based. Lamination textures reveal the progressive shift from *in situ* precipitation of aragonite and calcite encrusting the sea floor in Archean through Paleoproterozoic stromatolites to textures consistent with accretion of loose sediment through trapping and binding in Neoproterozoic stromatolites. This trend is interpreted to reflect the progressive decrease of abiotic factors and the concomittant increase of benthic microbial mats on controlling stromatolite growth. Neoproterozoic reefs witness the appearance of more complex textures that likely involve the participation of calcified microbes and noncalcified higher algae in colonizing the seafloor, increasing its surface complexity and resulting in highly porous frameworks for the first time in geologic history. Terminal Proterozoic thrombolitic reefs additionally contain the first calcified metazoans.

INTRODUCTION

Precambrian carbonate rocks have within them a legible record of earth history that spans more than three billion years. From the period of first continental accretion to the advent of ecologically diverse biomineralizing metazoans, these sedimentary rocks contain chemical, biological, and physical proxies for past tectonic regimes, environmental change, and the evolution of life. Their physical attributes reflect tectonic subsidence and sea-level fluctuation; their chemical variability provides insight into carbon burial rates, continental growth, and surficial redox; their paleontology illustrates how microorganisms have evolved and how the structure of early ecosystems developed.

Studies of Precambrian carbonates, like analyses of their younger counterparts, generally fall into two categories—one in which the former sedimentary facies, their constituent grains, and the platforms they form are of primary interest, and the other in which the sediments are viewed principally as carriers of a geochemical record (e.g., C and Sr isotopes), which is itself the object of study. In the first case, investigations are motivated by the desire to interpret sedimentation patterns that result from physical, chemical, and biological processes, whereas in the second studies are oriented more toward understanding biogeochemical cycles and the ancient ocean–atmosphere system.

In this volume, we have assembled papers that fall into either category. Having done so, an emerging trend is obvious—several of these studies accomplish both. This degree of integration is motivated by the realization that the clearest records of biogeochemical events are elucidated through careful study of sedimentary and diagenetic patterns. Conversely, sedimentation patterns are being explored in the context of the local and global microbiological and physicochemical variability that might influence textures and accumulations rates.

The study of Precambrian carbonate platforms necessitates such integrated approaches to problem solving. An apparently simple question asked of most Phanerozoic carbonates, such as: "Were the sediments produced biologically?", and answered affirmatively in scores of introductory-level textbooks and summary articles, is not so easily resolved for the Precambrian record. For rocks of this age, the absence of coarse skeletal debris in all but terminal Proterozoic carbonates does not provide an easy explanation for the many platforms that are as vast and compositionally diverse as any of Phanerozoic age. The problem of the origin of Phanerozoic carbonate mud, so easily explained through the post-mortem disintegration of green algae, does not find much basis in accounting for the mudstones present across the 600,000 km² late Archean Transvaal platform— at least 1.5 billion years older than the first direct evidence for green algae in the fossil record. Precambrian carbonate sedimentologists have thus had to rely on a number of different approaches to begin to address some of these simple yet essential questions, and so the integration of sedimentological, trace-element, isotopic, biomarker, and paleobiological data has become more widespread, even for studies devoted to the origin of the sediment itself.

Thirty years ago, it was not clear what facies comprised Precambrian carbonates, if they formed differentiated platforms, and if they were well enough preserved for detailed study. The prevailing view was, and to some extent still is, that Precambrian carbonate rocks were simply endless hectares of stromatolites and fabric-destructive dolostone. Several key papers in the mid-1970s, however, provided distinct answers to these questions and demonstrated the clear potential for additional, more detailed study (Hoffman, 1974; Serebryakov and Semikhatov, 1974; Beukes, 1977; Cecile and Campbell, 1978). These studies, in combination with the disovery of extensive fields of stromatolites in Shark Bay, ignited a major effort to better understand the paleoenvironmental and paleobiological significance of stromatolites in platform carbonates (Walter, 1976). This effort led, in turn, to a second generation of studies in which platforms were mapped, facies were interpreted in the context of modern analogs, and complementary diagenetic studies were aimed at trying to unravel primary mineralogy and carbonate precipitation mechanisms (Kerans, 1982; Grotzinger and Read, 1983; Bertrand-Sarfati and Moussine-Pouchkine, 1983; Tucker, 1983; Teitz and Mountjoy, 1985; Grey and Thorne, 1985; Grotzinger, 1986a, 1986b; Hofmann and Jackson, 1987; Beukes, 1987; Fairchild and Spiro, 1987; Zempolich et al., 1988). Syntheses of Precambrian carbonates at the close of the decade (Grotzinger, 1988, 1989b) summarized existing data and demonstrated that, to a first-order approximation, the geometries of carbonate platforms, their primary mineralogies, and the general distribution of facies since at least the late Archean were similar to those present in Paleozoic through Recent carbonates.

This phase of research, however, also pointed out that large parts of the Precambrian record were non-actualistic, with no analogues in the modern or, for that matter, in the Phanerozoic. The last ten years has been a watershed in our understanding in this regard, as Precambrian carbonates have been interpreted on their own merits and not viewed simply as variants on Phanerozoic models. Furthermore, new analytical techniques have allowed heretofore unimagined correlation and thus revealed previously unknown attributes of sediment dynamics. Finally, fresh geochemical techniques have permitted different proxies to speak about the compositions of the Precambrian oceans and atmospheres. Important papers on Precambrian carbonates that identify potentially age-dependent facies and/or processes include: Archean carbonates (Simonson et al., 1993; Sumner and Grotzinger, 1996a, 1996b; Simonson and Jarvis, 1996; Sumner, 1997a, 1997b); Paleoproterozoic carbonates (Burdett et al., 1990; Kah and Grotzinger, 1992; Karhu, 1993; Sami and James, 1993, 1994, 1996; Grotzinger and Rothman, 1996); Mesoproterozoic carbonates (Pelechaty and James, 1991; Pelechaty et al., 1991; Buick et al., 1995; Sergeev et al., 1995; Knoll et al., 1995b; Kah and Knoll, 1996; Frank et al., 1997; Furniss et al., 1998; Narbonne and James, 1996; Xiao et al., 1997; Knoll and Semikhatov, 1998); and Neoproterozoic carbonates (Aitken, 1988; Aitken and Narbonne, 1989; Southgate, 1989; Peryt et al., 1990; Wright et al., 1990; Fairchild, 1991, 1993; Knoll and Swett, 1990; Kaufman et al., 1991; Knoll et al., 1993, 1995a; Sumner and Grotzinger, 1993; Grotzinger and Knoll, 1995; Fairchild et al., 1997, 1989, 1990; Saylor et al., 1995, 1998; Pelechaty et al., 1996a, 1996b; Hoffman et al., 1998a, 1998b; Kennedy, 1996; Kennedy et al., 1998; Turner et al., 1993, 1997). The papers in this volume represent a milestone of that effort, and strive to extract some of the most important issues that make Precambrian carbonates so fascinating. The goal of this introductory paper is to review briefly some of the progress that has been made over the past decade and to identify the important outstanding problems. Not surprisingly, we find that many of these problems are not unique to Precambrian carbonates; rather, the record of Precambrian carbonate sedimentation simply illustrates the fundamental nature of these problems, providing a fresh perspective on Phanerozoic carbonates.

PLATFORM GEOMETRY AND ARCHITECTURE

The many detailed studies of individual late Archean and younger platforms confirm that the general structure and de-

velopment of Precambrian carbonate platforms is identical to modern ones. Important controls on platform geometry include patterns of differential subsidence, eustatic fluctuations, siliciclastic sediment flux, and paleoclimate. Ramps and rimmed shelves are both present, although Neoproterozoic rocks show a dominance of ramps over rimmed shelves. The reasons for this trend of abundant Neoproterozoic ramps are unclear, but may be related to the abundance of grainstones in some systems (e.g., Knoll and Swett, 1990; Clough and Goldhammer, this volume), the general decline of stromatolites that might have formed effective barriers (Grotzinger, 1988, 1990), and the rise of higher algae (Butterfield et al., 1988) that might have competed effectively for substrate space (Knoll and Swett, 1990).

Nevertheless, many platforms, beginning with the late Archean Campbellrand–Malmani structure (Beukes, 1980, 1987), show morphologic development from an initial ramp that undergoes progressive transition to a rimmed shelf (Fig. 1). Younger examples include the Paleoproterozoic Pethei and Rocknest platforms (Hoffman, 1974; Grotzinger, 1986b; Sami and James, 1993), the Neoproterozoic Yellowhead platform (Teitz and Mountjoy, 1985, 1989), and terminal Proterozoic carbonates of the Gourma basin (Bertrand-Sarfati and Moussine-Pouchkine, 1983) and the central Oman basin (Mattes and Conway Morris, 1990). In these cases, basin development is the dominant control on transitions from ramp to rimmed shelf, with intial flooding of antecedent topography, and rapid rates of accommodation giving way to slower, long-term subsidence and attendant reduced accommodation. This pattern is characteristic of many Phanerozoic transitions.

The sequence architecture of all well studied Precambrian platforms (Fig. 2) shows patterns that are identical to Phanerozoic platforms (e.g., Grotzinger, 1986b; Christie-Blick et al., 1988; Sami and James, 1993, 1994; Knoll et al., 1995a; Saylor et al., 1995; Pelechaty et al., 1996a; Sami et al., this volume; Clough and Goldhammer, this volume; Jackson et al., this volume), implying that the ratio of accommodation space creation to sediment flux was not significantly different. In most cases, sediment production rates were higher than what was required, so that the meter-scale shallowing-upward paradigm is as ubiquitous in Archean (Martin et al., 1980; Sumner and Grotzinger, this volume) and Proterozoic (Grey and Thorne, 1985; Grotzinger, 1986a; Southgate, 1989; Sami and James, 1994; Jackson et al., this volume) carbonates (Fig. 3) as it is in Phanerozoic carbonates (Pratt et al., 1992).

The architecture of Precambrian carbonates alone provides powerful evidence that sediment accumulation rates have always been anomalously high (in comparison to shallow marine siliciclastic systems), with sediment production easily matching and typically exceeding available accommodation space. High sediment production rates should not be viewed as a special attribute of Phanerozoic carbonate-producing systems, imparted through the advent of biocalcifying higher organisms at the dawn of Cambrian time (cf. Riding, 1982; Knoll et al., 1993). It seems likely that the calcium carbonate saturation state of seawater has always been at least as high as that in the Phanerozoic, and the reason for this is straightforward.

Inorganic carbon on earth is distributed between the atmosphere, the ocean, and the crust. Precipitation of calcium carbonate, biologically or inorganically, represents transfer from ocean to crust. Over long periods of time (millions of years),

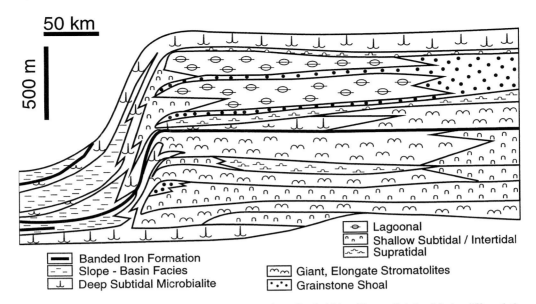

FIG. 1.—Late Archean (2.5 Ga) Campbellrand platform, northern Cape Province, South Africa. Note well-defined facies differentiation and transition from ramp to rimmed shelf morphology. After Beukes (1987) and Sumner and Grotzinger (this volume).

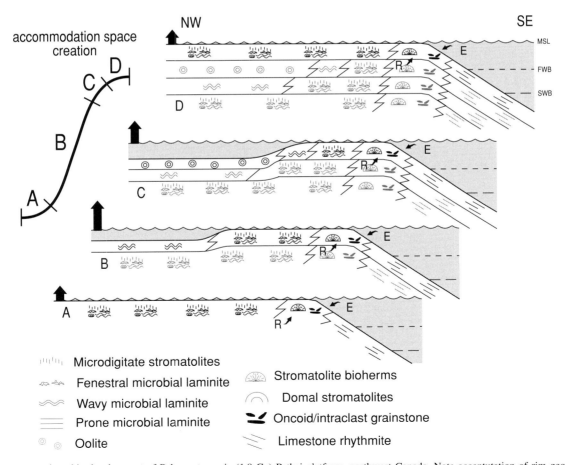

FIG. 2.—Sequence stratigraphic development of Paleoproterozoic (1.8 Ga) Pethei platform, northwest Canada. Note accentutation of rim geometry during times of accommodation increase, similar to Phanerozoic platforms. After Sami and James (1994).

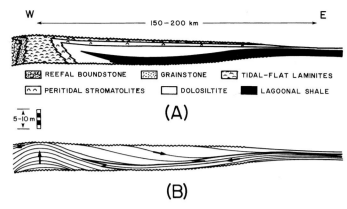

FIG. 3.—Facies architecture (A) and inferred chronostratigraphic relationships (B) in a single, meter-scale platform cycle, Paleoproterozoic (1.9 Ga) Rocknest platform, northwest Canada. A) Note that the shallowing-upward motif is best developed across middle section of cycle. To the west, near the platform shelf edge, cycles consist of unconformity-bounded tidal-flat facies, whereas to the east cycles consist of conformable successions of lagoonal shale and dolosiltites. B) Note that cycles nucleated near the rim and then prograded dominantly eastward. Downlapping shales were supplied by an eastern source region and are in turn downlapped by prograding carbonates. After Grotzinger (1986a).

the only way to decrease the oceanic inventory of inorganic carbon is to allow long-term partioning of carbonate minerals into the crust (Walker, 1985). In this way a new steady state is reached in which the oceanic reservoir becomes progressively smaller. The concentration of carbonate in seawater would therefore decrease, other factors being equal.

Prior to the advent of calcareous microplankton in Jurassic time, carbonates were precipitated abundantly only in shallow marine environments. Precipitation of shallow-water carbonates is limited to the space created as a result of sea level rising relative to the land surface (accommodation space). Unlike siliciclastic sediments, carbonate sediments cannot be deposited above sea level because they are produced in the marine environment (except for volumetrically trivial amounts of lacustrine carbonate). Transgression and onlap commonly result in net carbonate deposition, whereas regression and offlap lead to subaerial exposure and net carbonate dissolution. Consequently, the maximum amount of carbonate that could have been extracted from pre-Jurassic oceans is directly proportional to the accommodation space over the continents. As has been shown previously (Grotzinger, 1989b, 1994; Grotzinger and Kasting, 1993) carbonates have been able to fill the available accommodation space since at least the late Archean. In other words, their growth potential has always been high enough to effectively fill the space created by eustatic rises in sea level or accelerations in subsidence. Therefore, it is not clear that the inception of benthic biocalcification would have had an important effect on the saturation state of seawater; the amount precipitated would still have been restricted by the available accommodation space. Biocalcification acts only as a catalyst, restrained in its potential to sequester any more carbonate than by inorganic means because of the impositions of subsidence and eustasy.

Indeed, it seems that if there was a decrease in the saturation state of Paleozoic seawater it would be more attibutable to long-

term flooding of the continents than to the advent of biocalcification. The transgression that started with the breakup of the late Proterozoic supercontinent and culminated in late Cambrian time was responsible for the deposition, and therefore partitioning into the crust, of great volumes of carbonate over all the continents (Bond et al., 1989). As a consequence, much inorganic carbon was buried and removed from the oceanic realm.

CHEMOSTRATIGRAPHIC CORRELATION TECHNIQUES

Correlation techniques based on carbon and strontium have revolutionized Precambrian carbonate stratigraphy. Veizer and colleagues (Veizer and Compston, 1976; Veizer and Hoefs, 1976) first suggested that primary variations in the $\delta^{13}C$ and $^{87}Sr/^{86}Sr$ composition of Precambrian carbonates might reflect differences in the composition of contemporaneous seawater. Focus on the Neoproterozoic part of the record confirmed the potential magnitude and form of these major isotopic excursions (Knoll et al., 1986; Fairchild et al., 1989; Fairchild and Spiro, 1987). The ensuing decade resulted in a major effort to prove the utility of the excursions in providing a Neoproterozoic chronostratigraphy, useful in global correlation of otherwise poorly fossiliferous strata (Fairchild et al., 1990; Knoll, 1991; Kaufman et al., 1991; Kaufman et al., 1993; Knoll and Walter, 1992; Pell et al., 1993; Burns and Matter, 1993; Brasier et al., 1992, 1997; Narbonne et al., 1994; Kaufman and Knoll, 1995; Kennedy, 1996; Kennedy et al., 1998; Knoll et al., 1995a; Knoll et al., 1995b; Pelechaty et al., 1996b; Saylor et al., 1998; Hoffman et al., 1998a, 1998b). Most recently, the global carbon isotope curve has been used to subvide strata for the purpose of high-resolution intrabasinal correlation (Pelechaty et al., 1996a; Smith, 1998); when used in combination with sequence stratigraphic and biostratigraphic data, this approach promises a level of resolution for terminal Proterozoic strata that may rival that of Paleozoic time.

The conclusion of these studies is that correlation techniques based on carbon and strontium isotopes are a tremendous asset in subdivision of Neoproterozoic age strata, particularly the terminal Proterozoic part of the record. Initial studies of the isotopic variability of Mesoproterozoic and Paleoproterozoic carbonates, however, show that the signal may be of much lower amplitude, and thus the prospect for high-resolution correlation seems less promising (Veizer and Hoefs, 1976; Buick et al., 1995; Knoll et al., 1995b; Frank and Lyons, this volume; Frank et al., 1997; Kah, this volume). A possible exception may be the Paleoproterozoic "Lomagundi Event", when the amplitude of carbon-isotope anomalies seems to have been similar to that present in Neoproterozoic time (Schidlowski, 1988; Karhu, 1993).

SECULAR CHANGES IN FACIES

The past decade of research has confirmed that significant differences exist between Precambrian carbonate facies of different ages. It is necessary to view the record of Precambrian carbonate sedimentation in discrete intervals marked by important differences in the style and mode of carbonate production. Considered collectively, the progression of facies types provides the record of the long-term chemical evolution of sea water and, to a lesser extent, biological evolution.

In some cases facies types are distinctly bounded in time; however, in most cases the transitions are gradual (Fig. 4). Thus, unlike the Phanerozoic record, where abrupt changes in carbonate facies often coincide with major evolutionary pulses in carbonate-secreting organisms (e.g., Ordovician radiation), the Precambrian record appears to have been influenced mostly by inorganic processes that evolved over much longer time scales. Indeed, supposedly biologic parameters such as diversity of stromatolite taxa show little correlation with the actual record of fossil microbes; instead, correlation with the broader range of carbonate facies supports the possibility that long-term environmental change has influenced all carbonate facies, including stromatolites (Grotzinger and Knoll, 1999). Combined with the likely misrepresented history of Precambrian evaporite sedimentation (Grotzinger, 1989b; Grotzinger and Kasting, 1993; Pope and Grotzinger, this volume), these changes in the record of carbonate sedimentation provide the warrant for non-uniformitarian models of earth evolution and accounts of environmental secular change.

Archean Sea-Floor Encrusting Precipitates

Nature of the Precipitates.—

One of the most conspicuous age-dependent trends is the long-term decrease in the volume of carbonate precipitated directly on the sea floor (Fig. 4). These precipitates, in the form of aragonite and calcite pseudomorphs, are present as discrete sea-floor encrustations of both inorganic and microbial origin. Abiotic precipitates are morphologically and mineralogically identical to marine cements of Phanerozoic age (Grotzinger and

Read, 1983; Grotzinger, 1989b; Fairchild, 1991; Bartley et al., this volume; Pope and Grotzinger, this volume; Winefield, this volume), with the striking difference that they do not simply fill voids but are widespread as direct precipitates on the sea floor itself. Facies include large, upward-divergent crystal fans of calcite- and dolomite-replaced: 1) aragonite with radii commonly on the order of many tens to hundreds of centimeters (Fig. 5A); 2) much smaller upward-divergent aragonite forming microdigitate stromatolites (Fig. 5B); 3) isopachously encrusting, micron- to millimeter-thick layers of former (high-magnesium?) calcite (Fig. 5C); 4) isopachously encrusting layers of herringbone calcite (Fig. 5D); and rarely, 5) marine tufas with branching dendritic morphologies (Figure 5E).

The abundance of sea-floor calcite and aragonite precipitation shows, to a first-order approximation, a monotonic decrease from late Archean through Mesoproterozoic time (Grotzinger, 1989b, 1993, 1994; Grotzinger and Kasting, 1993; Grotzinger and Knoll, 1995; Sumner and Grotzinger, this volume). Decimeter- to meter-scale fans of former aragonite occur in virtually every well-preserved late Archean carbonate platform, and occur in open marine subtidal environments including storm-dominated shelves and reefal rims fronting major platforms (Sumner and Grotzinger, this volume). Sea-floor encrusting precipitates form discrete beds up to several meters thick and cements beds as thin as 20 centimeters can be traced laterally for over 100 kilometers (Sumner, 1995). Individual aragonite botryoids (now calcite) typically have radii on the order of tens of centimeters (Fig. 5A), and in some cases were as great as 150 centimeters (Grotzinger and Friedman, 1989; Grotzinger et al., 1993; Sumner and Grotzinger, 1996a; Sumner, 1997a; Sumner and Grotzinger, this volume).

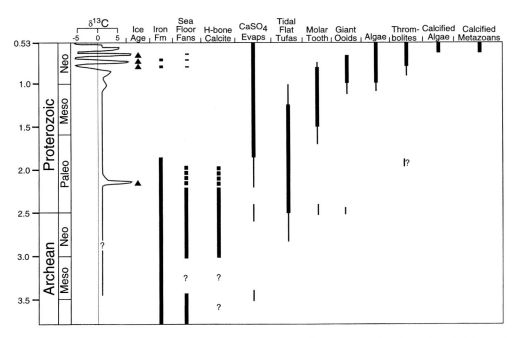

FIG. 4.—Temporal evolution of Archean and Proterozoic carbonate facies, calcium sulfate evaporites, iron formation, glacial deposits, and carbon-isotope composition of carbonates. "Sea Floor Fans" include mesoscopic peudomorphs of calcite- and dolomite-replaced aragonite forming beds in excess of 1 meter thick. The few occurrences of this facies in the Neoproterozoic record are specifically associated with the carbonates capping glaciogenic rocks, not including the exceptions mentioned in the text. "H-bone Calcite" includes beds of herringbone calcite precipitated directly on the sea floor. "Tidal Flat Tufas" includes calcite- and dolomite-replaced pseudomorphs of aragonite and calcite, precipitated as thin crusts and microdigitate stromatolites in restricted tidal-flat environments.

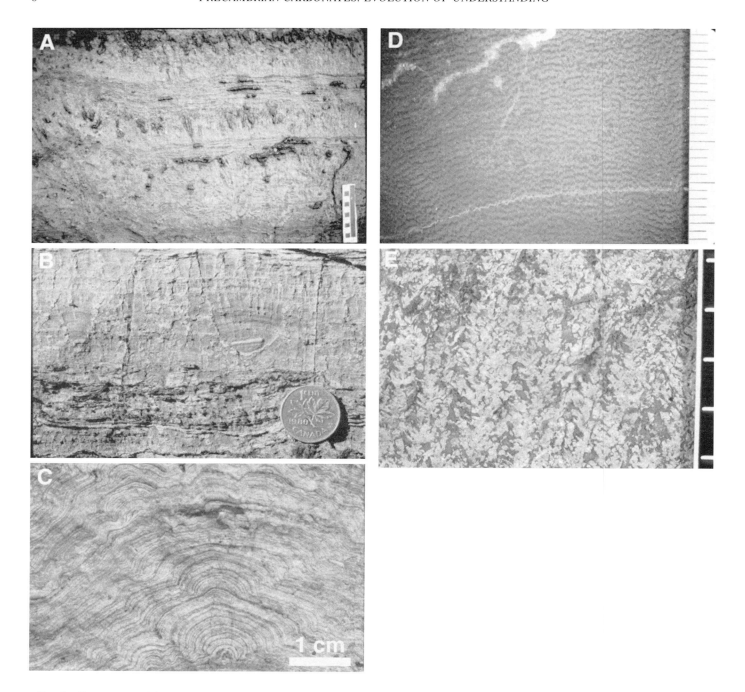

FIG. 5.—Textures created by precipitation of carbonate directly on the sea floor. A) Large, calcite-replaced aragonite fans interbedded with rippled ooid grainstone/lime mudstone, Late Archean (2.7 Ga) Cheshire Formation, Belingwe greenstone belt, Zimbabwe. Scale in centimeters. B) Microdigitate stromatolites, Paleoproterozoic (1.97 Ga) Kimerot platform, Kilohigok Basin, northwest Canada. Coin is 2 centimeters in diameter. C) Isopachous laminites, Late Archean (2.5 Ga) Malmani Subgroup, Transvaal Province, South Africa. D) Herringbone calcite, late Archean (2.5 Ga) Gamohaan Formation, northern Cape Province, South Africa. Scale in millimeters. E) Dendritically branching tufa, Paleoproterozoic (1.8 Ga) Hearne Formation, Pethei platform, northwest Canada. Scale in centimeters.

These facies are representative of open marine rather than restricted conditions (Sumner and Grotzinger, this volume), in contrast to most early interpretations, which assumed that the crystal fans were replaced gypsum and therefore deposited in restricted environments (e.g., Martin et al., 1980; see summary in Grotzinger, 1989b). Occurrences of crystal fans of this scale

are rare in younger rocks (Grotzinger, 1989b), with these exceptions often marking unusual local conditions in sea-water chemistry (Grotzinger and Knoll, 1995). One particularly well-developed instance occurs in the Paleoproterozoic Teena Dolomite, where the fans form continuous sheets within a restricted, likely anoxic basin (Winefield, this volume). Another exception includes thin sheets within foreland basin siliciclastic sediments of Paleoproterozoic age, formed along the maximum flooding surfaces of individual sequences where siliciclastic sedimentation rates were greatly reduced (Grotzinger and Friedmann, 1989).

Herringbone calcite was a common sea-floor precipitate in Archean carbonates that declined sharply in abundance at the end of early Paleoproterozoic time (Fig. 4; Sumner and Grotzinger, 1996a, 1996b). The constituent crystals of herringbone calcite have textures (Fig. 5D) that may indicate preferential growth of crystal faces forced by the presence of an inhibitor, possibly Fe^{2+} or Mn^{2+} (Sumner and Grotzinger, 1996a). Thus, its abundance in Archean carbonates has been explained in the context of environmental models in which lower oxygen concentrations in seawater lead to greater solubility of iron and manganese, which in turn interfered with calcite precipitation to the extent that calcite was precipitated with highly distorted crystals that recrystallized to form the distinctive herringbone texture. Herringbone calcite is rare in Phanerozoic rocks, where it may reflect locally dysaerobic to anaerobic pore fluids and seawater (Sumner and Grotzinger, 1996b).

Implications.—

The trend in declining sea-floor precipitates is considered to be only a first-order relationship and does not rule out transient reversals in response to short-term events. There are late Archean platforms that are dominated by muds, intraclasts, ooids, and/or nonprecipitated stromatolites and lack the abundant encrusting precipitates that define the late Archean norm. Similarly, the Neoproterozoic record contains exceptions to the general dearth of macroscopic seafloor encrustations and other precipitated carbonates. The exceptions occur in the so-called cap carbonates that overlie Neoproterozoic glaciogenic rocks (see discussion below).

In an attempt to highlight this distinctive trend, it should not be overlooked that all of these facies are associated with many conventional clastic carbonate facies. Large sea-floor fans of the late Archean carbonate platforms are often associated with wave-rippled ooid grainstones and wavy-bedded, interstratified rippled limestones with dolomitic lime mudstone drapes (Fig. 6A). These facies are identical in terms of their primary bedding textures and diagenesis (coarse grains, calcite; mudstones, dolomite) to the ubiquitous "ribbon limestones" of early Paleozoic age (Demicco, 1983). In other cases, the sea-floor fans are associated with broad expanses or thick buildups of stromatolites, although the stromatolites themselves may also be constructed, at least in part, of laminae that were precipitated *in situ*. In other cases, successions of micritic limestones and dolostones may be present (Fig. 6B), with uncommon development of fans.

Consequently, the development of the sea-floor fan facies is characterized by a high degree of variability, with some platforms apparently containing a smaller volume of sea-floor precipitates (e.g., Carawine Dolomite; Simonson et al., 1993), and others constituting 50% or more by volume (e.g., Cheshire and Gamohaan Formations; Grotzinger et al., 1993; Sumner, 1997a; Sumner and Grotzinger, this volume). The important point is that in addition to the usual association of stromatolites, grainstones, and mudstones, the late Archean seafloor commonly precipitated calcite and aragonite directly on the seafloor— sometimes in remarkable abundance.

FIG. 6.—Archean clastic carbonate sediments. A) Ripple cross-stratified ooid–intraclast grainstone, late Archean (2.5 Ga) Cheshire Formation, Belingwe greenstone belt, Zimbabwe. Hand lens is 2 cm wide. B) Thin-bedded dolomitic lime mudstone, Late Archean (2.5 Ga) Frisco Formation, Transvaal Province, South Africa. Hammer is 30 cm long.

The simplest interpretation is that Precambrian surface seawater was substantially oversaturated with respect to calcium carbonate, well above the factor of 3–5 that is typical of the oceans today (Li et al., 1969), so that the sea floor was directly encrusted with prolific marine carbonate precipitates (Grotzinger, 1989b; Grotzinger and Kasting, 1993). The only known Holocene analogs are nonmarine thermal spring and alkaline lake deposits in which extreme levels of oversaturation result in massive precipitation at the sediment–water interface (Chafetz and Folk, 1984; Bensen, 1994; Jones and Renaut, 1995; Fouke et al., 1999). Counter to intuition, extreme oversaturation does not result in spontaneous micritic "whitings" in these settings waters are generally clear, and sediment is uncommon in the precipitated crusts. Instead, the precipiated crusts commonly feature growth of large crystals, and in extreme cases with noncrystallographic and dendritic textures. Accordingly, the saturation state of Precambrian surface seawater is inferred to have been highest in the Archean, declining through the Paleoproterozoic and Mesoproterozoic, and reaching near-Phanerozoic values only during the the Neoproterozoic (Grotzinger, 1989b; Knoll and Swett, 1990; Fairchild et al., 1990; Grotzinger and Kasting, 1993; Grotzinger and Knoll, 1995). Grotzinger and Kasting (1993) noted that this interpretation is consistent with observations that the partial pressure of atmospheric carbon dioxide may have been much greater early in Earth history (Kasting, 1987) and that the total alkalinity in sea water may have been much higher as a result. Other theoretical arguments have been presented (Kempe and Degens, 1985; Kempe and Kazmierczak, 1994) that also favor elevated alkalinity in early "soda" oceans, albeit at extreme levels; a substantial geologic database on evaporite and carbonate deposits, however, refutes the interpretation of such extreme conditions (Young and Long, 1977; Jackson and Ianelli, 1981; Muir, 1987; Buick and Dunlop, 1987, 1990; Grotzinger and Kasting, 1993; Pope and Grotzinger, this volume). The long-term decrease in the saturation state of seawater is thought to be related to at least two factors: 1) long-term transfer of inorganic carbon from the atmosphere and ocean to the continents as a result of the formation, by 2.5–2.0 Ga, of large and stable continents capable of preserving substantial limestone and dolostone deposits, and 2) a major decrease in concentration of reduced (and therefore more soluble) iron and manganese in seawater as a result of a Paleoproterozoic increase in oxygen levels in the atmsophere and surface seawater (Sumner and Grotzinger, 1996b). It is postulated that Fe^{2+} and Mn^{2+} acted as in the same manner as Mg^{2+} does in inhibiting calcium carbonate precipitation (Berner, 1975; Mucci and Morse, 1983; Sumner and Grotzinger, 1996b). The major decline of seafloor precipitates, both inorganic and microbial, occurred hundreds of millions of years before the Precambrian–Cambrian boundary and, thus, cannot be related to the advent of carbonate-secreting metazoans and higher algae. In terms of its effects on carbonate facies and textures, this decline is as significant as the Cambrian radiation of skeletonized organisms and the Mesozoic evolution of calcareous microplankton.

Proterozoic Sea-Floor Precipitates

Nature of the Precipitates.—

Seafloor precipitates are widespread in Paleoproterozoic successions, but individual crystal fans and sheets more commonly have thicknesses measured in millimeters to centimeters rather than decimeters, and often form microdigitate stromatolites formed of radiating crystal fans (Fig. 5B). Furthermore, in contrast to the Archean sea-floor precipitates, these precipitated facies are mostly limited to restricted, often peritidal environments (Grotzinger and Read, 1983; Grey and Thorne, 1985; Grotzinger, 1986a, 1989b; Hofmann and Jackson, 1987; Sami and James, 1996). By Mesoproterozoic time, precipitated microdigitate stromatolites and laminar crusts were more limited in development, although they are locally abundant in peritidal strata that are associated with evaporites, such as in the Society Cliffs Formation (e.g., Kah and Knoll, 1996). Other peritidal strata generally lack these structures except for occasional intervals that represent only a small fraction of the overall platform (e.g., Bartley et al., this volume).

Petrographic studies indicate that the microdigitate stromatolites and smaller-scale botryoidal fans were precipitated as aragonite (Grotzinger and Read, 1983; Hofmann and Jackson, 1987; Kah and Knoll, 1996; Bartley et al., this volume). In contrast, the micron- to millimeter-scale laminated crusts (Fig. 5C) have textures more consistent with a calcite precursor (Grotzinger, 1986a; Bartley et al., this volume). In carbonates of the Paleoproterozoic Rocknest Formation and Mesoproter-

ozoic Kotuikan Formation, it is clear that these primary mineralogies were contemporaneous (Grotzinger, 1986a; Bartley et al., this volume).

Implications.—

When combined with the data from late Archean platforms, where sea-floor precipitates of both calcite and aragonite seem to have developed, it is not clear that any long-term trends in the primary mineralogy of shallow marine carbonates are present for this time interval. Similarly, primary mineralogy as inferred from ooids does not show any obvious trends (Simonson and Jarvis, 1996). Thus, there is no evidence through this time interval for a first-order trend in mineralogy, similar to that seen for the Phanerozoic (Sandberg, 1983; Wilkinson et al., 1985).

Macroscopically visible precipitate structures are rare in Neoproterozoic rocks (Fig. 4). In fact, the only significant occurrences are associated with the "cap carbonates", discussed below. One occurrence not associated with a cap carbonate comprises calcite-replaced aragonite botryoids associated with stromatolites in the circa 900 Ma Atar Group, Mauritania (Fairchild et al., 1990). In another occurrence, dolomite pseudomorphs of aragonite fans up to 25 cm in diameter are interpreted to have been deposited in hypersaline low-energy ponds represented by the Katakturuk Dolomite, northern Alaska (Clough and Goldhammer, this volume). The size of the Katakturuk fans are comparable to those seen in Archean carbonates and are anomalous with respect to other Neoproterozoic carbonates. Unfortunately, the age of the Katakturuk is poorly constrained (>543 Ma, <800 Ma), so it is difficult to place these carbonates within a broader framework of secular evolution.

Neoproterozoic Cap Carbonates

Attributes.—

Tillites and associated glaciogenic facies have long been known to occur in middle Neoproterozoic successions (e.g., Harland, 1965) and from the time they were first recognized, their intimate stratigraphic association with carbonates was considered paradoxical (e.g., Schermerhorn, 1974). Particularly puzzling are the "cap carbonates"—texturally unusual commonly pink or buff dolostones (less commonly, limestones) that form distinctive beds several meters thick above many Neoproterozoic tillites. The cap carbonates are extraordinary in that they were globally deposited directly on top of the glacial deposits, implying that carbonate sedimentation occurred worldwide at the onset of transgression over previously glaciated landscapes. In most cases, cap carbonates are remarkably pure; they commonly appear as laminated dolomicrospar (Fig. 7A) showing evidence of rapid lithification, but locally they include seafloor cements of originally aragonitic, centimeter- to decimeter-scale crystal fans (Fig. 7 B, C). Recently, cap carbonates have been characterized as thin, deep-water deposits (Kennedy, 1996). Although some cap carbonates may fit the deep-water description, it is also clear that in other cases the thin, deep-water facies pass laterally into much thicker platformal facies associations (Williams et al., 1974; Cloud et al., 1974; Hegenberger, 1993; Hoffman et al., 1998a, 1998b). Thus, it seems that despite potentially rapid sea-level rise associated with deglaciation, sediment production rates were high enough to match

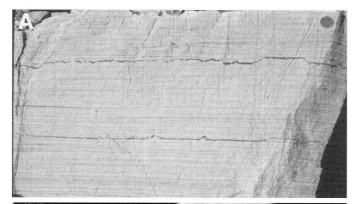

FIG. 7.—Cap carbonate facies. A) Thinly laminated, dolomite mudstone, Neoproterozoic Gariep Group, southern Namibia. Coin is 2 cm in diameter. B) Calcite-replaced aragonite fans interbedded with shaly lime mudstones, terminal Proterozoic Buschmannsklippe Formation, central Namibia. Coin is 2 cm in diameter. C) Calcite-replaced aragonite fans interbedded with lime mudstone, terminal Proterozoic Ravensthroat cap carbonate, Mackenzie Mountains, Canada. Scale in centimeters.

or exceed accommodation production, with resulting strong platform-to-basin differentiation.

Origin.—

Models for the origin of these enigmatic carbonates are diverse. Walter and Bauld (1983) proposed that the apparent dis-

cordance between tillites and carbonates can be explained in terms of stromatolite accretion in cold lakes, as occurs today in Antarctica; this mechanism, however, cannot account for either the texture or the distribution of most cap carbonates, or the observation that stromatolites are a minor facies in most cap carbonates. In contrast, Tucker (1986), Singh (1987), and Fairchild (1993) suggested that the carbonates might have been precipitated during warm interglacial intervals, implying that Neoproterozoic ice ages were terminated rapidly. This model invokes the thermodynamic relation between warming of seawater and its decreasing solubility of carbonate. Warming of seawater in shallow environments would have triggered carbonate precipitation. An additional mechanism would include turnover of a previously stratified ocean, driven by rapid melting of glacial ice, which would have forced upwelling of anoxic, isotopically depleted, alkaline deep water (Kaufman et al., 1991; Grotzinger and Knoll, 1995). This latter model can account for the strongly negative $\delta^{13}C$ isotopic values that are characteristic of virtually all cap carbonates (Kaufman and Knoll, 1995). The sedimentology of cap carbonates is consistent with this hypothesis, and independent evidence for deep-ocean anoxia comes from the iron formations found in association with some Neoproterozoic tillites (Beukes and Klein, 1993). The strongest evidence for sequential ocean stratification and turnover is, however, provided by carbon-isotope data. $\delta^{13}C$ values for later Neoproterozoic platform carbonates deposited prior to glaciation are unusually high—$+8$ to $+9‰$ and locally higher, whereas cap carbonates have values of -2 to -6% (Kaufman and Knoll, 1995). Co-occurring organic carbon shows the same secular variation, supporting petrological, geochemical, and geographic data that the isotopic signatures faithfully record secular changes in the isotopic composition of the surface ocean.

The surface waters of stratified oceans are typically enriched in ^{13}C because large volumes of ^{13}C-depleted organic matter are exported to anoxic bottom waters and the sediments beneath them (Deuser, 1970). Bacterial sulfate reduction of organic matter in the deep, anoxic water column produces HCO_3^- and CO_3^- that are depleted in ^{13}C. The magnitude and inferred duration of pre-glacial carbon-isotope excursions in Neoproterozoic successions are unusual, implying a protracted build-up of isotopically light deep ocean water. Remixing of this alkalinity-laden deep water into the surface ocean would have resulted in the precipitation of carbonates whose isotopic composition would be determined primarily by the composition of the large, deep alkalinity reservoir (Arthur, 1979; Holser, 1984).

Alternatively, the isotopic composition of cap carbonates could be explained by a model involving cessation of primary productivity in the ocean, thus shutting down the biological carbon pump, and driving ocean carbon-isotope compositions to riverine values of approximately $-4‰$ (Hoffman et al., 1998a). Eliminating primary productivity in the surface oceans for a time sufficiently long enough to drive carbon isotopic values to those consistent with nonbiologic sources requires dramatic causal mechanisms (cf. Hsü and McKenzie, 1985), such as covering the entire globe with ice (Kirschvink, 1992; Hoffman et al., 1998a). The differences between the ocean upwelling model and the snowball earth model predict fundamental differences in the regularity of carbon-isotope compositions and the duration of the negative anomalies. With the upwelling model, substantial variability in the carbon-isotope composition of cap carbonates is expected, and the duration of anomalies should be short—probably equal to or less than the residence time of carbon in the oceans, or about 10^5 years (Broecker and Peng, 1982). In terms of isotopic composition, it has been noted (Kennedy, 1996) that the diverse range of values in the global inventory of cap carbonates is consistent with this upwelling hypothesis. In the snowball earth model, the carbon-isotope composition of cap carbonates should be stable, near riverine and mantle input values of −4‰, and could be maintained continuously for much longer than 10^5 years—Hoffman et al. (1998a) suggest 10^7 years for isotopically depleted carbonates of northern Namibia based on inferences of sediment accumulation rates. Thus far, direct age constraints on the duration of any cap carbonates are non-existent, and proper calibration is required before any of these hypotheses are rejected.

Neoproterozoic Giant Ooids

Ooids are one of the basic platform-building components of both Phanerozoic and Precambrian carbonates. For Phanerozoic carbonates, variability in their abundance and mineralogy through time has provided insight into changes in environmental regimes and ocean chemistry (Sandberg, 1983, 1985; Wilkinson et al., 1985). The potential variability in the primary mineralogy of Precambrian ooids has only recently been summarized (Simonson and Jarvis, 1996).

It is also instructive to consider variations in the size of ooids (Sumner and Grotzinger, 1993). In general, modern ooids tend to be less than 1 mm in diameter (Bathurst, 1975). This is true of most Phanerozoic oolites, although there are exceptions (Swett and Knoll, 1989). Archean and Proterozoic ooids tend to be slightly larger but are still dominantly less than 2 mm in diameter. During early and middle Neoproterozoic time (Fig. 4), however, there were extreme exceptions to this size limit, and significant deposits of >2 mm sized ooids are found in diverse areas (Sumner and Grotzinger, 1993). For example (Fig. 7A), in the Akademikerbreen Group, Spitsbergen, 400 m of a 2000 m section are dominated by ooids with 4.0–9.0 mm diameters, reaching a maximum size of 14 mm (Swett and Knoll, 1989; Knoll and Swett, 1990). Why were such great volumes of giant ooids formed during Neoproterozoic time and what environmental changes could have generated these deposits?

Sumner and Grotzinger (1993) concluded that the combination of lower nucleation rate (imparted by the lower flux of nuclei), higher growth rate (due to higher carbonate saturation of seawater) and increased storminess (due to the prevalence of ramps, and possibly stormier climate) are all suggested to have conspired to produce the giant ooids of the Neoproterozoic. Of these, environmental agitation was likely the most important.

An increase in environmental energy of deposits in late Proterozoic platforms could have been due to the predominance of ramps over rimmed shelves (Grotzinger, 1989b). Unlike rimmed shelves, ramps feel the full force of storm events (Burchette and Wright, 1992). Sumner and Grotzinger (1993) suggested that the absolute level of Neoproterozoic storminess

may have increased relative to younger and older periods, because of climate fluctuations associated with the waxing and waning of the extensive Neoproterozoic ice sheets. Many giant ooid beds (see tabulation in Sumner and Grotzinger, 1993) occur stratigraphically below tillites deposited during glaciation (Tucker, 1983; Herrington and Fairchild, 1989; Swett and Knoll, 1989) or between glacial deposits (Singh, 1987). In either case, increased agitation cannot be the sole catalyst for development of giant ooids because they are absent in similar settings of Phanerozoic age, including the Neogene icehouse.

Molar-Tooth Structure

Attributes.—

Lack of body fossils means that any sedimentary features in Precambrian carbonates are inordinately important for paleoenvironmental interpretation. One such group of annoyingly enigmatic features is "molar-tooth structure". Molar-tooth structure (Fig. 8B) comprises mainly vertical, ptygmatically folded sheets of finely crystalline calcite spar in dolomitic or argillaceous lime mudstone (Smith, 1968; O'Connor, 1972; Horodyski, 1976). The calcite spar filling is

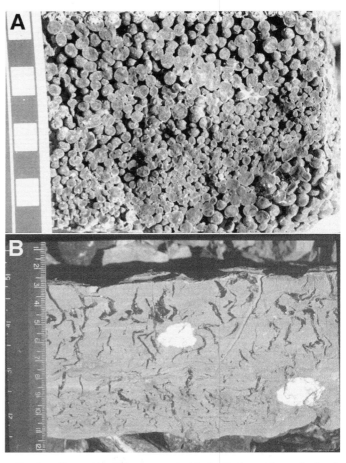

FIG. 8.—Giant ooids of Neoproterozoic Akademikerbreen Group, Svalbard. Scale in centimeters. Photograph by A. H. Knoll. B) Molar-tooth structure in finely crystalline dolostone, Neoproterozoic Little Dal Group, Mackenzie Mountains, northwest Canada. Scale in centimeters. Photograph by G. M. Narbonne.

peculiar. The crystals are pure, uniform, equant, polygonal, tightly packed, blocky calcite crystals 5–15 mm across and in sharp contact with surrounding sediment. Such crystals are unusual in carbonate rocks. They are neither obvious cement (cf. Bathurst, 1975; a precipitate filling a void) nor microspar (cf. Folk, 1965; a neomorphic product of preexisting carbonate). Fairchild et al. (1997) report that some crystals contain a luminescent rhomb-shaped core.

Molar-tooth structure is globally distributed but temporally restricted to rocks mostly of Mesoproterozoic and early Neoproterozoic age (Fig. 4; James et al., 1998). Molar-tooth structure is also facies-dependent, with most occurrences in shallow platform and inner/mid-ramp paleoenvironments (James et al., 1998). More specifically molar-tooth structure is a distinctly subtidal feature (Herrington and Fairchild, 1989; Knoll and Swett, 1990; Fairchild et al., 1997) and is particularly abundant in the lower parts of shallowing-upward cycles (O'Connor, 1972; Frank and Lyons, 1998; Pratt, 1998). Molar-tooth structure is not usually found in either basinal or peritidal facies.

Origin.—

The origin of molar-tooth structure has been debated for more than a century and continues to be highly contentious; recent interpretations include subaqueous shrinkage or synaeresis (Horodyski, 1976; Knoll and Swett, 1990), microbial growth (Smith, 1968; O'Connor, 1972), replacement of evaporites (Eby, 1975), microbially induced gas-bubble expansion (Furniss et al., 1998), and earthquake-induced dewatering (Fairchild et al., 1997; Pratt, 1998). The problem resembles that of "stromatactis" in Phanerozoic carbonates; the structures have no obvious modern counterpart, they are composed of calcite spar, they may have been open spaces originally, and while organisms may have been involved, physical processes were clearly important.

The cracks seem to belong to a family of structures that include synaeresis cracks in terrigenous clastic rocks and diastasis cracks in earliest Phanerozoic carbonates. They are not desiccation cracks. Recent thought points to the geotechnical properties of the sediment as playing an important role in the development of both diastasis and molar-tooth cracks. Diastasis cracks from Phanerozoic carbonates superficially resemble molar tooth, but they are clearly voids filled with grains from the overlying bed, not finely crystalline calcite as in molar tooth. The process of crack formation may involve the action of waves (diastasis; Cowan and James, 1992); or seismicity (molar-tooth; Fairchild et al., 1997; Pratt, 1998). Alternatively, and perhaps most likely, Furniss et al., (1998) provide compelling experimental evidence to show that biological, particularly microbial processes, are fundamental in the genesis of the cracks.

Pratt (1998) envisages the sediment as an original clay–lime mud sediment mixture. Seismic shaking 1) compacts the sediment and generates a variety of sheet-like cracks and pockets, and 2) segregates the lime mud, which is granular in character, from the clay, and the lime mud is carried into the fissures and cracks as a slurry. Continued shaking consolidates and shears the host sediment. The lime mud in the fissures starts to lithify almost immediately by grain growth, with $CaCO_3$ coming from seawater.

In an alternative model based on innovative experimental evidence, Furniss et al. (1998) visualize the formation of molar-tooth structure as a two-stage process. Biogenic gas, generated by decaying organic matter, creates a series of cracks, fissures, and bubbles filled with H_2S, CO_2, and CH_4 within a meter or so of the depositional surface. Experimental evidence shows that as the gas-generated fissures develop water is drawn from the sediment, promoting compaction. The gas cannot escape because the surface is sealed (perhaps by microbial mats; cf. James et al., 1998). Calcite spar, probably microbially mediated, precipitates in the open voids prior to compaction. $\delta^{13}C$ isotopic data (Frank and Lyons, 1998), however, do not show any difference between the sediment and the crack-filling.

Unfortunately, all current hypotheses fail to explain the scarcity of molar tooth structure in older Proterozoic and Archean carbonate rocks. The ubiquity of both earthquakes and microbes ensures that such processes should have been active throughout the geologic history of Precambrian carbonates, suggesting that as yet unrecognized factors must have been operative.

REEFS

General Attributes

The robust capacity of stromatolites to build reefs that are identical, in many respects, to the diversity of Phanerozoic reefs (Geldsetzer et al., 1988) has been addressed in previous studies (Grotzinger, 1988, 1989b, 1990, 1994). Existing data demonstrate that stromatolite reefs occupied a variety of different niches, similar to their younger counterparts. These include major barrier reefs (Fig. 9A) adjacent to large seaways (Grotzinger, 1986b, 1989a; Beukes, 1987; Clough and Goldhammer, this volume), patch reefs and pinnacle reefs (Fig. 9B, C) located on gentle ramps facing open seaways (Grotzinger and Khetani, 1994; Grotzinger et al., 1995; Narbonne et al., this volume), and even downslope bioherms that grew entirely within a deeper, quieter-water setting (Aitken, 1988; Kerans and Donaldson, 1988; Turner et al., 1993; Narbonne and James, 1996; Turner et al., this volume).

Research over the past three decades has established that many stromatolite buildups are true reefs (*sensu* James and Bourque, 1992). Stromatolitic reefs could grow from deeper, quiet-water settings upwards into the shallow zone of continual wave agitation, to resist and continue growth in the zone of wave action, and expand laterally to significant sizes so as to influence their surroundings by affecting circulation, salinity, and sediment production. Precambrian reefs commonly show the catch-up, keep-up, and give-up phases of development commonly associated with younger, Phanerozoic reefs.

Reef Construction

Stromatolites.—

Having established that Precambrian stromatolite reefs possess all the properties of true ecologic reefs, a first-order question remains: What serves as the basic frame-building constituent? For Phanerozoic reefs, rigid, metazoan skeletons ("supercalcifiers" of Stanley and Hardie, 1999) allow

FIG. 9.—Reefs. A) Prograding barrier reef of accretionary rimmed shelf, Paleoproterozoic (1.8 Ga) Abner Formation, northern Quebec, Canada. Large reefal mounds overlie reefal foreslope facies in progradational stacking pattern. Large mound in center of photograph is approximately 5 meters wide. B) Aggradational reef, about 100 m in height (background) developed on bedded slope ribbon and parted limestones (in gorge, foreground); Mesoproterozoic (1.2. Ga) Victor Bay Formation, Baffin Island, Canada. C) Thrombolitic pinnacle reef developed on platform as part of drowning succesion; covering deepwater shales have been mostly exhumed but are still visible on right side of photograph. Terminal Proterozoic Nama Group, southern Namibia.

tation, sediment infiltration, and bioerosion (James and Bourque, 1992). In this context individual stromatolites can be considered the frame-building element of stromatolite reefs (Grotzinger, 1986b, 1988, 1989b). This interpretation is based on the assumption that because stromatolites may have been produced primarily through the trapping and binding and/or precipitation-inducing activity of benthic microbial communities, they can be regarded as having had the same function as individual metazoans had during the development of Phanerozoic reefs—they are directly responsible for the vertical accretion of the structure. This view, however, necessarily ignores the microscopic aspects of stromatolite growth, in particular the specific roles of microorganisms in the accretionary process.

This may no longer be justifiable for several reasons. In the first case, recent studies of sediment–mat interactions in both modern and ancient stromatolites underscore the highly variable role of the organisms themselves in the generation of stromatolitic laminae (Grotzinger and Knoll, 1999). New data suggest that in addition to the well-established mechanism of trapping and binding (Black, 1933; Ginsburg and Lowenstam, 1958; Gebelein, 1974), stromatolites formed in mineralizing systems are dominated by in situ calcification of cyanobacteria (Golubic, 1991; Cady and Farmer, 1996) and by precipitation nucleation triggered by heterotrophic bacteria below the sediment–water interface (Canfield and Raiswell, 1991; Chafetz and Buczynski, 1992). In extreme cases the microbes behave passively, with accretion resulting from largely abiotic precipitation from highly oversaturated waters (Cady and Farmer, 1996; Fouke et al., 1999). These new studies of modern mineralizing systems provide better analogs for the Precambrian stromatolite textures, which represent growth not through processes related to sediment trapping by mats, but rather by crystal precipitation regulated by abiotic processes or mat degradation by heterotrophic bacteria (Grotzinger and Read, 1983; Hofmann and Jackson, 1987; Kah and Knoll, 1996; Grotzinger and Rothman, 1996; Sami and James, 1996; Bartley et al., this volume; Pope and Grotzinger, this volume; Seong-Joo and Golubic, this volume). Although most stromatolites were likely formed through the precipitation-inducing and/or trapping and binding activities of a diverse range of microbes, it is no longer clear exactly what specific role these microorganisms had in the construction of stromatolites, particularly for early Precambrian stromatolites.

What is now clear is that the unique influences of biology may be best expressed at microscopic scales, but difficult to distinguish from abiotic processes at macroscopic scales (Grotzinger and Rothman, 1996; Grotzinger and Knoll, 1999). Future advances in the study of stromatolite accretion processes are strongly dependent on the interpretation of the textures that define individual stromatolitic laminae, and thus the true framebuilding processes (Grotzinger and Knoll, 1999). In the most abiotic cases microbes likely resided at the sediment–water interface and therefore probably exerted some passive control on the accretion process (Seong-Joo and Golubic, this volume); on the other hand, the most obviously biological textures provide no evidence for the role of obligate calcifiers in the active construction of accretion textures (Grotzinger and Khetani, 1994; Grotzinger and Knoll, 1999). Thus, unlike metazoan reefs, in which the biochemistry of enzymatic secretion depends little

the reef to grow in any environment, from tranquil to wave-dominated settings, and thereby influence other environments. A "framework" results from a combination of the intertwining growth by calcified benthic organisms, cemen-

on the local physical environment, Precambrian microbial reefs were always critically dependent on the physical environment, either through providing a source of sediment to be trapped and bound, or in providing a high degree of oversaturation to enable local precipitation.

Thrombolites.—

A second problem in identifying the basic frame-building constituent of inferred microbial reefs arises from the occurrence of thrombolites (Fig. 10A) in addition to stromatolites in some Proterozoic reefs (Aitken and Narbonne, 1989; Kah and Grotzinger, 1992; Turner et al., 1993; Turner et al., this volume). Although known from Paleoproterozoic reefs, thrombolites are not important reef-building components until Neoproterozoic time (Fig. 4). For these reefs, the basic frame-building element is considered to be the thrombolitic mesoclot (Kennard and James, 1986). Because the growth of the irregular clots imparts a higher degree of irregularity to the actively accreting sediment–water interface, the final structure contains a greater number of large primary pores as compared to stromatolites.

The oldest thrombolites appear to derive their distinctive texture from early lithification of mats with high surface roughness, probably composed of coccoid cyanobacteria (Kah and Grotzinger, 1992). Evidence for this is provided by well-preserved fossil *Entophysalis* mats showing rough surface morphology in sediments of similar age (Golubic and Hofmann, 1976; Hofmann, 1975). In comparison, the high initial porosity of Neoproterozoic thrombolites also is likely related to the early lithification of coccoid-dominated mats; however, the complexity and surface roughness of the mats may also have been increased through the additional presence of green algae (Feldmann and McKenzie, 1998; Grotzinger and Knoll, 1999). This is supported by the presence of algae in rocks of this age (Fig. 4; Butterfield et al., 1988; Grant et al., 1991; Xiao et al., 1998).

Calcified Microbes.—

The other important development in later Precambrian time is the calcification of microbial filaments of many different types (calcimicrobes; James and Gravestock, 1990). Although the taxonomic and phylogenetic affinities are ambiguous, and many are products of diagenesis, morphologically they resemble (Fig. 10B) early Phanerozoic taxa such as *Girvanella* and *Renalcis* (Turner et al., 1993). These taxa are recognized as critical elements of early and middle Paleozoic reefs (James and Bourque, 1992). These calcimicrobes, because of their varied architecture, sometimes resulted in highly porous reef frameworks. Cavities produced in this way became sites for growth of cavity-dwelling biotas, cement precipitation, and internal, geopetal sediment accumulation.

Evolution of the Reef Archetype

Predictably, just as there is a secular change in the nature of sedimentary facies, so there is a parallel change in the nature of Precambrian reefs (Grotzinger, 1989b). Paleoproterozoic buildups are constructed by "cement-rich" stromatolites in which the influence of synsedimentary carbonate precipitation exceeds that of microbes. There is little variability in stromatolite form, mostly hemispherical, columnar, laminated, and conical types. Isolated buildups are not abundant; most are in-

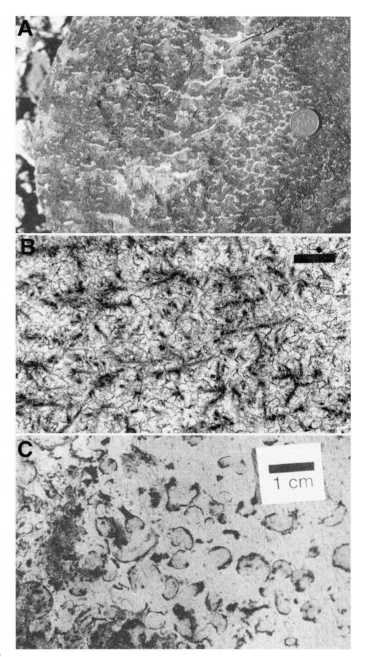

FIG. 10.—Biotic elements of Neoproterozoic reefs. A) Outcrop photograph of thrombolitic mesoclots (dark) forming framestone within pinnacle reef of Figure 9C. Primary pore space is infilled by geopetal lime mudstone (light gray) and void-filling marine cement and blocky spar (white). Coin is 2.5 cm in diameter. B) Filamentous calcimicrobes preserved as tubules and threads, Neoproterozoic Little Dal reefs, Canada. Interstitial porosity is filled with fibrous calcite cement. Scale bar, 500 microns. C) Calcified metazoan fossils associated with thrombolitic reefal facies, terminal Proterozoic Nama Group, Namibia.

tegrated into platforms and ramps as biostromes, because abiotic precipitation is so extensive and widespread.

Mesoproterozoic reefs record a long period of stasis, with stromatolites broadly similar to older growth forms. They are, however, more "muddy" and display increasing "diversity" in stromatolite form. It appears that the role of synsedimentary abiotic precipitation and microbial influence were roughly equal in importance (Knoll and Semikhatov, 1998). Increased stromatolite diversity relates more to environmental than biologic evolution (Grotzinger and Knoll, 1999).

The Neoproterozoic (1.0–0.54 Ga) was a period of dramatic global change. The appearance of calcimicrobes and thrombolites in the Tonian (1.0–0.85 Ga) coincides with the decline of conical elements and decline in stromatolites. It seems that the role of microbes became more important than that of synsedimentary cement in overall reef structure at this time. In deepwater buildups their activities led to rapid upward accretion and the formation of growth cavities containing both internal geopetal sediment and synsedimentary cement. The importance of calcimicrobes appears to be less in shallow-water reefs, where they are mostly spar-filled filament molds.

The first calcified metazoans appear in thrombolite reefs toward the end of Neoproterozoic post-glacial Vendian time (Fig. 4), further adding to their ecologic complexity (Grotzinger and Khetani, 1994; Grotzinger et al., 1995). Calcified fossils are abundant in thombolitic facies of the Nama Group, Namibia, and occur within both clotted domal and columnar structures that make up individual reefs, as well as within the intrachannel fill between domes and columns. This fill consists of trough cross-bedded skeletal packstone and grainstone of simple tubes, more complex cups and goblets, *Cloudina*, and their bioclastic detritus (Fig. 10C). The thrombolitic cores of domes and columns contain fossils and fossil fragments up to 1 centimeter wide, whereas the stromatolitic rinds of domes and columns contain millimeter-scale fossils and fragments. The thrombolitic reefal facies are considered to have developed within unrestricted shallow subtidal environments that, during platform drowning, developed pinnacle geometries (Fig. 9C). In this environmental context, the development of the Nama thrombolite-calcified fossil facies is analogous to younger Cambrian reefal facies, dominated by thrombolites and other microbialites with associated calcified higher organisms (Soja, 1994; Kruse et al., 1995; Riding and Zhuravlev, 1995).

SUMMARY AND CONCLUSIONS

The last decade has seen a surge in research on Precambrian carbonate rocks. These studies have been driven by the realization that many Precambrian platforms and ramps, despite their antiquity, are composed of beautifully preserved sedimentary rocks. The most important advances have been achieved by searching out these exceptionally well-preserved localities, documenting them in detail, and applying new geochemical techniques to resolve problems of stratigraphy, composition, and paleoceanography.

Precambrian platforms and ramps are strikingly similar to Phanerozoic structures with similar facies belts, both particulate and muddy sediment, ooids, reefs, seafloor cement precipitation, and recurring patterns of stratigraphic packaging. Yet, set against this uniformitarian background, perhaps the most important advance in the last decade has been the realization that different periods of the Precambrian have discrete carbonate depositional systems. Just as Cambrian and Cretaceous carbonates are distinctively different, so Paleoproterozoic and Neoproterozoic carbonates are quite dissimilar.

Late Archean and Paleoproterozoic carbonate deposition formed mostly rimmed platforms in which a large proportion of the carbonate was precipitated directly onto the seafloor as aragonite fans, microdigitate stromatolites, and beds of magnesian calcite. The decreasing abundance of such precipitates with time through the Paleoproterozoic suggests gradual depletion of the highly oversaturated Archean seawater. The sediments are otherwise grainy, reefs are composed of cement-rich stromatolites, and even though glaciation occurred, there are, surprisingly, no cap carbonates.

The Mesoproterozoic, long regarded as a time of stasis, was a period in which ramps as well as rimmed platforms are seen in the record. Seafloor cement precipitation was greatly diminished, except in platforms where contemporaneous evaporites were deposited, and stromatolites show greater textural diversity than in older rocks. The platforms are somewhat muddier, and molar-tooth calcite is a significant part of the sediment, with spar-clasts locally forming carbonate sands.

The Neoproterozoic is a period of dramatic changes in global tectonics, oceanography, and sedimentation. Carbonate platforms are mostly ramps, there is vanishingly little seafloor cement precipitation, sediments are commonly muddy, molar-tooth carbonate is abundant, and shoals formed of giant ooids are locally important. Although stromatolites still formed reefs, the appearance of thrombolites and calcified microbes in abundance dramatically altered their internal structure, creating void spaces that enabled both rapid vertical accretion and provided internal spaces for cement precipitation, sediment accumulation, and the growth of coelobites. Cap carbonates occur directly above glacigene sediments and, although their structure is reminiscent of Archean carbonates dominated by seafloor precipitation, they contain their own distinctive facies motifs.

We have only just begun to appreciate the holdings in this vast repository of information about the young earth, and it is clear that many unresolved problems still exist. The most important of these problems, such as the role of microbes in influencing precipitation mechanisms and sediment textures, must be approached carefully with regard to the potential role of modern analogs based on thermal springs and alkaline lakes rather than marine systems. In other cases, there may be no suitable modern analog, and research must utilize a non-actualistic approach, letting the rocks dictate the conditions for analysis. Only in this way will we be able to identify processes that may have changed over time, or even have been unique in the history of carbonate sedimentation.

ACKNOWLEDGMENTS

This work was supported by NSF Grant EAR-9628257 and NASA Astrobiology Institute grant NCC2-1053 to JPG and NSERC grant 2028-99 to NPJ. A. Knoll and G. Narbonne reviewed the manuscript and provided numerous helpful comments.

REFERENCES

AITKEN, J. D., 1988, Giant algal reefs, middle/upper Proterozoic Little Dal Group (>770, <1200 Ma), Mackenzie Mountains, N. W. T., Canada, *in*, Geldsetzer, H., James, N. P., and Tebbutt, G., eds., Reefs—Canada and Adjacent Areas: Canadian Society of Petroleum Geologists, Memoir 13, p. 13–23.

AITKEN, J. D., AND NARBONNE, G. M., 1989, Two occurrences of Precambrian thrombolites from the Mackenzie Mountains, Northwestern Canada: Palaios, v. 4, p. 384–388.

ARTHUR, M. A., 1979, Paleoceanographic events—recognition, resolution, and reconsideration: Review of Geophysics and Space Physics, v. 17, p. 1474–1494.

BATHURST, R. G. C., 1975, Carbonate Sediments and Their Diagenesis: Amsterdam, Elsevier, 658 p.

BENSEN, J., 1994, Carbonate deposition, Pyramid Lake subbasin, Nevada: 1. Sequence of formation and elevational distribution of carbonate deposits (tufas): Palaeogeography, Palaeoclimatology, Palaeoecology, v. 109, p. 55–87.

BERNER, R. A., 1975, The role of magnesium in the crystal growth of calcite and aragonite from sea water: Geochimica et Cosmochimica Acta, v. 39, p. 489–504.

BERTRAND-SARFATI, J., AND MOUSSINE-POUCHKINE, A., 1983, Platform-to-basin facies evolution: the carbonates of late Proterozoic (Vendian) Gourma (west Africa): Journal of Sedimentary Petrology, v. 53, p. 275–293.

BEUKES, N. J., 1977, Transition from siliciclastic to carbonate sedimentation near the base of the Transvaal Supergroup, northern Cape Province, South Africa: Sedimentary Geology, v. 18, p. 201–221.

BEUKES, N. J., 1980, Stratigrafie en litofasies van die Campbellrand-subgrop van die Proterofitiese Ghaap-groep, noord-Kaapland: Geological Society of South Africa, Transactions, v. 83, p. 141–170.

BEUKES, N. J., 1987, Facies relations, depositional environments and diagenesis in a major early Proterozoic stromatolitic carbonate platform to basinal sequence, Campbellrand Subgroup, Transvaal Supergroup, southern Africa: Sedimentary Geology, v. 54, p. 1–46.

BEUKES, N. J., AND KLEIN, C., 1993, Models for iron-formation deposition, in, Schopf, J. W., and Klein, C., eds., The Proterozoic Biosphere: Cambridge, U. K., Cambridge University Press, p. 147–151.

BLACK, M., 1933, The algal sediments of Andros Island, Bahamas: Royal Society [London], Philosophical Transactions, Series B, v. 222, 165–192.

BOND, G. C., KOMINZ, M. A., STECKLER, M. S., AND GROTZINGER, J. P., 1989, Role of thermal subsidence, flexure, and eustasy in the evolution of early Paleozoic passive-margin carbonate platforms, in Crevello, P. D., Wilson, J. L., Sarg, J. F., and Read, J. F., eds., Controls on Carbonate Platform and Basin Development: SEPM, Special Publication 44, p. 39–61.

BRASIER, M., GREEN, O., AND SHIELDS, G., 1997, Ediacaran sponge spicule clusters from southwestern Mongolia and the origins of the Cambrian fauna: Geology, v. 25, 303–306.

BRASIER, M. D., ANDERSON, M. M., AND CORFIELD, R. M., 1992, Oxygen and carbon isotope stratigraphy of early Cambrian carbonates in southeastern Newfoundland and England: Geological Magazine, v. 129, 265–297.

BROECKER, W. S., AND PENG, T. H., 1982, Tracers in the Sea: Palisades, New York, Lamont-Doherty Geological Observatory, 690 p.

BUICK, R., DES MARAIS, D. J., AND KNOLL, A. H., 1995, Stable isotopic compositions of carbonates from the Mesoproterozoic Bangemall Group, northwestern Australia: Chemical Geology, v. 123, 153–171.

BUICK, R., AND DUNLOP, J. S. R., 1987, Early Archean evaporitic sediments from the Warrawoona Group, North Pole, Western Australia (abstract): Geological Society of America, Abstracts with Program, v. 19, p. 604.

BUICK, R., AND DUNLOP, J. S. R., 1990, Evaporitic sediments of early Archean age from the Warrawoona Group, North Pole, Western Australia: Sedimentology, v. 37, p. 247–278.

BURCHETTE, T. P., AND WRIGHT, V. P., 1992, Carbonate ramp depositional systems: Sedimentary Geology, v. 79, p. 3–57.

BURDETT, J. W., GROTZINGER, J. P., AND ARTHUR, M. A., 1990, Did major changes in the stable-isotope composition of Proterozoic seawater occur?: Geology, v. 18, p. 227–230.

BURNS, S. J., AND MATTER, A., 1993, Carbon isotope record of the latest Proterozoic from Oman: Eclogae Geologicae Helvetiae, v. 86, p. 595–607.

BUTTERFIELD, N. J., KNOLL, A. H., AND SWETT, K., 1988, Exceptional preservation of fossils in an Upper Proterozoic shale: Nature, v. 334, p. 424–427.

CADY, S. L., AND FARMER, J. D., 1996, Fossilization processes in siliceous thermal springs: trends in preservation along thermal gradients, in Walter, M. R., ed., Evolution of Hydrothermal Ecosystems on Earth (and Mars?): Chichester, U. K., Wiley, p. 150–173.

CANFIELD, D. E., AND RAISWELL, R., 1991, Carbonate precipitation and dissolution: its relevance to fossil preservation, in Allison, P. A., and Briggs, D. E., ed., Taphonomy: Releasing the Data Locked in the Fossil Record: New York, Plenum Press, p. 411–453.

CECILE, M. P., AND CAMPBELL, F. H. A., 1978, Regressive stomatolite reefs and associated facies, middle Goulburn Group (lower Proterozoic), in Kilohigok Basin, N.W.T.: an example of environmental control of stromatolite form: Canadian Society of Petroleum Geologists, Bulletin, v. 26, p. 237–267.

CHAFETZ, H. S., AND BUCZYNSKI, C., 1992, Bacterially induced lithification of microbial mats: Palaios, v. 7, p. 277–293.

CHAFETZ, H. S., AND FOLK, R. L., 1984, Travertines: depositional morphology and the bacterially constructed constituents: Journal of Sedimentary Petrology, v. 54, p. 289–316.

CHRISTIE-BLICK, N., GROTZINGER, J. P., AND VON DER BORCH, C. C., 1988, Sequence stratigraphy in Proterozoic successions: Geology, v. 16, p. 100–104.

CLOUD, P. E., WRIGHT, L. A., WILLIAMS, E. G., DIEHL, P., AND WALTER, M. R., 1974, Giant stromatolites and associated vertical tubes from the upper Proterozoic Noonday Dolomite, Death Valley Region, eastern California: Geological Society of America, Bulletin, v. 85, p. 1869–1882.

CONWAY MORRIS, S., MATTES, B. W., AND MENGE, C., 1990, The early skeletal organism *Cloudina*: new occurrences from Oman and possibly China: American Journal of Science v. 290-A, 245–260.

COWAN, C. A., AND JAMES, N. P., 1992, Diastasis cracks: mechanically generated synaeresis-like cracks in Upper Cambrian shallow water oolitic and ribbon carbonates: Sedimentology, v. 39, p. 1101–1118.

DEMICCO, R. V., 1983, Wavy and lenticular-bedded carbonate ribbon rocks of the upper Cambrian Conococheague Limestone, central Appalachians: Journal of Sedimentary Petrology, v. 53, p. 1121–1132.

DEUSER, W. C., 1970, Carbon-13 in Black Sea waters and implications for the origin of hydrogen sulfide: Science, v. 268, p. 1575–1577.

EBY, D. E., 1975, Carbonate sedimentation under elevated salinities and implications for the origin of "molar-tooth" structure in the middle Belt carbonate interval (late Precambrian), northwestern Montana (abstract), Geological Society of America, Abstracts With Program, v. 7, p. 1063.

FAIRCHILD, I. J., 1991, Origins of carbonate in Neoproterozoic stromatolites and the identification of modern analogues: Precambrian Research, v. 53, p. 281–299.

FAIRCHILD, I. J., 1993, Balmy shores and icy wastes: the paradox of carbonates associated with glacial deposits in Neoproterozoic times: Sedimentology Review, v. 1, p. 1–15.

FAIRCHILD, I. J., EINSELE, G., AND SONG, T., 1997, Possible seismic origin of molar tooth structures in Neoproterozoic carbonate ramp deposits, north China: Sedimentology, v. 44, p. 611–636.

FAIRCHILD, I. J., HAMBREY, M. J., JEFFERSON, T. H., AND SPIRO, B., 1989, Late Proterozoic glacial carbonates in NE Spitsbergen: new insights into the carbonate–tillite association: Geological Magazine, v. 126, p. 469–490.

FAIRCHILD, I. J., MARSHALL, J. D., AND BERTRAND-SARFATI, J., 1990, Stratigraphic shifts in carbon isotopes from Proterozoic stromatolitic carbonates (Mauritania): influence of primary mineralogy and diagenesis: American Journal of Science, v. 290-A, p. 46–79.

FAIRCHILD, I. J., AND SPIRO, B., 1987, Petrological and isotopic implications of some contrasting Late Precambrian carbonates, NE Spitsbergen: Sedimentology, v. 34, p. 973–989.

FELDMANN, M., AND MCKENZIE, J., 1998, Stromatolite–thrombolite associations in a modern environment, Lee Stocking Island, Bahamas: Palaios, v. 13, p. 201–212.

FOLK, R. L., 1965, Some aspects of recrystallization in ancient limestones: In, Dolomitization and Limestone Diagenesis, in Pray, L. C., and Murray, R. C., eds., Society of Economic Paleontologists and Mineralogists, p. 14–48.

FOUKE, B. W., FARMER, J. D., DES MARAIS, D. J., PRATT, L., STURCHIO, N. C., BURNS, P. C., AND DISCIPULO, M. K., 2000, Depositional facies and aqueous–solid geochemistry of travertine-depositing hot springs (Angel Terrace, Mammoth Hot Springs, Yellowstone National Park, U.S.A.): Journal of Sedimentary Research, in press.

FRANK, T. D., AND LYONS, T. W., 1998, "Molar-tooth" structures: a geochemical perspective on a Proterozoic enigma: Geology, v. 26, p. 683–686.

FRANK, T. D., LYONS, T. W., AND C., L. K., 1997, Isotopic evidence for the paleoenvironmental evolution of the Mesoproterozoic Helena Formation, Belt Supergroup, Montana, USA: Geochimica et Cosmochimica Acta, v. 61, p. 5023–5041.

FURNISS, G., RITTEL, J. F., AND WINSTON, D., 1998, Gas bubble and expansion crack origin of "molar-tooth" calcite structures in the Middle Proterozoic Belt Supergroup, Western Montana: Journal of Sedimentary Research, v. 68, p. 104–114.

GEBELEIN, C. D., 1974, Biologic control of stromatolite microstructure: implications for Precambrian time stratigraphy: American Journal of Science, v. 274, p. 575–598.

GELDSETZER, H. H. J., JAMES, N. P., AND TEBBUTT, G. E., 1988, Reefs—Canada and Adjacent Areas: Canadian Society of Petroleum Geologists, Memoir 13, 775 p.

GINSBURG, R. N., AND LOWENSTAM, H. A., 1958, The influence of marine bottom communities on the depositional environment of sediments: Journal of Geology, v. 66, p. 310–318.

GOLUBIC, S., 1991, Modern stromatolites—a review, in Riding, R., ed., Calcareous Algae and Stromatolites: Heidelberg, Springer-Verlag, p. 541–561.

GOLUBIC, S., AND HOFMANN, H. J., 1976, Comparison of modern and mid-Precambrian Entophysalidaceae (Cyanophyta) in stromatolitic algal mats: cell division and degradation: Journal of Paleontology, v. 50, p. 1074–1082.

GRANT, S. W. F., KNOLL, A. H., AND GERMS, G. J. B., 1991, Probable calcified metaphytes in the latest Proterozoic Nama Group, Namibia: Journal of Paleontology, v. 65, p. 1–18.

GREY, K., AND THORNE, A. M., 1985, Biostratigraphic significance of stromatolites in upward shallowing sequences of the early Proterozoic Duck Creek Dolomite, Western Australia: Precambrian Research, v. 29, p. 183–206.

GROTZINGER, J. P., 1986a, Cyclicity and paleoenvironmental dynamics, Rocknest platform, northwest Canada: Geological Society of America, Bulletin, v. 97, p. 1208–1231.

GROTZINGER, J. P., 1986b, Evolution of early Proterozoic passive-margin carbonate platform: Rocknest Formation, Wopmay Orogen, N.W.T., Canada: Journal of Sedimentary Petrology, v. 56, p. 831–847.

GROTZINGER, J. P., 1988, Introduction to Precambrian reefs, in Geldsetzer, H., James, N. P., and Tebbutt, G., eds., Reefs—Canada and Adjacent Areas: Canadian Society of Petroleum Geologists, Memoir 13, p. 9–12.

GROTZINGER, J. P., 1989a, Construction of early Proterozoic (1.9 Ga) barrier reef complex, Rocknest platform, Northwest Territories, in Geldsetzer, H., James, N. P., and Tebbutt, G., eds., Reefs—Canada and Adjacent Areas: Canadian Society of Petroleum Geologists, Memoir 13, p. 30–37.

GROTZINGER, J. P., 1989b, Facies and evolution of Precambrian carbonate depositional systems: emergence of the modern platform archetype, in Crevello, P. D., Wilson, J. L., Sarg, J. F., and Read, J. F., eds., Controls on Carbonate Platform and Basin Development: SEPM, Special Publication 44, p. 79–106.

GROTZINGER, J. P., 1990, Geochemical model for Proterozoic stromatolite decline: American Journal of Science, v. 290-A, p. 80–103.

GROTZINGER, J. P., 1993, New views of old carbonate sediments: Geotimes, v. 38, p. 12–15.

GROTZINGER, J. P., 1994, Trends in Precambrian carbonate sediments and their implication for understanding evolution, in Bengtson, S., ed., Early Life on Earth: New York, Columbia University Press, Nobel Symposium No. 84, p. 245–258.

GROTZINGER, J. P., BOWRING, B. Z., SAYLOR, B. Z., AND KAUFMAN, A. J., 1995, Biostratigraphic and geochronologic constraints on early animal evolution: Science, v. 270, p. 598–604.

GROTZINGER, J. P., AND FRIEDMANN, J. S., 1989, Occurrence of thick crusts of former botryoidal aragonite, Rifle and Beechey Formations (1.97 Ga), Kilohigok Basin, N. W. T. (abstract): Geological Association of Canada, Program with Abstracts, v. 14, p. A77.

GROTZINGER, J. P., AND KASTING, J. F., 1993, New constraints on Precambrian ocean composition: Journal of Geology, v. 101, p. 235–243.

GROTZINGER, J. P., AND KHETANI, A., 1994, Facies and diagenesis of late Vendian thrombolite-shelly (Cloudina?) invertebrate pinnacle reefs, Nama Group, Namibia (abstract): Geological Society of America, Northeast Section, Abstracts with Program, p. 56.

GROTZINGER, J. P., AND KNOLL, A. H., 1995, Anomalous carbonate precipitates: Is the Precambrian the key to the Permian?: Palaios, v. 10, p. 578–596.

GROTZINGER, J. P., AND KNOLL, A. H., 1999, Stromatolites in Precambrian carbonates: Evolutionary Mileposts or Environmental Dipsticks?: Annual Review of Earth and Planetary Science, v. 27, p. 313–358.

GROTZINGER, J. P., AND READ, J. F., 1983, Evidence for primary aragonite precipitation, lower Proterozoic (1.9 Ga) dolomite, Wopmay orogen, northwest Canada: Geology, v. 11, p. 710–713.

GROTZINGER, J. P., AND ROTHMAN, D. R., 1996, An abiotic model for stromatolite morphogenesis: Nature, v. 383, p. 423–425.

GROTZINGER, J. P., SUMNER, D. Y., AND BEUKES, N. J., 1993, Archean carbonate sedimentation in an active extensional basin, Belingwe Greenstone Belt, Zimbabwe (abstract): Geological Society of America, Abstracts with Program, p. A64.

HARLAND, W. B., 1965, Critical evidence for a great Infra-Cambrian glaciation: Geologische Rundschau, v. 54, p. 45–61.

HEGENBERGER, W., 1993, Stratigraphy and sedimentology of the Late Precambrian Witvlei and Nama Groups, east of Windhoek: Geological Survey of Namibia, Memoir 17, 82 p.

HERRINGTON, P. M., AND FAIRCHILD, I. J., 1989, Carbonate shelf and slope facies evolution prior to Vendian glaciation, central East Greenland, in Gayer, R., ed., The Caledonide Geology of Scandinavia: London, Graham & Trotman, p. 263–273.

HOFFMAN, P. F., 1974, Shallow and deep-water stromatolites in lower Proterozoic platform-to-basin facies change, Great Slave Lake, Canada: American Association of Petroleum Geologists, Bulletin, v. 58, p. 856–867.

HOFFMAN, P. F., KAUFMAN, A. J., HALVERSON, G. P., AND SCHRAG, D. P., 1998a, A Neoproterozoic snowball earth: Science, v. 281, p. 1342–1346.

HOFFMAN, P. F., KAUFMAN, A. J., AND HALVERSON, G. P., 1998b, Comings and goings of global glaciation on a Neoproterozoic tropical platform in Namibia: GSA Today, v. 8, no. 5, p. 1–9.

HOFMANN, H. J., 1975, Stratiform Precambrian stromatolites, Belcher Islands, Canada: relations between silicified microfossils and microstructure: American Journal of Science, v. 275, p. 1121–1132.

HOFMANN, H. J., 1985, The mid-Proterozoic Little Dal macrobiota, Mackenzie Mountains, north-west Canada: Paleontology, v. 28, p. 331–354.

HOFMANN, H. J., AND JACKSON, G. D., 1987, Proterozoic ministromatolites with radial-fibrous fabric: Sedimentology, v. 34, p. 963–971.

HOLSER, W. T., 1984, Gradual and abrupt shifts in ocean chemistry during Phanerozoic time, in Holland, H. D. and Trendall, A. F., eds., Berlin, Springer-Verlag, p. 123–143.

HORODYSKI, R. J., 1976, Stromatolites of the upper Siyeh Limestone (Middle Proterozoic), Belt Supergroup, Glacier National Park, Montana: Precambrian Research, v. 3, p. 517–536.

HSÜ, K. J., AND MCKENZIE, J. A., 1985, A "Strangelove" ocean in the earliest Tertiary, in Sundquist, E. T., and Broecker, W. S., eds., The Carbon Cycle and Atmospheric CO_2: Natural Variations Archean to Present: American Geophysical Union, Geophysical Monograph 32, p. 487–492.

JACKSON, G. D., AND IANELLI, T. R., 1981, Rift-related cyclic sedimentation in the Neohelikian Borden Basin, northern Baffin Island, in Campbell, F. H. A., ed., Proterozoic Basins of Canada: Geological Survey of Canada, Paper 81-10, p. 269–302.

JAMES, N. P., AND BOURQUE, P.-A., 1992, Reefs and mounds, in Walker, R. G., and James, N. P., eds., Facies Models—Response to Sea Level Change: Geological Association of Canada, p. 323–348.

JAMES, N. P., AND GRAVESTOCK, D., 1990, Lower Cambrian shelf and shelf-margin buildups, Flinders Ranges, South Australia: Sedimentology, v. 37, p. 455–480.

JAMES, N. P., NARBONNE, G. M., AND SHERMAN, A. G., 1998, Molar-tooth carbonates: shallow subtidal facies of the Mid to Late Proterozoic: Journal of Sedimentary Research, v. 68, p. 716–722.

JONES, B., AND RENAUT, R., 1995, Noncrystallographic calcite dendrites from hot-spring deposits at Lake Bogoria, Kenya: Journal of Sedimentary Research, v. A65, p. 154–169.

KAH, L. C., AND GROTZINGER, J. P., 1992, Early Proterozoic (1.9 Ga) thrombolites of the Rocknest Formation, Northwest Territories, Canada: Palaios, v. 7, p. 305–315.

KAH, L. C., AND KNOLL, A. H., 1996, Microbenthic distribution of Proterozoic tidal flats: environmental and taphonomic considerations: Geology, v. 24, p. 79–82.

KARHU, J. A., 1993, Paleoproterozoic evolution of the carbon isotope ratios of sedimentary carbonates in the Fennoscandian Shield: Geological Survey of Finland, Bulletin 371, 87 p.

KASTING, J. F., 1987, Theoretical constraints on oxygen and carbon dioxide concentrations in the Precambrian atmosphere: Precambrian Research, v. 34, p. 205–229.

KAUFMAN, A. J., HAYES, J. M., KNOLL, A. H., AND GERMS, G. J. B., 1991, Isotopic compositions of carbonates and organic carbon from upper Proterozoic successions in Namibia: stratigraphic variation and the effects of diagenesis and metamorphism: Precambrian Research, v. 49, p. 301–327.

KAUFMAN, A. J., JACOBSEN, S. B., AND KNOLL, A. H., 1993, The Vendian record of Sr and C isotopic variations in seawater: Implications for tectonics and paleoclimate: Earth and Planetary Science Letters, v. 120, p. 409–430.

KAUFMAN, A. J., AND KNOLL, A. H., 1995, Neoproterozoic variations in the C-isotope composition of seawater: stratigraphic and biogeochemical implications: Precambrian Research, v. 73, p. 27–50.

KEMPE, S., AND DEGENS, E. T., 1985, An early soda ocean?: Chemical Geology, v. 53, p. 95–108.

KEMPE, S., AND KAZMIERCZAK, J., 1994, The role of alkalinity in the evolution of ocean chemistry, organization of living systems, and biocalcification processes, *in* Doumenge, F., Allemand, D., and Toulemont, A., eds., Past and Present Biomineralization Processes; Considerations about the carbonate cycle: Institut Océanographique [Monaco], p. 61–116.

KENNARD, J. M., AND JAMES, N. P., 1986, Thrombolites and stromatolites: Two distinct types of microbial structures: Palaios, v. 1, p. 492–503.

KENNEDY, M. J., 1996, Stratigraphy, sedimentology, and isotopic geochemistry of Australian postglacial cap dolostones: deglaciations, $\delta^{13}C$ excursions, and carbonate precipitation: Journal of Sedimentary Research, v. 66, p. 1050–1064.

KENNEDY, M. J., RUNNEGAR, B., PRAVE, A. R., HOFFMANN, K.-H., AND ARTHUR, M. A., 1998, Two or four Neoproterozoic glaciations?: Geology, v. 26, p. 1059–1063.

KERANS, C., 1982, Sedimentology and Stratigraphy of the Dismal Lakes Group: Ph. D. Dissertation, Carleton University, Ottawa, 304 p.

KERANS, C., AND DONALDSON, J. A., 1988, Deeper water conical stromatolite reef, Sulky Formation, middle Proterozoic, N. W. T., *in* Geldsetzer, H., James, N. P., and Tebbutt, G., eds., Reefs—Canada and Adjacent Areas: Canadian Society of Petroleum Geologists, Memoir 13, p. 81–88.

KIRSCHVINK, J. L., 1992, Late Proterozoic low-latitude global glaciation: the snowball earth, *in* Schopf, J. W., and Klein, C., eds., The Proterozoic Biosphere: Cambridge, U. K., Cambridge University Press, p. 569–581.

KNOLL, A. H., 1991, End of the Proterozoic Eon: Scientific American, v. 265, p. 64–73.

KNOLL, A. H., FAIRCHILD, I. J., AND SWETT, K., 1993, Calcified microbes in Neoproterozoic carbonates: Implications for our understanding of the Proterozoic/Cambrian transition: Palaios, v. 8, p. 512–525.

KNOLL, A. H., GROTZINGER, J. P., KAUFMAN, A. J., AND KOLOSOV, P., 1995a, Integrated approaches to terminal Proterozoic stratigraphy: an example from the Olenek uplift, northeastern Siberia: Precambrian Research, v. 73, p. 251–270.

KNOLL, A. H., HAYES, J. M., KAUFMAN, A. J., SWETT, K., AND LAMBERT, I. B., 1986, Secular variation in carbon isotope ratios from Upper Proterozoic successions of Svalbard and East Greenland: Nature, v. 321, p. 832–838.

KNOLL, A. H., KAUFMAN, A. J., AND SEMIKHATOV, M. A., 1995b, The carbon-isotope composition of Proterozoic carbonates: Riphean successions from northwestern Siberia (Anabar massif, Turukhansk uplift): American Journal of Science, v. 295, p. 823–850.

KNOLL, A. H., AND SEMIKHATOV, M. A., 1998, The genesis and time distribution of two distinctive Proterozoic stromatolite microstructures: Palaios, v. 13, p. 408–422.

KNOLL, A. H., AND SWETT, K., 1990, Carbonate deposition during the later Proterozoic Era: an example form Spitsbergen: American Journal of Science, v. 290-A, p. 104–132.

KNOLL, A. H., AND WALTER, M. R., 1992, Latest Proterozoic stratigraphy and Earth history: Nature, v. 356, p. 673–678.

KRUSE, P. D., ZHURAVLEV, A. Y., AND JAMES, N. P., 1995, Primordial metazoan–calcimicrobial reefs: Tommotian (early Cambrian) of the Siberian Platform: Palaios, v. 10, p. 291–321.

LI, T. H., TAKAHASHI, T., AND BROECKER, W. S., 1969, The degree of saturation of $CaCO_3$ in the oceans: Journal of Geophysical Research, v. 74, p. 5507–5525.

MARTIN, A., NISBET, E. G., AND BICKLE, M. J., 1980, Archean stromatolites of the Belingwe Greenstone Belt, Zimbabwe (Rhodesia): Precambrian Research, v. 13, p. 337–362.

MATTES, B. W., AND CONWAY MORRIS, S., 1990, Carbonate/evaporite deposition in the Late Precambrian–Early Cambrian Ara Formation of southern Oman, *in* Robertson, A. H. F., Searle, M. P., and Ries, A. C., eds., The Geology and Tectonics of the Oman Region: Geological Society of London, Special Publication, p. 617–636.

MUCCI, A., AND MORSE, J. W., 1983, The incorporation of Mg and Sr into calcite overgrowths: Influences of growth rate and solution composition: Geochimica et Cosmochimica Acta, v. 47, p. 217–233.

MUIR, M. D., 1987, Facies models for Australian Precambrian evaporites, *in* Peryt, T., ed., Evaporite Basins: Heidelberg, Springer-Verlag, p. 5–21.

NARBONNE, G. M., AND JAMES, N. P., 1996, Mesoproterozoic deep-water reefs from the Borden Penninsula, Arctic Canada: Sedimentology, v. 43, p. 827–848.

NARBONNE, G. M., KAUFMAN, A. J., AND KNOLL, A. H., 1994, Integrated chemostratigraphy and biostratigraphy of the upper Windemere Supergroup (Neoproterozoic), northwestern Canada: Implications for Neoproterozoic correlations and the early evolution of animals: Geological Society of America, Bulletin, v. 106, p. 1281–1292.

O'CONNOR, M. P., 1972, Classification and environmental interpretation of the cryptalgal organosedimentary "molar-tooth" structure of the Precambrian Belt–Purcell Supergroup: Journal of Geology, v. 80, p. 592–610.

PELECHATY, S. M., GROTZINGER, J. P., KASHIRTSEV, V. A., AND JERINOVSKY, V. P., 1996a, Chemostratigraphic and sequence stratigraphic constraints on Vendian–Cambrian basin dynamics, northeast Siberian craton: Journal of Geology, v. 104, p. 543–564.

PELECHATY, S. M., AND JAMES, N. P., 1991, Dolomitized middle Proterozoic calcretes, Bathurst Inlet, Northwest Territories, Canada: Journal of Sedimentary Petrology, v. 61, p. 988–1001.

PELECHATY, S. M., JAMES, N. P., KERANS, C., AND GROTZINGER, J. P., 1991, A middle Proterozoic paleokarst unconformity and associated rocks, Elu Basin, northwest Canada: Sedimentology, v. 38, p. 775–797.

PELECHATY, S. M., KAUFMAN, A. J., AND GROTZINGER, J. P., 1996b, Evaluation of $\delta^{13}C$ isotope stratigraphy for intrabasinal correlation: Vendian strata of the Olenek uplift and Kharaulakh Mountains, Siberian platform, Russia: Geological Society of America, Bulletin, v. 108, p. 992–1003.

PELL, S. D., MCKIRDY, D. M., JANSYN, J., AND JENKINS, R. J. F., 1993, Ediacaran carbon isotope stratigraphy of South Australia: Royal Society of South Australia, Transactions, v. 117, p. 153–161.

PERYT, T. M., HOPPE, A., BECHSTADT, T., KOSTER, J., PIERRE, C., AND RICHTER, D. K., 1990, Late Proterozoic aragonite cement crusts, Bambui Group, Minas Gerais, Brazil: Sedimentology, v. 37, p. 279–286.

PRATT, B. R., 1998, Molar-tooth structure in Proterozoic carbonate rocks: origin from synsedimentary earthquakes, and implications for the nature and evolution of basins and marine sediment: Geological Society of America Bulletin, v. 110, p. 1028–1045.

PRATT, B. R., JAMES, N. P., AND COWAN, C. A., 1992, Peritidal carbonates, *in* Walker, R. G., and James, N. P., eds., Facies Models—Response to Sea Level Change: Geological Association of Canada, p. 303–322.

RIDING, R., 1982, Cyanophyte calcification and changes in ocean chemistry: Nature, v. 299, p. 814–815.

RIDING, R., AND ZHURAVLEV, A. Y., 1995, Structure and diversity of oldest sponge–microbe reefs: Lower Cambrian, Aldan River, Siberia: Geology, v. 23, p. 649–652.

SAMI, T. T., AND JAMES, N. P., 1993, Evolution of an early Proterozoic foreland basin carbonate platform, lower Pethei Group, Great Slave Lake, northwest Canada: Sedimentology, v. 40, p. 403–430.

SAMI, T. T., AND JAMES, N. P., 1994, Peritidal platform growth and cyclicity in an early Proterozoic foreland basin, upper Pethei Group, northwest Canada: Journal of Sedimentary Research, v. B64, p. 111–131.

SAMI, T. T., AND JAMES, N. P., 1996, Synsedimentary cements as platform building blocks, Paleoproterozoic Pethei Group, northwestern Canada: Journal of Sedimentary Research, v. 66, p. 209–222.

SANDBERG, P. A., 1983, An oscillating trend in Phanerozoic non-skeletal carbonate mineralogy: Nature, v. 305, 19–22.

SANDBERG, P. A., 1985, Nonskeletal aragonite and pCO_2 in the Phanerozoic and Proterozoic, *in* Sundquist, E. T., and Broecker, W. S., eds., The Carbon Cycle and Atmospheric CO_2: Natural Variations Archean to Present: American Geophysical Union, Geophysical Monograph 32, p. 585–594.

SAYLOR, B. Z., GROTZINGER, J. P., AND GERMS, G. J. B., 1995, Sequence stratigraphy and sedimentology of the Neoproterozoic Kuibis and Schwarzrand Subgroups (Nama Group), Southwest Namibia: Precambrian Research, v. 73, p. 153–171.

SAYLOR, B. Z., KAUFMAN, A. J., GROTZINGER, J. P., AND URBAN, F., 1998, A composite reference section for terminal Proterozoic strata of southern Namibia: Journal of Sedimentary Research, v. 66, p. 1178–1195.

SCHERMERHORN, L. J. G., 1974, Late Precambrian mixtites: Glacial and/or nonglacial?: American Journal of Science, v. 274, p. 673–824.

SCHIDLOWSKI, M., 1988, A 3,800-million-year isotopic record of life from carbon in sedimentary rocks: Nature, v. 333, p. 313–318.

SEREBRYAKOV, S. N., AND SEMIKHATOV, M. A., 1974, Riphean and Recent stromatolites: a comparison: American Journal of Science, v. 274, p. 556–574.

SERGEEV, V. N., KNOLL, A. H., AND GROTZINGER, J. P., 1995, Paleobiology of the Mesoproterozoic Billyakh Group, Anabar Uplift, northern Siberia: Journal of Paleontology, Supplement to No. 1, v. 69, p. 1–37.

SIMONSON, B. M., AND JARVIS, D. G., 1996, Microfabrics of oolites and pisolites in the 2.5 Ga Carawine Dolomite of western Australia, *in* Rezak, R., and Lavoie, D., eds., Carbonate Microfabrics. Berlin: Springer-Verlag, p. 45–67.

SIMONSON, B. M., SCHUBEL, K. A., AND HASSLER, S. W., 1993, Carbonate sedimentology of the early Precambrian Hamersley Group of Western Australia: Precambrian Research, v. 60, p. 287–335.

SINGH, U., 1987, Ooids and cements from the late Precambrian of the Flinders Ranges, South Australia: Journal of Sedimentary Petrology, v. 57, p. 117–127.

SMITH, A. G., 1968, The origin and deformation of some "molar-tooth" structures in the Precambrian Belt–Purcell Supergroup: Journal of Geology, v. 76, p. 426–443.

SMITH, O. A., 1998, Terminal Proterozoic Carbonate Platform Development: Stratigraphy and Sedimentology of the Kuibis Subgroup (ca. 550–548 Ma), Northern Nama Basin, Namibia: MSc. Thesis, Massachusetts Institute of Technology, Cambridge, Massachusetts, 132 p.

SOJA, C. M., 1994, Significance of Silurian stromatolite–sphinctozoan reefs: Geology, v. 22, p. 355–358.

SOUTHGATE, P. N., 1989, Relationships between cyclicity and stromatolite form in the late Proterozoic Bitter Springs Formation, Australia: Sedimentology, v. 36, p. 323–339.

STANLEY, S. M., AND HARDIE, L. A., 1999, Hypercalcification: paleontology links plate tectonics and geochemistry to sedimentology: GSA Today, v. 9, no. 2, p. 1–7.

SUMNER, D. Y., 1995, Facies, Paleogeography, and Carbonate Precipitation in the Archean (2520 Ma) Campbellrand–Malmani Carbonate Platform, Transvaal Supergroup, South Africa: Ph.D. Dissertation, Massachusetts Institute of Technology, Cambridge, Massachusetts, 514 p.

SUMNER, D. Y., 1997a, Carbonate precipitation and oxygen stratification in late Archean seawater as deduced from facies and stratigraphy of the Gamohaan and Frisco formations, Transvaal Supergroup, South Africa: American Journal of Science, v. 297, p. 455–487.

SUMNER, D. Y., 1997b, Late Archean calcite–microbe interactions: Two morphologically distinct microbial communities that affected calcite nucleation differently: Palaios, v. 12, p. 302–318.

SUMNER, D. Y., AND GROTZINGER, J. P., 1993, Numerical modeling of ooid size and the problem of Neoproterozoic giant ooids: Journal of Sedimentary Petrology, v. 63, p. 974–982.

SUMNER, D. Y., AND GROTZINGER, J. P., 1996a, Herringbone calcite: Petrography and environmental significance: Journal of Sedimentary Research, v. 66, p. 419–429.

SUMNER, D. Y., AND GROTZINGER, J. P., 1996b, Were kinetics of Archean calcium carbonate precipitation related to oxygen concentration?: Geology, v. 24, p. 119–122.

SWETT, K., AND KNOLL, A. H., 1989, Marine pisolites from Upper Proterozoic carbonates of East Greenland and Spitsbergen: Sedimentology, v. 36, p. 75–93.

TEITZ, M., AND MOUNTJOY, E. W., 1985, The Yellowhead and Astoria carbonate platforms in the late Proterozoic Upper Miette Group, Jasper, Alberta: Geological Survey of Canada, Paper 85-1A, Current Research, Part A, p. 341–348.

TEITZ, M., AND MOUNTJOY, E. W., 1989, The late Proterozoic Yellowhead carbonate platform west of Jasper, Alberta, in, Geldsetzer, H., James, N. P., and Tebbutt, G., eds., Reefs—Canada and Adjacent Areas: Canadian Society of Petroleum Geologists, Memoir 13, p. 129–134.

TUCKER, M. E., 1983, Diagenesis, geochemistry, and origin of a Precambrian dolomite: The Beck Spring Dolomite of eastern California: Journal of Sedimentary Petrology, v. 53, p. 1097–1119.

TUCKER, M. E., 1986, Formerly aragonitic limestones associated with tillites in the late Proterozoic of Death Valley, California: Journal of Sedimentary Petrology, v. 56, p. 818–830.

TURNER, E. C., JAMES, N. P., AND NARBONNE, G. M., 1997, Growth dynamics of Neoproterozoic calcimicrobial reefs, Mackenzie Mountains, northwest Canada: Journal of Sedimentary Petrology, v. 67, p. 437–450.

TURNER, E. C., NARBONNE, G. M., AND JAMES, N. P., 1993, Neoproterozoic reef microstructures from the Little Dal Group, northwestern Canada: Geology, v. 3, p. 259–262.

VEIZER, J., AND COMPSTON, W., 1976, $^{87}Sr/^{86}Sr$ in Precambrian carbonates as an index of crustal evolution: Geochimica et Cosmochimica Acta, v. 40, p. 905–914.

VEIZER, J., AND HOEFS, J., 1976, The nature of $^{18}O/^{16}O$ and $^{13}C/^{12}C$ secular trends in sedimentary carbonate rocks: Geochimica et Cosmochimica Acta, v. 40, p. 1387–1395.

WALKER, J. C. G., 1985, Carbon dioxide on the early Earth: Origins of Life, v. 16, p. 117–127.

WALTER, M. R., 1976, Stromatolites: Amsterdam, Elsevier, 790 p.

WALTER, M. R., AND BAULD, J., 1983, The association of sulphate evaporites, stromatolitic carbonates and glacial sediments: examples from the Proterozoic of Australia and the Cainozoic of Antarctica: Precambrian Research, v. 21, p. 129–148.

WILKINSON, B. H., OWEN, R. M., AND CARROLL, A. R., 1985, Submarine hydrothermal weathering, global eustasy, and carbonate polymorphism in Phanerozoic marine oolites: Journal of Sedimentary Petrology, v. 55, p. 171–183.

WILLIAMS, E. G., WRIGHT, L. A., AND TROXEL, B. W., 1974, The Noonday Dolomite and equivalent stratigraphic units, southern Death Valley region, California, in Wright, L. A., and Troxel, B., eds., Guidebook: Death Valley Region, California and Nevada: Shoshone, California, Death Valley Publishing Company, p. 73–77.

WRIGHT, V. P., RIES, A. C., AND MUNN, S. G., 1990, Intraplatformal basin-fill deposits from the Infracambrian Huqf Group, east Central Oman, in Robertson, A. H. F., Searle, M. P., and Ries, A. C., eds., The Geology and Tectonics of the Oman Region: Geological Society of London, Special Publication 49, [London], p. 601–616.

XIAO, S., KNOLL, A. H., KAUFMAN, A. J., YIN, L., AND YUN, Z., 1997, Neoproterozoic fossils in Mesoproterozoic rocks? Chemostratigraphic resolution of a biostratigraphic conundrum from the North China Platform: Precambrian Research, v. 84, p. 197–220.

XIAO, S., KNOLL, A. H., AND YUAN, X., 1998, Morphological reconstruction of *Miaohephyton bifurcatum*, a possible brown alga from Neoproterozoic Doushantuo Formation, south China: Journal of Paleontology, v. 72, p. 1072–1086.

YOUNG, G. M., AND LONG, D. G. F., 1977, Carbonate sedimentation in a late Precambrian shelf sea, Victoria Island, Canadian Arctic Archipelago: Journal of Sedimentary Petrology, v. 47, p. 943–955.

ZEMPOLICH, W. G., WILKINSON, B. H., AND LOHMANN, K. C., 1988, Diagenesis of late Proterozoic carbonates: The Beck Spring Dolomite of eastern California: Journal of Sedimentary Petrology, v. 58, p. 656–672.

PART I
TECHNIQUES

GAMMA-RAY LOGS AND U–Pb ZIRCON GEOCHRONOLOGY—ESSENTIAL TOOLS TO CONSTRAIN LITHOFACIES INTERPRETATION OF PALEOPROTEROZOIC DEPOSITIONAL SYSTEMS

MICHAEL J. JACKSON, PETER N. SOUTHGATE, AND ROD W. PAGE

Australian Geological Survey Organisation, GPO Box 378, Canberra, ACT 2601, Australia

ABSTRACT: Outcrop-derived gamma-ray curves, lithofacies, and U-Pb SHRIMP zircon ages are integrated to provide a better understanding of accommodation history in the Paleo–Mesoproterozoic Nathan Group of northern Australia. This chronostratigraphic analysis significantly revises earlier lithostratigraphic interpretations of a 1200-m-thick succession of sandy carbonates. Rather than a continuous succession deposited in a complex series of lacustrine environments, it consists of three completely separate second-order supersequences, each a few hundred meters thick and deposited over a few million years. These supersequences are separated by major stratigraphic breaks (tectonically enhanced sequence boundaries) each approaching a duration of probably 10 million years. Each supersequence comprises several third-order sequences, which themselves contain many higher-order cycles, deposited in a series of continental, shoreline, and inner-ramp to outer-ramp environments. Transgressive, high-energy, continental to shallow marine, mixed clastic–carbonate facies dominate most of the sequences. The middle supersequence, however, preserves deeper-water (mostly sub-storm) stromatolitic facies in one sequence, and storm-reworked clastics in another. These are interpreted as condensed intervals deposited around their respective maximum flooding surfaces and are succeeded by regressive facies that probably represent highstand systems tracts.

New correlations between the Paleoproterozoic carbonate successions of the McArthur Basin and approximately time equivalent clastic successions in the Mt. Isa area, some 400 km to the southeast, are proposed.

INTRODUCTION

The development of a convincing sequence evolution for a succession of Proterozoic sedimentary rocks is hindered largely by the diachronous nature of lithofacies and the lack of biostratigraphic control. This paper provides a case history from the Paleoproterozoic of Northern Australia that illustrates how these constraints have largely been overcome by the use of two techniques—gamma-ray logging of outcrop sections and U–Pb SHRIMP dating of zircon crystals from tuffaceous intervals. Gamma-ray logs from drill holes have been used in the petroleum industry for many years. They provide an independent and objective method for identifying breaks in sedimentation and for subdividing stratigraphic successions, as well as for identifying potential source and reservoir beds (e.g., Rider, 1991). Gamma-ray logs also highlight radioactive intervals and hence are excellent for identifying previously unsuspected tuffaceous layers that may contain minerals suitable for isotopic dating. In this paper gamma-ray logs from surface sections and drill holes have been integrated with lithofacies descriptions and U–Pb SHRIMP ages to chronostratigraphically constrain depositional systems in a mixed carbonate–clastic succession of Mesoproterozoic–Paleoproterozoic age.

U–Pb SHRIMP dating of zircon crystals from tuffaceous layers in Paleoproterozoic rocks provides internal precision of ± a few million years (Page and Sweet, 1998), thereby enabling recognition of second-order and third-order, and perhaps even higher-order, stratigraphic sequences, and also resolving the relative time significance of erosion surfaces within these successions.

Although the dating technique requires expensive and highly sophisticated equipment, which may be difficult to access, the systematic collection of gamma logs from surface outcrops is a relatively simple and routine task involving inexpensive hand-held spectrometers. The manipulation and analysis of the information collected in the field is facilitated by simple spreadsheet programs available on small PCs.

In contrast to lithostratigraphy, which emphasizes the grouping together of rock bodies of similar composition, this paper highlights the benefits of integrating traditional lithofacies data together with sequence stratigraphic and gamma-ray data to (a) define depositional cycles that largely reflect changes in accommodation (at a range of scales); (b) identify significant breaks in sedimentation; and (c) correlate the large-scale accommodation patterns that emerge. This will not only improve our understanding of basin-fill evolution in widely separated parts of northern Australia but also help constrain the timing of generation and migration of metal-bearing brines involved in the deposition of Australia's largest sediment-hosted base metal deposits. Initial revised correlations between this area and the Mount Isa area proposed by Southgate et al. (1997) are, in places, very different from previously published correlations based on regional mapping and lithostratigraphic studies.

REGIONAL SETTING

The rocks described herein occur in the well exposed southern part of the McArthur Basin in the Northern Territory (Fig. 1). The McArthur Basin succession is unmetamorphosed, structurally simple, and of intracratonic origin (Jackson et al., 1987). It has a cumulative stratigraphic thickness of about 12,000 m and has been subdivided into several tectonic–stratigraphic packages (Fig. 2). The oldest package is the Tawallah Group, a 1760–1710 Ma package consisting largely of quartz-rich sandstones and mafic to felsic igneous rocks. The youngest package, the clastic Roper Group, has a tentative SHRIMP age of approximately 1494 Ma from near its base. These two clastic groups bracket a succession of stromatolitic carbonates with minor sandstone and shale, called the McArthur and Nathan Groups. The succession analyzed in this paper is around 1200 m thick and comprises mixed siliciclastic and carbonate rocks of the Nathan Group, together with the Amos Formation, the topmost unit from the underlying McArthur Group (Fig. 2). Most of the data come from two continuously measured sections supplemented by a stratigraphic drill hole, BMR Bauhinia Downs 3, located 10 km farther to the northeast (Fig. 1). Recent U–Pb SHRIMP dating of zircon crystals from tuffaceous beds, reported below, indicates that this succession was deposited within a time span of about 30 million years (from about 1615 Ma to about 1585 Ma). The interpretation presented below is essentially two dimensional in nature, and it is based mainly on detailed field observations. It does, however, represent a sig-

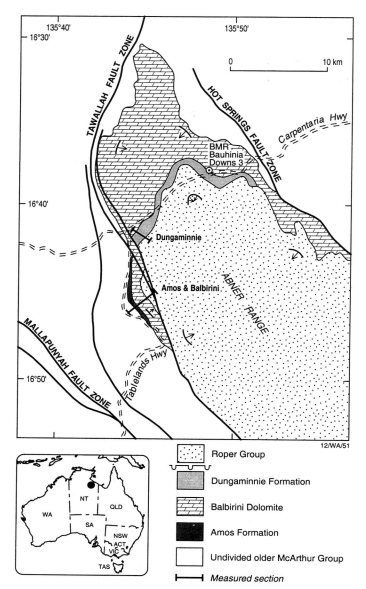

FIG. 1.—Simplified geological map of the northern end of the Abner Range (modified from Jackson et al., 1987), showing distribution of units examined, locations of measured sections, and drill hole used in the study. Main faults are also shown.

nificant improvement on previous regional studies (Muir, 1983; Jackson et al., 1987; Pietsch et al., 1991a, 1991b). There are poor, discontinuous outcrops of the Nathan Group north and northwest of this area (Haines et al., 1993), but the rocks are mostly intensely silicified so that the original textures and structures are poorly preserved. In addition, equivalent strata were recently identified and mapped in Arnhem Land (Rawlings et al., 1997; Haines et al., 1998), but detailed sedimentological studies have not been done in these areas.

LITHOSTRATIGRAPHY AND PREVIOUS SEDIMENTOLOGICAL
INTERPRETATIONS

On the basis of mapping in the late 1970s, the upper carbonate-rich part of the McArthur Basin succession was subdivided

into three formations—the Amos Formation, the Balbirini Dolomite, and the Dungaminnie Formation (Figs. 2, 3). The Amos Formation was defined as the uppermost formation of the McArthur Group, and the Balbirini Dolomite and the Dungaminnie Formation were combined together to form the Nathan Group. The base of the Nathan Group was described as a marked regional unconformity (Muir, 1983; Jackson et al., 1987).

In summary (Fig. 3) the lower part of this 1200-m-thick succession comprises intermittently exposed red beds, evaporitic shaly dolostones, and a prominent calcrete unit (Muir, 1983). Walter et al. (1988) suggest deposition in lacustrine, supralittoral, and alluvial-fan environments. The middle part of the succession (Fig. 3, 400–1000 m) is less sandy and dominated by stromatolitic, intraclastic and oolitic dolostones, with numerous domal, conical, and columnar biostomes. Walter et al. (1988) favor lacustrine or shallow marine environments. A return to sandier carbonates marks the top of the succession, but it also contains finer-grained clastics that Jackson et al. (1987, p. 145) suggest may indicate deposition in slightly deeper-water environments than those evident in the rest of the section.

In essence, the lithostratigraphic studies in the 1970s emphasized (a) the threefold subdivision into the Amos, Balbirini, and Dungaminnie formations, (b) the break between the Amos and Nathan Group, (c) the internal fourfold subdivision of the Balbirini Dolomite, and (d) the dominance of shallow-water environments. Although reservations were expressed on the dif-

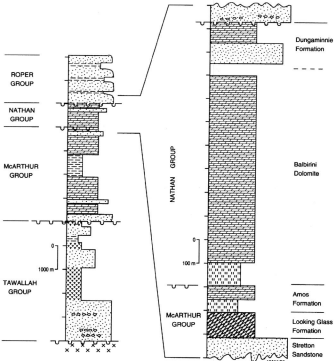

FIG. 2.—Simplified lithostratigraphy of the McArthur Basin Succession (from Jackson et al., 1987). Left-hand column shows the main groups that constitute the complete basin succession; the right-hand column shows a more detailed subdivision of the youngest part of the basin succession described in this paper.

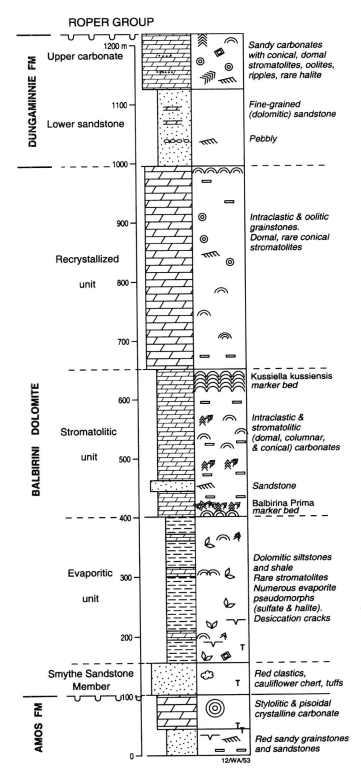

ROPER GROUP

DUNGAMINNIE FM

1200 m — Upper carbonate — Sandy carbonates with conical, domal stromatolites, oolites, ripples, rare halite

1100 — Lower sandstone — Fine-grained (dolomitic) sandstone — Pebbly

1000

Recrystallized unit — 900 — 800 — 700 — Intraclastic & oolitic grainstones. Domal, rare conical stromatolites

BALBIRINI DOLOMITE

Kussiella kussiensis marker bed

Stromatolitic unit — 600 — 500 — Intraclastic & stromatolitic (domal, columnar, & conical) carbonates

Sandstone

Balbirina Prima marker bed

400

Evaporitic unit — 300 — 200 — Dolomitic siltstones and shale. Rare stromatolites. Numerous evaporite pseudomorphs (sulfate & halite). Desiccation cracks

Smythe Sandstone Member — Red clastics, cauliflower chert, tuffs

AMOS FM

100 — Stylolitic & pisoidal crystalline carbonate

0 — Red sandy grainstones and sandstones

12/WA/53

FIG. 3.—Generalized composite column, showing the main lithofacies in the Amos, Balbirini, and Dungaminnie formations, based on information available up to 1979 (based on Muir, in Jackson et al., 1987). The informal subdivisions of the formations are also shown. Symbols are mostly self-explanatory, but they follow the scheme in Jackson et al. (1987, fig. 6).

ficulties of interpreting shallow water carbonate environments, most of these early studies favored deposition in a complex of lacustrine and associated continental environments (Muir, 1983; Jackson et al., 1987; Walter et al., 1988). During later mapping these lithostratigraphic subdivisions were traced to the north and west (Pietsch et al., 1991b; Haines et al., 1993), but because of the poor preservation little additional information on environments of deposition or evolution through time was provided.

METHODS—GAMMA-RAY LOGGING OF SURFACE OUTCROPS

The aim of the North Australian Basins Resource Evaluation (NABRE) Project, within which this work was done, is to provide a time-series predictive framework for Proterozoic basin evolution in northern Australia (Southgate et al., 1996). Sequence stratigraphic principles (e.g., Wilgus et al., 1988; Emery and Myers, 1996; Miall, 1997) are used to identify chronostratigraphic surfaces and better understand the stratigraphic architecture of the basin phases between these surfaces. The project is developing a chronostratigraphic framework for the Paleoproterozoic of northern Australia, and this framework is being used to better understand the origin of the stratiform Zn–Pb–Ag deposits of this region. To achieve this new understanding, well-exposed, key sections between Mount Isa and the Roper River were marked out at 1.5 m intervals and geologically logged using a Jacob's staff and Abney level. Concurrently, the sections were also gamma logged at 50 cm intervals using a hand-held Scintrex GRS-500 spectrometer. Although individual uranium, thorium, and potassium channels are available, the gamma-ray curves used in this study are total radiation counts only. Although there are a number of exceptions (for examples see Rider, 1991), gamma radiation correlates mostly to clay content, so that the curves show the relative shaliness of the rocks that constitute the Nathan Group. The gamma-ray curves are ideal for highlighting subtle trends in composition, which are commonly difficult to distinguish by lithofacies mapping alone. The validity of outcrop gamma logging for correlation purposes has been documented in several Phanerozoic examples, but we believe that this represents the first time they have been extensively used to help elucidate Paleoproterozoic accommodation history. Krassay (1998) provides a detailed description and discussion of the technique, and a full list of references.

COMPOSITE GAMMA-RAY CURVE

The composite gamma-ray log for the succession at the northern end of the Abner Range is shown in the left-hand side of Figure 4. This was measured in 1996 at 0.5 m intervals using a hand-held spectrometer as four separate sections, which were later combined into one composite, which was subsequently renumbered with 0 m at the base of the section (Jackson and Southgate, 1997). The interval from 960 to 1115 m was measured on core from stratigraphic drill hole BMR Bauhinia Downs 3. This core was gamma logged using AGSO's vehicle-mounted large crystal spectrometer—an Exploranium GR-320 Envispec model equipped with twin GPS-21 detectors. This is a much more sophisticated and sensitive system than the hand-held Scintrex spectrometers. The gamma-ray count values re-

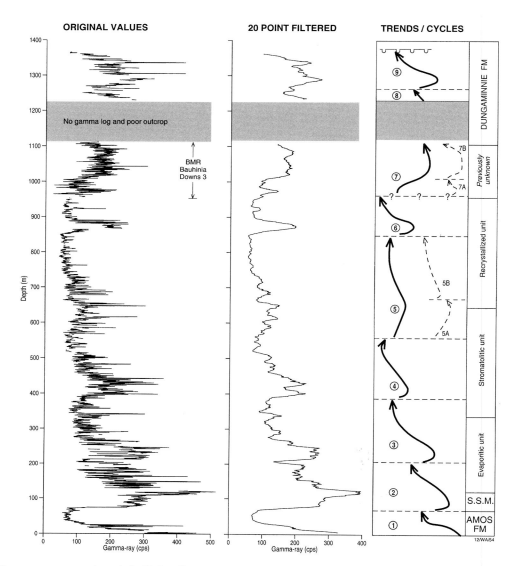

FIG. 4.—Composite gamma-ray curve through the Nathan Group and the upper part of the underlying Amos Formation. Left-hand column shows the original measurements at 50 cm spacing, and is an amalgamation of four separately measured sections. The next column is a simplified version of the left column; the original data have been smoothed, using a 20-point filtering routine, to elucidate and emphasize the broad trends in the log. The second column from the right is a schematic representation and interpretation of the main trends and breaks in the log; the numbered cycles are those described in the text. For comparison, the main lithostratigraphic subdivisions are shown on the far right-hand side of the diagram.

corded by the two systems are different in that the actual figures recorded and the amplitude of variations around a mean are about an order of magnitude different. In this study, we are not attempting to compare absolute measurements of gamma radiation, rather we are looking to analyze curve trends to facilitate sequence analysis, so values from the "Exploranium" spectrometer have been adjusted to give them a mean value and amplitude variation similar to that recorded by the Scintrex machine. The stratigraphic position of the well and the lithostratigraphic units summarized in the previous section are also shown in Figure 4.

There are several small gaps in the original gamma curve (around 10, 120, 190, 250, 280, 520, 820, 1280, 1300, and 1350 m) and one large break (between 1120 and 1250 m). These discontinuities are intervals of no outcrop. Gamma readings

were recorded only on definite, *in situ* outcrop. The large gap of no values near the top of the section relates to the lower sandstone part of the Dungaminnie Formation. Although this part of the section contains scattered small outcrops it consists largely of displaced float and scree. Tests elsewhere have indicated that spectral readings from this sort of "sub-crop" do not produce reliable results.

In the NABRE project the strategy for sequence stratigraphic interpretation mimics that of the capture of the original data. The gamma-ray logs and detailed lithofacies logs are collected together and integrated and interpreted in the field. However, to illustrate how powerful the gamma-ray curve may be, even in isolation, the following section provides a description and interpretation of the gamma log essentially on its own. As will become evident, the gamma-ray curve may provide a markedly different subdivision of a succession from that determined solely from lithofacies information.

On the basis of a rudimentary visual analysis of the logs a number of distinctive features are evident in Figure 4:

(a) There is a general overall trend in the gamma log from higher values near the base (0–200 m) to lower values higher up (i.e., around 960 m). This indicates that the succession is gradually becoming less silty or clay-rich upwards (i.e., the log and the associated facies are gradually "cleaning upwards").

(b) Gamma values above the no-outcrop interval (1230–1400 m) are noticeably higher than those just below it. Even without other constraints, the most obvious first suggestion would be for a subtle but distinct lithological change at this level, so that there might be a significant break in the poorly outcropping interval.

(c) Using curve shape the succession can be subdivided into nine larger-scale "cycles", around 100–150 m thick. Annotated as cycles 1 to 9 in Figure 4, they are more easily seen on the 20-point filtered curve, which smooths the gamma response. The lower four cycles all have a similar motif—they show a sharp deflection to higher count values at the base, followed by a gradual upward-decreasing ("cleaning") trend. The sharp change between cycles 1 and 2 equates to the lithostratigraphic boundary between the Amos Formation and the Smythe Sandstone, which, as noted earlier, was interpreted as a major group boundary. The breaks between cycles 2 and 3 and between 3 and 4 are at different levels from where the lithostratigraphic unit boundaries have been defined (see right-hand side of Figure 4). Cycles 5, 6, and 7 are not as clearly defined or as uniform as Cycles 1 to 4. Cycles 5 and 7 are more symmetrical than those below. Here again, the breaks between the cycles in the gamma logs do not equate with the previously defined lithostratigraphic subdivisions. In various parts of both the unedited and filtered curves it is possible to identify smaller-scale cycles. For example, between 70 and 100 m there are cycles about 15 m thick, whilst between 270 and 380 m there are probably three larger cycles, each a few tens of meters thick. We have not done enough research to adequately define the character and relationships of these finer-scale cycles, but some are described later, and the gamma curves does help to highlight parts of the section worthy of further research. The poorly defined cycle 9 at the top of the preserved section is most like cycle 4. The differentiation of these cycles using gamma trends alone may appear somewhat equivocal, as it is not based on a rigorous statistical analysis of the gamma-ray data. However, as we have pointed out above, this work is at a reconnaissance level, and we feel that a non-mathematical visual analysis is not unreasonable.

In summary, the gamma-ray logs, on their own, suggest a significantly different subdivision for this stratigraphic package than previously.

INTEGRATING GAMMA-RAY LOGS WITH NEW AND MORE DETAILED LITHOFACIES INFORMATION.

The initial interpretations for the gamma-ray logs can be significantly upgraded when combined with new lithofacies information. More detailed descriptions of the cycles shown in Figure 4 are presented below and illustrated graphically in Figures 5, 6, and 7.

Cycle 1

The basal part of the section (0–12 m) comprises mostly irregular, discontinuous, thin-bedded, red–brown siltstone and mudstone, with rare sandy laminae (Fig. 5). Small current ripples, desiccation cracks, and irregular carbonate crusts and pseudonodules suggest deposition in low-gradient alluvial-plain environments with soil formation and common emergence. Gamma-ray values are relatively high (around 300–400 counts). This facies coarsens upwards into a sandy dolarenite that contains larger asymmetric ripples, angular clasts of the red–brown siltstone, and clasts of dolomitic mudstone. Stratification is thicker, scouring and erosion of beds is common, and desiccation is still present. The associated gamma curve shows a gradual lowering in count values (cleaning upward) concomitant with the increase in dolomite content (12–30 m). The spikes around 25–30 m are related to 20–30-cm-thick pink beds, which are interpreted as waterlaid tuffs (see later); these contain a high content of potassium. At around 30 m the facies is a coarse-grained, trough cross-stratified, intraclastic, peloid grainstone with rare coarse quartz grains and thin interbeds of desiccated dolomitic mudstone. Deposition in a high-energy, intermittently exposed carbonate-rich environment (intertidal channel/flat) is favored. The overlying 60 m consists of massive, karstically weathered, extensively stylolitized gray crystalline dolostone with large "floating" pisoid structures. This is the archetypal Amos Formation facies, which has been described in detail by Muir (1983) and has been interpreted as a Proterozoic calcrete. This interval contains minimal clastic detritus (<2% floating coarse quartz grains) and consequently has a uniformly low gamma-ray curve (around 80 counts). The original (pre-calcrete) facies appears to have been a clean, porous, medium-grained peloid grainstone, as these rocks are evident in the gradational lower contact (30–35 m) and in rare patches within the calcrete. Before alteration in a calcrete profile, the Amos Formation represented a gradual transgression from a fluvial–mud-flat environment to an agitated and current-swept, shallow-water (?marine) carbonate shoreline environment. The related gamma curve has a smooth gradual "cleaning upward" character.

Cycle 2

The top of the Amos Formation, which is also the base of this cycle, is marked by a sharp lithofacies change and a distinct kick on the gamma log (at 75 m). The overlying Balbirini Dolomite consists of reddish-brown dolomitic and micaceous siltstone with thin, rippled sandstone lenses and numerous desiccation cracks—a facies almost identical to that seen at the base of the Amos Formation. The contact shows local erosional relief of at least 3 m, and is mantled by a ferruginous and manganiferous crust. Muir (1978) reported conglomerates at the base of the Balbirini Dolomite at the southern end of the Abner Range. Obviously there is a marked basinward shift in facies across this surface, indicating that it is a sequence boundary.

Cycle 2 comprises this basal continental red-bed facies (75–110 m) with high gamma values that is gradually replaced upwards by dolostones. These dolostones contain extensive diagenetic halite and sulfate pseudomorphs and rare stromatolites (Fig. 5, 110–221 m). The stromatolites are poorly developed and are mostly wavy to stratiform varieties. Muir (in Jackson

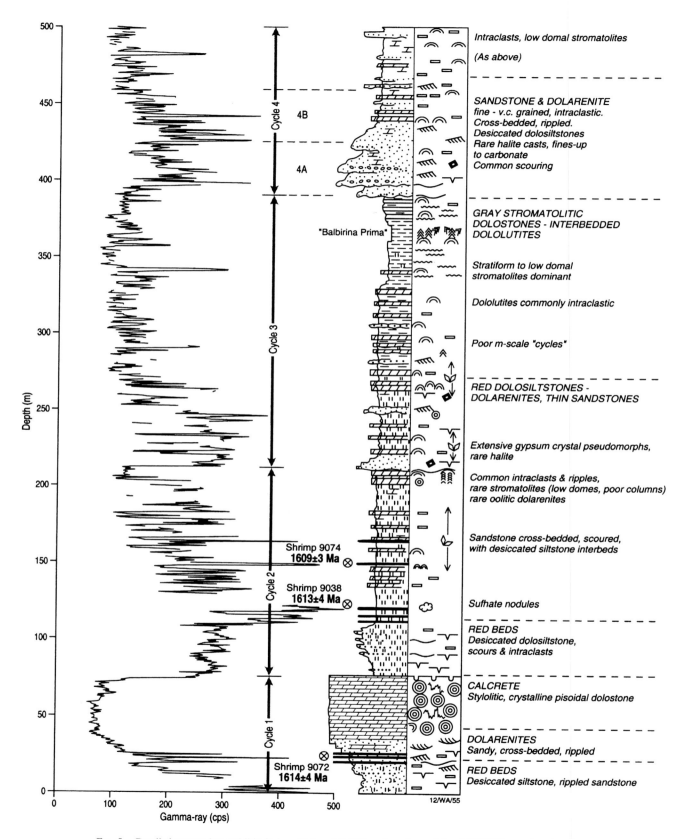

FIG. 5.—Detailed gamma log and lithofacies of interval 0–500 m. Locations of dated SHRIMP samples also shown.

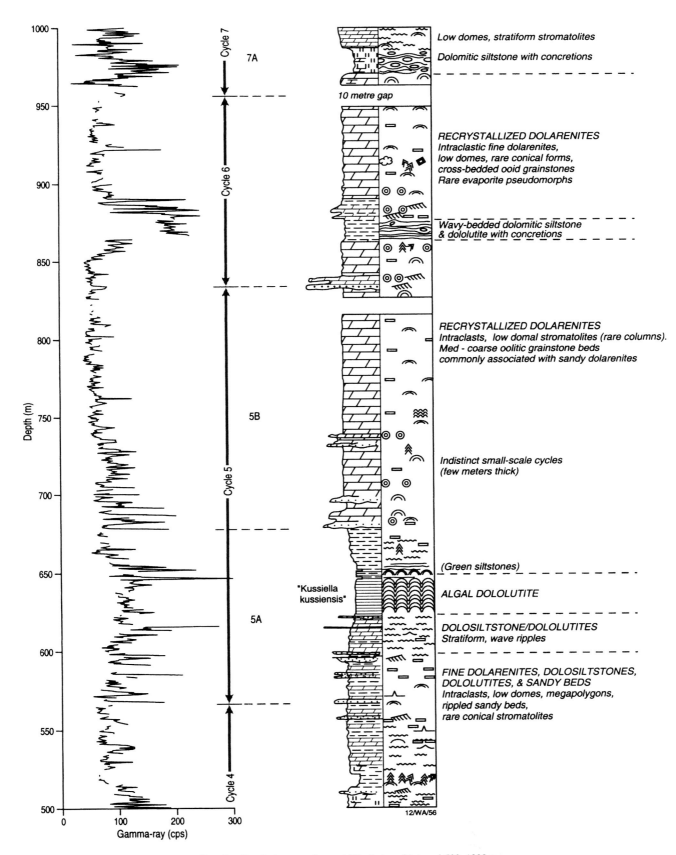

FIG. 6.—Detailed gamma log and lithofacies of interval 500–1000 m.

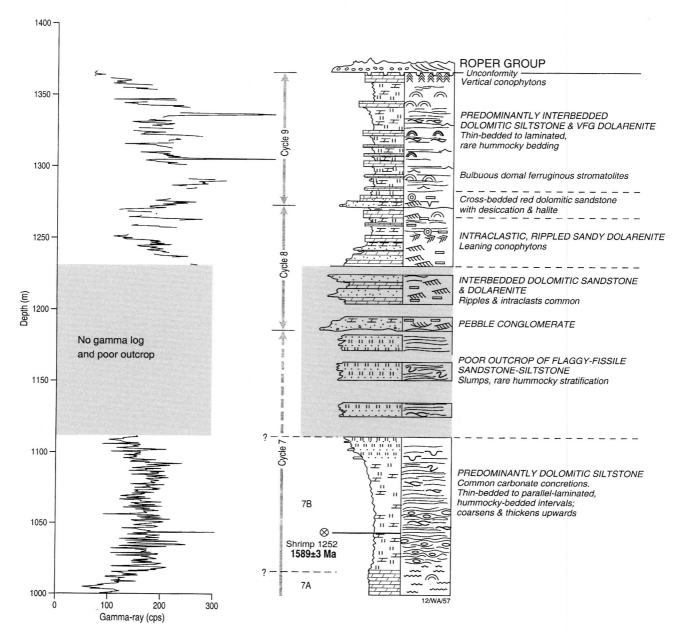

FIG. 7.—Detailed gamma log and lithofacies of interval 1000–1370 m.

et al., 1987) prefers deposition in largely continental environments. Oolitic and intraclastic beds occur in the uppermost few meters of cycle 2, which we interpret as indicating that the facies gradually deepen upwards; we prefer deposition in a marginal marine sabkha rather than a lake. The gamma curve has prominent peaks between 110 and 120 m, related to potassium-rich pink beds; these complicate the otherwise predictable relationship between facies and the gamma-ray curve. Between about 150 and 180 m the facies clearly differentiate smaller-scale (1–3 m thick) cycles consisting of shallow subtidal to intertidal, intraclastic and stromatolitic carbonates capped by supratidal evaporitic facies; these are more clearly evident on larger-scale gamma-ray logs.

Cycle 3

Here again, a sharp deflection to the right on the gamma-ray log defines the base at 213 m. This is caused by red–brown silty sandstones erosionally overlying "clean" stromatolitic dolo-stones (of uppermost cycle 2). The basal red beds, which are also evaporitic, were probably deposited in saline mudflats—the numerous desiccation cracks indicate regular emergence. The section gradually cleans upward to low gamma-ray values associated with carbonates (Fig. 5, between 213 and 390 m). The carbonates contain poorly defined cycles (each a few meters thick) with intraclasts and low domal stromatolites overlain by evaporitic and desiccation-cracked laminated beds. These higher-order cycles were probably deposited in more persistently submerged, storm-current-swept environments than those in cycle 2, but most of them still record periods of desiccation, so they are likely to be no deeper than shallow subtidal. Distinct low values on the gamma-ray log (at 345–355 m, 360–365 m, and 375 m) relate to stromatolite biostromes devoid of desiccation features. The 345–355 m interval consists of stratiform and very low domal forms interbedded with laminated dolomitic siltstone and dololutite; the presence of only a few small intraclasts and the preservation of thin lamination suggests quieter-water and deeper environments. The 360–365 m interval comprises the distinctive association of domal, branching-columnar, and branching-conical cherty stromatolites called the *Balbirina prima* bioherm series. Walter et al. (1988) describe this "marker bed" in some detail and interpret it as developing within a shallow subaqueous environment, at the end of a transgressive episode. The gamma low at 375 m comprises about 3 m of very fine grained dolarenite containing broad low domal stromatolites. These "clean" stromatolitic carbonates, surrounded by generally low-energy laminated fine-grained facies, are interpreted as the deepest facies so far encountered. If the *Balbirina prima* bioherm, which is the thickest of these, marks the maximum flooding (MFS) for cycle 3, the overlying 30–40 m would represent what is preserved of the overlying highstand systems tract (HST), but more detailed studies are required to confirm this.

Cycles 1, 2, and 3, although subtly different, have very similar gamma-ray signatures and internal lithofacies stacking patterns. They appear to contain at least two orders of thinner cycles—most of these kept up with accommodation and filled the available space generated by subsidence of the carbonate platform. However, there is an overall gradual deepening of facies, presumably related to increasing accommodation. The cycle motif of these mixed carbonate–clastic rocks is very different from the standard gamma log motifs developed from clastic rocks (e.g., Van Wagoner et al., 1990), where the gamma peak relates to shales laid down around the MFS, and not to early transgressive "dirty" sandstones.

Cycle 4

A similar succession of facies, together with a gradually upward-reducing gamma curve, occurs between 395 m and around 560 m (Figs. 5, 6). The marked kick on the gamma curve at 395 m defines a sharp incision surface cut into "clean" fine-grained stromatolitic dolostone. This surface is overlain by about 50 m of pebbly, cross-bedded, coarse-grained, dolomitic and limonitic sandstone with thin beds of red–brown siltstone and intraclastic and stromatolitic dolostone. In this cycle, the basal basinward shift of facies is not into low-energy saline mudflat environments, but rather to a higher-energy and much coarser-grained facies with lots of scouring and thicker cross beds (?braided fluvial facies or coastal). This clastic succession is gradually replaced upwards by shallow marine carbonates. Lower down these carbonates consist of fine-grained peloid intraclastic grainstones (commonly with quartz sand) interbedded with low domal and stratiform stromatolites. Higher up, dololutites and dolomitic siltstones replace the grainstones, and crinkly-flat stromatolites and rare conophyton-like forms replace the low domal forms. The interval 500–550 m contains only

rare, thin, fine-grained quartz sandstone beds. As with cycle 3 these lower-energy, finer-grained facies are interpreted as indicating gradual transgression into deeper-water environments.

Although not evident during geological logging, and somewhat masked by several high gamma spikes, the gamma-ray log between 395 and 460 m indicates that the lower part of cycle 4 comprises two distinctly asymmetric higher-order cycles, each around 20–25 m thick (annotated 4A and B in Figure 5). Despite the fact that lithologically this sand-rich interval looks like one event, the gamma-ray log clearly indicates it occurred as two distinct pulses—the reason for this is not known, but here again the gamma log highlights features for further research. The high individual spikes on the gamma log, mentioned above, commonly have count values about twice those of the enclosing sediments. These are produced by thin green shales between the carbonates or sandstones, and not pink beds, as was the case lower down in the section. These green shales may be related to floodings and probably define small-scale cycles. In contrast, the gamma spike at 482 m, in a section of mostly "clean" dolostones, is related to a fine-grained sandy doloarenite bed that contains obvious pink grains (?feldspar or clastic "pink bed" grains), indicating that tuffs were still being deposited. Clearly, to gain a better appreciation of events the gamma log and sedimentological information have to be interpreted closely together. A second bioherm of branching-conical stromatolites (similar to *Balbirina prima*) enclosed in quieter-water, flat-laminated dolosiltstones, occurs in an area of discontinuous outcrop around 520 m. By analogy with *Balbirina prima* in cycle 3, it would be sensible to interpret this biostrome as indicating where maximum flooding occurred in this cycle. The overlying (above 527 m) low-energy facies of thin-bedded, fine-grained dolarenites and dolosiltstones would then represent what remains of the succeeding HST.

The contact between cycles 4 and 5 is hard to define, both on the gamma logs and in the lithofacies. At about 550 m the gradually decreasing trend in gamma log values is replaced by a gradually increasing trend. In contrast to the cycles below, there is not a sharp deflection to the right in the gamma-ray curve, nor is there an obvious change in the lithofacies (Fig. 6). Where then is the most sensible place to put a boundary? Four specific features near 565 m indicate a change to shallower-water environments and suggest that this is where the sequence boundary, or its correlative conformity, may best be located. These features are: (1) the subtle, but obvious, change in trend of the gamma log with a gradual increase in values; (2) megapolygons at 570 m; (3) a quartz-rich intraclast conglomerate with rafts of desiccation-cracked dolomudstone (at 577 m); and (4) intraclast conglomerates containing well-rounded quartz granules between 580 and 600 m (Fig. 6). We interpret this as a new cycle with a base just below these features at about 565 m.

Cycle 5

Cycle 5 may be one thick cycle stretching from 565 to 835 m, or two separate cycles with a break around 680 m (Figs. 4, 6). With the currently available evidence a definitive decision cannot be made. Either way, both in gamma signature and facies this interval is substantially different from those described above.

Subcycle 5a.—The gamma log shows a gradual upward increase in values from around 100 cps near 565 m to about 150 cps at 650 m, then dropping back rapidly to <100 cps between 660 and 680 m. Above the basal sandy intraclastic facies (see preceding section) the rocks in this cycle are dominated by thin-bedded and laminated dolosiltstone and dolomitic mudstone with flat algal lamination, domal stromatolites, rare wavy ripples, and very rare intraclasts. Except near the base, and at 622 m, quartz sand is absent. The outcrop between 600 and 622 m is discontinuous and calcretized, and more extensively weathered. The interval 623 to 648 m comprises the stromatolite biostrome *Kussiella kussiensis* (Muir *in* Jackson et al., 1987; Walter et al., 1988). This is a distinctive tan–brown, 25-m-thick biostrome of superimposed beds (50–100 cm thick) of upright stromatolite columns, composed almost entirely of carbonate mud, that is laterally traceable for many tens of kilometers. In diameter, the columns range from about 5 cm up to about 80 cm wide, but most are in the 10–20 cm range. The carbonate forming the stromatolite columns is a fine-grained hypidiotopic dolomite. Inter-column areas are predominantly carbonate mudstone, but there are rare very fine peloids and small intraclasts (Walter et al., 1988). In plan, the stromatolite columns are mostly circular, but rare slightly elongate forms with a west–east orientation are present. Except for infrequent hardgrounds "micro unconformities", which imply some current movement (with minor erosion of the algal mats), the internal microstructure is regular and even (Walter et al., 1988, p. 97). Towards the top of the biostrome several green shale layers (20–50 cm thick) separate the individual stromatolite beds and give rise to the prominent spikes in the gamma log (Fig. 6). The uniformity of the biostrome, its local stratigraphic setting, lack of associated shallow-water features, and its widespread lateral distribution indicate that it must represent one of the deepest-water facies so far encountered. A low-energy environment, well beyond the effects of most storm-related activity, is suggested. In sequence stratigraphic terms, we see this stromatolitic biostrome as representing a larger-scale flooding with, perhaps, the green shales at the top smothering the stromatolites, which were unable to keep up with accommodation rates and were effectively drowned (MFS). The biostrome is overlain (648–680 m) by laminated dolosiltstone and dolomudstone, with rare intraclasts; these are a shallower facies and may represent what remains of the overlying HST.

Although most of the gamma spikes in this subcycle are related to green shale, the spike at 616 m is caused by a pinkish siliceous bed, which resembles the K-rich pink tuffs from near the base of the section.

Subcycle 5b.—The reason for separating out the interval 680–830 m as a potential separate cycle from 5a is threefold: (1) the gamma log shows an obvious deflection to the right followed by a smooth gradual return to the left, i.e., it shows a motif similar to the underlying cycles; (2) numerous quartz granules occur in the basal carbonates, above a 30-m-thick interval that lacks quartz grains, and (3) oolitic grainstones are common in the interval (Fig. 6). At 680 m a gritty dolarenite overlies a sharp erosion surface cut into a stromatolitic dololutite. This is interpreted as indicating a basinward shift in facies and hence a sequence boundary or its correlative conformity. The succeeding 60 meters comprises largely interbedded carbonates and shales. Extensive recrystallization masks textures and struc-

tures, but the gamma log suggests that this interval contains stacked cycles, each a few meters thick. Intraclastic, stromatolitic, and oolitic dolarenites are common components of the more resistant carbonate parts of the cycles. Stratiform to very low-relief, broad domal stromatolites dominate, but there are also thin (5–20 cm) biostromes of chertified columnar and conical forms. Prominent beds of ooid grainstones occur at 680 m, 707 m, and 738 m. These are 10–20 cm thick, tabular, cross-stratified beds and presumably represent thin ooid shoals. All of them have distinctly low gamma count values compared to the enclosing facies, consistent with their origin as winnowed, current-deposited material. Fine to medium quartz sand occurs in beds of intraclastic peloid grainstones at 733 m but appears to be absent from there to the top of the unit at 833 m—this interval is dominated by fine peloid grainstones with small intraclasts, ripples, and scour surfaces, and low domal stromatolites with rare west–east orientation. The gamma log of subcycle 5b shows an aggradational character, i.e., carbonate production and subsidence were evenly balanced.

At this reconnaissance level of study it is probably not too important which interpretation model we favor—one or two cycles. The facies and gamma logs indicate mainly transgressive trends low down (580–620 m), culminating in the drowning of the *Kussiella kussiensis* biostrome at a large-scale, regional MFS. This is then succeeded by either: (a) a thin HST of aggrading inner-ramp facies (upper cycle 5a), truncated by a sequence boundary, then a separate cycle (5b) that is characterized by relatively low accommodation so that the carbonate facies keep up; or, (b) a thick HST (650 m on) characterized by an initial weakly progradational trend, and then a fairly uniform aggradational phase.

Cycle 6

A thick interval of high gamma values between 860 and 890 m is the main distinguishing feature of this cycle (Fig. 6). This kick is related mainly to a 15-m-thick interval of fissile, laminated, dolomitic siltstone and dololutite. It is distinguished by continuous, parallel to wavy lamination with rare starved ripples, and incipient carbonate concretions. It indicates a general lowering of the energy of the depositional environment compared to those above and below and is interpreted as being deposited in deeper-water environments, but within reach of larger waves and occasional storms. This facies was not recognized below this level. It reflects an increase in the amount of fine clastic material available for deposition from suspension at a time or place on the ramp where carbonate production was fairly low. Like the *Kussiella kussiensis* biostrome, it is interpreted as marking the MFS of this cycle.

On the gamma log, the base of Cycle 6 would appear to be best placed at 850 m, where the curve changes from a decreasing to a markedly increasing trend (Fig. 6). However, when combined with the lithofacies, the base of the cycle is probably better placed at 833 m, at the base of an intraclastic and oolitic grainstones facies, where scattered quartz pebbles up to 10 mm in size rest on a scoured surface (sequence boundary or its correlative conformity). Because this basal facies is not "dirty" it does not produce a kick on the gamma log as in cycles 1 to 4. This is due to the similarity of facies between the late HST of cycle 5b and the initial transgressive part of cycle 6. So, here, we have an example where the facies are more discriminatory than the gamma logs, but together they are very powerful. Perhaps we should emphasize here that deflections in the gamma log in cycle 6 are interpreted more along the lines of traditional cycle motifs from the clastic literature (e.g., Van Wagoner et al., 1990) with deflections to the right to higher gamma values indicating transgression into deeper water—the opposite of the patterns seen below.

A shoaling of environments and increase in energy levels occurs in the HST (890–950 m) overlying the shaly unit. This is indicated between 880 and 888 m by several 1-m-thick, fining-up cycles with erosional bases capped by intraclast lags and climbing ripple-in-drift, interpreted as rapidly deposited ?tidal-channel deposits. Stromatolites above here also suggest shallowing. Several domal biostromes near the top of the outcropping Balbirini Dolomite (930–940 m) are oriented north–south, probably because of the effects of stronger currents. Chert pseudomorphs after sulfate and halite evaporites occur at 917 m—concentrated brines would also be consistent with reduced accommodation and gradual shallowing.

Cycle 7

Cycle 7 is represented only by the interval drilled in 1979 in BMR Bauhinia Downs 3, which was located specifically to intersect the non-outcropping uppermost part of the Balbirini Dolomite. As noted earlier, the gamma log from the drill hole has been fitted to the top of the outcrop section at 960 m. The lower 10 m of the drill hole consists largely of stromatolitic dolostone beds 2–3 m thick, separated by thin beds of green dolomitic siltstone–shale, which are probably small-scale cycles similar to those seen at the top of the outcropping section.

Basically, the gamma logs and facies in the drill hole can be subdivided into two symmetrical subcycles (Figs. 6, 7), but these are not as clearly differentiated as underlying cycles 1–6. The lower subcycle, between about 960 and 1000 m, comprises cyclic, stromatolitic carbonates, which give low values on the curve, bracketing a shale-dominated interval (970–980 m), with values around 150 cps. These middle green dolomitic siltstones and mudstones have even, parallel lamination commonly warped around incipient carbonate concretions. This facies is similar to that seen in the MFS shales of cycle 6; so here also it is interpreted as flooding into deeper-water environments. The upper subcycle (1000–1100 m) is thicker and is characterized by higher gamma values throughout. Although it is still dolomitic it contains a higher proportion of siltstone and mudstone with laminae of very fine-grained dolomitic sandstone. Stratification is mostly thin to laminated and parallel. Low-amplitude wavy lamination (?micro-HCS) is present between 1060 and 1090 m. Microloading and microconvolution occur between 1080 and 1100 m, and most sand laminae have microscoured bases. These features, together with well-developed carbonate concretions and glauconite between 1050 and 1080 m, indicate condensed deposition in low-energy environments—possibly in the mid to outer ramp, just within the range of the effects of the largest storms. The facies show a clear upward coarsening and thickening in the uppermost 20 m of the drill hole (1090–1110 m, Fig. 7). The facies at the top of the hole, very fine-grained sandstone and siltstone with loads, flame structures, and micro ball-and-pillow structures, is similar

to that which forms the poor outcrop at the base of the Dungaminnie Formation, described below.

Whereas carbonate production in the underlying units often kept up with accommodation, cycles 6 and 7 exhibit thick, deeper-water, clastic facies at their respective MFS, indicating that they were unable to keep up with accommodation, and the ramp at these times was thus effectively drowned.

Cycles 8–9

These are the youngest carbonate-rich sedimentary cycles in the McArthur Basin. They are preserved only through an area of about 10 km² at the northwest end of the Abner Range. Because the outcrop is also discontinuous, these are the least understood of this succession. There is a 130 m gap in the gamma-ray log between the top of BMR Bauhinia Downs 3 and the start of good outcrop at 1230 m (Fig. 7). In the absence of outcrop and a gamma-ray log we are not sure what happens to the top of cycle 7 or the lower part of cycle 8. However, a thin conglomerate at approximately 1185 m is interpreted as a possible sequence boundary, so this is used to separate cycle 7 from cycle 8. The section below this point comprises flaggy to fissile, thin- to medium-bedded, very fine-grained dolomitic sandstone, similar to that present in the upper 30–40 m of Bauhinia Downs 3. The bedding is mostly regular with wavy and hummocky surfaces, and there are dewatering structures, micro-scouring, and ?slump contortions; together these indicate shallow marine, reasonably rapid deposition above wave base. The conglomerate at 1185 m is a 2-m-thick, sharp-based, very coarse-grained sandstone–granule conglomerate. It is interpreted as indicating a basinward shift in facies. It is succeeded by mixed carbonate and clastic rocks; the clastics are poorly sorted, fine to coarse grained, micaceous and feldspathic sandstones; the carbonates are sandy, fine- to coarse-grained dolostones. The gamma log and revised lithofacies log in Figure 7 starts at about 45 m above the conglomerate. This upper part of the Dungaminnie Formation consists of interbedded dolomitic siltstones and sandy, stromatolitic, oolitic and intraclastic dolostones—facies not too dissimilar to those in the upper part of the Balbirini Dolomite. Between 1250 and 1275 m these facies appear to be are arranged into 3–5-m-thick, shallowing-upward cycles. The cross-stratification, intraclasts, and scoured surfaces together indicate high-energy current-swept environments.

A distinctive, 2-m-thick biostrome of "leaning" conical stromatolites in dark gray crystalline dolostone (see Jackson et al., 1987, fig. 171) occurs at 1250 m. The stromatolite cones are bilaterally symmetrical in plan view; most are ovate or lanceolate shaped. After rotation of the present bedding back to horizontal the attitude of the individual cones is consistently inclined at 60° from the vertical, towards the southwest. This is the most striking inclination of any conical or columnar stromatolites in the whole of the McArthur Basin succession. Because the biostrome is traceable only for about 100 m laterally, and is overlain and underlain by facies with lots of evidence of strong current activity, it is tentatively interpreted as being in a tidal channel. Sami and James (1993) interpret strongly inclined columnar microbialites from the Paleoproterozoic in Canada as indicating growth under the influence of basin-directed wave and/or tidal energies. Unfortunately, there is insufficient local outcrop to enable a consistent interpretation for this striking inclination to be made. A second impressive 5–6-m-thick biostrome of conical stromatolites occurs 100 m higher up in the formation (at 1360 m), immediately below the erosional base of the Roper Group. These conical forms are also bilaterally symmetrical (tear-shaped) in plan view, but in this case the cones were not inclined during growth. The azimuth of the axis of the plane of symmetry is consistently oriented towards 120°, indicating that the dominant (?tidal) palaeocurrents were oriented northwest–southeast at this stratigraphic level.

A 4-m-thick interval of red-brown, cross-bedded dolomitic sandstone and siltstone with desiccation cracks and halite casts occurs between 1276 and 1280 m. It is distinguished by a marked kick to the right in the gamma log. These red beds were deposited in intermittently exposed saline flats, farther inshore than the carbonate facies that form the bulk of this succession, and are, therefore, interpreted as marking a regression and basinward shift of facies. This is mainly why we have differentiated out the 9th cycle at the top of the Nathan Group. Cycle 9 contains several 4–8-m-thick cycles of wavy-laminated dolomitic siltstones capped by fine-grained dolarenites. Two of the cycles contain subspherical ferruginous stromatolite bioherms, 2 m across and with synoptic relief of 1–2 m, encased in hummocky-bedded dolomitic siltstones. The complete absence of intraclasts and oolites and the predominant wavy to hummocky stratification indicates deeper environments and possibly increased accommodation compared to cycle 8. Here, because of truncation, is where this reconnaissance level of understanding of the lithofacies would probably end in the absence of chronostratigraphic control.

In summary, using the gamma logs and sedimentological observations nine or, perhaps, eleven major episodes of sedimentation can be differentiated (Fig. 4). This is very different from the previously published five- to six-fold lithostratigraphic subdivision of this succession. Further, only one of the lithostratigraphic boundaries relates to what we would consider an important genetic change, defined by the gamma log and our refined lithofacies logs. The cycles we have defined consist of mixed carbonate and clastic sediments, commonly between 100 and 200 m thick, deposited on the inner to mid parts of a gently sloping ramp. In the absence of age control it would be logical to group most of these cycles together into one, or perhaps two, mega-cycles, somewhat along the lines of the previous Balbirini–Dungaminnie division, but with the boundary some 150 m higher. The overall similarity of the carbonate facies tracts suggests a gradually evolving platform, probably with a minor break at the Balbirini–Dungaminnie contact.

SHRIMP U–PB ZIRCON GEOCHRONOLOGY

SHRIMP Analytical Techniques

The ion microprobe study was carried out using SHRIMP II in the Research School of Earth Sciences at the Australian National University in Canberra. Detailed descriptions of the techniques for zircon U–Th–Pb analysis using SHRIMP are given by Compston et al. (1984) and Williams and Claesson (1987). Zircons from all except the Stretton Sandstone tuff sample were mounted with two different standards (SL 13 and QGNG) in an epoxy-resin disk, which was coated with a ~50 Å layer of Au. A 20–25 μm primary beam of singly negatively charged

O_2 was used for the production of positively charged secondary ions. Operation at a mass resolution in excess of 6500 ensured that there were no significant spectral interferences from either simple or compound isotopic species. Isotopic ratios were measured directly using an electron multiplier in ion counting mode, and no correction was made for the small amount of mass-dependent mass fractionation (~2.5 per mil per mass unit) that may be induced by the sputtering process and ion extraction system.

Corrections were made for initial Pb in the zircons, using values from Cumming and Richards (1975), based upon measured $^{204}Pb/^{206}Pb$. Pb/U was determined by reference to a standard zircon (SL13, 572 Ma old and having $^{206}Pb/^{238}U$ of 0.0928). Data on standards and unknowns were collected in sets of seven scans through the species of interest. Errors for individual grain measurements are derived from ion-counting statistics. The uncertainties in the measured isotopic ratios were augmented in cases of significant nonlinearity or scatter of the count rate with time (Williams et al., 1996). Uncertainties in Pb/U and Pb/Th included an additional component derived from uncertainty in the calibration curve for the standard for each session. This component, which dominated the uncertainty in these ratios, was between 1.3% and 2% (1σ). The secondary QGNG standard was separated from a quartz gabbronorite from the Lincoln Complex, Eyre Peninsula, South Australia (Mortimer et al., 1988). High-precision, conventional U–Pb zircon dating by C.M. Fanning and G.E. Mortimer (in Daly et al., 1998) has shown that the zircons in this rock have a crystallization age of 1849.8 ± 1.1 Ma, and have been little affected by isotopic disturbance since that time. The $^{207}Pb/^{206}Pb$ ages in unknowns and standards can be directly compared with each other, as they are derived independently of any standard. The high concentrations of ^{207}Pb and ^{206}Pb in QGNG render it particularly useful as a monitor of the integrity of $^{207}Pb/^{206}Pb$ measurements. Decay constants used are those recommended by the IUGS Subcommission on Geochronology (Steiger and Jäger, 1977). Uncertainties in calculated ages are quoted as 95% confidence limits, although analytical errors for individual analyses in the data tables and drawn on the concordia plots are quoted at the 1σ level. The analytical tables are available in Ozchron, AGSO's geochronological database.

U–Pb Zircon Geochronology

Stretton Sandstone.—This sample (9177.9043) was collected near Gum Yard, which is 36 km southeast of the Balbirini Dolomite measured section. The 30-cm-thick felsic tuff is one of three thinly laminated, slightly graded, pink to light brown beds within flaggy sandstone and siltstone in the basal part of the Stretton Sandstone. In thin section, the tuff consists of a fine mosaic of quartz, feldspar, and white mica with occasional remnant quartz phenocrysts. The zircon population in this tuff consists predominantly of squat euhedral, inclusion-free grains, and this pristine group, considered as having an igneous derivation, formed the main target for SHRIMP analysis. A few other grains are altered and/or subrounded; these are interpreted as a detrital component, and one such grain (37.1) has a $^{207}Pb/^{206}Pb$ age of 1861 Ma.

The SHRIMP U–Pb data were acquired in two sessions some months apart. Machine sensitivity in the first session was inferior, and given the low U content of these zircons this gave rise to large uncertainties in the pooled $^{207}Pb/^{206}Pb$ age of 1637 ± 20 Ma from 25 analyses. In the second session, with much improved sensitivity, the 43 analyses (Fig. 8A), including duplicate measurement on some grains analyzed earlier, have significantly smaller individual errors, and provide a pooled $^{207}Pb/^{206}Pb$ age of 1625 ± 2 Ma, with all data fitting to within experimental uncertainties ($\chi^2 = 0.96$). Grains 14, 15, and 21 have apparent ages of close to 1730 Ma. Although these three grains could be part of a reworked detrital suite, they are euhedral and have large individual errors, meaning that they cannot objectively be excluded from the main igneous suite. This low-U, high-Th/U zircon suite is not unusual compared to other Paleoproterozoic tuffs of northern Australia (Page and Sweet, 1998). Grouping of all 67 analyses (both analytical sessions) does not alter the 1625 ± 2 Ma result, nor does the inclusion or exclusion of twelve somewhat discordant analyses that show more than 10% recent Pb loss. The 1625 ± 2 Ma age is interpreted as an age of volcanic crystallization for the zircons, and hence the approximate depositional age of the Stretton Sandstone tuff.

Amos Formation.—This pink tuff bed (sample 9577.9072) is approximately 15 cm thick, and is one of four such beds within fine- to medium-grained, sandy dolarenites of the lower part of the Amos Formation. Some of these tuff beds fill channels cut into the enclosing carbonates. They are fragmented near their base, and the upper parts of some tuff beds themselves have eroded tops, fragmental remnants of which are found in younger adjacent sediment. Only three of these tuffs were actually crossed at the location where the section was measured (Fig. 5; 20 m). It could be considered unusual that tuffs are at all preserved in this relatively high-energy, fluvial to very shallow intertidal environment. Many of these tuff layers contain carbonate-filled "cross fractures" akin to the "cross fracture tuff marker beds" described from the Urquhart Shale in the Mount Isa Group (Croxford, 1964).

The analyzed zircons from the Amos tuff are clear, colorless euhedral grains only a few of which contain bubble-like inclusions or thin apatite prisms. Once again, this is a low-U zircon suite, and all 34 data points are concordant to within error (Fig. 8B). The group is also analytically coherent in $^{207}Pb/^{206}Pb$, providing an unambiguous igneous crystallization age of 1614 ± 4 Ma ($\chi^2 = 0.70$). This is regarded as a reliable depositional age, which is clearly consistent with the known stratigraphy and geochronology in this upper part of the McArthur Group.

Lower Balbirini Dolomite.—A number of pink to light brown tuffaceous beds occur in the lower part of the Balbirini Dolomite. These pink beds lie within a succession of stromatolitic and evaporitic carbonates, and are clearly alien to the sedimentary environment in which they are hosted. Two separate beds about 30 m apart stratigraphically were sampled for the geochronological study. Sample 9177.9038 is one of three massive tuffaceous beds between 0.3 and 0.5 m thick located about 45 m above the base of the formation (Fig. 5; 120 m). Although some of the zircon grains are broken, the squat, euhedral zircon population in this rock generally shows no signs of any mechanical abrasion, which, together with its uniform morphology, suggests that the zircons can be used to date the volcanic event that punctuated the sedimentary deposition. The pristine igneous morphology of these zircons and their homogeneous

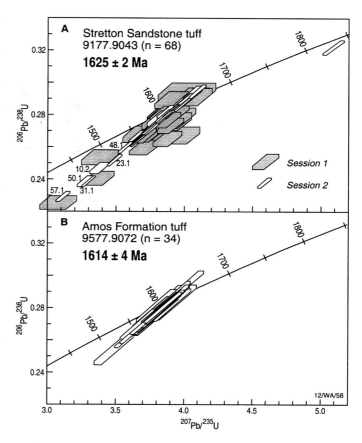

FIG. 8.—U–Pb concordia plot of zircon SHRIMP data from **A**) the Stretton Sandstone from Gum Yard, and **B**) the basal part of the Amos Formation from the type section. Errors in this and subsequent concordia plots are 1 σ uncertainties.

U/Pb systematics described below offer strong collaborative evidence for the igneous derivation of these particular pink layers and, therefore, we do not favor the suggest of Muir (in Walter et al., 1988, p. 81) that these rocks are metasomatized claystones. The zircons contain slightly more uranium than those previously discussed for the Stretton and Amos tuffs, and once again, all zircon U–Pb data (Fig. 9C) are concordant and form a close grouping in $^{207}Pb/^{206}Pb$ ($\chi^2 = 0.92$). This means that the weighted mean age, 1613 ± 4 Ma, can be taken as a good estimate for the age of deposition in this lower part of the Balbirini Dolomite.

Sample 9577.9074 was collected from a 40-cm-thick tuff at 150 m in the measured section, i.e., stratigraphically younger than sample 9177.9038. The sedimentary setting of the tuff, its petrography, and the morphology of its zircon population are similar to 9177.9038. Uranium and Th/U overlap with U and Th/U in 9177.9038, but four grains in 9577.9074 have unusually high U (220–500 ppm). The SHRIMP U–Pb data for 9577.9074 are concordant, and all 44 data points form a single cluster in $^{207}Pb/^{206}Pb$ ($\chi^2 = 0.92$), indicating a crystallization age of 1609 ± 3 Ma (Fig. 9B).

Uppermost Balbirini Dolomite.—Sample 9610.1252 was collected from a depth of 72.5 m from core in BMR Bauhinia Downs 3 drill hole. This depth was identified as a possible tuffaceous layer by the distinct kick on the gamma log. It occurs within a section of parallel-laminated, green dolomitic siltstone containing large dolomite concretions (Fig. 7). The sample appears to be a reworked tuffaceous rock—it consists of numerous medium to coarse, pink grains concentrated along scoured surfaces throughout a 20 cm interval. Even so, the clear, euhedral, zoned zircons contain a few bubble-like inclusions, and generally have a pristine igneous nature, suggesting that the reworking was not extensive and did not result in obvious contamination. Of the 44 SHRIMP analyses in Figure 9A, all but

three (grains 105, 120, 129) are concordant. This zircon suite is generally much higher in U (100–300 ppm) and has normal Th/U (<1) compared to others discussed above. Hence, the precision of individual analyses and overall precision of the clustered $^{207}Pb/^{206}Pb$ age result at 1589 $\pm$ 3 Ma ($\chi^2 = 1.35$) are improved. The discordance seen in three analyses is attributable to modern Pb loss, and has no effect on the pooled $^{207}Pb/^{206}Pb$ age.

We consider the 1589 $\pm$ 3 Ma age to represent volcanic crystallization of the zircon grains. Although the tuffaceous unit has been reworked, it is underlain and overlain by identical deep-water facies and does not appear to represent a major break in sedimentation. This age is considered to be close to the deposition age of this uppermost part of the Balbirini Dolomite; it is at least 14 million years younger than the ages found for the lower Balbirini Dolomite tuffs.

The new U–Pb zircon ages from this upper part of the McArthur Basin succession are summarized in Table 1, which also includes some recently published ages from the immediately underlying units. This consistent upward younging of the U–Pb SHRIMP age determinations through some 3000 m of section is geologically consistent with the stratigraphy and provides strong support for (a) the igneous lineage of the pink beds and (b) the veracity of the U–Pb zircon ages as reliable depositional ages.

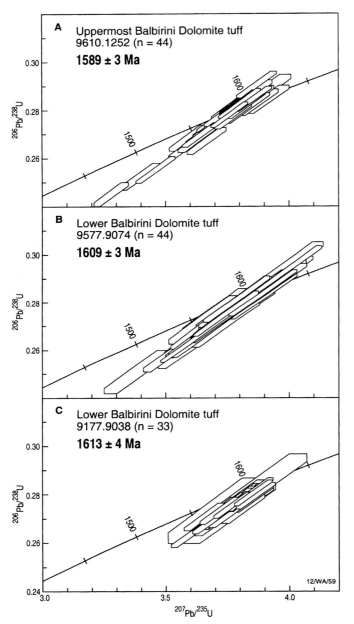

FIG. 9.—U–Pb concordia plot of zircon SHRIMP data from **A)** the upper part of the Balbirini Dolomite in drill hole BMR Bauhinia Downs 3 from a depth of 72.5 m; **B)** the lower part of the Balbirini Dolomite, 150 m above the basal contact; and **C)** the lower part of the Balbirini Dolomite, 45 m above the basal contact.

REVISED GEOLOGICAL INTERPRETATION USING SHRIMP AGES,
REGIONAL SUPERSEQUENCE CORRELATION CHART, AND
ACCOMMODATION HISTORY

This section presents a modified depositional history based on integrating the SHRIMP results with the earlier presented geological and gamma-ray data. It is constrained by new correlations of strata in the Lawn Hill–Mount Isa area published by Southgate et al. (1996) and Southgate et al. (1997). These regional constraints and correlations for part of the superbasin's history are summarized in Figure 10. Here the existing lithostratigraphic units, between 1645 and 1575 Ma, have been recorrelated using the new zircon ages and the gamma-ray curves in the light of sequence stratigraphic concepts (Haq et al., 1988; Vail et al., 1991) The key features correlated are a series of regional sequence and supersequence boundaries that are recognized in outcrop and on seismic sections in the Lawn Hill Platform area, approximately 350 km southeast of this area (Bradshaw et al., 1996a). Gamma-ray curves have been crucial in defining these surfaces and elucidating accommodation histories for the associated packages. The sedimentary rocks between these surfaces have been redefined into a series of supersequences and sequences (as used in Kennard et al., 1998). The largest-scale stratigraphic packaging is into second-order supersequences (Southgate et al., 1996). These are hundreds to thousands of meters thick and were deposited over periods of time of a few million up to about 20 million years. For ease of reference these have been informally named using an abbreviation of the formal lithostratigraphic unit that includes the MFS of that basin phase. For example, the Lawn Supersequence (~1615 to 1595 Ma) is informally named after the Lawn Hill Formation of the upper part of the McNamara Group (Hutton et al., 1981), because unit Pmh4 in the middle part of the Lawn Hill Formation contains the MFS of this basin phase (Fig. 10).

TABLE. 1.—SUMMARY OF NEW U–Pb ZIRCON SHRIMP RESULTS AND LOCATIONS OF FELSIC TUFFS FROM THE UPPER McARTHUR GROUP, NORTHERN TERRITORY, AND POOLED AGES OBTAINED FROM REPLICATE MEASUREMENTS OF STANDARD QGNG

Stratigraphic Unit	Sample #	Std QGNG Age (Ma)	Easting	Northing	U-Pb Age (Ma) (95% confidence)
UPPER McARTHUR GROUP FELSIC TUFFS					
1. Stretton Sandstone	9177.9043	—	612900	8135000	1625 ± 2
2. Amos Formation	9577.9072	1849 ± 4 (n = 12)	578600	8146700	1614 ± 4
3. Lower Balbirini Dolomite	9177.9038	1851 ± 3 (n = 17)	578799	8146934	1613 ± 4
4. Lower Balbirini Dolomite	9577.9074	1849 ± 4 (n = 12)	578400	8147400	1609 ± 3
5. Uppermost Balbirini Dolomite	9610.1252	1851 ± 3 (n = 14)	471900	7663200	1589 ± 3
MIDDLE McARTHUR GROUP (from Page and Sweet, 1998)					
6. Barney Creek Formation	7810.9001		617400	8182600	1638 ± 7
7. Barney Creek Formation	9177.9032		617400	8182600	1639 ± 3
8. Barney Creek Formation	9177.9031		617400	8182600	1640 ± 3

Middle McArthur group ages are from Page and Sweet (1998).

Smaller subdivisions of the supersequences—such as the numbered cycles described in this paper—would equate with higher-order (third-order and/or fourth- order) sequences. The smallest sedimentological "cycles" identified are the shoaling carbonate cycles, each a few meters thick, described earlier. These appear to be the most fundamental building blocks of this succession and are most likely parasequences (Posamentier et al., 1988; Sarg, 1988), although further studies are required to fully justify this assertion.

Lawn Supersequence Boundary in the Abner Range Area

Previously the surface separating cycles 1 and 2 was described as a major regional unconformity separating the McArthur and Nathan Groups (Jackson et al., 1987). On the basis of the new SHRIMP U–Pb results it is now evident that the depositional ages of cycles 1 and 2 are essentially indistinguishable. Further, the gamma log and facies show very similar trends for the two cycles, suggesting a similar depositional history. With this new information it would seem unlikely that there is a major time break between these two cycles. There is, however, approximately a 10 million year time difference between the Stretton Sandstone at 1625 ± 2 Ma, and cycle 1 at 1614 ± 4 Ma, indicating that a much more significant boundary may lie beneath the Amos Formation. We propose that a significant stratigraphic break be placed between the base of the Amos Formation and the top of the Looking Glass Formation (Fig. 2). The latter formation consists of shallow-water carbonates about 100 m thick that are everywhere (outcrop and drill hole) intensely silicified. The upper contact of the formation is generally not exposed, but at the few localities where it has been seen (Jackson et al., 1997, p. 130) it is erosional. The extensive and all-pervasive Paleoproterozoic silicification of the primary carbonates of the Looking Glass Formation is overprinted by a coarse, secondary porosity in the Beetle Springs area, 27 km east of this area (Muir et al., 1980). This is support for a prolonged period of deep weathering and alteration at the top of the Looking Glass Formation, which would also be consistent with a major stratigraphic break. The base of the Looking Glass Formation is also erosional, so there is geological time missing here as well, but without extensive studies, including coring, the comparative importance of this lower surface is hard to ascertain. We propose that the most logical stratigraphic level at which to locate a major basin phase boundary in this part of the history of the superbasin is at the base of the

Amos Formation/top Looking Glass (Fig. 10)—not at the top of the Amos Formation, as done previously (Fig. 2). The coarse clastics at the base of the Balbirini Dolomite, at the southeast end of the Abner Range (Walter et al., 1988), may still be correlatives of the red beds at the base of cycle 2, in which case, erosion during subaerial exposure has removed cycle 1. They could, however, be equivalent to the red beds at the base of cycle 1; in this case the calcreted upper part of cycle 1 is not preserved in this area.

Accommodation History, Cycles 1 to 7

With the new SHRIMP dating constraints, it is evident that the initial interpretations presented in the previous section on "Integrating gamma logs with new facies information" need major revision. There is clearly not the continuous, gradual evolution of a simple ramp through a series of 8–9 cycles as earlier suggested.

The oldest coherent package—Lawn Supersequence—is that represented by cycles 1–3 in Figure 11. These form three dominantly transgressive sequences comprising coastal-plain evaporitic deposits deepening up into shallow marine inner-ramp/shoreline deposits. An overall increase in accommodation space is suggested by the gradual upward increase in cycle thickness and also by the overall gradual deepening of the facies. Regressive trends are not evident in the two lowest cycles. This suggests slow subsidence and keep-up carbonate production. A potential MFS and part of an overlying HST may, however, be preserved in the upper 50 m of cycle 3. Here the condensed interval comprises dark gray, organic-rich, dolomitic mudstone with crinkly, flat algal mats (low energy, deeper environments) and the *Balbirina Prima* Bioherm.

Although there are not enough SHRIMP results to measure the time span for these three oldest cycles, broad equivalence of these with third-order or fourth-order sequences seems most reasonable on the basis of thickness, character of facies, log patterns, and similarity to similar better-dated cycles in other parts of the McArthur–Mount Isa area. Further, the *Balbirina prima* bioherm may represent the condensed section of the supersequence, with incision at the base of cycle 4 removing the bulk of any HST that may have been deposited.

The erosion surface at 395 m, at the base of cycle 4, overlain by a basinward shift in facies, is now interpreted as a more regionally significant surface. On the basis of the SHRIMP dating, it is correlated with the major surface at the base of the

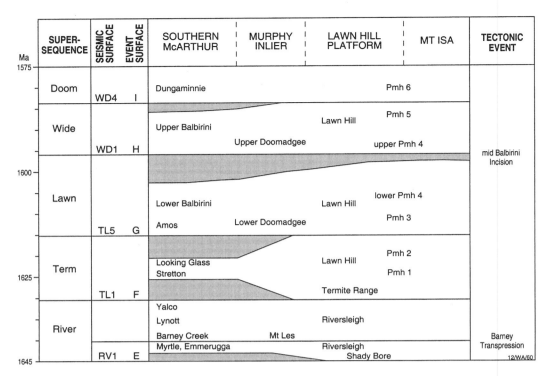

FIG. 10.—Part of NABRE's proposed chronostratigraphic correlation chart for the Mount Isa–southern McArthur River region (modified, after Southgate et al., 1996); based on data available to June 1998. The vertical axis is time in millions of years. The names of most of the existing formal lithostratigraphic units in the center of the diagram have been abbreviated to fit in the space available. New informal names for two tectonic events that are known to have affected sedimentation in some part of the superbasin are shown in the right-hand column. Gray areas indicate significant periods of erosion and/or nondeposition. Informal names for the supersequences are shown in the left-hand column. Seismic surfaces and events are from Bradshaw et al. (1996a).

Wide Supersequence on the Lawn Hill Platform (Southgate et al., 1997; Page, 1997). Consequently, the Balbirini Dolomite is split into two very different basin phases separated by a significant event of uplift and erosion, informally referred to as the "mid Balbirini Incision" (Fig. 10). SHRIMP dating from the two widely separated areas indicates that the duration of this hiatus is longer in the McArthur region.

There are no obvious major disconformities in the "upper Balbirini", so the SHRIMP U–Pb age of 1589 ± 3 Ma from cycle 7 is interpreted to indicate the broad depositional age of cycles 4–7. The age difference between cycle 2 at 1609 ± 3 Ma from the "lower Balbirini" and cycle 7 at 1589 ± 3 Ma from the "upper Balbirini" is around 20 million years. If these cycles are of fourth-order scale, each would represent a time span of less than 1 million years. This implies either significant time loss on internal erosion surfaces (which are not particularly obvious), or, more likely, major time loss at the base of one of these cycles, and we believe that this is most likely to be at the base of Cycle 4. If these cycles are of a third-order scale, their individual duration would be around 1 million years. Consequently, there would be proportionally less time loss on such surfaces, but, even so, the small number of cycles present in such a long time period still suggests significant erosion. Ongoing research on the thicker and more complete sections at Mt. Isa should help to clarify these interpretations.

Recent mapping in the Roper River area, 250 km northwest of this area (Abbott et al., personal communication) adds support to this suggestion for a significant break part way up the

Balbirini Dolomite. U–Pb SHRIMP dating confirms the presence of rocks of Balbirini age adjacent to a basement inlier called the Urapunga Tectonic Ridge (Plumb et al., 1996). Here, the succession is approximately 400 m thick and comprises four main facies associations: (a) an 80-m-thick, basal fluvial sandy unit; overlain by (b) a 70-m-thick shaly and stromatolitic carbonate unit; overlain by (c) a mixed mafic igneous and immature clastic suite, about 100 m thick; and (d) an uppermost 200-m-thick succession of cherty, oolitic, stromatolitic carbonate and interbedded sandstones. Assuming that the complete Nathan Group package is represented in this area, we speculate that units 1 and 2 at Urapunga may correlate with cycles 1–3 at Balbirini, and that the basaltic volcanogenic unit 3 correlates with cycle 4. A conglomerate within this volcanogenic unit contains clasts of exotic quartzite indicating erosion of much older clastic units from lower down in the succession. Laterally, therefore, the disconformity at Balbirini becomes a major surface at Urapunga with obvious localized tilting and expulsion of mafic magmas.

In contrast to the Lawn Supersequence, the Wide Supersequence contains thicker preserved HSTs in cycles 5, 6, and 7 (Fig. 11). The lowstand–transgressive parts of the sequences consist of shallow, high-energy sandy carbonate rocks rather than red beds, which dominated the Lawn Supersequence. The condensed interval in cycle 5B is defined by *Kussiella kussiensis*, whilst in cycles 6 and 7 it is characterized by low-energy, deeper-water, fine-grained shale facies. Carbonate starvation and shale deposition are interpreted to represent gradual drown-

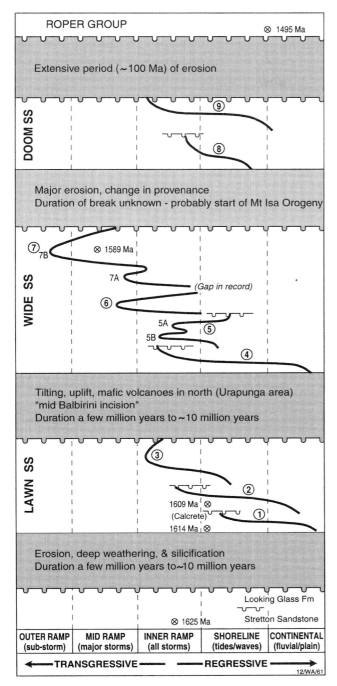

FIG. 11.—Revised evolution of the Nathan Group, using gamma data and SHRIMP U–Pb ages. Vertical axis is time, but, owing to limited control, it is only approximately linear. Contrast this with the previous lithostratigraphic scheme shown in Fig. 3. Heavy lines show the paleoenvironmental trends of the lithofacies in the individual cycles. Trends towards the left are transgressive (i.e., the facies are deepening), trends towards the right are shoaling. Sequence boundaries are shown by an unconformity symbol across which there is an obvious basinward shift of facies. The numbers in circles refer to the cycles described in the text. In this interpretation, the subdivisions of cycles 5 and 7 are shown as higher-order (smaller-scale) subdivisions of the main cycles. **Note:** (a) the overall (large-scale) transgressive nature of cycles 1 to 7; (b) second-order MFSs at cycles 3 and 7B; (c) the dominance of TSTs in the lower four cycles; (d) marked regressive shift between the Wide and Doom Supersequences, indicating a major change across this supersequence boundary. This figure, although schematic, represents the type of sequential stacking of genetic packages and events that are extremely useful for regional correlations.

ing of this second ramp, probably because of increased accommodation. The maximum drowning for this supersequence probably occurs in cycle 7B, where it is represented by 80 m of parallel-laminated dolomitic siltstone with glauconite and well-developed concretions. A gradual reduction in accommodation is evident in the upward-coarsening uppermost 25 m of BMR Bauhinia Downs 3 (top of cycle 7), but owing to poor outcrop, the character of the rest of this cycle is poorly constrained; but, again, it would appear that only a small part of the HST may have been preserved.

Accommodation History, Cycles 8 and 9

The accommodation history for these two cycles is poorly constrained, owing not only to poor outcrop but also to extensive erosion at the base of the overlying Roper Group. Cycles 8 and 9 are tentatively correlated with the Doom Supersequence (Fig. 10) from the better-constrained Lawn Hill Platform, 300 km to the southeast. A supersequence boundary has been mapped on seismic in the Lawn Hill area and correlated with a feldspathic sandstone at the base of a unit called Pmh6 in the Lawn Hill Formation (Bradshaw et al., 1996b). The sandstone forming the lower part of the Dungaminnie Formation is also distinctly feldspathic and micaceous, implying a marked change in paleogeography and provenance, which is consistent with our tentative correlation. There are at least two separate sequences in the Doom Supersequence in the Abner Range area, both of which contain high-energy shallow-water carbonate facies, with a high proportion of quartz sand. These facies are similar to the ramp carbonates in the older supersequences, and they appear to have mostly kept up and filled the accommodation space generated (Fig. 11). If we make a number of assumptions, especially constant carbonate supply and depositional rates, the wavy-laminated dolomitic siltstone with upright "conophytons" at the very top of the Dungaminnie Formation may represent a potential flooding into slightly deeper-water environments. In the Lawn Hill area, the Doom Supersequence comprises at least five sequences (Bradshaw et al., 1996c), suggesting increased erosion at the base of the overlying successions as one moves northwest across northern Australia.

SUMMARY AND CONCLUSIONS

By necessity, most Proterozoic stratigraphic reconstructions have relied on detailed lithofacies studies, constrained within geological-map-based lithostratigraphic frameworks. Some authors (e.g., Christie-Blick et al., 1988; Jackson et al., 1990) have attempted to use sequence stratigraphic concepts to analyze Proterozoic successions, by analyzing cyclic sedimentation patterns in terms of changes in sediment accommodation and identifying and tracing erosion surfaces (sequence boundaries) that separate genetically related strata. Chemostratigraphy has been applied successfully to the Neoproterozoic (Derry et al., 1992), but initial studies in this project indicate that it may not be as useful in the Paleoproterozoic (Brasier and Lindsay, 1998).

Gamma-ray logging of well-exposed surface sections of Precambrian strata should be considered as much a part of section-measuring as the description of rock type, grain size, and sedimentary structures. The collection and analysis of gamma logs will lead to an improved understanding of the lithofacies, it will enhance the identification of significant trends and breaks in the section, and lead to a much better understanding of the likely accommodation history (Fig. 11).

Further, gamma-ray logs highlight previously unsuspected tuffaceous intervals that can be accurately dated by SHRIMP techniques. In this example, U–Pb depositional ages from zircon crystals from several tuffaceous units have significantly changed the interpretation of the geological evolution of a 1200-m-thick package of Paleoproterozoic–Mesoproterozoic carbonates. The previous interpretation was for a gradually evolving complex of continental and lagoonal sediments. Now, the succession is interpreted as three distinctly different large-scale supersequences, separated from each other by regionally widespread events (Fig. 10). At a finer scale each supersequence comprises a number of largely transgressive, higher-order (third and/or fourth) sequences that have poorly developed or preserved HSTs. More convincing correlations between different parts of the superbasin containing markedly different facies should be facilitated by this type of genetic analysis.

In summary, gamma-ray logs and U–Pb SHRIMP geochronology are valuable tools that help constrain interpretations of Proterozoic depositional and accommodation history. The widespread adoption of these techniques is recommended.

ACKNOWLEDGMENTS

We acknowledge the pain and sweat that Scott Bain went through to help us log these sections. We are grateful to Marjorie Muir and Malcolm Walter, who made valuable comments on an early version of the manuscript. Tas Armstrong and Chris Foudoulis provided dedicated technical assistance for the SHRIMP geochronology. Angie Jaensch expertly drafted the figures. Eric Mountjoy and Paul Gammon are thanked for thorough and thought-provoking reviews of the manuscript.

This paper is published with approval from the Executive Director, Australian Geological Survey Organisation, Canberra.

REFERENCES

BRADSHAW, B. E., KRASSAY, A. A., SCOTT, D. L., McCONACHIE B. A., WELLS, A. T., AND DOMAGALA, J., 1996a, Sequence stratigraphic correlations and basin phase geometry of the Proterozoic Upper McNamara and Fickling Groups, Mt. Isa Basin, northwest Queensland (abstract), in Baker, T., et al., eds., MIC '96: New Developments in Metallogenic Research, The McArthur–Mt Isa–Cloncurry Minerals Province, Townsville, April 22–23, p. 20–23.

BRADSHAW B. E., KRASSAY A. A., JACKSON M. J., McCONACHIE B. A., SOUTHGATE P. N., SCOTT D. L., WELLS A. T., AND DOMAGALA J., 1996b, Further constraints on sequence stratigraphic correlations in the Mount Isa, McNamara and McArthur Groups—The Shady Bore Quartzite–Riversleigh Siltstone transition in 'NABRE'-hood of Riversleigh, northwest Queensland: AGSO Research Newsletter no. 25, p. 21–22.

BRADSHAW B. A., KRASSAY, A. A., McCONACHIE, B. A., LEVEN, J. H., FINLAYSON, D. M., AND DOMAGALA, J., 1996c, Sequence stratigraphy and basin phase geometry of the Proterozoic Upper McNamara Group, Mt. Isa Basin, northwest Queensland: Geological Society of Australia Abstracts no. 41, p. 51.

BRADSHAW, B. E., SCOTT, D. L., KRASSAY, A. A., AND SOUTHGATE, P. N., 1998, Elizabeth Creek Prospect: Buried mineral play in Century-equivalent strata, northern Lawn Hill Platform, Queensland: Australian Geological Survey Organisation Record 1998/4, 26 p.

BRASIER, M. D., AND LINDSAY, J. F., 1998, A billion years of environmental stability and the emergence of eukaryotes: New data from northern Australia: Geology, v. 26, p. 555–558.

CHRISTIE-BLICK, N., GROTZINGER, J. P., AND VON DER BORCH, C. C., 1988, Sequence stratigraphy in Proterozoic successions: Geology, v. 16, p. 100–104.

COMPSTON, W., WILLIAMS, I. S., AND MEYER, C. 1984, U–Pb Geochronology of zircons from Lunar breccia 73217 using a sensitive high mass-resolution ion microprobe. Proceedings 14th Lunar and Planetary Science Conference, Part 2: Journal of Geophysical Research, v. 89, Supplement, p. B525–B534.

CROXFORD, N. J. W., 1964, Origin and significance of volcanic potash-rich rocks from Mount Isa. Institution of Mining Metallurgy [London], Transactions, v. 74, p. 33–43.

CUMMING, G. L., AND RICHARDS, J. R. 1975, Ore lead isotopes in a continuously changing earth: Earth and Planetary Science Letters, v. 28, p. 155–171.

DALY, S. J., FANNING, C. M., AND FAIRCLOUGH, M. C., 1998, Tectonic evolution and exploration potential of the Gawler Craton, South Australia: AGSO Journal of Australian Geology & Geophysics, v. 17(3), p. 145–168.

DERRY, L. A., KAUFMAN, J., AND JACOBSEN, S. B., 1992, Sedimentary cycling and environmental changes in the Late Proterozoic: Evidence from stable and radiogenic isotopes: Geochimica et Cosmochimica Acta, v. 65, p. 1317–1329.

EMERY, D., AND MYERS, K., 1996, Sequence Stratigraphy: London, Blackwell, 297 p.

HAINES, P. W., PIETSCH, B. A., RAWLINGS, D. J., MADIGAN, T. L., AND FINDHAMMER, T. L. R., 1993, Mount Young 1:250 000 Geological Map Series, Explanatory Notes SD53–15, Northern Territory Geological Survey.

HAINES, P. W., RAWLINGS, D. J., SWEET, I. P., PIETSCH, B. A., PLUMB, K. A., MADIGAN, T. L. A., AND KRASSAY, A. A., 1998, Blue Mud Bay, Northern Territory—1:250 000 Geological Series, Explanatory Notes, SD53–7, Northern Territory Geological Survey.

HAQ, B. U., HARDENBOL, J., AND VAIL, P. R., 1988, Mesozoic and Cenozoic chronostratigraphy and eustatic cycles, in Wilgus, C. K., Hastings, B. S., Kendall, C. G. St. C., Posamentier H. W., Ross, C. A., and Van Wagoner, J. C. eds., Sea Level Changes—An Integrated Approach: SEPM, Special Publication 42, p. 71–108.

HUTTON L. J., CAVANEY R. J., AND SWEET I. P., 1981, New and revised stratigraphic units, Lawn Hill Platform, northwest Queensland: Queensland Government Mining Journal, v. 82, p. 423–434.

JACKSON, M. J., AND SOUTHGATE, P. N., 1997, Nathan Group Revisited, in NABRE Workshop—March 1997: Australian Geological Survey Organisation, Record 1997/12.

JACKSON, M. J., MUIR, M. D., PLUMB, K. A., LARGE, D. E., BROWN, M. C., AND ARMSTRONG, K. J., 1978, Field work report, McArthur Basin project, 1977: Australia, Bureau of Mineral Resources, Record 78/54.

JACKSON, M. J., MUIR, M. D., AND PLUMB, K. A., 1987, Geology of the southern McArthur Basin, Northern Territory: Australia, Bureau of Mineral Resources, Bulletin 220, 173 p.

JACKSON, M. J., SIMPSON, E. L., AND ERIKSSON, K. A., 1990, Facies and sequence stratigraphic analysis in an intracratonic, thermal-relaxation basin: the Early Proterozoic lower Quilalar Formation and Ballara Quartzite, Mount Isa Inlier, Australia: Sedimentology, v. 37, p. 1053–1078.

JACKSON, M. J., SOUTHGATE, P. N., KRASSAY, A. A., McCONACHIE, B. A., WELLS, A. T., AND SCOTT, D. L., 1996, New techniques/concepts for choosing the right ground for sediment-hosted mineralisation—Lower McNamarra Group, Lawn Hill Platform (abstract): Geological Society of Australia, Abstracts no. 41, p. 216.

KENNARD J. M., ALLEN, G. P., AND KIRK, R. B., 1999, Sequence stratigraphy—a review of fundamental concepts and their application to petroleum exploration and development in Australia: AGSO Journal of Australian Geology & Geophysics, v. 17(5/6), p. 77–104.

KRASSAY, A. A., 1998, Outcrop and drill core gamma-ray logging integrated with sequence stratigraphy: examples from Proterozoic sedimentary successions of northern Australia: AGSO Journal of Australian Geology & Geophysics, v. 17(4), p. 285–299.

MUIR, M. D., 1983, A Proterozoic calcrete in the Amos Formation, McArthur Group, Northern Territory, Australia, in Peryt, T.M. ed., Coated Grains: Berlin, Springer-Verlag, p. 548–558.

MUIR, M. D., ARMSTRONG, K. J., AND JACKSON, M. J., 1980, Precambrian hydrocarbons in the McArthur Basin, NT: BMR Journal of Australian Geology & Geophysics, v. 5(4), p. 301–304.

MIALL, A. D., 1997, The Geology of Stratigraphic Sequences: Berlin, Springer-Verlag, 433 p.

PAGE, R. W., 1997, Geological constraints provided by U–Pb zircon dating of basin phases in the Law Hill and McArthur Basins (abstract): NABRE Workshop, March 4–5: Australian Geological Survey Organisation, Record 1997/12.

PAGE, R. W., AND SWEET, I. P., 1998, Geochronology of basin phases in the western Mount Isa Inlier, and correlation with the McArthur Basin: Australian Journal of Earth Sciences, v. 45, p. 219–232.

PLUMB, K. A., PIETSCH, B. A., AND PAGE, R. W. 1996, Enhanced understanding of the McArthur Basin, Northern Australia—results from NGMA mapping in Arnhem Land (abstract): Geological Society of Australia, Abstracts no. 41, p. 345.

PIETSCH, B. A., WYCHE, S., RAWLINGS, D. J., CREASER, P. M., AND FINDHAMMER, T. L. R., 1991a, McArthur River region, 6065–6165. 1:100 000 Geological Map Series, Explanatory Notes: Northern Territory Geological Survey, Darwin, 38 p.

PIETSCH, B. A., RAWLINGS, D. J., CREASER, P. M., KRUSE, P. D., AHMAD, M., FERENCZI, P. A., AND FINDHAMMER, T. L. R., 1991b, Bauhinia Downs SE53–3, 1:250 000 Geological Map Series Explanatory Notes: Northern Territory Geological Survey, Darwin, 76 p.

RAWLINGS, D. J., HAINES, P. W., MADIGAN, T. L. A., PIETSCH, B. A., SWEET, I. P., PLUMB, K. A., AND KRASSAY, A. A., 1997, Arnhem Bay–Gove, Northern Territory, 1:250 000 Geological Series: Northern Territory Geological Survey, Explanatory Notes, SD53–3,4, 113 p.

RIDER, M. H., 1991, The Geological Interpretation of Well Logs: Caithness [Scotland], Whittles Publishing, 175 p.

SAMI, T. T., AND JAMES, N. P., 1993, Evolution of an early Proterozoic foreland basin carbonate platform, lower Pethei Group, Great Slave Lake, north-west Canada: Sedimentology, 40, p. 403–430.

SARG, J. F., 1988, Carbonate sequence stratigraphy, in Wilgus, C.K., Hastings, B.S., Kendall, C.G.St.C., Posamentier, H.W., Ross, C.A., and Van Wagoner, J.C. eds., Sea Level Changes—An Integrated Approach: SEPM, Special Publication 42, p. 155–181.

SOUTHGATE, P. N., JACKSON, M. J., KRASSAY, A. A., BRADSHAW, B. E., SCOTT, D. L., McCONACHIE, B. A., AND WELLS, A. T., 1996, Integrated Proterozoic basin analysis: constructing a regional structural and sequence stratigraphic framework for northern Australia (abstract), in Baker, T., et al.,

eds., MIC '96: New Developments in Metallogenic Research, The McArthur–Mt Isa–Cloncurry Minerals Province, Townsville, April 22–23, p. 132–136.

SOUTHGATE, P., BRADSHAW, B., DOMAGALA, J., JACKSON, J., KRASSAY, A., LINDSAY, J., McCONACHIE, B., SAMI, T., SCOTT, D., AND WELLS, A., 1997, Basin Fill Studies: Overview (abstract): NABRE Workshop, March 4–5: Australian Geological Survey Organisation, Record 1997/12.

STEIGER, R. H., AND JÄGER, E. 1977, Subcommission on geochronology: Convention on the use of decay constants in geo- and cosmochronology. Earth and Planetary Science Letters v. 36, p. 359–362.

VAN WAGONER, J. C., MITCHUM, R. M., JR., CAMPION, K. M., AND RAHMANIAN, V. D., 1990, Siliciclastic sequence stratigraphy in well logs, core, and outcrops: concepts for high-resolution correlation of time and facies: American Association of Petroleum Geologists, Methods in Exploration Series 7, 55 p.

VAIL, P. R., AUDEMARD, F., BOWMAN, S. A., EISNER, P. N., AND PEREZ-CRUZ, C., 1991, The stratigraphic signatures of tectonics, eustasy and sedimentology—an overview, in Einsele, G., Ricken, W., and Seilacher, A., eds., Cycles and Events in Stratigraphy: Berlin, Springer-Verlag, p. 617–659.

WALTER, M. R., KRYLOV, I. N., AND MUIR, M. D., 1988, Stromatolites from Middle and Late Proterozoic sequences in the McArthur and Georgina Basins and the Mount Isa Province, Australia: Alcheringa, v. 12(2), p. 79–106.

WILGUS, C. K., HASTINGS, B. S., KENDALL, C. G. ST. C., POSAMENTIER, H. W., ROSS, C. A., AND VAN WAGONER, J. C. EDS., 1988, Sea Level Changes—An Integrated Approach: SEPM, Special Publication 42, 407 p.

WILLIAMS, I. S., AND CLAESSON, S. 1987, Isotopic evidence for the Precambrian provenance and Caledonian metamorphism of the high grade paragneisses from the Seve Nappes, Scandinavian Caledonides. II. Ion microprobe zircon U–Th–Pb: Contributions to Mineralogy and Petrology, v. 97, p. 205–217.

WILLIAMS, I. S., BUICK, I. S., AND CARTWRIGHT, I., 1996, An extended episode of Mesoproterozoic metamorphic fluid flow in the Reynolds Range, central Australia: Journal of Metamorphic Geology, v. 14, p. 29–47.

CHEMOSTRATIGRAPHIC PROXY RECORDS: FORWARD MODELING THE EFFECTS OF UNCONFORMITIES, VARIABLE SEDIMENT ACCUMULATION RATES, AND SAMPLING-INTERVAL BIAS

PAUL M. MYROW

Department of Geology, The Colorado College, Colorado Springs, Colorado, 80903, U.S.A.

AND

JOHN P. GROTZINGER

Department of Earth, Atmospheric, and Planetary Sciences, Massachusetts Institute of Technology, Cambridge, Massachusetts, 02139, U.S.A.

ABSTRACT: Stratigraphic forward models are a significant asset in reconstructing the important processes controlling sedimentary basin development, stratigraphic architecture, and the distribution of facies. Generally, the models are used to make predictions concerning the rates and magnitudes of geologic processes operating at various temporal and spatial scales. Here, we use a recently developed stratigraphic forward modeling package (STRATA) to evaluate the impact of varying accommodation space and sediment fluxes, as well as sampling intervals, on the structure of chemostratigraphic curves preserved in the rock record.

The method assumes that a primary signal, say secular variations in the chemical composition of seawater, is embedded within the stratigraphic record of platform carbonate deposits. In principle, the method and underlying assumptions are generally independent of the particular primary signal that is being recorded (e.g., Sr isotopes), but for the sake of illustration we apply the approach to the terminal Proterozoic $\delta^{13}C$ record. If enough is known about the processes that regulate the primary signal, then a map of the primary signal can be used to infer how the controlling processes have varied through time and space—the stratigraphic record itself may be of little interest, depending on the question that is being asked. However, stratigraphic processes can exert a fundamental control on the structure of the primary signal, particularly if they are unsteady in time. Therefore, a forward stratigraphic model can be an essential tool in illuminating which processes may have influenced the final form of the primary signal as it is preserved in the rock record. Geologic processes such as variations in sea level, subsidence, and sediment supply can clearly influence the form of $\delta^{13}C$ curves as a result of variations in accommodation space and sediment preservation.

Another important influence on the construction of chemostratigraphic curves is the bias that is introduced through variations in sampling intervals. Samples are often collected in the field with spacings of 10–20 meters or more. The numerical experiments presented here show, particularly for epicratonic cover sequences (such as the Siberian platform), that sample spacings of >10 m can result in potentially severe distortion of the terminal Proterozoic and Early Cambrian $\delta^{13}C$ primary signal. On the other hand, sample spacings of 1–2 m or less result in recovery of even short duration events—provided that the data gaps associated with unconformities and siliciclastic intervals can be accounted for, as well as the overprinting effects of diagenesis.

INTRODUCTION

Forward models are a useful tool for reconstructing the history of basin evolution, including mechanisms for development of accommodation space, stratigraphic architecture, and the distribution of facies. Generally, such models allow for predictions concerning the rates and magnitudes of processes operating at various time scales (e.g., Read et al., 1986; Aigner et al., 1989; Kaufman et al., 1991a). We have recently modified a stratigraphic forward modeling package, STRATA (Flemings and Grotzinger, 1996), to provide chemostratigraphic proxy records that are superimposed on sequence-stratigraphic records of lithofacies and unconformities. Here, we use the modified program to illustrate the main controlling effects on the structure of chemostratigraphic curves preserved in the rock record. In particular, we illustrate how subsidence, sedimentation rate, and development of unconformities influence the shape and completeness of stratigraphic records. In addition, we explore the biases inherent to sampling intervals that are keyed to rock thicknesses rather than time.

To illustrate these controls on the chemostratigraphic record, we begin with a simple, arbitrarily produced curve of secular variations in the chemical composition of seawater. We assume that the signal in the rock is primary, or a primary signal can be corrected for the effects of diagenesis. Furthermore, we make no assumptions about the driving mechanisms behind the signal itself, and regulate only that it be uniform over the spatial scales of the carbonate platform that is sampled (i.e., not dependent on water depth). This signal will be imprinted in modified form in the stratigraphic record of platform carbonate deposits within the program. Ideally, if enough is known about the spatial and temporal changes in the processes that regulated the primary signal, then the chemostratigraphic record of basins could be used to reconstruct their depositional histories. Unfortunately, there is still much to be discerned about processes controlling the secular signal, let alone the various depositional and post-depositional factors that lead to partially or completely modified chemostratigraphic records. This is particularly true of Precambrian carbonate deposits. Therefore, we are less concerned with evaluating the integrity of published stratigraphic records, such as those for terminal Proterozoic time, than with demonstrating how various geologic processes and sampling strategies can result in highly distorted interpretations of a particular primary signal. Indeed, the stratigraphic record itself, with all its inherent biases, must be carefully analyzed before a global model curve is obtained. These effects are independent of the particular primary signal or the age of the strata in question, but they are particularly important for Precambrian successions because the lack of detailed biostratigraphic frameworks means that chemostratigraphic curves are more important tools for correlation and interpretation of strata of this age.

Our goal is to evaluate how various parameters that control patterns of basin filling, such as variations in sea level, subsidence, and sediment supply, influence the preserved form of a hypothetical $\delta^{13}C$ secular curve. In particular, we examine the effect of unconformities, sedimentation and subsidence rates, and sampling intervals on the preserved isotopic curve within a framework of the sequence-stratigraphic architecture of particular tectonic settings.

BACKGROUND

Much effort has been given recently to construction of chemostratigraphic curves for the Neoproterozoic and terminal Proterozoic, under the assumption that they represent secular changes in the global composition of sea water (see summary in Kaufman and Knoll, 1995). It is beyond the scope of this paper to address either this assumption or the validity of hypotheses that are put forth to explain various anomalies in this record. However, we recognize that the global curve is established and tested by accumulation of data from discrete sampling of outcrops on various continents. In almost every case, only one or two sections are produced for a particular basin, and usually with few, if any, geochronologic constraints or complementary chronostratigraphic markers. Because the processes that influence the physical stratigraphy must also affect the record of chemical proxies within it, high inter-basinal variability must be expected in data sets that are used for the construction of a global curve. As a result, global curves result from spatial averaging of data from sections that were chosen for various reasons including convenience, outcrop accessibility, outcrop exposure, and degree of tectonic overprinting, but not necessarily where the section might be most complete. Only through more extensive and detailed sampling can the most complete and representative curves of each basin be identified and then used to more accurately modify and/or improve the resolution of the global curve. Future work will necessarily be aimed at shorter-duration, and smaller-magnitude, excursions. This is particularly true for Neoproterozoic and older strata, in which correlation may ultimately rest with excursions of only a few per mil (e.g., Knoll et al., 1995a). Excursions of this magnitude and duration will require fine-scale sampling and particular care, given that the size of the excursions are approaching the scale of error associated with diagenesis and any averaging of components (e.g., cements, allochems, micrite) associated with sampling.

As advances lead to more accurate secular isotopic curves, the utility of these curves for basin analysis also improves. For Precambrian rocks, in which other chronostratigraphic proxies are rare or of very coarse resolution, chemostratigraphic approaches offer great potential. Utilizing global chemostratigraphic curves should become increasingly important in helping to reconstruct a wide variety of stratigraphic processes associated with basin evolution and deposition. This includes the recognition of unconformities, definition of two- and three-dimensional stratal geometries, depositional patterns associated with uplift or subsidence, and relative sediment accumulation rates within basins.

EFFECTS OF UNCONFORMITIES AND VARIABLE SEDIMENT ACCUMULATION RATES

The change in shape of preserved isotopic curves is well illustrated for different positions along a simple hinged carbonate platform with no changes in sea level, sediment accumulation rates, or subsidence patterns. Important input parameters (see Table 1 for a list of the major parameters used in the simulations) include simple, linearly increasing subsidence in the offshore direction and sediment accumulation rates that keep up with subsidence at all points across the basin, except for the right-hand side where a rimmed margin develops (Fig. 1). The rimmed geometry is created by imposing drastically lowered sedimentation rates for the right-hand side of the model during the initial growth of the platform, which results in local backstepping of the shelf margin.

A sinusoidal curve of rising and falling $\delta^{13}C$ was produced by providing the following information concerning the isotopic curve: (1) time of initiation and end of run, (2) maximum and minimum $\delta^{13}C$ values, and (3) curve shape. For this simulation and others, we defined $\delta^{13}C$ to be a simple sinusoidal function of time in which signal amplitude and period were specified a priori. However, it is also possible to generate curves by inputting sets of paired values of $\delta^{13}C$ and simulation times, followed by interpolation of the data using simple linear or cubic spline fits.

Figure 1A illustrates water depths for the accumulated sediment which, although not ideal (Wilborn and Wilkinson, 1998), may roughly correspond with facies. Time lines for the chemostratigraphic data are shown in Figure 1B. Note that the facies map indicates that most of the sediment across the shelf accumulated at the same depth; in other words, the carbonate platform kept up with accommodation in all locations. At the right-hand side, shallow platform facies deposited at sea level pass through a relatively abrupt rimmed-shelf transition into deeper facies.

Figure 1B illustrates the chemostratigraphic data displayed as a set of "logs", visually akin to what might be obtained from a series of 1D sections measured at a set spacing in the field. For the model simulation the spacing is 20 km. Relative to the shelf edge, the simulation shows a gradual compression of the chemostratigraphic curves in the up-dip direction, and a relatively more abrupt compression in the down-dip, offshore direction. The up-dip compression arises from condensation of the section in areas of lower accommodation space, whereas the downdip compression results from diminished sedimentation rates in deeper-water settings (sedimentation rates exponentially decline as a function of water depth; Schlager, 1981). In this run, the simulated sedimentary basin contains no unconformities and so every potential stratigraphic section would contain a complete temporal record, reflecting the original input record. However, the slope of both positive and negative excursions is distorted in shallow water to flatter geometries, meaning more stratigraphically rapid shifts towards higher or lower values. Without age control and a priori knowledge of sediment accumulation rates, data from outcrops representing areas of lower accumulation rates will appear to record more temporally rapid changes. This problem arises because, without such a priori control, the solution is not readily evident. In addition, if some evidence existed for variable accumulation rates, it would not be possible to calibrate for such variation and thus the principle of parsimony would generally lead one to not compress or expand time–thickness relationships.

The next level of complication is to create a similar sedimentary basin with several depositional sequences. This model run (Fig. 2) shows many effects that complex stratal geometry has on a preserved chemostratigraphic record. In this run, three cycles of eustatic sea-level changes were superimposed on a hinged carbonate shelf. The time lines in Figure 2A show patterns of onlap, offlap, and toplap, and thus highlight the stratigraphic position and lateral extent of unconformities.

Figure 2B shows a carbon-isotope record for the same run, using the same isotopic curve as Figure 1. Asymmetry in the isotopic curve results from condensation and expansion of the sedimentary section as a function of temporal variations in accumulation rates. Extreme asymmetry, ultimately resulting in

TABLE 1.—VALUES OF MAJOR PARAMETERS USED IN SIMULATIONS

	Sedimentation Rate (cm/ky)	Sea-Level Amplitude (m)	Sea-Level Period (My)	Left Subsidence Rate (cm/ky)	Right Subsidence Rate (cm/ky)	C-isotope Amplitude (ppt)	C-isotope Period (My)
Figure 1	100*	0	0	0	10	4	2
Figure 2	100*	30	2	0	15	4	2
Figure 3	100*	30	2	0	2	vend.iso	vend.iso
Figure 4	100	0	0	0.1	0.4	vend.iso	vend.iso

*On right-hand side the sedimentation rate is fixed at 10 cm/ky.

kinks in the isotopic curve, occur at or near unconformities, because of zero or lowered accumulation, respectively. (Note that in the display of chemostratigraphic logs STRATA deals with unconformities by drawing horizontal lines to represent absence of sediment, and also of isotopic record.) The degree of asymmetry increases from right to left because of diachrony associated with onlap. In other words, in this model run the older parts of the transgressive systems tracts are not represented in shallow water settings, and thus pre- and post-unconformity isotope values are increasingly offset updip.

The isotopic signature of the strata can also be displayed using continuous color (or gray-scale) mapping, similar to the way that facies water depths are plotted (Fig. 2C). Patterns of onlap and toplap are very clearly shown by the isotopic signatures. In the model shown in Figures 2C and 2D, there is preferential preservation of positive isotopic excursions because the sea-level curve and the isotopic curve were both sine functions that had the same period but were perfectly out of phase (see right side of Figure 2D). Shifting of the curves to in-phase positions would have resulted in preferential up-dip preservation of light isotopes. It is important to note that if isotopic ratios are coupled in some way to sea-level changes through geologic time, then natural systems may produce similar spatial segregation of isotopically light and heavy sediment in the rock record. Figure 2D shows a time–space (or "Wheeler") plot in which the vertical axis of Figure 2C (depth) is transformed to time and illustrates the temporal and spatial distribution of the isotopic signal, as preserved in sediment. Sea-level and isotope curves are shown on the right. Unconformities are partitioned into areas and times of nondeposition (hiatuses, shown in gray) and areas of erosion of previously deposited strata (vacuities, shown in black). The Wheeler plot emphasizes that proximal deposits may be considerably incomplete and that this may result in unusual chemostratigraphic patterns such as the stacking of positive excursions without intervening negative excursions.

EFFECTS OF SAMPLING BIAS

Sediment accumulation rates vary both spatially and temporally within sedimentary basins (Sadler, 1981). These rates are particularly poorly constrained for Precambrian basins, for which absolute ages have larger errors, and those ages which are available are not tied to a detailed chronostratigraphic framework (e.g., biostratigraphic zonation). As a result, it is extremely difficult to calibrate sampling intervals from locality to locality. This means that in sections deposited under different but constant accumulation rates, sampling at similar stratigraphic intervals means that proportionally different temporal resolution are represented in the isotopic data. Even in the case in which two sections cover a similar thickness of strata and a

similar total duration, time may be distributed very differently in each locality. Such differences in distribution of time results from condensation and expansion of strata (unsteadiness in sediment accumulation rate), and the number and duration of unconformities, both of which are ultimately related to differences in tectonics.

In the previous section of the paper, we illustrated the manner in which unconformities and changes in sediment accumulation rates alter chemostratigraphic signatures. Given the inability to temporally calibrate sampling intervals in most studies, particularly for Precambrian strata, it is readily apparent that sampling, simply by its discontinuous nature, compounds the problems outlined earlier. Therefore, it is important to recognize the nature and potential magnitude of distortions to chemostratigraphic curves that result from sampling procedures.

As part of its functionality, the new chemostratigraphic module of the program STRATA can sample model data at specified intervals to produce synthetic curves that smoothly integrate between selected data points without consideration of original isotopic input parameters. This is analogous to plotting an isotopic curve alongside a stratigraphic section without knowledge of how time is stratigraphically distributed. We consider this to be very realistic in the sense that, in general, almost no information is available concerning the duration of unconformities and the temporal and spatial variation in accumulation rates. Furthermore, even though some unconformities are obvious, the physical expression of many is subtle, a problem that again handicaps interpretation of Precambrian strata. Two examples from different tectonic settings are shown to illustrate how the inability to calibrate sampling intervals to geologic time, or to a chronostratigraphic framework, results in an inaccurate or incomplete reconstruction of a secular curve.

Terminal Proterozoic–Early Cambrian Passive Margin

Here we simulate development of a synthetic basin of terminal Proterozoic age with a spatially variable subsidence history, not unlike some of the world's better preserved terminal Proterozoic basins that were formed during passive-margin subsidence (e.g., Australia, Preiss and Forbes, 1981, von der Borch et al., 1988; Mackenzie Mountains, northwestern Canada, Ross, 1991, MacNaughton et al., 1997). Ideally, we would like to input the history of accommodation as controlled by sea level and subsidence, but no quantitative data are available for rocks of this age. Therefore, we focus on the effects of sampling interval. For this simulation, the terminal Proterozoic and Early Cambrian (Nemakit-Daldyn) carbon-isotope curves of Kaufman and Knoll (1995) and Brasier et al. (1997) were digitized to create a composite model curve. The key components of this model curve (maxima, minima, and zero crossings) are stored as data points, fixed in absolute time, in a file that STRATA

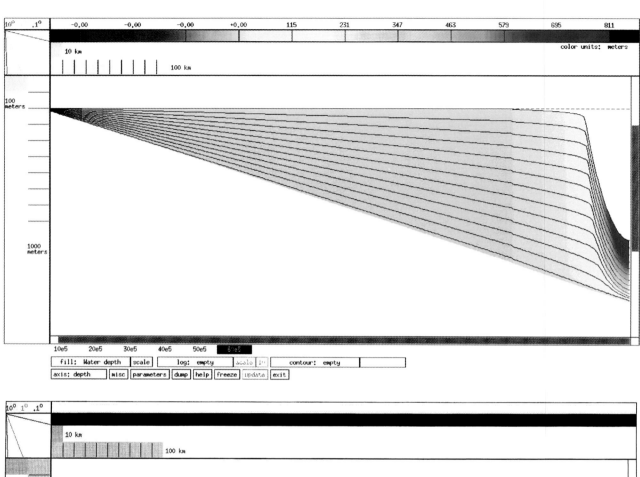

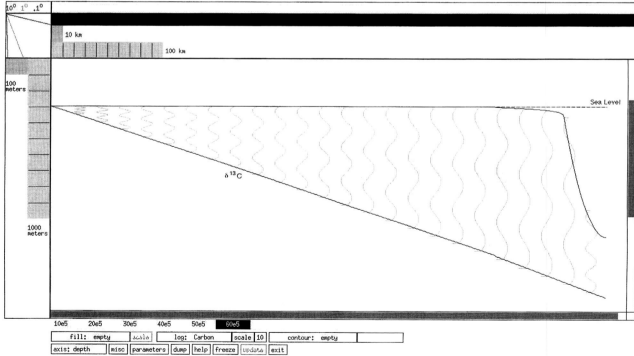

FIG. 1.—A) Synthetic carbonate platform showing development from initial ramp to rimmed shelf. Colors record the water depths (meters) in which sediment accumulated (see scale at top); subsidence rates increase linearly in the offshore direction and sediment accumulation keeps up with subsidence everywhere except for near the shelf margin, where a rapid transition to deep-water sedimentation occurs. B) Map of representative, evenly spaced isotopic curves as preserved in carbonate sediment across a hinged carbonate shelf. Subsidence rates increase linearly in the offshore direction, and sediment accumulation rates keep up with subsidence everywhere. A sinusoidal isotopic curve was input, and changing shapes reflect the influence of accumulation rate in areas of differing accommodation space.

then uses to fit either a simple linear interpolation (producing a saw-tooth pattern) or cubic spline (producing a smooth curve between data points), depending on the requirements of the user. In this case, we have fitted the data using the cubic spline option which yields an interpolated data set for values of carbon-isotope composition for all values of time (Δt) that are computed in the simulation.

A subsiding passive-margin basin is simulated in which carbonate sediment accumulation generally keeps pace with sea level; the facies map (not shown, but similar to that shown in Figure 2A) therefore shows no variation across most of the shelf, except near its rim, where an abrupt transition to deep-water facies occurs. Shelf deposits reach a maximum thickness of approximately 1000 m near the shelf edge for a total run time of 60 my. This is equivalent to 1.5 cm/1000 years, which is typical for a mature passive margin. Figure 3A displays the logs, with 20 km spacing, for the composite global carbon-isotope curve for the terminal Proterozoic and earliest Cambrian, covering the time span from 600 to 540 Ma. For reference (see arrows in Figure 3A), the upper part of the curve shows a prominent positive excursion (550–548 Ma), followed by a strong negative excursion at the Precambrian–Cambrian boundary (543 Ma), and some additional small, short-duration excursions of earliest Cambrian age.

The isotopic logs in Figure 3a, displayed at the full resolution that model calculations permit, show nearly complete preservation of the signal at all points on the profile, but with increasing compression in more proximal settings. Isotope output data for this simulation were then sampled at an interval of 20 m at each section across the profile, interpolated using a cubic spline fit, and replotted in Figure 3B. (Cubic splines smoothly fit the data much like field data often are fit by inspection using hand-drawn curves). This curve can be compared with the original isotopic curve in Figure 3A to illustrate the influence of sampling interval on curve geometry. Figure 3B illustrates progressively more inaccurate representations of the original curve in the more condensed sections updip. In general, most sections do not reproduce the Early Cambrian short-term variations with much accuracy, and only the two outermost shelf sections and the updip slope section reasonably capture the Precambrian–Cambrian negative spike.

In an attempt to recover the full structure of the model curve, the sampling interval can accordingly be reduced. In the next section we explore this procedure, but for the case of cratonic basins, where subsidence rates, and therefore sediment accumulations rates, are lower.

Cratonic Basin

Our second example illustrates similar effects for an intracratonic-basin and/or epicratonic setting, characterized by gentle subsidence (0.2 to 1 cm per 1000 yr). Such a scenario is very realistic for sections that have been described from the terminal Proterozoic–Early Cambrian cratonic platforms of Siberia (Khomentovsky and Karlova, 1993; Knoll et al., 1995b; Pelechaty et al., 1996). In this simulation, the same isotopic curve used in Figure 3A is plotted with cratonic (very low) subsidence rates for left-hand and right-hand sides (see Table 1), and this produces a depositional geometry with an expanding wedge without a shelf break (Fig. 4A). Using a sampling

interval of 10 m—one-half of that used for the passive-margin example illustrated in Figure 3B—produces an extraordinary range of isotopic curves, more than half of which bear little resemblance to the original curves (Fig. 4B). Decreasing the sampling interval to 5 m (Fig. 4C) produces a somewhat more complete recovery of the inputted global isotope curve, but still shows some of the problems illustrated in Figure 3B (which used a 20 m sampling interval), such as omission of the Precambrian–Cambrian boundary excursion.

A further decrease of the sampling interval to 1 m (Fig. 4D) results in a nearly perfect reproduction of the inputted global model curve. We consider this to be a significant result, which illustrates that for a very reasonable "worst-case" scenario of very low average sediment accumulation rates, the first-order structure of the terminal Proterozoic and Early Cambrian carbon-isotope curve can be faithfully reproduced using a sampling interval of 1 meter. In practice, of course, the potentially damaging effects of unconformities, diagenesis, and siliciclastic intervals unsuitable for isotope analyses will all exert their influence on the process. One goal of this exercise is to illustrate that in the tradeoff of cost and time versus chronostratigraphic precision, the best compromise for selection of the proper sampling interval is largely dependent on tectonic settings. More specifically, sampling interval should be adjusted (1) for sediment accumulation rate and (2) to capture the expected frequency of the signal being extracted. Whereas the perfect sampling interval would require *a priori* knowledge of these parameters, in practice rough estimates are helpful guidelines. For instance, estimates of sediment accumulation rates are known for various tectonic settings, and the major positive and negative excursions in carbon-isotope curves generally are on time scales of 1–2 million years.

Real Data and Sampling Intervals

A survey of chemostratigraphic studies of Neoproterozoic to Lower Cambrian deposits, summarized in Table 2, indicates a wide range of sampling intervals. The stratigraphic spacing of samples is in many cases highly variable, so much so that in several studies it is not readily evident that the researchers attempted to sample at a specific interval. This variability is the result of a number of factors. First, lithologies suitable for isotopic analysis are commonly interbedded with those that yield no data or unreliable results. In the case of carbon isotopes, intercalation of generally unsuitable siliciclastic deposits with carbonate beds will force adjustments in sampling schemes that result in gaps and uneven sampling intervals (e.g., Narbonne et al., 1994). A related cause for variability of sample intervals is due to differences in carbonate facies. Facies that tend to faithfully record primary signals, such as micrite and primary marine cements for carbon isotopes, are targeted for sampling, and those that commonly are altered during diagenesis, such as rudite and coarse grainstone, are avoided. As with mixed siliciclastic–carbonate deposits, the vertical distribution of these carbonate facies controls sampling intervals. Other processes that might make strata unsuitable for sampling, and thereby alter sampling intervals, would include tectonism (e.g., shear zones), hydrothermal alteration, baked zones around sills, and zones of massive recrystallization.

Some of the largest sampling intervals in Table 2, generally on the order of tens of meters, are associated with studies of

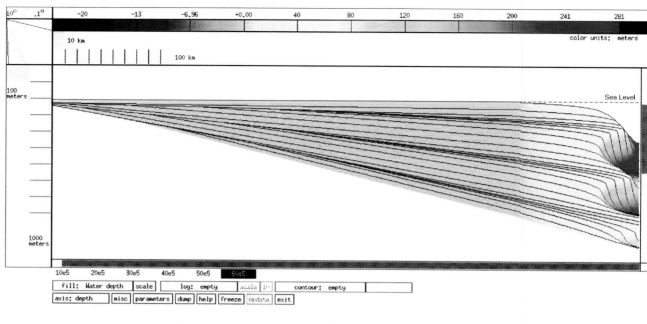

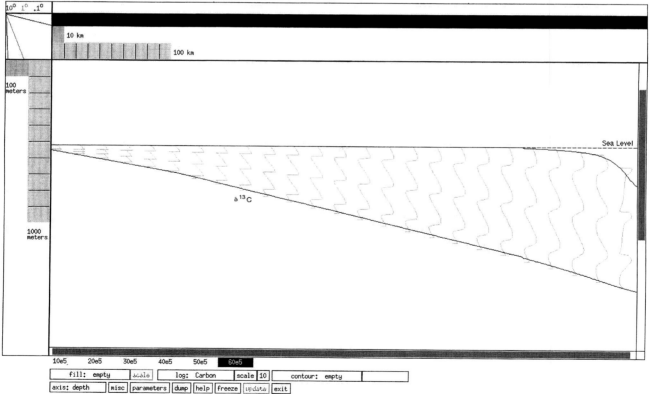

FIG. 2.—A) Synthetic depositional sequences produced for a hinged carbonate platform subjected to changing sea level (amplitude 30 m, period 2 My; see Table 1 for input parameters). Colors record the water depths in which sediment accumulated (see scale at top); long-lived sedimentation at sea level shows that sediment accumulation matched or exceeded accommodation production across the shelf. Lighter dashed lines represent time lines. Patterns of onlap and toplap show the position and extent of unconformities. B) Carbon isotopic record for the same shelf. Lateral changes in the shapes of isotopic curves reflect variations in sediment accumulation rates. Unconformities are clearly highlighted by kinks in the isotopic curves, which become progressively more extreme in the up-dip direction as more time is represented by the unconformity because of the combination of erosion and delayed onlap. C) Color map of the isotopic signature of the deposits; scale is shown at top. The same patterns of onlap and toplap shown by time lines in Figure 1A are evident in the isotope patterns. This pattern was

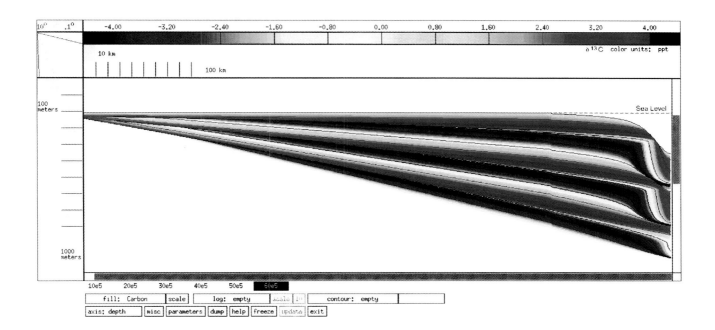

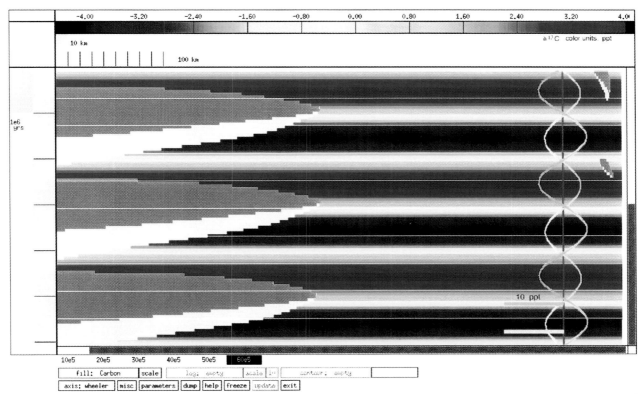

FIG. 2.—(Continued) generated using out-of-phase sinusoidal curves of sea level and isotopic changes. D) Wheeler or chronostratigraphic diagram (time on the vertical axis instead of thickness) for Figure 2C, mapping out the temporal and spatial distribution of the isotopic signal of shelf. Scaled sea level (meters) and isotope (parts per thousand) curves are shown on the right. Length of scale bar (green) for isotopic curve is 10 parts per thousand; length of scale bar (blue) for sea-level curve is 100 meters. Areas and times of nondeposition—lacunae—are shown in gray; black regions of the diagram represent areas and times of degradational vacuity, the removal of previously deposited sediment. Note how much of the primary signal is missing because of unconformities in proximal settings. In addition, note the potential for preferential preservation of either light or heavy isotopes (in this case heavy) in up-dip positions.

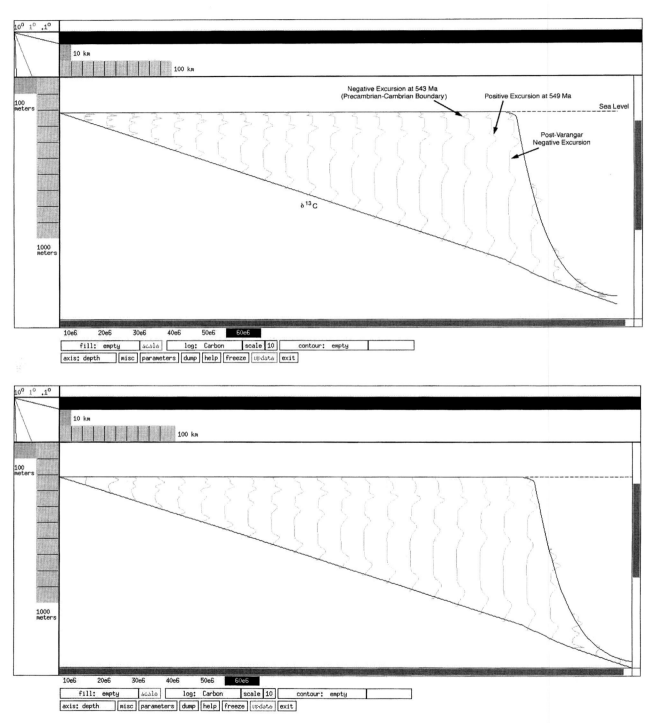

FIG. 3.—A) Composite global carbon curve for the terminal Proterozoic and earliest Cambrian (600 to 540 Ma; from Brasier et al., 1993; Kaufman and Knoll, 1995; Knoll et al., 1995b) input for a hinged carbonate platform without sea-level changes. The isotopic curves show nearly complete preservation of the signal at all points on the profile but are increasingly compressed in more proximal settings. Arrows delineate specific excursions referred to in the text. B) Isotopic output data from the simulation in Figure 3A were sampled at an interval of 20 m at each section on the profile, interpolated using a cubic spline fit, and then replotted. Compared with Figure 3A, this figure shows progressively more inaccurate representations of the original curve in the more condensed sections updip. This sampling interval in general does not capture the Early Cambrian short-term variations with much accuracy, and only the two outermost shelf sections reasonably capture the negative spike at the Precambrian–Cambrian boundary.

TABLE 2.—SAMPLING INTERVALS FOR CARBON ISOTOPES

Authors	Location	Sampling Interval
Narbonne et al. (1994) (Table 1)	Mackenzie Mountains	Highly variable; m's to 100's of m
Strauss et al. (1992) (Table A1)	Newfoundland	Most 10 m; others 20 m
Brasier et al. (1990)	China/Iran	China 1 m; Iran ~2.5 m
Brasier, Anderson, and Corfield (1992)	Newfoundland/England	Fortune Nfld: 2.5–5 m; Fosters Point Nfld: 0.8–2 m
Calver (1993)	Australia	Amadeus Basin 10 m or less; Officer Basin 20 m; Adelaide Basin 30–50 m
Smith et al. (1994)	Idaho	5–20 m
Kennedy (1996) (Table 1)	Australia	Mostly <1 m
Kaufman et al. (1992)	N.W. Territories	Mostly 1–3 m
Saylor et al. (1999) (Table 1)	Namibia	Some 1–4 m; some 10–25 m
Kaufman et al. (1991b)	Namibia	Table 1: Variable: some 1–3 m; some 10's–100's m
		Figure 9: 10–15 m (Nama Gp.)
		Figure 10: 25–30 m (Otavi Gp.)
Corsetti and Kaufman (1994)	White Inyo Mt.	Some 5–15 m; some 1.5–2.5
Brasier et al. (1996)	S. W. Mongolia	Variable: most 5–15 m
Pelechaty et al. (1996)	Siberia	Figure 2: 4–6 m; Figure 4: 2.5–3 m
Brasier et al. (1993) (Figure 2)	Siberia	2.5 m
Glumac and Walker (1998)	S. Appalachians	<1.5 m
Derry et al. (1994) [Sr]	Siberia	Variable: 5–50 m; ave ~20 m
Asmeron et al. (1991) [Sr]	Victoria Island, NW Territories	Variable: 25–125 m
Derry et al. (1989) [Sr] (Table 1)	Svalbard/E. Greenland	Variable: mostly 30–60 m

strontium isotopes. In the past, this may have been due in part to the cost and time necessary to process and run such samples, although it does not appear to be an issue in more recent studies (e.g., Montañez et al., 1996). The requirement of relatively unaltered limestone (not dolostone) for Sr analyses may make continuous sampling less likely in rocks of Precambrian age.

For those studies with relatively consistent sampling intervals, the goals of the study largely determined the magnitude of the intervals. For instance, Kennedy (1996) sampled primarily at intervals <1 m. In this case, he analyzed relatively thin cap carbonate beds to look at small-scale, presumably short-lived, changes in post glacial ocean chemistry. Studies such as that of Kaufman et al. (1991b) largely represent reconnaissance work with small numbers of samples over hundreds to thousands of meters of strata. Several of the Namibian successions analyzed in that study have subsequently been sampled at considerably finer detail (Saylor et al., 1998). Other studies, such as those of Smith et al. (1994) and Strauss et al. (1992), employed moderately wide sample spacings of 5–20 m, which our modeling suggests is pushing (or exceeding) the upper limit of sampling interval that will reasonably accurately reproduce the primary isotope signal.

DISCUSSION

The past decade of research aimed at refining the terminal Proterozoic time scale has produced a significant amount of chemostratigraphic data. In general, these data provide strong evidence for secular variations in the carbon (and strontium) isotopic composition of surface seawater (see Kaufman et al., 1997, and references therein), although it is important to note that published terminal Proterozoic secular curves are spatially- and time-averaged representations of ocean surface water composition. Acceptance of the first-order structure of the resulting model carbon-isotope curve is promoted, in large part, because of the great magnitude of many of its component isotopic anomalies, which apparently span at least an order of magnitude, as measured in parts per thousand. Nevertheless, some of these anomalies, such as the negative excursion at or near the Precambrian–Cambrian boundary, have been difficult to quantify

in magnitude (Bartley et al., 1998) owing to the likely short duration of the anomaly (<1 my; Grotzinger et al., 1995) and the fact that in several locations it is truncated by a probably globally correlative unconformity at or near the boundary (Pelechaty et al., 1996; Saylor et al., 1998). In order to further test the validity of the first-order model, as well as improve our understanding of the magnitude and form of specific excursions, it will be necessary in the future to pursue systematic studies involving many sections within a single basin. This is important because even the simplest basin (e.g., passive margin) can show remarkable along-strike variability in differential subsidence, leading to spatial and temporal variability in sediment accumulation rates (Read, 1989).

Inevitably, future work will also attempt to improve the resolution of the model curve by identifying excursions of smaller magnitude and/or duration. Such efforts are now underway for the Early Cambrian part of the time scale, where, in addition to short-duration excursions of large magnitude, short-duration excursions of 1 or 2 per mil are also thought to be significant (e.g., Brasier et al., 1994; Knoll et al., 1995b). Most recently, it has been suggested that small excursions might characterize part of latest terminal Proterozoic time as well (Kaufman and Knoll, 1997; Saylor et al., 1998). Furthermore, several pilot studies aimed at Mesoproterozoic and Paleoproterozoic carbon-isotope stratigraphy also reveal that only small-scale excursions of a few per mil are present (e.g., Knoll et al., 1995a), with rare exceptions such as the Paleoproterozoic "Lomagundi event", where carbon-isotope values of up to +10‰ are observed (Schidlowski, 1988; Karhu, 1993). In general, it seems that for rocks prior to about 900 Ma, chemostratigraphic correlation efforts using carbon isotopes may be limited to excursions of just a few per mil. Such attempts are laudable in that they promise, in principle, to improve chronostratigraphic resolution for correlation of relatively unfossiliferous Precambrian strata. However, as the magnitude and duration of the anomalies that define the chemostratigraphic signal decrease, the uncertainties that envelop that signal grow proportionally larger. Ultimately, between the inherent unsteadiness of sediment accumulation and the "noise" introduced through diagenetic resetting, the limit of highest practical resolution is approached.

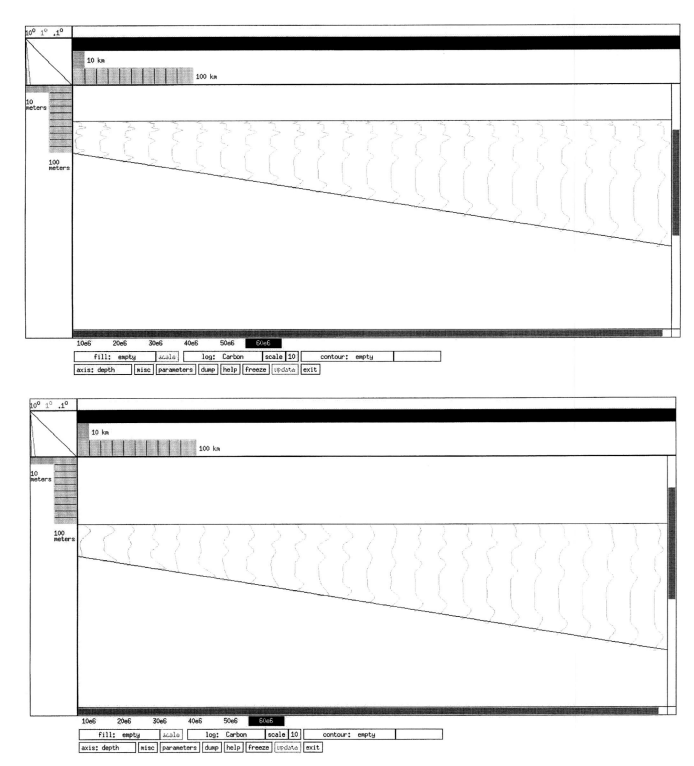

Fig. 4.—A) The same isotopic curve from Figure 3A is plotted with input parameters that simulate a cratonal setting: a wedge-shaped depositional geometry without a shelf break. B) The isotopic output data from Part A were sampled with an interval of 10 m and replotted. Note the remarkable range of shapes of isotopic curves. C) Plot of isotopic data using a sampling interval of only 5 m for the same data and input parameters as in Part A. The recovery of the original

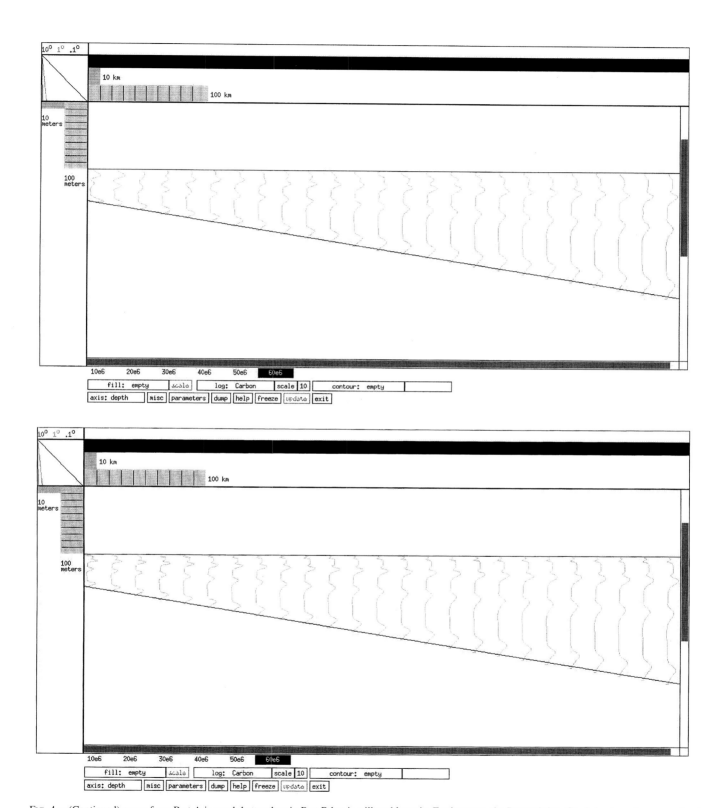

F𝗂ɢ. 4.—(Continued) curve from Part A is much better than in Part B but is still problematic. For instance, the Precambrian–Cambrian boundary excursion is not captured. D) Sampling interval of 1 m is applied to the same data and yields nearly complete preservation of the global curve shown in Part A.

Forward stratigraphic models are useful tools for illustrating what is theoretically possible and reasonable for a sensible range of input parameters. As data become available, model simulations can increasingly be restricted in their variability and can ultimately be used to address the inverse problem of attempting to recover the values of specific input parameters (e.g., sediment accumulation rates, subsidence rates, sea-level fluctuations). As applied here, STRATA can be used as a guide in helping to recover the values for missing parts of excursions in isotopic curves in sedimentary basins subjected to complex subsidence and sea-level histories. Although we have chosen to model only simple scenarios in this paper, STRATA has the capability to input a full range of geologic processes for the purpose of simulating complex geologic histories (see Flemings and Grotzinger, 1997, and the STRATA website at http://hydro.geosc.psu.edu).

Conclusions and Recommendations for Future Studies

The ability to establish an isotope-based or trace-element-based chronostratigraphy for Precambrian (and much of Phanerozoic) time is greatly influenced by data gaps created by unconformities and unsteady sediment accumulation rates. Furthermore, diagenetic overprinting may variably degrade any primary signals. While treatment of this latter problem is beyond the scope of the present paper, the former issues can be better addressed than at present through the application of numerical forward models such as STRATA, which can aid in more quantitative testing of conceptual hypotheses. The simple results presented in this paper make obvious several important steps that should be taken in future studies.

Clearly, it is essential to invest as much time as possible in the field searching for evidence of unconformities. Unfortunately, this is often difficult in single vertical sections; it has been recognized for a decade now (Christie-Blick et al., 1988; Grotzinger et al., 1989) that in Precambrian rocks it is essential to identify potential unconformity surfaces and trace them laterally searching for evidence of stratal truncation, meteoric dissolution, and stratigraphic onlap. Most importantly, samples for isotopic analyses need to be collected from multiple locations within the same basin so that stratal geometries can be used as a guide to how the form of a primary signal changes in response to both local and regional stratal relationships.

As a second point, it is important to keep sampling intervals as small as possible. Given that there must always be a lower interval limit that is greater than what might be ideal because of time, funding, outcrop expression, or other constraints, we recommend that particularly small sampling intervals be used in strata directly above and below potential unconformity surfaces. Simple modeling results, such as those presented here, demonstrate clearly that sediment accumulation rates are increasingly reduced as accommodation space is reduced prior to the development of an unconformity; sediment accumulation rates are low and then increase as deposition proceeds above an unconformity. Consequently, the effect on the chemostratigraphic record is increasingly compressed primary signals in strata adjacent to potential unconformities. Therefore, to best recover those signals, the sampling interval should be reduced.

More generally, however, when the sampling interval exceeds a critical level, the accuracy of the "sampled" curves

becomes misleading. The results of our simulations (Figs. 3, 4) indicate that for any particular sampling interval, sampling of expanded sections produce more accurate reconstructions of the original curves. For thick sections, such as those that accumulate in passive margins and foreland basins, sampling should certainly be less than 20 m, particularly in more proximal settings (5 m might be more reasonable in these thicker sections to capture most of the curve, although some short-term anomalies may be missed). For cratonic settings, the simulation indicates that sampling interval should be less than 5 m, preferably at 1 to 2 m or less. The simulations in Figures 3 and 4 do not contain unconformities, which tend to remove part of the signal and thereby cause stratigraphically instantaneous shifts across sequence boundaries. As stated above, capturing these shifts require finer-scale sampling intervals stratigraphically adjacent to the surfaces.

REFERENCES

AIGNER, T., DOYLE, M., LAWRENCE, D., EPTING, M., AND VAN VLIET, A., 1989, Quantitative modeling of carbonate platforms: some examples, *in* Crevello, P. D., Wilson, J. L., Sarg, J. F., and Read, J. F., eds., Controls on Carbonate Platform and Basin Development: SEPM, Special Publication 44, p. 27–38.

ASMEROM, Y., JACOBSEN, S. B., KNOLL, A. H., BUTTERFIELD, N. J., AND SWETT, K., 1991, Strontium isotopic variations of Neoproterozoic seawater: Implications for crustal evolution: Geochemica et Cosmochimica Acta, v. 55, p. 2883–2894.

BARTLEY, J. K., POPE, M., KNOLL, A. H., SEMIKHATOV, M. A., AND PETROV, P. Y., 1998, A Vendian–Cambrian boundary succession from the northwestern margin of the Siberian Platform: Stratigraphy, palaeontology, chemostratigraphy and correlation: Geological Magazine, v. 135, p. 473-494.

BRASIER, M. D., ANDERSON, M. M., AND CORFIELD, R. M., 1992, Oxygen and carbon isotope stratigraphy of early Cambrian carbonates in southeastern Newfoundland and England: Geological Magazine, v. 129, p. 265–279.

BRAISER, M., CORFIELD, R., DERRY, L., ROZANOV, A., AND ZHURAVLEV, A., 1994, Multiple δ13C excursions spanning the Cambrian explosion to the Botomian crisis in Siberia: Geology, v. 22, p. 455–458.

BRASIER, M., GREEN, O., AND SHIELDS, G., 1997, Ediacaran sponge spicule clusters from southwestern Mongolia and the origins of the Cambrian fauna: Geology, v. 25, p. 303–306.

BRASIER, M. D., KHOMENTOVSKY, V. V., AND CORFIELD, R.M., 1993, Stable isotopic calibration of the earliest skeletal fossil assemblages in eastern Siberia (Precambrian–Cambrian boundary): Terra Nova, v. 5, p. 225–232.

BRASIER, M. D., MAGARITZ, M., CORFIELD, R., LUO, H., WU, X., OUYANG, L., JIANG, Z., HAMDI, B., HE, T., AND FRASER, A. G., 1990, The carbon- and oxygen-isotopic record of the Precambrian–Cambrian boundary interval in China and Iran and their correlation: Geological Magazine, v. 4, p. 319–332.

BRASIER, M. D., SHIELDS, G., KULESHOV, V. N., AND ZHEGALLO, E. A., 1996, Integrated chemo- and biostratigraphic calibration of early animal evolution: Neoproterozoic–Early Cambrian of southwest Mongolia: Geological Magazine, v. 4, p. 445–485.

CALVER, C. R., 1993, Chemostratigraphy of Ediacaran successions in the Adelaide Geosyncline, Amadeus Basin and Officer Basin, *in* Jenkins, R. J. F., Lindsay, J. F., and Walter, M. R., eds., Field Guide to the Adelaide Geosyncline and Amadeus Basin, Australia: Australian Geological Survey Organization, Guidebook 35, 133 p.

CHRISTIE-BLICK, N., GROTZINGER, J. P., AND VON DER BORCH, C. C., 1988, Sequence stratigraphy in Proterozoic successions: Geology, v. 16, p. 100–104.

CORSETTI, F. A., AND KAUFMAN, A. J., 1994, Chemostratigraphy of Neoproterozoic–Cambrian units, White–Inyo Region, Eastern California: Implications for global correlation and faunal distribution: Palaios, v. 9, p. 211–219.

DERRY, L. A., BRASIER, M. D., CORFIELD, R. M., ROZANOV, A. Y., AND ZHURAVLEV, A. Y., 1994, Sr and C isotopes in Lower Cambrian carbonates from the Siberian craton: A paleoenvironmental record during the 'Cambrian explosion': Earth and Planetary Science Letters, v. 128, p. 671–681.

DERRY, L. A., KETO, L. S., JACOBSEN, S. B., KNOLL, A. H., AND SWETT, K., 1989, Sr isotopic variations in Upper Proterozoic carbonates from Svalbard and East Greenland: Geochemica et Cosmochimica Acta, v. 53, p. 2331–2339.

FLEMINGS, P. B., AND GROTZINGER, J. P., 1996, STRATA: Freeware for analyzing classic stratigraphic problems: GSA Today, v. 6, no. 12, p. 1–7.

GLUMAC, B., AND WALKER, K. R., 1998, A Late Cambrian positive carbon-isotope excursion in the southern Appalachians, U.S.A.: Relation to biostratigraphy, sequence stratigraphy, environments of deposition, and diagenesis: Journal of Sedimentary Research, v. 68, p. 1212–1222.

GROTZINGER, J. P., ADAMS, R. D., MCCORMICK, D. S., AND MYROW, P. M., 1989, Sequence stratigraphy, correlations between Wopmay Orogen and Kilohigok Basin, and further investigations of the Bear Creek Group (Goulburn Supergroup), District of Mackenzie, N. W. T.: Geological Survey of Canada, Paper 89–1C, Current Research, Part C, p. 107–119.

GROTZINGER, J. P., BOWRING, S. A., SAYLOR, B. Z., AND KAUFMAN, A. J., 1995, Biostratigraphic and geochronologic constraints on early animal evolution: Science, v. 270, p. 598-604.

KARHU, J. A., 1993, Paleoproterozoic evolution of the carbon isotope ratios of sedimentary carbonates in the Fennoscandian Shield: Geological Survey of Finland, Bulletin 371, 87 p.

KAUFMAN, P., GROTZINGER, J. P., AND MCCORMICK, D. S., 1991a, Depth-dependent diffusion algorithm for simulation of sedimentation in shallow marine depositional systems, *in* Franseen, E., Watney, W., Kendall, C., and Ross, W., eds., Sedimentary Modeling: Computer Simulations and Methods for Improved Parameter Definition: Kansas Geological Survey, Bulletin 233, p. 489–508.

KAUFMAN, A. J., HAYES, J. M., KNOLL, A. H., AND GERMS, G. B., 1991, Isotopic compositions of carbonates and organic carbon from upper Proterozoic succession in Namibia: stratigraphic variation and the effects of diagenesis and metamorphism: Precambrian Research, v. 49, p. 301–327.

KAUFMAN, A. J., AND KNOLL, A. H., 1995, Neoproterozoic variations in the C-isotopic compositions of seawater: stratigraphic and biogeochemical implications: Precambrian Research, v. 73, p. 27–49.

KAUFMAN, A. J., KNOLL, A. H., AND AWRAMIK, S. M., 1992, Biostratigraphic and chemostratigraphic correlation of Neoproterozoic sedimentary successions: Upper Tindir Group, northwestern Canada, as a test case: Geology, v. 20, p. 181–185.

KAUFMAN, A. J., KNOLL, A. H., AND NARBONNE, G. M., 1992, Isotopes, ice ages, and terminal Proterozoic Earth history: National Academy of Sciences, Proceedings, v. 94, 6600–6605.

KENNEDY, M. J., 1996, Stratigraphy, sedimentology, and isotopic geochemistry of Australian Neoproterozoic postglacial cap dolostones: Deglaciations, δ^{13}C excursions, and carbonate precipitation: Journal of Sedimentary Research, v. 66, p. 1050–1064.

KHOMENTOVSKY, V. V., AND KARLOVA, G. A., 1993, Biostratigraphy of the Vendian–Cambrian beds and the Lower Cambrian boundary in Siberia: Geological Magazine, v. 130, p. 29–45.

KNOLL, A. H., KAUFMAN, A. J., AND SEMIKHATOV, M. A., 1995a, The carbon-isotope composition of Proterozoic carbonates: Riphean successions from northwestern Siberia (Anabar Massif, Turukhansk Uplift): American Journal of Science, v. 295, p. 823–850.

KNOLL, A. H., KAUFMAN, A. J., SEMIKHATOV, M. A., GROTZINGER, J. P., AND ADAMS, W., 1995b, Sizing up the sub-Tommotian unconformity in Siberia: Geology, v. 23, p. 1139–1143.

MACNAUGHTON, R. B., DALRYMPLE, R. W., AND NARBONNE, G. M., 1997, Multiple orders of relative sea-level change in an earliest Cambrian passive-margin succession, Mackenzie Mountains, northwest Canada: Journal of Sedimentary Research, v. 67, p. 622–637.

MONTAÑEZ, I. P., BANNER, J. L., OSLEGER, D. A., BORG, L. E., AND BOSSERMAN, P. J., 1996, Integrated Sr isotope variations and sea-level history of Middle to Upper Cambrian platform carbonates: implications for the evolution of Cambrian seawater ^{87}Sr/^{86}Sr: Geology, v. 24, p. 917–920.

NARBONNE, G. M., KAUFMAN, A. J., AND KNOLL, A. H., 1994, Integrated chemostratigraphy and biostratigraphy of the upper Windemere Supergroup (Neoproterozoic), northwestern Canada: Implications for Neoproterozoic correlations and the early evolution of animals: Geological Society of America, Bulletin, v. 106, p. 1281–1292.

PELECHATY, S. M., GROTZINGER, J. P., KASHIRTSEV, V. A., AND ZHERNOVSKY, V. P., 1996, Chemostratigraphic and sequence stratigraphic constraints on Vendian–Cambrian basin dynamics, northeast Siberian craton: Journal of Geology, v. 104, p. 543–563.

PREISS, W. V., AND FORBES, B. G., 1981, Stratigraphy, correlation and sedimentary history of Adelaidean (Late Proterozoic) basins in Australia: Precambrian Research, v. 15, p. 255–304.

READ, J. F., 1989, Controls on evolution of Cambro–Ordovician passive margin, U.S. Appalachians, *in* Crevello, P., Wilson, J., Sarg, J. F., and Read, J. F., eds., Controls on Carbonate Platform and Basin Development: SEPM, Special Publication 44, p. 147–165.

READ, J. F., GROTZINGER, J. P., BOVA, J. A., AND KOERSCHNER, W. F., 1986, Models for generation of carbonate cycles: Geology, v. 14, p. 107–110.

ROSS, G. M., 1991, Tectonic setting of the Windemere Supergroup revisited: Geology, v. 18, p. 1125–1128.

SADLER, P. M., 1981, Sediment accumulation rates and the completeness of stratigraphic sections: Journal of Geology, v. 89, p. 569–584.

SAYLOR, B. Z., KAUFMAN, A. J., GROTZINGER, J. P., AND URBAN, F., 1998, A composite reference section for terminal Proterozoic strata of southern Namibia: Journal of Sedimentary Research, v. 68, p. 1223–1235.

SCHIDLOWSKI, M., 1988, A 3,800-million-year record of life from carbon in sedimentary rocks: Nature, v. 333, p. 313–318.

SCHLAGER, W., 1981, The paradox of drowned reefs and carbonate platforms: Geological Society of America, Bulletin, v. 92, p. 197–211.

SMITH, L. H., KAUFMAN, A. J., KNOLL, A. J., AND LINK, P. K., 1994, Chemostratigraphy of predominantly siliciclastic Neoproterozoic successions: a case study of the Pocatello Formation and Lower Brigham Group, Idaho: Geological Magazine, v. 131, p. 301–314

STRAUSS, H., BENGTSON, S., MYROW, P. M., AND VIDAL, G., 1992, Stable isotope geochemistry and palynology of the late Precambrian to Early Cambrian sequence in Newfoundland: Canadian Journal of Earth Sciences, v. 29, p. 1662–1673.

VON DER BORCH, C. C., CHRISTIE-BLICK, N., AND GRADY, A. E., 1988, Depositional sequence analysis applied to upper Proterozoic Wilpena Group, Adelaide Geosyncline, South Australia: Australian Journal of Earth Sciences, v. 35, p. 59–71.

WILBORN, R. E., AND WILKINSON, B. H., 1998, Inhomogeneous Poisson processes and the nature of facies mosaics on Holocene carbonate platforms (abstract): Geological Society of America, Abstracts with Programs, v. 30, p. 194.

PART II
STROMATOLITES AND PRECIPITATES

LITHIFICATION AND FABRIC GENESIS IN PRECIPITATED STROMATOLITES AND ASSOCIATED PERITIDAL CARBONATES, MESOPROTEROZOIC BILLYAKH GROUP, SIBERIA

JULIE K. BARTLEY
Geosciences Department, State University of West Georgia, Carrollton, Georgia 30118, U.S.A.
ANDREW H. KNOLL
Harvard University Botanical Museum, 26 Oxford St., Cambridge, Massachusetts 02138, U.S.A.
JOHN P. GROTZINGER
Department of Earth, Atmospheric, and Planetary Sciences, Massachusetts Institute of Technology, Cambridge, Massachusetts 02139, U.S.A.
AND
VLADIMIR N. SERGEEV
Geological Institute, Russian Academy of Sciences, Moscow 109017, Russian Federation

ABSTRACT: Early diagenetic chert in the upper Kotuikan and Yusmastakh formations, northeastern Siberia, preserves an exceptional record of carbonate textures and microfossils in an early Mesoproterozoic peritidal carbonate platform. Silicified lithologies include carbonate precipitates that formed at or near the sediment–water interface, as well as micritic event laminae that appear to have lithified more slowly. Precipitated textures include (1) radial–fibrous laminae nucleated on organic horizons and locally forming botryoids that stack vertically to produce microdigitite structures; and (2) micron–scale carbonate laminae. Both radial–fibrous carbonates and microlaminites contain abundant microfossils, some of which are preserved as uncompressed casts and molds that retain cellular detail. These indicate that lithification preceded microbial decay; actualistic taphonomy experiments on filamentous cyanobacteria suggest that lithification occurred on a timescale of days to weeks. In other silicified textures, microfossils show evidence of extensive post-mortem decay and compression, suggesting less rapid lithification. Papier-mâché carbonate sedimentation, characterized by essentially instantaneous lithification, appears to have been locally common in restricted tidal-flat environments during the Mesoproterozoic and earlier eras but uncommon in Neoproterozoic and later times.

INTRODUCTION

Conventionally, the domed, cylindrical, and digitate laminites found in Proterozoic carbonates have been identified as stromatolites and interpreted as the products of sediment trapping and binding and/or precipitation by microbial mat communities (e.g., Walter, 1976). Over the past decade, however, it has been recognized that the microdigitate stromatolites found widely in Paleoproterozoic carbonates accreted as stacked calcite or aragonite precipitates without the templating influence of microbial mats (Grotzinger and Read, 1983; Hofmann and Jackson, 1987; Grotzinger, 1989, 1994; Kah and Knoll, 1996). This does not necessarily indicate that organisms played no role in their precipitation, but rather that the role of biology was limited to the metabolic facilitation of carbonate precipitation. Knoll and Semikhatov (1998) have recently recognized a class of stromatolitic structures intermediate between these depositional extremes. Mesoproterozoic structures given the names *Omachtenia* and *Gongylina* by Russian stratigraphers appear to have accreted as micritic to arenitic event laminae stabilized between events by mats and cemented by carbonate precipitates nucleated on the sheet-like organic laminae left after extensive mat decomposition.

In Mesoproterozoic platform carbonates, microdigitate structures, *Omachtenia*-like domes and low columns, and conventional stromatolites are distributed along an environmental gradient from restricted tidal flats to open coastal subtidal regions (Knoll and Semikhatov, 1998). Broader observations show an equivalent gradient in time (Grotzinger, 1989, 1994). During the Archean and Paleoproterozoic, precipitated carbonate textures formed in a variety of environments, including unrestricted, open marine settings (Sumner and Grotzinger, 1996; Sumner, 1997a), although the relative abundance of precipitated carbonate textures varies widely from basin to basin (Simonson et al., 1993; Sami, this volume; Grotzinger, 1986, 1989, 1994). Most Mesoproterozoic carbonate successions, in turn, contain accretionary precipitates only in restricted coastal marine en-

vironments (Liang et al., 1985; Cao, 1992), at least some of which are associated with development of evaporites (Kah and Knoll, 1996; Kah, this volume). By the later Neoproterozoic Era, macroscopic precipitate textures formed only under anomalous conditions such as those associated with post glacial cap carbonates (Grotzinger and Knoll, 1995).

Petrologic textures can aid in the genetic interpretation of Proterozoic laminites, but care must be taken to distinguish primary features from diagenetic overprints. In many Proterozoic carbonates, later recrystallization and dolomitization have obscured depositional textures. Paleontologists, however, have long taken advantage of the fact that early diagenetic chert commonly preserves biological features not retained in surrounding rocks (e.g., Schopf, 1968). Chert nodules can also retain depositional textures (e.g., Hofmann, 1975), opening an unusually clear window onto ancient carbonate environments and depositional processes.

In this paper, we discuss the petrology of early diagenetic chert nodules in platform carbonates of the early Mesoproterozoic Billyakh Group, northern Siberia. These cherts preserve both depositional textures and microfossils, enabling us to evaluate the role of biology in facilitating carbonate accumulation and providing a means of constraining the timescale of carbonate lithification. In particular, these fossils and microfabrics allow us to evaluate the role played by microorganisms in the accretion of the laminated carbonate structures found in Billyakh carbonates.

GEOLOGIC SETTING

In the western Anabar uplift, the Billyakh Group comprises dominantly carbonate sediments of Mesoproterozoic age that lie conformably above the siliciclastic Mukun Group and unconformably beneath the terminal Proterozoic Staraya Rechka Formation (Sergeev et al., 1995). In ascending order, the Billyakh Group consists of the Ust'Il'ya, Kotuikan, and Yusmastakh formations (Fig. 1). The lower part of the 60-70-m-thick

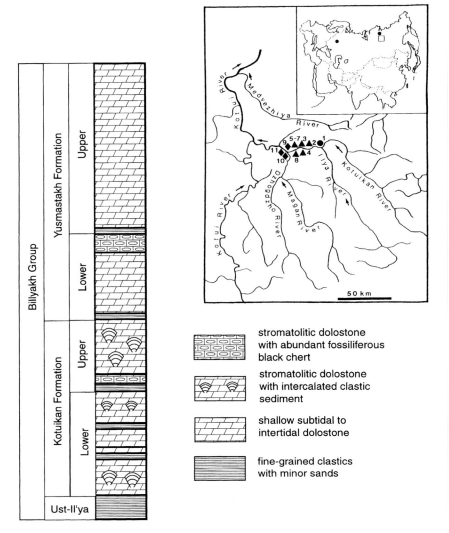

FIG. 1.—Location map, showing sampled localities (see Sergeev et al., 1995), and schematic stratigraphic column of the Billyakh Group. Western city labeled is Moscow; eastern city is Khatanga.

Ust'Il'ya Formation consists of shallow marine, wave- and storm-dominated shales, siltstones, and sandstones. Carbonate abundance increases upward, so that the upper half of the Ust'Il'ya succession is composed of mixed siliciclastic and carbonate rocks. Toward the top of the Ust'Il'ya Formation, domal stromatolites interfinger with siliciclastic rocks and grade upward into the bioherms of the carbonate-dominated lower Kotuikan Formation.

The 500-m-thick Kotuikan Formation has been divided into two members (Komar, 1966; Zlobin and Golovanov, 1970; Shenfil' and Yakschin, 1982). The base of the formation is marked by patchy to laterally continuous *Colonnella* and *Kussiella* biostromes (Fig. 2A; Komar, 1966), whereas the bulk of the 300-m-thick lower member consists of open-shelf carbonates with abundant stromatolitic bioherms (Fig. 2B) interbedded with fine-grained dolarenites, intraformational conglomerates (Fig. 2C), and fine-grained clastic sediments. The upper member consists of light gray peritidal dolostones characterized by

thickly- to thin-laminated, wavy-bedded dolosiltites and microbial laminites deposited in a more restricted environment. Rare ooids and intraformational conglomerates occur in the upper member, as do occasional asperiform structures (Fig. 2D) and rare, very thinly laminated travertine-like carbonates. Original carbonate was replaced by early diagenetic chert sporadically throughout this member (similar to Figure 2E), preserving a rich microbiota (Sergeev et al., 1995) and original carbonate textures.

The Yusmastakh Formation disconformably overlies the Kotuikan. The lower member of the Yusmastakh consists of laminated to medium-bedded dolomicrite and contains a moderately diverse assemblage of domal to conical stromatolites. Oolites occur throughout this member (Fig. 2F), and early diagenetic chert nodules are common. A sequence boundary separates the lower and upper members and is marked by several erosional surfaces and glauconitic sands. The upper member comprises dolomitic laminites interbedded with thin beds of

FIG. 2.—Outcrop photos: Kotuikan and Yusmastakh formations. A) Columnar stromatolites within bioherms of the lower Kotuikan Formation. Pocketknife for scale is 8 cm. B) A succession of bioherms in the lower Kotuikan Formation. The curved surface on which the geologist stands is the top of a large bioherm; the small bioherm to the geologist's right (arrow) accreted from the top of the underlying structure and was subsequently buried by the massive bioherm that dominates the rock face. Interbiohermal sediments can be seen below and to the right of the small bioherm. Person for scale is 200 cm. C) Intraformational conglomerate deposited by storms in basinal facies of the lower Kotuikan Formation. D) Asperiform stromatolites of the Upper Kotuikan Formation. The asperiform structures are a macroscopic manifestation of radial–fibrous carbonate fabrics. The layer in the middle of the photograph shows exceptional development of this fabric. E) Chert nodules in the upper member of the Yusmastakh Formation. Chert nodules similar in size, distribution, and microfossil content occur throughout the Upper Kotuikan and Yusmastakh formations. Silicification was very early, predating carbonate recrystallization, and preserves original carbonate textures as well as microfossils. F) Silicified ooids from the Yusmastakh Formation. Note that dissolution of nuclei and cortical deformation preceded silicification.

marly shales and minor stromatolitic, oolitic, and intraclastic dolomites. Chert nodules (Fig. 2E) are also present in this member. Occasional evidence of shallow evaporitic settings includes mudcracks, symmetrical ripples, and dolomitic vugs after gypsum or halite.

Age Constraints

The Ust'Il'ya and Kotuikan formations contain acritarch assemblages that compare closely with Mesoproterozoic assemblages found elsewhere (Sergeev et al., 1995; Knoll and Sergeev, 1995). Carbon-isotope chemostratigraphy also suggests an early Mesoproterozoic age and is inconsistent with a late Mesoproterozoic or Neoproterozoic age (Knoll et al., 1995). Additionally, the distinctive precipitate textures observed in the more restricted facies of the Billyakh Group, particularly in the upper Kotuikan Formation, bear a striking similarity to those that characterize other Mesoproterozoic peritidal successions (Kah and Knoll, 1996; Xiao et al., 1997) and that are largely absent from Neoproterozoic peritidal carbonates (Grotzinger, 1989, 1994; Grotzinger and Kasting, 1993; Knoll and Swett, 1990; Knoll et al., 1993). The few radiometric ages obtained on these successions do little to further constrain the age of the succession. Mineralogically characterized glauconite from the lower Ust'Il'ya Formation yielded a Rb/Sr age of 1483 ± 5 Ma (Gorokhov et al., 1991), and K/Ar ages from the Billyakh Group yield broadly similar ages (Gorokhov et al., 1991; Semikhatov and Serebryakov, 1983). Thus, although the absolute age of this succession is not well constrained, the chemostratigraphy and micropaleontology taken in combination suggest an early Mesoproterozoic ($>$1300 Ma) age.

DEPOSITIONAL ENVIRONMENT

In a sequence stratigraphic framework, the Ust'Il'ya Formation represents a transgressive systems tract. The base of the unit contains abundant hummocky cross-stratified sandstones interpreted to have formed in a midshelf environment that grade upward into less frequent, thinner-bedded shelf deposits with hummocky cross-stratification and quasi-planar stratification, interpreted to have formed in a deeper-water setting. In general, deposition occurred on a storm-dominated open shelf. Across the formation boundary into the lower Kotuikan, sediments are transitional into highstand systems tract deposition in which patchy bioherms coalesced upward to form a regionally extensive biostrome.

The base of the Kotuikan Formation was deposited at highstand, and siliciclastic influx was restricted to the marginal shelf. Several shallowing-upward parasequences are preserved in the lower Kotuikan, each comprising tens of meters of shale with intercalated hummocky cross-stratified sandstone beds overlain by tens of meters of stromatolitic dolomite (Fig. 2A, B). Edgewise conglomerates consisting of dolosiltite intraclasts are abundant in the lower parts of parasequences (Fig. 2C). These show polygonal packing, indicating strong oscillatory currents. The lower member grades into the upper Kotuikan over about 10 m. Microdigitate stromatolites (Fig. 2D) and isopachous, laminated crusts are developed in the upper member. The lower Kotuikan is interpreted to have formed under open-shelf conditions, as indicated by the abundance of shale, hummocky cross-stratification, and flat-pebble conglomerate. Stro-

matolites are the dominant sedimentary features; precipitated textures are significant only in the restricted peritidal environments of the upper member and form a minor proportion of the overall facies.

The Yusmastakh Formation comprises thick-laminated, wavy-bedded dolosiltites, small domal stromatolites, microbialaminites, calcareous shales, and oolites. Desiccation-cracked microbialaminites, fenestral laminites, and tepee structures are developed locally. Very sparse precipitate textures are observed in the Yusmastakh Formation. Coarse recrystallization during dolomitization has obliterated much of the original primary carbonate texture. Overall, the Yusmastakh represents alternation of restricted marine tidal-flat environments with less restricted shallow marine settings. Facies consistent with more open marine conditions include oolites, bioherms, and laterally continuous biostromes, and represent transgressive flooding of an otherwise peritidal platform.

PRIMARY TEXTURES AND STRUCTURES

Carbonates of the Billyakh Group are dolomitized, generally resulting in poor preservation of primary textures. Several well-preserved textures, however, are observed in early diagenetic cherts of the Kotuikan and Yusmastakh formations. Because silicification generally occurred prior to neomorphism and/or replacement by dolomite, these cherts record the textures of a primary carbonate phase (likely calcite in some instances and aragonite in others). Examination of the silica-replaced carbonate textures permits inferences about the origin of the carbonate precipitation mechanisms. Because early silicification also preserves microfossil assemblages, paleontological information can be used in combination with petrographic data to constrain interpretations of fabric genesis and diagenesis. In particular, silicified carbonates permit evaluation of the contribution of biological activity to texture formation, the timescale of lithification, and the relationship between microscale structures and larger-scale patterns.

Radial–Fibrous Texture

This texture is common in cherts of the upper unit of the Kotuikan Formation. It is composed of radiating to subparallel bladed or fibrous crystals. Each fiber is 2 to 5 μm across and 200 to 2000 μm long, and is replaced by cryptocrystalline quartz of random optical orientation (crystals $<$ 1 μm in diameter). Diameter does not vary along fiber length. Crystals propagate normal to their nucleation surface. Laminae within this texture are delineated by concentrations of finely divided organic matter, which outline accretion surfaces perpendicular to the direction of crystal growth. Nucleation of these crystals generally occurred within organic-rich horizons, and fiber bundles may be distributed sporadically or continuously along a lamina. When sporadically nucleated, the radial–fibrous crystals form small botryoids, which grow upward and may branch, forming microdigitate stromatolites (Fig. 3A, B). When nucleation was continuous over a horizon, palisade laminae developed (Fig. 3C). Rarely, crystal growth includes downward-directed as well as upward-directed sheaves (Fig. 3D), demonstrating that, in some cases, nucleation occurred slightly below the sediment–water interface. In general, however, growth is upward directed, supporting the hypothesis that nu-

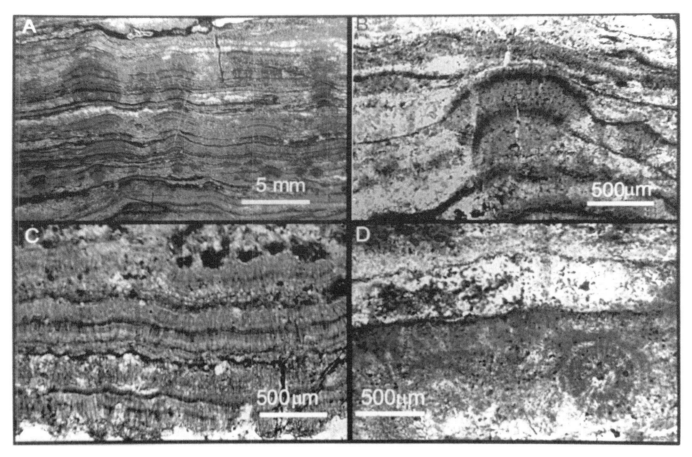

FIG. 3.—Photomicrographs of radial–fibrous texture preserved in chert. A) Low-magnification illustration showing localized radial–fibrous crystal growth from organic-rich laminae in tidal-flat carbonates of the upper Kotuikan. B) Detail of A, showing spatial relationships among detrital laminae that fill in microtopographic lows, organic laminae, and precipitates. C) Palisade texture, composed of isopachous crystals continuously nucleated along a horizon. D) Three-dimensional radial–fibrous crystals. Note that the radial structure overgrows primary features such as organic fragments, indicating growth within the sediment.

cleation generally occurred at the sediment–water interface. Similar forms are found in the Mesoproterozoic Society Cliffs Formation of Baffin Island, Arctic Canada (Kah and Knoll, 1996) and the Huanglianduo Formation of China (Xiao et al., 1997).

Crystal growth is commonly truncated by drapes of sediment or organic matter, or through interference with other, laterally propagating fiber bundles. Interfering crystal bundles may terminate sharply, or crystals may interpenetrate for a small distance (generally less than 20 μm) before terminating. The shape of crystal terminations is poorly preserved; thus, this criterion cannot be used to infer original mineralogy. The size and shape of the fibrous crystals, however, resembles the fibers that constitute botryoidal aragonite (Ginsburg and James, 1976; Folk and Assereto, 1976; Grotzinger and Read, 1983; Hofmann and Jackson, 1987), although this growth habit may also occur in calcite (e.g., flowstone). Where dolomitized rather than silicified, fibrous or bladed crystals have been replaced by mosaics of anhedral, equant to elongate dolomite crystals, 10–450 μm in diameter, that have ragged, irregular boundaries. The optic axes of replacive crystals show no preferred orientation. Thus, both texture and crystallographic attributes are consistent with

dolomitization of an aragonitic precursor (Loucks and Folk, 1976; Mazzullo, 1980; Sandberg, 1975). Microfossils are moderately abundant in this texture, with both filamentous and coccoidal forms often occurring within the crystal bundles.

Microlaminated Texture

This texture is restricted to a small interval of the upper Kotuikan Formation. It consists of laminae 1 to 3 μm thick with planar to convex–upward shape. Laminae are much smaller than the microfossils they contain, and much thinner than those of typical microbial mats. Laminae are defined by concentrations of organic matter, producing an alternating pattern of extremely thin dark laminae and thicker light laminae. Individual laminae are of uniform thickness and are traceable throughout their lengths, which may exceed 2 cm. Where curved, laminae form overlapping domes, with younger laminae truncating against older structures (Fig. 4A). These domes commonly display isopachous–fibrous textures, with crystals preferentially elongated normal to local curvature (Fig. 4B); crystals nucleate in topographic lows or sporadically along flat surfaces. Where visible, crystals are smaller than those of the radial–fibrous texture, generally < 1 μm across and 10 to 50 μm long.

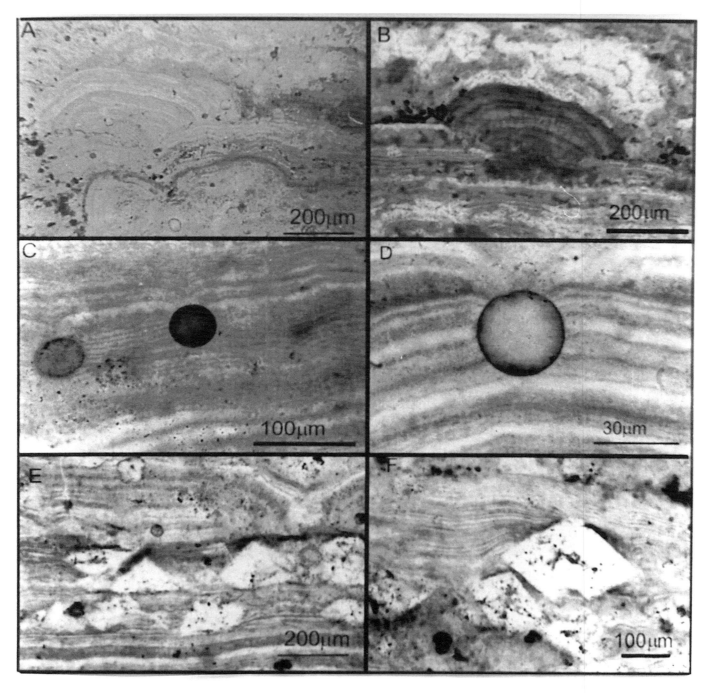

FIG. 4.—Photomicrographs of microlaminated texture. A) Low-magnification view, showing overlapping microlaminae. Note the isopachous character of the laminae. Dark circles are entombed microfossils. B) Radial to isopachous texture within the microlaminated texture. The radially textured region appears to have nucleated within a small depression in the microlaminated texture. This relationship may indicate carbonate nucleation at a single point on a surface, a change in mineralogy, or perhaps a change in local water chemistry. The black structures to the left of the radial feature are *Eoentophysalis belcherensis* colonies. Their presence along this surface may indicate a hiatus in carbonate precipitation. C) Uncompacted microfossils (*Myxococcoides grandis*) contained in the microlaminated texture. Note the very small scale of laminations. D) Well–preserved microfossil (*Myxococcoides grandis*) in microlaminated texture. Scale of laminations is markedly smaller than the size of most microfossils. Note the downward warping of laminae near the microfossil, which may result from interaction of the hydrophobic cell wall with seawater. E) Silicified dolomite rhombohedra within microlaminated texture, displaying flattened bottom edges and well-developed, euhedral upper surfaces. Flattened bottom edges may indicate growth of dolomite at or below the sediment–water interface rather than in the water column. F) Silicified microlaminated texture, showing onlapping relationship of microlaminae to dolomite rhombohedron.

The original carbonate mineralogy is difficult to determine with certainty, because of silicification where texture is preserved, and coarsely crystalline dolomite replacement elsewhere. Several features of this texture, including crystal size, presence of relict isopachous texture, and overlapping nature of the small domes, bear a striking similarity to high-Mg calcite dome masses precipitated in modern landlocked pools with seasonally fluctuating salinity (Braithwaite et al., 1989). Where recrystallization is less severe, primary crystallographic orientations are apparently retained such that sweeping extinction of crystals is observed upon stage rotation under plane-polarized light; crystals are preferentially elongate normal to layering, and optic axes parallel crystal elongation. This crystallographic feature, in which the optic axes of the replacive crystals are apparently inherited from its precursor mineral, is most consistent with replacement of former calcite (Kendall, 1985). Therefore, on the basis of petrographic evidence, this texture is inferred to have replaced former (high-Mg?) calcite, with individual equant to acicular crystals likely growing normal to substrate to produce isopachous lamination.

Microfossils are abundant in this texture, locally exceeding 1 cell/100 μm^2. Microfossil preservation is excellent and fossils are entirely uncompacted (Fig. 4C). Microlaminae onlap the margins of cell walls and then overstep the tops of cells (Fig. 4D). This suggests that the fluids from which the mineral precipitated were either so thin that they did not cover the microfossils completely—so that a single layer might drape over cells—or that the cells themselves were not preferred sites of mineral nucleation. The two explanations are not mutually exclusive. Many organisms secrete molecules that inhibit calcium carbonate precipitation (Marin et al., 1996), and cyanobacterial surfaces are hydrophobic. In light of this, it is interesting to note that laminae are deflected downward in the regions immediately adjacent to cell walls (Fig. 4D). Regardless of cyanobacterial wall chemistry, the extraordinary thinness of laminae suggests that accreting carbonates were wetted only by thin films of water. This suggests deposition in the supratidal zone, which may have been wetted only by ocean spray during storms, similarly to the pelagosite crusts of the Persian Gulf region (Purser and Loreau, 1973). In this case, the effects of fluid surface tension would dominate, leading to exposure of cell tops and preferential precipitation of minerals adjacent to cells. Accordingly, deflection of laminae away from the cell wall (Fig. 4D) might reflect the hydrophobic properties of certain organic compounds, which would have prevented the buildup of fluids where surface tension might normally be highest—where local curvature is greatest, adjacent to the junction between cell and seafloor. Consequently, where laminae might normally be expected to thicken, similar to "meniscus" cements (Dunham, 1969), they instead thin as observed in Figure 4D.

Dolomitized patches and horizons, now silicified, are common in the microlaminites, but rare in other textures, perhaps indicating differences in original porosity, solubility, or mineralogy. Individual dolomite rhombohedra are often aligned with c axes normal to lamination (Fig. 4E). Dolomite rhombohedra are commonly flattened along their bottoms, and may also show flattening along their tops. In rare instances, dolomite rhombs can be seen to be onlapped by microlaminae (Fig. 4F), also now silicified, suggesting that that some dolomite was precipitated as a primary mineral near or at the sediment–water interface, perhaps in an environment similar to that observed in shallow, evaporitic lagoons in Brazil (Vasconcelos et al., 1995; Vasconcelos and McKenzie, 1997). Uncompacted fossils in the same textures suggest that microlaminite occurred within weeks or months of deposition, sharply constraining the timescale for dolomite precipitation. Several hypotheses have been put forward to explain the formation of primary dolomite in modern coastal environments, and the Kotuikan examples do little to constrain those suggestions. The important point, however, is that primary dolomite rhombs are uncommon in this facies and unknown from associated facies. Most of the massive dolomite that characterizes Kotuikan carbonates obliterates primary texture and postdates early silicification. Where late diagenetic chert occurs, individual dolomite rhombohedra are not discernible in preserved textures; dolomite crystals form anhedral, interlocking mosaics. In these regions, fine laminae are overprinted, but relict structure remains, producing a coarsely laminated texture. An additional insight, then, that results from the early silicification of these rocks is the preservation of an early diagenetic window, which suggests strongly that primary dolomite was about as common on this Mesoproterozoic tidal flat as it is today in similar environments (Zenger et al., 1980). This, in turn, suggests that the factors that inhibit dolomite precipitation in modern oceans were already in place in the Mesoproterozoic era and, therefore, that the abundance of dolomite in Mesoproterozoic carbonate successions cannot be ascribed mainly to ancient seawater chemistry.

Poorly Laminated to Fenestral Texture

This texture comprises irregular laminae of relatively dense organic matter, often with recognizable fossils. Generally, these laminae are flat-lying to gently convex upward (Fig. 5A), although in some cases the laminated character is not visible, and a disordered, often fenestral, organic-rich texture results (Fig. 5B). When mat-forming organisms are discernible, they may be filamentous cyanobacterial sheaths such as *Siphonophycus* (Fig. 5C), or coccoids, generally referable to the Entophysalidaceae (Fig. 5D). This texture is inferred to have been produced by the accumulation of mat-building benthic microorganisms, which were buried and lithified prior to significant compaction.

Within thicker accumulations of microbial mats, possible primary fenestrae are commonly observed (Fig. 5B). In chert-replaced regions, these fenestrae are filled with void-filling chalcedony, which may have filled primary void space or replaced early, marine void-filling carbonate spar. In most cases, significant decomposition of the component microorganisms has occurred, resulting in indistinct morphological preservation and virtual absence of cellular preservation.

Thin organic laminae in this fabric are flat lying to convex upward, and are often discontinuous. They are inferred to be decomposed and/or compacted microbial mats that were lithified after compaction and/or decomposition.

Laminated, Micritic Texture

Laminae formed of micrite are generally light-colored and fine-grained (2–30 μm, with a mean value of 10–15 μm). This texture is abundant in the Yusmastakh Formation, and, when

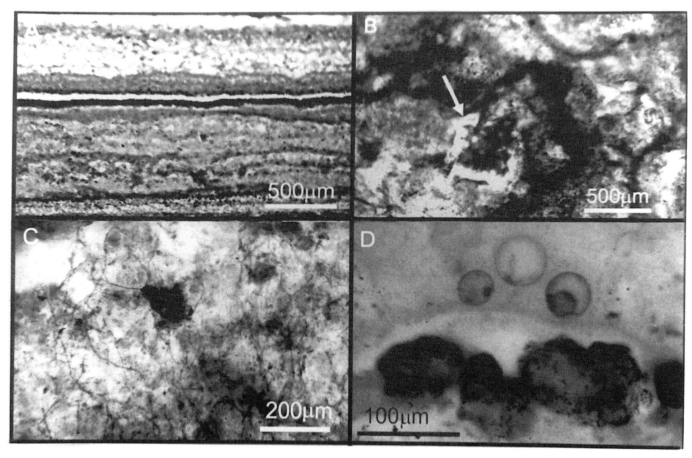

FIG. 5.—Photomicrographs of microbial mat texture. A) Flat-laminated mats. Laminae are produced by alternation of organic-rich and organic-poor horizons. The bright white layer is a micritic drape over a particularly dense mat layer. Mat constructors in this thin section are poorly preserved morphologically, and some mats are compacted. B) Fenestral mats. Laminae are absent or poorly defined, and fenestrae are filled with silicified sparry calcite (bright white regions in the photograph). Morphological preservation is poor, but individual filaments were detectable. C) Filamentous mats composed of *Siphonophycus* sp., showing variable quality of microfossil preservation and uncompacted nature of mat horizon. D) Coccoidal mats, composed of *Eoentophysalis belcherensis*. These coccoidal mats colonize hard substrates, and accumulations of *E. belcherensis* probably represent times of slow carbonate accumulation and consequent exposure of a lithified surface at the seafloor. Uncompacted cells of *Myxococcoides grandis* occur in the micritic layer above these mats. The modern counterparts of these coccoidal fossils colonized firm substrates. Thus, it may be that the coccoids colonized lithified surfaces during times of slow carbonate accumulation and were preserved by rapid burial when accumulation resumed.

interlaminated with mats or organic laminae, form distinctive stratiform laminites (Fig. 6A). The micritic texture is replaced by the same cryptocrystalline chert that replaces other textures. Occasional intraclast breccia beds preserve deformed clasts of this texture.

The micritic laminae commonly entomb solitary and colonial coccoidal microfossils (Fig. 6B), which generally are uncompacted. The disordered arrangement of microfossils and the occasional presence of micritic intraclasts suggest episodic transport of both sediments and microfossils from shallow subtidal environments to a tidal-flat setting. This texture represents deposited carbonate mud that was rapidly lithified by carbonate cement, in contrast to the radial–fibrous and microlaminated textures, which were primary sea-floor precipitates. Laminae formed of micrite are interpreted to have formed in intertidal to shallow subtidal environments, where sediment accumulation would have been related to precipitation of suspended carbonate mud as whitings, followed by slow settling from suspension.

CONSTRAINING THE TIMING OF LITHIFICATION

Because these early diagenetic cherts preserve both the carbonate texture and a rich microbiota, we can use the taphonomy of the microfossils to constrain the timing of lithification of these carbonate sediments and thereby independently test the hypothesis that some of the textures are primary sea-floor precipitates (Grotzinger and Read, 1983). Experimental taphonomy indicates that significant morphological decomposition of cyanobacteria occurs on timescales of days to weeks (Bartley, 1996). In some cases, significant morphological losses occurred in only 10 days; in others degradation was somewhat slower, progressing over 125 days to conditions of morphological obliteration. Because microorganisms are rapidly decomposed by heterotrophic bacteria, even in the absence of oxygen, excellent preservation can be expected only when lithification occurs on the same timescale as decomposition.

We have evaluated the taphonomy of the microbiota in the early-silicified carbonates of the Yusmastakh and Kotuikan for-

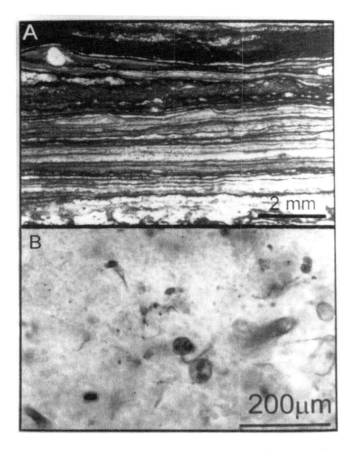

FIG. 6.—Photomicrographs of detrital micritic laminae. A) Low-magnification view of micritic laminae (white) alternating with organic-rich layers (dark). Note the stacking of thin organic-rich laminae without morphologically discernible microfossils. B) Photomicrograph of fossils within micritic laminae. These are uncompacted, chaotically oriented within the laminae, and—in the case of filaments—fragmented. These features collectively suggest that the fossils were transported to the tidal flat and, along with the micrite, deposited in a thin event bed.

mations. By examining assemblages of fossils and correlating fossil preservation with the carbonate textures that host them, we can evaluate the impact of primary depositional environments on fossil content and preservation, and independently establish a timescale for carbonate lithification.

Methods

Microfossils were examined in petrographic thin sections of cherts. A taphonomic grade (Kowalewski et al., 1995; Bartley, 1996) of good, fair, or poor was assigned to each unicellular coccoidal microfossil evaluated. The taphonomic grade "good" indicates little or no alteration to the original (spherical) shape of a unicell, and little or no loss of cell-wall fidelity (Fig. 7A). Fossils were assigned a taphonomic grade of "fair" when some shape alteration and/or moderate loss of cell-wall structure was observed (Fig. 7B). "Poor" was assigned when shape distortion or cell-wall alteration was significant (Fig. 7C). Although the assignment of taphonomic grade is based on a qualitative measure of alteration, the results of taphonomic evaluation are reproducible. Each microfossil was assigned a taphonomic grade,

and several hundred or more microfossils were evaluated on each thin section. Microfossils were assessed by a modified point-counting technique. The stage was moved incrementally, the fabric type was assessed, and all microfossils in the field of view were evaluated. This process was repeated until the entire thin section had been systematically evaluated. The resulting "population" of taphonomic grades can be represented as a single point on a ternary diagram. This diagram, called a ternary

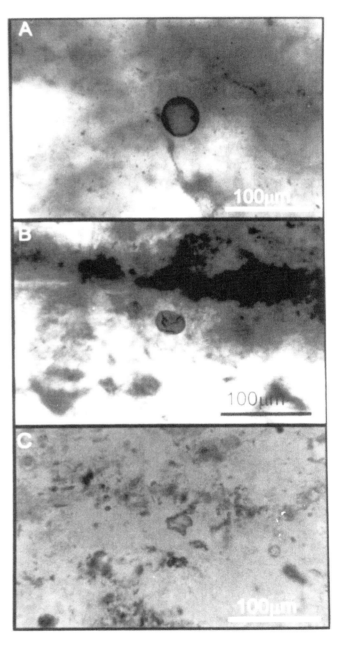

FIG. 7.—Photomicrographs of *Myxococcoides*, illustrating qualitative taphonomic grade scale. A) Good. The cell is uncompacted and the cell wall is intact, indicating that little post-mortem alteration has affected the morphology of this cell. B) Fair. The cell is partially collapsed and may be torn, but most of the cell morphology is recognizable. C) Poor. The cell displays significant alteration; the cell is shriveled and the cell wall is broken.

taphogram (Kowalewski et al., 1995), summarizes the distributions of taphonomic grades for several assemblages of microfossils.

Results and Discussion

Figure 8 shows the distribution of microfossil taphonomic grades, sorted according to the texture type that contains the fossils evaluated (Fig. 8A), and compared to the results of laboratory taphonomic experiments (Fig. 8B; Bartley, 1996). All fossiliferous texture types are included in this diagram. We believe that differences in taphonomic grade distribution reflect differences in the timing of lithification among the texture types preserved in the Kotuikan and Yusmastakh cherts.

Microlaminated Texture.—

Of the texture types evaluated, the microlaminated (travertine-like) texture contains the best-preserved microfossils. Nearly all the unicellular microfossils observed had taphonomic grades of good or fair (Figs. 4D, 8A, 9A), and microfossils are uniformly uncompressed in this texture (Fig. 4C), indicating that lithification took place very rapidly. The microorganisms were entombed on the timescale of decomposition, probably within days to weeks. Even where little organic matter remains, it is clear that the external morphology was preserved by cast and mold in original carbonate very soon after the organism

settled on the seafloor (Fig. 9A). The microlaminated texture was likely precipitated at the sediment–water interface, and allochthonous microfossils were rapidly entombed as they settled on the accumulating carbonate crust.

The formation of this texture was probably also highly episodic. When production of the seafloor crust stopped, the surface was colonized by *Eoentophysalis belcherensis*, occurring as thin mat coatings and as scattered well-developed colonies (Figs. 5D, 9B). Depressions in the topography are often filled by accumulations of microfossils and occasional fine-grained clastic material. This facies was probably supratidal; water covered the sediment only during storms or unusually high tide, during which time rapid carbonate precipitation ensued. This scenario may also explain why mat development is minimal in this facies.

Radial–Fibrous Texture.—

The radial–fibrous texture type contains a higher proportion of fair and poor microfossils. The vertical position of a microfossil in a radial–fibrous crystal array is an important factor in its taphonomic grade. Although the radial–fibrous crystals usually nucleate in areas with high organic-matter content (Fig. 10A), no microfossils are observed in areas of nucleation. The organic matter is amorphous and often finely divided. Above the areas of nucleation, however, microfossils are often well preserved (Figures 8A, 10B). We interpret this taphonomic evidence to suggest that the radial–fibrous texture probably had a more biologically influenced precipitation history than did the microlaminated texture. Nucleation of this texture generally occurs in association with an organic-rich but microfossil-poor horizon, suggesting facilitation of precipitation by an active community of heterotrophic bacteria. Radial–fibrous crystals nucleated within organic horizons, at or just below the sediment–water interface, then propagated rapidly upward (Fig. 10A). Well-preserved allochthonous microfossils often were encompassed by expanding fans (Fig. 10B), isolating them within crystalline carbonate before morphologies were obliterated by bacterial decomposers. Organic matter (Fig. 10A) commonly drapes horizons of radial–fibrous texture, suggesting either that newly established mats truncated crystal growth or that mats rapidly overgrew crystal fans when precipitation slowed.

This facies probably represents the intertidal to supratidal region of an arid tidal flat, where evaporation represents an important part of the local water budget. Evaporation of seawater concentrated carbonate ions locally, resulting in progressively higher values of carbonate oversaturation. Significant mat development was possible, perhaps because of overall wetter conditions. The growth of radial–fibrous texture was likely intermittent, with periods of low precipitation rate punctuated by rapid growth of radial–fibrous fabric. It is also possible that the decomposing mats themselves influenced precipitation. As decomposition of a mat progressed, organic molecules that inhibit carbonate precipitation were consumed heterotrophically, making the microenvironment more favorable for carbonate precipitation. Additionally, many heterotrophic processes, of which sulfate reduction is a particularly important example, increase $[HCO_3^-]$ locally, raising alkalinity and favoring carbonate deposition (Canfield and Raiswell, 1991). This mechanism has been linked to the formation of biologically mediated car-

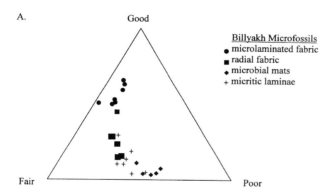

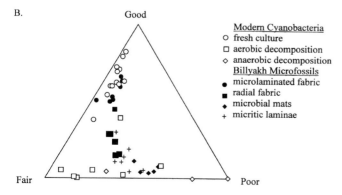

FIG. 8.—Ternary taphograms. A) Ternary taphogram illustrating the relationship between preservation quality and texture type. B) Ternary taphogram comparing decomposition of modern cyanobacteria (data from Bartley, 1996) with preservation of fossils from cherts of the Kotuikan and Yusmastakh formations.

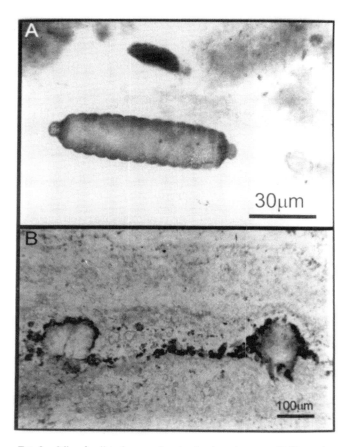

FIG. 9.—Microfossil taphonomy in microlaminated texture. A) Photomicrograph of *Filiconstrictosus cephalon*, illustrating excellent preservation with little residual organic matter (cast-and-mold structure). B) Photomicrograph of *Eoentophysalis belcherensis* colonies growing on an exposure surface within the microlaminated fabric.

seawater carbonate concentrations may have been much higher on average, producing a highly supersaturated seawater, which was further concentrated in tidal-flat settings through evaporation (Grotzinger, 1989). Tidal-flat precipitates are less common in Mesoproterozoic rocks (Grotzinger, 1989, 1994) and are best developed in arid tidal flats associated with evaporite deposition (Kah and Knoll, 1996; Jackson and Iannelli, 1981). All other factors being equal, the role of microbes in these settings was to induce preferential carbonate nucleation in areas of high initial concentrations of organic matter.

Poorly Laminated to Fenestral Texture.—

Microfossil preservation in the microbial mat microfacies is generally poorer than in the precipitated textures (Fig. 5C). Microfossils almost always show evidence of decomposition, with fair and poor taphonomic grades dominant (Fig. 8A). Compaction of fossils is occasionally evident in this texture. These characteristics indicate that lithification occurred more slowly in the microbial mat microfacies than in precipitate-dominated facies, perhaps indicating less restricted waters. The preservation of fossils in mats indicates that decomposition was frequently arrested prior to complete loss of morphology, perhaps because

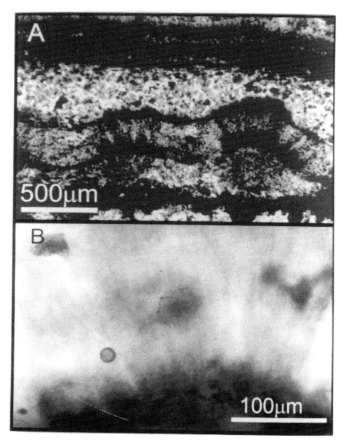

FIG. 10.—Photomicrographs of radial–fibrous texture. A) Photomicrograph illustrating nucleation of radial–fibrous crystals in organic-rich horizons, and termination of radial–fibrous crystals by a drape of organic matter. B) Photomicrograph illustrating nucleation in a zone of undifferentiated organic matter, possibly a decomposed microbial mat, and excellent microfossil preservation within the radial–fibrous crystals.

bonates in many depositional environments (Chafetz and Buczynski, 1992; Canfield and Raiswell, 1991; Sumner, 1997b; Vasconcelos and McKenzie, 1997). In some cases, nucleation may have occurred directly at the sediment–water interface, stimulated by carbonate-supersaturated brines percolating upward from within the decaying mat. Whether or not the presence of microbial mats initiated precipitation, once carbonate nucleated in this supersaturated environment, it grew rapidly from the site of nucleation, penetrating the mat and intersecting the sediment–water interface. The radial–fibrous crystals then trapped allochthonous microfossils, rapidly entombing them. Growth of radial–fibrous texture would be quenched by a change in water chemistry, resulting from flooding, reduced concentrations of inorganic carbon, and/or rapid overgrowth by a microbial mat. The fact that these facies are almost entirely absent from younger carbonates (Grotzinger, 1989; Grotzinger and Knoll, 1995), despite the ubiquitous presence of microbes throughout earth history, indicates that while microbes may play a role as catalysts in development of the precipitated crystal structures, the presence of the structures themselves must relate to the composition of seawater (Grotzinger, 1989). Accordingly, these structures are best developed in Paleoproterozoic rocks (Grey and Thorne, 1985; Grotzinger, 1989), when

of formation of a cement phase in an otherwise soft-sediment environment.

Laminated, Micritic Texture.—

Micritic, millimeter-scale laminae are interlaminated with organic-rich horizons (fossil mats or sapropels) in the tidal-flat facies of the Yusmastakh Formation, although event beds of micritic sediment occasionally occur in the Kotuikan Formation. Preservation of microfossils in the micritic laminae is generally better than in the interlaminated fossil mats (Fig. 8A) or sapropels. Evidence of compaction is absent, and microfossils (Fig. 11A, B) typically consist of *Archaeoellipsoides* and *Myxococcoides*, which are thought to be planktonic microfossils (Sergeev et al., 1995). Significantly, *Archaeoellipsoides* is interpreted as an akinete of a nostocalean cyanobacterium (Golubic et al., 1995), the modern representatives of which thrive in brackish water rather than in normal marine waters. We suggest that micrite was sporadically transported to tidal flats during storms, having formed under subtidal conditions. Cementation must have been rapid, entombing organisms prior to decomposition or compaction.

That micrite was rapidly cemented is further supported by the observation that fossil mats colonizing the upper surfaces of micritic laminae generally are *Eoentophysalis belcherensis*, which commonly colonizes firm substrates (Golubic and Hof-

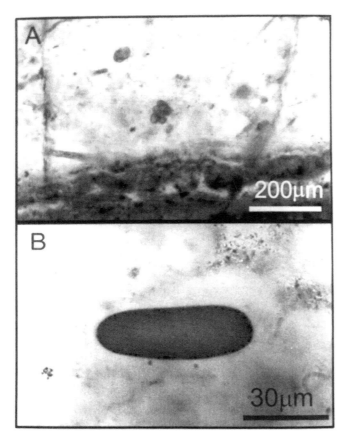

FIG. 11.—Preservation of fossils within detrital micritic laminae. A) Photomicrograph demonstrating good to moderate preservation in micritic horizons. B) Well-preserved *Archaeoellipsoides major* in a micritic horizon.

mann, 1976). Colonization of the substrate was possible only when deposition of suspended sediment was slow or when a stable hardground was available. The dark horizons interlaminated with light layers are often filamentous mats, which are not restricted to hard substrates (Horodyski, 1977), and probably colonize any available surface when water and light are available. We conclude that the environment in which the millimeter-scale laminae formed was probably submerged most of the time, may have been sporadically brackish, and that evaporative concentration of ions was less important than in facies where abiotic carbonate precipitates formed.

DISCUSSION

Given that morphology is an uncertain guide to stromatolite biogenicity (Hoffman, 1976; Buick et al., 1981; Grotzinger and Rothman, 1996), decoding primary textures is an essential step in determining the role of microbes in stromatolite development. Unfortunately, evaluation of textures preserved only in carbonates can be difficult, because of loss of detail associated with aggrading neomorphism, dolomitization, and obliterative recrystallization of fossils and primary crystal textures. By comparison, however, primary textures preserved in early diagenetic chert such as those of the Kotuikan Formation permit evaluation of timing of carbonate precipitation, and the relative impact of biogenic and abiogenic processes on stromatolite development. Microfossil taphonomy provides an estimate of the duration of microbial decomposition before cementation entombed microfossils and therefore serves as an independent constraint on the rapidity of carbonate precipitation. By comparing the taphonomy of microfossils in the various Kotuikan textures to results of decomposition experiments (Bartley, 1996), we conclude that microfossils were entombed by carbonate lithification prior to significant decomposition, suggesting that these carbonates precipitated rapidly, accreting on a timescale of days to weeks.

Sea-floor carbonate precipitates in the Kotuikan Formation are present only in peritidal facies, consistent with earlier interpretations that considered tidal-flat precipitates to be carbonate evaporites (Grotzinger, 1986, 1989, 1990). It seems unlikely that the biota played an active templating role in the formation of the radial–fibrous carbonate texture or the larger-scale structures these carbonates form, such as microdigitate stromatolites and the low-domal, finely laminated, stratiform stromatolites. If biological processes were involved, their impact was likely limited to catalysis of carbonate precipitation, perhaps by sulfate reduction during early remineralization of organic matter. In this sense, the radial–fibrous Kotuikan precipitates may share a common origin with the precipitated textures described by Knoll and Semikhatov (1998) where mineral precipitation is triggered by extensive decomposition of mats but the precipitated crystals bear no systematic relationship to the texture of the original mat. In this model of stromatolite growth, the texture is considered to be partly abiogenic in the sense that the crystals that define it do not precipitate on a template formed by an actively growing mat community. On the other hand, the texture is considered to be partly biogenic in the sense that episodic growth of mats may have intermittently terminated crystal growth, thus producing primary lamination. Further, crystal nucleation may have been aided by heterotrophic bacterial sulfate reduction. Thus, depending on one's viewpoint, the radial–fibrous texture has a hybrid origin, reflecting a variety of competing processes.

The microlaminated texture forms in relatively organic-carbon-poor sediments, and contains very well preserved microfossils trapped in the rapidly mineralizing sediments. The taphonomic characteristics of microfossils in this texture are similar to those of cyanobacteria in living cultures, suggesting that little if any decomposition occurred prior to lithification. These microfossils are largely allochthonous, although autochthonous mats of *Eoentophysalis belcherensis* formed during hiatuses in precipitation. *E. belcherensis* mats from the Yusmastakh Formation (Fig. 9E) have teeth-like and mushroom-like colony shape, similar to modern *Entophysalis* colonies, which evidently adopt this morphology to escape burial and indicate a high instantaneous rate of sediment deposition (Golubic, 1985). Laminae are smaller in scale than the microfossils they contain, and the laminated structure is likely a result of intermittent and rapid carbonate precipitation. The downward deflection of laminae at microfossil margins (Fig. 4D) may reflect cell surface hydrophobicity, the retention of cell-surface macromolecules that inhibit carbonate precipitation, or both. Small domal and stratiform stromatolites formed by radial and isopachous growth of precipitated carbonate, rather than from the buildup of microbial mats. The laminated, stratiform to low domal shapes of these stromatolites are controlled by carbonate precipitation, rather than by the activities of microorganisms; thus, this texture and the larger-scale stromatolites it comprises are considered to be abiotic in origin.

Peritidal precipitates are present in varying abundance in other Mesoproterozoic carbonates. Though locally well developed in the Kotuikan Formation, peritidal precipitates are far more abundant in the Society Cliffs Formation of Baffin Bay (Kah and Knoll, 1996), the Debengda Formation of Siberia (Sergeev et al., 1994), the Huanglianduo Formation of Shanxi, North China (Xiao et al., 1997), and the Wumishan Formation (Liang et al., 1985; Cao, 1992). To a certain extent, the abundance of peritidal precipitates at any specific location may correlate with inferred paleoenvironment: in more humid settings (e.g., Kotuikan; Sergeev et al., 1995) decreased precipitation potential may have favored low abundance, whereas in more arid settings, particularly those associated with evaporites (e.g., Society Cliffs; Jackson and Ianelli, 1981; Kah and Knoll, 1996), increased precipitation potential might have favored higher abundance. Fortunately, the evaporative regime that apparently favors peritidal sea-floor carbonate precipitation also promotes early diagenetic silicification (Maliva et al., 1990), which makes it possible to glimpse both the taphonomic and the petrographic aspects of these textures in remarkable detail.

It is interesting to note that whereas the preferential relationship between early diagenetic silicification and peritidal environments continues into the early Paleozoic (Maliva et al., 1990), the association with peritidal sea-floor precipitates does not (Grotzinger, 1989, 1990, 1994; Grotzinger and Knoll, 1995). Given that microbes capable of photosynthesis, sulfate reduction, and methanogenesis have been present from the Archean onwards in the interstitial pores and on the exposed surface of tidal flats, it is unlikely that a change in either their abundance or functionality is responsible for this secular facies transition. However, the potential role of paleoclimate in controlling peritidal precipitated stromatolites may have been modulated by a long-term decrease in the carbonate saturation of the world's oceans throughout Mesoproterozoic time. It is now reasonably well established that sea-floor precipitates are abundant in unrestricted, subtidal as well as restricted, peritidal environments in late Archean carbonates, and that the abundance of subtidal sea-floor precipitates declines during Paleoproterozoic time, followed by a decline in the abundance of peritidal sea-floor precipitates during Mesoproterozoic time (Grotzinger, 1989, 1994; Kah and Knoll, 1996; Sumner and Grotzinger, 1996; Sumner, 1997a). With rare exceptions, Neoproterozoic and later carbonates do not contain carbonate sea-floor precipitates (Grotzinger, 1989; Grotzinger and Knoll, 1995). Although the causes of this decline are still largely speculative (Grotzinger, 1989; Grotzinger and Kasting, 1993; Sumner and Grotzinger, 1996), it is reasonable to posit on the basis of available data that the absence of peritidal sea-floor precipitates in Neoproterozoic carbonates is related more to environment than to life. The occurrence of carbonate precipitates in close spatial and temporal proximity with more slowly lithified fabrics in the Billyakh Group and in other Mesoproterozoic successions suggests that the occurrence of precipitates in the Mesoproterozoic is controlled principally by local environmental factors, such as evaporation rate and freshwater influx, that were superimposed on a generally high level of sea-water supersaturation with respect to $CaCO_3$ minerals. The broader environmental distribution of seafloor precipitates in older successions and their general absence from even evaporitic portions of younger carbonate platforms suggest that Mesoproterozoic seawater lay at a critical threshold with respect to carbonate precipitation.

ACKNOWLEDGMENTS

We thank Peter Yu. Petrov for field assistance and Misha A. Semikhatov for field assistance and helpful discussions. We acknowledge Linda C. Kah for discussions regarding carbonate microfabrics, and for thoughtful comments on early versions of this manuscript. Bruce Simonson and Jim Jackson contributed thoughtful reviews that greatly improved the quality of this manuscript. This research was supported in part by National Aeronautics & Space Administration grant NAGW–893 and NAG5–3654 to AHK, National Aeronautics & Space Administration grant NAGW–2795 to JPG, and Russian Federation Basic Research grant 98–05–64259 to VNS.

REFERENCES

BARTLEY, J. K., 1996, Actualistic taphonomy of cyanobacteria: Implications for the Precambrian fossil record: Palaios, v. 11, p. 571–586.
BRAITHWAITE, C. J. R., CASANOVA, J., FREVERT, T., AND WHITTON, B. A., 1989, Recent stromatolites in landlocked pools on Aldabra, western Indian Ocean: Palaeogeography, Palaeoclimatology, Palaeoecology, v. 69, p. 145–165.
BUICK, R., DUNLOP, J. S. R., AND GROVES, D. I., 1981, Stromatolite recognition in ancient rocks: an appraisal of irregularly laminated structures in an Early Archean chert–barite unit from North Pole, Western Australia: Alcheringa, v. 21, p. 161–181.
CANFIELD, D. E., AND RAISWELL, R., 1991, Carbonate precipitation and dissolution. Its relevance to fossil preservation, *in* Allison, P. A., and Briggs, D. E. G., eds., Taphonomy: Releasing the Data Locked in the Fossil Record: New York, Plenum Press, Topics in Geobiology, 9, p. 411–453.
CAO, R., 1992, A preliminary study on microstructure of the Precambrian stromatolites, *in* Qui, S., Liang, Y., Cao, R., and Zhang, L., eds., Late Precambrian Stromatolites and Its Related Ore Deposits: Xi'an, Northwest University Press, p. 1–7 (in Chinese with English abstract).

CHAFETZ, H. S., AND BUCZYNSKI, C., 1992, Bacterially induced lithification of microbial mats: Palaios, v. 7, p. 277–293.

DUNHAM, R. J., 1969, Meniscus cement, *in* Bricker, O. P., ed., Carbonate Cements: Baltimore, Johns Hopkins University Press, p. 297–300.

FOLK, R. L., AND ASSERETO, R., 1976, Comparative fabrics of length-slow and length-fast calcite and calcitized aragonite in a Holocene speleothem, Carlsbad Caverns, New Mexico: Journal of Sedimentary Petrology, v. 46, p. 486–496.

GINSBURG, R. N., AND JAMES, N. P., 1976, Submarine botryoidal aragonite in Holocene reef limestones, Belize: Geology, v. 4, p. 431–436.

GOLUBIC, S., 1985, Microbial mats and modern stromatolites in Shark Bay, Western Australia, *in* Caldwell, D. E., James, A. B., and Corale L. B., eds., Planetary Ecology: New York, Van Nostrand Reinhold Company, p. 3–16.

GOLUBIC, S., AND HOFMANN, H. J., 1976, Comparison of Holocene and mid-Precambrian Entophysalidaceae (Cyanophyta) in stromatolitic algal mats: Cell division and degradation: Journal of Paleontology, v. 50, p. 1074–1082.

GOLUBIC, S., SERGEEV, V. N., AND KNOLL, A.H., 1995, Mesoproterozoic Archaeoellipsoides: Akinetes of heterocystous cyanobacteria: Lethaia, v. 28, p. 285–298.

GOROKHOV, I. M., SEMIKHATOV, M. A., AND DRUBETSKOI, E. P., 1991, Rb–Sr and K–Ar vozrast osadochnyh geochronometrov nizhnego rifeya Anabarskogo massiva [Rb–Sr and K–Ar ages of sedimentary geochronometers from the Lower Riphean deposits of the Anabar Massif]: Akademiya Nauk SSSR, Izvestiya, Seriya Geologicheskaya, v. 7, p. 17–32.

GREY, K., AND THORNE, A. M., 1985, Biostratigraphic significance of stromatolites in upward shallowing sequences of the early Proterozoic Duck Creek Dolomite, western Australia, *in* Young, G. M, Chen, J. B., and Zhang, H., eds., Stratigraphic Methods as Applied to the Proterozoic Record: Precambrian Research, v. 79, p. 183–206.

GROTZINGER, J. P., 1986, Cyclicity and paleoenvironmental dynamics, Rocknest platform, northwest Canada: Geological Society of America, Bulletin, v. 97, p. 1208–1231.

GROTZINGER, J. P., 1989, Facies and evolution of Precambrian carbonate depositional systems: Emergence of the modern platform archetype, *in* Crevello, P.D., Wilson, J.L., Sarg, J.F., and Read, J.F., eds., Controls on Carbonate Platform and Basin Development: SEPM, Special Publication 44, p. 79–106.

GROTZINGER, J. P., 1990, Geochemical model for Proterozoic stromatolite decline: American Journal of Science, v. 290–A, p. 80–103.

GROTZINGER, J. P., 1994, Trends in Precambrian carbonate sediments and their implication for understanding evolution, *in* Bengtson, S., ed., Early Life on Earth: New York, Columbia University Press, p. 245–258.

GROTZINGER, J. P., AND KASTING, J.F., 1993, New constraints on Precambrian ocean composition: Journal of Geology, v. 101, p. 235–243.

GROTZINGER, J. P., AND KNOLL, A.H., 1995, Anomalous carbonate precipitates: Is the Precambrian the key to the Permian?: Palaios, v. 10, p. 578–596.

GROTZINGER, J. P., AND READ, J.F., 1983, Evidence for primary aragonite precipitation, lower Proterozoic (1.9 Ga) Rocknest dolomite, Wopmay orogen, northwest Canada: Geology, v. 11, p. 710–713.

GROTZINGER, J. P., AND ROTHMAN, D. H., 1996, An abiotic model for stromatolite morphogenesis: Nature, v. 383, p. 423–425.

HOFFMAN, P., 1976, Stromatolite morphogenesis in Shark Bay, western Australia, *in* Walter, M.R., ed., Stromatolites: Amsterdam, Elsevier, Developments in Sedimentology 20, p. 261–271.

HOFMANN, H. J., 1975, Stratiform Precambrian stromatolites, Belcher Islands, Canada: relations between silicified microfossils and microstructure: American Journal of Science, v. 275, p. 1121–1132.

HOFMANN, H. J., AND JACKSON, G. D., 1987, Proterozoic ministromatolites with radial–fibrous fabric: Sedimentology, v. 34, p. 963–971.

HORODYSKI, R. J., 1977, Lyngbya mats at Laguna Mormona, Baja California, Mexico: Comparison with Proterozoic stromatolites: Journal of Sedimentary Petrology, v. 47, p. 1305–1320.

JACKSON, G. D., AND IANNELLI, T. R., 1981, Rift–related cyclic sedimentation in the Neohelikian Borden Basin, northern Baffin Island, *in* Campbell, F. H. A, ed., Proterozoic Basins of Canada: Geological Survey of Canada, Paper 81–10, p. 269–302.

KAH, L. C., AND KNOLL, A. H., 1996, Microbenthic distribution of Proterozoic tidal flats: Environmental and taphonomic considerations: Geology, v. 24, p. 79–82.

KENDALL, A. C., 1985, Radiaxial fibrous calcite: A reappraisal, *in* Schneidermann, N., and Harris, P. M., eds., Carbonate Cements: SEPM, Special Publication 36, p. 59–78.

KNOLL, A. H., FAIRCHILD, I. J., AND SWETT, K., 1993, Calcified microbes in Neoproterozoic Carbonates: Implications for our understanding of the Proterozoic/Cambrian Transition: Palaios, v. 8, p. 512–525.

KNOLL, A. H., KAUFMAN, A. J., AND SEMIKHATOV, M. A., 1995, The carbon isotopic composition of Proterozoic carbonates: Riphean successions from northwestern Siberia (Anabar Massif, Turukhansk uplift): American Journal of Science, v. 295, p. 823–850.

KNOLL, A. H., AND SERGEEV, V. N., 1995, Taphonomic and evolutionary changes across the Mesoproterozoic–Neoproterozoic transition: Neues Jahrbuch für Geologie und Paläontologie, Abhandlungen, v. 195, p. 289–302.

KNOLL, A. H., AND SEMIKHATOV, M. A., 1998, The genesis and time distribution of two distinctive Proterozoic stromatolitic microstructures: Palaios, v. 13, p. 407–421.

KNOLL, A. H., AND SWETT, K., 1990, Carbonate deposition during the late Proterozoic Era: An example from Spitsbergen: American Journal of Science, v. 290–A, p. 104–131.

KOMAR, V. A., 1966, Stromatolity verkhnedokembriiskikh otlozhenii severa Sibirskoi platformy i ikh stratigraficheskoe znachenia [Stromatolites of the upper Precambrian deposits in the northern Siberian Platform and their stratigraphic significance]: Moscow, Nauka, 122 p.

KOWALEWSKI, M., FLESSA, K. W., AND HALLMAN, D. P., 1995, Ternary taphograms: Triangular diagrams applied to taphonomic analysis: Palaios, v. 10, p. 478–483.

LIANG Y., ZHU, S., ZHANG, L., CAO, R., GAO, Z., AND BU, D., 1985. Stromatolite assemblage of Late Precambrian in China: Precambrian Research, v. 29, p. 15–32.

LOUCKS, R. G., AND FOLK, R. L., 1976. Fanlike rays of former aragonite in Permian Capitan Reef pisolite: Journal of Sedimentary Petrology, v. 46, p. 483–485.

MALIVA, R. G., KNOLL, A. H., AND SIEVER, R., 1990, Secular change in chert distribution: A reflection of evolving biological participation in the silica cycle: Palaios, v. 4, p. 519–532.

MARIN, F., SMITH, M., ISA, Y., MUYZER, G., AND WESTBROEK, P., 1996, Skeletal matrices, muci, and the origin of invertebrate calcification: National Academy of Sciences [USA], Proceedings, v. 93, p. 1554–1559.

MAZZULLO, S. J., 1980, Calcite pseudospar replacive of marine acicular aragonite, and implications for aragonite cement diagenesis: Journal of Sedimentary Petrology, v. 50, p. 409–422.

PURSER, B. H. AND LOREAU, J. P., 1973, Aragonitic, supratidal encrustations on the Trucial Coast, Persian Gulf, *in* Purser, B. H., ed., The Persian Gulf: New York, Springer-Verlag, p. 343–376.

SANDBERG, P. A., 1975, New interpretations of Great Salt Lake ooids and of ancient non-skeletal carbonate mineralogy: Sedimentology, v. 22, p. 497–537.

SCHOPF, J. W., 1968, Microflora of the Bitter Springs Formation, Late Precambrian, central Australia: Journal of Paleontology, v. 42, p. 651–688.

SEMIKHATOV, M. A., AND SEREBRYAKOV, S. N., 1983, Sibirskii gipostratotip rifeya [The Siberian Hypostratotype of the Riphean]: Moscow, Nauka, 224 p.

SERGEEV, V. N., KNOLL, A. H., AND GROTZINGER, J. P., 1995, Paleobiology of the Mesoproterozoic Billyakh Group, Anabar Uplift, Northern Siberia: Journal of Paleontology, Memoir 39, p. 1–37.

SERGEEV, V. N., KNOLL, A. H., KOLOSOVA, S. P., AND KOLOSOV, P. N., 1994, Microfossils in cherts from the Mesoproterozoic Debengda Formation, Olenek Uplift, Northeastern Siberia: Stratigraphy and Geological Correlation, v. 2, p. 23–38.

SHENFIL', V. Y., AND YAKSHCHIN, M. S., 1982, K stratigrafii rifeiskikh otlozhenii zapadnogo sklona Anabarskogo massiva [Stratigraphy of the Riphean deposits of the western slope of the Anabar Uplift], *in* Anonymous, ed., Novye dannye po stratigrafii pozdnego dokembriya Sibiri [New data on the stratigraphy of the Late Precambrian of Siberia]: Moscow, Nauka, p. 31–42.

SIMONSON, B. M., SCHUBEL, K. A., AND HASSLER, S. W., 1993, Carbonate sedimentology of the early Precambrian Hamersley Group of Western Australia: Precambrian Research, v. 60, p. 287–335.

SUMNER, D. Y., 1997a, Carbonate precipitation and oxygen stratification in late Archean seawater as deduced from facies and stratigraphy of the Gamohaan and Frisco formations, Transvaal Supergroup, South Africa: American Journal of Science, v. 297, p. 455–487.

SUMNER, D. Y., 1997b, Late Archean calcite–microbe interactions: Two morphologically distinct microbial communities that affected calcite nucleation differently: Palaios, v. 12, p. 302–318.

SUMNER, D. Y., AND GROTZINGER, J. P., 1996, Were kinetics of Archean calcium carbonate precipitation related to oxygen concentration?: Geology, v. 24, p. 119–122.

VASCONCELOS, C., AND MCKENZIE, J. A., 1997, Microbial mediation of modern dolomite precipitation and diagenesis under anoxic conditions (Lagoa

Vermelha, Rio De Janeiro, Brazil): Journal of Sedimentary Research, v. 67, p. 378–390.

VASCONCELOS, C., MCKENZIE, J. A., BERNASCONI, S., GRUJIC, D., AND TIEN, A. J., 1995, Microbial mediation as a possible mechanism for natural dolomite formation at low temperatures: Nature, v. 377, p. 220–222.

WALTER, M. R., 1976, Stromatolites: Amsterdam, Elsevier, Developments in Sedimentology 20, 790 p.

XIAO, S., KNOLL, A. H., KAUFMAN, A. J., YIN, L., AND YUN, Z., 1997, Neoproterozoic fossils in Mesoproterozoic rocks? Chemostratigraphic resolution of a biostratigraphic conundrum from the North China Platform: Precambrian Research, v. 84, p. 197–220.

ZENGER, D. H., DUNHAM, J. B., AND ETHINGTON, R. L., 1980, Concepts and Models of Dolomitization: Society of Economic Paleontologists and Mineralogists, Special Publication 28, 320 p.

ZLOBIN, M. N., AND GOLOVANOV, N. P., 1970, Stratigraficheskii ocherk verkhnedokembriiskikh otlozhenii zapadnogo sklona Anabarskogo podniatia [A stratigraphic outline of the Upper Precambrian deposits of the Western Slope of the Anabar Uplift], in Anonymous, ed., Opornyi razrez verkhnedokembriiskikh otlozhenii Zapadnogo Sklona Anabarskogo Podniatia [The basic section of the Upper Precambrian deposits of the Western Slope of the Anabar Uplift]: Leningrad, Nauchno-issledovatel'skii Institut Geologii Arktiki, p. 6–21.

GEOCHEMICAL SCENARIOS FOR THE PRECIPITATION OF BIOMIMETIC INORGANIC CARBONATES

JUAN MANUEL GARCÍA-RUIZ

Laboratorio de Estudios Cristalográficos. Instituto Andaluz de Ciencias de la Tierra. CSIC–Universidad de Granada.
Av.uentenueva s/n, Granada 18002, Spain

ABSTRACT: The precipitation of carbonate into alkaline silicate solutions results in the formation of self-assembled crystal aggregates with noncrystallographic morphologies. These precipitates emulate biologically induced mineral textures as well as display forms typical of primitive microfossils. The precipitation behavior varies with pH, i.e., as a function of the species created by dissociation of the silicic acid under alkaline conditions. Calcite single crystals and crystal aggregates precipitated in these media display complex forms derived from the specific inhibition of some crystal faces, and eventually, noncrystallographic shapes such as sheaf-of-wheat with self-organized banding develop. When strontianite and witherite precipitate in these environments at pH higher than 10, their crystal aggregates display in addition very specific morphologies, such as target patterns, scrolls, twisted ribbons, spirals, fingers, etc., with typical sizes ranging from microns to millimeters. The crystallites of the metal carbonate are embedded in a silicate matrix and are co-oriented and parallel to each other, suggesting that both the loci for nucleation and the orientation of the carbonate groups are controlled by the silica phase.

The silica concentration (>250 ppm SiO_2), ionic force, and pH values (>8.5) required for the phenomenon to be observed are well within the range of values measured in contemporary alkaline lakes. A number of geological scenarios where the phenomenon could occur have been identified, among which are: a) contemporary lakes and thermal springs associated with alkaline magmatism such as those in the African rift valley; b) Precambrian (particularly Archean) terranes where cherts formed as a result of direct precipitation of silica; and c) a scenario on Earth-like planets where the existence of a silica-rich environment derived from hydrolysis of alkaline rocks is predicted.

INTRODUCTION

One of the long-standing challenges in geological studies has been to decode the genetic information enclosed in mineral (morphological and textural) patterns in order to learn about past geochemical scenarios. The variety of growth morphologies (the combination of crystal forms and habit of actual crystals as the result of a growth process), the existence of polymorphs, and the variability of aggregation patterns and disequilibrium shapes make calcite, in principle, a good candidate for these decodification studies. However, studies reported to date indicate that it is difficult to demonstrate a one-to-one correlation between a set of morphological and/or textural features and a specific physicochemical environment. The problem can be illustrated by one of the more interesting cases: the detection of biological signatures in sedimentary carbonates. It is known that living organisms are able a) to synthesize calcite and other polymorphs of calcium carbonate (Simkiss, 1986); b) to control the critical supersaturation value for the nucleation process (Williams, 1984); c) to modify growth behavior by the specific interaction of macromolecules with crystal surfaces (Albeck et al., 1993; Aizenberg et al., 1995); and d) even to "switch" the precipitating polymorphic phase (Belcher et al., 1996). Using information obtained from laboratory studies of the interface between organic compounds and inorganic materials and from contemporary mineralizing systems, undoubtedly linked to biological activity, many investigators have undertaken the task of finding signals of life in the texture and morphology of carbonates (see for instance: Chafetz and Folk, 1984; Folk et al., 1985; Jones and Kahle, 1986; Pentecost, 1990; Buczynski and Chafetz, 1992; Folk, 1993).

Although self-assembled aggregation of carbonate crystals to create shape-controlled ceramic materials is currently thought to be a specific feature of life, the morphological and textural carbonate patterns reminiscent of those designed by interaction with biological macromolecules can also be obtained by purely inorganic precipitation mechanisms within alkaline solutions enriched in silica (García-Ruiz, 1985). The interaction of calcium salts with silica-derived species forming at high pH modifies the morphology of calcite rhombohedral crystals. The point symmetry group ($-3\ 2/m$) maintained initially is eventually lost through a dendrification process governed by noncrystallographic branching. Moreover, for precipitated barium and strontium carbonate crystals (orthorhombic aragonite-type structure), such an interaction extends to the formation of inorganic self-assembled precipitates where the silica spreads as a two-dimensional matrix and acts as the main morphogenetic agent. In this case, the morphology is clearly unrelated to the structure of the carbonate and the precipitates show an amazing morphological similarity to primitive organisms within a size range from microns to millimeters.

These inorganic self-organized structures are of interest as a laboratory model for biomineralization and biomimetic ceramics (García-Ruiz, 1985) in that they enhance the search for new materials and new ways to produce them (Mann, 1996). If the phenomenon of morphological and textural modification of carbonate minerals in silica-rich environments can be demonstrated to occur under geological conditions, it will also be interesting as a geochemical tool when deciphering the genesis of carbonate mineral textures. Furthermore, the morphological convergence of the inorganic precipitates with microstructures found in Precambrian cherts, some currently identified as biological remnants and some of them of unknown origin, could shed light on the early evolution of life on Earth.

The aim of this work is to survey the plausible geochemical scenarios where the above interaction of silica with carbonate could have been operating in the past and the contemporary environments where it could occur. For the sake of clarity, I will first present relevant experimental results illustrating the main morphological and textural features of carbonate precipitating from alkaline solutions with a high concentration of silica.

LABORATORY FORMATION OF INDUCED-MORPHOLOGY CRYSTAL AGGREGATES

Morphological and Textural Features

To tailor the morphology of carbonate crystals growing in silica-rich solutions, the precipitation experiments must be performed using values of the relevant parameters within the region where both carbonate precipitation and dissociation and polymerization of silicic acid occur (Fig. 1). Such experimental conditions can be attained by mixing solutions of calcium, barium, or strontium chloride with sodium silicate solutions and adjusting the pH of the dilution between 8.5 and 12. A commercial sodium silicate solution (for instance, from Aldrich, with a Na/Si ratio of 0.65 and a pH = 11.3), previously diluted with bi-distilled water to the desired concentration, can be used as the silica source. The NaOH concentration of this commercial solution is 13.8% and the total Si concentration is 12.2%. This silicate solution is then mixed with aliquots of alkaline-earth metal chloride solutions and the pH set to the desired value with diluted HCl or NaOH solutions. Performing the experiments under atmospheric conditions in the open air to equilibrate CO_2 ensures the formation of HCO_3^- and $CO_3^=$ within the working pH range (Garrels and Christ, 1965) and the subsequent precipitation of carbonate. Carbonate concentration can be increased by adding soluble carbonate or by bubbling CO_2 in the system. Because of the high solubility of silica in alkaline media, it is mandatory to avoid the use of glass reservoirs for quantitative studies.

A systematic study of the precipitation behavior reveals that the morphological modification starts at silica concentrations above 250 ppm and at pH values higher than 8.5 (Fig. 2). The silica concentration is, no doubt, a relevant parameter for the

morphogenetical process, but the key factor is related to the pH value, i.e., to the relative concentration of silica-derived species in the solution. For the sake of clarity, it is convenient to distinguish between the precipitation behavior of calcite and that of witherite and strontianite, because they are not identical.

For the case of calcite, no precipitation occurs until pH 9, when equant crystals with rhombohedric {104} faces form. At higher pH, the crystals elongate along the {001} direction, basically maintaining the rhombohedrical faces but creating a set of nonsingular faces tautozonal with the c axis, forming elongated shapes. Increasing the pH value to 10.5–11 results in the formation of crystals composed of mosaic blocks that retain the memory of the space-group symmetry of the calcite structure. Further increase in the concentration of silica results in the development of spherulitic textures via sheaf-of-wheat morphologies (Fig. 3).

For the case of witherite and strontianite, a typical morphological sequence obtained from low to high pH values is as follow (silica concentration of 260 ppm of SiO_2 at 20°C and a $BaCl_2$ concentration of 0.01 M): at pH below 9.5–10, single crystals with prismatic {010} and {110} faces appear; the {110} faces later split along the [001] axis and dumbbell–type dendrites form. Repeated splitting of the crystal provokes dendritic open forms that look like sheaves of wheat that ultimately form globular shapes. These are beautiful structures, appearing under transmitted optical microscopy as bundles of globules or colonies of several globules up to 60 μm in size, made up of a radiating array of crystalline fibers that branch at noncrystallographic angles, resulting in the continuous bending of crystal surfaces after bifurcation (Fig. 4). At pH higher than 10.2, the observed morphological behavior is completely different, and, according to experimental observations, specific to Ba and Sr carbonates (Figs. 5, 6). At this pH, vesicles up to 300 μm in diameter form, which, with time, experience several morphological changes leading to yeast-like and burst-like forms, encapsulations, rosettes, and sheets. An amazing morphological behavior is then observed: from all the above forms, but mostly from sheets, the precipitates adopt beautiful helicoidal patterns. When viewed under an optical microscope these forms appear as braids. The scanning electron microscope, however, reveals that this morphology results from a precise twisting of the sheets. When the silica concentration or the working temperature is increased, the same morphological trend with pH is observed but it is shifted slightly towards lower pH values. In all of these batch experiments performed by mixing solutions, which are obviously closed systems, the pH falls to a value of 7.5–8 as a result of the carbonate precipitation.

The above-described morphological dependence on pH can also be demonstrated for open systems working out of equilibrium by using a silica concentration high enough to form a gel of initial high pH (García-Ruiz and Amorós, 1981a, 1981b; García-Ruiz, 1985; Baird et al., 1992). The convection-free environment in the gel ensures diffusive transport of the acid metal chloride solution through the highly basic gel containing CO_3 groups. As the diffusion front advances, the starting pH value of the gel decreases locally, and precipitation of carbonate takes place at different locations that are spatially discriminated from low pH near the gel/solution interface to high pH far from that interface. The morphological sequence obtained with many batch experiments using a low silica concentration can then be

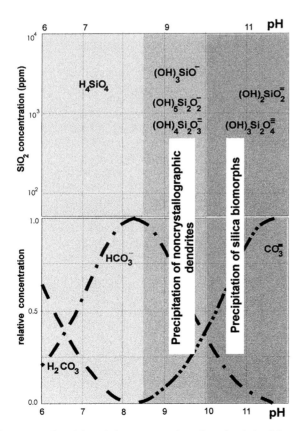

Fig. 1.—A plot of the relative concentration of species derived from SiO_2 and CO_2 dissociation as a function of pH. Note the correlation between the two main types of carbonate precipitation observed and the dominant silica-derived species in the solution.

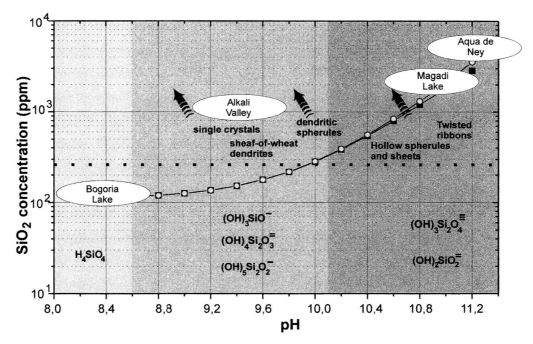

FIG. 2.—The solubility of silica as a function of pH (full-symbol line considering $(OH)_3SiO^-$ contribution; open-symbol line considering also $(OH)_2SiO_2^-$ contribution). The morphologies experimentally observed at various pH values are indicated as well as the location in the plot of some contemporary lakes. The horizontal dashed line parallel to the abscissa axis indicates the minimum silica concentration required to observe the morphological modifications. The arrows indicate the shift of the morphological trend observed at increasing silica concentration or temperature.

clearly observed to appear across the silica gel in a single experiment. In addition, the experimental system working out of equilibrium for a long time yields well developed structures that reveal new morphological and textural features, among which the self-organized banding structures of calcite crystal aggregates arising from sheaf-of-wheat morphologies are noteworthy (Fig. 7; García-Ruiz, 1980; Dominguez-Bella, 1986; Dominguez-Bella and García-Ruiz, 1986; 1987).

While crystal aggregates obtained at pH lower than 10 are made up mainly of carbonate crystals with traces of silica species, the precipitates obtained at higher pH are composite materials, as demonstrated by dissolution experiments, X-ray diffractometry, infrared spectroscopy, and electron microscopy. They are made of a crystalline carbonate phase plus an amorphous or ill-defined metal silicate hydrate phase (García-Ruiz, 1985). Neither infrared nor X-ray analysis reveals the existence of a special silica phase; all the spectra show characteristic vibrations of silica gel (Farmer, 1974) and broad peaks characteristic of X-ray powder diffraction pattern of amorphous silica. Small-angle X-ray scattering and transmission electron microscopy studies are under way to seek the existence of microscopic order and the potential mechanisms that could be responsible for mesoscopic ordering.

The loci and orientation of the carbonate crystals within the precipitate are not at all randomly distributed. The existence of an ordered textural arrangement of carbonate crystals can be inferred when they are observed under cross-polarized light and appears clearly from scanning electron microscope observations and from electron diffraction (Fig. 8). The textural arrangement can be observed directly in crystal aggregates of induced morphology that form at mild pH values. They are built

of a number of blocks that form a mosaic crystal (Figs. 3, 4). The degree of misalignment of these building blocks increases as the interaction with the dissociation species of silicic acid increases. It is noticeable that even when precipitation takes places at discrete time intervals, leading to the formation of self-organized banding, the co-orientation of the building blocks forming the whole aggregate is maintained in either two-dimensional or three-dimensional crystal aggregates (Fig. 8). Although more subtle, such an ordered arrangement also exists in the silica-rich aggregates formed at higher pH values. To demonstrate this, the silica matrix must be dissolved carefully, using NaOH solutions, and then the residue washed with water. The extreme case of noncrystallographic complex shapes of twisted ribbons is shown in Fig. 8B. The arrangement of the carbonate crystals is made evident, showing their alignment perpendicular to the helicoidal surface of the particle.

The internal structure of the silica-rich aggregates is also interesting. Most of the spherules are hollow and can be considered as vesicles (Fig. 9). From these vesicles, burst-like morphologies form, probably as a result of the increment of the internal pressure. In many cases, the vesicles undergo a development leading to sheet-like morphologies that are also hollow. Each wall of these lamellae is made up of an asymmetric bilayer, with co-oriented carbonate crystals facing the outer part while the inner part seems to be made up mainly of a silica-rich phase (Fig. 9). At some nonspecific points within these sheet-like forms, or even in some cases from the initial vesicles themselves, twisted ribbons that are also hollow may form. For a single ribbon, the twist period is constant and maintained for the whole length except at the end of the twisted ribbon. When

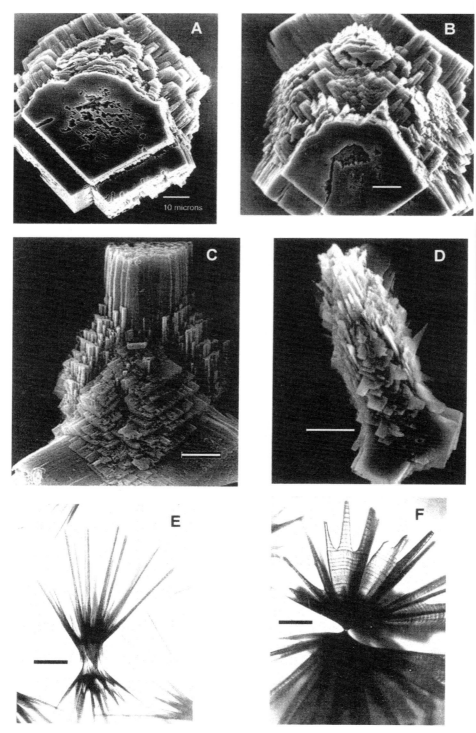

FIG. 3.—Morphological behavior of calcite precipitating from silica-rich media at pH ≅ 10. A, B) Note the existence of smooth rhombohedral {104} faces and the formation of rough faces tautozonal with the *c* axis ({hk0} faces) causing the elongation of the crystal shape but maintaining the point group symmetry of the crystal. Scale bar = 10 μm. C) A view along the *c* axis of the crystal, showing the tendency of the rhombohedral faces to acquire a columnar structure. Note the mosaic character of the crystals (which, at this stage, can actually be interpreted as a crystal aggregate) and the arrangement of the fibrous growth units. Scale bar = 5 μm. D) From the growth behavior shown in Part A, hexa-radiated crystals form. Scale bar = 10 μm. E) The iterative accretion of these large growth units (micron size) causes a progressive misalignment of the columnar stuctures, leading to the formation of multibranched crystals. Scale bar = 50 μm. F) Lateral growth of these branches creates a continuous film, which displays self-organized banding. When the misalignment is large, the crystals adopt the dumbbell forms that eventually lead to spherulitic shapes. Scale bar = 150 μm.

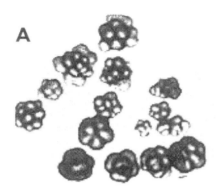
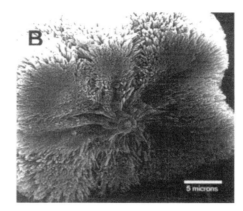

FIG. 4.—Morphology of witherite and strontianite in silica gel at pH 9–10. A) The multi-globular morphologies observed under optical microscopy are actually dendrites formed by noncrystallographic branching of a single crystal nucleus. B) The morphogenetical process is similar to that of calcite, shown in Figure 3.

the ribbons are obtained in silica gel the twist period does not vary when the viscosity of the media is altered.

Thus, we can differentiate two different precipitation behaviors for carbonates precipitated in silica-rich solutions: (1) At mildly alkaline conditions, the precipitate is mainly made up of crystalline carbonate, the silicic species inducing a strong modification of the textural and aggregation features, leading eventually to loss of the point symmetry group of carbonates and formation of self-organized banding, producing textural properties reminiscent of biomineral structures and biologically induced structures. (2) At higher pH, the silica-rich phase is the main component. It controls the nucleation loci and orientation of the carbonate crystals and the overall morphology of the forming composite material. The development of noncrystallographic shapes reminiscent of primitive living organisms leads me to term them "silica biomorphs" in order to underline their inorganic character but emphasize their peculiar morphological behavior.

Control of the nucleation sites and orientation of carbonate crystals made by organic molecules secreted by living organisms is a wonderful example of self-organization leading to highly specific ceramic materials. It is remarkable that the self-assembled aggregation of carbonate crystals created by the interaction with silicate species formed at alkaline pH demonstrates not only that such a textural emulation of the mineral products of life occurs but also that this emulation extends to the morphology observed in the simplest organisms.

Morphogenetic Mechanisms

The equilibrium solubility of silica is approximately independent of pH up to about pH 8.3, with values in the range of 100–150 ppm (1.67–2.5×10^{-3} M) but increases greatly with pH, being 1120 ppm at pH 10.6 (Alexander et al., 1954; Krauskopf, 1956, 1979). In neutral aqueous solutions at a low salt concentration, the solubility is almost the same as in pure water but decreases with increasing salt concentration. The equilibrium solubility at low pH increases with temperature, from 50 ppm at 0°C to 750 ppm at 100°C (Siever and Scott, 1963). The increase in the solubility of silica in an alkaline media is explained by the presence of silicate anions in addition to silicic acid in these conditions. At pH less than 9, silicic acid is mainly undissociated (Fig. 1). At pH higher than 9, three monomeric species of silicic acid are present in solution, and at pH 9.7, the first deprotonation of silicic acid becomes dominant while the second deprotonation starts to be significant only at pH 11. In addition, at pH higher than 9 the dimers $Si_2O_2(OH)_5^-$ and $Si_2O_3(OH)_4^{2-}$ are also present in significant concentrations. At above pH 11, $Si_2O_4(OH)_3^{3-}$ is also a relevant species (Iler, 1979).

As demonstrated by Alvarez and Sparks (1985), even at low silicate concentrations (70 ppm) a substantial part of the silicate solution is non-monomeric, mainly present as dimers. Nevertheless, the polymerization of silica also depends on its concentration and on the silica/cation ratio, temperature, and solution aging. Commercial sodium silicate solutions with Na/Si values of 0.6 and silica concentrations of 4 M show the existence of all the four Q^n groups with many different configurations. In general, the degree of polymerization of the silicate anions increases with increasing silica concentration and decreasing Na/Si ratio.

Taking into account the above data, a correlation between the morphology of the precipitates and the pH value exists. This correlation is due to the different types of interaction expected from neutral to moderately alkaline solutions. At pH below 8, no interaction exists, because carbonate is not present at a concentration sufficient to nucleate witherite; moreover, no condensation of silica occurs. At higher pH (>9), $H_3SiO_4^-$, as well as the dimers $Si_2O_2(OH)_5^-$ and $Si_2O_3(OH)_4^{2-}$, become important. The interaction with the witherite crystals is most likely to take place via OH^- groups bonded to barium-rich crystal surfaces such as the pinacoid {001}. This interaction is nonspecific, in the sense that there are no epitactic relationships, the phenomenon being rather a heterogeneous nucleation of silica on the witherite crystal surfaces, which enhances silica condensation. Adsorption of condensed silica apparently causes splitting of the {001} witherite faces along the c axis and development of the branched cauliflower-type structures observed at pH below 9.5.

At higher pH, between 9.5 and 10.5, the percentage of silicate ions in solution is higher in comparison with monomeric acid. Above pH 10, silica particles in the presence of barium ions in solution reverse their charges to become positive, and react with

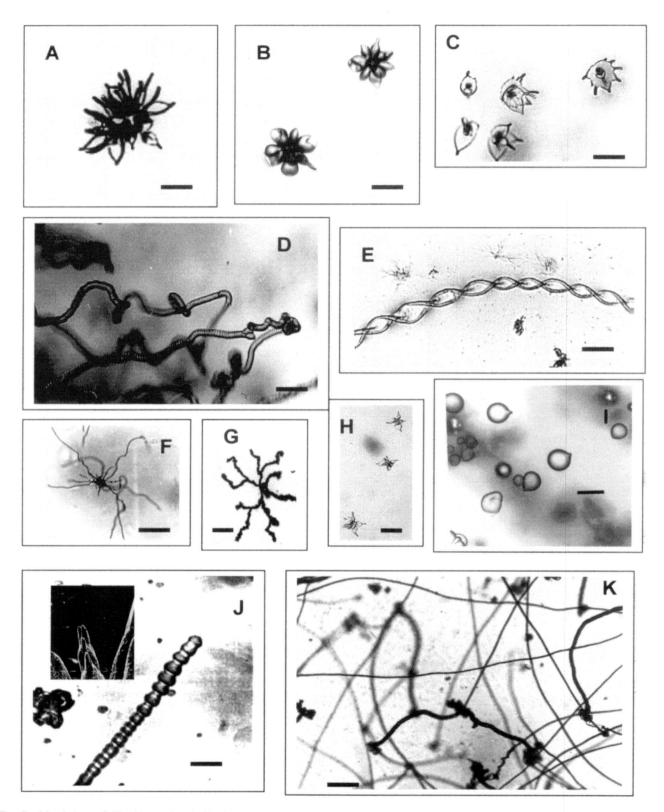

FIG. 5.—Morphology of silica biomorphs of witherite and strontianite precipitated at pH ≥ 10, at different stages of development. A–C, and H) Burst-like shapes showing multivesicular or sheet-like morphology. D, E) Twisted ribbons with different degrees of torsion. F, G) Filamentary structure arising from a single growth center. I) Spherical vesicles and yeast-like morphologies. J) Septate filament with tip (shown in the insert). (K) Filaments formed by ribbons with very small twist period. Scale bars: A, B, C. G, H, and I, = 100 μm; D = 200 μm; E, = 40 μm; F, = 150 μm; J, = 40 μm.

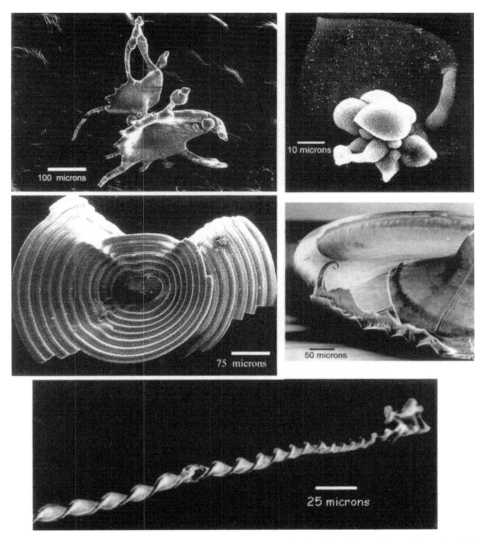

FIG. 6.—Scanning electron microscope views of witherite and strontianite silica biomorphs precipitated at pH ≥ 10.

witherite, most likely via hydroxyl groups, a mechanism that provokes silica flocculation (Ottewill, 1983). The precipitate can be considered a metal silicate hydrate gel (Fuji and Kondo, 1981), which is then pervaded by water, creating a silica-rich enclosed region surrounded by a semipermeable membrane. Because of the chemical similarity with the so-called silica garden (Birchall et al., 1980; Double, 1983), an osmotic driving force was suggested to account for the formation of noncrystallographic shapes (García-Ruiz, 1985). According to the membrane osmotic model developed for cement chemistry (Coatman et al., 1980), the membrane thus formed is semipermeable and the influx of solution creates an osmotic pressure in the inner part of the crystal–membrane arrangement. The subsequent cracking of the membrane provokes an injection of the inner acid solution into the outer basic gel, and a new membrane traces the fluid structure created during the mixing. In principle, the interface created by this injection should behave like a self-performed viscous fingering experiment (Nittmann et al., 1985), i.e., a Saffman–Taylor instability forming when a

fluid is injected and pushes another one of higher viscosity (Saffman and Taylor, 1958). However, a number of observations suggest that such a mechanism does not offer a complete explanation of the shapes obtained during precipitation of barium and strontium carbonate at high pH. Among these observations García-Ruiz and Moreno (1997) have noted the following: (1) the twist period of the helicoidal pattern is independent of gel viscosity; (2) the aggregates grow at a constant rate; and (3) the precipitation behavior is sensitive to temperature. These observations, along with the bi-layer symmetry of the precipitates (Fig. 9), suggest the existence of a structural control of chemical nature, which needs to be studied further in detail.

The correlation found between precipitation behavior and pH, the existence of a reasonable explanation for the morphogenetical process, and the fact that the same precipitates were observed when the experiments were performed under Ar atmosphere as well as in the presence of fungicide and bactericide, rule out any biological origin for this phenomenon of morphological induction.

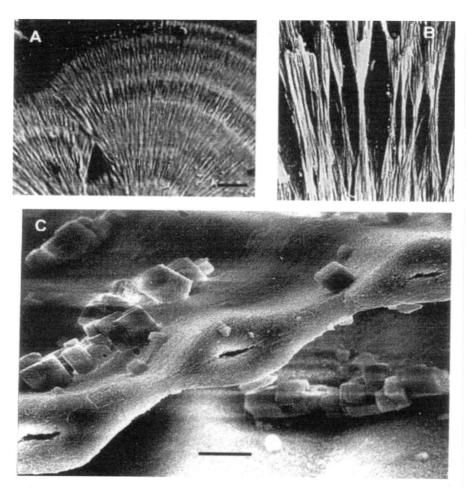

FIG. 7.—Scanning electron microscope observation of induced-morphology crystal aggregates of calcite. A) Self-organized banding structure. Scale bar = 100 μm. B) Detail of A showing the banding as formed by the alignment of sheaf-of-wheat crystals, the low-density bands corresponding to the center of the sheaves, the high-density bands corresponding to the ends of the sheaves. C) Note that the pattern of the banding is the same for the case of three-dimensional crystal aggregates shown in this figure. Scale bar = 30 μm.

FIG. 8.—Sheet-like crystal aggregate of witherite observed under crossed polarizers. The pseudo-uniaxial Maltese cross indicates the existence of order in the distribution of the carbonate crystallites forming the aggregate. Note the Archimedean trend followed during the development of the sheet-like shape. Scale bar = 100 μm. B) Scanning electron microscope view of a twisted ribbon once the silica matrix was removed. The delicate and precise arrangement of the carbonate crystallites forming the aggregate is made evident.

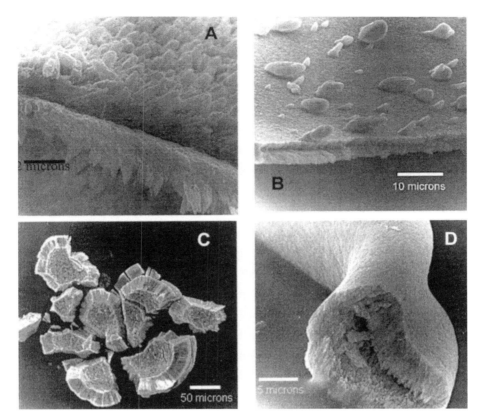

FIG. 9.—Scanning electron microscope views of the inner structure of silica biomorphs. A, B) Cross section of sheet-like morphologies showing the two-wall structure, each wall made up of a bi-layer with a carbonate-rich and a silica-rich surface. C) Spherical vesicle showing its hollow character. D) Twisted ribbons are hollow tubules.

PRESENT-DAY GEOCHEMICAL SCENARIOS

The usual silica content in natural waters, including rivers and seas, rarely exceeds 100 ppm and in general is much lower than the equilibrium concentration of opaline amorphous silica in water (Krauskopf, 1956; Davis, 1964; Siever, 1992). This undersaturated level of silica in modern oceans is due to the activity of silica-secreting organisms (Maliva et al., 1989) and to sorption by clay minerals (Mackenzie et al., 1967). In addition, the pH value of the ocean is fairly neutral and has been found to be acidic in most of rivers. Therefore, the formation of silica biomorphs is unlikely in natural environments. However, there are currently a few regions on Earth where waters containing a high concentration of silica can be found (Icole and Perinet, 1984). These anomalies occur, for instance, in some hot springs and lakes in the African Rift Valley, such as Lake Magadi (Kenya), where silica contents of up to 2700 ppm have been measured (Jones et al., 1967). The Alkali Valley (Oregon, USA) and the active volcanic region of eastern Anatolia are also regions with alkaline brines. The most extreme case known by the author is the Aqua de Ney vent, where a silica concentration of 5000 ppm has been reported (Feth et al., 1961). In general, closed-basin waters where the main inflow comes from alkaline sodium carbonate/bicarbonate springs associated with volcanic terrains (Kempe and Degens, 1985) are candidates to become highly concentrated in silica. The dissolved silica in these environments comes from incongruent dissociation of silicate minerals rather than from quartz dissolution (Garrels and Mackenzie, 1971) may later precipitate as amorphous silica or as silicates.

According to the results of our laboratory experiments, morphological induction in carbonates occurs when the pH is higher than 8.5 and the concentration of silica is beyond a threshold of about 300 ppm. Note that these values are within the range of values measured in some contemporary alkaline lakes (Fig. 2), suggesting that the phenomenon, although rare, may be active in some natural present-day localities. Thus, if the silicate solution used in the laboratory experiments is replaced by water samples from these alkaline lakes and mixed with $BaCl_2$, $SrCl_2$, or $CaCl_2$ solutions, the same precipitation behavior of carbonate is expected.

PAST GEOCHEMICAL SCENARIOS

The silica cycle seems to have operated as today during the Phanerozoic (Siever, 1957, 1992). Since about 600 millions years ago: (1) no changes in the physicochemical properties of the ocean relevant to silica solubility occurs; and (2) the different influx of silica to surface waters was efficiently balanced by the activity of silica-secreting organisms, which are able to maintain the concentration of silica far below the equilibrium concentration. In fact, there is field evidence that the origin of most Phanerozoic cherts is unequivocally linked to the sedimentation of the exoskeletons of silica-secreting organisms

(Maliva et al., 1989). During that time, precipitation of opaline silica was dominated by siliceous sponges, radiolarians, and diatoms (Brasier et al., 1997) and with very few exceptions (i.e., some deep-sea deposits), opal is completely absent in older rocks (Knauth, 1994).

However, there is no evidence of any Precambrian biomineralization process leading to silica precipitation, and in fact, recent isotopic studies suggest the absence of any biogenic contribution to Archean chert formations (Minami et al., 1995). Therefore, for Precambrian times, we have to imagine a silica cycle completely controlled by abiotic reactions among dissolved silica, organic matter, clay minerals, and zeolites (Siever, 1992).

The importance of cherts during the Precambrian, particularly in Archean times, is difficult to overestimate (Knauth, 1994). Chert, the most common chemical sediment in the Early and Middle Precambrian, is found in carbonates, banded iron formations, as beds in argillites, and as stratiform jasper beds in silicic volcanic sequences. It is associated with the oldest volcanic sequences, such as greenstone belts, and contains the oldest remnants of living organisms. Although these cherts now consist entirely of microquartz, fibrous silica, or megaquartz (many have been metamorphosed), the nature of the primary precursors and the source of silica remains a matter for discussion. In any case, purely abiotic processes must account for the precipitation of silica during the Precambrian.

An abiotic mechanism for chert formation, described by Eugster (1969), was inspired by the contemporary alkaline lakes in the rift valley of East Africa. Eugster and coworkers proposed that changes in the pH value due to influx of more dilute brines or by evaporation leads to varve-like precipitates initially made up of hydrous sodium silicates (such as magadiite), which convert to quartz by volume-to-volume replacement and by addition of void-filling microquartz. This mechanism has been further discussed by Williams and Crerar (1985) and experimentally tested by Muraishi (1989). Eugster and Jones (1968) extrapolated this mechanism to Precambrian cherts on the basis that intrabasin alkaline lakes must have been much more extensive on the early Earth because of the intense hydrothermal activity likely to have been associated with syndepositional volcanism. As derived from the geological record of sedimentary rocks, the continuous degassing of the Earth's interior, linked to volcanic activity, provoked the first accumulation of liquid water during the Archean, no later than 4 Ga ago. Weathering of volcanic rocks and degassing through bicarbonate vents provided these waters with saturated high silica concentrations and high pH values. What is relevant to the present work is that it seems reasonable to infer that a number of continental ponds, intrabasin lakes, and regions with little marine influence were scattered in the Archean with a much higher density and total volume than nowadays. Evaporation of these waters, sometimes linked to meteorite impact (particularly before 3.7 Ga) would supersaturate them, provoking large deposit of silica gel.

This "conservative" extrapolation, with mildly alkaline environments are restricted to areas with little or no marine influence (Eugster and Chou, 1973), was later extended and developed by Kempe and Degens (1985), who claimed that the whole Precambrian ocean was dominated by high-alkalinity values rather than by present-day sodium chloride waters. Even for those geochemical models that support on a more neutral ocean (Siever 1992), silica influx during the Archean would have been larger than the sorptive capacity of silicates and organic matter in the ocean, thereby enabling formation of supersaturated brines and eventually leading to precipitation of silica. Note also that the availability of strontium and barium in Archean brines was higher than now (Maisonneuve, 1982) because of the low concentration of sulfate (as low as 10^{-3} M, as estimated by Walker and Brimblecombe, 1985), although the existence of evaporitic deposits in the Early Archean (Buick and Dunlop, 1990) may alter these estimates. The enrichment in Sr, Mn, and Fe in greenstone-belt carbonate sequences has been interpreted as the result of a strong mantle influence in Archean times (Veizer et al., 1989). For instance, cherts such as those of the Warrawoona Group are linked to barium anomalies of debated origin (Strother, 1992) but probably related to hydrothermal activity (Buick and Dunlop, 1990). Thus, the laboratory experiment described above to form self-organized carbonate structures in silica-rich alkaline solutions fits this geochemical scenario very well, with barium and strontium available along with calcium in Archean brines. Therefore, it can be proposed that the formation of silica biomorphs may have been a natural process on the primitive Earth.

Finding observational evidence of this would be relevant to the chemistry of Archean waters because today there is no general consensus on the chemical features either of the early atmosphere or of the primitive ocean (Walker, 1983; Holland and Kasting, 1992; Kasting, 1993). While it seems clear that the early atmosphere contained very little free oxygen during the first 2000 million years, the values for temperature and partial CO_2 pressure vary widely for different models; the general trend, however, is to estimate these at values similar to or higher than present-day values. Ocean alkalinity and pH values are also a matter of debate, with models ranging from neutral and even acidic marine waters (Grotzinger and Kasting, 1993) to the alkaline and basic ocean proposed by Kempe and Degens (1985), atmospheric CO_2 pressure being a key parameter. Note that higher CO_2 partial pressure and higher temperatures (García-Ruiz, 1985; García-Ruiz and Moreno, 1997) enhance the interaction of silicate species with metal carbonate, the mechanism governing the formation of silica biomorphs. In this framework, the search for induced-morphology crystal aggregates in the Precambrian rocks has an immediate application: their striking morphology and the specific range of pH values (8.5–12) within which they form make them a useful geochemical indicator to set the boundary conditions for geochemical models.

NONTERRESTRIAL SCENARIOS

Any rational proposal to search extraterrestrial alkaline silica-rich environments must focus on Earth-like planets. For planets of this kind, where alkaline volcanic activity plays an essential role in early crust formation, the proper scenario to precipitate silica biomorphs and induced-morphology calcium carbonate becomes available as soon as condensed water appears. Mars is the first candidate because there are several lines of evidence that suggest that the geochemical conditions of the Archean Earth were similar to those of its early history (i.e., during the Noachian and probably part of Hesperian time) (Mc-

Kay, 1986; Chyba and McDonald, 1995). That is, it was a warm planet (warmer than now), with a CO_2 atmosphere where liquid water would have been widespread, most probably as the result of strong hydrothermal activity (Squyres and Kasting, 1994) leading to the formation of intrabasinal lakes in volcanic terrains. Therefore, primary Archean cherts might have counterparts in the remaining Noachian terrain on Mars, perhaps providing the conditions necessary to form silica biomorphs. It is noteworthy that geochemical studies of Martian meteorites (shergottites) indicate enrichment in barium and strontium with respect to rare earth elements, possibly suggesting preferential extraction of the alkaline earth elements from the rocks and subsequent transport by internal fluid. Because barium and strontium were likely to have been available in these alkaline silica-rich environments, silica biomorphs can be predicted to have formed on Mars, and because of the reduced weathering of the Mars crust, they may be widely distributed today on the Martian surface and subsurface.

The geological parallelism of the early history of Mars and Earth suggests also that life might have originated simultaneously on both planets and evolved until atmospheric conditions on Mars became too extreme for life to persist (McKay and Stoker, 1989; Davis and McKay, 1996). Testing this hypothesis requires a search for Martian microfossils (Farmer, 1995), a difficult task but one that may have been shortcut by McKay et al. (1996a). They collected different types of data from a Martian meteorite that, when considered collectively, they thought to indicate the existence of primitive life on Mars. Among these data, the existence of carbonate textures consistent with biological activity and the existence of microstructures that look like microfossils were crucial to their argument (McKay et al., 1996b). The ALH84001 meteorite studied by McKay and coworkers is basically made up of pyroxenes with olivine as a minor component. If we consider the abrasion pH of pyroxenes, i.e., the pH value obtained by hydrolysis of a mineral when ground in water (Stevens and Carron, 1948), the solution derived by leaching is alkaline, particularly at high temperatures. Shearer et al. (1996) measured the fractionated isotopic signature of sulfur in the pyrite identified in this meteorite and found values that support the existence of an alkaline hydrothermal system with a pH no lower than 8. If we assume that brines of pH 10 circulated through the olivine/pyroxene matrix, influx of CO_2 into the system would have decreased the pH and precipitated carbonate minerals in the meteorite fractures. Note that these are the right conditions to produce induced-morphology carbonate crystals. Therefore, the remarkable morphologies reminiscent of life forms observed in the carbonate globules of ALH84001 could be interpreted as the result of carbonate precipitation from alkaline silica-rich brines. For instance, see Plate II for carbonates globules and Figure 3 for ovoids and septated filaments in Dominguez–Bella and García-Ruiz (1983). Laboratory experiments to further test this explanation emulating plausible geochemical context for the carbonate found in the ALH84001 meteorite are under way.

SEARCH FOR FIELD EVIDENCE

To date, no natural occurrence of carbonate crystals with shapes and aggregation patterns controlled by silicate species has been reported in the literature on evaporites. Because of the low concentration of barium and strontium in contemporary waters—with the exception of some oilfield brines (White, 1967)—it is very unlikely that witherite and/or strontianite are precipitating from the few alkaline brines that exist today. On the contrary, calcium carbonate generally precipitates from these waters. However, finding observational evidence of calcite precipitation tailored by silicate species just by scanning the literature demonstrates the problem posed by the morphological similarities between biologically controlled and abiotically induced calcite crystallization as remarked above. Thus, we must consider only those cases where the role of organic matter or living organisms has been reasonably discarded. A good candidate appears in a site where the phenomenon was, in fact, predicted to occur (García-Ruiz, 1993), i.e., the African rift-valley lakes. Jones and Renaut (1995) recently described noncrystallographic calcite dendrites collected from Lake Bogoria (Kenya), which according to these authors appear to form by purely inorganic precipitation. These are multi-branched dendrites with curved branches (feather dendrites), as well as what the authors call scandulitic dendrites formed by stacking of plate-like crystals. These morphological patterns fit very well those displayed by induced-morphology crystal aggregates of $CaCO_3$. Both feather and scandulitic dendrites are coated with a mucus-like porous precipitate, in which Jones and Renaut found a high content of silica. Although the silica concentration of hot and warm spring waters feeding Lake Bogoria is close to 120 ppm, evaporation and possible further dissolution of silicates may increase the concentration. So, these bizarre forms may result from the interaction of silicic acid species and silicates with calcite surfaces, leading to the noncrystallographic behavior of the precipitates.

For past environments, again no reference has been found in the literature for witherite/strontianite precipitates. For the case of noncrystallographic calcite, the most likely candidate is the herringbone texture recently described in detail by Sumner and Grotzinger (1996). This is a mineral pattern that appears to be much more abundant and widely distributed in Archean than in Proterozoic rocks, suggesting a change in the physicochemical conditions of the marine precipitation system about 2.5 billion years ago. Herringbone calcite patterns are made up of bundles of fibrous calcite crystals that arise from growth centers that present two additional features: (1) noncrystallographic branching, i.e., they are dendritic crystals but the secondary branches do not form angles corresponding to specific interplanar angles of the calcite structure, instead they display a continuous change of curvature; and (2) a self-organized banding structure revealed as light and dark concentric layers with serrated profiles. On the basis of a theory proposed by Keith and Padden (1963), which was formally applied to spherulitic crystallization from melts, Sumner and Grotzinger (1996) suggested a mechanism for herringbone pattern formation that requires adsorption of impurities on specific crystal planes of the calcite structures. From further geochemical considerations, these authors suggested that Mn and Fe impurities are the most likely candidates responsible for the dendritic pattern. Nonspecific adsorption of impurities on crystal faces is known to provoke the sheaf-of-wheat morphology as an intermediate stage towards the characteristic spherulitic growth of chainfolded polymers studied by Keith and Padden, a mechanism that has also been applied to the growth of crystals from aqueous solution (Williamson, 1968). However, as Sumner and Grotzinger realized, this fails to explain the existence of self-organized banded structures in crystal aggregates. In addition, there is no experimental evidence that Mn and Fe tailor the morphology of calcite in such a way. The available information indicates self-organized zoning of the Mn atoms in calcite crystals maintaining the {104} rhombohedral crystal form (Reeder et al., 1990) and also the reduction of some growth faces (Dromgoole and Walter, 1990), but neither sheaf-of-wheat morphology nor the self-banded textures characteristic of herringbone patterns have been reported to occur as a result of the Fe/Mn tailoring.

Note that the noncrystallographic branching and the self-organized banding displayed by herringbone calcite are also characteristic of calcite crystallized into high-pH silica gels. This suggests that several questions need to be resolved before the origin of herringbone calcite can be clarified. Is gel (i.e., a viscous medium restricting mass transport processes) a requirement for the existence of self-organizing banding? Is polymeric organic matter able to force the precipitation of calcite with these peculiar features, as do silica-derived species? Is iron and/or manganese able to create such patterns under non-oxidation conditions? Currently, experimental evidence exists only for the case of silica, but there are a number of clues suggesting that other alternatives must also be experimentally tested. Under anoxic conditions, precipitation of ferrous carbonate could also produce patterns similar to those reported above for Ba, Sr, and Ca carbonates. We lack experimental evidence, but the precipitation structures found by Russell and Hall (1997) for iron sulfide support that hypothesis. Recently, Gower and Tirrell (1998) found the same aggregation pattern described here for barium and strontium carbonates when calcium carbonate is grown in the presence of charged polypeptides. Helical crystal aggregates made of (possibly) vaterite and calcite crystals with the same inhibition trends observed for silica-rich alkaline solutions were obtained in the presence of poly-aspartate.

The Case of Precambrian Microflora

The existence of a morphological convergence of inorganic biomorphs with primitive organisms creates a problem that requires separate discussion (see Cady, 1998). Since the pioneering work of Barghoon and Tyler (Tyler and Barghoon, 1954; Barghoon and Tyler, 1965), the search for remnants of primordial life has been performed by decoding both direct and indirect information found in the rocks. The accuracy of the indirect chemical fossils, such as aliphatic hydrocarbons and the fractional isotopic ratio (particularly ^{13}C to ^{12}C) thought to be characteristic of biological activity, is rather low. Although bearing interesting information, they do not provide an unambiguous signature of life, particularly for very old rocks, because postprecipitation processes may have altered the original signature. Mineral structures, such as stromatolites, known to result from biological activity and thought to be characteristic of the presence of living organisms, have recently been questioned by Grotzinger and Rothman (1996), who offer a set of four possible biotic and abiotic mechanisms fitting the fractal properties of stromatolitic structures. Thus, the search for definitive signals of primordial life today relies on the information stored in direct biological remnants. In practice, the absence of hard parts

and functional division in these very simple organisms (bacteria and cyanobacteria) reduces the identification to a morphological study. Thus, as revealed by the recent investigation of the ALH84001 Martian meteorite (McKay et al., 1996a; McKay et al., 1996b), the detection of primordial life may be reduced to the issue of deciphering when a morphological pattern is unequivocally biotic and not the result of an inorganic precipitation process (Cady, 1998).

During the search for biological remnants in Proterozoic and more recently in Archean rocks, micropaleontologists discovered a number of microstructures reminiscent of biological forms. To decipher the biogenic character of lifelike Precambrian microstructures there are a number of criteria (Buick, 1990) that any putative biological remnant must fulfill. On the basis of the degree of fulfillment of these criteria, such structures are classified into three main categories: actual fossils, dubious structures, and nonfossil structures (Schopf, 1983). The inorganic processes leading to biological-like morphologies has been discussed extensively in the paleontological literature. However, to the best of my knowledge, in none of the papers discussing the biogenicity of the Precambrian microstructures has the silica biomorph phenomenon been considered (see for instance, Cloud, 1973; Cloud and Morrison, 1979; Schopf and Walter (1983); Buick, 1990; Strother, 1992; Oehler and Schopf, 1971).

Some of the self-organized inorganic structures produced by the interaction of silicate solution with carbonate are morphologically similar to what are generally taken to be Precambrian microfossils (see figures in this paper and in García-Ruiz, 1994). In fact, the ability of colloidal silicates and other abiotic organic and inorganic materials to emulate life-like forms has been recognized for many years (Herrera, 1910; Leduc, 1914; Merek, 1973). This morphological similarity, close as it may be, is not, however, by itself a reason to propose silica biomorphs as an alternative for some of these Precambrian microstructures. Other reasons are: (1) their size, which varies from microns to millimeters depending on the chemical conditions, and size distribution, which is very narrow for specific experimental conditions; (2) their hollowness, which has been demonstrated above; and (3) their structured surface, which is a direct consequence of the formation mechanism itself. In addition, it is very significant that most of the Precambrian microfossils, particularly those from the Archean, are embedded in cherts. Those primary cherts forming from gel precursors are the right geochemical scenario required for the precipitation of silica biomorphs. Silica biomorphs made in silica-rich alkaline waters may be transported to locations where primary carbonate precipitation takes place, where they are engulfed. Cherts resulting from secondary replacement of carbonate rocks would maintain the silica biomorphs after silicification, as they do with living organisms. Finally, as discussed by García-Ruiz (1998), silica biomorphs may attach organic compounds, thus emulating the organic composition of actual microfossils. In relation with this, Ng and García-Ruiz (unpublished work) investigated the potential for uptake of aminoacids and nucleic acids by the inner compartment of silica biomorph. It was found that selective molecules of varying charges and sizes can be absorbed on the biomorph vesicle structure and taken up inside the vesicle lumen. The most notable preference for uptake was the arginine and lysine amino acids as well as the adenine nucleotide.

All these reasons make the formation of silica biomorphs a most powerful process to emulate highly complex biological-like micromorphologies in geochemically plausible scenarios. Leaving aside those microfossils preserved in phosphates (for instance, Xiao et al., 1998) and clays and perhaps those found in replacement cherts, it seems reasonable to reexamine the described Precambrian microflora with silica biomorphs in mind. Such a study should include those microstructures considered dubious fossils or nonfossils, for which an alternative explanation has not been offered, e.g., the globules and filamentary structures found by LaBerge (1967, 1973) in Precambrian iron formations and the forms described by McBride and Folk (1977, fig. 15) within chalcedony in the Caballos novaculite formation. Given the geochemical trend for the likelihood of alkaline environments to decrease in time, special attention should be paid to Archean cherts. Nevertheless, more recent cherts, such as those in the Gunflint (Cloud, 1965) and Bitter Spring Formations (Southgate, 1986), which may be primary chemical precipitates and were originally deposited at the time when the putative microbiota was embedded, should also be reconsidered.

CONCLUSIONS

The existence of purely inorganic mechanisms to produce carbonate precipitates that emulate in detail the shape of primitive organisms and the carbonate textures currently associated with life has been experimentally demonstrated. The ability of silicate species and silicic acid to modify the morphology and aggregation of carbonate crystals was demonstrated to work at an SiO_2 concentration as low as 250 ppm. Thus, the phenomenon of morphological induction of carbonate (calcite, witherite, and strontianite) crystals by silicate species at alkaline pH is plausible in some contemporary alkaline lakes. The fact that these mechanisms operate within geochemically plausible scenarios characteristic of the early stages of planetary development (interfaces between volcanic rocks and condensed water) introduces new complications when searching for ancient microbial life with morphological and textural tools. The search for field evidence of these inorganic structures is of interest because it may provide information on: (1) the chemistry of Precambrian waters, because the narrow range of pH where silica biomorphs and induced morphology crystal aggregates form make them useful geochemical markers; (2) the biological or abiotic character of Precambrian microstructures of debated origin; (3) the ability of chemical species derived from silica at high pH to emulate crystal patterns characteristic of biologically induced carbonates and the role that such an emulation might have in prebiotic chemistry; and (4) the correct interpretation of morphological and textural patterns in the context of the search for life on other planets.

ACKNOWLEDGMENTS

I would like to thank Miss Eva Herrera for assistance in laboratory work and Dr. Alicia Gonzalez Segura and Dr. Isabel Guerra Tschuschke for help with the scanning electron microscope. I also thank Francisco Higes-Rolando, Otto Kalim, Juli Pereto, Mike Russell, Graham Cairns-Smith, and John Grotzinger for very useful discussions on this subject. The manuscript was enhanced during the referee process by the suggestions of Roger Buick and Sherry L. Cady. Financial support from DGI-CYT of the Ministerio de Educación y Ciencia (Project PB94–0220) and from Junta de Andalucía are gratefully acknowledged.

REFERENCES

AIZENBERG, J., HANSON, J., ILAN, M., LEISROWITZ, L., KOETZLE, T. F., ADDADI, L., AND WEINER, S., 1995, Morphogenesis of calcite sponge spicules: a role for specialized proteins interacting with growing crystals: FASEB Journal, v. 9, p. 262–268.

ALBECK, S., AIZENBERG, J., ADDADI, L., AND WEINER, S., 1993, Interactions of various skeletal intracrystalline components with calcite crystals: American Chemical Society Journal, v. 115, p. 11,691–11,697.

ALEXANDER, G. B., HESTON W. M., AND ILER, R. K., 1954, The solubility of amorphous silica in water: Journal of Physical Chemistry, v. 58, p. 453–455.

ALVAREZ R., AND SPARKS, D. L., 1985, Polymerization of silicate anions in solutions at low temperature: Nature, v. 318, p. 649–651.

BAIRD, T., BRATERMAN, P., CHEN, P., GARCÍA-RUIZ, J. M., PEACOK, R., AND REID, A., 1992, Morphology of gel–grown barium carbonate aggregates—pH effect on control by a silicate–carbonate membrane: Materials Research Bulletin, v. 27, p. 1031–1040.

BARGHOON, E. S., AND TYLER, S. A., 1965, Microorganisms from the Gunflint chert: Science, v. 147, p. 563–577.

BELCHER, A. M., WU, X. H., CHRISTENSEN, R. J., HANSMA, P. K., STUCKY, G. D., AND MORSE, D. E., 1996, Control of crystal phase switching and orientation by soluble molusc-shell proteins: Nature, v. 381, p. 56–58.

BIRCHALL, J. D., HOWARD, A. J., AND DOUBLE, D. D., 1980, Some general considerations of a membrane/osmosis model for Portland cement hydration: Cement and Concrete Research, v. 10, p. 145–155.

BRASIER, M., GREEN, O., AND SHIELDS, G., 1997, Ediacarian sponge spicule clusters from southwestern Mongolia and the origins of the Cambrian fauna: Geology, v. 25, p. 289–384.

BUCZYNSKI, C., AND CHAFETZ, H. S., 1991, Habit of bacterially induced precipitates of calcium carbonate and the influence of medium viscosity on mineralogy: Journal of Sedimentary Petrology, v. 61, p. 226–233.

BUICK, R., 1990, Microfossil recognition in Archean rocks: An appraisal of spheroids and filaments from a 3500 m.y. old chert–barite unit at North Pole, western Australia: Palaios, v. 5, p. 441–459.

BUICK, R., AND DUNLOP, J. S. R., 1990, Evaporitic sediments of Early Archean age from the Warrawoona Group, North Pole, Western Australia: Sedimentology, v. 37, p. 247–277.

CADY, S. L., 1998, Astrobiology: A new frontier for 21st century paleontologists: Palaios, v. 13, p. 95–97.

CHAFETZ, H. S., AND FOLK, R. L., 1984, Travertines: Depositional morphology and the bacterially constructed constituents: Journal of Sedimentary Petrology, v. 54, p. 289–216.

CHYBA, C. F., AND MCDONALD, G. D., 1995, The origin of life in the solar system: current issues: Annual Review of Earth and Planetary Sciences, v. 23, p. 215–249.

CLOUD, P. E., 1965, Significance of the Gunflint (Precambrian) microflora: Science, v. 148, p. 27–35.

CLOUD, P. E., 1973, Pseudofossils: a plea for caution: Geology, v. 1, p. 123–127.

CLOUD, P. E., AND MORRISON, K., 1979, On microbial contaminants, micropseudofossils, and the oldest records of life: Precambrian Research, v. 9, p. 81–91.

COATMAN, R. D., THOMAS, N. L., AND DOUBLE, D. D., 1980, Studies on the growth of "silicate gardens" and related phenomena: Journal of Materials Science, v. 15, p. 2017-2026.

DAVIS, S. N., 1964, Silica in streams and ground water: American Journal of Science, v. 262, p. 870–891.

DAVIS, W. L., AND MCKAY, C. P., 1996, Origins of life: A comparison of theories and application to Mars: Origins of Life and Evolution of the Biosphere, v. 26, p. 61–73.

DOMINGUEZ BELLA, S., 1986. Estudio morfológico y textural de agregados cristalinos de morfología inducida de CaCO₃. [unpublished Ph.D. dissertation]: Universidad Complutense, Madrid, 340 p.

DOMINGUEZ-BELLA, S., AND GARCÍA-RUIZ, J. M., 1983, Agregados cristalinos de morfología inducida de carbonato de calcio. I. Secuencias morfológicas a pH 10: Real Sociedad Española de Historia Natural (Geología), Boletín, v. 81, p. 173–185.

DOMÍNGUEZ BELLA, S. AND GARCÍA-RUIZ, J. M., 1986, Textures in induced morphology crystal aggregates of $CaCO_3$: Sheaf of wheat aggregates: Journal of Crystal Growth, v. 79, p. 236–240.

DOMÍNGUEZ BELLA, S., AND GARCÍA-RUIZ, J. M., 1987, Banding structures in induced morphology crystal aggregates of $CaCO_3$: Journal of Materials Science, v. 22, p. 3095–3102.

DOUBLE, D. D., 1983, New developments in understanding the chemistry of cement hydration: Royal Society [London], Philosophical Transactions, v. A310, p. 53–66.

DROMGOOLE, E. L., AND WALTER, L. M., 1990, Inhibition of calcite growth rates by Mn^{2+} in $CaCl_2$ solutions at 10, 25, and 50°C: Geochimica et Cosmochimica Acta, v. 54, p. 2991–3000.

EUGSTER, H. P., 1969, Hydrous sodium silicate from Magadi Lake, Kenya: Precursors of bedded cherts: Science, v. 157, p. 1177–1179.

EUGSTER, H. P., AND JONES, B. F., 1968, Gels composed of sodium–alumnium silicate, lake Magadi, Kenya: Science, v. 161, p. 160–164.

EUGSTER, H. P., AND CHOU, I.-M., 1973, The depositional environment of Precambrian iron formation: Economic Geology, v. 68, p. 1144–1168.

FARMER, V. C., ed., 1974, Infrared Spectra of Minerals: London, Mineralogical Society of London, 539 p.

FARMER, J. D., 1995, Mars exopaleontology: Palaios, v. 10, p. 3–4.

FETH, J. H., ROGERS, S. M., AND ROBERSON, C. E., 1961, Aqua de Ney, California, a spring of unique chemical character: Geochimica et Cosmochimica Acta, v. 22, p. 75–86.

FOLK, R. L., CHAFETZ, H. S. AND TIEZZI, P., 1985, Bizarre forms of depositional and diagenetic calcite in hot-spring travertines, central Italy, in, Schneidermann, N., and Harris, P.M., eds., Carbonate Cements: SEPM, Special Publication 36, p. 349–369.

FOLK, R. L., 1993, SEM imaging of bacteria and nannobacteria in carbonate sediments and rocks: Journal of Sedimentary Petrology, v. 63, p. 990–999.

FUJI, K., AND KONDO, W., 1981, Heterogeneous equilibrium of calcium silicate hydrate in water at 30°C: Chemical Society Journal, Dalton, v. 2, p. 645–651.

GARCÍA-RUIZ, J. M., 1980, Teoría del crecimiento de cristales en geles. Precipitación polimórfica y agregados cristalinos de morfología inducida [unpublished Ph.D. dissertation]: Universidad Complutense, Madrid, 380 p.

GARCÍA-RUIZ, J. M., 1985, On the formation of induced morphology crystal aggregates: Journal of Crystal Growth, v. 73, p. 251–262.

GARCÍA-RUIZ, J. M., 1994, Inorganic self-organisation in Precambrian cherts: Origins of Life and Evolution of the Biosphere, v. 24, p. 451–467.

GARCÍA-RUIZ, J. M., AND MORENO, A., 1997, On the growth mechanism of twisted ribbons of barium carbonate: Anales de Química International Edition, v. 93, p. 1–2.

GARCÍA-RUIZ, J. M., 1998, Carbonate precipitation into alkaline silica-rich environments: Geology, v. 26, p. 843–846.

GARCÍA-RUIZ, J. M., AND AMORÓS, J. L., 1981a, Morphological aspects of some symmetrical crystal aggregates grown by silica gel technique: Journal of Crystal Growth, v. 55, p. 379–83.

GARCÍA-RUIZ, J. M., AND AMORÓS, J. L., 1981b, Crystal aggregates with induced morphologies grown by silica gel technique: Bulletin Mineralogique, v. 104, p. 107–113.

GARRELS, R. M., AND CHRIST, C. L., 1965, Solutions, Minerals and Equilibria: New York, Harper & Row, 450 p.

GARRELS, R. M., AND MACKENZIE, F. T., 1971, Evolution of Sedimentary Rocks: New York, W. W. Norton & Co., 397 p.

GOWER, L. A., AND TIRRELL, D. A., 1998, Calcium carbonate films and helices grown in solutions of poly-aspartate): Journal of Crystal Growth, v. 191, p. 153–160.

GROTZINGER, J. P., AND KASTING, J. F., 1993, New constraints on Precambrian ocean composition: Journal of Geology, v. 101, p. 235–243.

GOTZINGER, J. P., AND ROTHMAN, D. H., 1996, An abiotic model for stromatolite morphogenesis: Nature, v. 383, p. 423–425.

HERRERA, A. L., 1910, Sur la vie apparente de corpuscules obtenues par évaporation de solutions de silice et de carbonate de calcium dans l'eau saturée d'acide carbonique: Sociedad Científica A. Alzate, Memoria, v. 29, p. 43–67.

HOLLAND, H. D., AND KASTING, J. F., 1992, The environment of the Archean Earth, in Schopf, J. W., and Klein, C., eds., The Proterozoic Biosphere: Cambridge, U.K., Cambridge University Press, p. 21–24.

ICOLE, M., AND PERINET, G., 1984, Les silicates sodiques et les milieux carbonat's bicarbonat's sodiques: une revue: Revue de Géologie Dynamique et de Géographie Physique, v. 26, p. 167–176.

ILER, R. K., 1979, The Chemistry of Silica: New York, Wiley, 866 p.

JONES, B., AND KAHLE, C. F., 1986, Dendritic calcite crystals formed by calcification of algal filaments in a vadose environment: Journal of Sedimentary Petrology, v. 56, p. 217–227.

JONES, B., AND RENAUT, R. W., 1995, Non-crystallographic calcite dendrites from hot-spring deposits at lake Bogoria, Kenya: Journal of Sedimentary Research, v. A65, p. 154–169.

JONES, B. F., RETTIG, S. L., AND EUGSTER, H. P., 1967, Silica in alkaline brines: Science, v. 158, p. 1310–1314.

KASTING, J. K., 1993, Earth's early biosphere: Science, v. 259, p. 920–926.

KEITH, H. D., AND PADDEN, F. J., 1963, A phenomenological theory of spherulitic crystallization: Journal of Applied Physics, v. 34, p. 2409–2421.

KEMPE, S., AND DEGENS, E. T., 1985, An early soda ocean?: Chemical Geology, v. 53, p. 95–108.

KNAUTH, L. P., 1994, Petrogenesis of cherts, in Heaney, P. J., Prewitt, C. T., and Gibbs, G. V., eds., Silica: Reviews in Mineralogy, v. 29, p. 233–256.

KRAUSKOPF, K. B., 1956, Dissolution and precipitation of silica at low temperatures: Geochimica et Cosmochimica Acta, v. 10, p. 1–26.

KRAUSKOPF, K. B., 1979, Introduction to Geochemistry, 2nd Edition: New York, McGraw–Hill, 617 p.

LABERGE, G. L., 1967, Microfossils and Precambrian iron formations: Geological Society of America, Bulletin, v. 78, p. 331–342.

LABERGE, G. L., 1973, Possible biological origin of Precambrian iron-formations: Economic Geology, v. 68, p. 1098–1109.

LEDUC, S., 1914, The Mechanisms of Life: New York, Rebman Co., 172 p.

MACKENZIE, F. T., GARRELS, R. M., BRICKER, O. P., AND BICKLEY, F., 1967, Silica in sea water: control by silica minerals: Science, v. 155, p. 1404–1405.

MAISONNEUVE, J., 1982, The composition of the Precambrian ocean waters: Sedimentary Geology, v. 31, p. 1–11.

McBRIDE, E. F., AND FOLK, R. L., 1977, The Caballos novaculite revisited: Part II: Chert and shale members and synthesis: Journal of Sedimentary Petrology, v. 47, p. 1261–1286.

MALIVA R. G., KNOLL, A. H., AND SIEVER, R., 1989, Secular change in chert distribution: A reflection of evolving biological participation in the silica cycle: Palaios, v. 4, p. 519–532

MANN, S., ed., 1996, Biomimetic Materials Chemistry: New York, VCH Publishers, 383 p.

McKAY, C. P., 1986, Exobiology and future Mars missions: the search for Mars earliest biosphere: Advances in Space Research, v. 6, p. 269–285.

McKAY, C. P., AND STOKER, C. R., 1989, The early environment and its early evolution on Mars: Reviews of Geophysics, v. 27, p. 189–214.

McKAY, D. S., GIBSON, E. K., JR., THOMAS–KEPRTA, K. L., VALI, H., ROMANEK, C. S., CLEMMETT, S. J., CHILLIER, X. D. F., MAECHLING, C. R., AND ZARE, R. N., 1996a, Search for past life in Mars: Possible relic biogenic activity in Martian meteorite ALH84001: Science, v. 273, p. 924–930.

McKAY, D. S., THOMAS–KEPRTA, K. L., ROMANEK, C. S., GIBSON, E. K., JR., AND VALI, H., 1996b, Evaluating the evidence for past life in Mars; Response: Science, v. 374, p. 2123–2124.

MEREK, E. L., 1973, Imaging and life detection: Bioscience, v. 23, p. 153–159.

MINAMI, M., SHIMIZU, H., MASUDA, A., AND ADACHI, M., 1995, Two Archean Sm–Nd ages of 3.2 and 2.5 Ga for the Marble bar chert, Warrawoona group, Pilbara block, Western Australia: Geochemical Journal, v. 29, p. 347–362.

MURAISHI, H., 1989, Crystallization of silica gel in alkaline solutions at 100–180°C: Characterization of SiO_2–Y by comparison with magadiite: American Mineralogist, v. 74, p. 1147–1151.

NITTMANN, J., DACCORD, G., AND STANLEY, G., 1985, Fractal growth of viscous fingers: quantitative characterization of a fluid instability phenomenon: Nature, v. 314, p. 141–144.

OEHLER, J. H., AND SCHOPF, J. W., 1971, Artificial microfossils: Experimental studies of permineralization of blue–green algae in silica: Science, v. 174, p. 1229–1231.

OTTEWILL, R. H., 1983, Chemistry of colloidal silicates and cements: Royal Society [London], Philosophical Transactions, v. A310, p. 67–78.

PENTECOST, A., 1990, The formation of travertine shrubs, Mammoth hot springs, Wyoming: Geological Magazine, v. 127, p. 159–168.

REEDER, R. J., FAGIOLI, R. D., AND MEYER, W. J., 1990, Oscillatory zoning of Mn in solution grown calcite crystals: Earth-Science Reviews, v. 29, p. 39–46.

RUSSELL, M. J., AND HALL, A. J., 1997, The emergence of life from iron monosulphide bubbles at a submarine hydrothermal redox and pH front: Geological Society of London, Journal, v. 154, p. 377–402.

SAFFMAN, P. G. AND TAYLOR, G., 1958, The penetration of a fluid into a medium or Hele-Shaw cell containing a more viscous liquid: Royal Society [London], Proceedings, v. A245, p. 312–329.

SCHOPF, W., ed., 1983, Earth's Earliest Biosphere: Princeton, New Jersey, Princeton University Press, 543 p.

SCHOPF, W., AND WALTER, M. R., 1983, Archean microfossils: New evidence of ancient microbes, *in* Schopf, J. W., ed., Earth's Earliest Biosphere: Princeton, New Jersey, Princeton University Press, p. 214–239.

SHEARER, C. K., LAYNE, G. D., PAPIKE, J. J., AND SPILDE, M. N., 1996, Sulfur isotopic systematics in alteration assemblages in martian meteorite Allan Hills 84001: Geochimica et Cosmochimica Acta, v. 60, p. 2921–2926.

SIEVER, R., 1957, The silica budget in the sedimentary cicle: American Mineralogist, v. 42, p. 821–841.

SIEVER, R., 1992, The silica cycle in the Precambrian: Geochimica et Cosmochimica Acta, v. 56, p. 3265–3272.

SIEVER, R., AND SCOTT, R., 1963, Silica solubility, 0–200°C, and the diagenesis of siliceous sediments: Journal of Geology, v. 70, p. 127–150.

SIMKISS, K., 1986, The process of biomineralization in lower plants and animals—anoverview, *in* Leadbeater, B. S. C., and Riding, R., eds., Biomineralization in Lower Plants and Animals: Oxford, U.K., Clarendon Press, p. 19–37.

SOUTHGATE, P. N., 1986, Depositional environment and mechanism of preservation of microfossils, upper Proterozoic Bitter Spring formation, Australia: Geology, v. 14, p. 683–686.

SQUYRES, S. W., AND KASTING, F., 1994, Early Mars: how warm and how wet: Science v. 265, p. 744–749.

STEVENS, R. E., AND CARRON, M. K., 1948, Simple field test for distinguishing minerals by abrasion pH: American Mineralogist, v. 33, p. 31–49.

STROTHER, P., 1992, Evidence of earliest life, *in* Margulis, L., and Olendzenski, L., eds, Environmental Evolution: Cambridge, Massachusetts, MIT Press, p. 87–101.

SUMNER, D. Y., AND GROTZINGER, J. P., 1996, Herringbone calcite: petrography and environmental significance: Journal of Sedimentary Research, v. 66, p. 419–429.

TYLER, S. A., AND BARGHOORN, E. S., 1954, The occurrence of structurally preserved plants in Precambrian rocks of the Canadian Shield: Science, v. 119, p. 606–608.

VEIZER, J., HOEFS, J., LOWE, D. R., AND THURSTON, P. C., 1989, Geochemistry of Precambrian carbonates: II. Archean Greenstone belts and Archean sea waters: Geochimica et Cosmochimica Acta, v. 53, p. 859–871.

WALKER, J. G., 1983, Possible limits on the composition of the Archean ocean: Nature, v. 302, p. 518–520.

WALKER, J. G., AND BRIMBLECOMBE, P., 1985, Iron and sulphur in the prebiologic ocean: Precambrian Research, v. 28, p. 205–222.

WHITE, D. E., BRANNOCK, W. W., AND MURATA, K. J., 1956, Silica in hot-spring waters: Geochimica et Cosmochimica Acta, v. 10, p. 27–59.

WHITE, D. E., 1967, Magmatic, connate and metamorphic waters: Geological Society of America, Bulletin, v. 68, p. 1659–1682.

WILLIAMS, R. J. P., 1984, An introduction to biominerals and the role of organic molecules in their formation: Royal Society [London], Philosophical Transactions, v. B304, p. 411–424.

WILLIAMS, L. A., AND CRERAR, D. A., 1985, Silica diagenesis, II. General mechanisms: Journal of Sedimentary Petrology, v. 55, p. 312–321.

WILLIAMSON, R. B., 1968, Constitutional supersaturation in Portland Cement solidified by hydration: Journal of Crystal Growth, v. 3–4, p. 787–794.

XIAO, S., ZHANG, Y., AND KNOLL, A. H., 1998, Three-dimensional preservation of algae and animal embryos in a Neoproteorozoic phosphorite: Science, v. 391, p. 553-558.

BIOLOGICAL AND MINERAL COMPONENTS OF AN ANCIENT STROMATOLITE: GAOYUZHUANG FORMATION, MESOPROTEROZOIC OF CHINA

LEE SEONG-JOO
Department of Earth System Sciences, Yonsei University, Seoul, Korea
AND
STJEPKO GOLUBIC
Biological Science Center, Boston University, Boston, Massachusetts 02215, U.S.A.

ABSTRACT: Silicified Mesoproterozoic stratiform stromatolites of the ca. 1400 Ma Gaoyuzhuang Formation in northern China contain microbial fossils preserved in a synsedimentary context rich in carbonate precipitates. Benthic microbial fossils were preserved by early silicification in growth position. Carbonate precipitation took place concurrently with accumulation of fine-grained sediment, and within the time frame of microbial growth and movements. The kinetics of the sedimentary process is thus calibrated by the rates commensurate with the behavioral responses of ancient microorganisms. Since both mineral and organic components of these ancient stromatolites remained preserved, their mutual relationship could be assessed. Extensive microbial growth, mat formation, and accumulation of organic matter required time and indicated the extent of sedimentary pauses. Carbonate precipitation took place in the absence of microorganisms, inhibiting their successful colonization and growth. The interplay between biological and abiotic forces in the formation of Gaoyuzhuang stromatolite permits an approximation of actual rate of carbonate precipitation, which often exceeds that of microbial settlement and growth. The relationship between microbial growth and precipitates in stromatolites under study is generally antagonistic, indicating limited involvement of microbial activities in the precipitation process.

INTRODUCTION

Since Kalkowsky (1908) defined the terms oolite and stromatolite, applications of these terms have vacillated between genetic and descriptive (cf. Krumbein, 1983; Ginsburg, 1991). Kalkowsky understood stromatolites (as well as oolites) to be organo-sedimentary structures, the genesis of which involved microorganismal participation, although the fossil materials (Buntsandstein Formation, Lower Triassic of Germany) on which his descriptions and definitions were based did not contain any preserved microorganisms. His conclusions about stromatolite genesis, although convincing, were conjectural. Actual interactions between microorganisms and sediments in the formation of stromatolitic structures were studied much later on presumed modern counterparts (reviewed by Golubic, 1991). Such interactions are supposed to involve trapping and binding of mineral particles as well as mineral precipitation (Awramik and Margulis, 1974; Awramik et al., 1976). The latter process invokes the question of biomineralization, requiring determination of the nature and the degree of biological control over the process of mineral formation. The more recent formulations define a stromatolite in more general terms as an "accretion product of the on-going interaction between the organisms of the mat community and the physical process of sedimentation" (Knoll, 1986, p. 118). The implication is that the degree of microbial participation may vary and, thus, needs to be determined from case to case. A significant proportion of Archean and early Proterozoic stromatolitic structures have recently been interpreted as rhythmic precipitates that formed with little or no direct microbial participation (Grotzinger, 1989b; Grotzinger and Knoll, 1995).

In geological practice, the stromatolites are usually encountered as laminated rocks, recognizable on the basis of their macromorphology and microtextural properties (Walter, 1976; Walter et al., 1992). The majority of ancient stromatolites are preserved as carbonate rocks, but their original mineralogy is usually altered by diagenetic recrystallizations (aragonite-to-calcite conversions, dolomitization, or metamorphism). Remains of microorganisms in these ancient stromatolitic structures are rarely recognizable, so that the microbial origins are implied rather than observed.

Ancient stromatolites in which both sedimentary fabrics and the resident microorganisms remained preserved by early silicification offer an opportunity to study the relations between microorganisms and the surrounding sediments (cf. Hofmann, 1975; Knoll and Golubic, 1979). In the current contribution, we present a case where early silicification of Mesoproterozoic stratiform stromatolites preserved *in situ*, both microbial fossils and synsedimentary mineral formations, including the evidence of periodic massive carbonate precipitation. The dynamics of the sedimentary process is thus "frozen in time" disclosing an interplay between biological and mineral components in the course of the formation of an ancient stromatolite.

GEOLOGICAL SETTING, MATERIALS, AND METHODS

Stromatolitic chert samples were collected from the Mesoproterozoic Gaoyuzhuang Formation near the area of Pangjapu Iron Mine in Hebei Province, about 115 km northwest of Beijing, northern China (Fig. 1). In this region, the Gaoyuzhuang Formation forms a 900 m thick succession of dolostones, dolomitic shales, siltstones, and manganiferous dolostones. It is underlain conformably by the Dahongyu Formation and overlain disconformably by the Wumishan Formation (see Zhang, 1981, for details). Radiometric dating based on Pb–Pb isotope analysis of galena, obtained from the upper part of the Gaoyuzhuang Formation, yielded an average age of 1434 ± 50 Ma (Zhong, 1977; Chen et al., 1980; Yu and Zhang, 1985). The succession is divided in members I–VI (Fig. 1, right). Cherts are found throughout the formation, but are especially abundant and fossiliferous in members I and II, where they are associated with distinctive domal to columnar stromatolites which developed above the fossiliferous chert layers. The depositional paleoenvironment is interpreted as peritidal, possibly representing small intertidal pools. Evaporitic conditions and subaerial exposure are indicated by the abundance of precipitates and fenestral structures in the sediment. This interpretation is consistent with microfossil composition (cf. Knoll et al., 1991; Sergeev, 1993). Microfossil assemblages include organisms which were protected from excessive radiation by extracellular pigmentation and have modern intertidally occurring ana-

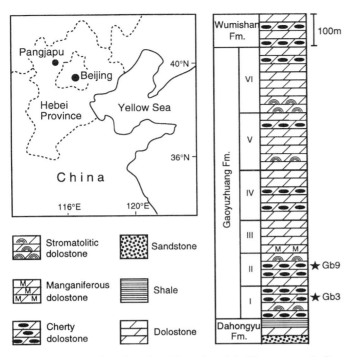

FIG. 1.—Geographic and stratigraphic setting of the Mesoproterozoic Gao-yuzhuang Formation in northern China. Horizon of stromatolitic cherts containing *in situ*–preserved microbial fossils and mineral precipitates are marked by asterisks.

logues. The fossiliferous cherts are characterized by flat to wavy millimeter-scale lamination.

Petrographic thin sections were cut perpendicular to lamination and analyzed with a Zeiss Universal microscope using transmitted plain and cross-polarized light. Samples from two stratigraphic horizons (Gb 3 and 9), which exhibit considerable concentrations of *in situ* preserved microorganisms, were analyzed in detail for the purpose of the present contribution. Petrographic thin sections are stored in the collection of the Biological Science Center at Boston University, slide numbers: Gb92-3b and Gb92-4c (precipitates); Gb31-1a (*Eoentophysalis*); Gb92-4b and Gb92-1a (*Coccostratus*); Gb92-4b and Gb92-1a (*Siphonophycus*); Gb94–2a, 2b, and 2c (multitrichmous filaments).

RESULTS

Petrographic Relations Preserved in Cherts

Petrographic thin sections of a silicified stratiform laminated rock, cut perpendicular to the bedding plane, reveal discrete wavy to billowy lamination of alternating organic-rich and mineral-rich layers. The original orientation of both organic and mineral elements remained preserved in these stromatolites, embedded in a mineral matrix of microquartz and, less commonly, chalcedony. The mineral textures of replacement silica are revealed in cross-polarized light, whereas plain-transmitted-light microscopy shows microorganismal remains as well as the outlines of the original carbonate minerals. Well-preserved, darkly outlined microbial fossils appear to be oriented in growth position, suggesting an early onset of silicification accompanied

by little or no disturbance of the original interrelationships between microbial populations and the surrounding sediment. Early silicification and burial preserved the sedimentary context as it was set within a few millimeters of the ancient sediment–water interfaces. An early onset of silicification is also supported by the presence of uncompacted pores and fenestral voids in the sediment. These appear clear in transmitted light, showing primary silica fill with centripetal increase in grain size (Fig. 2A), or centripetal fibrous chalcedony when viewed in cross-polarized light (Fig. 2B). Some of these spaces demonstrate undisturbed growth of carbonate botryoid cements (cf. Ross, 1991), which were later replaced by silica (Fig. 2C). Carbonate and organic fabrics are both embedded in a microquartz matrix, which also surrounds the fenestrae (Fig. 2D). Organic-

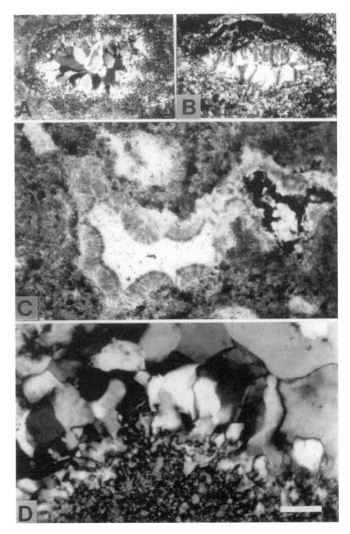

FIG. 2.—Chert mineral composition: microquartz is embedding and replacing carbonate sediment and enclosing microfossils, whereas megaquartz and chalcedony fills the fenestrae. A) Fenestral void fill with centripetally increasing megaquartz grain size. B) A void filled with length-fast chalcedony. C) A large fenestra with marginal growth of primary carbonate botryoid cement. D) Edge of a fenestra showing a gradient in sizes of quartz grains. A, B, and D are in cross-polarized light; C in plain transmitted light. Scale bar in D is 50 μm for A–C and 10 μm for D.

rich laminae are composed of microbial mats of prostrate filamentous microfossils, whereas sediment-rich laminae contain numerous local precipitates with fewer, interspersed, mostly vertically oriented microfossils. Crystallization and recrystallization processes in silica proved to be less destructive to the preexisting textures, as compared with carbonate minerals, preserving the remains of microorganisms, as well as the outlines of earlier mineral precipitates. However, synsedimentary carbonate precipitation did provide a rigid support to the sediment prior to silicification, and was apparently instrumental for *in situ* preservation of microfossils (cf. Sergeev et al., 1995). The chert provided a stable medium for preservation of biogenic and mineral fabrics with a minimum of diagenetic alterations. No microfossils were found in carbonate rocks outside chert areas. Carbonate in the chert is present as large, late diagenetic crystals of dolomite, with intact edges, which locally interfere with silica and destroy the embedded fabrics (cf. Hofmann, 1976).

Preserved Microbiota

Populations of coccoid microfossils form dense cellular masses, concentrated in convex-upward hemispherical colonies, interspersed in sediment or fused laterally into contiguous billowy mats (Fig. 3A). Individual coccoid units consist of simple cellular outlines (Fig. 3B) or of multiple encapsulated cellular outlines (Fig. 3C, D), locally including single or paired, isodiametric or elongated granules (Fig. 3E). These outlines are best interpreted as cyanobacterial exopolymer envelopes, which locally contain shriveled remains of cells (Golubic and Barghoorn, 1977). Convex-upward bumps and protrusions of the dark coccoid mat surface identify the areas of most intense microbial growth, whereas the pale or hollow interiors of individual colonies appear to be caused by bacterial decomposition of older mat parts (Fig. 3F). The colonies and mats are always darker pigmented on their upper surfaces, comparable to the modern *Entophysalis* mats (Golubic and Hofmann, 1976). Dark surface pigmentation in many modern subaerial and mat-forming cyanobacteria is caused by the extracellular pigment scytonemine, which protects the cell from excessive light and UV radiation (Garcia-Pichel and Castenholz, 1991). This protection was particularly important during early Proterozoic times, when lower atmospheric oxygen levels produced a weaker ozone shield (Garcia-Pichel, 1998). Microfossils, which dominate Gaoyuzhuang coccoid assemblages, are *Eoentophysalis belcherensis* Hofmann (1976) and *Coccostratus dispergens* Seong-Joo and Golubic (1999).

Populations of filamentous microfossils form mats and networks of intertwined simple and bundled tubules (Fig. 4). These tubules are best interpreted as empty cyanobacterial sheaths (Golubic and Barghoorn, 1977), which may contain rows of cell remains in various stages of shrinkage and separation (cf. Knoll and Golubic, 1979; Seong-Joo and Golubic 1998). In the sediment-rich layers, the sheaths are mostly upright and simple (Fig. 4A). In contrast, the organic-rich layers are composed of mostly horizontally spread mats of tubular filaments, including simple and enveloped tubules, as well as bundled, double, triple, and multiple tubules inside a common external sheath (Fig. 4B). Most tubules have conspicuously clear lumens (Fig. 4C). The interior diameters of these tubules fall consistently into the same narrow size range of 3–6 µm, probably representing the closest approximation of the original width of cellular trichomes that produced them. Narrow size distribution and smooth transitions between prostrate and erect filaments support the interpretation that these filamentous fossils probably represent a single biological taxon, with closest affinity to modern multitrichomous cyanobacteria of the type of *Schizothrix* and *Microcoleus* (Seong-Joo and Golubic, 1998). Alternative possible taxonomic affinities to heterotrophic bacteria or sheathed sulfur-oxidizing bacteria are unlikely. Filamentous microfossils, which dominate in these assemblages, are *Siphonophycus inornatum* Zhang (1981) and *Eoschizothrix composita* Seong-Joo and Golubic (1998).

Preserved Mineral Deposits

Sediment-rich layers in this sequence abound with autochthonous mineral precipitates that grew in place, excluding organic matter and microorganisms in the process. These textured mineral fabrics are best interpreted as outlines of originally aragonitic crystal fans precipitated in shallow hypersaline pools. Acicular aragonite was apparently directly replaced by silica, preserving the outlines of individual crystals and crystal aggregates (cf. Grotzinger and Read, 1983; Hofmann and Jackson, 1987; Seong-Joo and Golubic, 1999).

Textured grains include radiating spheroid and botryoid clusters, single and stacked upward-radiating fans, and crustous mineral coatings (Figs. 5, 6). The internal texture of all these grains consists of fine, straight, reddish-brown fibers radiating from point sources. The intensity of coloration of radiating fibers changes in rhythmic pulses, resulting in concentric darker and lighter growth zones, without interrupting the course of individual fibrous crystals (Fig. 5A). Fibers in spheroid and botryoid grains radiate in all directions (Fig. 6A); they are upward-radiating in crystal fans (Fig. 6B) and more or less upward-parallel in crustous coatings (Fig. 5B). Frequent interpenetration of these fibers along contacts between two adjacent grains identifies them as outlines of individual radiating needle-like crystals (Fig. 5C). All textured grains are conspicuously free of microbial fossils. Incorporation of single fossils or fossil fragments is rare and marginal (cf. Hofmann and Jackson, 1987).

There are numerous transitions between different mineral structures, indicating that they are parts of a single, continuous process. Botryoid clusters represent the early stages. They are commonly located directly on top of organic-rich layers, and underneath upward radiating fans (Fig. 6B). They regularly contain discrete dark nucleation centers. Crystal nucleation centers in botryoid spherulites contain pseudomorphs to the initial aragonitic crystal bundles, dumbbells, and paired hemispheres (Fig. 6E, F, G). A primary acicular crystal or bundle of parallel needles generates at both poles a secondary, divergent burst of needles, which fan out into a dumbbell-shaped body (Fig. 6E) and then, by increasing the angle of divergence, a paired hemisphere bundle is formed radiating in all directions (Fig. 6G). Crossing of initial needle crystals (cf. Castanier, 1987, Pl. A, fig. 6) may generate two intersecting dumbbells and form a rosette (Fig. 6F). Further crystal growth is radial and continuous, forming spherulites with concentric growth zones.

We have studied comparable initial crystal formations of aragonite precipitates in carbonate-saturated Mammouth Hot

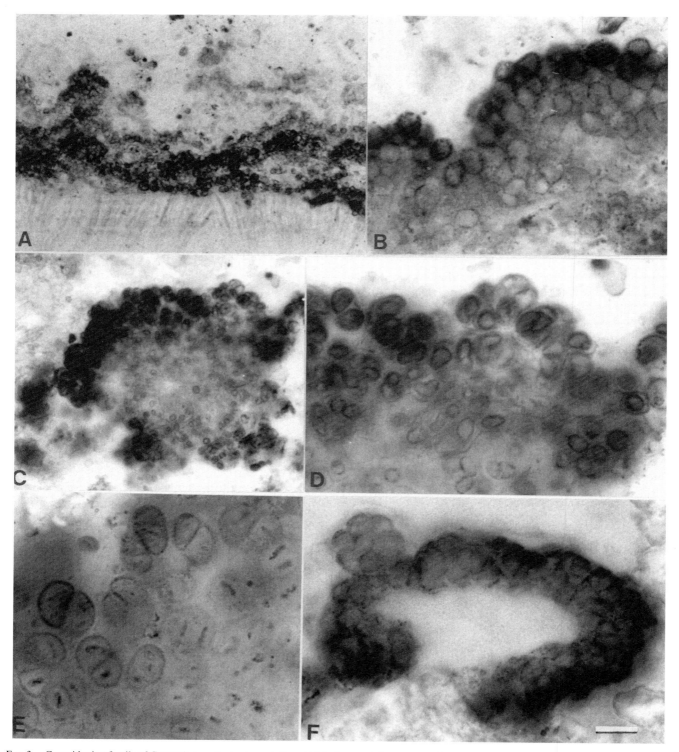

FIG. 3.—Coccoid microfossils of Gaoyuzhuang cherty stromatolites. A) Mat layers of *Coccostratus dispergens* Seong-Joo and Golubic growing on and above the surface of a crystal fan. B) Detail of A, showing simple cellular units with protective pigmentation concentrated along the upper surface of the mat. C) A colony of *Eoentophysalis belcherensis* Hofmann, preserved in growth position, with distinctive protective pigmentation staining the periphery of the colony. D) Detail of B, showing encapsulated multiple envelopes. E) Detail from a different colony in which shriveled remains of *Eoentophysalis* cells, arrested in different stages of cell division, are enclosed within envelopes. F) A colony of *Eoentophysalis* with hollow interior showing signs of structural degradation. Scale bar in F is 25 μm for A and C, and 10 μm for B, D, E, and F.

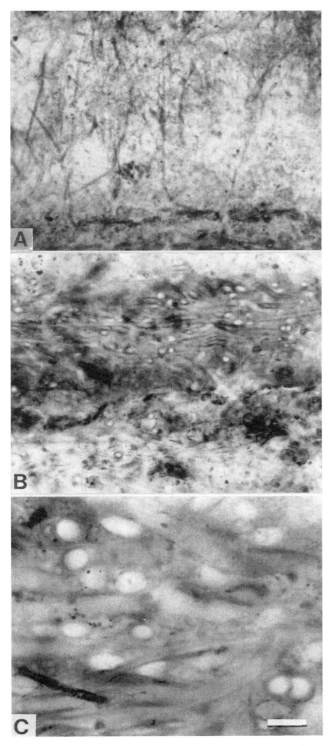

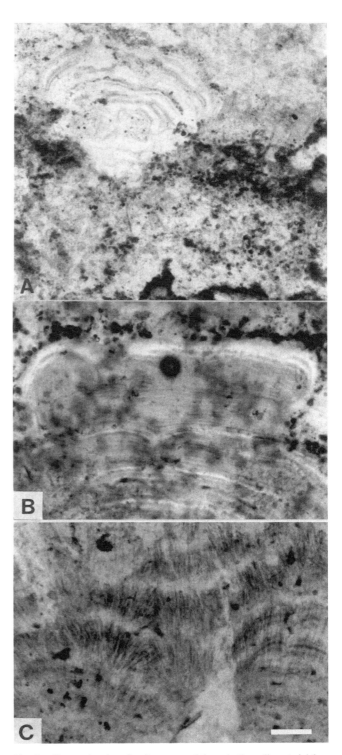

FIG. 4.—Filamentous microfossil *Eoschizothrix composita* Seong-Joo and Golubic. A) Vertically oriented tubular sheaths left in the sediment-rich layer as cyanobacterial trichomes moved upward to escape burial and cementation. Note the transition from horizontal to vertical orientation in the center below. B) Predominantly prostrate distribution of simple and bundled sheaths building an organic-rich layer of the stromatolite. C) Detail of B: interwoven, uncompacted tubules with clear lumens. The trichomes abandoned their sheaths when the mat was buried by sediment. Scale bar in C is 100 μm for A, 50 μm for B, and 10 μm for C.

FIG. 5.—Textured grains of carbonate precipitates in the sediment-rich layers of silicified Gaoyuzhuang stromatolties. A) An expanding crystal fan on top of a mat of coccoid microfossils, originating from two separate botryoid clusters, each with several dark nucleation centers. B) Flat-topped crustous coating with densely arranged growth lines, colonized by a biofilm of coccoids. C) Interpenetration of acicular crystal fibers at the interferences between competing crystal fans. Scale bar in C is 100 μm for A, 50 μm for B, and 10 μm for C.

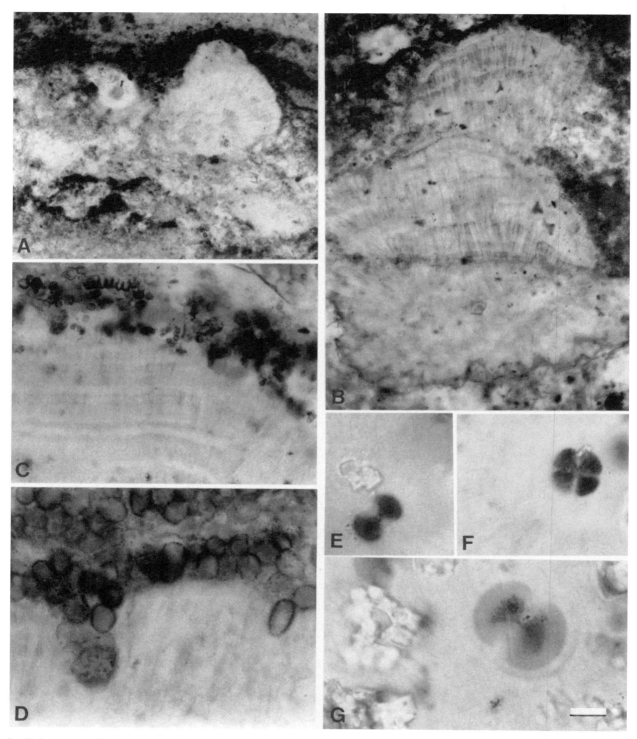

FIG. 6.—Carbonate precipitates, microfossils, and nucleation centers. A) A large, upward-expanding botryoid cluster between microbial mats of *Coccostratus dispergens*. B) A laterally expanding cluster of botryoid spherulites (below) gave rise to upward-diverging crystal fans (above). Dark areas are colonies of coccoid cyanobaceria. C) Sessile, polarly differentiated coccoids colonizing the surface of a crystal fan. Note the high density of growth zones in the fan. D) Contact between the top of a crystal fan and the biofilm of sessile, *Chamaesiphon*-like coccoids. E) Dumbbell-shaped initial crystal bundle in the nucleation center of a spheroid grain. F) A rosette formed by intersection of two dumbbell-shaped crystal bundles. Note the texture of faint fibers radiating in all directions from the initial nucleation center. G) Intitial crystal bundle in the form of paired hemispheroids with a halo of the first growth zones. The scale in G is 100 μm for A and B, 30 μm for C, and 10 μm for D–G.

Spring in Yellowstone. Aragonite dumbbells and paired hemispheroids formed there at high temperature and by highest rates of precipitation (cf. Seong-Joo et al., 1999). The precipitation gradually shifted to calcite as the water cooled and the precipitation rates slowed down. Similar observations were reported earlier from thermal springs (Farmer and Des Marais, 1994) and hypersaline evaporitic settlings (Krumbein, 1979; Chafetz and Buczynski, 1992).

Botryoid clusters originate from fusion of individual competing spherulites (Figs. 5A, 6A, and 6B, below), whereas preferentially upward crystal growth of spherulites leads to formation of crystal fans. Stacked fans originate when precipitation is locally favored but periodically interrupted (Fig. 6B, above). During such interruptions in the formation of crystal fans, they were intermittently coated by microbial biofilms (Figs. 7, 8). Uninterrupted upward crystal growth leads to formation of "microstromatolitic" (<1 mm) and "ministromatolitic" (>1 mm) columns, whereas crustous coatings originate from multiple competing botryoid clusters and lateral spreading of the precipitation process.

In addition to textured grains, sediment-rich layers contain light, smooth, nontextured areas where the outlines of individual sediment particles are not preserved. Nontextured mineral matrix in the Gaoyuzhuang stromatolites is interpreted as fine-grained sediment, possibly precipitated in the water column above, and then settled (cf. Grotzinger, 1990). This matrix appears transparent in plain-transmitted-light and consists of uniform fields of microquartz under cross-polarized light. Such nontextured areas extend in horizontal layers. Adjacent to crystal fans, these layers are slightly concave upward or sloping down from the protruding columns of stacked fans (Fig. 8). In the Gaoyuzhuang stromatolites, the smooth layers are preferentially colonized by filamentous microfossils.

Kinetics of the Sedimentary Process

Lamination is generally regarded as a salient property of stromatolites. In Gaoyuzhuang stromatolites, as in many other sedimentary settings, the lamination reflects recurring changes in sedimentation over time. It is customary to count the laminae as couplets of organic-rich and sediment-rich layers expressing this cyclicity. Each layer observed in an oriented petrographic thin section can be interpreted as a synoptic profile (Hofmann, 1969) reflecting the sediment–water interface at a particular time. As the sediment–water interface moved upward in the course of sediment accumulation, the changes in sedimentary conditions over time were recorded in the rock fabric as a sequence of laminar alternation of organic-rich and sediment-rich layers.

In the stromatolitic laminae of the Gaoyuzhuang cherts, dense populations of well-preserved microfossils characterize organic-rich layers, which include only few interspersed mineral grains. In contrast, sediment-rich layers contain fewer microorganisms between numerous nodular, fan-shaped, and stratiform precipitates. These differences in depositional pattern appear to be dictated by changing rates of sedimentation, to which the microorganisms responded by growth and movement. Microbial populations grew, and organic matter accumulated, during the times when inorganic sedimentation rates were low. Sediment-rich layers, on the other hand, represent events of high sediment flux and/or high rates of autochthonous mineral precipitation. These events buried and displaced microorganisms, and elicited their behavioral responses, engaging in various escape strategies (Seong-Joo and Golubic, 1999). Therefore, the top of each organic-rich layer should logically be regarded as the surface of each laminar couplet, because these surfaces remained exposed for extended time at the concurrent sediment–water interface, where they were overgrown by microorganisms and stabilized (cf. Krumbein et al., 1994).

The concept of synoptic profile (Hofmann, 1969) is also useful in reconstructing horizontal variations in the rates of microbial growth vs. sediment accumulation, and in estimating the relative importance of these co-occurring processes. Local differences in the rates of sediment accumulation along the same time profile are expressed as waviness and irregularities of laminar surfaces. Changes and trends may then be followed in upward direction from lamina to lamina. Upward-extending protuberances along the laminar surface indicate faster, and depressions slower, rates of growth and sediment accumulation. These relationships are illustrated in the following two examples.

A view of an oriented petrographic thin section of the Gaoyuzhuang stromatolite (Fig. 7) includes about 2 cm of depositional height and about a dozen laminae. The highest rates of sediment accumulation are shown in the central part of the illustration by a series of upward-protruding stacked crystal fans. The sequence starts from a relatively flat lamina (Fig. 7, level 1) showing minor irregularities in organic-rich layers apparently due to varying growth rates of microorganisms at the sediment surface at the time. More pronounced local microbial growth can be seen in two organic-rich layers above (levels 2 and 3), particularly on the right side of the picture. These bubbly, dark coatings, formed during a period of extensive microbial growth, were interrupted by several fluxes of sedimentation and mineral precipitation, evident as wide sediment-rich layers in between. The appearance and expansion of two spherulites (level 2) then disturb the relatively uniform sedimentation regime at level 1. These spherulites, which originated from clearly identifiable nucleation centers, were formed by rapid precipitation of aragonite. They rest here on top of a cavity (arrow), currently filled with megaquartz with centripetally increasing grain size. The cavity is one of many original pores and "birdseye" structures found in the same thin section. It is conceivable that a gas bubble originally uplifted the microbial mat at this spot, thus modifying the microenvironmental condition sufficiently to trigger carbonate precipitation.

As crystal growth slowed down, coccoid microorganisms settled on the newly emerging grains, forming a thin but well-defined microbial biofilm. Subsequent sedimentation and establishment of a new microbial mat partially buried the precipitate (level 3), but the topography retained sufficient elevation to become the preferred nucleation site at the next carbonate precipitation events (level 4). The result was a series of stacked upward-radiating crystal fans, with brief interruptions in their growth, which permitted only partial colonization by microorganisms. This entire sediment-rich layer is loaded with competing precipitates, creating a clotted microfabric.

The presence of loose sediment can be detected at level 4, by observing the tent-like slopes, draping down from the tips of the protruded column of stacked fans. Organic growth on

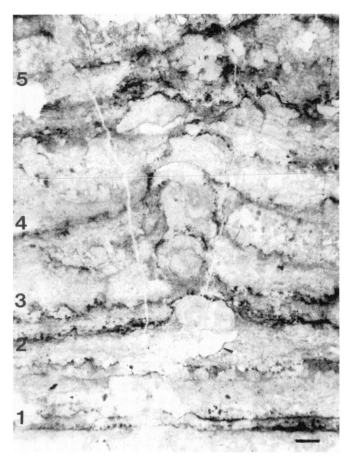

FIG. 7.—Series of a dozen stromatolitic laminae characterized by thin organic-rich and thick sediment-rich layers. Dark layers are mats and biofilms of coccoid microfossils. Light layers contain numerous mineral precipitates and fenestral voids. Stacked upward-radiating crystal fans that persist though several laminae and show highest rates of accumulation are in the center of the picture. Numbers 1–5 indicate subsequent synoptic profiles as discussed in the text. Scale bar is 1 mm.

nature of the substrate is different. A sedimentary pause that followed permitted an overgrowth of the sediment surface by benthic microorganisms, forming an organic-rich layer (level 2). Filamentous multitrichomous cyanobacteria formed the thicker mats over the soft, loose sediment to the left, while a compact thin layer of coccoid cyanobacteria colonized the top of the hard crystal fan to the right. The next tier of the stacked fan column (center right) nucleated from the coccoid horizon at several separate points. The resulting fans fused into a single one about 2/3 of the height of the fan. The rate of crystal fan accretion at that level was higher than the sediment accumulation rate of its surroundings, resulting in protrusion of the fan above the average level of the next-higher synoptic profile (level 3). During the next sedimentary pause, another compact coating of coccoids covered the top of this fan. The sediment accumulating concurrently to the left of the column was predominantly fine-grained. It was colonized profusely by filamentous cyanobacteria, forming several mat layers. The same scenario is repeated even more dramatically in the next-higher lamina (level 4), featuring crystal fan growth in three impressive spurts (top right). The accumulation rate of the fine sedi-

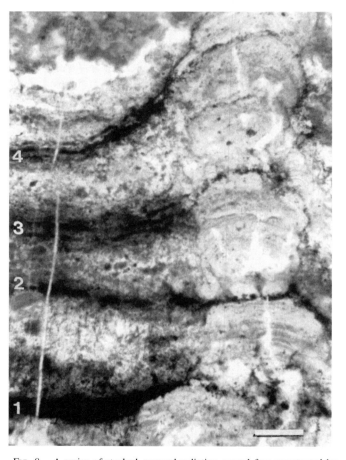

FIG. 8.—A series of stacked, upward-radiating crystal fans punctuated by coccoid biofilm coatings (right) next to thinly laminated mats of filamentous microfossils permeating and stabilizing loose fine-grained sediment (left). An upward trend in increasing accretion rate of precipitates relative to accumulation of fine-grained sediment is evident from changing synoptic profiles. Scale bar is 1 mm.

top of this lamina is modest. A more intense microbial growth and leveled sedimentation return later as seen at the top of the picture (level 5).

Another detail of the same stromatolite (Fig. 8) illustrates the distinction in fabrics, microbial settlements, and accumulation rates between autochthonous benthic precipitates and fine-grained clastic sediment. The precipitates on the right side of the picture formed a column of stacked fans, each with upward-radiating zoned fabric. The left side of the picture shows fine layering of predominantly loose sediment supporting intense microbial growth (dark layers). As in the previous example, the column persisted through several laminae. Precipitation was triggered locally, starting a series of positive reinforcements, in which precipitation rates increased upward with each subsequent event. The base of the column nucleated on one side of a buried fan (level 1), from where it radiated upward, forming the first fan. Subsequent events include crystal fan growth on the right and formation of several botryoid grains mixed with fine-grained sediment to the left. The combined rates of sediment accumulation are even across the profile, although the

ment to the left of the column showed a significant lag behind the accretion rate of the column. These surfaces are curved concave upward, leaning on the column at increasingly steeper angles. They were consistently characterized by thin lamination formed by motile filamentous cyanobacteria.

During the intervals between precipitation events, the hard upper surfaces of crystal fans were recognized by microorganisms as hard grounds. They became preferentially colonized by sessile coccoid cyanobacteria. These organisms show polarized cell symmetry with basal attachment (Fig. 6C, D). They are similar to modern epilithic cyanobacteria, of the genera *Cyanocystis* (cf. Hua et al., 1989) and *Chamaesiphon*. The loose clastic sediment to the left of the column was recognized and preferentially colonized by motile, sheathed filamentous cyanobacteria, which stabilized these sediment layers. Sediment stabilization probably involved trapping and binding of sediment particles. Brief episodes of mat burial by loose sediment, evident as thin lamination (at a scale of 100 μm of vertical distance), was overcome by upward movement of trichomes and recolonization of the sediment surface. The sheaths were left behind, contributing to the organic input to the sediment. These organisms were similar to modern cyanobacteria of the genera *Schizothrix* and *Microcoleus*. (cf. Golubic and Browne, 1996; Seong-Joo and Golubic, 1998).

The series of four stromatolitic laminae in the latter example illustrates a trend toward increased mineral saturation and increased precipitation rates over the time period of their formation. The process was interrupted four to five times by shorter or longer sedimentary pauses. The absolute timing for this process was within the biological time scale commensurate with microbial colonization, growth, and migration.

Preservation and Diagenesis

Precambrian cherts of various ages contain organically preserved microbial fossils. This is in contrast to chert nodules of Phanerozoic age, in which fossil remains, if present, are found mostly in an advanced stage of degradation. Only primary silica deposition, usually associated with volcanic or hydrothermal activities, incorporates microorganisms in a good state of preservation (e.g., Rhynie chert; Trewin and Rice, 1992; Taylor et al., 1995). Early silicification, which permineralized the sediment–water interface together with microbial communities growing there, appears to be critical for their structural preservation. Such conditions are generally favored under hypersaline conditions, which may constitute a preservational bias in favor of evaporitic and intertidal settings (reviewed by Horodyski and Donaldson, 1983). Even so, preservation of microorganisms in silica was apparently more common during Precambrian times than later. It is conceivable that the saturation levels of silica in ancient sea water, and the readiness to precipitate was higher, particularly in coastal settings (Knoll, 1985). The saturation levels may have declined gradually in the course of the Phanerozoic as silica became sequestered by eukaryotic organisms that evolved siliceous skeletons (e.g., sponges, silicoflagellates, diatoms, and radiolaria). Chert formation was then associated with diagenetic mobilization of skeletal silica.

Cherts provide a stable preservational medium, particuraly when silicification took place early, before microbial degrada-

tion of organic structures was completed. Microbial metabolic activities change the chemical properties of the interstitial waters, which permeate the sediment, and these changes may have a positive or negative feedback effect. The onset of anoxic conditions, for example, which commonly follows intensive microbial decomposition of organic matter, tends to retard the degradation process, thus increasing the chances for preservation and extending the time window for fossilization in silica (cf. Knoll and Golubic, 1979). This effect may be enhanced if combined with an increase in salinity. The fossil record is biased in favor of environments in which recycling of organic matter is incomplete, and in favor of resistant and chemically recalcitrant structures and compounds. Consequently, microbial fossils found are representative only of a fraction of the total microbial diversity at any time.

The syndepositional precipitation of carbonate in the case of Gaoyuzhuang stromatolites provided an additional favorable circumstance for preservation of microorganisms in growth position prior to silicification. It provided a rigid support of the sediment, prevented compaction and collapse of pore spaces, and, consequently, shearing and distortion of accumulated organic matter and displacement of microbial communities. Such a favorable relationship between biological and mineral components in the Gaoyuzhuang stromatolites also influenced their conservation during later diagenesis. Organic-rich layers within the same stromatolites, in the absence of local precipitates when associated only with fine-grained sediment, contain few preserved microfossils. Most of the organic matter is then hashed into shapeless streaks, displaced along progressing mineralization fronts or compressed and deformed along stylolitic contacts. Such deformations took place during sediment compaction prior to silicification or along silicification fronts. There appears to be a positive correlation, if not a causal relation, between silicification and the presence of organic matter in rocks (cf. Knoll, 1986). Silicification has incorporated the organic remains, including nonsoluble impurities, while it has replaced carbonate minerals. This replacement process must have taken place gradually, without disturbing the arrangement of crystal outlines, marked by reddish insoluble impurities. The sequence of these events is revealed along the contacts between the various mineral phases. The fronts of advancing silica infringe upon older carbonate deposits. Islands of incorporated carbonate become preferentially dolomitized in the process of later diagenetic recrystallization.

DISCUSSION

Recent studies of the origins of carbonate platforms and reef architecture have identified unequivocal patterns of massive benthic, rhythmic carbonate precipitation, which resulted in laminated sedimentary structures (Grotzinger, 1989a, 1990; Grotzinger and Knoll, 1995). Some of these laminated cements include complex tufa-like patterns that followed a fractal geometry reiterated over several orders of magnitude. These studies called for caution against an *a priori* assumption of biogenicity of all stromatolites, on the grounds that, in many cases, abiotic genesis of the observed patterns as null hypotheses could not be falsified (Grotzinger and Rothman, 1996). In the perspective of the Earth's history, it is fair to assume that purely physicochemical processes have preceded the biological ones.

It is also understood that physicochemical laws underlie and are inclusive in the processes controlled by living systems. For these reasons, the burden of proof when determining the causative agents in stromatolite morphogenesis befalls the support of the claims of biogenicity, which also requires an exclusion of plausible alternative abiotic explanations.

The above view challenges the very definition of stromatolites (Kalkowsky, 1908) as biosedimentary structures formed by microbial activities such as trapping and binding of sediment particles and/or (biogenic) mineral precipitation (Awramik and Margulis, 1974). At the least, this view calls for a more precise sorting out of the biological and sedimentary constituents and processes involved in the formation of stromatolitic structures.

In the case of "trapping and binding" it is important to consider that these activities are based on responses of microorganisms to burial by sediments. They are usually associated with microbial exopolymer production and have a stabilization of loose sediments as a consequence (cf. Neumann et al., 1970; Krumbein et al., 1994). In the case of mineral precipitation, it is important to specify at which stage of the process a microbial influence may have taken place and how it related to the associated abiotic processes. Biogenic influences on mineral formation can potentially take place at different stages in the course of mineral and sediment formation: at the stage of (a) solution chemistry, (b) mineral nucleation, (c) crystal growth, and (d) sediment grain arrangement. The nature and extent of these influences may vary from case to case, and may be differently distributed from stage to stage (cf. Golubic, 1991).

Fortuitous preservation of 1400 Ma benthic microbial communities in growth position, in a synsedimentary context rich in autochthonous carbonate precipitates, facilitated a close inspection of the relations between biological and mineral components of a stratiform, laminated organo-sedimentary structure. The lamination has been analyzed as a microstratigraphic upward progression of temporal profiles in a dynamic system, which allowed reconstruction of relative rates that lead to the observed accumulations of organic and mineral matter. The rates of microbial growth and, by inference, the role of microbiota in the formation of Gaoyuzhuang stromatolite are inversely proportional to the rates of sedimentation and mineral precipitation. Maximum microbial development, leading to formation of biofilms and mats, took place concurrently with the lowest sedimentation rates, and during brief sedimentary pauses. Conversely, microbial growth was suppressed, or even excluded, during periods of rapid sedimentation and mineral precipitation, which prevailed in the sediment-rich layers. In this context, the timing of precipitation is gauged by the rates of microbial growth and movement, which are measured in days and weeks rather than in millions of years.

The exclusion of microbial fossils from areas with textured mineral fabrics argues for rapid precipitation rates (cf. Grotzinger and Knoll, 1995), and against direct microbial involvement in crystal growth. However, the observed association of nucleation centers with organic-rich layers indicates a possible role of organisms and/or organic products in crystal nucleation. The preserved early crystallization stages immediately following carbonate nucleation in the Gaoyuzhuang stromatolites have characteristic shapes of bi-radiating crystal bundles, dumbbell shapes, and paired hemispheroids (Fig. 6E–G). These early crystallization patterns are strikingly similar to those reported from modern hypersaline (Krumbein, 1974, 1979; Novitsky, 1981; Castanier, 1987) and hydrothermal (Farmer and Des Marais, 1994) environments. They were also obtained experimentally in bacterial cultures (Buczynski and Chafetz, 1991; Chafetz and Buczynski, 1992). All these natural and artificial settings had high levels of carbonate supersaturation in common; however, within the same supersaturation range, crystal nucleation was promoted by the presence of microorganisms and dead organic matter (Krumbein, 1979; Chafetz and Buczynski, 1992). Once nucleation took place, further crystal growth proceeded spontaneously along aragonitic or calcitic crystal lattices, depending on precipitation rates. Similar crystal formation was also achieved in purely inorganic experimental settings (García-Ruiz, 1985; Bella and García-Ruiz, 1986, 1987) providing alternative means of crystal nucleation.

The aragonitic crystal bundles, dumbbells, and paired hemispheroids that we observed at Mammouth Hot Spring, Yellowstone, formed over a size range of several orders of magnitude, but followed similar patterns of development and maintained the same basic organization and shape (Golubic et al., 1999). Although these aragonite crystal aggregates were associated with microbial mats, their shapes and sizes could not be related to any of the resident microorganisms. The observed pattern may, in fact, represent another case where fractal geometry (cf. Grotzinger and Rothman, 1996) could be applied as a model.

In Gaoyuzhuang botryoids and spherulites, crystal growth proceeded continuously from the moment of nucleation, through the formation of initial radiating crystal bundles outward, resulting in textural continuity throughout the entire spherulite (Fig. 7, level 2). Dense arrangement of nucleation sites resulted in competitive crystal growth, so that clusters of nuclei fused and remained encapsulated inside a single spherulite (Fig. 5A). These observations suggest that spontaneous crystal growth of primary aragonite took place at extremely high rates.

Crystal growth in mineral fans and crusts resulted in an internal fabric indistinguishable from that of the spherulites but upward oriented. The existence of fine, regular, reddish-colored growth zones (5 to 20 μm apart) as a part of the crystal fabric (also called stromatolitic intralamination), indicates some kind of rhythmicity in mineral growth. The frequency of these crystal growth zones (e.g., in Figure 7) is orders of magnitude higher than that of the stromatolitic laminar couplets, and of the microbial biofilms, which punctuate the growth of stacked fans (which are millimeters apart). Considering the timing inherent in microbial growth as a measure, assigning diurnal rhythm to fine crystal growth zonation appears reasonable. Diurnal changes in chemistry of interstitial waters may conceivably be responsible for these pulsations, and microbial metabolic activities may well be among the causes of these changes. The density of zones is typically lowest close to the centers of spherulites and increases peripherally. Similarly, it is highest at the base of crystal fans and decreases upward (Fig. 6B vs. 6C). Such patterns indicate a slowing down of precipitation rate, leading to a pause, which commonly introduces the formation of coccoid biofilms (Fig. 6C, D). The internal fabrics with fine, rhythmic zonation are reminiscent of those observed in other carbonate precipitates such as those observed in speleothem and travertine deposits.

The stacking of mineral fans is punctuated by intermittent colonization by biofilms composed of coccoids, whereas mat-forming filaments simultaneously colonize the surrounding sediments. As in modern environments, the coccoids prefer to settle on hard mineral surfaces of the precipitates, while filaments cover and stabilize fine-grained sediment that accumulated between precipitates. This selective microbial colonization was helpful in recognition of fossil substrates when original grain outlines were not preserved. These areas of fine-grained sediment are free of siliciclastic material. They were probably filled with micritic carbonate, which may have originated from whitings in the water column above (cf. Grotzinger, 1990, fig. 5B). The timing of these biological events is also evident from their arrangement. Several distinct mat layers of filaments formed concurrent to a single coccoid coating (Fig. 8, center), contrasting the speed of microbial motility in escaping burial by sediments to the timing of colonization and settlement of sessile forms. Because the filamentous organisms persisted through several consecutive burial events, they contributed to the frame construction of the stromatolite, trapping and binding sediment particles in the process and provided a supportive organic texture to the loose micritic matrix around them (Seong-Joo and Golubic, 1998; Seong-Joo et al., 1999). The effect of the coccoid biofilm on the substrate appears to be limited to local dissolution of mineral surfaces, because some coccoids appear to "sink" into the fan fabrics below them (Fig. 6C, D).

Rapid accretion rates of mineral precipitates are also expressed in the laminar synoptic profiles. Stacked mineral fans regularly protrude above the average sediment levels, and sometimes persist through several laminae (Fig. 7). When not interrupted and coated by biofilms, individual fans fuse into vertical "microstromatolitic", "ministromatolitic", and "microdigitate" columnar units spanning a single sediment-rich lamina or crossing several lamina boundaries. These thinly and regularly intralaminated columns formed in the absence of microorganisms and are a chemical product of highly supersaturated interstitial fluids. Such mineral constructs may take different size, depending on the continuity of the precipitation process.

Larger columnar arrangements of crystal fans in Gaoyuzhuang stromatolites that persist through several laminae are similar in texture to those described as "ministromatolites" by Hofmann and Jackson (1987) and "microstromatolites" by Zhang et al. (1995). By analogy to our observations, these structures were all formed by rapid mineralization under similarly supersaturated conditions. All these systems may have contained microorganisms, but the role of such microorganisms in crystal formation was probably negligible or at least subordinate to mineral processes, which were predominant. It is noteworthy that these upright-growing precipitates also occur in a broad spectrum of sizes and, by extrapolation, may easily include megascopic crystal fans described from the Archean and early Proterozoic (Grotzinger and Knoll, 1995).

A historically relevant analogy to "microstromatolitic" precipitates discussed in this paper refers to the microscopic fabric of Kalkowsky's oolitic grains (Kalkowsky, 1908). These grains are significantly larger than most ooids formed today, and are commonly beset with surface bumps resembling raspberries (Paul, 1982). Such framboid oolite grains are composed internally of radiating "microstromatolitic" columns, with fine-grained sediment accumulated between them. Thus, the paleoenvironments of the Buntsandstein sea (Lower Triassic) at Heseberg, Germany, where the terms stromatolite and oolite were first used in comparison, were also characterized by a predominance of precipitation processes rather than by microbial stabilization of loose clastic sediments through "trapping and binding".

ACKNOWLEDGMENTS

We are grateful for encouragement, field guidance, and friendship of the late professor Zhang Yun of Beijing University. Drs. A.H. Knoll, H.J. Hofmann, and B. Jones read the earlier versions of the manuscript and provided valuable suggestions. S. Golubic was supported by the Hanse Institute for Advanced Study, Delmenhorst, Germany. L. Seong-Joo was supported by the post-doctoral fund of French Government 238024K through the laboratory of Dr. E. Verrecchia, U.M.R. 5561 C.N.R.S., Biogeosciences, University of Bourgogne, Dijon, France. Boston University provided partial travel support to L. Seong-Joo.

REFERENCES

AWRAMIK, S. M., AND MARGULIS, L., 1974, Definition of stromatolite: Stromatolite Newsletter, v. 2, p. 1–5.

AWRAMIK, S. M., MARGULIS, L., AND BARGHOORN, E. S., 1976, Evolutionary processes in the formation of stromatolites, in Walter, M. R., ed., Stromatolites: Amsterdam, Elsevier, Advances in Sedimentology, v. 20, p. 149–162.

BELLA, S. D., AND GARCÍA-RUIZ, J. M., 1986, Textures in induced morphology crystal aggregates of CaCO₃: Sheaf of wheat morphologies: Journal of Crystal Growth, v. 79, p. 236–240.

BELLA, S. D., AND GARCÍA-RUIZ, J. M., 1987, Banding structures in induced morphology crystal aggregates of CaCO₃: Journal of Materials Science, v. 22, p. 3095–3102.

BUCZYNSKI, C., AND CHAFETZ, H. S., 1991, Habit of bacterially induced precipitates of calcium carbonate and the influence of medium viscosity on mineralogy: Journal of Sedimentary Petrology, v. 61, p. 226–233.

CASTANIER, S., 1987, Micorbiogéologie: Processus et modalites de la carbonatogénèse bactériénne: Unpublished Ph.D. Dissertation, University of Nantes, Nantes, France, 541 p.

CHAFETZ, H. S., AND BUCZYNSKI, C., 1992, Bacterially induced lithification of microbial mats: Palaios, v. 7, p. 227–293.

CHEN, J., ZHANG, H., ZHU, S., ZHAO, Z., AND WANG, Z., 1980, Research on Sinian Suberathem of Jixian, Tianjin, in Tianjin Institute of Geology and Mineral Resources, ed., Research in Precambrian Geology, Sinian Suberathem in China: Tianjin, Tianjin Science and Technology Press, p. 56–114 (in Chinese with English abstract).

FARMER, J. D., AND DES MARAIS, D. J., 1994, Biological versus inorganic processes in stromatolite morphogenesis: Observations from mineralizing sedimentary systems, in Stal, L. J., and Caumette, P., eds., Microbial Mats: Structure, Development and Environmental Significance: Heidelberg, Springer-Verlag, NATO ASI Series, p. 61–68.

GARCIA-PICHEL, F., 1998, Solar ultraviolet and the evolutionary history of cyanobacteria: Origins of Life and Evolution of the Biosphere, v. 28, p. 321–347.

GARCIA-PICHEL, F., AND CASTENHOLZ, R. W., 1991, Characterization and biological implications of scytonemin, a cyanobacterial sheath pigment: Journal of Phycology, v. 27, p. 395–409.

GARCÍA-RUIZ, J. M., 1985, On the formation of induced morphology crystal aggregates: Journal of Crystal Growth, v. 73, p. 251–262.

GINSBURG, R. N., 1991, Controversies about stromatolites: Vices and virtues, in Muller, D. W., McKenzie, J. A., and Weissert, H., eds., Controversies in Modern Geology: London, Academic Press, p. 25–36.

GOLUBIC, S., 1991, Modern Stromatolites—a review, in Riding, R., ed., Calcareous Algae and Stromatolites: Heidelberg, Springer-Verlag, p. 541–561.

GOLUBIC, S., AND BARGHOORN, E. S., 1977, Interpretation of microbial fossils with special reference to the Precambrian, in Flügel, E., ed., Fossil Algae: Heidelberg, Springer-Verlag, p. 1–14.

GOLUBIC, S., AND BROWNE, K. M., 1996, *Schizothrix gebeleinii* sp. nov. builds subtidal stromatolites, Lee Stocking Island, Bahamas: Algological Studies, v. 83, p. 273–290.

GOLUBIC, S., AND HOFMANN, H. J., 1976, Comparison of modern and mid-Precambrian Entophysalidaceae (Cyanophyta) in stromatolitic algal mats: cell division and degradation: Journal of Paleontology, v. 50, p. 1074–1082.

GOLUBIC, S., SEONG-JOO, L., AND BROWNE K. M., 1999, Cyanobacteria: architects of sedimentary structures, *in* Riding, R., and Awramik, S. M., eds., Microbial Sediments: Heidelberg, Springer-Verlag, in press.

GROTZINGER, J. P., 1989a, Facies and evolution of Precambrian carbonate depositional systems: Emergence of the modern platform archetype, *in* Crevello, P. D., Wilson, J. L., Sarg, J. F., and Read, J. F., eds., Controls on Carbonate Platform and Basin Development: SEPM, Special Publication 44, p. 79–106.

GROTZINGER, J. P., 1989b, Introduction to Precambrian reefs, *in* Geldsetzer, H. H. J., James, N. P., and Tebbut, G. E., eds., Reefs, Canada and Adjacent Areas: Canadian Society of Petroleum Geologists, Memoir 13, p. 9–12.

GROTZINGER, J. P., 1990, Geochemical model for Proterozoic stromatolite decline: American Journal of Science, v. 290-A, p. 80–103.

GROTZINGER, J. P., AND KNOLL, A. H., 1995, Anomalous carbonate precipitates: Is the Precambrian key to the Permian?: Palaios, v. 10, p. 578–596.

GROTZINGER, J. P., AND READ, J. F., 1983, Evidence of primary aragonite precipitation, Lower Proterozoic (1.9 Ga) dolomite, Wopmay Orogen, Northwest Canada: Geology, v. 11, p. 710–713.

GROTZINGER, J. P., AND ROTHMAN, D. H., 1996, An abiotic model for stromatolite morphogenesis: Nature, v. 383, p. 423–425.

HOFMANN, H. J., 1969, Attributes of stromatolites: Geological Survey of Canada, Paper 69, p. 1–43.

HOFMANN, H. J., 1975, Stratiform Precambrian stromatolites, Belcher Islands, Canada: Relations between silicified microfossils and microstructure: American Journal of Science, v. 275, p. 1121–1132.

HOFMANN, H. J., 1976, Precambrian microflora, Belcher Island, Canada: significance and systematics: Journal of Paleontology, v. 50, p. 1040–1073.

HOFMANN, H. J., AND JACKSON, G. D., 1987, Proterozoic ministromatolites with radial-fibrous fabric: Sedimentology, v. 34, p. 963–971.

HORODYSKI, R. J., AND DONALDSON, J. A., 1983, Distribution and significance of microfossils in cherts of the Middle Proterozoic Dismal Lakes Groups, District of Mackenzie, Northwest Territories, Canada: Journal of Paleontology, v. 57, p. 271–288.

HUA, M., FRIEDMANN, E. I., OCAMPO-FRIEDMANN, R., AND CAMPBELL, S. E., 1989, Heteropolarity in unicellular cyanobacteria: structure and development of *Cyanocystis violacea*: Plant Systematics and Evolution, v. 164, p. 17–26.

KALKOWSKY, E., 1908, Oolith und Stromatolith im norddeutschen Buntsandstein: Deutsche Geologische Gesellschaft, Zeitschrift, v. 60, p. 68–125.

KNOLL, A. H., 1985, Exceptional preservation of photosynthetic organisms in silicified carbonates and silicified peats: Royal Society [London], Philosophical Transactions, v. B311, p. 111–122.

KNOLL, A. H., 1986, Geological evidence for early evolution: Societat Catalana de Biologia, Treballs, v. 39, p. 113–141.

KNOLL, A. H., AND GOLUBIC, S., 1979, Anatomy and taphonomy of a Precambrian algal stromatolite: Precambrian Research, v. 10, p. 115–151.

KNOLL, A. H., SWETT, K., AND MARK, J., 1991, Paleobiology of a Neoproterozoic tidal flat/lagoonal complex: the Draken Conglomerate Formation, Spitsbergen: Journal of Paleontology, v. 65, p. 531–570.

KRUMBEIN, W. E., 1974, On the precipitation of aragonite on the surface of marine bacteria: Die Naturwissenschaften, v. 61, p. 167.

KRUMBEIN, W. E., 1979, Photolithotrophic and chemoorganotrophic activity of bacteria and algae as related to beachrock formation and degradation (Gulf of Aqaba, Sinai): Geomicrobiology Journal, v. 1, p. 140–203.

KRUMBEIN, W. E., 1983, Stromatolites—the challenge of a term in space and time: Precambrian Research, v. 20, p. 493–531.

KRUMBEIN, W. E., PATERSON, D. M., AND STAL, L. J., eds., 1994, Biostabilization of Sediments: Oldenburg, Biblioteks und Informationssystem der Carl von Ossietzky Universität, 529 p.

NEUMANN, A. C., GEBELEIN, C. D., AND SCOFFIN, T. P., 1970, The composition, structure and erodability of subtidal mats, Abaco, Bahamas: Journal of Sedimentary Petrology, v. 40, p. 274–297.

NOVITSKY, J. A., 1981, Calcium carbonate precipitation by marine bacteria: Geomicrobiology Journal, v. 2, p. 275–388.

PAUL, J., 1982, Der Untere Bundsandstein des Germanischen Beckens: Geologische Rundschau, v. 71, p. 795–811.

ROSS, D. J., 1991, Botryoidal high-magnesium calcite marine cements from the Upper Cretaceous of the Mediterranean region: Journal of Sedimentary Petrology, v. 61, p. 349–353.

SEONG-JOO, L., AND GOLUBIC, S., 1998, Multi-trichomous cyanobacterial microfossils from the Mesoproterozoic Gaoyuzhuang Formation, China: Paleoecological and taxonomic implications: Lethaia, v. 31, p. 169–184.

SEONG-JOO, L., AND GOLUBIC, S., 1999, Microfossil populations in the context of synsedimentary micrite deposition and acicular carbonate precipitation: Mesoproterozoic Gaoyuzhuang Formation, China: Precambrian Research, v. 96: p. 183-208.

SEONG-JOO, L., BROWNE, K. M., AND GOLUBIC, S., 1999, On stromatolite lamination, *in* Riding, R., and Awramik, S.M., eds., Microbial Sediments: Heidelberg, Springer-Verlag, in press.

SERGEEV, V. N., 1993, Silicified Riphean microfossils of the Anabar Uplift: Stratigraphy and Geological Correlation, v. 1, p. 264–278.

SERGEEV, V. N., KNOLL, A. H., AND GROTZINGER, J. P., 1995, Paleobiology of the Mesoproterozoic Billyakh Group, Anbar Uplift, northern Siberia: Palaeontological Society [London], Memoir 39, p. 1–37.

TAYLOR, T. N., HASS, H., REMY, W., AND KERP, H., 1995, The oldest fossil lichen: Nature, v. 378, p. 244.

TREWIN, N. H., AND RICE, C. M., 1992, Stratigraphy and sedimentology of the Devonian Rhynie chert locality: Scottish Journal of Geology, v. 28, p. 37–47.

WALTER, M. R., ed., 1976, Stromatolites: Amsterdam, Elsevier, Developments in Sedimentology, v. 20, 790 p.

WALTER, M. R., GROTZINGER, J. P., AND SCHOPF, J. W., 1992, Proterozoic stromatolites, *in* Schopf, J.W., and Klein C., eds., The Proterozoic Biosphere: Cambridge, U.K., Cambridge University Press, p. 253–260.

YU, R., AND ZHANG, X., 1985, Study of geochronology of Late Precambrian in the Yanshan Ranges: Tianjin Institute of Geology and Mineral Resources of the Chinese Academy of Geological Sciences, Bulletin, v. 11, p. 1–22.

ZHANG, Y., 1981, Proterozoic stromatolite microfloras of the Gaoyuzhuang Formation (Early Sinian, Riphean), Hebei, China: Journal of Paleontology, v. 55, p. 485–506.

ZHANG, Y., YANG, C., YIN, C., AND SHAO, H., 1995, Microbial mat communities and related sedimentary–geochemical aspects of the Mesoproterozoic Changcheng Group, Pangjiapu, Hebei, North China: Acta Micropalaeontologica Sinica, v. 12, p. 221–240 (in Chinese with English abstract).

ZHONG, F., 1977, On the Sinian geochronological scale of China based on isotopic ages for the Sinian strata in the Yanshan region, North China: Scientia Sinica, v. 22, p. 818–834.

CONTROLS ON FABRIC DEVELOPMENT AND MORPHOLOGY OF TUFAS AND STROMATOLITES, UPPERMOST PETHEI GROUP (1.8 GA), GREAT SLAVE LAKE, NORTHWEST CANADA

MICHAEL C. POPE* AND JOHN P. GROTZINGER

Department of Earth, Atmospheric, and Planetary Sciences, Massachusetts Institute of Technology, Cambridge, MA 02139, U.S.A.

ABSTRACT: A unique tufa and stromatolite succession, represented by the uppermost 10 m of the 1.8 Ga Hearne Formation (Pethei Group), northern Canada, developed across a large carbonate platform during a transition from normal marine to evaporitic conditions. In ascending order, the facies that document this transition consist of dendritically branching tufa, irregularly laminated flat to domal stromatolites, and even, iso-pachously laminated domal stromatolites. The morphologies and textures of these tufas and stromatolites are similar to structures produced in heavily mineralized depositional environments (e.g., hot-spring and hypersaline depositional systems). Comparison with structures produced in the mineralizing systems, as well as with laboratory experiments of biological growth and abiotic mineral precipitation, provide insight into the mechanistic processes that contributed to development of the unusual facies of the uppermost Hearne Formation.

This comparison suggests that the Hearne tufa and stromatolites were formed by biotic and abiotic processes whose influence on morphology fluctuated during the deposition of these facies. The key to understanding the dominant role of abiotic processes in development of these unusual carbonate fabrics lies in recognizing that these features formed during a transition from normal marine to evaporite conditions when seawater became warmer, increasingly saline, and more conducive to *in situ* mineralization. The tufa facies and domal, isopachously laminated stromatolite facies are both considered to have resulted from abiotic precipitation of carbonate mud induced by progressive oversaturation of seawater associated with increasing temperature and salinity during restriction of the Pethei basin. These facies are not observed in normal marine carbonates of this age and younger, and so the presence of such extreme environmental conditions are considered essential for the development of this facies. The generic growth mechanism of diffusion–limited aggregation (or similar depositional process) is invoked here to account for growth of micritic, dendritically branching tufa as a dominantly abiotic process. Similarly, domal stromatolites with even, isopachous laminae and evidence for surface–normal growth may have been produced mainly by abiotic mineral precipitation of micrite cement at the sediment–water interface. Whether or not micrite precipitation was kinetically aided by the presence of microbes remains uncertain, because there is no preserved evidence of such structures. However, the characteristically irregular lamination of the flat to domal stromatolites is most consistent with the former presence of discontinuous microbial mats, which would have trapped and bound loose sediment. Abundant precipitation is not indicated in this facies, because no calcified sheaths are preserved.

INTRODUCTION

Stromatolites are a conspicuous feature of many Precambrian open marine carbonate platforms and are commonly interpreted as the products of sediment trapping, binding, and/or precipitation as a result of growth and metabolic activity of microorganisms, principally cyanophytes (Awramik and Margulis, 1974, 1976; Riding, 1991). Today, stromatolites form in very limited environments in oceans and lakes although structures that are similar to stromatolites also form in hot-spring and cave settings (Walter, 1976; Chafetz and Folk, 1984; Riding, 1991). On the basis of comparisons with modern marine examples (e.g., Logan et al., 1964), distinctive morphologies of Precambrian stromatolites are oftentimes invoked to make paleogeographic and paleoceanographic interpretations of carbonate-platform geometries (cf. Serebryakov and Semikhatov, 1974; Hoffman, 1974; Cecile and Campbell, 1978; Grotzinger, 1986). However, some stromatolites that formed in the early Precambrian, when *in situ* seafloor precipitation was more common, may have been produced abiotically (Grotzinger and Read, 1983; Hofmann and Jackson, 1988; Grotzinger 1989, 1990; Sami and James, 1996; Kah and Knoll, 1996; Sumner and Grotzinger, 1996; Sumner 1997a, 1997b; Bartley et al., this volume), or at least the role of biogenic processes in affecting texture and morphology may be minimal or indistinguishable in the resultant rock (Grotzinger and Rothman, 1996).

Because biological records are sparse in Precambrian stromatolites, the biogenicity of these structures is difficult to prove (Buick et al., 1981), and interpretations are commonly inferential, based on comparison with morphologically similar structures formed in modern environments (Walter, 1976; Semi-

khatov et al., 1979; Burne and Moore, 1987; Schopf, 1994). Biological structures produced in the laboratory (Fujikawa and Matsushita, 1989; Ben-Jacob et al., 1992, 1994) as well as biologically induced structures forming in modern travertine systems support a biogenic role for development of some of these structures (Chafetz and Folk, 1984; Guo and Riding, 1994; Cady and Farmer, 1996). However, some abiotically constructed tufa and stromatolite fabrics, which are morphologically similar to ancient stromatolites, are present in modern travertine deposits (e.g., Pentecost, 1990; Guo and Riding, 1994; Jones and Renaut, 1995, 1996; Renaut and Jones, 1997) and also are similar to structures produced by abiotic mineral deposition systems in the laboratory (Galathra et al., 1992). This indicates that some tufa and stromatolite fabrics may form without the significant morphological influence of biological communities and that the assessment of morphology, in many cases, may be an indiscriminant parameter for establishing biogenicity (cf. Grotzinger and Rothman, 1996). This does not mean that microorganisms (cyanophytes and other bacteria) are not present in most if not all natural settings; rather it emphasizes that the role of biology in certain systems may be passive in the development of structures (e.g. Pentecost, 1990; Jones and Renaut, 1995, 1996; Renaut and Jones, 1997; Bartley et al., this volume), or may not result in development of a uniquely biologic morphology. Thus, determining the relative roles of biology, sedimentation, and *in situ* mineral precipitation becomes more difficult to decipher in these and other ancient stromatolites. However, certain unique structures in stromatolites, specifically those that can be replicated in the laboratory or closely monitored in modern depositional systems, will likely provide insights into the depositional processes during their formation.

In the East Arm of Great Slave Lake, northwest Canada, a transition from a carbonate platform into marine redbeds with carbonates and vanished evaporites is marked on the inner shelf

---

*Present Address: Department of Geology, Washington State University, Pullman, WA, 99164, U.S.A.

of the Hearne Formation (1.8 Ga; uppermost Pethei Group) by 10 m of distinctive morphologies and textures, including: dendritically branching tufa, flat-to-domal irregularly laminated stromatolites, and isopachous, evenly laminated stromatolites. These facies are unusual, resembling no other unit in the underlying Pethei carbonate platform, which is up to 600 m thick. However, by studying and reconstructing the likely growth processes in these stromatolites, and through comparison to appropriate modern (e.g., nonmarine and coastal salina) and experimental analogs, we hope to further understanding of the processes for growth of ancient stromatolites, at both the macroscale and the microscale.

In this paper we use a nongenetic definition for the term "stromatolite" because of the difficult problems associated with definitively establishing a biogenic origin for most ancient stromatolites (Grotzinger and Knoll, 1999). According to Semikhatov et al. (1979), "Stromatolites are laminated, lithified, sedimentary growth structures that accrete away from a point or limited surface attachment. They are commonly, but not necessarily, of microbial origin and calcareous composition".

TECTONIC AND STRATIGRAPHIC SETTING

The Great Slave Lake Supergroup was deposited in a compound transpressional–transtensional foreland basin (Fig. 1) that developed in response to collision of the Slave craton and the Taltson–Thelon volcanic arc (Hoffman, 1987, 1989) between 1.93 and 1.85 Ga (Bowring et al., 1984). The Great Slave Lake Supergroup crops out in a narrow, elongate synclinorium along the shores of the East Arm of Great Slave Lake (Fig. 1). Previous work on regional basin architecture is provided by Stockwell (1933, 1936), Hoffman et al. (1977), and Hoffman (1981, 1987).

The Great Slave Lake Supergroup (~12 km thick) records four distinctive periods (Fig. 1) of basin development and sedimentation (Hoffman, 1968, 1988): 1) rifting and thermal cooling (Union Island and Sosan Groups); 2) establishment of a foredeep (Kahochella Group) and attendant volcanism (Seton Island Volcanics) during initial collision (Ross and Smith, 1985); 3) carbonate platform development (Pethei Group); and 4) filling of the basin by progradation of marine and nonmarine siliciclastics (Christie Bay Group). The transition from the Pethei Group into the overlying Christie Bay Group records a change in deposition from marine carbonate platform into marine siliciclastics, carbonates, and evaporites, capped by nonmarine siliciclastic rocks. The tufa and stromatolites described in this paper are found as part of the inner-platform facies assemblage and represent the transition from the marine carbonate platform to overlying marine carbonates, evaporites, and siliciclastics.

The Pethei carbonate platform records three distinctive transgressive–regressive depositional sequences (Fig. 2). The lower two of the Pethei sequences display well-defined platform-to-basin transitions with transgressive phases corresponding to platform-submerged events and regressive phases marked by platform-shoaled events (Hoffman, 1974; Sami and James, 1993, 1994). The uppermost sequence architecture is less clear because of subsequent tectonic imbrication and erosion. However, outcrops of the uppermost Hearne Formation (inner-platform position), indicate that this formation also shallows up-

ward but there is little preserved evidence of a clear platform-to-basin transition and the regressive part of the sequence likely continues into the basal Stark Formation. The uppermost Hearne Formation is regionally correlative with deep-water facies of the uppermost Pekanatui Point Formation (Hoffman, 1974; Sami and James, 1994). Detailed work on carbonate sedimentology and stratigraphy, with special emphasis on gross stromatolite morphology in the Pethei Group, is provided by Hoffman (1967, 1968, 1969, 1974, 1989) and Sami and James (1993, 1994, 1996). Sami and James (1996) considered the Pethei carbonate platform to be composed predominantly (~57–75%) of abiogenically precipitated, synsedimentary sparry and micritic cements and crusts similar to many other Paleoproterozoic and Archean carbonate platforms (Grotzinger, 1989; Sumner and Grotzinger, 1996).

The Hearne Formation, the uppermost unit of the inner-platform facies of the Pethei Group is approximately 100 m thick and is best exposed at Blanchet Island (Figs. 1, 3). The basal limestone of the Hearne Formation sharply overlies dolomitized laterally-linked domal stromatolites at the top of the underlying Wildbread Formation (Figs. 2, 4). The contact between these two formations is a sharp, irregular surface that commonly is overlain by clasts of the underlying domal stromatolites. Dolomitization limited to the upper part of the Wildbread Formation and rip-up clasts in the base of the Hearne Formation suggests that the bounding surface was subaerially exposed prior to deposition of the Hearne.

The Hearne Formation is conformably overlain by the Stark Formation, although minor submarine erosion of uppermost Hearne lithologies may have occurred locally. The Stark Formation is a breccia consisting of rounded to angular clasts of dolostone, siltstone, and shale in a calcareous shale matrix (Hoffman, 1968; Hoffman et al., 1977; Badham and Stanworth, 1977; Pope and Grotzinger 1997). Brecciation in the Stark Formation was produced by dissolution of bedded evaporites (mainly halite) deposited near the base of this unit and subsequent collapse of overlying units (Badham and Stanworth, 1977; Hoffman et al., 1977; Pope and Grotzinger, 1997). Consequently, the upper Hearne records conditions of increasing restriction leading up to this basin-wide salinity crisis. This salinity crisis may have been regional in extent, covering most of the Slave craton (Hoffman et al., 1977; Grotzinger et al., 1985; Hoffman and Grotzinger, 1993).

HEARNE FORMATION

Lower Hearne Formation

The lower ~90 m of the Hearne Formation is dominated by thick-bedded, irregularly laminated red or gray limestone and lesser amounts of dolomite (Hoffman, 1968), corresponding to the Prone Microbial Laminite facies of Sami and James (1994, 1996). Laminae are 1–2 mm thick and composed of irregular, discontinuous layers of fibrous sparry calcite overlain by thin, discontinuous micritic films. Fenestrae and voids in this facies commonly are filled by clear, blocky, equant sparry calcite or dolomite formed during later diagenesis.

Subvertical red and gray limestone with a columnar texture are found as thin discontinuous units in the lower Hearne For-

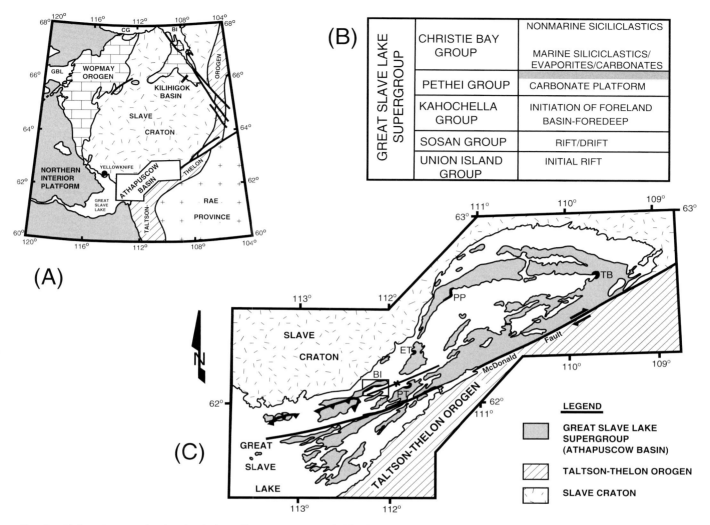

FIG. 1.—A) Location map showing the Archean Slave craton surrounded by three synchronous Paleoproterozoic foredeeps located in: Wopmay Orogen, Kilohigok basin, and the Athapuscow basin of the Great Slave Lake area (inset map). GBL = Great Bear Lake; CG = Coronation Gulf; BI = Bathurst Inlet. B) The generalized stratigraphic column in the upper right shows the units and phases of basin development in the Great Slave Lake Supergroup (modified from Hoffman, 1988). The stratigraphic position of the uppermost Hearne Formation tufa and stromatolites is shown by an inset black square. C) Simplified geologic map, Athapuscow Basin, East Arm of Great Slave Lake. The Great Slave Lake Supergroup outcrops in a gently south–plunging synclinorium with shallow dips on the north–northwest limb and steep, often overturned dips on the south–southeast limb. Areas of uppermost Hearne Formation outcrops studied for this paper are shown in black (see Figure 1B for stratigraphic position) and labeled BI, Blanchet Island; ET, Et–then Island; PT, Pte a Tuer; PP, Pethei Peninsula; and TB, Tochatwi Bay. The area for Figure 3 is shown by the black rectangle. Modified from Hoffman (1988).

mation. The columns are 1 to 3 cm wide and are defined by segregations of dark red dolomicrite with lighter gray, fibrous marine (?) cement between columns. Laminae are irregular and cannot be followed from one column to another. The columnar limestone makes elliptical domes (1 to 3 m wide), with synoptic relief of less than 0.5 m in the basal Hearne Formation. These domes are oriented perpendicular to the paleoshoreline and are similar to domes in the underlying Utsingi Formation (Hoffman, 1967, 1974). Cross-bedded intraclastic limestone is found as discontinuous units in the upper part of the lower Hearne Formation. The cross-bedding is low angle and the intraclasts consist of small (2–10 mm diameter) micritic fragments supported in a sparry matrix.

Interpretation.—The lack of subaerial exposure indicators (mudcracks, prism cracks, sheet cracks, and dissolution surfaces) indicate that all units in the lower Hearne Formation were deposited in a shallow subtidal setting (Hoffman, 1968, 1974; Sami and James, 1994). The irregular laminae accreted by precipitation of primary sea-floor cements and settling of lime muds from suspension, followed by early lithification through precipitation of spar cement (Sami and James, 1994). Irregularly shaped, clotted micrite bodies within laminae are interpreted to represent precipitation of magnesian calcite associated with microbial bodies (Sami and James, 1994, 1996). The presence of cross-bedding near the top of this unit indicates that water depths decreased or high-energy wave or current events became more common during the later stages of deposition of this unit, indicating overall shallowing of the sea floor.

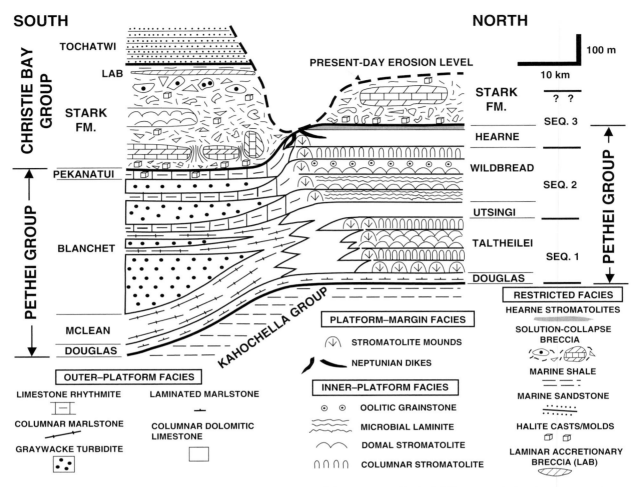

FIG. 2.—Stratigraphy of the uppermost Kahochella, Pethei and lowermost Christie Bay groups. The Pethei Group records three large transgressive–regressive depositional sequences with inner–platform and equivalent outer platform facies (right-hand and left-hand sides, respectively). The location of the Hearne Formation tufa, flat–to–domal irregularly laminated stromatolites, and isopachous, evenly–laminated stromatolites is shown by gray shading. Modified from Hoffman (1968, 1974) and Sami and James (1996).

Upper Hearne Formation

The upper 10 m of the Hearne Formation is composed of three distinctive facies, in ascending order: 1) dendritically branching tufa; 2) flat, irregularly laminated stromatolites grading up into domal irregularly laminated stromatolites; and 3) isopachous, evenly laminated stromatolites forming geometric, self-similar domes. The characteristics of these facies are presented in Table 1.

Dendritically Branching Tufa.—Dendritically branching tufa (~3 m thick) consists of subvertically oriented micritic bushes (20 to 80 mm wide) composed of a primary stalk and secondary branches (Fig. 5A, C). Crude layering, on the order of 1 to 2 cm thick, is produced by horizontal accumulations of insoluble residues, dark organic (?) material, silica, and stylolites. Locally, the subhorizontal layering is subdued and tufa fabrics are stacked to produce larger composite structures 30 to 50 cm high and 10 to 30 cm wide with divergent (Fig. 5B) or irregularly inclined geometries. The stalk and secondary branches of the tufas are composed of irregular clumps of micritic calcite (<10 μm); however, the stalk and branches commonly are not well

preserved because of later diagenetic recrystallization of the carbonate mud. Cross-sections of individual bushes are circular and up to 1 cm in diameter. A sharp irregular surface marks the boundary with overlying flat, irregularly laminated stromatolite units on Blanchet Island, but on the Pethei Peninsula the contact between these units is gradational. Tufa bushes contain brown, possibly organic residues, and spherical particles 20 mm in diameter that are preserved in crystals of coarse spar cement. Many of the micritic clumps appear to be coated with fibrous calcite cement (<10 mm length). Voids between and within bushes commonly are filled with neomorphic bladed or fibrous rim cement and a later coarse, equant spar cement. Voids rarely contain fine crystalline silica, or are now unfilled.

These distinctive tufas with their stalk and secondary branches have a more organized structure than irregular micritic tufa-like clots described from the Prone Microbial facies of the Hearne Formation (Sami and James, 1994, 1996). Also, these dendritically branching tufas comprise the entire thickness of this 3-m-thick unit, and although they are commonly encrusted by radial calcite cements they are not interbedded with subhor-

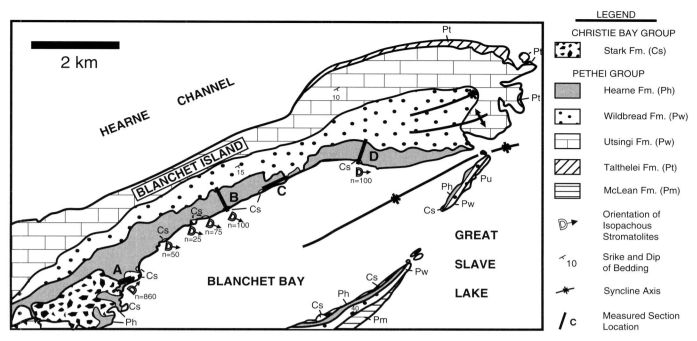

FIG. 3.—Close–up map from Figure 1 of outcrops of the Pethei Group and Stark Formations surrounding Blanchet Bay. Hearne Formation outcrops are marked by gray shading. Orientation of isopachous evenly laminated stromatolite domes is shown by double "D" and arrow. The straight side of the "D" corresponds to the steep side of the domes, and the rounded side of the "D" is the gently sloping side. The arrow shows the preferred northeast orientation of the gently sloping side of the domes. Number of measurements = *n*. Locations of measured sections in Figure 4 are labeled A, B, C, D. The paleocurrent direction of these stromatolites (~E/NE) is roughly parallel to a wind direction predicted for deposition at 10–20° north of the Paleoproterozoic equator (Hoffman and Grotzinger, 1993).

izontal crusts of radial fibrous precipitate, as are the micritic clots of the Lower Hearne (Sami and James, 1996).

Interpretation.—The dendritically branching tufa facies represents subaqueous deposition in a quiet-water setting that allowed the stalks to grow upright or slightly inclined and develop branches. The subhorizontal laminae in these tufas serve as growth markers to indicate that growth of individual shrubs did not extend far above the sediment–water interface, probably less than 2 cm. Constant thickness and lateral continuity of the dendritically branching tufa unit (3 m × tens to hundreds of square kilometers) indicates that processes which formed these structures were widespread during later Hearne time. The uniform, fine grain size of calcite crystals in the dendritic structures indicates that they formed by direct precipitation of calcite crystals from the water column. The preservation of delicate branching structures and abundance of primary void space (filled by later cements) indicate that the structures were either lithified at the time of growth or as a result of very early marine cementation. *In situ* calcite precipitation and filling of voids with fibrous marine cements produced the rigid framework around and within the dendritic micritic bushes.

The morphology of the Hearne dendritic tufas are remarkably similar to Holocene travertine samples (cf. Chafetz, 1981, his fig. 1a, b; Chafetz and Folk, 1984, their fig. 1; Pentecost, 1995, his fig. 3a) though their scales may be slightly different, being more representative of larger forms in these deposits (e.g., Guo and Riding, 1992, their fig. 10; Pursell and Folk, 1990; Jones and Renaut, 1995; Jones et al., 1996). The morphology of these dendritically branching tufas in travertine are commonly attrib-

uted to bacterial growth (Folk et al., 1985; Chafetz and Folk, 1984; Guo and Riding, 1994; Chafetz, 1981), although abiotic growth mechanisms for similar fabrics, even in the presence of bacteria, also have been proposed (Pentecost, 1990; Jones and Renaut, 1995, 1996; Renaut and Jones, 1997).

Dendritic shrubs in most Holocene travertine deposits are composed of low-Mg calcite, and the elementary building block is a bacterial clump (10–40 mm diameter) encased in a single calcite crystal (Folk et al., 1985; Guo and Riding, 1994; Jones and Renaut, 1995). However, some abiotically produced dendritic shrubs in travertines may be composed of radiating needles of aragonite (Pentecost, 1990). Modern travertine shrubs commonly are composed of upward-radiating chains and groups of calcite crystals (including individual bacterial clumps). Layering in Recent travertine is commonly 1 to 3 cm thick and many have daily to yearly laminae (0.1 to 0.5 mm thick) (Chafetz and Folk, 1984; Pentecost, 1990; Guo and Riding, 1992). Bacteria forming modern travertine tufa shrubs are photosynthetic, growing only during daylight hours and commonly producing 1–3 cm thick beds (range 1 mm to 8 cm); alternation of tufa shrubs and thinly laminated sediment may form daily cycles (Pentecost, 1995). Shrubs form thin-bedded deposits (3 cm thick) in shallow-level ponds of warm, bacteria- and H_2S-rich waters (Chafetz and Folk, 1984; Cady and Farmer, 1996). Micritic carbonate crusts in such settings commonly are formed by bacterially mediated, *in situ* carbonate precipitation (Chafetz and Bucynski, 1992).

Dendritic fabrics in modern travertine systems develop only under extreme environmental conditions: shallow water that is

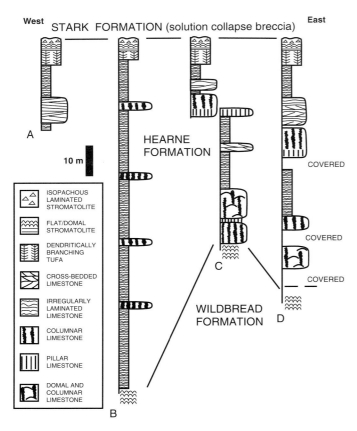

FIG. 4.—Detailed measured sections of the Hearne Formation along the north side of Blanchet Bay. The unique tufa and stromatolites that are the focus of this paper occur in uppermost 10 m.

highly oversaturated with respect to CaCO$_3$, elevated pH (>7.5), and elevated temperatures (>30°C and commonly >80°C) (Chafetz and Folk, 1984; Folk et al., 1985; Jones and Renaut, 1995, 1996; Pentecost, 1990, 1995; Guo and Riding, 1994; Guo et al., 1996; Renaut and Jones, 1997). Laboratory experiments and observation of modern travertines indicate that dendritic fabrics develop rapidly under unusual disequilibrium depositional conditions, which include highly supersaturated solutions, elevated temperatures, and enhanced CO$_2$ degassing (Jones and Kahle, 1986; 1993, discussion and references therein; Jones and Renaut, 1995, 1996; Renaut and Jones, 1997). Organic or inorganic impurities in the water column may also facilitate the growth of dendritic structures by altering the saturation state necessary for dendritic growth (Jones and Kahle, 1986 and references therein). Electrochemical deposition of zinc and copper oxides in the laboratory produces purely abiotic dendritic branching structures that are morphologically similar to the Hearne tufa (Matsushita et al., 1985; Galathra et al., 1992). These dendritic structures form through aggregation of particles that precipitate directly from solution. However, dendritic structures develop only when the electrochemical potential is high (Galathra et al., 1992; Grier et al., 1986), otherwise flat-laminated, domal, and simple columnar structures are formed (Galathra et al., 1992). These laboratory experiments indicate that dendritic structures could be produced in natural mineralizing systems, but probably only during very restricted chemical conditions. In such settings biotic processes might also play a role in development of dendritic tufa morphology, but its role is unclear at present.

Supersaturation of ordinary, open-marine Paleoproterozoic seawater was likely high (Grotzinger, 1989; Grotzinger and Kasting, 1993; Sumner and Grotzinger, 1996), and evaporation during terminal Hearne time probably increased the carbonate saturation and seawater temperature. The metabolic activities of cyanobacteria or bacteria also may have helped increase the carbonate saturation in the latest Hearne time, but modern trav-

TABLE 1.—CHARACTERISTICS OF UPPERMOST TUFA AND STROMATOLITE FACIES—HEARNE FORMATION

Unit/Type (Thickness)	Mineralogy	Description	Interpretation
Isopachous, Evenly Laminated Stromatolite (3 meters)	Dolomite	Small asymmetric domes (less than 40 cm wide) with crudely triangular cross–sections, formed of isopachous, even laminae composed of dolomicrite (<10 mm diameter); domes have a steep and gently inclined side; laminae on gently inclined side contain small-scale ridges and swales that resemble sheet–flow structures in hot springs; laminae are commonly 1 to 10 mm thick and are internally graded; many micritic layers are clotted or irregular with possible subvertical structures	*In situ* chemical precipitate structure produced by settling and aggregation of dolomite mud from the water column; little or no biological influence over morphology; clotted to irregular subvertical textures in finest micrite layers may be remnants of filamentous bacteria; slow to moderate accretion rate, growth normal to antecedent domal topography; extreme environmental restriction
Flat to Domal Irregularly Laminated Stromatolite (4 meters)	Limestone	Irregular domes up to 15 cm across composed of irregular laminae (1 to 10 mm thick); laminae composed of sparry calcite (20 to 150 mm diameter) layer alternating with organic-rich micritic (<10 mm diameter) calcite layer; contains portions of subvertical micritic structures similar to dendritic "bushes" described below	Combined biological and chemical structure; uneven laminae likely produced by irregularities in the microbial substrate (mat) and irregularities produced by production of micritic bushes; domes produced by response to chemical precipitation fluctuation in physicochemical parameters; normal to restricted environmental setting
Dendritically Branching Tufa (3 meters)	Limestone	Bushes 10 to 30 cm wide, 30 to 50 cm high in outcrop; individual bushes composed of irregular, micritic clumps (<20 mm diameter) that form "stalks" with divergent "branches" surrounded by neomorphic bladed or fibrous calcite cements with coarse, equant, blocky calcite cements infilling remaining pore space; bushes are circular in cross–section; subhorizontal laminae defined by accumulations of organic matter and insoluble residues, but not accumulated sediment layers	Chemically precipitated structures produced by *in situ* precipitation, settling and aggregation of calcite; biological influence unknown; rapid (?) depositional rate, extreme environmental restriction

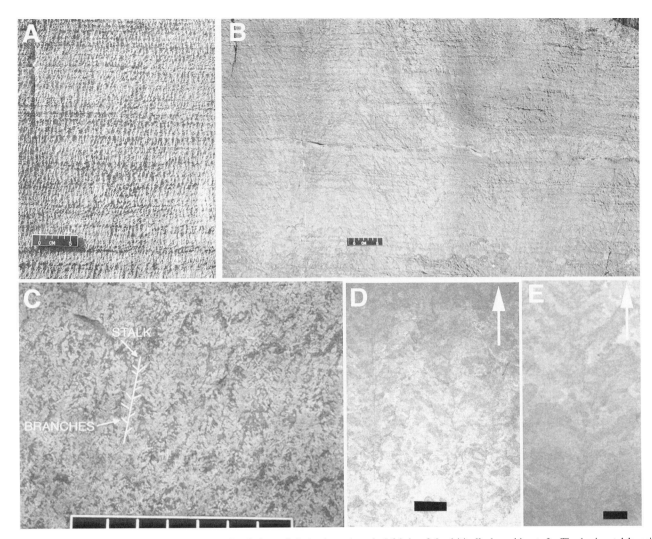

FIG. 5.—Dendritically branching tufa. A) Cross–sectional view of distinctive subvertical fabric of dendritically branching tufa. The horizontal layering is subdued in this view. B) Cross–sectional view shows a large scale (>10 cm wide, >50 cm high) divergent, branching fabric that is composed of multiple smaller layers of dendritically branching tufa. C) Close–up of the dendritically branching tufa. Light gray micrite forms the stalks and branches of each tufa element, whereas dark gray fibrous marine cement fills voids between the tufa elements. Scale bar is in centimeters. D) Photomicrograph of multiple dendritically branching tufa elements. The vertically oriented central stalks and dendritically aligned branches are dense dark brown micrite, and the rest of the slide is light gray fibrous marine cement. Scale bar is ~0.5 cm. E) Photomicrograph of an individual dendritically branching tufa element. Scale bar is ~0.2 cm.

ertine examples indicate that this mechanism is not necessary for the production of dendritic structures in this setting (Pentecost, 1990; Guo and Riding, 1994; Jones and Renaut, 1995; Renaut and Jones, 1997). Thus, the Hearne tufa is postulated to have grown through *in situ* calcite precipitation in warm, highly oversaturated sea water, with either direct settling and aggregation of carbonate mud, or diffusion of ions to the sediment–water interface, where carbonate precipitated to form the dendritically branching structures, in a manner similar to laboratory deposition of zinc and copper dendrites (e.g., Matsushita et al., 1985; Galathra et al., 1992).

Tufa Morphology: Formational and Depositional Processes.—
The most important aspect of the depositional model presented here is that bacteria in modern, oversaturated oceans (Li et al., 1969) do not form dendrites under normal marine conditions, even though surfaces are covered with bacteria. In contrast,

dendritic, tufa fabrics most commonly are produced in highly oversaturated conditions (Jones and Kahle, 1986, 1993; Jones and Renaut, 1995). Consequently, regardless of whether the Hearne tufas were formed biologically or abiologically, their presence in the uppermost Hearne Formation suggests that seawater at that time was highly oversaturated with respect to calcium carbonate. Development of such highly oversaturated marine waters was likely produced by increasing restriction and evaporation immediately prior to deposition of evaporites.

Morphologies of biotic and abiotic dendritic, tufa-like structures produced in modern settings and laboratory experiments are qualitatively indistinguishable, and the scant evidence for biotic activity makes it difficult to determine the most important processes in development of the Hearne tufas. Nevertheless, reference to modern analogues indicates that environmental conditions during tufa formation were highly restricted, and out of equilibrium. Under these conditions formation of the dendritic tufa probably was very rapid (Galathra et al., 1992; Pentecost, 1990). Aggregation of carbonate ions (or a similar mechanism) at the sediment–water interface to form *in situ* precipitates is the most likely growth mechanism for Hearne tufa. Microbes present on the growing surface might have helped induce *in situ* precipitation, but their effect is uncertain because of the paucity of fossil evidence. Furthermore, because microbes, especially bacteria, are common in nearly all surficial environments (Walter, 1996) we consider the absence of dendritic tufa formed under normal marine conditions to be critical evidence in establishing the fundamental importance of environmental parameters in controlling the growth of Hearne tufa.

Irregularly laminated, Flat to Domal Stromatolites.—Subhorizontal, irregularly-laminated stromatolites (~4 m thick) overlie the dendritic, branching tufa. The basal 0.5 to 1.0 m of this unit consists of flat, irregularly laminated stromatolites that grade up into domal, irregularly laminated stromatolites that become more irregular in an upward direction by increasing their surface roughness (Fig. 6). Plan view of the domal stromatolites shows many irregular elliptical shapes (Fig. 7A). Thin (<5 cm thick), discontinuous intraclastic layers are locally developed. Laminae (1–10 mm thick) in the irregularly laminated stromatolites are defined by variations in grain size of carbonate, with light-colored coarser layers composed of sparry calcite (20–150 mm) and finer-grained, dark brown layers of micritic

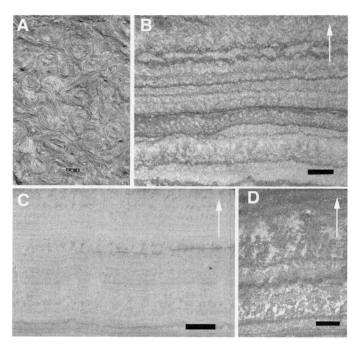

FIG. 7.—Flat to domal stromatolites. A) Plan view of domal stromatolites. The domal shapes are quite irregular and randomly oriented. Individual laminae show variable thickness and are locally discontinuous. B) Photomicrograph of uneven laminae in this facies. Light layers are sparry calcite with micritic clots; dark layers are carbonate mud. Irregularities in the laminae are produced by irregularities in both the upper surface of the upward-propagating, coarser calcite spar portion of the laminae and the upper surface of the micritic portion of the laminae, which formed by settling of crystals from suspension in the water column. Dark brown, micritic clots in the sparry parts of the laminae may be tufa–like clots (*sensu* Sami and James 1996). Scale bar is 2.5 mm. C) Polished slab showing cross–section of uneven, subhorizontal laminae and small micritic tufa layers within the flat to domal stromatolites. This facies is developed only locally in these stromatolites, but it suggests that minor tufa growth did occur during development of this facies. Scale bar is ~0.5 cm. D) Photomicrograph of the tufa fabrics within the flat to domal stromatolites. The tufa consists of irregular clots of micrite surrounded by coarse sparry cement. These tufa fabrics are much less organized than the underlying dendritically branching tufa. Scale bar is 2 mm.

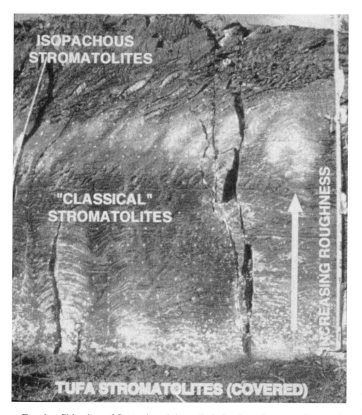

FIG. 6.—Side view of flat to domal, irregularly laminated stromatolites grading upward into isopachously laminated stromatolites located near measured section A. Dots on rock face are 10 cm apart. The length of individual laminae increases upsection, indicating an increase in surface roughness.

(<10 mm) calcite (Fig. 7B). Some of the thicker laminae contain micritic clots that resemble tufa-like micritic clots of the Prone Microbial Laminite facies (Sami and James, 1996). The micritic clots are oriented perpendicular to the depositional surface and in plan view are nearly circular. Alternating layers of micritic clots and lime mudstone (each 0.2 to 1 cm thick) are locally common in this facies (Fig. 7C, D). The lime mudstone drapes the bushes, producing subhorizontal, irregular laminae. Locally, irregular topography produced by mud layers draping bushes is propagated upward to produce upward-widening, smoothed domes (Fig. 7C). Neomorphism of calcite and diagenetic recrystallization to dolomite cement does not preserve original textures. Finer-grained micritic layers commonly include organic detritus, stylolites, and angular quartz grains less than 100 mm in diameter. Brown organic (?) spheres (50–200 mm in diameter) occur in both the sparry and micritic layers. The domal stromatolites at the top of this unit grade upward into the overlying isopachous, evenly laminated stromatolites (Fig. 6).

Interpretation: Macrotextures.—The irregularly laminated flat to domal stromatolites are morphologically similar to laminated Precambrian stromatolites formed under normal-marine conditions (Walter, 1976; Semikhatov et al., 1979; Grotzinger, 1986; Knoll, 1985). Traditionally, changes in stromatolite morphology are interpreted to represent changes in biologic communities (e.g., Walter, 1976) or physical conditions such as current flow directions and velocities (e.g., Semikhatov et al., 1979). A third possibility recognizes the potentially important role of changing seawater chemistry (Grotzinger, 1990). In highly oversaturated conditions, abiotic growth through *in situ* precipitation may have led to a similar transition as a result of fluctuations in the chemical composition of seawater.

The first mechanism, principally biological, would invoke the role of microbial mats, which may have influenced the development of the uneven laminae, acting mainly as irregular substrates for deposited carbonate mud (Monty, 1976; Golubic, 1991; Pentecost, 1995). The transition from flat to domal morphology also may record a change in microbial communities within this structure. However modern stromatolites showing similar morphologies can be produced by more than one microorganism or community of microorganisms. For example, modern pinnacle mats from Shark Bay, China, and Mexico were produced by communities dominated by *Schizothrix, Phormidium,* and *Lyngbya,* respectively (Golubic, 1985; Javor and Castenholz, 1981; Zhang and Hoffmann, 1992). Flat to domal morphologic transitions in stromatolites and microbial mats are documented in normal marine, evaporite, polar lake, and travertine settings (Hoffman, 1974; Chafetz and Folk, 1984, Logan et al., 1964; Feldmann and McKenzie, 1997; Love et al., 1983). These settings are characterized by subtidal deposition in environmentally restricted conditions, which preserves their morphologic shapes and microbial components. In the case of the Hearne stromatolites, no direct evidence of fossil mats is preserved.

Alternatively, the upward transition from flat to domal morphology of the upper Hearne stromatolite laminae may record a change in response to fluctuating physical processes, such as an increase in water depth to produce a decrease in wave-generated current velocities (e.g., Logan et al., 1964; Semikhatov et al., 1979; Casanova, 1994). Flat stromatolites commonly are interpreted to have formed in shallow intertidal conditions (Logan et al., 1964); however, the lack of exposure features in the flat Hearne stromatolites indicate that they formed in a subtidal setting. Similarly, modern domal stromatolites commonly form in deeper subtidal settings (e.g., Dill et al., 1986), so a flat to domal transition commonly is interpreted to represent upward-deepening conditions.

Finally, chemically-based depositional systems produced in the laboratory commonly produce morphological transitions that are similar to the flat to domal transition in the Hearne stromatolites. In the experiments of Galathra et al. (1992), a flat to domal transition is produced as the growth surface reaches a steady-state equilibrium morphology for a given set of initial conditions—the morphology changes (time-dependent roughening), but the external conditions are not varied. Once this type of self-organizing depositional system reaches a steady state, the surface roughness remains constant in time; however, the depositional surface may evolve through several different geometries on the way to this final steady state. The important point is that substantial changes in morphology, expressed in a vertical succession, may relate only to time-dependent evolution of the depositional surface to steady state, and not necessarily to fluctuations in any external or internal parameters. This can be true for both abiotic and biotic systems.

Interpretation: Microtextures.—The micritic clots in the coarser-grained layers look like arrays of irregular cauliflower–shaped heads interbedded within irregularly laminated carbonate mud. Couplets of laminated carbonate mud and clotted micritic bushes indicate subtle variations in environmental conditions during deposition and are similar to couplets produced in modern travertine and hot-spring settings (Chafetz and Folk, 1984; Guo and Riding, 1992). Alternating layers of micritic clots and laminated micrite indicate that clot growth was not a continuous process and that increased sediment flux or *in situ* precipitation of micrite could disrupt and interfere with continuous clot growth. Couplets of continuous carbonate mud and micritic tufa clots surrounded by coarser sparry calcite cement indicates that *in situ* cementation was early—otherwise, flat, overlying micritic sediment would have filled the primary void space within the clots. Discontinuous intraclastic layers indicate early cementation, local erosion, and sediment reworking and deposition by waves.

The rare, dark brown organic-rich spherules likely are fossil coccoid cyanobacteria, and their presence in both coarser-grained and finer-grained layers suggests that they did not influence the morphology of the resultant laminae (see also Bartley et al., this volume). The angular quartz grains in the finer-grained layers are interpreted as eolian detritus, analogous to wind-blown dust interbedded with Permian carbonates in the Permian basin of west Texas (Fischer and Sarnthein, 1988).

Flat-to-Domal Stromatolite Morphologies: Formational and Depositional Processes.—Micritic tufa clots indicate *in situ* precipitation of carbonate mud. It is not clear whether these micritic clots were produced biotically (e.g., Sami and James, 1996) or abiotically in a process similar to that described for the underlying tufa fabric. Nonetheless, development of these tufa fabrics does indicate that environmental conditions during deposition of this facies were occasionally highly oversaturated with respect to calcium carbonate.

The irregularly laminated carbonate mud layers, which form most of this facies, also could have been produced biotically (e.g., trapping and binding of precipitated mud) or abiotically (e.g., *in situ* precipitation of carbonate mud). It is not possible at present to definitively determine which of these is the dominant process in formation of this facies.

The gross morphologic transition from flat to domal stromatolites in this facies could represent changes in biologic processes or communities or fluctuations in environmental conditions. However, because microorganisms are only rarely preserved in this facies, and there is no independent sedimentological evidence suggestive of fluctuations in physical conditions (e.g., Serebryakov and Semikhatov, 1974; Chafetz and Folk, 1984; Casanova, 1994), we must consider the possibility that this transition was produced abiotically by *in situ* precipitation of carbonate mud from a highly oversaturated body of water. Highly oversaturated waters may lead to deposition of dendritic structures (Jones and Kahle, 1986, 1993; Jones and Renaut, 1995), and experimental (Galathra et al., 1992) and numerical modeling studies (Barabasi and Stanley, 1995) suggest that initial perturbations in surface topography could have been propagated upward to form the highly irregular domes. It is likely that both biotic and abiotic processes contributed to development of the flat to domal stromatolites, but we cannot now determine which processes were dominant.

Isopachous, Evenly Laminated Stromatolites.—Irregularly laminated domal stromatolites of the underlying unit grade up into dolomitic, isopachous, evenly laminated stromatolites (~3 m thick). Bedding-plane exposures that reveal the depositional growth morphology of these stromatolites show randomly oriented large, smooth, composite domes with up to 40 cm of synoptic relief between the tops of the domes and their intervening troughs (Fig. 8A). These larger domes are composed of smaller, geometrically self-similar domes with isopachous, evenly laminated stromatolites. Individual laminae can be traced continuously across outcrops (Fig. 8B), from one dome to another, while maintaining a remarkably uniform thickness. In plan view (Fig. 8C) the individual stromatolite domes have a distinctive "D" shape (<40 cm across), and in cross-section they are highly asymmetric domes (~5 to 20 cm in length) with a steep, nearly vertical side and a more gradually inclined side (Fig. 8D). The gradually inclined sides of the domes are preferentially oriented to the E–NE (Fig. 4). Laminae on the gradually inclined sides have smaller asymmetric ridges and swales (Fig. 8D) that are propagated upward through the unit (Fig. 6). Three-dimensional preservation of these stromatolites produces very distinctive, asymmetrically tetrahedral domes (Fig. 8D).

Individual laminae (0.4 to 1 mm thick) are composed mainly of dolomicrite (<10 mm) and are extremely even and isopachous (Figs. 8E, F). Internal layering in laminae is defined by grading from fine dolosparite or coarser dolomicrite crystals into finer dolomicrite. The coarser layers commonly have irregular upper surfaces and crystal size grades upward into finer-grained dolomicrite. The transition from finer-grained layers into coarser sparry layers commonly is more abrupt. Internally the laminae contain thinner (<0.2 mm) discontinuous sublaminae or lamellae (Fig. 8F). Abundant stylolites in this facies commonly distort the original laminae. Stable-isotope values of these isopachous stromatolites are relatively heavy (~–4‰ $\delta^{18}O$; +3‰ $\delta^{13}C$) compared to the rest (–12 to –5‰ $\delta^{18}O$; 0 to +2‰ $\delta^{13}C$) of the Pethei Group (Whitaker et al., in press; Hotinski and Kump, 1997).

Interpretation.—The domal shape of the isopachous, evenly laminated stromatolites and the lack of exposure features in this unit indicate that they formed subaqueously. Preservation of very steep primary dips, the great lateral continuity and isopachous geometry of submillimeter-scale laminae, and general lack of sedimentary particles (except diffuse quartz silt) in this facies indicate that cementation likely took place syndepositionally. The uniformity of depositional morphologies and laminae thickness indicates these structures formed by *in situ* pre-

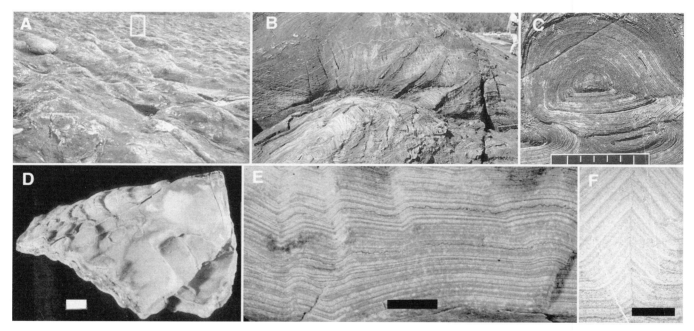

FIG. 8.—Isopachously laminated stromatolites. A) Outcrop bedding plane showing morphometric view of irregular domes at top of Hearne Formation, Blanchet Bay. Relief on the surface is ~40 cm. Hammer for scale. B) Cross–sectional view of isopachously laminated stromatolites. Individual laminae are continuous across the outcrop, and a few are highlighted by white chalk lines. Scale on right is in centimeters. C) Plan view of a single isopachously laminated stromatolite dome in cross–section. The distinctive "D" morphology of this dome is representative of plan-view cross–sections for most domes in this facies and was used to make the oriented measurements plotted in Figure 4. The straight side (toward bottom of photo) and the more curved side (toward top of photo) correspond to similar parts of the double "D" symbol in Figure 4. All domes in the basin are oriented with the flat side to the NW/SE and the curved side oriented to the N/NE. Superimposed upon the larger distinctive shape are smaller, regularly shaped structures protruding from both sides of the curved part. Note that each lamina retains its approximate uniform thickness throughout the dome. D) Side view of a three–dimensional isopachously laminated dome. Straight, steeper side (right) corresponds to straight side of dome in Figure 8C. Gently sloping side (left) corresponds to the curved side of dome in Figure 8C. Small ridges and swales appear only on the gently inclined side and correspond to smaller structures superimposed on the larger geometry of Figure 8C. Scale is ~2 cm. E) Polished hand sample showing cross–section of isopachous laminae. Laminae thickness is approximately uniform and isopachous across bumps and into troughs. Dark, irregular subhorizontal lines are stylolites. Scale is ~0.8 cm. F) Photomicrograph of isopachous laminae. Bases of laminae are light gray, coarser dolomicrite, and darker gray, finer dolomicrite marks the upper part of laminae. White cracks are late fractures filled with coarse spar, and dark fractures are filled with late silica. Scale is 2.5 mm.

cipitation of carbonate at the sediment–water interface, accounting for the surface-normal (isopachous) growth geometry that is so characteristic of this facies (e.g., Fig. 8F).

The uniform orientation of both large-scale domes and superposed ridge-and-swale structures suggests that a unidirectional physical parameter (e.g., wind-generated waves or currents) played a large part in formation of this facies. The preferred orientation of domes in this unit indicate that fluid flow during deposition was from the southeast toward the northeast and that the steep side of each dome faced basinward. The irregular ridge-and-swale structures on the gently sloping sides of mounds are morphologically similar to the micro-terrace sets of mineralizing hot-spring systems (Guo and Riding, 1994).

The extreme uniformity of laminae thickness throughout this unit indicates that the processes that formed these laminae were stable in both time and space. Very low flow velocities are indicated by the absence of current-formed features or lenses of sedimentary particles. Velocities must have been just high enough to impart an anisotropy to the domal structures, but not so much as to prevent mostly surface–normal growth, which creates the isopachous lamination.

The absence of laminoid fenestrae and concentrated organic matter suggests that if filamentous microbes were present they were not dense enough to form mats. Such a scenario would be very similar to that suggested for the "microlaminated" facies discussed by Bartley et al. (this volume).

Isopachous, even laminae are morphologically similar to laminae produced in modern terraced travertine deposits (Guo and Riding, 1992; Chafetz and Folk, 1984), Silurian carbonates directly beneath evaporites of the Michigan Basin (Huh et al., 1977; Petta, 1980), Permian stromatolites of the evaporitic Zechstein Basin (Smith, 1995), and Miocene stromatolites in Spain (Feldmann and McKenzie, 1997) and Egypt (Monty et al., 1987; Haddad et al., 1984; James et al., 1988) deposited just prior to the Messinian salinity crisis. The association of these lamination types with highly evaporative settings suggests that they preferentially formed in environments dominated by evaporatively concentrated seawater, with higher temperatures which led to enhanced chemical precipitation (Pope et al., in review). In such a setting the effects of biotic activity are likely overwhelmed by chemical (abiotic) processes. However, any cyanobacteria or bacteria that live in such settings produce a mucous coating that may act to trap and bind precipitated carbonate grains that formed in the overlying water column (Renaut and Jones, 1997). Alternatively, if these laminae formed by *in situ* precipitation of micrite (i.e., micrite cement) on the seafloor, then the coarser layers could reflect lower *in situ* nucleation rates, and thus crystals grow larger, and the finer crystals nucleate faster. In this scenario of nucleation control, growth rate is constant throughout the lamination. The alternative is to hold nucleation rate constant and change growth rate in time. However, the alternation of coarse and finer dolomite crystal layers may also just be an artifact of diagenetic recrystallization or neomorphism.

The even, isopachous laminae in the uppermost Hearne are suggestive of primary chemical precipitation in response to physicochemical processes related to increased evaporation and salinity immediately preceding Stark evaporite deposition. This is supported by the relatively heavy stable-isotope values recorded near the top of the Hearne Formation, which are con-

sistent with evaporitic conditions immediately prior to deposition of the Stark Formation (Whitaker et al., in press; Hotinski and Kump, 1997).

Isopachous Laminated Stromatolite Morphologies: Formational and Depositional Processes.—Deposition of fine-grained dolomite mud is interpreted to be a primary precipitate induced by the restrictive (i.e., highly oversaturated with respect to calcium carbonate) environmental conditions just prior to development of the overlying evaporites. This is supported by the uniformly fine grain size and preservation of sublamellae within laminae (Fig. 8F). Surface-normal growth and evenness of laminae in this facies indicates *in situ* precipitation of dolomite mud, probably at the sediment–water interface, as the dominant process in formation of these unique stromatolites. The uniform orientation of these stromatolites indicates that they formed under the influence of a slight, consistently uniform, probably wind-induced unidirectional current.

The observation of isopachous layering is significant and indicates growth normal to the depositional surface, so that all local slopes, no matter how steep or how shallow, were equally well accreted with carbonate. This provides an important constraint on the growth mechanism and suggests strongly that fallout of loose sediment, and by implication trapping and binding by microbial mats, was not the likely basis for growth. Assuming that all sediment settled and was trapped perfectly well, this mechanism would favor constant thickness of layering as measured vertically across the stromatolite. Instead, the lamination in these stromatolites is constant as measured normal to the interface, regardless of local curvature. Accordingly, this implies a local growth process in which sediment is produced at the sediment–water interface itself, such as *in situ* crystal growth (see below for further discussion). However, petrographic observations show a lack of palimpsest fibers of formerly large crystals, which differs from other well-described precipitated stromatolites (Grotzinger and Read, 1983; Hofmann and Jackson, 1988; Grotzinger and Knoll, 1995; Bartley et al., this volume). We interpret the lack of this texture and the presence of uniformly fine crystal size to indicate that nucleation of "micrite cement" was the mechanism by which these stromatolites grew—that accretion occurred by *in situ* precipitation as opposed to settling of micritic sediment is shown by the presence of surface-normal layering. Although this is geometrically consistent with abiotic growth (cf. Grotzinger and Rothman, 1996), it is possible that carbonate nucleation was controlled by the presence of thin biofilms (cf. Jones, 1995).

SEM ANALYSES

Broken fresh surfaces and surfaces etched in weak HCl of dendritically branching tufa and isopachous, evenly laminated stromatolites samples were observed with no coating in an Electroscan environmental scanning electron microscope at 30 kV. Irregular crystal outlines are clearly visible in these scans (Fig. 9), but none of the samples contained abundant filamentous or spherical nannostructures that might be interpreted as fossil microbes (cf. Chafetz and Folk, 1984; Folk, 1993). Bacteria commonly are called upon to mediate carbonate precipitation in mineralizing environments (Chafetz and Buczynski, 1992; Chafetz and Folk, 1984). The lack of abundant fossil cells in these samples should not be taken to indicate that microbes had

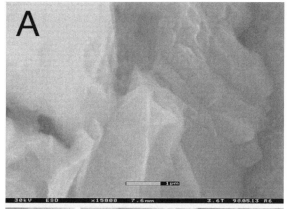

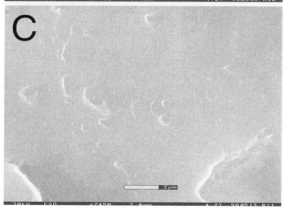

FIG. 9.—SEM views of etched isopachously laminated stromatolite (A) and tufa (B, C). A) Note abundant irregular crystal faces of dolomite and absence of organic remains. B) Sharp surface irregularities in the center are interpreted to be the edges of a micritic clump. C) The flat surface represents one of the calcite rhombohedrons, which is neomorphic, surrounding the micritic shrubs.

it is important to establish whether these structures formed in a marine or a nonmarine setting. Furthermore, comparison of the Hearne fabrics to similar structures produced in modern mineralizing systems places important constraints on microscopic growth mechanisms. Finally, the morphological variations between these facies and their interpreted growth mechanisms places constraints on the chemistry of the water body from which they precipitated.

Marine vs. Nonmarine Stromatolites

Given that many of the most suitable analogs for the Hearne tufa and stromatolites are found in modern nonmarine thermal springs and lacustrine settings, it is important to establish the depositional environment of these Hearne carbonates. Determination of a marine vs. a nonmarine origin for Precambrian stromatolites may be difficult in certain cases, and so each interpretation requires careful consideration of tectonic setting and sedimentologic, stratigraphic, and geochemical criteria that are independent of the stromatolites themselves.

The Pethei Group formed in a large pericratonic foreland basin (>300 km long and >100 km wide) at the edge of the Archean Slave craton, and so is not an intracratonic basin (Hoffman, 1981, 1987). The carbonate platform includes a distinctive platform-to-basin transition between shallow-water and deep-water carbonates; deep-water facies are interbedded with siliciclastic turbidites derived from uplifted orogenic highlands (Hoffman, 1974). The presence of stromatolite mounds, edgewise conglomerate, ooid grainstone, and fenestral fabrics indicates that the Pethei Group formed in a shallow subaqueous environment (Hoffman, 1968; Sami and James, 1995, 1996). Additionally, bimodal paleocurrents in shallow-water ripples indicate that the shallow part of the platform formed under the influence of tidal currents (Hoffman, 1967, 1968, 1974). The thickness and lateral extent of the Pethei carbonate platform, the abundance of fibrous cements in the branching, dendritic tufa, and the presence of herringbone calcite cement in neptunian dikes and voids along the shelf margin all suggest that the Pethei platform was developed in a marine environment (Hoffman, 1968; Sami and James, 1996; Pope and Grotzinger, 1997). Oxygen and carbon isotope values (Whitaker et al., in press; Hotinski and Kump, 1997) are not anomalous with respect to other contemporaneous carbonates (Burdett et al., 1990) that have an established marine origin (Grotzinger, 1986).

Uppermost Hearne tufas and stromatolites are found as tabular units over areas (many hundreds to several thousands of km^2) that are orders of magnitude larger than most modern or ancient travertine deposits, which form as irregularly shaped, discontinuous units over smaller areas (< a few km^2). Furthermore, the depositional setting of a large carbonate platform overlain by restricted marine siliciclastics and evaporites in foreland basins is common throughout Earth's history (Peryt and Kovalevich, 1997, and references therein) whereas the occurrence of a thick (> 200 m) lacustrine deposit directly overlying a large marine carbonate platform in this depositional setting has not been documented. Nevertheless, during periods of basin isolation leading up to evaporite precipitation the internal chemistry of a basin may evolve to the point where it is difficult to distinguish marine from transitionally lacustrine settings (Hardie, 1984). The abundance of halite and paucity of gypsum

no impact in influencing the formation of these textures, but rather emphasizes the difficulties in ascertaining the specific roles of microbes in ancient rocks.

DISCUSSION

The Hearne tufa and stromatolites are unique structures that provide insights into the depositional conditions immediately prior to development of widespread evaporites. However, given that these structures formed during very restricted conditions, and anhydrite in the overlying Stark Formation might suggest that these evaporites, and possibly the underlying stromatolites of the uppermost Hearne, were deposited in a lacustrine setting (Hardie, 1984). However, the conformable nature of the uppermost Hearne tufa and stromatolites with underlying marine Pethei carbonates and overlying Stark siliciclastics, subtidal carbonates, and evaporites all suggest that these rocks formed in a marine setting. While a lacustrine origin—in the sense of an extremely evolved marine parent water (Hardie, 1984)—may be difficult to rule out, the Hearne tufa certainly is not a thermal spring deposit, because its geometry is a thin sheet, deposited over an enormous area in comparison to known thermal-spring deposits, and is not associated with any known contemporaneous volcanism or hydrothermal rocks.

Comparison of Upper Hearne Stromatolites with Modern Mineralizing Systems

The dendritically branching tufa and isopachous, evenly laminated stromatolites are morphologically very similar to structures produced in modern travertine and hot-spring settings, thus providing an important analog from which to derive insight concerning the chemical and biological processes that may have influenced development of these structures. Given the abundant evidence for prolific early marine cementation in Paleoproterozoic and Archean subtidal carbonates, travertine and hot-spring settings may be particularly relevant because they are characterized by waters that are highly oversaturated with respect to $CaCO_3$, are commonly slightly alkaline, and contain abundant carbonate precipitates formed in non-agitated subaqueous settings. Although the Hearne structures were not deposited in a thermal-spring setting, as discussed above, and thus the geologic setting of the modern analog differs markedly from the ancient features described here, the value in the comparison is in the relationship between depositional texture and water composition.

Morphologic similarities between the Hearne dendritically branching tufa and even, isopachously laminated stromatolites and Tertiary travertine deposits (Folk et al., 1995; Guo and Riding, 1992, 1994) suggest these structures formed by similar processes. Biologic activities may be an important process in development of some modern stromatolites and tufas in these settings (e.g., Buczynski and Chafetz, 1991; Chafetz and Buczynski, 1992). However, because we cannot directly determine the role of biology in formation of these rocks and because similar forms can be produced abiotically (Pentecost, 1990; Jones and Renaut, 1995, 1996; Renaut and Jones, 1997), it should not be assumed that biological processes were necessarily essential or even important in the construction of these ancient tufas and stromatolites. *In either interpretation*, however, it is important to recognize that the growth and preservation of delicately branching tufa and isopachously laminated stromatolites in 1.8 Ga carbonate rocks indicate that they formed rapidly by *in situ* carbonate precipitation in a mineralizing system that was likely highly oversaturated with respect to calcium carbonate.

During the transition from carbonate to evaporite depositional conditions at the end of Hearne time, seawater temperatures likely were increased and higher than normal (>30°C). In modern mineralizing systems, as temperatures increase cyanophytes become more restricted but thermophilic bacteria be-

come more abundant (Golubic, 1976, 1991; Brock, 1976). Research in modern hot springs and travertine settings indicates that these bacteria may be geochemically passive (i.e., they neither induce nor suppress carbonate precipitation), but their sticky mucous may limit the lateral movement of suspended crystals that settle on the sediment surface (Renaut and Jones, 1997). Increasing temperature and salinity in this Paleoproterozoic carbonate-to-evaporite transition may have facilitated the transition from *in situ* calcite to dolomite precipitation (e.g., Folk and Land, 1975) in the uppermost Hearne units. If dolomite was not primary, then it probably occurred very early through neomorphism of metastable high-Mg calcite or aragonite directly to dolomite, resulting in its excellent fabric preservation.

Morphological Variations: Implications about Depositional Processes

Theory, experiments, and observations on the nature of dynamically evolving interfaces place important constraints on the possible range of growth mechanisms for the Hearne tufas and stromatolites. The texture, particularly the roughness,[1] of any depositional surface (interface) is subject to certain force balances and the presence of noise or randomness. In general, and regardless of whether growth is abiologic or solely microbial, there are two end-member models that account for the morphology of an accretionary interface. These different models feature local versus nonlocal growth processes. In cases where interface growth is controlled by **local** growth processes, the rate of growth is dependent only on the local properties of the interface such as height of the interface and its nearest neighbors (e.g., Kardar et al., 1986). However, for other systems there are a number of **nonlocal** effects that contribute to interface morphology and growth velocity, the most important of which is the presence of a diffusing field, which may reflect pressure, electric potential, temperature, and chemical or nutrient concentration (e.g., Witten and Sander, 1983). In the case of growth by local processes, interface morphologies may be smooth or irregular, but are always relatively compact (Fig. 10), whereas nonlocal processes lead to steady-state morphologies that are usually highly ramified, featuring columnar to dendritic branching patterns (Fig. 11).

The very significant aspect of both local and nonlocal models is that examples of each can be found for microbial systems (compare Ben-Jacob et al., 1994, with Matsushita and Fujikawa, 1990) as well as purely abiotic systems (cf. Kardar et al., 1986; Matsushita et al., 1985; Galathra et al., 1992), which have qualitatively identical appearances and often quantitatively similar scaling relationships (see summary in Barabasi and Stanley, 1995). This may be frustrating in the attempt to use the morphology of depositional surfaces as a parameter to ascertain the biogenicity of stromatolites (cf. Grotzinger and Rothman, 1996), but on the other hand is fascinating in that it implies that microbes, as simple cells, may behave almost atomistically in their self-organization to form clusters, biofilms, and mats.

---

[1]The roughness of the interface is defined by the rms fluctuation in the height of the interface. By definition, growth starts from a horizontal line; the interface is initially a simple straight line, but as deposition occurs, peaks and valleys form and the interface gradually roughens.

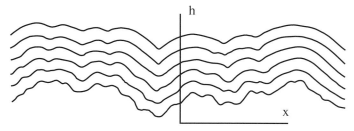

FIG. 10.—Cross–sectional view of KPZ model (Kardar et al. 1986) for dynamical surface growth of interfaces. The surface is growing parallel to the H–axis. In generating these curves, Kardar et al. (1986) let an initially rough (noisy) surface evolve through time without the input of additional noise. Consequently, surface–normal growth results in smoothing through time, producing fewer domes of increasingly greater wavelength. In contrast, the Hearne isopachous laminites produce increasingly irregular and rough shapes with time (Fig. 6), thus suggesting that in addition to accreting in a surface–normal fashion, the system was also being perturbed at randomly short wavelengths. However, in both cases the accretionary systems share the common property of surface–normal growth, which demonstrates their essential similarity.

FIG. 11.—Dendritically branching zinc leaf trees produced by diffusion–limited aggregation in an abiotic precipitation experiment (Matsushita et al. 1985). The dendritic structures are qualitatively similar to the Hearne dendritically branching tufa. The width of the Fig. is ~5 cm.

The Hearne stromatolites (smooth to irregular, but compact) and tufa (dendritic) with their distinctive morphologies, lend themselves well to interpretation using local versus nonlocal growth models. The Hearne stromatolites, which show a high degree of surface-normal accretion, are best explained through comparison with local growth models such as the KPZ model (Kardar et al., 1986). This growth model (Fig. 10) predicts smoothing and broadening of domes with time because particles (ions, nutrients, sediment) that arrive at the surface stick to the first particle that they meet on the surface—the probability of attaching, say, to the side of a bump is the same as attaching to the top of a bump or the depression between bumps. Thus, lateral growth in this model is very important. An initially rough surface grows with constant velocity normal to all local surfaces and, with time, larger domes overtake smaller domes, leading to a smoother interface, with a smaller number of broader domes than in the initial condition (Fig. 10). Growth of this type is characteristic not only of the Hearne stromatolites but also of many other early Precambrian stromatolites and reflects the fact that only local processes influence their growth (Grotzinger and Rothman, 1996). This type of growth also best describes the geometry of layering in the walls of agates, botryoidal mineral clusters, speleothems, and at least certain types of stromatolites in a quantitative manner where sea-floor precipitation is thought to have been important (Grotzinger and Rothman, 1996). Significantly, the Hearne stromatolites fit this description well in having isopachous lamination that displays

constant thickness as measured normal to local curvature, clear evidence of outward as well as upward growth (Fig. 8F), and a general lack of sediment filling depressions between domes. However, we do note that the minor siliciclastic component within the Hearne stromatolites shows evidence of having preferentially accumulated in depressions, as seen using plain-light petrography as well as X-ray mapping for silica concentration (see Okinawa et al., 1997).

The role of microbes, bacteria, and their attendant biofilms in development of modern and ancient marine carbonates is uncertain. However, recent SEM investigations of Mn and Fe precipitates from travertines, composed of chains of nanobacteria, clearly organize themselves to form microscopic isopachous laminae on the order of 50–100 mm thick (Chafetz et al. 1998, their fig. 8). Unfortunately, the morphologic response is also exactly what is predicted for abiotic mineralizing systems (cf. Kardar et al., 1986; Grotzinger and Rothman, 1996). Again, the lack of nanostructures consistent with fossil bacteria in the Hearne laminites does not preclude a role for the influence of microbial biofilms, but it does point out the difficulty in establishing biogenicity given only morphology.

In contrast, the Hearne tufas fundamentally differ from the Hearne stromatolites in having a complexly branched morphology, which implies that nonlocal effects were important in controlling growth. The most common model used to account for dendritic growth, biologic or abiotic, is known as diffusion-limited aggregation, or DLA (Witten and Sander 1983). As the name of the model implies, aggregation in DLA is controlled by the dynamics of diffusion away from the interface, rather than the kinetics of reaction at the interface—the essential difference between nonlocal and local growth dynamics. The key premise of the DLA model is that particles (ions, nutrients, sediment) arrive at the site of deposition through a random walk that simulates Brownian motion (diffusion). Particles are successively released, each undergoing a random walk, until a macroscopic cluster is formed. Numerical models have shown that the dendritic structures that are formed by DLA have fractal geometry, and experiments in both biological and abiotic systems have confirmed the essential role of diffusion in controlling the geometry. The complex branching of the dendritic structures best illustrates the nonlocality of the DLA model. As branches begin to develop, they create a screening effect, which makes it increasingly improbable (exponentially so) that new particles will ever find their way into the depressions between branches (Fig. 12). Thus, no matter what may take place at the interface itself, the growth process is fundamentally controlled by effects away from the interface (i.e., nonlocal effects), in this case diffusion of particles in a potential field. Furthermore, the growth rate at any given point depends on the entire geometry of the growing structure, not only on the local morphology.

The DLA model has significant implications for the geologic interpretation of the Hearne tufas. Most importantly, it implies a highly restricted depositional environment—so restricted that the mass flux of ions or nutrients was essentially limited to a diffusive process. However, it seems hard to envision a basin with the dimensions of the Hearne Formation in which wind-driven currents (advection) were slowed to the point where mass flux by diffusion became dominant over mass flux by advection. As Jorgensen and Des Marais (1990) have noted, for reasonable flow velocities (0.5–10 cm s^{-1}) where modern mats

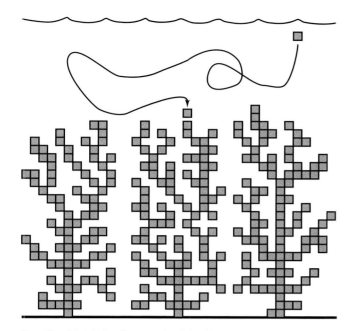

FIG. 12.—Model showing growth of dendritically branching structures by diffusion–limited aggregation (DLA). A particle, such as an ion, moves by Brownian motion through the water column and sticks to the growing interface through a reaction at the interface (either abiotic or biotically induced) that produces a mineral precipitate. Particles that attach next to each other may lead to growth of lateral branches, which are positively reinforced with time because they prevent the migration of ions to greater depths within the structure. This capturing or "screening" effect is the cause of the highly ramified branching that is characteristic of diffusion limited growth. Further reinforcement and prevention of precipitation in deep nooks and crannies also is driven by accumulation of chemical inhibitors at those sites.

form, the diffusive boundary layer immediately overlying a mat is very thin (<1 mm) as compared to the surface roughness of the growing mat. This observation is also applicable to any abiotic surface, and really is a manifestation of the fact that for any current moving over any surface, the current velocity must slow to zero at the surface itself. At some point there will always be a transition from a turbulent regime, where mass flux is efficiently accomplished through eddy diffusion, to a boundary layer in which mass flux is accomplished by less efficient simple diffusion. However, the individual branching structures of the Hearne tufas persist for up to 50 cm vertically, although the true synoptic relief may have been limited to millimeters or centimeters. As was noted earlier, some laminae do run through the dendritic texture of the Hearne tufas, supporting this interpretation. Even if the latter values are representative of the true synoptic relief, these are much greater than what might be predicted for the diffusive boundary layer in a shallow, restricted basin. The problem then is to account for the growth of dendritic structures in a regime where their characteristic scale is substantially larger than that of the diffusive boundary layer. If the structures protrude above the diffusive boundary layer, then DLA cannot be invoked to explain their growth.

Perhaps the reconciliation between model and observation lies in understanding that the Hearne basin, in an advanced state of chemical evolution, likely became stratified with dense, saline brines pooling within topographic lows, much in the same way that occurs in highly evaporitic coastal salinas today (e.g.,

Solar Lake; Gavish 1980). During stratification the lower layer resists advective mixing by wind-driven surface shear stress and is increasingly stable against increases in water depth and increases in density gradient. On the other hand, higher wind shear at the surface favors decreasing stability of the lower layer. Because advective mixing does not take place across the halocline, mass flux across that boundary and through the lower layer is dominated by simple diffusion. Consequently, it is very likely that in the Hearne basin, just prior to deposition of the Stark evaporites, stratification developed and that at times accretion of sediment on the seafloor was limited by diffusion, giving rise to the dendritic structures observed in the upper Hearne.

Although reference to modern analogs is useful to show that stratification and advection inhibition of the lower layer is indeed physically plausible for the environmental setting that we postulate for the upper Hearne, we can reinforce this conclusion with a simple calculation that takes into account the relevant factors for the Hearne basin. The Richardson number (Ri) predicts whether or not the interface between two density-stratified fluid layers is stable, and is given by

$$ \text{Ri} = \frac{g\beta \dfrac{\Delta s}{\Delta z}}{\left(\dfrac{\Delta u}{\Delta z}\right)} \qquad (1) $$

where g is the gravitational constant, β is the coefficient of haline expansion, Δs is the salinity difference between top and bottom layers, Δz is the water depth, and Δu is the wind-generated shear velocity at the surface. $\Delta s/\Delta z$ and $\Delta u/\Delta z$ give the salinity and velocity gradients, respectively. For Ri < 0.25, turbulent mixing is effective at all depths and stratification does not occur; for values greater than 0.25, stratification is stable (Baines, 1995). Assuming reasonable and conservative values (Fig. 13) for the basin at the time that the Hearne tufa may have

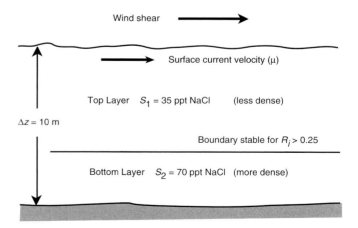

FIG. 13.—Schematic diagram showing how the densities of a two–layered water mass can maintain its stratification. If the Richardson number for the interface (boundary) between the two water masses stays above 0.25, then stratification remains in place (see text). Alternatively, large perturbations of the interface, possibly induced by increased surface currents, changes in water depth or changes in salinity, cause the Richardson number to decrease below 0.25, and stratification destabilizes.

formed, for example water depths of 10 m, a surface salinity of 35 ppt (normal seawater) and a bottom salinity of 70 ppt (still within the carbonate precipitation field), and an average surface current velocity of 1 m/s (relatively high), then we obtain Ri $\sim$ 3, about an order of magnitude larger than what is required to induce stability. Therefore, we consider it very likely that the dendritic tufas of the Hearne Formation grew under highly restricted conditions, in a shallow but density-stratified basin. Therefore, it is possible that the complex dendritic structures in the Hearne Formation result from diffusion-limited aggregation, thereby implying a very restricted phase of development in the basin regardless of whether or not growth of the tufa was biologically influenced.

Another interesting point derives from comparison of the Hearne basin with that of modern thermal springs. In the latter case, diffusion-limited growth is promoted by a constant state of high disequilibrium involving high oversaturation with respect to calcium carbonate, due to degassing at the vent associated with decompression of rising waters, as well as fluid turbulence within the pool. Here the comparison breaks down because the Hearne tufas formed in a large, very restricted, shallow marine basin. It is hard to imagine that any of the processes that maintain the high state of oversaturation in modern thermal springs apply in this setting, particularly decompression-induced degassing of rising vent fluids. What factors could have maintained the Hearne basin at high state of oversaturation for a long enough time to deposit three meters of tufa? The answer may lie in recognizing that it represents part of a transition into evaporite deposition where seawater would have become increasingly concentrated with respect to *all* ionic constituents as the gypsum and/or halite precipitation fields were approached. Thus, not only was the concentration of Ca^{2+} and CO_3^{2-} ions increased, but so were all the other ions that might have served to inhibit carbonate precipitation. Growth at the interface may have featured local depletion of Ca^{2+} and CO_3^{2-} ions from the solution, while at the same time the solution was being enriched in the ions that may have acted as kinetic inhibitors, such as Mg^{2+}, SO_4^{2-}, PO_4^{2-}, Fe^{2+}, and Mn^{2+}. Thus, growth was dependent not only on the diffusion of mineral-forming ions to the interface, but also on simultaneous diffusion of precipitation-inhibiting ions *away* from the interface. The inhibiting ions would have tended to concentrate in the depressions between branches, reinforcing and creating a positive feedback mechanism for continued growth of a dendritic morphology.

The unusual stromatolites in the upper 10 m of the Hearne Formation in the East Arm of Great Slave Lake, Canada, can be accounted for mainly by abiotic depositional processes. With increased evaporation and salinity, and possibly alkalinity, dendritically branching tufa and isopachous evenly laminated stromatolites could have been formed by mineral precipitation regardless of the presence of any microbes on the surface. The changes from dendritic, branching tufa to irregularly laminated flat to domal stromatolites to isopachous, evenly laminated stromatolite morphologies and textures possibly represent the interplay between abiotic and biotic depositional systems. Dendritic, branching stromatolites and isopachous, evenly laminated stromatolites reflect extreme environmental conditions where chemical processes dominate, whereas flat-domal irregularly laminated stromatolites record a combination of bio-

logical and chemical processes influencing stromatolite growth. The isopachous, evenly laminated stromatolites inherit their domal shape from the underlying stromatolites but modify the laminae in a more chemically dominated system, with low-velocity, directed flow creating their striking anisotropic geometry. Although microbes may have been present at or near the depositional surfaces of dendritically branching tufa and isopachously laminated stromatolites, it is unclear if, or how, they affected the resulting morphologies.

It is important to recognize that the growth processes that influence the morphology of any interface, whether populated by microbes or not, create many similar geometries that may not be distinguishable qualitatively, or even quantitatively. This serves to underscore the point of Grotzinger and Rothman (1996) that stromatolite and other "microbialite" morphologies, such as tufas, may have multiple origins. The apparent universality of growth processes that fascinates physicists and drives them to study both bacterial and abiotic systems in an attempt to determine generalized dynamical models may be a plague for earth scientists who seek only to establish that the structure is biologic in origin. However, the good news is that whatever is lost in terms of our ability to establish the former role of life in stromatolite morphogenesis will likely be replaced with the ability to use these generalized models to infer a broader understanding of the environmental processes that operated on the early Earth. At this point, our understanding of how these structures formed is still meager. But through comparison to well-studied physical models developed for both biologic as well as abiotic systems, we can begin to formulate more specific hypotheses that can be evaluated objectively using various geochemical, paleontological, textural, and morphologic tests.

ACKNOWLEDGMENTS

This research was supported by National Aeronautics and Space Agency Grant NAG5–6722 to JPG. We thank Paul Hoffman for supplying us with field maps and aerial photos of the East Arm and discussions concerning the unique flatiron stromatolites. Bill Padgham, Mike Beauregard, and Mike Pollock of DIAND are thanked for their hospitality, field support, and expediting. We thank Hank Chafetz for his advice on preparing and interpreting SEM analyses. Discussions with Jochem Marotzke clarified our understanding of ocean stratification, although any remaining errors are our responsibility. Odin Smith, Kelvin Chan, Lee Kump, and Roberta Hotinski are thanked for discussions and assistance in the field. M. Matsushita is thanked for providing the original photograph of manganese dendrites. David Bell is thanked for assistance with the SEM. Brian Jones and Steve Golubic provided excellent reviews of the final manuscript. John Southard's thorough handling of the final editing is greatly appreciated.

REFERENCES

AWRAMIK, S. M., AND MARGULIS, L., 1974, Stromatolite newsletter, unpublished, v. 2, p. 5.
AWRAMIK, S. M., AND MARGULIS, L., 1976, Unpublished manuscript, cited by M. R. Walter, ed., of Stromatolites, Amsterdam, Elsevier, Developments in Sedimentology v. 20, p. i.
BADHAM, J. P. N., AND STANWORTH, C. W., 1977, Evaporites from the Lower Proterozoic of the East Arm, Great Slave Lake: Nature, v. 268, p. 516–518.
BAINES, P. G., 1995, Topographic Effects in Stratified Flows: Cambridge, U.K., Cambridge University Press, 482 p.

BARABASI, A. L., AND STANLEY, H. E., 1995, Fractal Concepts in Surface Growth: Cambridge, U.K., Cambridge University Press, 366 p.

BEN–JACOB, E., SCHOCHET, O., TENEBAUM, A., COHEN, I., CZIROK, A., AND VICSEK, T., 1994, Communication, regulation and control during complex patterning of bacterial colonies: Fractals, v. 2, p. 15–44.

BEN–JACOB, E., SCHOCHET, O., TENEBAUM, A., COHEN, I., CZIROK, A., AND VICSEK, T., 1992, Generic modelling of cooperative growth patterns in bacterial colonies: Nature, v. 368, p. 46–49.

BOWRING, S. A., VAN SCHMUS, W. R., AND HOFFMAN, P. F., 1984, U–Pb zircon ages from Athapuscow Aulocogen, East Arm of Great Slave Lake, N.W.T., Canada: Canadian Journal of Earth Sciences, v. 21, p. 1315–1324.

BROCK, T. D., 1976, Environmental microbiology of living stromatolites, in Walter, M. R., ed., Stromatolites: Amsterdam, Elsevier, Developments in Sedimentology v. 20, p. 141–148.

BUCZYNSKI, C., AND CHAFETZ, H. C., 1991, Habit of bacterial induced precipitates of calcium carbonate and the influence of medium viscosity on mineralogy: Journal of Sedimentary Petrology, v. 61, p. 226–233.

BUICK, R., DUNLOP, J. S. R., AND GROVES, D. I., 1981, Stromatolite recognition in ancient rocks; an appraisal of irregularly laminated structures in an early Archean chert–barite unit from North Pole, western Australia: Alcheringa, v. 5, p. 166–179.

BURDETT, J. W., GROTZINGER, J. P., AND ARTHUR, M. A., 1990, Did major changes in the stable-isotope composition of Proterozoic seawater occur?: Geology, v. 18, p. 227–230.

BURNE, R. V., AND MOORE, L. S., 1987, Microbialites: Organosedimentary deposits of benthic microbial communities: Palaios, v. 2, p. 241–254.

CADY, C., AND FARMER, J., 1996, Fossilization processes in siliceous thermal spring: trends in preservation along thermal gradients, in Evolution of Hydrothermal Ecosystems of Earth (and Mars?): CIBA Foundation Symposium 202, New York, John Wiley and Sons, p. 150–172.

CASANOVA, J., 1994, Stromatolites from the East Africa rift: A synopsis, in Bertrand-Sarfati, J. and Monty , C., eds., Phanerozoic Stromatolites II: Dordrecht, The Netherlands, Kluwer Academic Publishers, p. 193–226.

CECILE, M. P., AND CAMPBELL, F. H. A., 1978, Regressive stromatolite reefs and associated facies, middle Goulburn Group (Lower Proterozoic) in Kilihigok Basin, N. W. T: an example of environmental control on stromatolite forms: Bulletin of Canadian Petroleum Geology, v. 26, p. 237–267.

CHAFETZ, H. S., 1981, Photographs of bacterial shrubs in travertine, Idaho and Italy: Journal of Sedimentary Petrology, v. 51, p. 1162.

CHAFETZ, H. S., AND BUCZYNSKI, C., 1992, Bacterially induced lithification of microbial mats: Palaios, v. 7, p. 277–293.

CHAFETZ, H. S., AND FOLK, R. L., 1984, Travertines: depositional morphology and bacterially constrained constituents: Journal of Sedimentary Petrology, v. 54, p. 289–316.

CHAFETZ, H. S., AKDIM, B., JULIA, R., AND REID, A., 1998, Mn- and Fe-rich black travertine shrubs: Bacterially (and nanobacterially) induced precipitates: Journal of Sedimentary Research, v. 68, p. 404–412.

DILL, R. F., SHINN, E. A., JONES, A. T., KELLY, K., AND STEINEN, R. P., 1986, Giant subtidal stromatolites forming in normal salinity waters: Nature, v. 324, p. 55–58.

FELDMANN, M., AND McKENZIE, J. A., 1997, Messinian stromatolite–thrombolite associations Santa Pola, SE Spain: an analogue for the Palaeozoic?: Sedimentology, v. 44, p. 893–914.

FISCHER, A. G., AND SARNTHEIN, M. 1988, Airborne silts and dune-derived sands in the Permian of the Delaware Basin: Journal of Sedimentary Petrology, v. 58, p. 637–643.

FOLK, R. L., 1993, SEM imaging of bacteria and nannobacteria in carbonate sediments and rocks: Journal of Sedimentary Petrology, v. 63, p. 990–999.

FOLK, R. L., AND LAND, L. S., 1975, Mg/Ca ratio and salinity, two controls over crystallization of dolomite: American Association of Petroleum Geologists, Bulletin, v. 59, p. 60–68.

FOLK, R. L., CHAFETZ, H. S., AND TIEZZI, P.A., 1985, Bizarre forms of depositional and diagenetic calcite in hot-spring travertines, central Italy: Journal of Sedimentary Petrology, v. 55, p. 349–369.

FUJIKAWA, H., AND MATSUSHITA, M., 1989, Fractal growth of Bacillus subtilis on agar plates: Physical Society of Japan, Journal, v. 58, p. 3875–3878.

GALATHRA, L. M., KAHANDA, K. S., XIAO-QUN, Z., FARRELL, R., AND WONG, P., 1992, Columnar growth and kinetic roughening in electrochemical deposition: Physical Review Letters, v. 68, p. 3741–3744.

GAVISH, E., 1980, Recent sabkhas marginal to the southern coasts of Sinai, Red Sea, in Nissenbaum, A., ed., Hypersaline Brines and Evaporitic Environments: Amsterdam, Elsevier, p. 233–251.

GOLUBIC, S., 1976, Organisms that build stromatolites, in Walter, M. R., ed., Stromatolites: Elsevier, Amsterdam, Developments in Sedimentology, v. 20, p. 113–126.

GOLUBIC, S., 1985, Microbial mats and modern stromatolites in Shark Bay, western Australia, in Caldwell, D. E., Brierly, J. A., and Brierly, C. L., eds., Planetary Ecology: New York, Van Nostrand-Reinhold, p. 3–16.

GOLUBIC, S., 1991, Modern Stromatolites: A review, in Riding, R., ed., Calcareous Algae and Stromatolites: Berlin, Springer–Verlag, p. 541–561.

GRIER, D. BEN–JACOB, E., CLARK, R., AND SANDER, L, M., 1986, Morphology and microstructure in electrochemical deposition of zinc: Physical Review Letters, v. 56, p. 1264–1267.

GROTZINGER, J. P., 1986, Cyclicity and paleoenvironmental dynamics, Rocknest platform, northwest Canada: Geological Society of America, Bulletin, v. 97, p. 1208–1231.

GROTZINGER, J. P., 1989, Facies and evolution of Precambrian carbonate depositional systems: Emergence of the modern platform archetype, in Crevello, P. D., Wilson, J. L., Sarg, J. F., and Read, J. F., eds., Controls on Carbonate Platform and Basin Development: SEPM, Special Publication 44, p. 79–106.

GROTZINGER, J. P., 1990, Geochemical model for Proterozoic stromatolite decline, in Knoll, A. H., and Ostrom, J. H., eds., Proterozoic Evolution and Environments: American Journal of Science, v. 290-A, p. 80–103.

GROTZINGER, J. P., AND READ, J. F., 1983, Evidence for primary aragonite precipitation, Lower Proterozoic (1.9 Ga) dolomite, Wopmay Orogen, northwest Canada: Geology, v. 11, p. 710–713.

GROTZINGER, J. P., HOFFMAN, P. F., AND TIRRUL, R., 1985, Interacting early Proterozoic foredeeps flanking a small Archean continent (abstract): International symposium on foreland basins, Fribourg, Switzerland, 2–4 September, Programme and Abstracts.

GROTZINGER, J. P., AND KASTING, J. F., 1993, New constraints on Precambrian ocean chemistry: Journal of Geology, v. 101, p. 235–243.

GROTZINGER, J. P. AND KNOLL, A. H., 1995, Anomalous carbonate precipitates: Is the Precambrian the key to the Permian?: Palaios, v. 10, p. 578–596.

GROTZINGER, J. P., AND KNOLL, A. H., 1999, Stromatolites in Precambrian carbonates: Evolutionary mileposts or environmental dipsticks?: Annual Review of Earth and Planetary Sciences, v. 27, p. 313–358.

GROTZINGER, J. P., AND ROTHMAN, D. H., 1996, An abiotic model for stromatolite morphogenesis: Nature, v. 383, p. 423–425.

GUO, L., AND RIDING, R., 1992, Aragonite laminae in hot water travertine crusts, Rampolano, Italy: Sedimentology, v. 39, p. 1067–1079.

GUO, L., AND RIDING, R., 1994, Origin and diagenesis of Quaternary travertine shrub fabrics, Rapolano Terme, central Italy: Sedimentology, v. 41, p. 499–520.

GUO, L., ANDREWS, J., RIDING, R., DENNIS, P., AND DRESSER, Q., 1996, Possible microbial effects on stable carbon isotopes in hot-spring travertines: Journal of Sedimentary Research, v. A66, p. 468–473.

HADDAD, A. E., AISSAOUI, D. M., AND SOLIMAN, M. A., 1984, Mixed carbonate siliciclastic sedimentation on a Miocene fault-block, Gulf of Suez: Sedimentary Geology, v. 37, p. 185–202.

HARDIE, L. A., 1984, Evaporites: marine or non-marine?: American Journal of Science, v. 284, p. 193–240.

HOFFMAN, P. F., 1967, Algal stromatolites: use in stratigraphic correlation and paleocurrent determination: Science, v. 157, p. 1043–1045.

HOFFMAN, P. F., 1968, Stratigraphy of the Great Slave Lake Supergroup (Aphebian), east arm of Great Slave Lake, District of Mackenzie: Geological Survey of Canada, Paper 68-42, 93 p.

HOFFMAN, P. F., 1969, Proterozoic paleocurrents and depositional history of the East Arm fold belt, Great Slave Lake, northwest Territories: Canadian Journal of Earth Sciences, v. 6, p. 441–462.

HOFFMAN, P. F., 1974, Shallow and deepwater stromatolites in Lower Proterozoic platform-to-basin facies change, Great Slave Lake, Canada: American Association of Petroleum Geologists, Bulletin, v. 58, p. 856–867.

HOFFMAN, P. F., 1981, Autopsy of Athapuscow Aulocogen: A failed arm affected by three collisions, in Campbell, F. H. A., ed., Proterozoic Basins of Canada: Geological Survey of Canada, Paper 81-10, p. 97–102.

HOFFMAN, P. F., 1987, Early Proterozoic foredeeps, foredeep magmatism and Superior-type iron-formations of the Canadian Shield, in Kroner, A., ed., Proterozoic Lithospheric Evolution: Washington, D. C., American Geophysical Union, p. 85–98.

HOFFMAN, P. F., 1988, Geology and tectonics, East Arm of Great Slave Lake, Northwest Territories: Geological Survey of Canada, Map 1628A, 2 Sheets.

HOFFMAN, P. F., 1989, Pethei Reef Complex (1.9 Ga), Great Slave Lake N.W.T., in Geldsetzer, H. J., James, N. P., and Tebbutt, G. E., eds., Reefs: Canada and Adjacent Areas: Canadian Society of Petroleum Geologists, Memoir 13, p. 38–48.

HOFFMAN, P. F., BELL, I. R., HILDEBRAND, R. S., AND THORSTAD, L., 1977, Geology of the Athapuscow Aulocogen, east arm of Great Slave Lake, District of Mackenzie: Geological Survey of Canada, Report of Activities, Part A, v. 77-1A, p. 117–129.

HOFFMAN, P. F., AND GROTZINGER, J. P., 1993, Orographic precipitation, erosional unloading, and tectonic style: Geology, v. 21, p. 195–198.

HOFMANN, H. J., AND JACKSON, G. D., 1988, Proterozoic mini-stromatolites with radial fibrous fabric: Sedimentology, v. 34, p. 963–971.

HOTINSKI, R. M., AND KUMP, L. R., 1997, A geochemical investigation of the Pethei Group, Northwest Territories, Canada: Implications for Paleoproterozoic ocean chemistry (abstract): Canadian Society of Petroleum Geologists–SEPM, Abstracts with Programs, p. 132.

HUH, J. M., BRIGGS, L. I., AND GILL, D., 1977, Depositional environments of Pinnacle Reefs, Niagaran and Salina Groups, northern shelf, Michigan Basin, in Fisher, J. H., ed., Reefs and Evaporites; Concept and Depositional Models: American Association of Petroleum Geologists, Studies in Geology no. 5, p. 1–21.

JAMES, N. P., CONIGLIO, M., AISSAOUI, D. M., AND PURSER, B. H., 1988, Facies and geologic history of an exposed Miocene rift-margin carbonate platform: Gulf of Suez, Egypt: American Association of Petroleum Geologists, Bulletin, v. 72, p. 555–572.

JAVOR, B. J., AND CASTENHOLZ, R. W., 1981, Laminated microbial mats, Laguna Guerrero Negro, Mexico: Geomicrobiology, v. 2, p. 237–273.

JONES, B., 1995, Processes associated with microbial biofilms in the twilight zone of caves: Examples from the Cayman Islands: Journal of Sedimentary Research, v. A65, p. 552–560.

JONES, B., AND KAHLE, C. F., 1986, Dendritic calcite crystals formed by calcification of algal filaments in a vadose environment: Journal of Sedimentary Petrology, v. 56, p. 217–227.

JONES, B., AND KAHLE, C. F., 1993, Morphology, relationship, and origin of fiber and dendritic calcite crystals: Journal of Sedimentary Petrology, v. 63, p. 1018–1031.

JONES, B., AND RENAUT, R. W., 1995, Noncrystallographic calcite dendrites from hot-spring deposits at Lake Bogoria, Kenya: Journal of Sedimentary Research, v. A65, p. 154–169.

JONES, B., AND RENAUT, R. W., 1996, Influence of thermophilic bacteria on calcite and silica precipitation in hot springs with temperatures above 90°C: Evidence from Kenya and New Zealand: Canadian Journal of Earth Sciences, v. 33, p. 72–83.

JONES, B., RENAUT, R. W., AND ROSEN, M. R., 1997, Biogenecity of silica precipitation around geysers and hot-spring biotas, North Island, New Zealand: Journal of Sedimentary Research, v. 67, p. 88–104.

JORGENSON, B. B., AND DES MARAIS, D. J., 1990, The diffusive boundary layer of sediments: Oxygen microgradients over a microbial mat: Limnology and Oceanography, v. 35, p. 1343–1355.

KAH, L. H., AND KNOLL, A. H., 1996, Microbenthic distribution of Proterozoic tidal flats, environmental and taphonomic considerations: Geology, v. 24, p. 79–82.

KARDAR, M., PARISI, G., AND ZHANG, Y.-C., 1986, Dynamic scaling of growing interfaces: Physical Review Letters, v. 56, p. 889–892

KNOLL, A. H., 1985, Exceptional preservation of photosynthetic organisms in silicified carbonates and silicified peats, in Whittington, H. B., and Conway-Morris, S., eds., Extraordinary Fossil Biotas: Their Ecological and Evolutionary Significance: Royal Society [London], Philosophical Transactions, Series B, Biological Sciences, v. 311, p. 111–122.

LI, Y. H., TAKAHASHI, T., AND BROECKER, W. S., 1969, Degree of saturation of $CaCO_3$ in the oceans: Journal of Geophysical Research, v. 74, p. 5507–5526.

LOGAN, B. W., REZAK, R., AND GINSBURG, R. N., 1964, Classification and environmental significance of algal stromatolites: Journal of Geology, v. 72, p. 68–83.

LOVE, F. G., SIMMONS, G. M., JR., PARKER, B. C., WHARON, R. A., JR., AND SEABURG, K. G., 1983, Modern conophyton-like microbial mats discovered in Lake Vanda, Antarctica: Geomicrobiology Journal, v. 3, p. 33–48.

MATSUSHITA, M., HAYAKAWA, Y., AND SAWADA, Y., 1985, Fractal structure and cluster statistics of zinc-metal trees deposited on a line electrode: Physical Review A, v. 32, p. 3814–3816.

MATSUSHITA, M., AND FUJIKAWA, H., 1990, Diffusion-limited growth in bacterial colony formation: Physica A, v. 168, p. 498–506.

MONTY, C. L. V., 1976, The origin and development of cryptalgal fabrics, in Walter, M. R., ed., Stromatolites: Amsterdam, Elsevier, Developments in Sedimentology, v. 20, p. 193–249.

MONTY, C. L. V., ROUCHY, J. M., MAURIN, A., BERNET–ROLLANDE, M. C., AND PERTHUISOT, J. P., 1987, Reef-stromatolite-evaporite facies relationships from middle Miocene examples of Suez and the Red Sea, in Peryt, T. M., ed., Evaporite Basins: Berlin, Springer-Verlag, Lecture Notes in Earth Sciences v. 13, p. 133–188.

OKANIWA, T., TAKANO, M., KUMAZAWA, M., KAWAKAMI, S., AND ISOZAKI, Y., 1997, Rhythm and event analysis of lamination of stromatolites (1.9 Ga) part 1, description of lamination (abstract): Geological Association of Canada, Annual Meeting, Abstract Volume, 22, p. A110.

PENTECOST, A., 1990, The Formation of travertine shrubs: Mammoth Hot Springs, Wyoming: Geological Magazine, v. 127, p. 159–168.

PENTECOST, A., 1995, Formation of laminite travertines at Bagno Vignone, Italy: Geomicrobiology Journal, v. 12, p. 239–251.

PERYT, T. M., AND KOVALEVICH, V. M., 1997, Association of redeposited salt breccias and potash evaporites in the lower Miocene of Stebnyk (Carpathian foredeep, west Ukraine): Journal of Sedimentary Research, v. 67, p. 913–922.

PETTA, T. J., 1980, Silurian pinnacle reef diagenesis—northern Michigan: Effects of evaporites on pore space distribution, in Halley, R. B., and Loucks, R. G., eds., Carbonate Reservoir Rocks: SEPM, Core Workshop 1, p. 32–42.

POPE, M. C., AND GROTZINGER, J. P., 1997, The 1.8 Ga Stark megabreccia, facies association and reconstruction of a major Paleoproterozoic evaporite (abstract): American Association of Petroleum Geologists Annual Meeting, Program with Abstracts, p. 94.

POPE, M. C., GROTZINGER, J. P., AND SCHREIBER, B. C., in press, Evaporitic subtidal stromatolites produced by in situ precipitation: textures, facies associations, and temporal significance: Journal of Sedimentary Research, v. 70.

PURSELL, V. J., AND FOLK, R. L., 1990, Aragonite, calcite dendrites and microfluorite in Mammoth Hot Springs travertine, Yellowstone National Park, Wyoming (abstract): Geological Society of America, Annual Meeting, Program with Abstracts, p. A 90.

RENAUT, R. W., AND JONES, B., 1997, Controls on aragonite and calcite precipitation in hot spring travertines at Chemurkeu, Lake Bogoia, Kenya: Canadian Journal of Earth Sciences, v. 34, p. 801–818.

RIDING, R., 1991, Classification of microbial carbonates, in Riding, R., ed., Calcareous Algae and stromatolites: Berlin, Springer-Verlag, p. 21–51.

ROSS, G. M., AND SMITH, T. L., 1985, Physical volcanology and stratigraphy of the Seton Formation: foredeep volcanism in Athapuscow Aulocogen, District of Mackenzie: Geological Survey of Canada, Paper 85-1A, Current Research, Part A, p. 681–692.

SAMI, T. T., AND JAMES, N. P., 1993, Evolution of an early Proterozoic foreland basin carbonate platform, lower Pethei Group, Great Slave Lake, northwest Canada: Sedimentology, v. 40, p. 403–430.

SAMI, T. T., AND JAMES, N. P., 1994, Peritidal carbonate platform growth and cyclicity in an early Proterozoic foreland basin, upper Pethei Group, Northwest Canada: Journal of Sedimentary Research, v. B64, p. 111–131.

SAMI, T. T., AND JAMES, N. P., 1996, Synsedimentary cements as Paleoproterozoic platform building blocks, Pethei Group, northwestern Canada: Journal of Sedimentary Research, v. 66, p. 209–222.

SCHOPF, J. W., 1994, The oldest know records of life: Early Archean stromatolites, microfossils and organic matter, in Bengston, S., ed., Early Life on Earth: New York, Columbia University Press, Nobel Symposium No. 84, p. 193–206.

SEMIKHATOV, M. A., GEBELIN, C. D., CLOUD, P., AWRAMIK, S. M., AND BENMORE, W. C., 1979, Stromatolite morphogenesis: progress and problems: Canadian Journal of Earth Sciences, v. 16, p. 992–1014.

SEREBRYAKOV, S. M., AND SEMIKHATOV, M. A., 1974, Riphean and Recent stromatolites: A comparison: American Journal of Science, v. 274, p. 556–574.

SMITH, D. B., 1995, Marine Permian of England: London, Chapman & Hall, 205 p.

STOCKWELL, C. H., 1933, Great Slave Lake–Coppermine River area, Northwest Territories: Geological Survey of Canada, Annual Report, Part C, p. 37–63.

STOCKWELL, C. H., 1936, East Arm of Great Slave Lake: Geological Survey of Canada, Map 377A (East Half) and 378 A (West Half) with descriptive notes.

SUMNER, D. Y., 1997a, Carbonate precipitation and oxygen stratification in Late Archean seawater as deduced from facies and stratigraphy of the Gamohaan and Frisco Formations, Transvaal Supergroup, South Africa: American Journal of Science, v. 297, p. 333–354.

SUMNER, D. Y., 1997b, Late Archean calcite–microbe interactions; two morphologically distinct microbial communities that affected calcite nucleation differently: Palaios, v. 12, p. 302–318.

SUMNER, D. Y., AND GROTZINGER, J. P., 1996, Were the kinetics of calcium carbonate precipitation related to oxygen concentration?: Geology, v. 24, p. 119–122.

WALTER, M. R., 1976, Introduction, *in* Walter, M. R., ed., Stromatolites: Amsterdam, Elsevier, Developments in Sedimentology, v. 20, p. 790.

WALTER, M. R., 1996, Old fossils could be fractal frauds: Nature, v. 383, p. 385–386.

WHITAKER, S. G., SAMI, T. T., KYSER, T. K., AND JAMES, N. P., in press, Petrogenesis of 1.9 Ga limestones and dolostones and their record of Paleoproterozoic environments: Precambrian Research.

WITTEN, T. A., AND SANDER, L. M., 1983, Diffusion-limited aggregation: Physical Review B, v. 27, p. 5686–5697.

ZHANG, Y., AND HOFFMANN, L., 1992, Blue–green algal mats of the salinas in San-ya, Hainan Island (China): structure, taxonomic composition, and implications for the interpretation of Precambrian stromatolites: Precambrian Research, v. 56, p. 275–290.

LATE ARCHEAN ARAGONITE PRECIPITATION: PETROGRAPHY, FACIES ASSOCIATIONS, AND ENVIRONMENTAL SIGNIFICANCE

DAWN Y. SUMNER

Geology Department, University of California, Davis, CA 95616, U.S.A., sumner@geology.ucdavis.edu

AND

JOHN P. GROTZINGER

Earth, Atmospheric and Planetary Sciences, Massachusetts Institute of Technology, Cambridge, MA, U.S.A., grotz@mit.edu

ABSTRACT: Large crystal pseudomorphs, composed of limestone and dolomite, that radiate upward to form centimeter- to meter-tall fans are known from every well-preserved Late Archean carbonate platform on earth. In many cases these crystal fans are an important facies, constituting as much as 50% of the observed volume of carbonate rock. Texturally, the fans are composed of elongate blades consisting of a mosaic of crystals with randomly oriented optic axes. In some pseudomorphs, trains of inclusions define the fibrous character of the precursor mineral, and the blades exhibit blunt terminations when draped by micritic sediment. Some of the pseudomorphs contain strontium concentrations of up to 3700 ppm. Associated facies include strongly elongate giant stromatolites, hummocky cross-stratified sandstones, ooid-intraclast packstone to grainstone, small domal stromatolites, and several thinly laminated micritic facies that may display desiccation cracks.

Previously, some of these crystal fans have been interpreted as calcite-and dolomite-replaced pseudomorphs after gypsum, formed under restricted conditions resulting from evaporative concentration of seawater. However, replacement textures and elevated strontium concentrations suggest that the crystal fans are more likely the result of neomorphism of large botryoids of aragonite that formed thick crusts directly on the sea floor. Furthermore, occurrence of the crystal fans in direct association with strongly elongate giant stromatolites and hummocky cross-stratified sediments suggests precipitation of the fans in open marine, wave- and current-swept environments. Although evaporation of seawater may have contributed to the growth of fans in some peritidal environments, most occurrences are not associated with any other indicators of evaporitic conditions such as halite or gypsum pseudomorphs.

The reinterpretation of most reported occurrences of Late Archean gypsum pseudomorphs as aragonite pseudomorphs indicates that calcium sulfate precipitation from Late Archean seawater was rare, and that precipitation of aragonite as thick crusts on the sea floor was significantly more abundant than during any subsequent time in earth history. Rapid aragonite precipitation rates and the paucity of calcium sulfate precipitation can be accounted for in a model for Late Archean seawater featuring, relative to present-day seawater, higher supersaturation with respect to calcium carbonate and high HCO_3^- concentrations.

INTRODUCTION

Ocean chemistry varies on time scales ranging from thousands to billions of years. Many of these changes are tracked by changes in the chemistry of carbonates and other minerals that precipitate from seawater (e.g., Broecker and Peng, 1987; Grotzinger, 1989; Hardie, 1996; Opdyke and Wilkinson, 1993; Sandberg, 1985b; Wilkinson et al., 1985; Wilkinson and Given, 1986). Recent changes are relatively easy to constrain because the chemistry of seawater is similar to that in the modern oceans. However, developing constraints on ocean chemistry becomes increasingly difficult with increasing age because wider variations in seawater chemistry may have occurred, and interpretations of ambient chemical conditions become less precise because of changes in depositional processes, evolution of carbonate secreting organisms, preservation of fewer rocks, and potentially extensive diagenesis. The difficulty of constraining ancient seawater chemistry is demonstrated by the variety of models proposed for Archean and Proterozoic oceans. In a uniformitarian model, the concentrations of dominant cations and anions in seawater have been fairly constant through time, with the exceptions of higher pCO_2 and higher iron and manganese concentrations in Archean oceans (e.g., Walker, 1983; Holland, 1984). In contrast, Kempe and Degens (1985) and Kempe and Kazmierczak (1990, 1994) suggest dramatically different chemical conditions by proposing that prior to ~800 Ma, Earth had a "soda ocean" that was dominated by bicarbonate rather than chlorine. Calcium would have been a limiting element for life, the oceans would have had a pH of 9 to 11, and atmospheric pCO_2 would have been low (Kempe and Degens, 1985; Kempe and Kazmierczak, 1990, 1994). A third model using higher atmospheric pCO_2 and an observed paucity of gypsum pseudomorphs in Mesoproterozoic and older evaporites results in an

increase in bicarbonate such that the HCO_3^- concentration, $[HCO_3^-]$, of seawater was greater than twice $[Ca^{2+}]$ in seawater (Grotzinger, 1989; Grotzinger and Kasting, 1993). This model produces Paleoproterozoic oceans with pH = 6.5–7.5 if $[Ca^{2+}]$ was about the same as or slightly lower than in modern oceans. However, pH is even lower for the very high pCO_2 suggested by climate models for the Archean atmosphere (e.g., Owen et al., 1979; Walker, 1985; Kasting, 1987).

One way to distinguish between these models of ocean chemistry is to document the mineralogy and chemistry of primary marine precipitates. For example, evaporation of seawater from a "soda ocean" would result in precipitation of dolomite and Na_2CO_3 in addition to calcite and aragonite (Kempe and Degens, 1985; Kempe and Kazmierczak, 1994). In the "soda ocean" model, $[Ca^{2+}]$ is too low to drive gypsum precipitation (Kempe and Degens, 1985; Kempe and Kazmierczak, 1994), because gypsum precipitation requires the presence of significant Ca^{2+} after much of the HCO_3^- has been removed through $CaCO_3$ precipitation. Thus, expected minerals would include primary calcite and dolomite and pseudomorphs of less stable aragonite and Na_2CO_3 (Kempe and Degens, 1985; Kempe and Kazmierczak, 1994). The presence of gypsum pseudomorphs would be inconsistent with a "soda ocean", as would halite pseudomorphs, because of the proposed low $[Cl^-]$ (Kempe and Degens, 1985; Kempe and Kazmierczak, 1994).

The interpretation of the absence or presence of gypsum pseudomorphs in the rock record also distinguishes between the models proposed by Walker (1983) and by Grotzinger and Kasting (1993). The interpretation that gypsum pseudomorphs are present in most of the sedimentary rock record has been used to argue that $[HCO_3^-] < 2[Ca^{2+}]$ for oceans during most of Earth history (Walker, 1983; Holland, 1984). In contrast, marine evaporite sequences prior to about 1500 Ma may lack significant quantities of gypsum (Grotzinger, 1989, 1994), suggesting that $[HCO_3^-] > 2[Ca^{2+}]$ (Grotzinger and Kasting, 1993), which produces a very different interpretation for the carbonate chemistry of Archean through Mesoproterozoic seawater. Both predict halite precipitation, and neither predicts the precipitation of Na_2CO_3, in contrast to the "soda ocean" model. Grotzinger and Kasting (1993) suggest that the paucity of calcium sulfate minerals might also be due to critically low concentrations of sulfate, due to lower pO_2 at that time. Given the diversity of predicted minerals for various chemical models, the identification of the primary precipitates from ancient seawater can provide constraints on the viability of each model.

Archean carbonates commonly contain large crystal pseudomorphs that radiate upward in centimeter- to meter-tall fans that have been interpreted as either gypsum (e.g., Bertrand-Sarfati, 1976; Martin et al., 1980; Walter, 1983; Holland, 1984; Abell et al., 1985; Hofmann et al., 1985; Wilks, 1986) or aragonite (e.g., Hofmann, 1971; Bertrand-Sarfati and Eriksson, 1977; Martin et al., 1980; Simonson et al., 1993). Given the dependence of Archean seawater models on the chemistry and timing of mineral precipitates, it is important to document the primary mineralogy of these pseudomorphs, the range of depositional environments in which they precipitated, and their morphological diversity. Here, we document the occurrences, depositional environments, modes of growth, and crystal characteristics of fanning, botryoidal, and fringing pseudomorphs from various depositional environments in the 2.55 to 2.52 Ga Campbellrand–Malmani carbonate platform, South Africa; ~2.7 Ga Belingwe Greenstone Belt, Zimbabwe; ~2.6 Ga Bulawayo Greenstone Belt, Zimbabwe; and ~2.7 Ga Steeprock Group, Ontario.

GEOLOGICAL AND DEPOSITIONAL SETTINGS

Campbellrand–Malmani Carbonate Platform

The 2550–2520 Ma (Barton et al., 1994; Walraven and Martini, 1995; Altermann, 1996; Sumner and Bowring, 1996) Campbellrand and Malmani subgroups, Transvaal Supergroup, South Africa, are correlative and compose a ~1.5 km-thick carbonate platform that is preserved over 190,000 km² and was probably deposited over >600,000 km² on the Kaapvaal Craton (Fig. 1; Button, 1973; Eriksson and Truswell, 1974; Beukes, 1980, 1987; Sumner, 1995). It was deposited on the transgressive fluvial to marine Black Reef sandstones (Button, 1973; Clendenin et al., 1991) and the Schmidtsdrif Subgroup (Beukes, 1987), and it is overlain by the thick Kuruman and Penge iron formations, which were deposited after drowning of the carbonate platform. Preservation of the Campbellrand–Malmani platform for 800 km perpendicular to strike, the thickness of the platform, the identification of sequence boundaries with all the associated systems tract architecture, and the presence of basinal facies, indicate that the platform formed in a pericratonic, probably passive-margin setting and thus represents precipitation from seawater (Beukes, 1987; Sumner, 1995).

Structural disruption of the Campbellrand–Malmani carbonate platform is limited to gentle warping over most of the craton with locally steeper dips around the Bushveld Complex and intense folding and faulting coincident with the western boundary of the Kaapvaal craton (Stowe, 1986; Beukes and Smit,

1987). Metamorphic alteration is limited, with most outcrops below greenschist facies equivalent metamorphism except around the Bushveld Complex (Button, 1973; Miyano and Beukes, 1984). Early, fabric-retentive dolomite replaced most of the Malmani Subgroup, whereas a significant volume of the Campbellrand Subgroup still consists of limestone.

Eight lithofacies assemblages have been defined for the platform (Fig. 2; Sumner, 1995). 1) **Slope and basinal lithofacies** include rhythmites with interbedded turbidites, chert and dolostone breccias, carbonaceous shales, iron-formation, and tuffaceous turbidites. The presence of turbidites as well as possible debris-flow breccias near the platform margin strongly supports a basinal depositional environment for this lithofacies assemblage (Beukes, 1980, 1987). 2) The **deep subtidal microbialite lithofacies** assemblage consists of a variety of "fenestrate microbialites," which are a newly characterized group of microbial structures that consist of three components: draping, mat-like laminae; vertically oriented structures called supports; and voids filled with carbonate cements (Sumner, 1997b, 2000). The fenestrate microbialites show diverse morphologies due to varying proportions and relationships among the laminated mat, supports, and cement-filled voids, in addition to physicochemical processes. The delicate morphology of the microbialites, the lack of evidence for scouring, and the absence of clastic carbonate all suggest a deep subtidal, sub-wave-base depositional environment for the microbialite assemblage (Sumner, 1997a, 1997b). 3) The **subtidal giant stromatolite lithofacies** consists of giant elongate mound stromatolites composed of columnar stromatolites, smooth to peaked laminae, and fanning pseudomorphs. The giant, elongate mound stromatolites range from 2 to 10 meters wide and from 5 to >45 meters long (Truswell and Eriksson, 1972; Button, 1973; Eriksson et al., 1976; Eriksson and Truswell, 1974; Eriksson, 1977: Beukes, 1987). Giant elongate mound stromatolites are common in Precambrian carbonate platforms, and above-wave-base, open marine subtidal depositional environments for them have been well established (e.g., Hoffman, 1969; Button, 1973; Truswell and Eriksson, 1973; Eriksson and Truswell, 1974; Grotzinger, 1986b; Pelechaty and Grotzinger, 1988). Isolated crystal fans and continuous layers of crystal fans within the giant mound stromatolites previously have been interpreted as domal stromatolites with a radiating internal fabric (Truswell and Eriksson, 1973; Eriksson, 1977) and as gypsum rosettes (Bertrand-Sarfati, 1976). 4) The **lagoonal lithofacies** assemblage contains fenestral microbial laminites and small domal stromatolites. An abundance of local truncation surfaces and the lack of cross-stratification and channeling suggest a shallow subtidal depositional environment with little agitation. The stratigraphic position of these lithofacies platformward of a rimmed margin suggests a lagoonal depositional environment (Fig. 2; Beukes, 1987). 5) The **intertidal to shallow subtidal lithofacies** assemblage is dominated by columnar stromatolites, oolitic and non-oolitic grainstones, and large fanning and fringing pseudomorphs. An abundance of erosional unconformities, rare channeling, and ripple, small dune, and low-angle cross-stratification in grainstones suggest a lower intertidal to shallow subtidal depositional environment. 6) The **supratidal to upper intertidal lithofacies** assemblage consists of domal stromatolites, intraclast and ooid grainstones, intraclast breccias, tepee structures, small fanning pseudomorphs, halite pseudomorphs, and

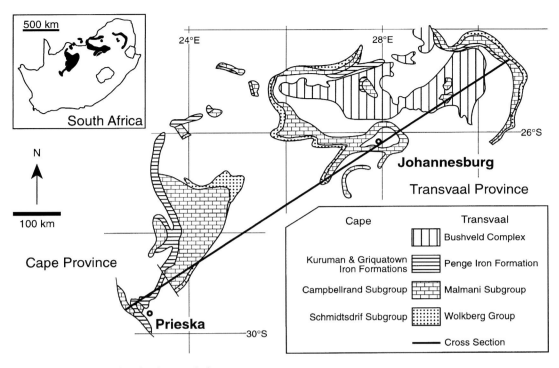

FIG. 1.—Map of the Campbellrand–Malmani carbonate platform.

minor micrite. Grainstones contain wave-ripple stratification, desiccation cracks, intraclasts, and channels. The sedimentary structures support a shallow intertidal to supratidal depositional environment. 7) The **grainstone-dominated lithofacies** assemblage consists of beds of oolitic grainstones, non-oolitic grainstones, and wavy-laminated dolomite. They commonly are recrystallized to the extent that primary sedimentary features are difficult to identify. However, rare wave, interference, climbing, and current ripples are present. Hummocky cross-stratification and trough cross-stratification also are present locally. The range in cross-stratification styles suggests deposition in environments ranging from shallow subtidal to supratidal. 8) Rare **quartz sands, siltstones, and siliciclastic shales** are associated with exposure surfaces and form a lithofacies assemblage consisting of shallow marine to fluvial siliciclastic deposits.

Crystal pseudomorphs.—Pseudomorph fans are abundant across the Campbellrand–Malmani carbonate platform from the platform margin to the interior and in open subtidal to evaporitic supratidal environments (Fig. 2). All of the fanning pseudomorphed crystals grew upward from bedding planes (Fig. 3) or outwards from the sides of stromatolites as botryoids (Fig. 4). The pseudomorphs consist of millimeter- to centimeter-wide linear zones of clear calcite, dolomite, and/or recrystallized chert that exclude all surrounding sediment. They radiate from a single nucleation point and reach lengths of over 50 cm. Commonly, they are draped by laminated sediment that infilled inter-pseudomorph space and produced stromatolite-like domes (Fig. 3A–C). Rare pseudomorphs are not draped by sediment, and inter-pseudomorph space is filled with calcite cement.

Pseudomorph fans typically are spaced from centimeters to tens of meters along specific bedding planes. In shallow subtidal environments of the giant stromatolite and intertidal to shallow subtidal lithofacies assemblages, 3–50 cm-thick beds of closely spaced pseudomorph fans are common. In these beds, the crystal fans grew into each other; the most inclined pseudomorphed crystals abut crystals in neighboring fans whereas more vertically oriented crystals continued to grow upward (Fig. 3B). These beds had variable sediment influx. Beds with a high influx of sediment relative to growth rate of the original crystals are characterized by small pseudomorph fans and thick layers of draping sediment. Usually, growth of the precursor crystals was terminated by thick layers of sediment, but rarely the most vertically oriented crystals projected above the sediment layer and continued to grow. In beds with lower sediment influx, pseudomorphed crystals that radiated at a low angle to bedding commonly are overlain by a layer of sediment that terminated their growth whereas more vertically oriented crystals continued to grow (Fig. 5A–C). Some fans grew as giant botryoids on bedding planes and lack clastic carbonate between the original crystals. The pseudomorphs in these fans radiate 180° outward from the nucleation sites and abut pseudomorphs from neighboring fans (Fig. 5E). Individual pseudomorphs diverge outward, and small crystal fans are present in the intervening space. Remaining inter-pseudomorph space is filled with calcite cement rather than detrital carbonate.

Where fans are very closely spaced, only the most upright crystals continued to grow, and a fringe of crystals oriented perpendicular to bedding developed (Figs. 3D, E, 5C, D). Similarly, some thinly laminated beds contain crystal pseudomorphs that were elongate perpendicular to bedding without a botryoidal geometry. These pseudomorphs of fine fibrous crystals extend through multiple laminae (Button, 1973; Eriksson, 1977). They always are oriented perpendicular to bedding and parallel to each other. Laminated sediment fills space between

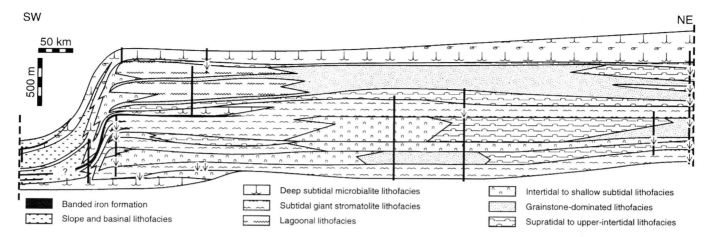

FIG. 2.—Cross section of the Campbellrand–Malmani carbonate platform. Fans mark occurrences of aragonite pseudomorphs logged in stratigraphic sections, which are shown by vertical bars. The line of section is shown in Figure 1.

the crystals (Figs. 3D, 5C). These textures are common in the giant stromatolite lithofacies and are present in supratidal deposits.

Commonly, crystal fringes grew off the sides of stromatolites in shallow subtidal depositional environments and in the reef-like margin of the platform (Fig. 4; Bertrand-Sarfati and Eriksson, 1977). These pseudomorphs consist of parallel fine fibers that grew perpendicular to the stromatolite surface. They sometimes coat the entire stromatolite, but more frequently grew as <1 mm to 10 cm thick lenticular to botryoidal coatings projecting into inter-stromatolite troughs (Fig. 4). The fibrous fringes often are coated by later fibrous calcite marine precipitates, including herringbone calcite (a marine cement texture; Sumner and Grotzinger, 1996), or are overlain by grainstone.

Cheshire Formation, Belingwe Greenstone Belt

The Belingwe Greenstone Belt, Zimbabwe, unconformably overlies a gneissic basement complex, as old as 3.6 Ga (Bickle et al., 1975; Martin, 1978; Nisbet, 1987). The volcanics-dominated "lower greenstone assemblage", the Mtshingwe Group, is overlain unconformably by an "upper greenstone assemblage", the ~2.7 Ga (Hawkesworth and Bickle, 1976) Ngezi Group (Macgregor, 1951; Laubscher, 1963; Bickle et al., 1975). The Ngezi Group consists of three units (Fig. 6): the predominantly sedimentary Manjeri Formation, the volcanic Reliance and Zeedersbergs formations, and the predominantly sedimentary Cheshire Formation. The Cheshire Formation is distributed along the main synclinal axis of the Belingwe greenstone belt. It is about 2.5 km thick and consists of a heterogeneous succession of sedimentary rocks including conglomerate, sandstone, siltstone, limestone, and minor banded iron-formation (Martin, 1978). Thicker and more abundant conglomerates characterize the eastern flank of the syncline. They pass laterally across depositional strike into thinner and finer-grained conglomerates toward the western flank of the syncline. Cheshire carbonates are developed in the western flank and pinch out to the east (Martin, 1978).

The Cheshire carbonates occur in a mixed siliciclastic and carbonate interval approximately 500 m thick. The principal outcrop belt studied by Martin et al. (1980) contains stromatolitic limestones, locally interbedded with siltstone and sandstone, and coarse limestone breccia. Martin et al. (1980) described the stromatolitic facies as a series of shallowing-upward cycles that are one to a few meters thick and extend laterally for at least several kilometers. The cycles consist of two subfacies: 1) well-laminated, stromatolitic limestone and dolomitic limestone, with minor chert, and rare argillaceous limestone; and 2) well-preserved upward-fanning bundles of crystal pseudomorphs that were interpreted as calcite pseudomorphs after either aragonite (Martin et al., 1980) or sulfates (Martin et al., 1980; Walter, 1983).

We studied these outcrops to refine the sedimentologic framework in which the carbonates were deposited, as well as better define the tectonic setting of the basin (see also Grotzinger et al., 1993). Our work involved mapping and logging of detailed measured sections from the main stromatolite outcrop. The lower part of the Cheshire Formation comprises siltstones and shales with rarer interstratified fine- to medium-grained sandstone beds. Sandstone beds are dominated by planar lamination, ripple cross-lamination, and low-angle quasiplanar stratification. In some cases, they contain well-developed hummocky cross-stratification. Other beds consist of centimeter-scale interstratified sandstones and shales that form lenticular to wavy bedding. In these beds, thin sandstones are dominated by symmetrical to slightly asymmetrical ripples with internal stratification exhibiting bundled, chevron-type upbuilding. Ball-and-pillow structures, convolute bedding, and small slump structures are common, particularly near the tops of thicker sandstone beds. Amalgamated sandstone beds form units up to 2.5 m thick.

Upwards in the section, partially dolomitized limestones become interstratified with siliciclastic facies, forming discrete beds 20–50 cm thick. The limestones contain fine-grained oolites, numerous beds of upward-radiating fans of pseudomorphed crystals, and uncommon simple domal stromatolites. Pseudomorph fans commonly form small mounds that are onlapped by rippled oolites. The proportion of siliciclastic facies decreases upward in the section, and carbonate beds thicken,

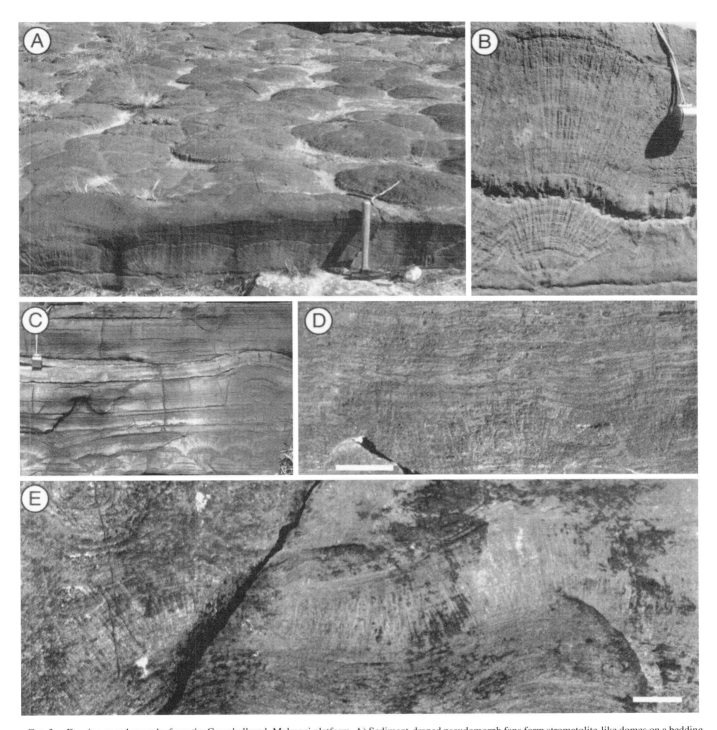

FIG. 3.—Fanning pseudomorphs from the Campbellrand–Malmani platform. A) Sediment-draped pseudomorph fans form stromatolite-like domes on a bedding surface. Hammer for scale. B) Closely spaced sediment-draped pseudomorph fans grew into each other. Hand lens is 2 cm across. C) Widely spaced sediment-draped pseudomorph fans nucleated on a single bedding plane at the base of the photo. A later pseudomorph fan nucleated higher up. Sediment draping the upper fan is rippled. D) Small pseudomorph fans and fibers project upwards and are draped with abundant sediment. Scale bar is 2 cm long. E) A fringe of closely spaced pseudomorphs coats a surface and contains abundant sediment. Scale bar is 2 cm long.

reaching up to 3 m thick, and are dominated by small mounds of fanning pseudomorphs. Ultimately, siliciclastic facies give way to a 50-m-thick continuous carbonate interval called the "main stromatolitic outcrop" (Martin et al., 1980).

The bedding characteristics and assemblages of sedimentary structures in the Cheshire Formation below the main stromatolitic outcrop typically are associated with wave- or storm-dominated open marine shelf settings (Clifton et al., 1971; de Raaf

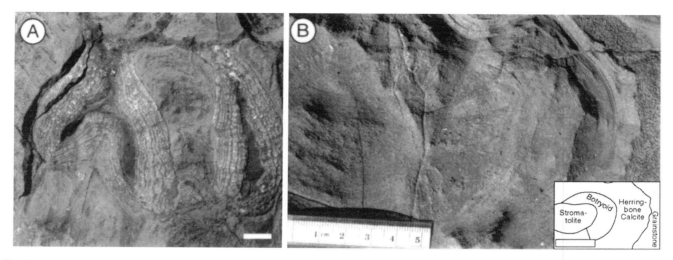

FIG. 4.—Fibrous pseudomorphs from the Campbellrand–Malmani platform. A) A several-centimeter-thick fringe of pseudomorphs coats the sides of bulbous stromatolites. The stromatolites are composed of calcite that precipitated *in situ* and fine organic laminae. Final fill of the troughs is coarsely dolomitized, and probably initially consisted of a fine grainstone. Scale bar is 2 cm long. B) Plan view of a botryoidal pseudomorph that grew off the side of a columnar stromatolite. The stromatolite had a herringbone calcite microtexture, and herringbone calcite continued to precipitate contemporaneously with botryoid growth. The botryoid is coated with a later layer of herringbone calcite. Final void fill is coarse dolomite and late diagenetic calcite. It probably initially was grainstone.

et al., 1977; Dott and Bourgeois, 1982; Arnott, 1993). Sediment deposition seems to have been greatest during times of strong unidirectional to oscillatory flows, interspersed with more prolonged intervals of settling from suspension and reworking by gentle wave-produced currents. Siliciclastic facies of the lower Cheshire Formation suggests a shallow subtidal environment, with water depths on the order of 5–50 m. The oolite facies is consistent with these depths; only thin oolitic sheets formed, rather than the thick lenticular units characteristic of shoals. These facies assemblages are most consistent with subtidal deposition of pseudomorph fan facies under normal marine conditions in an open, wave-swept shelf setting. There is no evidence to indicate that the pseudomorph fans in the lower Cheshire Formation formed in a restricted lagoonal setting as proposed by Martin et al. (1980).

The main stromatolite outcrop comprises asymmetric cyclic limestones with stromatolites and fans of pseudomorphs (Martin et al., 1980). Cycles typically are bounded by erosional surfaces with up to a few centimeters of relief that are overlain and draped by centimeter-thick beds of shale, transgressive lag deposits consisting of oolite–intraclast grainstone/packstone, and rare flat-pebble conglomerate (Fig. 7). In several cases, pseudomorph fans and stromatolites nucleated directly on the erosional surfaces, but most appear to have grown on lag deposits. Pseudomorph fans form beds 10–200 cm thick that alternate with small domal to columnar stromatolites 2–10 cm wide and 5–20 cm high. Pseudomorphs grew off of stromatolitic laminae and vice versa. These facies are gradationally overlain by a crinkly laminite facies composed of submillimeter- to millimeter-thick microsparitic laminae that have a constant thickness normal to layering. The crinkly laminites commonly are truncated by a minor erosional surface, and the cyclic facies motif is repeated (Fig. 7). Transition styles between facies suggest that cycle boundaries occur at the bases of pseudomorph fan and stromatolitic units, coincident with stratal surfaces that show evidence for erosion and draping overlap. Because the

pseudomorph fan and stromatolite beds usually are overlain gradationally by the crinkly laminite facies, which is truncated by the erosion surfaces, the crinkly laminite facies represents the top of any given cycle. This interpretation is distinct from that reported by Martin et al. (1980), who placed cycle boundaries at the tops of pseudomorph fan and stromatolitic beds, which were interpreted as the final stage of deposition in evaporative cycles.

Our reinterpretation of the Cheshire cycles suggests a nonevaporitic depositional environment. Rather, the sedimentary characteristics best fit the shallow flooding of subaerial exposure surfaces followed by deposition of shale, ooids, and intraclasts in a zone of active wave reworking; surfaces of this type with overlying lag deposits are extremely common in the record of shallow marine carbonate platforms (e.g., James, 1984). The crystal fan facies would have a shallow subtidal origin, consistent with open marine environmental interpretations for the pseudomorph fans in the lower Cheshire Formation. The transition to crinkly laminite facies is interpreted as shallowing to the peritidal zone, where deposition occurred in a more restricted setting. The crinkly laminite facies is similar to other peritidal laminites of early Precambrian age that show monotonous, fine lamination, often with extreme lateral continuity, which suggests a precipitated origin (Grotzinger and Rothman, 1996). However, the crinkly laminite facies differs somewhat from other peritidal laminites in that it shows remarkable local surface roughness across a broad range of length scales. In that sense, the facies is more comparable to the peaked laminite facies of the Paleoproterozoic Cowles Lake Formation, which is interpreted as a shallow subtidal facies (Jackson, 1989; Grotzinger and Rothman, 1996). With the reinterpretation of crystal pseudomorphs replacing aragonite rather than gypsum, combined with the absence of casts and molds of standard evaporite minerals, we find no evidence that would contradict the interpretation that the pseudomorph fan facies developed in a shallow subtidal setting that ranged from open marine shelf, to somewhat more restricted, peritidal conditions.

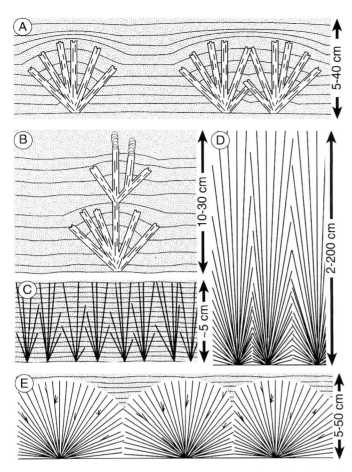

FIG. 5.—Various geometries of fanning pseudomorphs. A) Pseudomorph fans draped by laminated sediment tend to nucleate on specific surfaces. Where closely spaced, neighboring fans interpenetrate and the original crystals competed for growth space. Note that more inclined crystals commonly were buried by sediment earlier than more vertically oriented ones. B) Thick layers of sediment often bury fans. Sometimes the most vertically oriented pseudomorphed crystals projected through thick sediment layers and new fans nucleated on them. In rare cases where crystals projected significantly above the sediment–water interface, pseudomorphs acted as nucleation sites for digitate stromatolites. C) In areas with abundant fine-grained sediment and closely spaced fans, thin, fibrous pseudomorphs project through multiple laminae, often resulting in beds with a strong vertical fabric at right angles to a fine horizontal lamination. D) Some beds consist entirely of closely spaced pseudomorphs. A fanning geometry is apparent only at the bases of the beds where fans nucleated. The tops of the beds consist of nearly vertically oriented pseudomorphs. E) Rare beds consist entirely of widely spaced fanning pseudomorphs. The individual pseudomorphs radiate out at 180°. New fans nucleated on the sides of the precursor crystals as they diverged outward. Calcite cement typically fills the remaining pore space.

Crystal pseudomorphs.—Pseudomorph fans form a substantial fraction of the carbonates in the Cheshire Formation. In the lower Cheshire Formation, they commonly form localized buildups or lithoherms and laterally continuous beds (Fig. 8). The lithoherms have widths of tens of centimeters to tens of meters and up to 20 cm of synoptic relief. They are onlapped by wavy-laminated grainstone or siltstone (Fig. 8A), and grainstone commonly fills space between individual pseudomorphs. In most cases, pseudomorph fans nucleated on a single surface and grew into each other laterally, resulting in vertically ori-

ented pseudomorphs in the upper parts of the beds (Fig. 5C, D). In rare cases, however, new fans nucleated within a bed, producing upward-diverging pseudomorph orientations throughout the bed. In the main stromatolitic outcrop, the pseudomorphed crystals nucleated on erosional surfaces, lag deposits, or stromatolitic laminae. Pseudomorphed fans that nucleated on erosional surfaces or lag deposits usually form continuous layers of fans. However, some beds contain widely spaced, 5–10 cm tall pseudomorphed crystals that nucleated on highs on the underlying bed and are separated by grainstone with rare intraclasts. Crystal pseudomorphs are intimately associated with stromatolitic laminae. In many cases, stromatolitic laminae coat the tops of the crystals and mimic the relief of the underlying crystals. Centimeter–diameter digitate stromatolites grew off of the tips of some individual pseudomorphed crystals (Fig. 8C), and troughs between both the pseudomorphs and digitate stromatolites are filled with oolitic grainstone. Some crystal fans nucleated on the tops of columnar stromatolites, and rare pseudomorph fans are present between stromatolitic laminae, commonly, but not always, forming continuous layers (Fig. 7).

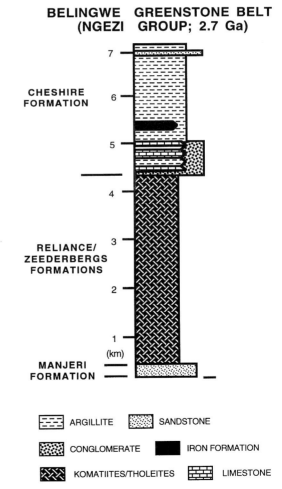

BELINGWE GREENSTONE BELT (NGEZI GROUP; 2.7 Ga)

FIG. 6.—Generalized stratigraphy of the Ngezi Group in the Belingwe Greenstone Belt illustrating relative position of the Cheshire Formation. After Martin (1978) and Martin et al. (1980).

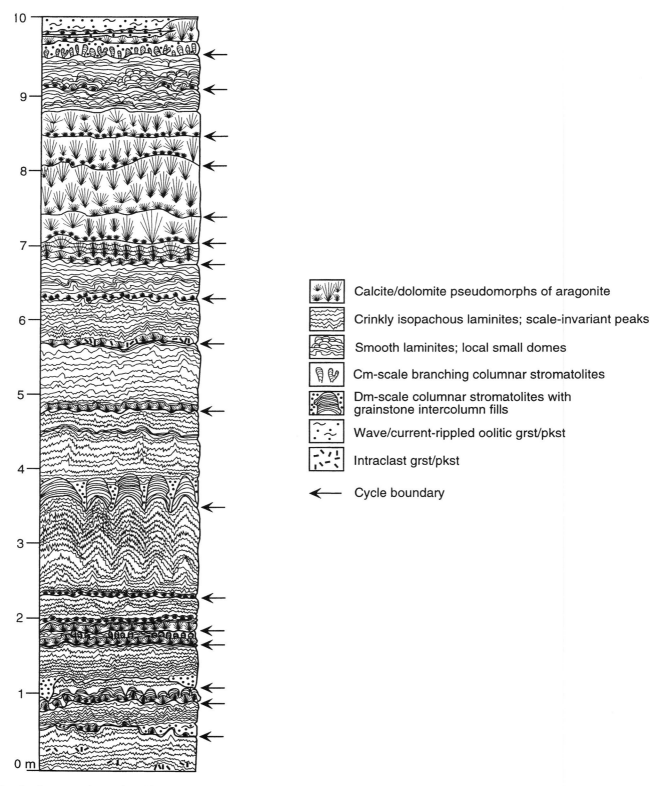

FIG. 7.—Representative stratigraphic section of the Cheshire Formation, from the "Main Stromatolite Outcrop" of Martin et al. (1980). This interval forms the uppermost 10 m of the outcrop, and is directly overlain by a siliciclastic-rich interval, containing fine sandstones and siltstones similar to the lower Cheshire Formation. Note cyclic repetition of facies, with fans and grainstones directly overlying cycle boundaries, interpreted as subaerial exposure and transgressive surfaces.

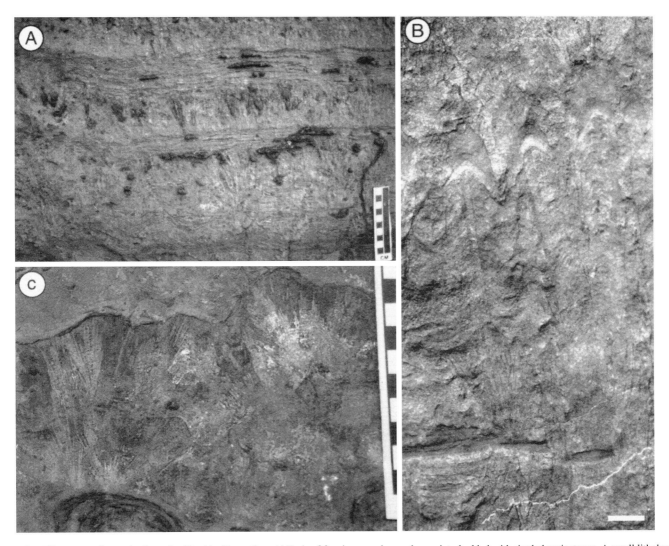

FIG. 8.—Fibrous pseudomorphs from the Cheshire Formation. A) Beds of fanning pseudomorphs are interbedded with rippled grainstones. A small lithoherm is developed on the left. B) The base of this bed consists of fanning pseudomorphs surrounded by grainstone. In the middle, only the most vertically oriented pseudomorphs remain and are surrounded by grainstone. Digitate stromatolites nucleated on the tips of the pseudomorphs and more fans precipitated on the digitate stromatolites. Compare with Figure 5B. Scale bar is 1 cm long. C) Abundant small crystal fans nucleated on a stromatolite and on each other.

Huntsman Limestone, Bulawayo Greenstone Belt

The ~2.6 Ga (Hawkesworth and Bickle, 1976) Bulawayo greenstone belt, Zimbabwe, contains a thick succession of mafic and ultramafic lavas interspersed with thin units of felsic volcanics, phyllites, banded iron formation, and rare carbonate (Wilson, 1979). In general, outcrop is poor and little is known about this belt. However, local occurrences of limestone are present and are clearly part of the thick succession of mafic and ultramafic rocks. These carbonates have been studied only in a very general way starting with their discovery by Macgregor (1941) and followed by hand-sample descriptions of stromatolites (Schopf et al., 1971; Walter, 1983).

In 1993, excellent exposures were available for study at Huntsman Quarry because of a long drought, which lowered water levels in the normally flooded pits. We measured two short sections that revealed a diverse suite of structures including stromatolites, fenestrate microbialites, abundant fanning pseudomorphs, and laminated clastic carbonates. The stratigraphically lower section from the southeast pit (Fig. 9) consists predominantly of beds of fanning pseudomorphs with calcite cement crusts and interbeds of fenestral carbonate and rare micritic sediment. These facies are typically arranged into decimeter-thick cycles. The base of each cycle consists of light tan pseudomorph fans that darken upward. They are capped by 0.1–5 cm-thick crusts of herringbone calcite that form either continuous layers or digitate stromatolites. The crusts are dark and abruptly overlain by light pseudomorph fans. In several cycles, micritic layers filled the relief on top of the herringbone calcite crusts before the nucleation of new pseudomorphed crystals. No evidence of erosion or dissolution was observed along these surfaces. The origin of fenestral beds that are occasionally interbedded with these cycles is unknown, but may be due to microbial mat growth.

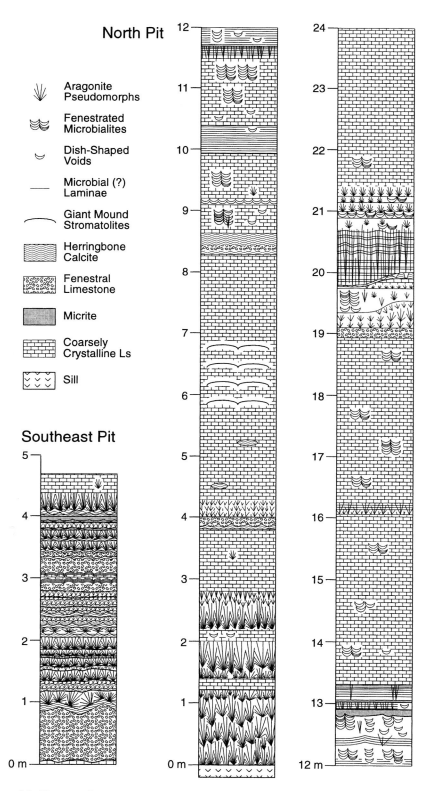

FIG. 9.—Stratigraphic sections of the Huntsman limestone. The southeast pit contains abundant layers of fanning pseudomorphs and fenestral limestone. The north pit contains abundant pseudomorph fans intergrown with fenestrate microbialites. Because of abundant shearing and recrystallization, microbial structures are commonly recognized only by the presence of dish-shaped voids preserved as sparry calcite in darker limestone.

The upper section is from the west face of the north pit (Fig. 9). It starts with beds of fanning pseudomorphs with rare fenestral interbeds. After a recrystallized massive interval, the large domal stromatolites described by Macgregor (1941) are developed. Internal textures are poorly preserved, but faint lamination occasionally is visible. Above the giant domes, abundant fenestrate microbial structures with scattered fanning pseudomorphs are the dominant lithofacies. The microbial structures consist of laminated mat, supports, and dish-shaped voids that are similar to cuspate fenestrate microbialites of the deep subtidal microbialite lithofacies assemblage in the Campbellrand–Malmani carbonate platform (Sumner, 1997a, 1997b). Because of extensive recrystallization, often only the dish-shaped voids are visible because of their light color relative to the laminated mat and supports. However, in less altered beds, the microbialite structure is well preserved. Upward in the section, beds of vertically oriented pseudomorphs are interstratified with beds of fenestrate microbialites. The pseudomorphs in these beds commonly are draped by black laminae that are vertically separated by one to several millimeters of white calcite that appears to fill centimeter-long, bedding-parallel fenestrae. The sides of these fenestrae are defined by the edges of pseudomorphs, whereas the tops and bottoms are defined by the dark laminae. Upward in the section, pseudomorphed fan lithoherms developed, and one layer of columnar stromatolites with a herringbone calcite internal texture was deposited. The top of the upper section is extensively sheared, and few sedimentary features are preserved.

The lack of cross-stratification and a larger stratigraphic context for the Huntsman limestone makes interpretation of the depositional environment equivocal. However, facies in the upper section are consistent with a subtidal depositional environment (Macgregor, 1941). The delicate fenestrate microbialites were probably deposited below wave base or during episodes of low agitation (Sumner, 1997a, 1997b), whereas the large domal stromatolites may have been deposited above wave base (Macgregor, 1941). No sedimentary structures suggesting intertidal or restricted depositional environments were observed.

Crystal pseudomorphs.—In the Huntsman Limestone, the pseudomorph fans commonly nucleated at the bases of 3–20 cm-thick beds that usually consist solely of pseudomorphs (Fig. 10A), and rarely contain small amounts of draping sediment. Lithoherms consisting solely of pseudomorph fans developed synoptic relief of up to 20 cm. The fans in the lithoherms commonly nucleated along specific surfaces, overgrowing the underlying pseudomorphs. They range in height from 1 to 20 cm.

Pseudomorphs associated with the fenestrate microbialites are poorly preserved because of extensive recrystallization and strain. We identified only widely separated pseudomorphs in microbialite-rich beds, where they project through the fenestrate microbialites irrespective of the microbial textures (Fig. 10B). Walter (1983) described an acicular crystal texture corresponding to our fanning pseudomorphs that projected through both the microbial mat and the dish-shaped voids. He reported that the acicular texture was pervasive, which suggests that it may be more common than we observed. Walter (1983) suggested that the voids in the microbialites were due to separation of laminae from the force of crystallization of the acicular pseudomorph growth. However, the microbial structures are identical to cuspate microbialites in the Campbellrand–Malmani

platform, where voids are filled with isopachous calcite cements (Sumner, 1997b, 2000). Thus, the voids are probably a result of microbial processes rather than precipitation of primary crystals. We did not observe any evidence that growth of the original crystals affected the microbialite textures by producing voids, forming surfaces that were colonized by mats, or disrupting the lateral continuity of the mat.

Beds of vertically oriented pseudomorphs that are interstratified with microbialites commonly are draped by black laminae and contain oblong, bedding-parallel fenestrae distinct from those in the microbialite beds (Fig. 10C). The fenestrae-filling calcite typically is extensively recrystallized, so its origin is unknown. However, the texture of the laminae is similar to the laminated mat in the fenestrate microbialites, which suggests that they may have been microbial mats. If so, these beds may have consisted of vertically oriented crystals that were draped by microbial mats, leaving voids beneath the mats and between the crystals that were later filled with calcite cement. In this case, the original crystals may have formed a surface on which microbial mats grew.

Steeprock Group

The ~2.7 Ga Steeprock Group, Ontario, Canada, unconformably overlies much older crystalline basement and consists of a platform of siliciclastic sands and conglomerate, carbonate, and altered iron-formation, followed by a "typical" greenstone belt sequence of thick pyroclastic ashrock, mafic volcanics, and turbiditic sediments (Jollife, 1966; McIntosh, 1972). The contact between the ashrock and overlying thick mafic volcanics is strongly sheared, suggesting that the volcanics have been thrust over Steeprock platform sediments (Hoffman, 1989). Carbonates in the Steeprock Group have been studied for over 100 years from regional, economic, paleontologic, and sedimentologic perspectives (Smyth, 1891; Walcott, 1912; Lawson, 1913; Jollife, 1955; Hofmann, 1971; Walter, 1983; Wilks and Nisbet, 1985; Wilks, 1986).

The Steeprock carbonates were deposited on a veneer of fluvial (Wilks, 1986) and possibly shallow marine siliciclastic sediments that covered the exposed crystalline basement (Fig. 11). The carbonates are up to 500 m thick and extend continuously along strike for 12 km, with the exception of one locality where the entire unit has been cut out beneath a major karstic unconformity developed at the top of the sequence (Wilks, 1986; Hoffman, 1989). The upper karstic carbonates are overlain by a carbonate soil-like sequence containing the minerals goethite, gibbsite, hematite, and kaolinite, as well as including lenses of pisolitic ferruginous bauxite (Jollife, 1955; Wilks, 1986). This deeply weathered soil unit is overlain by a sequence of altered probable banded iron-formation, which is thought to have accumulated subaqueously, following transgression of the paleosol and foundering of the platform (McIntosh, 1972; Wilks, 1986).

A crude stratigraphy (Fig. 11) based on stromatolite morphology has been defined for the Steeprock carbonates (Wilks and Nisbet, 1985; Wilks, 1986). Grainstones apparently are absent from the sequence, which is dominated by stromatolitic lithologies. Small domal stromatolites up to 15 cm wide with up to 10 cm synoptic relief occur near the base of the sequence and are associated with units containing microbial laminites and

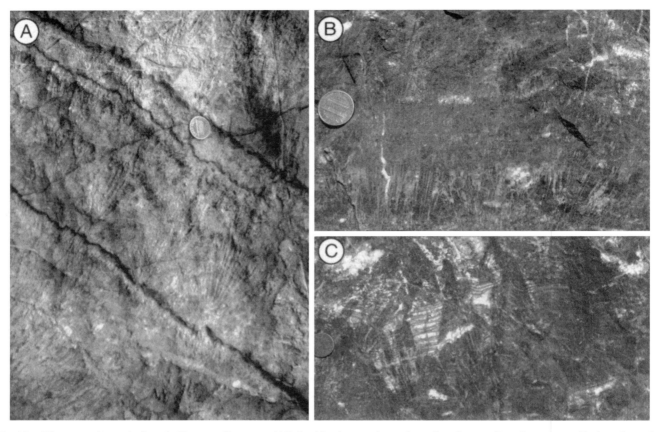

Fig. 10.—Fibrous pseudomorphs from the Huntsman limestone. A) Beds of fanning pseudomorphs nucleated repeatedly and are separated by irregular surfaces. B) The fanning texture is emphasized by dolomitization of fill between pseudomorphs. C) Pseudomorph fans (dark) are draped by dark microbial(?) laminae leaving white voids. Coins are 2 cm in diameter.

irregular to wavy-laminated stromatolites (Wilks and Nisbet, 1985; Wilks, 1986). Digitate columnar stromatolites and linked conical stromatolites are developed locally, and pseudomorphs after a fibrous, radiating precursor mineral are present (Hofmann, 1971). These pseudomorphs were first described and interpreted by Walcott (1912) as biogenic structures, and assigned the name *Atikokania*. Subsequently, these were reinterpreted to be crystal structures identical to the pseudomorphs described here. Hofmann (1971) suggested gypsum or aragonite as a precursor mineralogy, but later authors have favored only the gypsum interpretation, on the basis of the large size of the crystals, which extend for up to 25 cm (Walter, 1983; Wilks, 1986). Overlying carbonates contain large, elongate stromatolite mounds up to 3 m wide and 5 m long, and with up to 1 m of synoptic relief (Wilks, 1986). Stromatolites form biostromes that extend across most outcrops. Lamination in stromatolites is defined by variations in the organic content of the carbonate, as well as fenestrae that are up to 3 cm long (Wilks, 1986). Walter (1983) noted that the laminae are defined in part by the presence of acicular crystal fibers, similar to those of the "*Atikokania*" facies.

The overall stratigraphy of the Steeprock carbonate sequence has been interpreted by Wilks (1986) as a subtidal, shallowing-upward depositional package, with smaller stromatolites at the base and larger stromatolites at the top. However, many docu-mented Proterozoic shallowing-upward sequences contain larger-scale stromatolites that are overlain by smaller varieties (Cecile and Campbell, 1978; Grotzinger, 1986a; Beukes, 1987). Thus, the Steeprock sequence probably deepens upward. A subsequent fall in relative sea level exposed the top of the platform and a karstic unconformity developed.

Crystal pseudomorphs.—Continuous sections were not measured at Steeprock, but fans of pseudomorphs, identical to *Atikokania*, are abundant as laterally continuous beds interstratified with columnar stromatolites and fenestrate microbialites. In beds, the crystal fans typically nucleated very close to each other and grew continuously upward for 1 to 160 cm. The fan-like geometry is predominant at the very bases of beds, and upward, the pseudomorphs are predominantly parallel and vertically oriented (Figs. 5D, 12). Pseudomorphs draped with sediment were not observed.

Pseudomorph fans commonly are found within fenestrate microbialites that form wavy layers with alternating void-rich and void-poor microbialites (Fig. 12B; Sumner, 2000). Rare layers of cuspate fenestrate microbialites with dish-shaped voids are present, but most of the fenestrate microbialites have 0.5–5 mm equant rather than dish-shaped voids and form a net-like texture. Void-rich, net-like microbialites contain abundant equant voids separated by supports draped by thin mat layers. The supports commonly show small amounts of compactional fold-

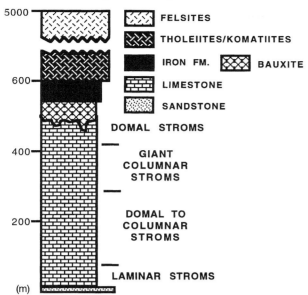

FIG. 11.—Stratigraphy of the Steep Rock Group illustrating relations between stromatolites of the carbonate unit. After Wilks and Nisbet (1985) and Wilks (1986).

ing. Void-poor microbialites contain abundant compacted supports draped by filmy laminae. Voids are rare in the compacted microbialites and are flattened parallel to the filmy laminae where present. In some cases, pseudomorphs project through the microbialites. They are more abundant or better preserved in void-poor microbialite layers that show evidence for post-growth compaction than in less compacted microbialites. In the compacted microbialites, the pseudomorphs are typically densely spaced with few to no identifiable gaps between them. In some samples, the pseudomorphs form fans that grew against one another (Fig. 12). The microbial laminae dome up over the centers of the fans and have a trough-filling geometry where neighboring fans intersect. The pseudomorphs project through the microbial components without directly affecting the morphology of the microbialites. The microbialites are encased in the pseudomorphs, and the laminated mat and supports continue from pseudomorph to pseudomorph without deflecting upward or downward at the pseudomorph boundaries (Sumner, 2000). In addition, the supports and pseudomorphed crystals are not always oriented parallel to each other. At the sides of fans, the pseudomorphs radiate slightly outward whereas the supports are oriented more vertically. Compaction probably modified the original orientation of the supports, but they are not oriented parallel to the elongation of the pseudomorphs, which implies that their orientation was not affected by precipitation of the precursor mineral.

The origin of the carbonate in the void-rich microbialites is unclear. Pseudomorphs are less abundant in them, because of either poor preservation or precipitation of fewer precursor crystals. Sumner (2000) interprets the differences in void-rich and void-poor net-like microbialites as due to variable synse-

dimentary compaction. In void-rich microbialites, carbonate precipitation probably occurred on the supports during growth of the microbialites, giving them rigidity. In contrast, there was probably little contemporaneous precipitation on void-poor microbialites, allowing them to compact. However, Walter (1983) reports acicular crystals projecting through voids in what look to be void-rich microbialites, suggesting that originally the pseudomorphed crystals did precipitate within both void-rich and void-poor microbialites.

Timing and Environments of Pseudomorph Precipitation

In all four carbonate platforms studied, the pseudomorph fans grew upward or outward from depositional surfaces. The abundance of beds of crystal pseudomorphs up to 160 cm thick and lacking evidence for detrital carbonate demonstrates that they did not grow within sediment. The growth of lithoherms consisting solely of fans and surrounded by siltstone, grainstone, and intraclasts demonstrates that they could form current-resistant highs on the sea floor. In addition, the growth of digitate stromatolites on the tips of individual pseudomorphs demonstrates that some crystals projected above the sea floor and formed sites favorable for stromatolite growth. Sediment that draped growing fans or infilled troughs between fans was deposited contemporaneously with or after growth of the pseudomorphed crystals. Thus, most of the pseudomorphs replace a primary mineral that grew directly from ambient seawater at or projecting above the sediment–water interface.

The timing of precipitation of the fine, vertically oriented pseudomorphed crystals that project through laminated sediment is more difficult to interpret. The primary crystals probably did not project far above the sedimentary surface because traction transport of sediment would have broken off the fine crystals. In contrast, they may have precipitated either at or just below the sediment–water interface.

The timing of precipitation of pseudomorphed crystals preserved in fenestrate microbialites is also somewhat ambiguous. The primary crystals show no evidence of having influenced the growth morphology of the microbialites, which implies that precipitation of the original crystals may have occurred below the mat surface and encased the mat as they grew upward. In addition, the evidence for compaction in some microbialites containing abundant pseudomorphs suggests that crystal growth occurred below the mat surface after minor compaction of the microbialites (Sumner, 2000). In contrast, the beds of pseudomorphed crystals in the upper Bulawayo section that appear draped by mats may have provided a surface for microbial colonization, and thus influenced the texture of the microbial structures. Even where the pseudomorphed crystals may have grown below a microbial mat, there is no evidence for preexisting sediment that was replaced by growth of the crystals. The textural evidence suggests that the crystals formed the original sediment within microbial mats consisting of organic residue with abundant water-filled voids. Thus, the pseudomorphs likely reflect the primary precipitation of the precursor mineral from microbially modified seawater.

The environments in which the pseudomorph precursor precipitated are diverse, ranging from agitated subtidal to evaporitic facies. Depositional environments are best constrained in the Campbellrand–Malmani carbonate platform, where preser-

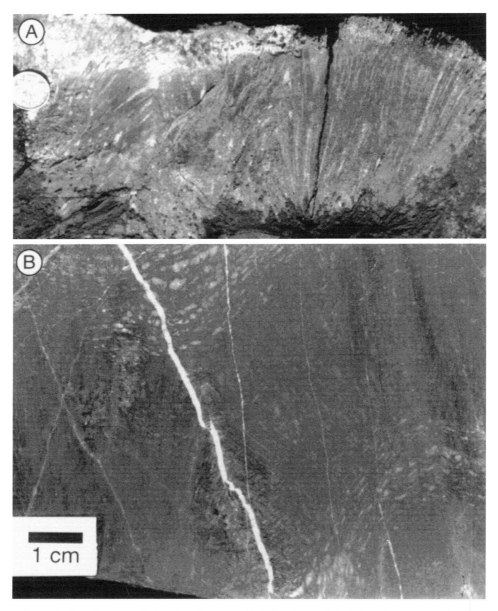

FIG. 12.— Fibrous pseudomorphs from the Steep Rock carbonates. A) Field photo of fans. Coin is 2 cm in diameter. B) Two pseudomorph fans project through microbialites and abut each other in the trough near the white tension crack.

vation of the platform for 800 km across strike allows evaluation of the extent of restriction during growth of the fans. Fans are abundant throughout the platform, including the wave-swept subtidal giant stromatolite facies belt in the ramp that developed at the base of the platform and during a major transgression in the middle of the platform (Fig. 2). In addition, the fans are present throughout the reef margin. The presence of fans in these agitated, open marine environments implies that they precipitated from open seawater and not solely from evaporitically concentrated waters. Fans that grew in more restricted facies of the Campbellrand–Malmani carbonate platform tend to be substantially smaller, suggesting that crystal precipitation in restricted facies had different morphological characteristics, possibly because of a higher influx of detrital

carbonate. In the Cheshire Formation, pseudomorph fans also are abundant in open-shelf, agitated depositional environments, as well as possibly more restricted environments. Although similar evaluations of the extent of restriction are not as reliable for the Bulawayo and Steep Rock greenstone belt carbonates, facies studied are consistent with near-wave-base subtidal deposition. Thus, precipitation of the precursor mineral in these four carbonates of diverse age probably reflects global Late Archean seawater chemistry.

PSEUDOMORPH CHARACTERISTICS

Petrographic Characteristics

The fanning and botryoidal crystal pseudomorphs now consist of calcite, dolomite, and chert. Their morphology is defined by trains of inclusions and their relationships to the surrounding sediment. Where the pseudomorphs are draped by fine sediment, they have flat to feathery terminations. In addition, they have hexagonal cross sections. Petrographic preservation is best in pseudomorphs now consisting of calcite.

Calcite replacement of the original crystals can be texturally classified into four petrographic facies (Fig. 13): 1) inclusion-rich, equant mosaic; 2) scattered inclusion, interlocking mosaic; 3) elongate mosaic; and 4) equant mosaic. The optically best preserved pseudomorphs are replaced by an **inclusion-rich, equant mosaic** of calcite. This petrographic facies contains abundant trains of inclusions that run parallel to elongation in the pseudomorphs and preserve the original fibrous character of the precursor mineral. They crosscut calcite crystal boundaries. The optically unoriented calcite crystals are 50–250 μm in diameter and are equant to rarely elongate parallel to inclusion trains. Crystal boundaries are usually planar compromise boundaries with rare irregular to interlocking boundaries. Some crystals overstep the edges of pseudomorphs and replace both the primary mineral and inter-pseudomorph fill. The **scattered inclusion, interlocking mosaic** petrographic facies contains fewer inclusions, which are scattered throughout with only very faint linear trends parallel to pseudomorph elongation. The optically unoriented calcite crystals are about 300 μm in diameter and are sometimes elongate parallel to pseudomorph elongation. They have well defined, interlocking crystal boundaries.

Commonly, well defined crystals contain about four subdomains with slightly different extinction orientations and indistinct domain boundaries. The **elongate mosaic** petrographic facies lacks inclusions defining original crystal structure. The optically unoriented calcite crystals are variable in size but are typically smaller than 175 x 500 μm and are elongate parallel to pseudomorph elongation. Rare crystals contain subdomains with slightly different extinction, which are also elongate parallel to pseudomorph elongation. The crystals have irregular boundaries that tend to be more linear when parallel to pseudomorph elongation. The **equant mosaic** petrographic facies includes most other replacement textures that do not preserve characteristics of the primary minerals. The equant crystals vary in size and are optically unoriented.

All four petrographic facies are abundant in the pseudomorphs from the Campbellrand–Malmani carbonate platform. The facies grade laterally into each other. Individual pseudomorphs sometimes contain all four facies and often contain the scattered inclusion, elongate, and equant mosaics. Pseudomorphs from the Cheshire Formation typically consist of scattered inclusion mosaic facies that grades into equant mosaics. Pseudomorphs from the Huntsman limestone and the Steeprock Group are poorly preserved and consist of equant mosaics. The pseudomorphs from the Steeprock Group typically contain bimodal mosaics with 80% of crystals <50 μm in diameter and 20% >200 μm in diameter.

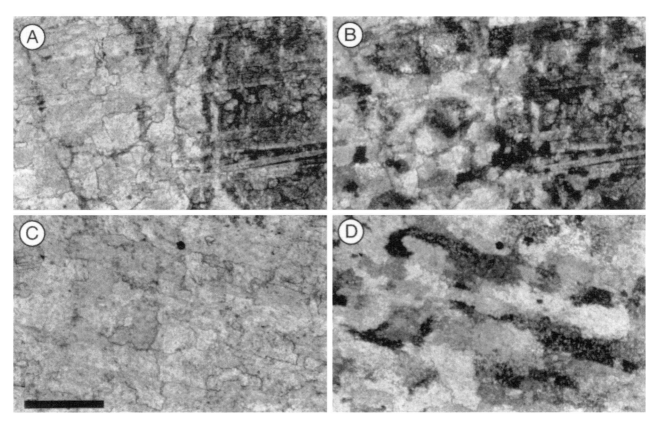

FIG. 13.—Photomicrographs of fibrous pseudomorphs in sample BT 22 from the Campbellrand–Malmani platform. A) The right half of the pseudomorph consists of the inclusion-rich, equant mosaic whereas the left half consists of the scattered inclusion, interlocking mosaic. B) Same view under crossed polarizers. C) Pseudomorph consisting of the elongate mosaic facies. The high [Sr] measured in sample BT 22 came from this area. D) Same view under crossed polarizers. Scale bar is 500 μm long for all photographs.

Fig. 14.—Fibrous pseudomorphs from the Carawine Formation. A) Silicified pseudomorphs form a decimeter-thick layer at the base, and smaller fanning pseudomorphs are preserved in dolomite near the top. Scale bar is 5 cm long. B) This small acicular fan is preserved in dolomite and is encased in herringbone calcite. Scale bar is 2 cm long.

Primary Mineralogy

Several of the petrographic characteristics of the fanning pseudomorphs strongly suggest an aragonite precursor mineralogy. First, the relict morphological characteristics of the original crystals are most consistent with an aragonite precursor: the fibrous nature of the primary mineral and the blunt to feathery terminations of the pseudomorphs are typical of aragonite (Loucks and Folk, 1976; Mazzullo, 1980; Sandberg, 1985a; Peryt et al., 1990). Gypsum crystals usually have well developed crystal faces (e.g., Hardie et al., 1983; Lowenstein, 1988), none of which were observed. Second, optically unoriented, equant to elongate calcite crystals with unit extinction are characteristic of calcite replacement of aragonite (Assereto and Folk, 1980; Mazzullo, 1980; Sandberg, 1985a). Gypsum and anhydrite typically are replaced by calcite in a dissolution–precipitation process, so preservation of inclusions defining the internal texture of a gypsum precursor is not expected (e.g., Harwood, 1980; Folk et al., 1993). Also, secondary calcite mosaics filling gypsum molds would show either a void-filling geometry or an equant neomorphic texture rather than elongation parallel to pseudomorph elongation. Solution-collapse features, which can be associated with replaced gypsum pseudomorphs, were not observed in any of the Archean carbonates described. Thus, a combination of the primary crystal morphology and the petrographic textures of the pseudomorphs are inconsistent with gypsum as the precursor mineral.

The pseudomorph characteristics also are inconsistent with recrystallized primary calcite cements. Recrystallization of fibrous calcite usually produces optically oriented neomorphic calcite mosaics (Assereto and Folk, 1980; Mazzullo, 1980; Sandberg, 1985a) rather than the unoriented mosaics observed. These recrystallized calcite textures are present adjacent to, but not within, the pseudomorphs. Also, the hexagonal cross sections of the pseudomorphs are consistent with either gypsum or twinned aragonite (e.g., Sandberg, 1985a; Buick and Dunlop,

1987; Riccioni et al., 1996) but are not characteristic of fibrous calcite.

Strontium Concentrations

Aragonite commonly contains high [Sr] whereas calcite and gypsum typically contain less strontium, because the strontium partition coefficient for aragonite is 1.13 (Kinsman, 1969; Kinsman and Holland, 1969) whereas the partition coefficients for calcite and gypsum are <0.1 (Katz et al., 1972; Lorens, 1981) and 0.2 (Kushnir, 1980), respectively. Marine aragonite commonly contains tens of thousands of ppm strontium initially, and thousands of ppm strontium can be preserved in aragonite pseudomorphs during conversion of aragonite to calcite at low water-to-rock ratios (e.g., Katz et al., 1972; Sandberg, 1985a). Concentrations of several thousand ppm are rare in primary calcite and would not be expected in recrystallized calcite because of Sr loss during recrystallization. Similarly, gypsum replaced by calcite should not contain high [Sr] because of the relatively low distribution coefficient of Sr into gypsum, and substantial volumes of water are necessary to alter gypsum to calcite, which would further dilute the [Sr] of the secondary calcite. Thus, high preserved [Sr] supports the interpretation of an aragonite precursor to the pseudomorphs. Low [Sr] may reflect either high water-to-rock ratios or a different precursor mineral.

Strontium concentrations of pseudomorphs from the Campbellrand–Malmani platform were measured using an electron microprobe with a 15 keV beam acceleration, 5 nA beam current, and a 10 μm spot size. Counting times were 10 s for Ca, Mg, and Fe and 30 s for Sr and Mn. Yield weights were calculated for stoichiometric carbonate using [Ca], [Mg], [Mn], [Fe], and [Sr] and were 98–103%. The Sr, Mn, and Fe detection limits were 400 ppm, 600 ppm, and 1200 ppm, respectively.

Analyses were performed on 1–4 pseudomorphs in each of six samples and on fibrous calcite cement in one sample. [Sr]

in each pseudomorph and the calcite cement was measured at six spots separated by 15–50 μm. The calcite cement (sample MV104-1) contained less than or equal to 600 ± 400 ppm Sr, and pseudomorphs in the same sample contained up to 900 ± 400 ppm Sr, although most analyses were below the detection limit (Table 1). Highest [Sr] were measured in an area of sample BT 20 consisting of the elongate mosaic facies replacing a botryoidal pseudomorph, where concentrations from 1800 to 3700 ± 400 ppm were measured. [Sr] varied from 1800 ppm to 3200 ppm over a distance of <50 μm. Strontium concentrations greater than 900 ± 400 ppm were also measured in the scattered-inclusion interlocking-mosaic facies in both botryoidal and fanning crystal pseudomorphs. Concentrations are extremely variable and jump from >900 ppm to below the detection limit in a distance of <50 μm. This local heterogeneity demonstrates that water–rock interactions were variable over very small distances during recrystallization of the original crystals.

The preservation of several thousand ppm Sr in the pseudomorphs supports an aragonitic precursor. The composition of recrystallized calcite cements associated with less well preserved pseudomorphs overlaps [Sr] in the pseudomorphs, so results do not unambiguously demonstrate that the pseudomorphs contain higher [Sr] than associated calcite. However, the high concentrations in better preserved pseudomorphs and local heterogeneity are supportive of an aragonitic precursor that recrystallized to calcite with variable but low water-to-rock ratios. This distribution of Sr would not be expected with the large water-to-rock ratios required for calcite replacement of gypsum.

DISCUSSION

Other Archean Occurrences

Similar aragonite pseudomorphs have been reported from two other Archean carbonates. In the 2.6 Ga Carawine Dolomite, Hamersley Basin, Australia, pseudomorphs are found in shallow-water, low-energy depositional environments and consist of prismatic pseudomorphs forming sediment-draped fans and acicular pseudomorphs forming fringes and botryoids (Fig. 14; Simonson et al., 1993). The prismatic pseudomorphs are 3–20 cm long, have hexagonal cross sections, and show irregular crystal terminations. Neighboring pseudomorphs show evidence of competitive growth. The replacing dolomite and chert appear to have filled molds of the original crystals (Simonson et al., 1993). Acicular pseudomorphs are up to 4 cm long and are closely spaced forming parallel to botryoidal masses. Some of these masses were reworked and abraded (Simonson et al., 1993). Morphologically, the acicular pseudomorphs are similar to the prismatic pseudomorphs, but petrographically, they show replacement rather than dissolutional textures (Simonson et al., 1993). Simonson et al. (1993) interpret these pseudomorphs as replacing aragonite, which is consistent with our aragonitic interpretation for the pseudomorphs described here. The aragonite pseudomorphs are distinct from stubby pseudomorphs that Simonson et al. (1993) interpreted as gypsum on the basis of their growth geometry and chevron crystal terminations. The possible gypsum pseudomorphs were found in three layers, each <2 cm thick. At one location, they occur in conjunction with hollow-faced cubes, interpreted as halite pseudomorphs.

Fanning crystal pseudomorphs are also present in the 2925–2940 Ma Uchi Greenstone Belt at Red Lake, Ontario (Hofmann et al., 1985). They form fans up to 1.2 m in diameter that consist of chert and carbonate. The pseudomorphs are centimeter- to decimeter-wide bundles of acicular crystals that nucleated on bedding planes and grew upward. Neighboring fans have interpenetrating pseudomorphs indicative of competitive growth (Hofmann et al., 1985). The pseudomorphs were interpreted as replacing either gypsum or aragonite (Hofmann et al., 1985). They are morphologically more similar to the pseudomorphs documented here, and we propose that they replace aragonite rather than gypsum.

Aragonite Precipitation Rates

The growth of crystal fans >1 m high in beds lacking evidence for detrital sediment requires that there was little sediment influx during aragonite precipitation, aragonite precipitation rates were very high, or a combination of both. If crystal growth rates were not substantially higher than modern aragonite cement precipitation rates, long intervals of no sediment influx are required. Maximum aragonite cement precipitation rates estimated from modern reefs are about 25 mm/100 yr or 1 cm/40 yr (Grammer et al., 1993; Grammer et al., 1996). If Late Archean aragonite precipitation occurred at the same rate, it would take a 10 cm fan 400 yr to precipitate and a 1 m fan 4000 yr to precipitate. It is unrealistic to expect no sediment influx into agitated shallow subtidal to intertidal depositional environments for hundreds to thousands of years. Also, in many cases, grainstones filled space between aragonite pseudomorphs and finer sediment draped some fans, demonstrating the availability of at least some detrital sediment. Thus, to get the observed decimeter heights of Archean aragonite fans, aragonite precipitation must have been substantially faster than it is in modern reefs. Rapid precipitation may have been a result of higher than modern supersaturation of seawater with respect to aragonite (Grotzinger, 1989; Grotzinger and Kasting, 1993).

Older Late Archean carbonates, i.e., those from Steep Rock, Belingwe, Bulawayo, and Uchi greenstone belts, tend to have larger aragonite fans and more fan lithoherms that are associated with grainstones than the younger Campbellrand–Malmani and Carawine carbonates, which have aragonite pseudomorph fans and fine crystals draped by fine-grained sediment. Fans in the Campbellrand–Malmani platform rarely are associated with grainstones. If the thickness of aragonite fan beds reflect crystal growth rates, aragonite supersaturation may have been higher around 2.7–2.6 Ga than around 2.6–2.5 Ga. Alternatively, if the thickness of aragonite fan beds reflects sediment influx, a difference in production of grainstones and/or grain transport is required. A paucity of large aragonite fans in Proterozoic and Phanerozoic carbonates could be due to either a decrease in aragonite precipitation rate or an increase in deposition of detrital carbonate. Each effect, either by itself or in combination, would allow burial of any aragonite crystals that started to grow on the sea floor. Thus, it appears that the Campbellrand–Malmani and Carawine carbonates reflect a transition from more abundant and large aragonite pseudomorphs in older Late Archean carbonates to the rare pseudomorphs found in unusual environments in Proterozoic and Phanerozoic carbonates.

TABLE 1.—MICROPROBE ANALYSES OF ARAGONITE PSEUDOMORPHS

Sample	Petrographic Texture	CaCO$_3$ (mol%)	2σ	MgCO$_3$ (mol%)	2σ	Mn (ppm)	2σ	Fe (ppm)	2σ	Sr (ppm)	2σ
bt 20-1_1	Inclusion-rich equant mosaic	98	2	0.7	0.2	5500	1800	—	—	—	—
bt 20-1_2	,,	98	2	1.2	0.2	4800	1700	—	—	500	400
bt 20-1_4	,,	96	2	2.3	0.3	7700	2310	2200	900	700	400
bt 20-1_5	,,	97	2	1.6	0.3	6600	1900	2500	900	—	—
bt 20-1_6	,,	97	2	1.1	0.2	5100	1800	3000	900	—	—
bt 20-2_1	Scattered inclusion interlocking mosaic	97	2	1.5	0.3	3100	1500	2900	900	500	400
bt 20-2_2	,,	98	2	1.2	0.2	5200	1800	—	—	700	400
bt 20-2_3	,,	98	2	1.8	0.3	1800	1400	—	—	600	400
bt 20-2_4	,,	98	2	1.0	0.2	5200	1800	1300	700	500	400
bt 20-2_5	,,	98	2	1.1	0.2	5300	1800	1600	700	—	—
bt 20-2_6	,,	99	2	0.8	0.2	2500	1500	—	—	1500	400
bt 20-3_1	Elongate mosaic	98	2	1.3	0.3	—	—	—	—	1800	400
bt 20-3_2	,,	99	2	0.2	0.2	—	—	—	—	3200	400
bt 20-3_3	,,	99	2	0.1	0.1	—	—	—	—	2900	400
bt 20-3_4	,,	99	2	0.3	0.2	—	—	—	—	2100	400
bt 20-3_5	,,	99	2	0.1	0.1	—	—	—	—	3500	500
bt 20-3_6	,,	99	2	0.1	0.1	—	—	—	—	3700	600
bt 22-1_1	Scattered inclusion to equant mosaic	98	2	2.1	0.3	—	—	—	—	—	—
bt 22-1_2	,,	98	2	2.1	0.3	1200	1200	—	—	—	—
bt 22-1_3	,,	97	2	2.5	0.3	1200	1200	—	—	—	—
bt 22-1_4	,,	98	2	0.8	0.2	2500	1500	1700	800	—	—
bt 22-1_5	,,	98	2	1.3	0.2	1700	1400	—	—	—	—
bt 22-1_6	,,	98	2	0.5	0.2	4000	1700	2700	900	—	—
bt 22-2_1	Inclusion-rich to scattered inclusion mosaic	98	2	1.4	0.3	3900	1700	1400	700	600	400
bt 22-2_2	,,	98	2	0.7	0.2	6500	1900	1700	700	400	400
bt 22-2_3	,,	98	2	0.8	0.2	4700	1700	—	—	—	—
bt 22-2_4	,,	98	2	0.7	0.2	4500	1600	—	—	—	—
bt 22-2_5	,,	98	2	1.5	0.3	2300	1500	—	—	600	400
bt 22-2_6	,,	97	2	2.7	0.3	3200	1500	—	—	500	400
bt 22-3_1	Equant to elongate mosaic	97	2	2.5	0.3	1500	1400	—	—	600	400
bt 22-3_2	,,	98	2	1.5	0.2	1800	1300	—	—	—	—
bt 22-3_3	,,	96	2	2.5	0.3	3600	1600	1800	700	—	—
bt 22-3_4	,,	98	2	1.2	0.2	4300	1600	—	—	—	—
bt 22-3_5	,,	97	2	1.8	0.3	4600	1700	1300	700	1000	400
bt 22-3_6	,,	98	2	1.1	0.2	4500	1600	—	—	—	—
bt 25-1_1	Scattered inclusion to equant mosaic	98	2	0.6	0.2	6000	1900	1300	700	—	—
bt 25-1_2	,,	77	2	18.1	0.7	20200	3000	4000	1000	700	400
bt 25-1_4	,,	97	2	1.0	0.2	8400	2100	1300	800	—	—
bt 25-1_5	,,	97	2	1.0	0.2	9900	2200	—	—	—	—
bt 25-1_6	,,	98	2	0.5	0.2	6300	1800	—	—	—	—
bt 25-2_1	Equant mosaic	97	2	2.4	0.3	4100	1700	—	—	500	400
bt 25-2_2	,,	98	2	0.9	0.2	5400	1800	—	—	—	—
bt 25-2_3	,,	98	2	0.6	0.2	6100	1800	—	—	—	—
bt 25-2_4	,,	97	2	0.9	0.2	10200	2200	—	—	600	400
bt 25-2_6	,,	98	2	0.5	0.2	6200	1900	—	—	500	400
bt 26-1_1	Recrystallized inclusion-rich equant mosaic	98	2	1.0	0.2	4200	1700	—	—	800	400
bt 26-1_2	,,	98	2	0.9	0.2	5900	1900	—	—	700	400
bt 26-1_3	,,	98	2	0.8	0.2	5200	1800	—	—	—	—
bt 26-1_4	,,	86	2	10.7	0.5	4100	1700	15200	5000	—	—
bt 26-1_5	,,	98	2	0.7	0.2	4100	1700	1300	700	—	—
bt 26-1_6	,,	99	2	0.6	0.2	3500	1600	—	—	—	—
bt 26-2_1	Scattered inclusion interlocking mosaic	81	2	16.1	0.6	9600	2200	7000	1700	600	400
bt 26-2_2	,,	97	2	1.6	0.3	6600	2100	1300	700	1000	400
bt 26-2_3	,,	96	2	1.3	0.2	11300	2400	—	—	—	—
bt 26-2_4	,,	97	2	0.8	0.2	8000	2100	—	—	—	—
bt 26-2_5	,,	98	2	0.5	0.2	5700	1800	—	—	—	—
bt 26-2_6	,,	98	2	0.7	0.2	5700	1800	1900	800	—	—
bt 26-3_1	Equant to elongate mosaic	94	2	5.7	0.3	2500	1500	—	—	500	400
bt 26-3_2	,,	95	2	4.9	0.3	1200	1200	—	—	700	400
bt 26-3_3	,,	98	2	1.0	0.2	—	—	—	—	1500	400
bt 26-3_4	,,	98	2	0.9	0.2	4700	1700	1300	700	—	—
bt 26-3_5	,,	97	2	0.8	0.2	12300	2500	—	—	500	400
bt 26-3_6	,,	98	2	0.9	0.2	4800	1700	—	—	600	400
mv 104-1_1	Calcite cement between pseudomorphs	98	2	1.1	0.2	6500	1800	—	—	500	400
mv 104-1_2	,,	92	2	5.6	0.3	8600	2100	1600	700	400	400
mv 104-1_3	,,	98	2	0.9	0.2	7200	1900	—	—	600	400
mv 104-1_4	,,	97	2	1.2	0.2	6100	1800	—	—	—	—
mv 104-1_5	,,	97	2	0.8	0.2	7400	1900	1400	700	—	—
mv 104-1_6	,,	97	2	0.9	0.2	8700	2100	—	—	—	—
mv 104-2_1	Equant mosaic	98	2	1.3	0.2	—	—	—	—	700	400
mv 104-2_2	,,	99	2	1.0	0.2	—	—	—	—	500	400
mv 104-2_3	,,	98	2	1.3	0.2	—	—	—	—	900	400
mv 104-2_4	,,	98	2	1.1	0.2	3000	1500	—	—	—	—
mv 104-2_5	,,	98	2	1.3	0.2	—	—	—	—	—	—
mv 104-2_6	,,	99	2	1.1	0.2	—	—	—	—	400	400

TABLE 1.—(Continued) MICROPROBE ANALYSES OF ARAGONITE PSEUDOMORPHS

Sample	Petrographic Texture	CaCO₃ (mol%)	2σ	MgCO₃ (mol%)	2σ	Mn (ppm)	2σ	Fe (ppm)	2σ	Sr (ppm)	2σ
mv 104-3_1	Scattered inclusion interlocking mosaic	98	2	0.9	0.2	3100	1500	—	—	—	—
mv 104-3_2	,,	99	2	0.9	0.2	2600	1500	—	—	—	—
mv 104-3_3	,,	98	2	0.4	0.2	7500	1900	—	—	—	—
mv 104-3_4	,,	98	2	0.5	0.2	5000	1700	—	—	500	400
mv 104-3_5	,,	98	2	0.5	0.2	9300	2200	—	—	—	—
mv 104-3_6	,,	98	2	0.6	0.2	6900	1900	—	—	—	—
mv 104-4_1	Equant mosaic	97	2	1.2	0.2	6700	1900	—	—	—	—
mv 104-4_2	,,	97	2	1.9	0.3	5600	1800	1300	700	700	400
mv 104-4_3	,,	98	2	0.8	0.2	8100	2000	—	—	400	400
mv 104-4_4	,,	98	2	0.7	0.2	5600	1800	—	—	—	—
mv 104-4_5	,,	98	2	0.8	0.2	6500	1800	—	—	—	—
mv 104-4_6	,,	98	2	1.2	0.2	4300	1600	—	—	700	400
mv 105-1_1	Equant mosaic	98	2	0.7	0.2	8800	2100	—	—	—	—
mv 105-1_2	,,	98	2	0.7	0.2	6400	1900	—	—	—	—
mv 105-1_3	,,	98	2	0.6	0.2	8100	2100	—	—	—	—
mv 105-1_4	,,	98	2	0.6	0.2	6200	1800	—	—	600	700
mv 105-1_5	,,	98	2	0.2	0.2	7900	2100	—	—	—	—
mv 105-1_6	,,	98	2	0.6	0.2	7300	2100	—	—	—	—

—Concentration below detection limit

Implications for Seawater Chemistry

The reinterpretation of most of the reported occurrences of Late Archean gypsum pseudomorphs as aragonite pseudomorphs implies that gypsum precipitation from Late Archean seawater was rare. Although rare gypsum pseudomorphs are present in one Late Archean carbonate deposit (e.g., Simonson et al., 1993), the sedimentological contexts of observed halite casts in the Carawine Dolomite and Campbellrand–Malmani carbonate platform do not allow for the precipitation and subsequent dissolution of substantial volumes of gypsum prior to halite precipitation (e.g., Simonson et al., 1993; Sumner, 1995). The lack of abundant Late Archean gypsum pseudomorphs or solution-collapse features within sediments below or laterally equivalent to those containing halite casts implies that gypsum was not a volumetrically important evaporite mineral.

Either low $[SO_4^{2-}]$ or high $[HCO_3^-]$ can explain the absence of abundant gypsum (Grotzinger and Kasting, 1993). With an oxidizing surface ocean, SO_4^{2-} should have been abundant, allowing gypsum precipitation unless much of seawater Ca^{2+} was removed through carbonate precipitation (Grotzinger and Kasting, 1993). This situation would imply $[HCO_3^-] > 2[Ca^{2+}]$. However, prior to the rise in atmospheric oxygen, this argument is complicated by the possibility of low oceanic $[SO_4^{2-}]$, which would also have limited gypsum precipitation. Currently, the $[SO_4^{2-}]$ of Archean seawater is poorly constrained, so low $[SO_4^{2-}]$ cannot be eliminated as the reason gypsum precipitation was rare. However, high $[HCO_3^-]$ is consistent with the necessary rapid aragonite precipitation rates, as is high $[Ca^{2+}]$. Even if $[HCO_3^-]$ was high, the presence of rare gypsum pseudomorphs in the Carawine Dolomite indicates that gypsum saturation was attained at least locally. Thus, the possibility that $[HCO_3^-]$ was *much* greater than $2[Ca^{2+}]$ for all of Late Archean time in all environments is unlikely. Rather, it seems more likely that $[HCO_3^-]$ was close to $2[Ca^{2+}]$, which is consistent with simultaneous saturation of siderite and calcite (Grotzinger and Kasting, 1993). This would allow for locally minor gypsum precipitation when and where $[HCO_3^-]$ locally dropped below $2[Ca^{2+}]$.

The paucity of gypsum is also consistent with the "soda ocean" model, which implies $[HCO_3^-] \gg 2[Ca^{2+}]$. However, this model is not consistent with the accumulation of large carbonate platforms dominated by $CaCO_3$ precipitation. Widespread aragonite precipitation in open marine environments suggests that bulk seawater was capable of precipitating substantial volumes of aragonite, especially by about 2.5 Ga, when the Campbellrand–Malmani carbonate platform was deposited. Kempe and Kazmierczak (1994) suggest that the "soda ocean" $[Ca^{2+}]$ was between 8×10^{-5} and 1×10^{-4} mol/l. At these low $[Ca^{2+}]$, it is difficult to accumulate significant quantities of $CaCO_3$ in reasonable lengths of time. For example, the Campbellrand–Malmani carbonate platform is over 1 km thick and is preserved over 190,000 km² (Beukes, 1987; Button, 1973; Sumner, 1995). Even assuming that 25% of the volume of the platform is noncarbonate and ignoring the eroded part of the platform, which originally covered more than 600,000 km² (Button, 1973; Beukes, 1987; Sumner, 1995), more than 10^{18} mol Ca^{2+} are required even if the entire platform was dolomitized soon after deposition. At 10^{-4} mol Ca^{2+}/l, more than 10^{22} l of seawater would be necessary to provide sufficient Ca^{2+} for accumulation of the preserved part of the platform. The current volume of the ocean is 1.37×10^{18} l. Thus, in order for the Campbellrand–Malmani carbonate platform to have accumulated from a "soda ocean", high fluxes of Ca^{2+} from weathering would be required to rapidly replenish seawater Ca^{2+}. If Ca^{2+} is delivered to the oceans in rivers, carbonate precipitation would be concentrated at the mouths of rivers draining siliciclastic interiors. In the case of the Campbellrand–Malmani carbonate platform, the development of a rimmed margin, the widespread deposition of subtidal lithofacies across the entire platform, and the lack of siliciclastic sediment from a weathering craton imply that precipitation occurred from seawater as opposed to the mixing of river water with seawater. Thus, the low Ca^{2+} concentrations required by the "soda ocean" are unrealistic given abundant calcium carbonate accumulation by 2.5 Ga.

CONCLUSIONS

Abundant aragonite precipitated from Late Archean seawater, forming fans of crystals meters tall. This precipitation occurred in diverse depositional environments ranging from evaporitic to open marine subtidal shelves. The crystals grew directly on the sea floor and projected up into open water, sometimes forming lithoherms that were resistant to abrasion during deposition of surrounding grainstones. Precipitation of large aragonite crystals on the sea floor requires that: 1) later Archean seawater was supersaturated with respect to aragonite; 2) aragonite precipitation rates were rapid relative to the influx of detrital carbonate; and 3) aragonite precipitation was more rapid than the fastest rates observed in modern reefs. In addition, a decline in the abundance and size of aragonite fans from the older (2.7–2.6 Ga) to the younger (2.6–2.5 Ga) Late Archean carbonates studied suggests that there were secular variations in aragonite precipitation rates in Late Archean time.

ACKNOWLEDGMENTS

We are grateful to Nicolas Beukes for great discussions over the years and for help with field work in South Africa and Zimbabwe. DYS also is grateful to Geerat Vermeij for stimulating discussions on ocean chemistry. Tim Lowenstein and B. Charlotte Schreiber are thanked for reviewing the manuscript. Financial support was provided by National Aeronautics and Space Administration grant NAGW-2795 to JPG.

REFERENCES

ABELL, P. I., MCCLORY, J., MARTIN, A., AND NISBET, E. G., 1985, Archean stromatolites from the Ngezi Group, Belingwe Greenstone Belt, Zimbabwe; preservation and stable isotopes—preliminary results: Precambrian Research, v. 27, p. 357–383.

ALTERMANN, W., 1996, Discussion on 'Zircon Pb-evaporation age determinations of the Oak Tree Formation, Chuniespoort Group, Transvaal Sequence: Implications for the Transvaal–Griqualand West basin correlations': South African Journal of Geology, v. 99, p. 337–338.

ARNOTT, R. W. C., 1993, Quasi-planar-laminated sandstone beds of the Lower Cretaceous Bootlegger Member, north-central Montana: Evidence of combined-flow sedimentation: Journal of Sedimentary Petrology, v. 63, p. 488–494.

ASSERETO, R., AND FOLK, R. L., 1980, Diagenetic fabrics of aragonite, calcite, and dolomite in an ancient peritidal–spelean environment: Triassic Calcare Rosso, Lombardia, Italy: Journal of Sedimentary Petrology, v. 50, p. 371–394.

BARTON, E. S., ALTERMANN, W., WILLIAMS, I. S., AND SMITH, C.B., 1994, U–Pb zircon age for a tuff in the Campbell Group, Griqualand West Sequence, South Africa: Implication for Early Proterozoic rock accumulation rates: Geology, v. 22, p. 343–346.

BERTRAND-SARFATI, J., 1976, Psedomorphoses de gypse en rosettes dans un calcaire cryptalgo-laminaire du Précambrien infériur (système du Transvaal. Afrique du Sud): Société Géologique de France, Bulletin, v. 18, p. 99–102.

BERTRAND-SARFATI, J., AND ERIKSSON, K. A., 1977, Columnar stromatolites from the Early Proterozoic Schmidtsdrift Formation, northern Cape Province, South Africa—Part 1: Systematic and diagnostic features: Palaeontologia Africana, v. 20, p. 1–26.

BEUKES, N. J., 1980, Stratigrafie en litofasies van die Campbellrand-subgroep van die Proterofitiese Ghaap-groep, noord-Kaapland: Geological Society of South Africa, Transactions, v. 83, p. 141–170.

BEUKES, N. J., 1987, Facies relations, depositional environments and diagenesis in a major early Proterozoic stromatolitic carbonate platform to basinal sequence, Campbellrand Subgroup, Transvaal Supergroup, southern Africa: Sedimentary Geology, v. 54, p. 1–46.

BEUKES, N. J., AND SMIT, C. A., 1987, New evidence for thrusting in Griqualand West, South Africa: Implications for stratigraphy and the age of red beds: South African Journal of Geology, v. 90, p. 378–394.

BICKLE, M. J., MARTIN, A., AND NISBET, E. E., 1975, Basaltic and peridotitic komatiites and stromatolites above a basal unconformity in the Belingwe Greenstone Belt, Rhodesia: Earth and Planetary Science Letters, v. 27, p. 155–162.

BROECKER, W. S., AND PENG, T. H., 1987, The role of $CaCO_3$ compensation in the glacial to interglacial atmospheric CO_2 change: Global Biogeochemical Cycles, v. 1, p. 15–29.

BUICK, R., AND DUNLOP, J. S. R., 1987, Early Archean evaporitic sediments from the Warrawoona Group, North Pole, Western Australia (abstract): Geological Society of America, Abstracts with Programs, v. 19, p. 604.

BUTTON, A., 1973, The stratigraphic history of the Malmani dolomite in the eastern and north-eastern Transvaal: Geological Society of South Africa, Transactions, v. 76, p. 229–247.

CECILE, M. P., AND CAMPBELL, F. H. A., 1978, Regressive stromatolite reefs and associated facies, middle Goulburn Group (lower Proterozoic), in Kilohigok Basin, N.W.T.: An example of environmental control of stromatolite form: Canadian Society of Petroleum Geologists, Bulletin, v. 26, p. 237–267.

CLENDENIN, C. W., HENRY, G., AND CHARLESWORTH, E. G., 1991, Characteristics of and influences on the Black Reef depositional sequence in the eastern Transvaal: South African Journal of Geology, v. 94, p. 321–327.

CLIFTON, H. E., HUNTER, R. E., AND PHILLIPS, R. L., 1971, Depositional structures and processes in the non-barred high-energy nearshore: Journal of Sedimentary Petrology, v. 41, p. 651–670.

DE RAAF, J. F. M., BOERSMA, J. R., AND VAN GELDER, A., 1977, Wave generated structures and sequences from a shallow marine succession, Lower Carboniferous, County Cork, Ireland: Sedimentology, v. 24, p. 451–483.

DOTT, R., JR., AND BOURGEOIS, J., 1982, Hummocky stratification: Significance of its variable bedding sequences: Geological Society of America, Bulletin, v. 93, p. 663–680.

ERIKSSON, K. A., 1977, Tidal flat and subtidal sedimentation in the 2250 M.Y. Malmani dolomite, Transvaal, South Africa: Sedimentary Geology, v. 18, p. 223–244.

ERIKSSON, K. A., AND TRUSWELL, J. F., 1974, Stratotypes from the Malmani Subgroup northwest of Johannesburg, South Africa: Geological Society of South Africa, Transactions, v. 77, p. 211–222.

ERIKSSON, K. A., TRUSWELL, J. F., AND BUTTON, A., 1976, Palaeoenvironmental and geochemical models from an early Proterozoic carbonate succession in South Africa, in Walter, M.R., ed., Stromatolites: New York, Elsevier, p. 635–643.

FOLK, R. L., TIEZZI, P. A., PURSELL, V. J., GRABER, E. R., GREENBERG, J. G., AND MILLER, J., 1993, Overturned geopetal structures formed by solution of sulfates, Triassic (Rhaetian) Portoro Limestone, Portovenere area (La Spezia), Liguria, Italy: Carbonates and Evaporites, v. 8, p. 39–49.

GRAMMER, G. M., GINSBURG, R. N., SWART, P. K., MCNEILL, D. F., JULL, A. J. T., AND PREZBINDOWSKI, D. R., 1993, Rapid growth rates of syndepositional marine aragonite cements in steep marginal slope deposits, Bahamas and Belize: Journal of Sedimentary Petrology, v. 63, p. 983–989.

GRAMMER, G. M., MCNEILL, D. F., AND CRESCINI, C. M., 1996, Quantifying rates of syndepositional marine cementation across a carbonate platform and margin, Bahamas (abstract): Geological Society of America, Abstracts with Programs, v. 28, p. 337.

GROTZINGER, J. P., 1986a, Cyclicity and paleoenvironmental dynamics, Rocknest platform, northwest Canada: Geological Society of America, Bulletin, v. 97, p. 1208–1231.

GROTZINGER, J. P., 1986b, Evolution of early Proterozoic passive-margin carbonate platform: Rocknest Formation, Wopmay Orogen, N.W.T., Canada: Journal Sedimentary Petrology, v. 56, p. 831–847.

GROTZINGER, J. P., 1989, Facies and evolution of Precambrian carbonate depositional systems: Emergence of the modern platform archetype, in Crevello, P. D., Wilson, J. L., Sarg, J. F., and Read, J. F., eds., Controls on Carbonate Platform and Basin Development: SEPM, Special Publication 44, p. 79–106.

GROTZINGER, J. P., 1994, Trends in Precambrian carbonate sediments and their implication for understanding evolution, in Bengtson, S., ed., Early Life on Earth: New York, Columbia University Press, Nobel Symposium no. 84, p. 245–258.

GROTZINGER, J. P., AND KASTING, J. F., 1993, New constraints on Precambrian ocean composition: Journal of Geology, v. 101, p. 235–243.

GROTZINGER, J. P., AND ROTHMAN, D. H., 1996, An abiotic model for stromatolite morphogenesis: Nature, v. 383, p. 423–425.

GROTZINGER, J. P., SUMNER, D. Y., AND BEUKES, N. J., 1993, Archean carbonate sedimentation in an active extensional basin, Belingwe Greenstone Belt, Zimbabwe (abstract): Geological Society of America, Abstracts with Programs, v. 25, p. A64.

HARDIE, L. A., 1996, Secular variation in seawater chemistry: An explanation for the coupled secular variation in the mineralogies of marine limestones and potash evaporites over the past 600 m.y.: Geology, v. 24, p. 279–283.

HARDIE, L. A., LOWENSTEIN, T. K., AND SPENCER, R. J., 1983, The problem of distinguishing between primary and secondary features in evaporites, *in* Schreiber, B. C., ed., Sixth International Symposium on Salt: Alexandria, Virginia, Salt Institute, p. 11–39.

HARWOOD, G. M., 1980, Calcitized anhydrite and associated sulphides in the English Zechstein First Cycle Carbonate (EZ1 Ca), *in* Füchtbauer, H., and Peryt, T., eds., The Zechstein Basin: Stuttgart, E. Schweizerbart'sche Verlagsbuchhandlung, Contributions to Sedimentology no. 9, p. 61–72.

HAWKESWORTH, C. J., AND BICKLE, M. J., 1976, Rhodesian Rb–Sr geochronology from 3.8–2.0 b.a.—a brief review, *in* Annual Report: Leeds, England, University of Leeds, Research Institute of African Geology, p. 22–27.

HOFFMAN, P. F., 1969, Proterozoic paleocurrents and depositional history of the East Arm fold belt, Great Slave Lake, Northwest Territories: Canadian Journal of Earth Sciences, v. 6, p. 441–462.

HOFFMAN, P. F., 1989, Precambrian geology and tectonic history of North America, *in* Bally, A. W., and Palmer, A. R., eds., The Geology of North America—An Overview: Boulder, Colorado, Geological Society of America, p. 447–512.

HOFMANN, H. J., 1971, Precambrian fossils, pseudofossils, and problematica in Canada: Geological Survey of Canada, Bulletin 189, p. 1–146.

HOFMANN, H. J., THURSTON, P. C., AND WALLACE, H., 1985, Archean stromatolites from Uchi greenstone belt, Northwestern Ontario, *in* Ayres, L. D., Thurston, P. C., Card, K. D., and Weber, W., eds., Evolution of Archean Supracrustal Sequences: Geological Association of Canada, Special Paper 28, p. 1125–1132.

HOLLAND, H. D., 1984, The Chemical Evolution of the Atmosphere and Oceans: Princeton, New Jersey, Princeton University Press, 582 p.

JACKSON, M. J., 1989, Lower Proterozoic Cowles Lake foredeep reef, N.W.T., Canada, *in* Geldsetzer, H. H. J., James, N. P., and Tebbutt, G. E., eds., Reefs: Canada and Adjacent Areas: Canadian Society of Petroleum Geologists, Memoir 13, p. 64–71.

JAMES, N. P., 1984, Shallowing-upward sequences in carbonates, *in* Walker, R. G., ed., Facies Models: Geoscience Canada, Reprint Series 1, p. 213–228.

JOLLIFE, A. W., 1955, Geology and iron ores of Steep Rock Lake: Economic Geology, v. 50, p. 373–398.

JOLLIFE, A. W., 1966, Stratigraphy of the Steep Rock Group, Steep Rock Lake, Ontario, *in* Goodwin, A. M., ed., Precambrian Symposium: Geological Association of Canada, Special Paper 3, p. 75–98.

KASTING, J. F., 1987, Theoretical constraints on oxygen and carbon dioxide concentrations in the Precambrian atmosphere: Precambrian Research, v. 34, p. 205–229.

KATZ, A., SASS, E., STARINSKY, A., AND HOLLAND, H. D., 1972, Strontium behavior in the aragonite–calcite transformation: An experimental study at 40–98°C: Geochimica et Cosmochimica Acta, v. 36, p. 481–496.

KEMPE, S., AND DEGENS, E. T., 1985, An early soda ocean?: Chemical Geology, v. 53, p. 95–108.

KEMPE, S., AND KAZMIERCZAK, J., 1990, Chemistry and stromatolites of the sea-linked Satonda Crater Lake, Indonesia: A recent model for the Precambrian sea?: Chemical Geology, v. 81, p. 299–310.

KEMPE, S., AND KAZMIERCZAK, J., 1994, The role of alkalinity in the evolution of ocean chemistry, organization of living systems, and biocalcification processes (abstract), *in* Doumenge, F., ed., Past and Present Biomineralization Processes. Considerations About the Carbonate Cycle: Institut Océanographique, Bulletin, v. 13, p. 61–117.

KINSMAN, D. J. J., 1969, Interpretation of Sr^{2+} concentrations in carbonate minerals and rocks: Journal of Sedimentary Petrology, v. 49, p. 937–944.

KINSMAN, D. J. J., AND HOLLAND, H. D., 1969, The co-precipitation of cations with $CaCO_3$ IV. The co-precipitation of Sr^{2+} with aragonite between 16° and 96°: Geochimica et Cosmochemica Acta, v. 33, p. 1–17.

KUSHNIR, J., 1980, The coprecipitation of strontium, magnesium, sodium, potassium and chloride with gypsum: An experimental study: Geochimica et Cosmochimica Acta, v. 44, p. 1471–1482.

LAUBSCHER, D. H., 1963, The origin and occurrence of chrysotile asbestos and associated rocks in the Shabani and Mashaba areas [unpublished Ph.D. thesis]: Johannesburg, South Africa, University of the Witwatersrand.

LAWSON, A. C., 1913, The geology of Steeprock Lake, Ontario: Geological Survey of Canada, Memoir 18, p. 7–15.

LORENS, R. B., 1981, Sr, Cd, Mn and Co distribution coefficients in calcite as a function of calcite precipitation rate: Geochimica et Cosmochimica Acta, v. 45, p. 553–561.

LOUCKS, R. G., AND FOLK, R. L., 1976, Fanlike rays of former aragonite in Permian Capitan Reef pisolite: Journal of Sedimentary Petrology, v. 46, p. 483–485.

LOWENSTEIN, T. K., 1988, Origin of depositional cycles in a Permian "saline giant": The Salado (McNutt zone) evaporites of New Mexico and Texas: Geological Society of America, Bulletin, v. 100, p. 592–608.

MACGREGOR, A. M., 1941, A pre-Cambrian algal limestone in Southern Rhodesia: Geological Society of South Africa, Transactions, v. 43, p. 9–16.

MACGREGOR, A. M., 1951, Some milestones in the Precambrian of southern Rhodesia: Geological Survey of Southern Rhodesia, Proceedings, v. 38, p. 27–71.

MARTIN, A., 1978, The geology of the Belingwe–Shabani schist belt: Rhodesia Geological Survey, Bulletin 83, 220 p.

MARTIN, A., NISBET, E. G., AND BICKLE, M. J., 1980, Archean stromatolites of the Belingwe Greenstone Belt, Zimbabwe (Rhodesia): Precambrian Research, v. 13, p. 337–362.

MAZZULLO, S. J., 1980, Calcite pseudospar replacive of marine acicular aragonite, and implications for aragonite cement diagenesis: Journal of Sedimentary Petrology, v. 50, p. 409–422.

MCINTOSH, J. R., 1972, The Caland Ore Company Limited deposit: A geological description: Ontario Department of Mines and Northern Affairs, Geological Report 18, p. 82–105.

MIYANO, T., AND BEUKES, N. J., 1984, Phase relations of stilpnomelane, ferri-annite, and riebeckite in very low-grade metamorphosed iron-formations: Geological Society of South Africa, Transactions, v. 87, p. 111–124.

NISBET, E. G., 1987, The Young Earth: An Introduction to Archean Geology: London, Allen & Unwin, 402 p.

OPDYKE, B. N., AND WILKINSON, B. H., 1993, Carbonate mineral saturation state and cratonic limestone accumulation: American Journal of Science, v. 293, p. 217–234.

OWEN, T., CESS, R. D., AND RAMANATHAN, V., 1979, Early Earth: An enhanced carbon dioxide greenhouse to compensate for reduced solar luminosity: Nature, v. 277, p. p. 640–642.

PELECHATY, S. M., AND GROTZINGER, J. P., 1988, Stromatolite bioherms of a 1.9 Ga foreland basin carbonate ramp, Beechey Formation, Kilohigok Basin, Northwest Territories, *in* Geldsetzer, H. H. J., James, N. P., and Tebbutt, G. E., eds., Reefs: Canada and Adjacent Areas: Canadian Society of Petroleum Geologists, Memoir 13, p. 93–104.

PERYT, T. M., HOPPE, A., BECHSTAEDT, T., KOESTER, J., PIERRE, C., AND RICHTER, D. K., 1990, Late Proterozoic aragonitic cement crusts, Bambui Group, Minas Gerais, Brazil: Sedimentology, v. 37, p. 279–286.

RICCIONI, R.-M., BROCK, P. W. G., AND SCHREIBER, B. C., 1996, Evidence for early aragonite in paleo-lacustrine sediments: Journal of Sedimentary Research, v. 66, p. 1003–1010.

SANDBERG, P., 1985a, Aragonite cements and their occurrence in ancient limestone, *in* Schneidermann, N., and Harris, P. M., eds., Carbonate Cements: SEPM, Special Publication 36, p. 33–57.

SANDBERG, P. A., 1985b, Nonskeletal aragonite and pCO_2 in the Phanerozoic and Proterozoic, *in* Sundquist, E. T., and Broecker, W. S., eds., The Carbon Cycle and Atmospheric CO_2: Natural Variations Archean to Present: American Geophysical Union, Geophysical Monograph 32, p. 585–594.

SCHOPF, J. W., OEHLER, D. Z., HORODYSKI, R. J., AND KVENVOLDEN, K. A., 1971, Biogenicity and significance of the oldest known stromatolites: Journal of Paleontology, v. 45, p. 477–485.

SIMONSON, B. M., SCHUBEL, K. A., AND HASSLER, S. W., 1993, Carbonate sedimentology of the early Precambrian Hamersley Group of Western Australia: Precambrian Research, v. 60, p. 287–335.

SMYTH, H. L., 1891, Structural geology of Steep Rock Lake, Ontario: American Journal of Science, v. 43, p. 317–331.

STOWE, C. W., 1986, Synthesis and interpretation of structures along the northeastern boundary of the Namaqua tectonic province, South Africa: Geological Society of South Africa, Transactions, v. 89, p. 185–198.

SUMNER, D. Y., 1995, Facies, Paleogeography, and Carbonate Precipitation on the Archean (2520 Ma) Campbellrand–Malmani Carbonate Platform, Transvaal Supergroup, South Africa [unpublished Doctoral thesis]: Cambridge, Massachusetts, Massachusetts Institute of Technology, 514 p.

SUMNER, D. Y., 1997a, Carbonate precipitation and oxygen stratification in late Archean seawater as deduced from facies and stratigraphy of the Gamohaan and Frisco formations, Transvaal Supergroup, South Africa: American Journal of Science, v. 297, p. 455–487.

SUMNER, D. Y., 1997b, Late Archean calcite–microbe interactions: Two morphologically distinct microbial communities that affected calcite nucleation differently: Palaios, v. 12, p. 300–316.

SUMNER, D. Y., 2000, Microbial versus environmental influences on the morphology of Late Archean fenestrate microbialites, *in* Riding, R. E., and Awramik, S. M., eds., Microbial Sediments: Berlin, Springer-Verlag, p. 307–314.

SUMNER, D. Y., AND BOWRING, S. A., 1996, U–Pb geochronologic constraints on deposition of the Campbellrand Subgroup, Transvaal Supergroup, South Africa: Precambrian Research, v. 78, p. 25–35.

SUMNER, D. Y., AND GROTZINGER, J. P., 1996, Herringbone calcite: Petrography and environmental significance: Journal of Sedimentary Research, v. 66, p. 419–429.

TRUSWELL, J. F., AND ERIKSSON, K. A., 1972, The morphology of stromatolites from the Transvaal Dolomite north-west of Johannesburg, South Africa: Geological Society of South Africa, Transactions, v. 75, p. 99–110.

TRUSWELL, J. F., AND ERIKSSON, K. A., 1973, Stromatolitic associations and their palaeo-environmental significance: A re-appraisal of a lower Proterozoic locality from the northern Cape Province, South Africa: Sedimentary Geology, v. 10, p. 1–23.

WALCOTT, C. D., 1912, Notes on fossils from limestones of Steeprock Series, Ontario: Geological Survey of Canada, Memoir 28, p. 16–22.

WALKER, J. C. G., 1983, Possible limits on the composition of the Archean ocean: Nature, v. 302, p. 518–520.

WALKER, J. C. G., 1985, Carbon dioxide on the early Earth: Origins of Life, v. 16, p. 117–127.

WALRAVEN, F., AND MARTINI, J., 1995, Zircon Pb-evaporation age determinations of the Oak Tree Formation, Chuniespoort Group, Transvaal Sequence: Implications for Transvaal–Griqualand West basin correlations: South African Journal of Geology, v. 98, p. 58–67.

WALTER, M. R., 1983, Archean stromatolites: evidence of the Earth's earliest benthos, *in* Schopf, J. W., ed., Earth's Earliest Biosphere: Princeton, New Jersey, Princeton University Press, p. 187–213.

WILKINSON, B. H., AND GIVEN, R. K., 1986, Secular variation in abiotic marine carbonates: Constraints on Phanerozoic atmospheric carbon dioxide contents and oceanic Mg/Ca ratios: Journal of Geology, v. 94, p. 321–333.

WILKINSON, B. H., OWEN, R. M., AND CARROLL, A. R., 1985, Submarine hydrothernal weathering, global eustasy, and carbonate polymorphism in Phanerozoic marine oolites: Journal of Sedimentary Petrology, v. 55, p. 171–183.

WILKS, M. E., 1986, The geology of the Steep Rock Group, N.W. Ontario: A major Archean unconformity and Archean stromatolites [unpublished M.Sc. thesis]: University of Saskatchewan, 206 p.

WILKS, M. W., AND NISBET, E. G., 1985, Archean stromatolites from the Steep Rock Group, northwestern Ontario, Canada: Canadian Journal of Earth Sciences, v. 22, p. 792–799.

WILSON, J. F., 1979, A preliminary reappraisal of the Rhodesian basement complex: Geological Society of South Africa, Special Publication 5, p. 1–23.

DEVELOPMENT OF LATE PALEOPROTEROZOIC ARAGONITIC SEAFLOOR CEMENTS IN THE McARTHUR GROUP, NORTHERN AUSTRALIA

PETER R. WINEFIELD*

Centre for Ore Deposit Research, University of Tasmania, G.P.O. Box 252-79, Hobart 7001, Australia

ABSTRACT: Laterally extensive beds of acicular, radiating carbonate fans, locally known as "Coxco needles", are particularly common within a distinct stratigraphic interval (~1640 Ma) in the Proterozoic of northern Australia. In the southern McArthur Basin, they are the distinctive feature of the Coxco Dolomite Member and occur throughout a number of lithofacies across the platform. Mounding and onlapping of sediment laminae, their upwardly divergent aspect, brecciated Coxco needle clasts infilling synsedimentary fractures, and their intimate association with stromatolites supports the precipitation of Coxco fans from ambient seawater directly onto the seafloor. Individually, they consist of acicular crystal casts up to 10 cm long, which form radiating, bottom-nucleated fans. Needle terminations are commonly blocky or square and in cross section appear pseudohexagonal with crystal casts generally having six-sided forms. Needles consist internally of an irregular mosaic of dolospar cement easily distinguished from the more finely crystalline dolomicrite matrix. These features are entirely consistent with criteria for the recognition of aragonite in ancient carbonate sequences and imply an original aragonitic mineralogy for the Coxco fans.

The sequence through the middle McArthur Group (Emmerugga Dolomite, Teena Dolomite, Coxco Dolomite Member, and Barney Creek Formation) is broadly transgressive, and precipitation of Coxco needles occurred during the onset of a period of tectonically induced subsidence. The mechanism for the widespread chronostratigraphic precipitation of $CaCO_3$ is thought to be upwelling of highly alkaline, HCO_3^--rich anoxic bottom water onto the carbonate platform coeval with changes in the bathymetry of the basin. Mixing with relatively Ca^{2+}-rich surface waters resulted in widespread precipitation of carbonate seafloor cement (i.e., Coxco fans) across the platform in several distinct lithofacies. The reason that macroscopic carbonate cement formed in preference to widespread precipitation of finely crystalline micrite remains unclear, although it is suggested that elevated concentrations of Fe^{2+} and Mn^{2+} in the basin waters may have inhibited micrite precipitation and thus favored development of macroscopic seafloor Coxco fans.

INTRODUCTION

Several stratigraphic units in the Palaeoproterozoic McArthur Group of the southern McArthur Basin (Fig. 1) contain abundant marine carbonate cements, with the most widespread and best developed being the enigmatic, colloquially named "Coxco needles." These consist of radiating fans of acicular crystal casts up to 10 cm long, which are pervasively pseudomorphed by sparry dolomite cement. Coxco fans are the most characteristic feature of the Coxco Dolomite Member, which is stratigraphically overlain by carbonaceous and pyritic dolomitic siltstone of the Barney Creek Formation (Fig. 2), host to the giant HYC (Here's Your Chance) Zn–Pb–Ag deposit at McArthur River (Logan et al., 1990).

In the past, a number of different precursors have been suggested for the original mineralogy of the Coxco needles, including aragonite, gypsum, and trona. Brown et al. (1978) interpreted the shape and habit of the needles as being indicative of dolomite pseudomorphs after botryoidal aragonite. However, Walker et al. (1977) put forward an alternative hypothesis that the needles represented pseudomorphs of gypsum, largely on the basis of comparison of the interfacial angles of individual Coxco needles with that of aragonite and gypsum, and also purported analogies with modern examples observed growing in shallow brine pools on the sabkha of the Trucial Coast. Jackson et al. (1987) suggested that at least some of the Coxco needle casts are morphologically similar to trona described from the Eocene Green River Formation (Fahey, 1962). This tentative interpretation led Jackson et al. (1987) to speculate the depositional environment of the Coxco Dolomite Member was lacustrine, inasmuch as trona does not form in a marine environment.

Regional mapping of several northern Australian Proterozoic Basins during the 1990s by the Northern Territory Geological Survey (NTGS) has identified several other stratigraphically equivalent occurrences of Coxco-like fans (Fig. 1). Independent radiogenic SHRIMP (Super High Resolution Ion Microprobe) dating of zircons from tuffaceous sediments associated with these units supports the widespread coeval precipitation of Coxco needle fans.

Recent literature has increasingly documented fan-like seafloor carbonate precipitates within late Archean and Proterozoic carbonates, and the general consensus is for an aragonitic precursor (Table 1). The study and description of these carbonate cements often provides important insights into understanding temporal changes in depositional environments and ocean chemistry (Sandberg, 1983, 1985; Wilkinson et al., 1984; Given and Wilkinson, 1985; Wilkinson and Given, 1986; Sumner and Grotzinger, 1996a, 1996b; Grotzinger and Knoll, 1995). This paper describes the Coxco needle fans, determines their depositional setting, and discusses possible implications of widespread development of carbonate seafloor precipitates prior to the deposition of carbonaceous and pyritic dolomitic siltstone of the mineralized Barney Creek Formation.

GEOLOGICAL SETTING

The intracratonic McArthur Basin is located along the western and southern margins of the Gulf of Carpenteria in northern Australia and is exposed over about 200,000 km³ of the Northern Territory (Fig. 1). The tectonic framework of the McArthur Basin is dominated by two north–south trending fault zones (Fig. 1), the southern Batten Fault Zone (Fig. 3) and the northern Walker Fault Zone, separated by the east–west trending Urapunga Fault Zone. These fault zones are elongate, relatively deformed corridors up to 80 km wide by several hundreds of kilometers long and contain up to 10 km of preserved section. In contrast, the flanking "shelves" are only mildly deformed and preserve only approximately 4 km of section with minimal thickness and facies variation (Plumb et al., 1990).

The McArthur Basin stratigraphic sequence consists of an unmetamorphosed section of platformal carbonates and silici-

*Present address: Shell U.K. Exploration and Production, 1 Altens Road, Nigg, Aberdeen AB12 3FY, United Kingdom

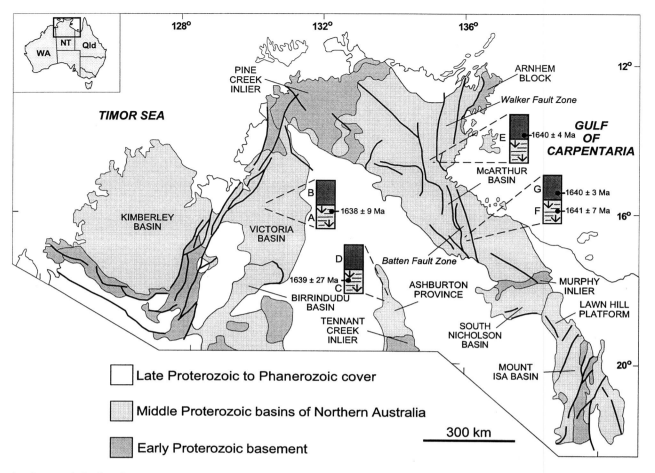

Fig. 1.—Proterozoic Basins of Northern Australia; adapted from Plumb et al. (1990). Unit A = Campbell Springs Dolomite; B = Fraynes Formation; C = Mt. Shillinglaw Formation; D = undifferentiated Pmx; E = Vizard Formation; F = Coxco Dolomite Member, Teena Dolomite; G = Barney Creek Formation. SHRIMP dates for the Teena Dolomite and Barney Creek Formation quoted from Page (1997). The SHRIMP date for the Mt. Shillinglaw Formation is quoted from Stephens (1997), and SHRIMP dates for the Vizard Formation and Campbell Springs Dolomite was obtained via personal communication with Rod Page (AGSO) and Peter Beier (NTGS), respectively. Stratigraphic information for the Campbell Springs Dolomite, Mt. Shillinglaw Formation, and Vizard Formation was kindly supplied from personal communication with Steve Abbott (NTGS), Peter Beier (NTGS), and Jim Jackson (AGSO), respectively.

clastic sediment, with minor carbonaceous siltstone and bi-modal volcanics. Four major unconformity-bounded groups are recognized, which are, from oldest to youngest: Tawallah Group (dominated by quartz sandstone with lesser conglomerate, dolostone, fine-grained clastics, and mafic and felsic volcanics); McArthur and Nathan Groups (dominated by dolostone with lesser sandstone and fine-grained clastics); Roper Group (dominated by quartz sandstone and fine-grained clastics).

The McArthur Group forms a relatively thick, carbonate-dominated sequence (~5 km) of interbedded stromatolitic and evaporitic dolostone, sandstone, siltstone, and shale (Fig. 2). The deposition and distribution of McArthur Group facies is strongly fault controlled and largely constrained within the Batten Fault Zone (Plumb and Wellman, 1987). Overall, the depositional pattern of the McArthur Group alternates between carbonate and clastic sediments. Alluvial and shallow marine environments are dominant at the base and top of the group, and deeper conditions are thought to characterize the middle McArthur Group formations, especially the Barney Creek and lower Lynott Formations (Pietsch et al., 1991a).

STRATIGRAPHY

The Teena Dolomite and Barney Creek Formation form a broad transgressive sequence with maximum water depths culminating in the deposition of carbonaceous, pyritic dolomitic siltstones within localized, fault-controlled sub-basins (Brown et al., 1978; Pietsch et al., 1991b; Bull, 1998). The Teena Dolomite conformably overlies the Emmerugga Dolomite, which consists largely of cyclic, subtidal stromatolitic dolostone. The Teena Dolomite is subdivided by Jackson et al. (1987) into a lower undifferentiated unit and the overlying Coxco Dolomite Member. The lower unit is regionally extensive and consists of oolitic and oncolitic grainstones, coarse dolarenite, imbricated flat-pebble conglomerate, or ripple-marked quartz arenite "grits". These lithofacies represent a marked shallowing in the sequence when compared to the underlying Emmerugga Dolomite. This shallowing and basinward shift in facies is interpreted to represent a sequence boundary, which can be recognized throughout the central Batten Fault Zone (Fig. 4).

In general, the Coxco Dolomite Member has been identified solely by the presence of Coxco needle fans within gray crys-

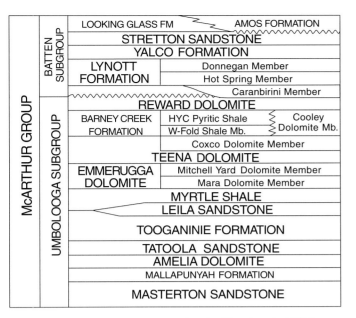

FIG. 2.—McArthur Group stratigraphy (Pietsch et al., 1991a).

talline dololutite. Rare "conical" stromatolites and thin intervals of dolomitic shale and siltstone are also reported (Pietsch et al., 1991a). Detailed logging of measured sections and drill core from throughout the central Batten Fault Zone during the course of this study has resulted in the recognition of several distinct, stratigraphically equivalent Coxco needle lithofacies (Fig. 4).

The Barney Creek Formation is a generally recessive unit dominated by finely laminated to thin-bedded, planar-laminated, dolomitic, carbonaceous and locally pyritic siltstone (Pietsch et al., 1991a). Two distinct depositional models have been proposed for the unit: a deeper-water, sub-wave-base environment or a shallow to emergent, sabkha or lagoonal environment. Brown et al. (1978) and a more recent study by Bull (1998) both concluded that the Barney Creek Formation represented "deeper water shaly carbonates" that were deposited at the height of a broad sea-level transgression. They argue that the abundance of carbonaceous, pyritic shales is indicative of

a quiet, anoxic, sub-wave-base depositional environment, and that the lack of features suggestive of shallow water or emergent conditions (e.g. desiccation cracks, shallow-water microbialites, agitated-water deposits such as oolite and flat-pebble conglomerates) supports this interpretation. Bull (1998) and Large et al. (1998) argued further that the shallow-water marine or lacustrine sabkha depositional model for the Barney Creek Formation, as proposed by Williams and Logan (1981), Muir (1983), and Jackson et al. (1987), is untenable on a regional scale, and that critical evidence cited in support of the shallow-water model (i.e., proposed evaporitic pseudomorphs) could be the result of hydrothermal alteration associated with the genesis of the deposit.

The contact between the Teena Dolomite and the Barney Creek Formation is generally a sharp transition from light-colored dolostone to dark-colored, pyritic dolomitic siltstone. In some areas, the contact is brecciated and the underlying Coxco Dolomite Member is highly fractured and fissured. These fissures are infilled with alternating generations of fibrous dolomite cement and laminated internal sediment. Less commonly, brecciated clasts of Coxco needles rimmed with fibrous cement are included within larger fissures. These fissures are interpreted as neptunian dikes formed as the result of localized extension or dilation within the carbonate platform, generated by the onset of basin subsidence prior to the deposition of Barney Creek Formation (Winefield et al., 1997).

COXCO NEEDLE LITHOFACIES AND DEPOSITIONAL RELATIONSHIPS

Detailed lithofacies analysis of the Teena Dolomite has identified the following depositional relationships that together suggest that Coxco needle fans were precipitated from ambient seawater directly onto the seafloor: (1) they form decimeter-thick, laterally continuous beds; these beds are non-stromatolitic and follow topography (Figs. 5A); (2) they are exclusively upward diverging (Fig. 5B) and in plan form circular bundles; (3) fine micritic laminae truncates against, onlaps, and mounds over individual Coxco fans (Fig. 5B, D; 7C, D); (4) brecciated, rotated clasts of Coxco needles are commonly included within neptunian fissures (which themselves crosscut Coxco beds) and are rimmed by fibrous dolomite cement and internal sediment (Fig. 7A, B); (5) Coxco needles are locally intimately associ-

TABLE 1.—KNOWN OCCURRENCES OF ARAGONITIC MARINE SEAFLOOR CEMENTS

Age	Stratigraphy/Location	Environment	Reference
~ 280 Ma	Laborcita Formation, Sacramento Mountains, New Mexico	algal mounds—shallow marine, near shelf edge	Mazzullo and Cys (1979)
~ 600 Ma	Nucculeena Formation, Adelaide Geosyncline, Australia	transgressive sequence overlying a glacigenic succession	Kennedy (1996)
~ 1.2-0.6 Ga	Bushmansklippe Formation, Namibia	transgressive deposits that cover shelf carbonates	Hegenberger (1993)
~ 1.64 Ga	Teena Dolomite, Batten Fault Zone, McArthur Basin, Australia	peritidal → subtidal → deep subtidal	Winefield and McGoldrick, (1998); this study
~ 1.64 Ga	Vizard Formation, Mt. Birch, Urapunga Fault Zone, McArthur Basin, Australia	intertidal-subtidal	M. Jackson, pers. comm. (1998)
~ 1.64 Ga	Mt. Shillinglaw Formation, northern Tennant Creek Inlier, Australia	subtidal?	P. Beier, pers. comm. (1996)
~ 1.64 Ga	Campbell Springs Dolomite, Victoria Basin, Australia	subtidal?	S. Abbott, pers. comm. (1998)
~ 1.9 Ga	Rocknest Formation, Wopmay Orogen, Canada	subtidal	Grotzinger and Read (1983)
1.97 Ga	Rifle & Beechey Formations, Kilohigok Basin, Canada	transgressive stromatolitic reefs	Grotzinger and Friedman, (1989)
2.52 Ga	Campbellrand-Malmani Platform, Transvaal Supergroup, South Africa	peritidal → deep subtidal	Sumner (1995)
~ 2.7 Ga	Steep Rock Group, SW Province, Canada	associated with elongate stromatolites	Hofmann (1971); Grotzinger (1989)
~ 2.7 Ga	Cheshire Formation, Ngezi Group, Zimbabwe	??	Martin et al., (1980); Grotzinger, (1989)

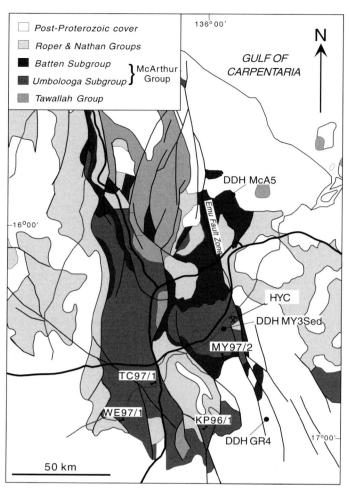

FIG. 3.—Geology of the central Batten Fault Zone, with locations of representative sections and DDH shown (map adapted from Pietsch et al., 1991b).

ated with plumose structured microbialite, and conical and columnar stromatolites (Fig. 5E, F, G).

In addition to noting the above features, five distinct Coxco needle lithofacies have been identified (Fig. 6), which demonstrate the widespread precipitation of Coxco fans throughout several depositional environments.

The most widespread and best recognized is *Lithofacies II*, which consists of finely laminated light- and dark-gray dololutite. The lack of carbonate sand or cross-lamination suggests a quiet subtidal depositional environment. Fine dololutite or dolomicritic laminae commonly onlap against and or mound over individual Coxco needle fans, beds of which can be traced laterally for hundreds of meters in areas of good outcrop. The contact with the overlying carbonaceous shale and siltstone of the Barney Creek Formation is generally sharp. Synsedimentary or neptunian dikes infilled with fibrous cement, brecciated Coxco clasts (rimmed by fibrous cement), and laminated internal sediment are commonly associated with this lithofacies.

Coxco needle fans are often observed in association with various stromatolitic or microbialite forms. The most common association is with cyclic, subtidal "plumose" structures where

Coxco fans are evident as distinct beds and as internal components within the microbial structure (*Lithofacies III*). Plumose structures consist of complex, tree-like structures with individual branches being defined by irregular, silicified filaments. Although there is no modern analogue for these plumose structures, a microbial origin is favored from morphological and textural observations. Sumner (1995) documented similar structures within units of the Archean Campbellrand–Malmani Carbonate Platform, South Africa, and interpreted them as being the products of biological processes within a deep subtidal, sub-wave-base depositional environment. This lithofacies is also associated with large (~1.5 m high) columnar or *Conophyton*-like microbialite. The association of *Lithofacies III* with *Conophyton*-like microbialite, the absence of any elongation of plumose-structured microbialite, and their relatively delicate morphology all suggests a deep subtidal depositional environment.

Lithofacies I consists of a peritidal sequence of microbially laminated pale red dololutite with periodic beds of well-developed Coxco needles. Low-relief, undulatory domal microbialite forms distinctive layers throughout this lithofacies and is analogous to the "crinkly mat" zone described by Kendall and Skipworth (1968) in an evaporitic lagoon in the Persian Gulf, and to *Lyngbya* mats growing in the Laguna Mormona, Mexico (Horodyski, 1977). Beds are commonly deformed by tepee-like structures that consist of asymmetrically buckled dololutite layers. These tepee-like structures are overlain by unaffected dololutite beds, and in some instances sediment layers truncate against these features, suggesting that they are synsedimentary. The identification of this distinctive microbialite form, the red oxidized coloration of the dolostone, and the presence of tepee-like structures in this lithofacies indicates a supratidal or shallow intertidal depositional setting.

Less commonly, Coxco needle fans are interspersed with thinly laminated carbonaceous, dolomitic siltstone. *Lithofacies IV* consists of diffusely laminated, alternating light green and red dolomitic siltstone, with several tuffaceous intervals marked by fissile green clayey layers. Interestingly, the Coxco needle fans are commonly preferentially situated within slightly redder (oxidized?) dolomitic siltstone. The presence of common tuffaceous beds up to 15 cm thick throughout this lithofacies, in addition to the lack of any obvious tractional sedimentary structures, suggests a relatively quiet, sub-wave-base depositional environment. The alternation between red dolomitic siltstone with well-developed Coxco needle layers and green dolomitic siltstone with few if any Coxco needles suggests a gradational deepening and the transgression of more reduced lithologies (i.e., green dolomitic siltstone) prior to deposition of carbonaceous, pyritic siltstone. Rarely, Coxco needle dololutite layers are interbedded with thinly laminated carbonaceous, pyritic dolomitic siltstone (Fig. 5D; *Lithofacies V*) generally considered characteristic of the Barney Creek Formation. An anoxic, sub-wave-base depositional environment is inferred for this lithofacies (Bull, 1998) and therefore, by association, Coxco needle fans must have formed in a similar depositional environment. The interbedding of Coxco needle dololutite and pyritic dolomitic siltstone probably represents a gradual transition from oxidized to more reduced basin waters during Barney Creek Formation deposition.

MORPHOLOGY AND PETROGRAPHY DESCRIPTION

Coxco needles characteristically form bottom nucleated, upward-radiating fans of acicular crystal casts that grew from a

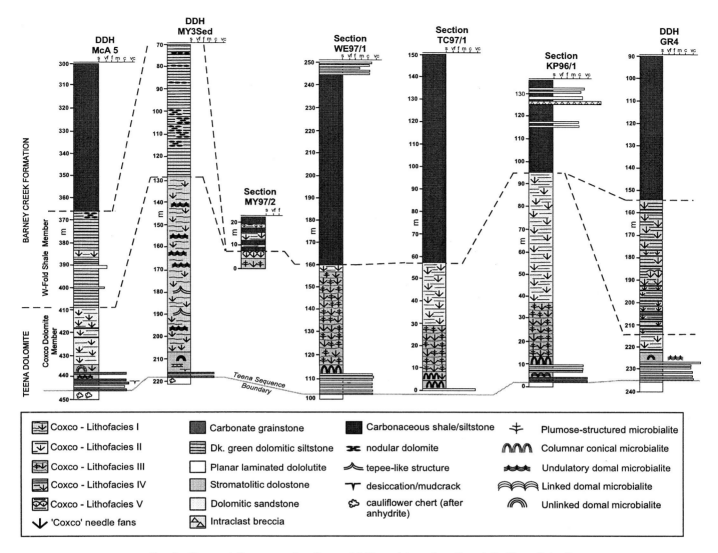

Fig. 4.—Representative measured sections and drill core intersections through the Teena Dolomite.

single point. Fans are generally up to 10 cm in height, and neighboring fans commonly intersect each other to form laterally extensive, decimeter-thick layers. Where fans grew very close together, divergent growth of crystal casts was prevented by the presence of neighboring fans and only upright crystals were able to continue growing, producing a layer of acicular crystals mostly oriented perpendicular to bedding. Individual, isolated Coxco fans are also common. These are generally more radially divergent, with bed-to-crystal angles ranging from 20° to 90°, reflecting the increased area available for unimpeded fan growth. In plan, crystal fans form roughly circular bundles.

Coxco fans are always associated with beds of finely crystalline carbonate, and the space between individual Coxco needles is commonly composed of micritic dolomite. The dimensions of each individual needle is approximately in the ratio of 1:10 (width:height), with 6 cm being the average length of needle casts measured in this study. The terminations of each needle are commonly square or blocky, although "feathery" terminations also occur (Figs. 5C, 7G). In cross section, Coxco

needles are pseudohexagonal with crystal casts having six-sided forms depending on the intersection between the needle and the surface being examined. Cross sections of Coxco needles are rarely preserved in enough detail to measure interfacial angles accurately. Any study of this feature would also be complicated by the splayed, radiating habit of Coxco needles, making identification of needle cross sections exactly perpendicular to the c axis difficult. However, it has been possible to examine a few silicified needle forms with a scanning electron microscope (SEM), which revealed paired or twinned pseudohexagonal crystal forms with interfacial angles of close to 60° (Fig. 8).

Coxco needle fans are subtle features that are best observed in preferentially weathered outcrop, polished slabs, or drill core. The distinctive fan morphology and its constituent needles persist through all but the most fabric-destructive recrystallization, although the size and character of the neomorphic dolospar changes noticeably. Commonly, needles consist of an irregular mosaic of clear, equant dolospar, which is in stark contrast to the more finely crystalline dolomicrite matrix (Fig. 7F, G). This

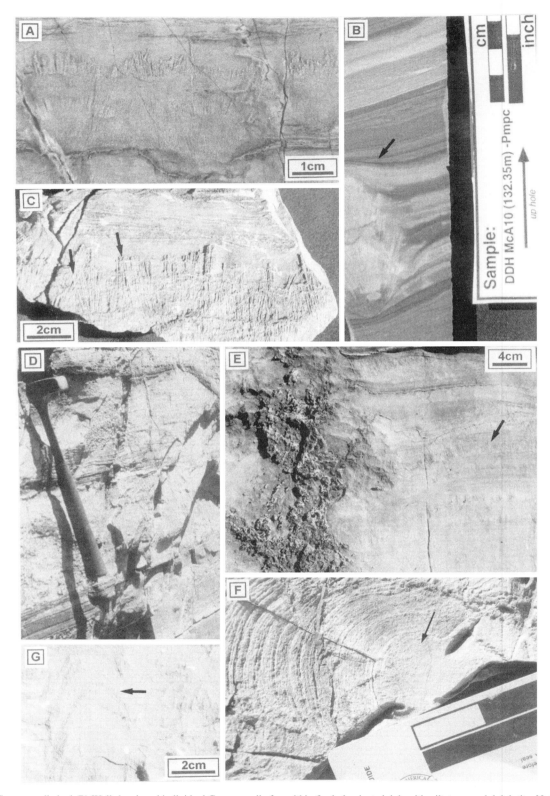

Fig. 5.—A) Coxco needle bed. B) Well-developed individual Coxco needle fan within finely laminated dolomitic siltstone, and dololutite. Note the mounding of sediment laminae and pinching out of the marked layer. C) Weathered face with blocky or square terminated Coxco needles. Note the mostly upright growth of needles. D) Interbedded Coxco needle dololutite and finely laminated carbonaceous, pyritic shale. E) Coxco needle fans forming layers associated with plumose-structured stromatolites. F) Large domal microbialite with Coxco needle fan "nucleus". G) Radiating Coxco fan forming a mounded, columnar microbialite-like form.

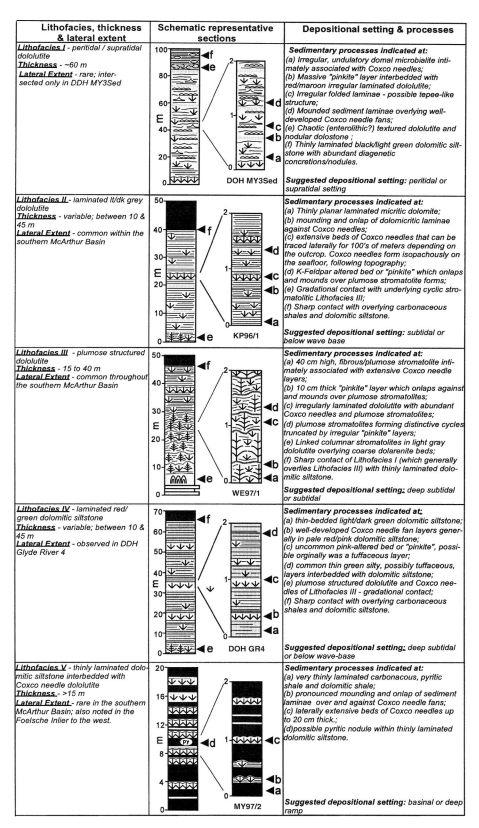

Lithofacies, thickness & lateral extent	Schematic representative sections	Depositional setting & processes
Lithofacies I - peritidal / supratidal dololutite **Thickness** - ~60 m **Lateral Extent** - rare; intersected only in DDH MY3Sed	DOH MY3Sed	**Sedimentary processes indicated at:** (a) Irregular, undulatory domal microbialite intimately associated with Coxco needles; (b) Massive "pinkite" layer interbedded with red/maroon irregular laminated dololutite; (c) Irregular folded laminae - possible tepee-like structure; (d) Mounded sediment laminae overlying well-developed Coxco needle fans; (e) Chaotic (enterolithic?) textured dololutite and nodular dolostone ; (f) Thinly laminated black/light green dolomitic siltstone with abundant diagenetic concretions/nodules. **Suggested depositional setting:** peritidal or supratidal setting
Lithofacies II - laminated lt/dk grey dololutite **Thickness** - variable; between 10 & 45 m **Lateral Extent** - common within the southern McArthur Basin	KP96/1	**Sedimentary processes indicated at:** (a) Thinly planar laminated micritic dolomite; (b) mounding and onlap of dolomicritic laminae against Coxco needles; (c) extensive beds of Coxco needles that can be traced laterally for 100's of meters depending on the outcrop. Coxco needles form isopachously on the seafloor, following topography; (d) K-Feldpar altered bed or "pinkite" which onlaps and mounds over plumose stromatolite forms; (e) Gradational contact with underlying cyclic stromatolitic Lithofacies III; (f) Sharp contact with overlying carbonaceous shales and dolomitic siltstone. **Suggested depositional setting:** subtidal or below wave base
Lithofacies III - plumose structured dololutite **Thickness** - 15 to 40 m **Lateral Extent** - common throughout the southern McArthur Basin	WE97/1	**Sedimentary processes indicated at:** (a) 40 cm high, fibrous/plumose stromatolite intimately associated with extensive Coxco needle layers; (b) 10 cm thick "pinkite" layer which onlaps against and mounds over plumose stromatolites; (c) irregularly laminated dololutite with abundant Coxco needles and plumose stromatolites; (d) plumose stromatolites forming distinctive cycles truncated by irregular "pinkite" layers; (e) Linked columnar stromatolites in light gray dololutite overlying coarse dolarenite beds; (f) Sharp contact of Lithofacies I (which generally overlies Lithofacies III) with thinly laminated dolomitic siltstone. **Suggested depositional setting:** deep subtidal or subtidal
Lithofacies IV - laminated red/green dolomitic siltstone **Thickness** - variable; between 10 & 45 m **Lateral Extent** - observed in DDH Glyde River 4	DOH GR4	**Sedimentary processes indicated at:** (a) thin-bedded light/dark green dolomitic siltstone; (b) well-developed Coxco needle fan layers generally in pale red/pink dolomitic siltstone; (c) uncommon pink-altered bed or "pinkite", possible orginally was a tuffaceous layer; (d) common thin green silty, possibly tuffaceous, layers interbedded with dolomitic siltstone; (e) plumose structured dololutite and Coxco needles of Lithofacies III - gradational contact; (f) Sharp contact with overlying carbonaceous shales and dolomitic siltstone. **Suggested depositional setting:** deep subtidal or below wave-base
Lithofacies V - thinly laminated dolomitic siltstone interbedded with Coxco needle dololutite **Thickness** - >15 m **Lateral Extent** - rare in the southern McArthur Basin; also noted in the Foelsche Inlier to the west.	MY97/2	**Sedimentary processes indicated at:** (a) very thinly laminated carbonacous, pyritic shale and dolomitic shale; (b) pronounced mounding and onlap of sediment laminae over and against Coxco needle fans; (c) laterally extensive beds of Coxco needles up to 20 cm thick.; (d)possible pyritic nodule within thinly laminated dolomitic siltstone. **Suggested depositional setting:** basinal or deep ramp

FIG. 6.—Coxco needle lithofacies and their characteristics.

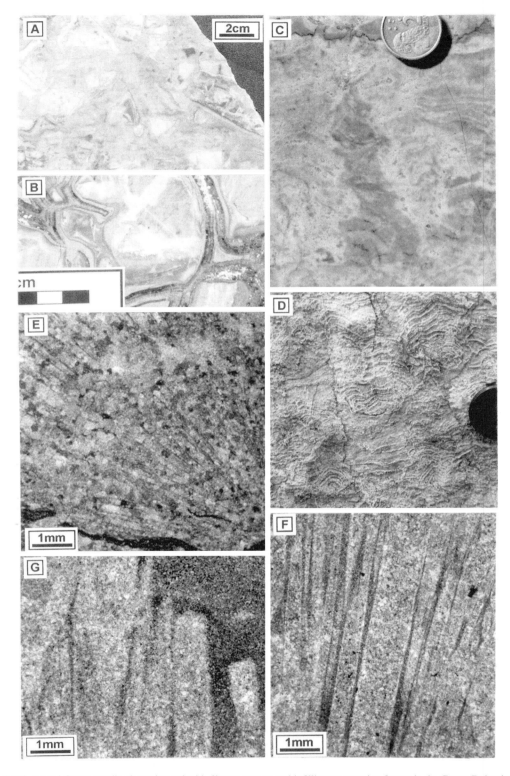

Fig. 7.—A) Brecciated, rotated Coxco needle clasts rimmed with fibrous cement and infilling a neptunian fissure in the Coxco Dolomite Member. B) Rotated clasts of Coxco needle dolomite cemented by fibrous dolomite cement and internal sediment. C) Sediment laminae mounding associated with Coxco needle growth (polished slab). Coin is 2 cm in diameter. D) Relationship similar to part C but in outcrop. Lens cap is 5.2 cm in diameter. E) Irregular mosaic of dolospar replacing original fan structure. Note also that the fan structure radiates from sub-horizontal to almost 180°. F) Coarser dolospar preserving the morphology of individual Coxco needles with finely crystalline dolomicrite evident between individual needles. G) Blocky and square terminations of individual Coxco needles preserved by replacive dolospar.

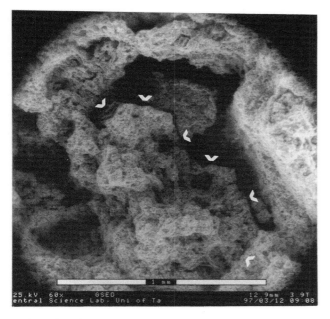
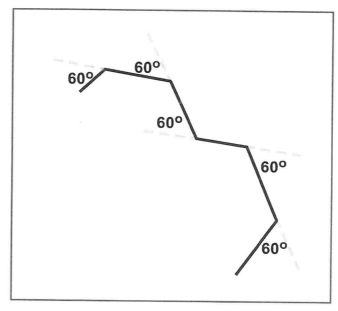

FIG. 8.——SEM image looking in plan down the *c* axis of a silicified, twinned Coxco needle. White symbols indicate crystal faces, and the accompanying diagram demonstrates interfacial angles of 60°.

contrast allows clear identification of individual needle shapes in thin sections and on most weathered outcrops. Further alteration is manifested as entire fans being composed of irregular dolospar that crosscuts relics of the original needle morphology, with the primary needle or fiber structure evident only from inclusion trails within the dolospar (Fig. 7E). Thus, with progressive alteration the crystal size of the dolospar becomes larger and extinction patterns become increasingly complex and chaotic, with no systematic relationship between the optical orientation of the replacive dolospar crystals and the replaced needle structure.

GEOCHEMISTRY

Elevated Sr^{2+} concentrations of calcitized or dolomitized cements is commonly used as one of the criteria for recognition of primary aragonite cements in ancient carbonate sequences (Sandberg, 1985). Elemental (Mg, Ca, Fe, Mn, Sr) concentrations of Coxco needle dolospar and the dolomicrite matrix were determined from several samples using an electron microprobe at the University of Tasmania. This data is included as Appendix 1 and can be obtained in digital form from the author on request. Errors for Mg were ± 0.05 wt%; Ca ± 0.05 wt%; Mn ± 200 ppm; Fe ± 200 ppm; and Sr ± 100 ppm.

The average values for Mn and Fe for Coxco needle dolospar are 902 ppm and 6012 ppm, respectively. Although the average Sr value falls within the range of operational error, several analyses were greater than 600 ppm (Fig. 9). Sr analyses of the dolomicrite matrix were also commonly less than detection limits, although two values greater than 200 ppm were recorded. Mn values for both the Coxco needle dolospar and dolomicrite matrix have a wide range (Fig. 9), although the average Mn value for each is below the operational error. The average Fe compositions for both are over 6000 ppm, although a wide range of values is recorded (Fig. 9).

DISCUSSION

The transgressive sequence through the Teena Dolomite and Barney Creek Formation culminated in the deposition of the carbonaceous, pyritic, dolomitic siltstones of the Barney Creek Formation during a period of pronounced tectonically controlled basin subsidence (Brown et al., 1978; Neudert and McGeough, 1996; Bull, 1998). The observation of a number of distinct, stratigraphically equivalent Coxco needle lithofacies (from peritidal to deep subtidal depositional environments) supports their precipitation over a wide area during the initial drowning of the carbonate platform and prior to the deposition of sub-wave-base, carbonaceous siltstone of the Barney Creek Formation.

Precipitation of Coxco needles occurred prior to complete lithification or compaction of the surrounding sediment. It is therefore considered highly unlikely that they originated in the subsurface from a later diagenetic process. Indeed, the exclusively upright, radial growth of Coxco fans, sediment–fan relationships, and the presence of Coxco needles in beds generally lacking in detrital carbonate all indicate that they grew as positive relief structures at the sediment–water interface (Fig. 11). This is supported by observations of Coxco needle clasts infilling synsedimentary fissures, and the lack of any zoning or evidence of sediment inclusions within individual needles during their growth.

Morphologically, the radial fan-like geometry, pseudohexagonal cross sections, and acicular nature of individual Coxco needles are all consistent with a primary aragonite mineralogy (Loucks and Folk, 1976; Mazzullo, 1980). In addition, blocky to square terminations of each needle are very distinctive and are commonly used to recognize aragonite cements in ancient carbonate sequences (Sandberg, 1985; James and Choquette, 1990; Sumner and Grotzinger, 1996a). The elongation directions of needles or fibers in a single fan diverge away from the

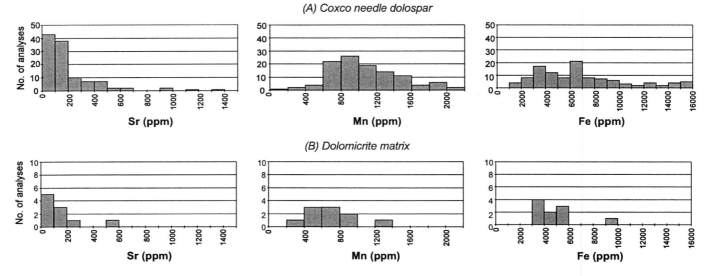

FIG. 9.—Results of electron microprobe analyses of Sr²⁺, Mn²⁺, and Fe²⁺ for Coxco needle dolospar, and dolomicritic matrix.

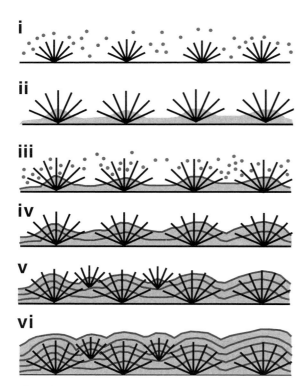

FIG. 10.—Schematic diagram of Coxco fan development and associated sediment mounding: (i) precipitation of fans directly onto the seafloor with micritic sediment also precipitating in the water column; (ii) micritic sediment forms the distinctive mounded laminae associated with some Coxco fans; (iii–v) continued precipitation of fans and mounding of micritic sediment forming decimeter-scale beds of Coxco needles. Note that proximity of some neighboring fans causes the preferential upward rather than lateral growth of needles, which in turn affects the overall morphology of individual fans.

substratum in a manner that is remarkably similar to Holocene aragonite druses (Mazzullo, 1980; James and Choquette, 1990). In contrast, the proposal of a gypsum precursor for the Coxco needles contradicts the fact that subaqueous bottom-nucleated gypsum forms "swallow-tail" or spear-like terminations (Warren, 1996).

The replacive dolospar which pseudomorphs Coxco needles consists of a mosaic of randomly oriented crystals, with ragged dolospar crystal boundaries commonly crosscutting the original needle structure. Sandberg (1985) describes this relationship as a common feature of calcitized aragonite cements, and a similar relationship is documented for dolomitized cement fans interpreted to have originally been aragonite in the Paleoproterozoic Rocknest Formation of Northwest Canada (Grotzinger and Read, 1983).

The excellent fabric preservation of Coxco needles implies very early dolomitization of needle fans. Such dolomitization of an aragonitic precursor to the fans could produce the irregular mosaic observed. In contrast, the dolomitization or calcitization of gypsum generally requires a significant solid volume loss or the movement of large quantities of pore water through the rock (Pierre and Rouchy, 1988). The absence of brecciation or solution-collapse features in the Coxco Dolomite Member, or evidence of significant pore-water movement, appears to discount this process. Furthermore, analysis of the Sr²⁺ content of Coxco needle dolospar reveals that although the Sr concentrations are within operational error and are typical of most ancient dolostones, rare high Sr values (up to 1250 ppm) are compatible with an aragonitic precursor mineralogy for Coxco needles. The high degree of fabric preservation, rare elevated Sr values, and the similarity of replacement fabrics to those of neomorphic calcite (Loucks and Folk, 1976; Mazzullo, 1980; Grotzinger and Read, 1983; Sandberg, 1985) all suggest that the dolospar directly replaced the Coxco needle fans rather than replacing an intermediate calcitized phase.

Walker et al. (1977) documented apparent similarities between the interfacial angles of acicular Coxco needles and gyp-

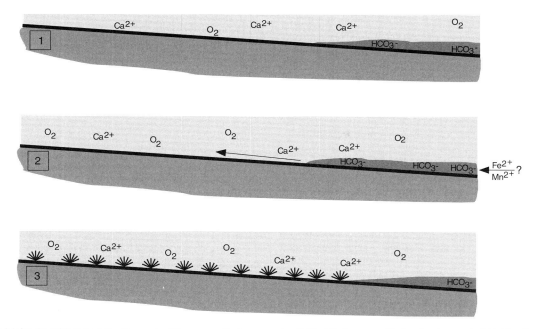

FIG. 11.—Model for the widespread development of Coxco needle fan cements. 1) Stratified ocean with the development of highly alkaline bottom waters associated with microbial activity in anoxic conditions. 2) Onset of tectonically induced basin subsidence forces a change in the basin bathymetry, resulting in upwelling of HCO_3^--charged bottom waters onto the carbonate platform. At the same time, hydrothermal processes are active within the basin. 3) Mixing with oxygenated, relatively Ca^{2+}-rich surface waters results in widespread precipitation of carbonate. Fe^{2+} and Mn^{2+} possibly inhibits micrite nucleation, favoring macroscopic Coxco fan growth.

sum crystals elongated parallel to the c axis, but they showed no cross sections and presented no quantitative data. They also note that the pseudomorphs appear to be zoned, having cores of dark dolomite containing abundant fine-grained inclusions interpreted to be clay minerals. These observations are clearly contrary to the results of this study.

Although there are problems that preclude an accurate study of the interfacial angles of individual Coxco needles, rare cross sections are sufficiently preserved to allow examination under a SEM. This reveals that casts have almost perfect hexagonal forms and commonly are twinned. Measurement of the interfacial angles of these cross sections demonstrates that they are 60° (Fig. 8). Studies of numerous polished thin sections of Coxco needles from each of the five Coxco needle lithofacies have also failed to recognize any zoning with the Coxco needle dolospar, although inclusion trails are observed defining the acicular, needle shape in most samples.

Much of the early work on the Teena Dolomite (e.g., Plumb and Brown, 1973; Walker et al., 1977) was centered on a few scattered outcrops situated close to the McArthur River Mine. A number of other crystal cast morphologies, including crystal pseudomorphs tentatively identified as after trona or gypsum by Jackson et al. (1987), were recognized associated with Coxco needle fans from these outcrops. *Lithofacies I*, consisting of a shallow peritidal sequence with well-developed Coxco needle beds, was identified in a drill core close to the mine. It is possible that *Lithofacies I* extended throughout the immediate mine area to include the outcrops originally studied, in which case the development of sulfate evaporites associated with Coxco needle fans within a peritidal setting is not inconceivable.

However, I believe that it is difficult to reconcile the results of the more regional sedimentological study presented here with the interpretation, based largely on a superficial comparison of interfacial angles, that Coxco needles were originally gypsum. Similarly, the interpretation of Jackson et al. (1987) that some of the relic casts were morphologically similar to trona, used as evidence that the Coxco Dolomite Member was deposited within a lacustrine lagoon, is also tenuous. This interpretation is inconsistent with both the lateral extent and lithofacies that host the Coxco needle fans, which support the inclusion of the Coxco Dolomite Member within a broad transgressive sequence culminating with the deposition of the Barney Creek Formation.

Other Northern Australian Examples of Coxco Fans

Radiating carbonate fans identical to the Coxco examples are present in stratigraphically equivalent sequences in the northern McArthur Basin, the northern Tennant Creek Inlier, and Victoria Basin (Fig. 1). Although no detailed sedimentological studies of these sequences has yet been completed, initial work by NTGS and Australian Geological Survey Organisation (AGSO) geologists suggests that the carbonate fans occur within broadly trangressive sequences capped by deep-water carbonaceous, dolomitic siltstone (Abbott, personal communication, 1998; Jackson, personal communication, 1998). Correlation between these sequences is constrained on the basis of their lithological and stratigraphic similarities, and by SHRIMP U–Pb dating of zircons within tuffaceous, pink-altered (locally termed "pinkites") beds associated with Coxco fans.

SIGNIFICANCE OF AN ARAGONITIC PRECURSOR

The widespread precipitation of carbonate during a broad chronostratigraphic transgressive event, as indicated by the development of macroscopic Coxco needle fans, suggests a subtle but extensive change in the basin water chemistry during the early phase of the corresponding sea-level rise. A similar relationship is described by the coral-reef hypothesis for deglaciation in the Holocene (Berger, 1982; Opdyke and Walker, 1992) and also for the formation of Australian Neoproterozoic postglacial cap dolostones (Kennedy, 1996). Both models invoke upwelling of, or flooding of the shelf, by HCO_3^--rich deep water during postglacial sea-level rises or transgression. These flooding events initiate rapid precipitation of carbonate, resulting in growth of coral or in the widespread formation of cap dolostone such as documented in the Australian Neoproterozoic.

Carbonate precipitation is known to occur occasionally as chemical whitenings (Kempe and Degens, 1985; Knoll and Swett, 1990; Grotzinger and Kasting, 1993; Kennedy, 1996) and given the increased saturation state of the Proterozoic ocean with respect to carbonate (Knoll et al., 1993), it is not unreasonable to attribute the widespread precipitation of Coxco needles to a broad transgression. This event could have flooded the subsiding carbonate platform with HCO_3^--charged deep water prior to the deposition of deeper-water sediments.

The Archean and early Proterozoic oceans are generally considered to have been stratified, with anoxic bottom water overlain by a thin layer of oxidized water sustained by microbial activity in the uppermost part of the water column (Beukes and Klein, 1993; Grotzinger and Knoll, 1995). Anoxic deep waters are known to have elevated alkalinity due to production of bicarbonate by microbial activity (Goyet et al., 1991; Kempe and Kazmierczak, 1994), and mixing of upwelling highly alkaline anoxic bottom waters with relatively Ca^{2+}-rich surface waters is known to result in precipitation of large amounts of $CaCO_3$ (Kempe, 1990).

A change in the bathymetry of the central Batten Fault Zone in response to the initiation of basin subsidence is suggested here as the mechanism for the upwelling of HCO_3^- anoxic bottom water and subsequent precipitation of carbonate fans throughout a number of lithofacies across the platform (Fig. 11). The reason that macroscopic precipitation of Coxco needle fans is favored over precipitation of more finely crystalline micritic carbonate (such as associated with the Neoproterozoic cap dolostones) is unclear. Sumner and Grotzinger (1996a) postulated that increased Fe^{2+} and Mn^{2+} contents in the Archean and Early Proterozoic acted to inhibit carbonate nucleation and micrite formation, in a way similar to how Mg^{2+} is thought maintain supersaturation of modern surface seawater (Berner, 1975). By reducing the precipitation rate of carbonate, various ions acting as inhibitors kinetically maintain highly $CaCO_3$-saturated waters, favoring precipitation of macroscopic carbonate cements. The subsequent decline in the number of documented examples of macroscopic carbonate seafloor cement in younger successions was interpreted to relate to the progressive oxidation of the atmosphere and oceans. However, it is possible that the concentration of Fe^{2+} and Mn^{2+} in McArthur Basin waters remained sufficiently elevated to inhibit precipitation of finely crystalline micrite from upwelling HCO_3^--charged waters. As yet, not enough work has been done on the effect of elevated Fe^{2+} and Mn^{2+} concentrations on aragonite precipitation.

Interestingly, Large et al. (1998) invoke the release of hydrothermally sourced Fe^{2+} and Mn^{2+} from active faults to explain an anomalous Mn halo around the HYC deposit. These faults were active during the latter stages of Teena Dolomite deposition and the onset of hydrothermal fluid discharge provides an alternative explanation for elevated Fe and Mn in the "Coxco" basin water.

The identification of stratigraphically equivalent occurrences of Coxco needle fans throughout northern Australia (Fig. 1) suggests that a transgression or upwelling mechanism similar to that inferred within the southern McArthur Basin was in effect over a much larger area. Therefore, any process invoked to explain the chronostratigraphic occurrence of Coxco fans must also explain the lateral extent of this phenomena.

Grotzinger and Knoll (1995) suggest that the Proterozoic decrease in carbonate saturation and seafloor precipitates is a first-order relationship that does not rule out any transient reversals in response to short-term events. Thus the presence of Coxco needles within a distinct stratigraphic interval is most likely a short-lived reversal in the overall decline of seafloor carbonate cement precipitation through the Proterozoic. Because the oceans are not considered to have been completely mixed until the Mesoproterozoic, upwelling of HCO_3^--rich waters from partly stratified oceans would have been possible until 1.5 Ga. However, the critical factor in the precipitation of macroscopic Coxco needles, as opposed to increased micrite accumulation, is likely to have been the effect of an inhibitor such as Fe^{2+} or Mn^{2+} on carbonate precipitation.

CONCLUSIONS

Detailed stratigraphic and petrographic study of the occurrence of Coxco needle fans in the middle McArthur Group has recognized a number of criteria (e.g., radial divergent morphology; blocky/square terminations; pseudohexagonal cross sections; mosaic of irregular neomorphic dolospar) that are consistent with an original aragonitic mineralogy. Field relationships demonstrate that precipitation occurred from ambient seawater directly onto the seafloor, and the identification of five distinct Coxco lithofacies supports the widespread precipitation of Coxco fans across the platform.

The onset of basin subsidence and related sea-level transgression is thought to have triggered the upwelling of highly alkaline, anoxic deep waters onto the platform. These subsequently mixed with Ca^{2+}-rich surface waters, resulting in widespread precipitation of Coxco needle fans across the platform. The development of aragonitic Coxco needle fans is considered to be a relatively short-lived reversal in the decline of Proterozoic carbonate saturation and occurrence of macroscopic seafloor cements. The reason that macroscopic carbonate cements were favored over the widespread precipitation of micrite remains an enigma. Elevated Fe^{2+} and Mn^{2+} may have been a factor, acting as inhibitors on the formation of micrite, thus allowing the growth of macroscopic Coxco fan cements.

ACKNOWLEDGMENTS

This work formed part of a Ph.D. study on the sedimentology and diagenesis of Proterozoic McArthur Group carbonates of the southern McArthur Basin, northern Australia. Funding originated from an Australian Commonwealth Postgraduate Research Award, and the AMIRA P384A Proterozoic Sediment-Hosted Base Metal Deposits project provided additional logistical support. The author would like to thank Peter Beier

APPENDIX 1.

	Mg (wt%)	Ca (wt%)	Mn (ppm)	Fe (ppm)	Sr (ppm)		Mg (wt%)	Ca (wt%)	Mn (ppm)	Fe (ppm)	Sr (ppm)
COX	12.43	21.10	860	5590	b.d.	COX	10.59	19.54	13	4703	b.d.
COX	13.13	22.07	430	2458	b.d.	COX	11.92	21.87	2020	14024	b.d.
COX	12.90	22.23	621	1542	358	COX	11.90	21.95	1483	11977	b.d.
COX	11.91	20.78	621	7180	b.d.	COX	12.09	21.81	1729	13898	b.d.
COX	12.68	21.74	526	7855	1253	COX	10.98	20.38	1266	13801	b.d.
COX	12.69	21.76	526	3952	1014	COX	11.70	21.76	1235	13620	b.d.
COX	12.22	21.23	764	8048	477	COX	11.66	22.22	1033	11380	b.d.
COX	12.79	21.94	669	4530	298	COX	11.14	21.38	1352	16825	b.d.
COX	12.02	21.25	717	6988	239	COX	11.85	21.83	902	14038	b.d.
COX	12.73	22.00	526	6602	358	COX	11.81	21.85	1586	10902	b.d.
COX	12.32	20.86	573	5542	895	COX	11.43	21.97	1295	15385	b.d.
COX	12.57	21.66	382	5927	b.d.	COX	11.69	21.63	1353	14453	b.d.
COX	12.28	21.09	764	6409	298	COX	12.21	21.59	1689	10808	b.d.
COX	12.20	21.58	573	4289	b.d.	COX	12.16	21.69	1994	11946	b.d.
COX	12.62	22.31	621	5301	358	COX	11.82	21.39	1617	11094	b.d.
COX	12.90	21.70	287	5686	b.d.	COX	11.91	21.00	817	7875	b.d.
COX	12.72	21.78	478	7084	298	COX	12.39	22.18	1151	7538	b.d.
COX	12.28	21.26	573	5445	418	COX	12.23	21.99	1151	9546	224
COX	12.78	22.17	334	3470	537	COX	12.20	22.03	2098	9466	b.d.
COX	12.56	21.69	b.d.	5253	b.d.	COX	12.17	21.84	1982	12006	b.d.
COX	12.81	22.01	478	5494	b.d.	COX	12.15	21.73	1472	8959	b.d.
COX	12.86	22.21	573	3229	358	COX	12.25	21.56	1736	7598	b.d.
COX	11.93	20.85	430	5349	b.d.	COX	12.13	22.12	1371	8102	b.d.
COX	12.74	22.60	956	2554	b.d.	COX	12.27	22.12	949	6278	b.d.
COX	12.88	22.45	956	2458	b.d.	COX	11.86	21.40	1355	14086	b.d.
COX	12.47	22.02	812	5735	b.d.	COX	12.12	21.21	1793	14272	b.d.
COX	12.76	22.33	764	2169	b.d.	COX	11.56	20.81	1341	12466	b.d.
COX	12.37	21.86	764	2072	b.d.	COX	12.61	21.93	438	2645	b.d.
COX	12.02	21.75	956	2313	b.d.	COX	12.07	20.78	1112	5657	b.d.
COX	12.49	22.61	1003	1735	b.d.	COX	12.20	21.31	760	4228	b.d.
COX	11.88	21.37	1003	3036	358	COX	12.89	22.29	789	3437	b.d.
COX	12.47	22.42	956	1879	b.d.	COX	12.14	21.33	629	3849	b.d.
COX	12.30	21.92	1003	3759	358	COX	12.53	22.07	483	2040	b.d.
COX	12.25	22.30	669	2024	537	COX	11.72	20.45	1083	5966	b.d.
COX	11.90	21.24	1051	2410	b.d.	COX	12.57	21.88	907	4126	b.d.
COX	12.15	21.99	908	2747	b.d.	COX	12.97	22.14	717	3082	b.d.
COX	12.51	22.05	1433	3132	b.d.	COX	12.35	21.56	907	5248	b.d.
COX	12.48	22.21	1003	2313	239	COX	12.71	22.03	512	5272	b.d.
COX	13.53	21.13	401	1128	b.d.	COX	12.71	22.20	745	5702	b.d.
COX	13.41	20.79	826	1187	b.d.	COX	12.75	21.86	950	5195	b.d.
COX	13.56	21.19	b.d.	404	b.d.	COX	12.64	22.21	483	2293	b.d.
COX	13.41	20.96	618	5316	b.d.	COX	12.54	21.99	1141	6061	b.d.
COX	13.39	20.59	1668	8979	b.d.	COX	12.57	21.81	1331	5884	b.d.
COX	12.93	20.55	687	13193	254						
COX	13.26	21.03	936	6726	b.d.	AVERAGE =	12.48	21.61	902	6012	b.d.
COX	13.14	21.26	386	b.d.	b.d.	STDEV. =	0.57	0.57	429	3946	b.d.
COX	13.47	21.13	418	2295	b.d.	MAX. =	13.70	22.61	2098	16825	1253
COX	13.48	20.79	936	3641	b.d.	MIN. =	10.59	19.54	b.d.	b.d.	b.d.
COX	13.24	21.28	675	4047	b.d.						
COX	13.42	20.86	b.d.	108	b.d.	MIC	12.56	21.70	382	3229	537
COX	13.41	20.86	1087	6086	b.d.	MIC	11.97	21.04	478	4337	b.d.
COX	13.28	20.97	441	586	b.d.	MIC	12.55	21.82	621	3662	b.d.
COX	12.49	22.39	740	2573	807	MIC	12.51	21.94	812	3084	b.d.
COX	13.64	20.98	614	1111	b.d.	MIC	12.51	21.72	812	3084	b.d.
COX	13.70	20.89	568	1073	320	MIC	10.48	18.68	1338	5542	b.d.
COX	13.40	20.86	591	1078	b.d.	MIC	11.23	19.88	526	9060	b.d.
COX	13.07	21.07	1064	9124	b.d.	MIC	12.35	21.61	669	4482	239
COX	12.58	21.80	1075	8374	b.d.	MIC	12.45	21.62	621	5253	b.d.
COX	12.03	21.25	1309	8134	b.d.	MIC	12.30	21.51	526	5927	b.d.
COX	12.36	21.32	1265	7394	b.d.						
COX	12.66	22.07	654	4507	b.d.	AVERAGE =	12.09	21.15	678	4766	388
COX	11.70	20.69	495	5938	b.d.	STDEV. =	0.70	1.05	269	1830	211
COX	12.68	22.06	698	5723	b.d.	MAX. =	12.56	21.94	1338	9060	537
COX	12.70	21.82	974	6634	b.d.	MIN. =	10.48	18.68	382	3084	b.d.
COX	12.80	21.97	728	3751	b.d.						
COX	12.72	22.38	859	3726	b.d.						
COX	12.77	22.24	800	2762	b.d.						
COX	12.44	21.74	713	5549	b.d.						
COX	12.51	21.79	873	4284	b.d.						
COX	12.63	22.27	597	2485	b.d.						

(NTGS) and Steve Abbott (NTGS) for providing samples of the Mt. Shillinglaw Formation and Campbell Springs Dolomite respectively for inclusion in this study, and Jim Jackson (AGSO) for providing information on the Vizard Formation. I am particularly grateful to John Warren for providing the impetus for this work and discussions related to precipitation of subaqueous gypsum. The following are gratefully acknowledged for providing stimulating discussions and for reading and improving earlier versions of the manuscript: Malcolm Wallace, Peter McGoldrick, Stuart Bull, David Rawlings, Malcolm Walter, and John Dunster. Reviewers Maria Mutti and Dawn Sumner are thanked both for their constructive criticism and encouragement.

REFERENCES

BERGER, W. H., 1982, Increases of carbon dioxide during deglaciation: the coral reef hypothesis: Naturwissenschaften, v. 69, p. 87–88.

BERNER, R. A., 1975, The role of magnesium in the crystal growth of calcite and aragonite from seawater: Geochimica et Cosmochimica Acta, v. 39, p. 489–504.

BEUKES, N. J., AND KLEIN, C., 1993, Models for iron-formation deposition, *in* Schopf, J. W., and Klein, C., eds., The Proterozoic Biosphere: Cambridge, United Kingdom, Cambridge University Press, p. 147–151.

BROWN, M. C., CLAXTON, C. W., AND PLUMB, K. A., 1978, The Proterozoic Barney Creek Formation and some associated units of the McArthur Group, Northern Territory: Australian Bureau of Mineral Resources, Record 1969/145, 59 p.

BULL, S. W., 1998, Sedimentology of the Palaeoproterozoic Barney Creek Formation in DDH BMR McArthur 2, southern McArthur Basin, Northern Territory: Australian Journal of Earth Sciences, v. 45, p. 21–31.

FAHEY, J. J., 1962, Saline minerals of the Green River Formation: U.S. Geological Survey, Professional Paper 405, 50 p.

GIVEN, R. K., AND WILKINSON, B. H., 1985, Kinetic control of morphology, composition, and mineralogy of abiotic sedimentary carbonates: Journal of Sedimentary Petrology, v. 55, p. 109–119.

GOYET, C., BRADSHAW, A. L., AND BREWER, P. G., 1991, The carbonate system in the Black Sea: Deep-Sea Research, v. 38, p. 1049–1068.

GROTZINGER, J. P., 1989, Facies and evolution of Precambrian carbonate depositional systems: emergence of the modern platform archetype, *in* Crevello, P. D., Wilson, J. L., Sarg, J. F., and Read, J. F., eds., Controls on Carbonate Platform and Basin Development: SEPM, Special Publication 44, p. 79–106.

GROTZINGER, J. P., AND FRIEDMAN, S. J., 1989, Occurrence of thick crusts of botryoidal aragonite, Rifle and Beechey Formations (1.97 Ga), Kilohigok Basin, N.W.T. (abstract): Geological Association of Canada, Program with Abstracts, v. 14, p. A77.

GROTZINGER, J. P., AND KASTING, J. F., 1993, New constraints on Precambrian ocean composition: Journal of Geology, v. 101, p. 235–243.

GROTZINGER, J. P., AND KNOLL, A. H., 1995, Anomalous carbonate precipitates: Is the Precambrian the key to the Permian?: Palaios, v. 10, p. 578–596.

GROTZINGER, J. P., AND READ, J. F., 1983, Evidence for primary aragonite precipitation, lower Proterozoic (1.9 Ga) dolomite, Wopmay Orogen, northwest Canada: Geology, v. 11, p. 710–713.

HEGENBERGER, W., 1993, Stratigraphy and sedimentology of the late Precambrian Witvlei and Nama Groups, east of Windhoek: Geological Survey of Namibia, Memoir 17, 82 p.

HOFMANN, H. J., 1971, Precambrian fossils, pseudofossils, and problematica in Canada: Geological Survey of Canada, Bulletin 189, 146 p.

HORODYSKI, R. J., 1977, *Lyngbya* mats at Laguna Mormona, Baja California, Mexico: comparison with Proterozoic stromatolites: Journal of Sedimentary Petrology, v. 47, p. 1303–1320.

JACKSON, M. J., MUIR, M. D., AND PLUMB, K. A., 1987, Geology of the southern McArthur Basin, Northern Territory: Australia, Bureau of Mineral Resources, Bulletin 220, 173 p.

JAMES, N. P., AND CHOQUETTE, P. W., 1990, Limestones—The sea floor diagenetic environment, *in* Diagenesis: Geoscience Canada, Reprint Series 4, p. 13–35.

KEMPE, S., 1990, Alkalinity: The link between anaerobic basins and shallow water carbonates?: Naturwissenschaften, v. 77, p. 426–427.

KEMPE, S., AND DEGENS, E. T., 1985, An early soda ocean?: Chemical Geology, v. 53, p. 95–108.

KEMPE, S., AND KAZMIERCZAK, J., 1994, The role of alkalinity in the evolution of ocean chemistry, organisation of living systems, and biocalcification processes, *in* Doumerge, F., ed., Past and Present Biomineralisation Processes: Monaco, Musée Océanographique, Bulletin 13, p. 61–116.

KENDALL, C. G. ST. C., AND SKIPWORTH, P. A. D'E., 1968, Recent algal mats of a Persian Gulf Lagoon: Journal of Sedimentary Petrology, v. 38, p. 1040–1058.

KNOLL, A. H., AND SWETT, K., 1990, Carbonate deposition during the late Proterozoic era: an example from Spitsbergen: American Journal of Science, v. 290A, p. 104–132.

KNOLL, A. H., FAIRCHILD, I. J., AND SWETT, K., 1993, Calcified microbes in Neoproterozoic carbonates: implications for our understanding of the Proterozoic/Cambrian transition: Palaios, v. 8, p. 512–525.

KENNEDY, M. J., 1996, Stratigraphy, sedimentology, and isotopic geochemistry of Australian Neoproterozoic postglacial cap dolostones: deglaciation, $\delta^{13}C$ excursions, and carbonate precipitation: Journal of Sedimentary Research, v. 66, p. 1050–1064.

LARGE, R. R., BULL, S. W., COOKE, D. R., AND McGOLDRICK, P. J., 1998, A genetic model for the HYC deposit, Australia: based on regional sedimentology, geochemistry and sulfide-sediment relationships: Economic Geology, v. 93, p. 1345–1368.

LOGAN, R. G., MURRAY, W. J., AND WILLIAMS, N., 1990, HYC silver–lead–zinc deposit, McArthur River: Australian Institute of Mining and Metallurgy, Monograph 14, p. 907–911.

LOUCKS, R. G., AND FOLK R. L., 1976, Fan-like rays of former aragonite in Permian Capitan Reef pisolite: Journal of Sedimentology, v. 46, p. 483–485.

MARTIN, A., NISBET, E. G., AND BICKLE, M. J., 1980, Archaean stromatolites of the Belingwe Greenstone Belt, Zimbabwe (Rhodesia): Precambrian Research, v. 13, p. 337–362.

MAZZULLO, S. J., 1980, Calcite pseudospar replacive of marine acicular aragonite, and implications for aragonite cement diagenesis: Journal of Sedimentary Petrology, v. 50, p. 409–422.

MAZZULLO, S. J., AND CYS, J. M., 1979, Marine aragonite sea-floor growths and cements in Permian phylloid algal mounds, Sacramento Mountains, New Mexico: Journal of Sedimentary Petrology, v. 49, p. 917–936.

MUIR, M. D., 1983, Depositional environments of host rock to northern Australian lead–zinc deposits, with special reference to McArthur River: Mineralogical Association of Canada, Short Course Handbook, no. 8, p. 141–174.

NEUDERT, M., AND McGEOUGH, M., 1996, A tectonostratigraphic framework for the deposition of the upper McArthur Group, N.T. (abstract), *in* Baker, T., Rotherham, J. K., Richmond, J. M., Mark, G., and Williams, P. J., eds., MIC '96—New Developments in Metallogenic Research: The McArthur–Mount Isa–Cloncurry Minerals Province: Economic Geology Research Unit, Contribution 55, James Cook University, Queensland, 161 p.

OPDYKE, B. N., AND WALKER, J. C. G., 1992, Return of the coral reef hypothesis: basin to shelf partitioning of $CaCO_3$ and its effect on atmospheric CO_2: Geology, v. 20, p. 733–736.

PAGE, R. W., 1997, Geological constraints provided by U–Pb zircon dating of basin phases in the Lawn Hill and McArthur Basins (abstract): Australian Geological Survey Organisation, Record 1997/12.

PIERRE, C., AND ROUCHY, J. M., 1988, The carbonate replacements after sulphate evaporites in the middle Miocene of Egypt: Journal of Sedimentary Petrology, v. 58, p. 446–456.

PIETSCH, B. A., RAWLINGS, D. J., CREASER, P. M., KRUSE, P. D., AHMAD, P., FERERCZI, P. A., AND FINDHAMMER, T. L. R., 1991a, Bauhinia Downs: 1:250,000 Geological Map Series, Northern Territory Geological Survey, Explanatory Notes SE53-3.

PIETSCH, B. A., WYCHE, S., RAWLINGS, D. J., CREASER, P. M., AND FINDHAMMER, T. L. R., 1991b, McArthur River Region: 1:100,000 Geological Map Series, Northern Territory Geological Survey, Explanatory Notes SE53-3.

PLUMB, K. A., AND BROWN, M. C., 1973, Revised correlations and stratigraphic nomenclature in the Proterozoic carbonate complex of the McArthur Group, Northern Territory: Australia Bureau of Mineral Resources, Bulletin 139, p. 103–115.

PLUMB, K. A., AND WELLMAN, P., 1987, McArthur Basin, Northern Territory: mapping of deep troughs using gravity and magnetic anomalies: Australia Bureau of Mineral Resources, Journal of Australian Geology and Geophyics, v. 10, p. 243–251.

PLUMB, K. A., AHMAD, M., AND WYGRALAK, A.S., 1990, Mid-Proterozoic Basins of the North Australian Craton—Regional Geology and Mineralisation, *in* Hughes, F. E., ed., Geology of the Mineral Deposits of Australia and Papua New Guinea: Australasian Institute of Mining and Metallurgy, Monograph 14, p. 881–902.

SANDBERG, P., 1983, An oscillating trend in Phanerozoic non-skeletal carbonate mineralogy: Nature, v. 305, p. 19–22.

SANDBERG, P., 1985, Aragonite cements and their occurrence in ancient limestones, *in* Schneidermann, N., and Harris, P.M., eds., Carbonate Cements: SEPM, Special Publication 36, p. 33–57.

STEPHENS, D. I., 1997, EL's 9022, 9023 and 9325–Willeray Project, McArthur

Basin (Final Report): Northern Territory Department of Mines and Energy, Open File Company Report, 97-781 (unpublished).

SUMNER, D. Y., 1995, Facies, Paleogeography and Carbonate Precipitation on the Archean (2520 Ma) Campbellrand–Malmani Carbonate Platform, Transvaal Supergroup, South Africa [unpublished Ph.D. thesis]: Massachusetts Institute of Technology, Cambridge, Massachusetts, 516 p.

SUMNER, D. Y., AND GROTZINGER, J. P., 1996a, Were kinetics of Archean calcium carbonate precipitation related to oxygen concentration?: Geology, v. 24, p. 119–122.

SUMNER, D. Y., AND GROTZINGER, J. P., 1996b, Herringbone calcite: petrography and environmental significance: Journal of Sedimentary Research, v. 66, p. 419–429.

WALKER, R. N., MUIR, M. D., DIVER, W. L., WILLIAMS, N., AND WILKINS, N., 1977, Evidence of major sulphate evaporite deposits in the Proterozoic McArthur Group, Northern Territory, Australia: Nature, v. 265, p. 526–529.

WARREN, J. K., 1996, Evaporites, brines and base metals: what is an evaporite? Defining the rock matrix: Australian Journal of Earth Sciences, v. 43, p. 115–132.

WILKINSON, B. H., AND GIVEN, R. K., 1986, Secular variation in abiotic marine carbonates: Constraints on Phanerozoic atmospheric carbon dioxide contents and oceanic Mg/Ca ratios: Journal of Geology, v. 94, p. 321–333.

WILKINSON, B. H., BUCZYNSKI, C., AND OWEN, R. M., 1984, Chemical control of carbonate phases: implications from Upper Pennsylvanian calcite–aragonite ooids of southeastern Kansas: Journal of Sedimentary Petrology, v. 54, p. 932–947.

WILLIAMS, N., AND LOGAN, R. G., 1981, Depositional environments of the sediments hosting the McArthur River stratiform Pb–Zn deposits (abstract), *in* Groves, D. I., McNamara, K., Brown, R. G., and Johnstone, M. H., eds., Sediments through the Ages: Geological Society of Australia, Abstracts, no. 3, p. 8.

WINEFIELD, P. R., SELLEY, D., AND BULL, S. W., 1997, Examples of synsedimentary deformation related to slope development in Proterozoic carbonates (abstract): Geological Society of Australia, Abstracts, no. 47, p. 32.

WINEFIELD, P. R., AND MCGOLDRICK, P., 1998. Evidence of Proterozoic primary $CaCO_3$ precipitation from the McArthur Group of northern Australia (abstract), *in* Arehart, G.B., and Hulston, J.R., eds., Water–Rock Interaction: International Association of Geochemistry and Cosmochemistry Conference Proceedings, WRI-9, p. 373–376.

PART III
REEFS

EARLY NEOPROTEROZOIC (TONIAN) PATCH REEF COMPLEXES, VICTORIA ISLAND, ARCTIC CANADA

G. M. NARBONNE, N. P. JAMES
Queen's University, Kingston, Ontario, Canada
R. H. RAINBIRD
Geological Survey of Canada, Ottawa, Ontario, Canada
AND
J. MORIN
Environnement Canada, Ste. Foy, Québec, Canada

ABSTRACT: The Boot Inlet Formation (Reynolds Point Group, Shaler Supergroup) is an early Neoproterozoic (<1077 MA, >723 Ma) succession that crops out within the Minto Inlier on northern Victoria Island in the Canadian Arctic archipelago, and consists of strata that accumulated on a carbonate ramp. Inner-ramp facies comprise molar-tooth lime mudstone and current-bedded ooid grainstone (locally herringbone cross-laminated) with scalloped erosional surfaces. Ooid shoals (3–4 m thick) and sheets (0.5–1.0 m thick) are interbedded with 10–15 m thick stromatolite bioherms and biostromes forming complexes 0.5 to 5.0 km wide. The most common mid-ramp facies is parted to ribbon-bedded limestone with conspicuous ripples, gutter casts, hummocky cross-stratification, and intraformational breccias readily interpretable as storm deposits; these fine-grained rocks form shallowing-upward, meter-scale cycles capped by oolitic limestone and small reefs. Outer-ramp facies comprise shale with large carbonate concretions.

Reefs are most common in the lower half of the succession, where overall sea-level rise combined with higher-order transgressions to produce maximum accommodation space. A pronounced zonation of reef types occurs across the ramp. A current-oriented biostrome of *Baicalia?* is the only reef type on the inner ramp. Patch reefs and table reefs characterize the inner- to mid-ramp transition, and consist of stacked meter-scale bushes of *Tungussia* that pass upward into broad domal sheets of parallel, columnar stromatolites (*Baicalia*) oriented at a high angle to the sheets. Overall upward decrease in diversity of growth form is accompanied by evidence for increasing wave and current energy. Concentric-sheet bioherms up to 60 m in diameter and 15 m high, composed of sheets of closely spaced "pencil stromatolites" (*Jurusania*), grew in outer-ramp facies during rapid transgression.

The Boot Inlet reefs are similar to other Proterozoic reefs in being composed entirely of stromatolites, including some of the same forms as characterize other early Neoproterozoic patch reefs. Calcimicrobes are conspicuously absent, despite their abundance in coeval deeper-water reefs in the Mackenzie Mountains. The presence of kalyptra-like stromatolitic structures in the Boot Inlet reefs is similar to that of Early Cambrian calcimicrobe–archaeocyathan reefs, and lends support for the view that the Phanerozoic reef archetype originated during the Neoproterozoic.

INTRODUCTION

Reefs are arguably the most complex of marine ecosystems, and are preserved in the rock record as a variety of structures united by similarities in geometry, composition, and fabric (Fagerstrom, 1987; James and Bourque, 1992). While much is known about Phanerozoic buildups, comparatively little is understood about reefs prior to the appearance of calcareous benthic metazoans. It has become increasingly evident in recent years that Precambrian reefs, especially those of Neoproterozoic age, contain important information about the early history of this important ecosystem.

Early Neoproterozoic (Tonian) reefs are especially well exposed in northern Canada (Aitken, 1988; Jefferson and Young, 1988; Turner et al., 1993, 1997, this volume). This study documents mainly shallow-water stromatolitic buildups exposed on Victoria Island, in the Canadian Arctic Archipelago. The focus is on their morphology, temporal and spatial settings, internal structure, and their place in the evolving late Proterozoic to Phanerozoic reef system.

GEOLOGICAL SETTING

The rocks of this study were deposited in the intracratonic Amundsen Basin, which formed between Laurentia and an outboard continent, possibly Siberia, during late Paleoproterozoic through early Neoproterozoic time (Young, 1981; Rainbird et al., 1996). Strata of interest belong to the early Neoproterozoic Shaler Supergroup, a sequence of shallow-water siliciclastic, carbonate, and evaporite rocks preserved on the Arctic mainland coast, north of Great Bear Lake, on Banks Island, and on Victoria Island (Rainbird et al., 1994a; Rainbird et al., 1997). This report focuses on carbonates of the ca. 500 m thick Boot

Inlet Formation of the Reynolds Point Group, which is well exposed at the northeastern end of Minto Inlier on northern Victoria Island (Fig. 1).

Mafic sills and dikes of the Franklin magmatic event intrude the Shaler Supergroup and provide a minimum U–Pb (baddeleyite) age of 723 Ma (Heaman et al. 1992). A maximum U–Pb age of 1077 Ma is provided by dating detrital zircons of the underlying Nelson Head Formation (Rainbird et al., 1997).

The striking lithological similarlity between the Shaler Supergroup and the coeval Mackenzie Mountains Supergroup of the western N.W.T. (Aitken et al., 1978; Rainbird et al., 1994a, Rainbird et al., 1996) implies that the Boot Inlet stromatolite reefs are the shallow-water equivalents of the huge calcimicrobial reefs in the "basinal assemblage" of the Little Dal Group (Turner et al., 1993, 1997, this volume). As such, they provide an important insight into the environmental spectrum of reefs that grew across an early Neoproterozoic ramp and deep-basin floor.

METHODS

Field work for this study was undertaken during a two-week period during the summer of 1996. The 25 km² area of investigation is located southwest of Wynniatt Bay in the vicinity of section 92-M2 (Morin and Rainbird, 1993; Rainbird et al., 1994b). This locality was selected because of the numerous reported buildups and excellent exposure. Sections were logged in detail (Fig. 2), reef localities were sampled and mapped, and units were traced laterally for several kilometers to determine continuity.

The area is one of moderate relief (~200 m) with excellent exposure as low eroded cuestas that dip gently southwestward.

Carbonate Sedimentation and Diagenesis in the Evolving Precambrian World
Copyright © 2000, SEPM (Society for Sedimentary Geology) Special Publication 67, ISBN 1-56576-072-7

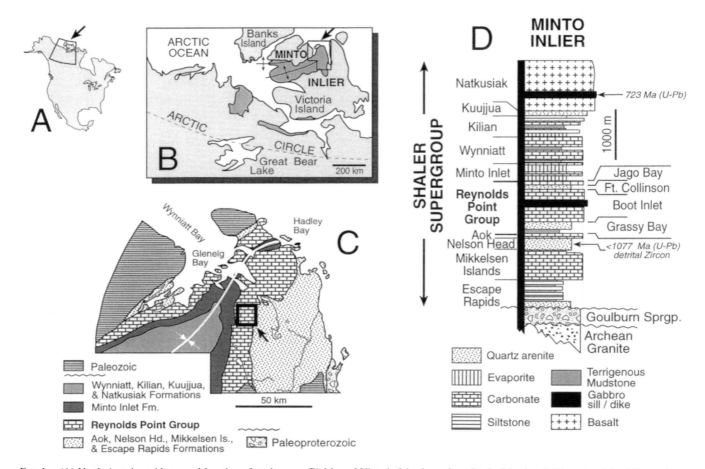

FIG. 1.—(A) North America with general location of study area. (B) Map of Victoria Island, southern Banks Island and adjacent mainland illustrating the location of the early Neoproterozoic Shaler Supergroup. (C) Generalized geological map of the northeast Minto Inlier; study area within box; after Rainbird et al., 1994b. (D) Stratigraphic column of the Shaler Supergroup (after Rainbird et al., 1994a) highlighting the position of the Reynolds Point Group and component formations. This study is focused on the Boot Inlet Formation.

Glaciation has exposed a rolling terrain variably covered with glacial till, till veneer, and outwash gravels, dotted with small lakes and incised by shallow, broad river valleys. Diabase sills and dikes, although abundant, do not substantially affect the original stratigraphy and are omitted from stratigraphic sections. Specific lithological problems were resolved through study of 24 petrographic thin sections.

Stromatolite description follows the terminology of Walter (1972) and Grey (1989).

STRATIGRAPHY

The Shaler Supergroup and its constituent formations were originally defined by Thorsteinsson and Tozer (1962). Formational nomenclature was recently revised by Rainbird et al. (1994a), who established the name "Boot Inlet Formation" for the Lower Carbonate member of the former Reynolds Point Formation. Attributes of the Boot Inlet Formation and associated strata were first described by Young and Long (1977a) and have been more thoroughly documented by Morin and Rainbird (1993) on the basis of reconnaissance mapping.

The Boot Inlet Formation is underlain by the Grassy Bay Formation, a 60–200 m-thick terrigenous clastic unit interpreted

to have been deposited by a prograding river-dominated delta (Young and Long, 1977b; Rainbird et al., 1994a). Cross-bedded quartz arenites pass upward into heterogeneous, hummocky cross-stratified and parallel-laminated dolosiltite and dololutite with interbedded guttered rhythmite. The upper sediments, with broad scours, loads, gutters, and HCS at various scales are envisaged to be a storm-wave-influenced inner-shelf deposit.

The overlying Boot Inlet Formation exhibits oolitic grainstone, stromatolite boundstone, and thin-bedded dolosiltite and dololutite interpreted to have accumulated on a storm-dominated carbonate ramp. Mostly limestone, the rocks have undergone relatively little fabric-destructive diagenesis except directly adjacent to diabase intrusives.

Overlying Fort Collinson Formation strata are mainly sandstones with bidirectional cross-stratification, interpreted as a beach barrier system strongly influenced by tidal-current flow.

SEDIMENTOLOGY

The sedimentology of these rocks has been described by Morin and Rainbird (1993), who viewed the overall depositional setting as a storm-dominated carbonate ramp. This study fully supports that interpretation, and the rocks are easily placed

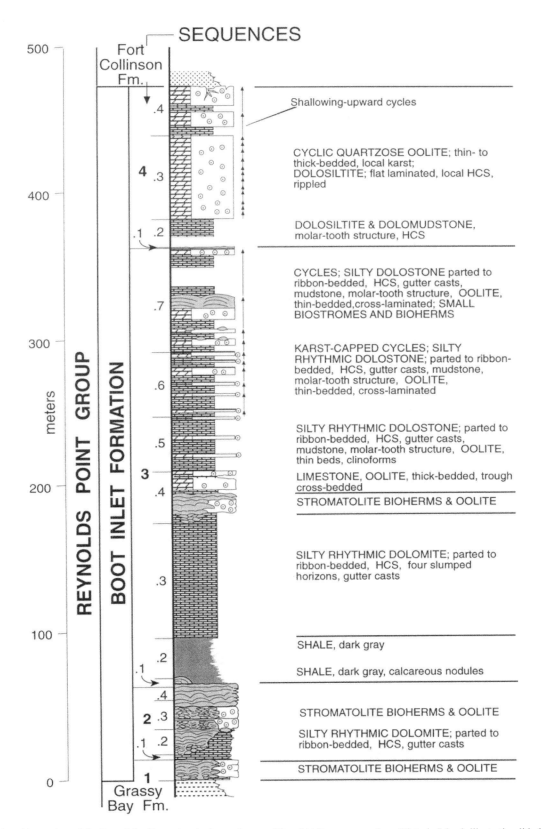

FIG. 2.—Stratigraphic section of the Boot Inlet Formation in the study area, Wynniatt Bay area, northern Victoria Island, illustrating lithological succession and stratigraphic sequences. Arrows indicate shallowing-upward cycles.

in the overall framework of carbonate ramps (Fig. 3) as outlined by Read (1985) and Burchette and Wright (1992).

Sedimentary Facies

Inner-Ramp Facies.—

These heterogeneous facies are interbedded ooid grainstone, molar-tooth lime mudstone, dolosiltite, and cryptmicrobial and laminated lime mudstone. Ooid grainstone forms beds up to 2 m in thickness, with bidirectional, trough and planar unidirectional cross-bedding and local scalloped paleokarst upper surfaces. Although composed mostly of ooids, grapestones and microbially coated intraclasts are common. Thin-bedded lime mudstone is generally massive with molar-tooth structure (see James et al., 1998, and references therein) or is cryptmicrobially laminated. Dolosiltites are typically parallel-laminated, wave and current rippled, or hummocky and swaly cross-stratified. Thin graded beds comprise lenticular ooid packstone at the base through parallel and cross-laminated dolosiltite to dololutite at the top. Desiccation cracks are conspicuously absent. All these muddy and grainy deposits are laterally equivalent to stromatolite bioherms and biostromes.

Mid-Ramp Facies.—

The most common mid-ramp facies is parted to locally ribbon-bedded dolostone with numerous features typical of storm-wave deposition, including current and wave ripples, gutter casts, hummocky to local swaly cross-stratification, and graded beds. The most abundant rocks are rhythmites 5–15 cm thick, which consist of beds of parallel-laminated dolosiltite to dolarenite with common basal gutter casts overlain by hummocky cross-laminated to cross-bedded dolosiltite with dololutite interbeds 1–4 cm thick. These strata locally are punctuated by 0.3 to 0.5 m thick slumped horizons. The rhythmic parted dolostones locally are interbedded with ooid packstone, in the form of graded and erosionally based units of oolite and laminated dolosiltite. These thin-bedded dolostones and minor shales form thick sequences and surround extensive stromatolite bioherms.

Outer-Ramp Facies.—

Argillaceous dolosiltite and shale form the deepest-water facies. Decimeter-scale ovoid dololutite to dolosiltite concretions are common. Primary sedimentary structures are restricted to a few thin parallel laminae. These strata locally encase bioherms and biostromes composed of thin columnar "pencil" stromatolites.

Interpretation

Together these facies indicate a simple paleoramp setting that was strongly influenced by storm deposition. The inner ramp is interpreted as series of tidal ooid sand shoals and wide stromatolite banks behind which lay small open lagoons. These stromatolites and shoals were variably effective as nearshore barriers because storm-bedded dolosiltites occur even in these protected lagoonal settings. Ooids were commonly reworked and swept both landward into the lagoon and seaward down the ramp. The mid-ramp was a site of mostly fine-grained event sedimentation. Slumped horizons are most common in the distal regions of the mid-ramp, and suggest that the incline may have been "distally steepened" (cf. Read, 1985) in this position. The outer ramp, generally below storm wave base, was a site of quiet-water accumulation of terrigenous clay, silt, and carbonate mud.

SEQUENCE STRATIGRAPHY

The succession is divisible into four sequences (Fig. 2). Sequence boundaries are interpreted to lie at the abrupt upward passage from shallow-water inner-ramp ooid grainstone or stromatolite boundstone to overlying mid- or outer-ramp shale and dolostone. This reflects the shoaling and then abrupt flooding of the ramp, and in all but the lowest sequence this contact is also marked by the presence of a biostrome or bioherm composed of "pencil" stromatolites interpreted to represent the earliest stages of the transgression. The sequences are subdivided into segments for ease of discussion.

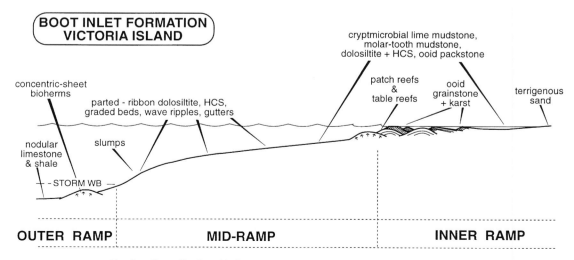

FIG. 3.—Generalized profile illustrating the major facies of the Boot Inlet Formation.

Sequences

Sequence 1.—

This package comprises the upper part of the Grassy Bay and the basal 17 m of the Boot Inlet formations. Terrigenous clastic mid-ramp siltstones and shales grade up into rhythmic parted dolostones and discrete stromatolite bioherms and are capped by a thick succession of inner-ramp ooid grainstones and stromatolite biostromes.

Sequence 2.—

The transgressive systems tract (TST) segment (2.1) of this 60-m-thick sequence is a parted rhythmic dolostone with small meter-scale bioherms at the base. The early highstand systems tract (HST) is a series of extensive bioherms and laterally equivalent parted rhythmite (2.2) and the late HST is a 35-m-thick complex series of mid-inner ramp ooid-rich grainstones, packstones, mudstones, and associated bioherms and biostromes (2.3 and 2.4).

Sequence 3.—

This 200 m package is the thickest sequence and comprises a relatively thin TST and thick HST, with the HST divisible into an early 80-m-thick, noncyclic part and a later 120-m-thick, cyclic part.

The base of the TST (3.1) is a pencil-stromatolite biostrome that becomes distinctly biohermal upward, likely reflecting rapid rise in sea level. The bulk of the TST (3.2) is a shale with calcareous concretions at the base that becomes less calcareous upward with maximum flooding within dark gray shale.

Early phases of the noncyclic HST (3.3) is mid-ramp, locally slumped, parted rhythmite with stromatolite bioherms near the top capped by inner-ramp oolite–stromatolite complexes (3.4). These upper oolites are tabular, 1.0–5.0 m-thick beds, and comprise 50% of the unit, are trough cross-bedded with sets 20–40 cm in height and are locally wave rippled with mudstone drapes. They contain numerous grapestone lumps and rip-up clasts. Intervening dolostones are heterogeneous with interbedded, platy hummocky cross-stratified dolosiltite, molar-tooth mudstone, and graded oolite grainstone-to-mudstone on a 2–4 cm scale.

Package 3.5 is a predominantly thin-bedded inner-ramp dolomudstone to ooid packstone/wackestone. Finer-grained beds contain abundant molar tooth, microbial laminae, local gutter casts, and broad hummocky cross-stratification. Discrete ooid-grainstone beds up to 1.5 m in thickness punctuate the succession (ca. 20%), and are a series of low-angle clinoforms, likely representing prograding storm washover deposits. One unit with prominent slump structures contains numerous intraclasts of ooid grainstone.

The upper, cyclic part begins as package 3.6, a series of discrete inner-ramp shallowing-upward, paleokarst-capped, meter-scale cycles (Fig. 2). Each cycle comprises a lower heterogenous unit, 2.0–7.0 m thick, of thin-bedded parted dolostone formed by units of ooid packstone, hummocky cross-stratified and guttered dolosiltite, rippled dolosiltite, and microbial and molar-tooth dolomudstone. The upper unit, 0.5–2.0 m thick, is a cross-bedded ooid grainstone, locally with ooid intraclasts. The cycle is capped by a paleokarst surface. Ooids directly

beneath this surface have distinctive early first-stage meniscus cement.

Package 3.7 is a similar series of inner-ramp cycles, but they are much thicker, averaging 15 m, lack obvious paleokarst, and the upper ooid unit is capped with stromatolite bioherms or biostromes. The uppermost of these cycles is capped by herringbone cross-laminated quartzose ooid grainstone, flat-clast conglomerate, and columnar stromatolites.

Sequence 4.—

This 100-m-thick sequence is a succession of meter-scale inner-ramp shallowing-upward cycles. The thin TST (4.1) is a pencil stromatolite biostrome. Above a covered interval the rest of the TST is a molar-tooth mudstone (4.2). Most of the sequence (4.3) is a cyclic HST in which cycles are similar to those in 3.5 in that each has a lower heterolithic unit 1–3 m thick and an upper oolite unit. Sequence 4 oolites can be distinguished from those lower in the Boot Inlet Formation in that they are more quartzose, with some units containing more than 50% quartz. Where the cycle is <2 m thick the lower unit is parallel-laminated mudstone, but cycles 2–3 m thick are more variable, with additional ooid packstone, molar-tooth mudstone, and hummocky cross-stratified dolosiltite. The ooid units, 0.5–6 m thick, are planar and locally herringbone cross-laminated, and have irregular upper surfaces but no convincing karst; large, rounded clasts of microbially coated ooid grainstone locally occur near the top. Unit 4.4 is similar but the fine units contain terrigenous clay and silt. The sequence is capped by a complex of ooid shoals and stromatolite dolostone that has been brecciated, with cracks filled by oolite and quartzose sand from the overlying Fort Collinson Formation. This contact is interpreted to be a paleokarst surface of prolonged subaerial exposure.

Interpretation.—

The Boot Inlet Formation is sandwiched between two predominantly terrigenous clastic units, but during deposition of this formation the ramp was largely cut off from terrigenous clastic supply. Similarities in facies associations throughout the succession suggest consistent depositional controls, yet different packaging implies varying control by allogenic and autogenic factors.

We interpret the Boot Inlet Formation as a major transgressive–regressive sequence, with the Grassy Bay and Fort Collinson formations representing major sea-level lowstands and siliciclastic progradation. Sequences within the Boot Inlet would seem to be best explained by several superimposed higher-order sea-level fluctuations. Meter-scale cycles are likely a product of some as-yet-undetermined combination of carbonate factory dynamics and sea-level movement.

This interpretation implies that the study area was located in the middle of a broad area of carbonate deposition, because both basinward and landward shifts in facies belts are well recorded in the section. Deeper-water (e.g., basin floor) depositional environments are not recorded in strata of the Boot Inlet Formation in the Minto Inlier but are represented in correlative strata of the "basinal facies" of the Little Dal Group in the Mackenzie Mountains (see Aitken, 1981; Turner et al., 1997).

In such an interpretation, and assuming constant subsidence, carbonates in Sequence 1 reflect abbreviated TST and HST because of a rapid rise in relative sea level. Sequence 2 implies an overall slowing of large-scale sea-level rise allowing for more prolonged production of shallow-water carbonate and basinward facies shift. This progradation is, however, most strikingly manifested in Sequence 3. Here the TST is mostly shale, with early highstand systems tract (EHST) in the form of progressively shallower packages of noncyclic inner-ramp facies. The late highstand systems tract (LHST), with reduced overall accommodation, is reflected by the karst-capped and bioherm-capped meter-scale cycles. Sequence 4, dominated by meter-scale inner-ramp cycles with the quartzose carbonates, suggests again reduced accommodation and a nearby terrigenous clastic source. Finally, the major karst surface at the top of the Boot Inlet Formation is interpreted to represent the major lowstand of sea level before commencement of the next cycle of deposition, represented by the quartz arenites of the Fort Collinson Formation.

STROMATOLITE REEFS

General Attributes

Reefs range in size from less than 0.5 m in all dimensions to several tens of meters in diameter and height, and in morphology from isolated meter-scale bioherms to decameter-scale patch reefs, table reefs, and concentrically layered deep-water bioherms to large biostromes (Fig. 4). Reefs are most abundant in sequences 1 and 2 in the lower part of the Boot Inlet Formation, occur sporadically in sequence 3, and are not known from sequence 4 (Fig. 2). Reefs in the upper part of the succession have been dolomitized, but most reefs in the lower half of the Boot Inlet Formation are limestone with excellent preservation of fabrics.

Reefal Elements

Reefs are constructed almost entirely of columnar stromatolites, with a few hemispherical and stratiform stromatolites. Fill between the stromatolite columns consists of lime mudstone, stromaclast-rich lime mudstone, and oolitic and/or muddy rocks similar to that of the inter-reef.

These components combine into the two basic structural elements of the reefs: meter-scale mounds and meter-scale sheets. Either can appear as an isolated element, or be stacked or grouped to form larger and more complex reef types (Fig. 5). Biostromes and concentric-sheet bioherms consist of stacked meter-scale sheets of differing geometries—stratiform for the biostromes and strongly arched for the concentric-sheet bioherms. Patch reefs are formed by stacking the two basic elements, meter-scale mounds overlain by meter-scale sheets. Table reefs consist of several separate concentrations of meter-scale mounds overlain by a single continuous meter-scale sheet (Fig. 5).

Meter-Scale Mounds.—

These consist of decimeter- to meter-scale (average 1 m diameter by 0.5 m high) bushes of branching columnar stromatolites. Individual stromatolite columns are 2–3 cm wide and show highly divergent branching patterns, with numerous inclined and even horizontal columns at the base passing upward into erect, slightly divergent branches (Fig. 6A). Laminae are gently to steeply convex. Among described stromatolites, these

most closely resemble *Tungussia*, particularly *T. erecta* from the Bitter Springs Formation of central Australia (Walter, 1972). Meter-scale mounds occur either as isolated bioherms or in concentrations that form the base of patch and table reefs (Figs. 5, 6A–B).

Meter-Scale Sheets.—

These consist of sheets (average 0.5 m thick) of numerous parallel, erect, columnar stromatolites. Partings between sheets have been enhanced by pressure solution but fundamentally reflect termination of growth of all stromatolites in the underlying sheet and growth of new stromatolite columns in the overlying sheet. Stromatolite sheets are typically flat to domed but become strongly curved, vertical, or even overhanging at the peripheries of the mounds (Fig. 7A). Stromatolite columns throughout the sheet are parallel with each other and can be oriented either vertically or perpendicular to the orientation of the sheet (irrespective of the original horizontal), even in adjacent sheets (Fig. 7B). Orientations of sheets and of individual stromatolites are inconsistent with growth due to trapping and binding loose sediment, and instead imply that the stromatolites grew by precipitation of micrite, as has been inferred for many Proterozoic stromatolites (cf. Donaldson, 1976; Grotzinger, 1989; Grotzinger and Rothman, 1996; Narbonne and James, 1996). Vertical growth of columns is consistent with the hypothesis that light was essential to their growth. Absence of reef-derived blocks from the inter-reef, despite growth of the reefs on a wave- and storm-dominated ramp (see above), implies complete early lithification of the stromatolites during growth.

Two distinctive stromatolite types characterize the meter-scale sheets in different reef-types. Patch reefs, table reefs, and most biostromes consist of "finger-sized" stromatolite columns that expand upward to a maximum width of 2–3 cm (Fig. 7C). Branching is parallel, mainly lateral but including bifurcate and multifurcate styles; lamellae are gently convex to rectangular. These stromatolites closely resemble *Baicalia* in growth form but exhibit streaky rather than distinctly banded microstructure.

Concentric-sheet bioherms and thin biostromes directly overlying sequence boundaries consist of decimeter- to meter-scale sheets of closely spaced, erect, straight, "pencil" stromatolites typically 7–8 mm in diameter (Fig. 7D). Stromatolite columns are unwalled, with bumpy to lobate ornamentation and abundant cornices and bridges between adjacent columns; laminae are steeply convex. Branching is extremely rare and virtually restricted to the top of the uppermost sheet in the mound, where lateral α- and β-style branching occurs. Total column length is difficult to determine because columns commonly pass out of the plane of section but is at least several tens of centimeters and possibly considerably more in some reefal facies. These stromatolites resemble *Jurusania*, particularly *J. nisvensis* from the late Riphean of Siberia and the Bitter Springs Formation of Australia, in exhibiting long, narrow, naked, infrequently branching columns.

These basic building blocks form four different types of buildups: (1) single-mound small bioherms, (2) sheet biostromes, (3) patch reefs and table reefs of multi-mound bioherms and stacked sheets, and (4) large concentric-sheet bioherms (Fig. 5).

FIG. 4.—Aerial views of reefs of the Boot Inlet Formation. (A) Patch reefs (P), table reefs (T), and concentric-sheet bioherm (B), units 2.3 to 3.1. The concentric-sheet bioherm is 60 m in diameter. (B) Elongate domes on top of biostrome in unit 3.7. Domes are approximately 10–25 m wide.

Single-Mound Small Bioherms

Description.—

The smallest buildups are individual meter-scale mounds that occur as isolated small bioherms (Fig. 5). Each mound consists of a decimeter- to meter-scale (average 1 m diameter by 0.5 m high) bush of the stromatolite *Tungussia* and associated lime mudstone between the columns. Meter-scale bioherms are best developed in rhythmites in the basal units of sequence 2. They also occur in rhythmites at the bases of some parasequences in

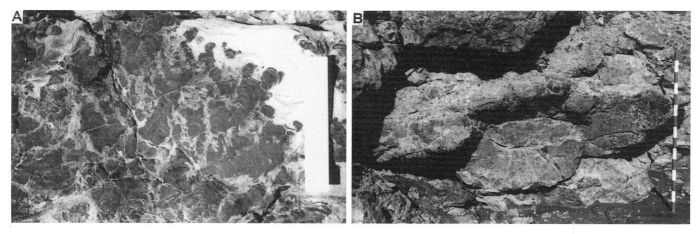

FIG. 5 .—Meter-scale stromatolite mounds. (A) Meter-scale mound consisting of a large head of the stromatolite *Tungussia*. Unit 2.2. 15 cm ruler for scale. (B) Basal patch reef facies consisting of a cluster of meter-scale *Tungussia* mounds. Unit 2.2. Staff is marked in 10 cm increments.

the upper part of sequence 3, but fabric-destructive dolomitization makes it difficult to determine their original composition.

Interpretation.—

These small bioherms, developed in mid-ramp rhythmites immediately above the bases of sequences and parasequences, probably represent transgressive deposits.

Biostromes

Description.—

The mesoscale structure of most biostromes is that of either broad, laterally linked domes or subhorizontal sheets (Fig. 5). The upper surfaces of most are smooth. Biostromes are finite within outcrop of the study area, generally grading laterally into and/or covered by ooid grainstone. At other localities biostromes terminate abruptly, with bioherms at their margins.

Two distinct biostromes are present. A 7–8 m thick biostrome occurs at the top of a parasequence in unit 3.7 (Fig. 2). This biostrome overlies and interfingers at its base with oolitic and rhythmitic carbonates. Upward, it consists entirely of decimeter- to meter-scale sheets of mainly poorly preserved digitate stromatolites similar to *Baicalia*. Stratiform stromatolites commonly encrust the margins of the digitate forms. The top of the biostrome exhibits low elongate domal ridges 10–30 m wide and several tens to hundreds of meters long oriented 065°–080°, normal to structural strike (Fig. 4B).

Thin (10–20 cm thick) biostromes of "pencil" stromatolites (*Jurusania*) immediately overlie sequence boundaries 2, 3, and 4. They are overlain by rhythmitic carbonates and shales interpreted to represent deep mid-ramp or outer-ramp deposits (Fig. 2).

Interpretation.—

These distinct biostrome types appear to have formed at opposite ends of the environmental spectrum. Position at the top of a parasequence, interbedding with oolitic carbonate, evidence for significant wave and/or current action in at least the later stage of biostrome growth, and minor occurrence of stratiform stromatolites all imply that the inner-ramp biostrome rep-

resents the shallowest reef type in the succession. In contrast, the thin biostromes of pencil stromatolites that overlie major sequence boundaries appear to represent deeper-water TST deposits.

Bioherm-Biostrome Complexes: Patch Reefs and Table Reefs

Description.—

Large bioherms occur throughout sequences 1 and 2 and in unit 3.4 of sequence 3 (Fig. 2) and can conceptually be viewed

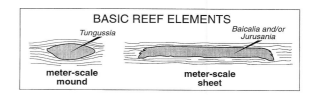

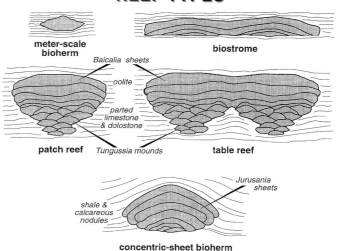

FIG. 6.—Basic elements and types of the stromatolite reefs of the Boot Inlet Formation.

FIG. 7.—Meter-scale stromatolite sheets. (A) Stromatolite sheets on the edge of reef in unit 2.4, illustrating progressive steepening of sheets towards the periphery of the mound. Staff is marked in 10 cm increments. (B) Detail of a sheet in Part A, showing erect digitate stromatolites. 15 cm ruler for scale. (C) Sheet of finger stromatolites *(Baicalia)*, unit 2.4. (D) Sheet of pencil stromatolites *(Jurusania)*, unit 3.1.

as patch reefs. They occur as single patch reefs, linked patch reefs, or in clusters of 10–30 reefs in which the upper facies of adjacent reefs have coalesced to form table-reef complexes (Fig. 4A). The reefs are either reliefs composed of stacked mounds or stacked mounds grading upwards into sheets. All of these reefs occur at the same stratigraphic levels and show similar initial stages and facies successions, and thus can be regarded as parts of a genetic continuum.

Bioherms composed of stacked mounds are 2.5–9 m thick and 7–25 m in diameter. They are subcircular to elliptical in plan view, with no consistent asymmetry. A few patch reefs are hemispherical, but most expand upward (Fig. 8A–C).

Basal patch-reef facies comprise concentrations of meter-scale mounds, in which each mound is a bush of the branching stromatolite *Tungussia* (Fig. 5). Bedded sediment (rhythmite) occurs between the stromatolite heads, and imparts the characteristic knobby appearance to weathered outcrops of this facies (Fig. 6B). The knobby, multi-mound facies generally passes upwards into stacked, meter-scale sheets of the digitate stromatolite *Baicalia* (Figs. 5, 8A–C). Growth of a patch reef on a preexisting reef results in a complex of stacked reefs (Fig. 8D) in which the basal knobby, multi-mound facies is reduced or absent.

Although each of the four levels of patch-reef development is similar in character, some significant differences exist, even along strike, at the same level (Figs. 9–10). Sequence 2 comprises a TST (2.1) with isolated small, meter-scale mounds, and a HST (2.2) of patch reefs grading up into table reefs and oolite. This patch reef to table reef succession is repeated again (2.3), likely the result of smaller-scale sea-level fluctuations and locally capped by a paleokarst unconformity. The upper unit is wholly biostromal (2.4). Patch reefs are developed both in parted dolosiltite and in intraclast-peloid grainstone, reflecting their growth in a variety of subtidal settings. The extent of the biostromes is illustrated by their lateral gradation into thick oolite. Table-reef complexes are as wide as 300 m across, with the margins grading into patch reefs (Fig. 4A).

Patch reefs and table reefs in the HST of Sequence 3 illustrate a similar succession, although here patch reefs are locally developed in quartzose oolite, highlighting their development in a variety of facies (Fig. 11).

Interpretation.—

Patch and table reefs are associated with rhythmite and oolite facies that formed near the inner-ramp to mid-ramp transition (Fig. 3). Stratigraphic relationships suggest that the upward

FIG. 8.—Patch reefs of the Boot Inlet Formation. (A) Patch reef, showing characteristic upward expansion. Reef flanked by rhythmites, with oolite increasing toward the top of the reef. Unit 3.4. Person for scale. (B) Patch reef in rhythmite, with basal meter-scale mound facies passing upward into stromatolite sheet facies, unit 2.2. Staff is marked in 10 cm increments. (C) Patch reef, flanked by rhythmite and overlain by oolite, showing basal meter-scale mound complex and upper stromatolite sheet facies. Unit 3.4. Staff marked in 10 cm increments. (D) Stacked patch reef complexes (center) flanked by oolite on both sides. Unit 2.3. Person for scale.

transition from *Tungussia* mounds to *Baicalia* sheets reflects shoaling during highstand: *Tungussia* mounds occur mainly in the lower parts of sequences and parasequences whereas *Baicalia* sheets occur most commonly immediately below sequence and parasequence boundaries; the transition from mounds to sheets commonly corresponds to a change from muddy to oolitic sediments in the inter-reef. These are interpreted as "catch-up" reefs in the terminology of Neumann and Macintyre (1985).

Tracing of sheets of stromatolites implies that the largest patch and table reefs exhibited at least 3–5 m of topographic relief above the sea floor.

Large Concentric-Sheet Bioherms

Description.—

These are the most spectacular reefs in the Boot Inlet Formation, ranging up to 60 m across. All are nearly perfectly circular in plan view (Figs. 4, 12B). They occur on the top of sequence 2 patch and table reefs, and protrude 8–15 m into the overlying outer-ramp shales at the base of sequence 3 (Figs. 2, 9). The contact between the top of sequence 2 reefs and the base of the concentric-sheet bioherms was not observed.

Basal facies consists of 4–6 m of stacked bushes and aggregates of *Tungussia*, each 1–2 m in diameter, with bedded carbonate between the stromatolite knobs (meter-scale mound facies). This is overlain by the main facies of the concentric-sheet bioherms, which consists of meter-scale sheets of vertical, slender "pencil" stromatolites (*Jurusania*). The contact between these facies is complex—it ranges from gradational (where it can vary laterally even within a single sheet) to abrupt (where sheets of pencil stromatolites have grown down the sides of the concentric-sheet bioherms to envelope *Tungussia* heads).

Tracing of sheets implies that the concentric-sheet bioherms exhibited depositional relief above the sea floor similar to their present topographic relief of 8–15 m. One reef contains a vertical neptunian crack 6 m deep filled with horizontally layered calcareous shale (Fig. 12C–D), but no blocks of reefal detritus were encountered adjacent to any burial mound despite evidence for obvious topographic relief. Where observable, tops of the mounds are slightly corroded and iron stained, reflecting condensation.

Interpretation.—

Concentric-sheet bioherms are considered to be the deepest reef facies in the Boot Inlet Formation, because they are sur-

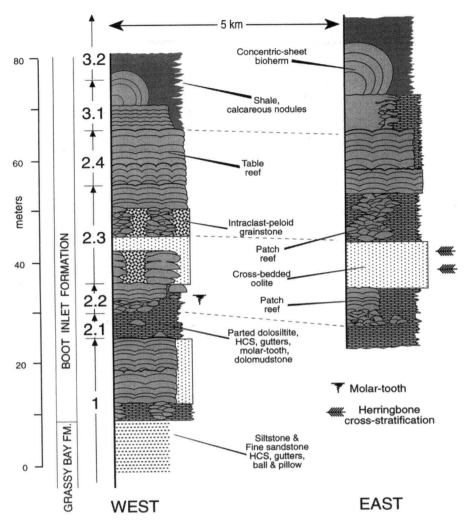

FIG. 9.—Detail of two stratigraphic sections illustrating reef development in the middle part of the Boot Inlet Formation.

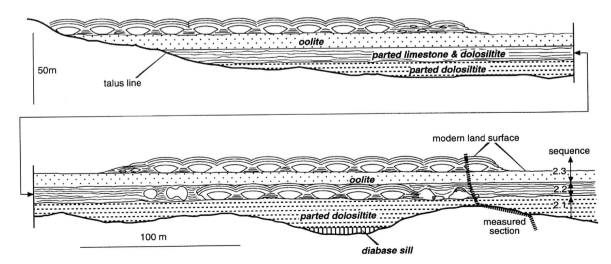

FIG. 10.—A sketch, constructed from photograph mosaics and field sketches, of the lateral distribution of facies in sequence 2. Measured stratigraphic section is the right-hand (eastern) column in Figure 9.

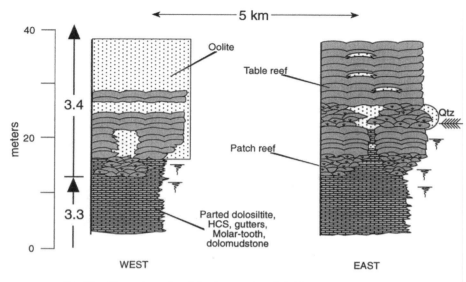

FIG. 11.—Comparison of reef development in unit 3.4 in two sections 5 km apart.

FIG. 12.—Concentric-sheet bioherms, unit 3.1. (A) Side view of the concentric-sheet bioherm in Figure 4A. Person for scale. (B) Top of a small concentric-sheet bioherm approximately 4 m high. (C) Cross section of a concentric-sheet bioherm in shale. Staff is marked in 10 cm increments. (D) Detail of the north side of the mound in "C", showing recumbent sheets near the edge and a neptunian fracture filled with calcareous shale (marked by arrows).

rounded by shale and concretionary shale of the outer ramp (Fig. 3). The concentric-sheet bioherms nucleated on or grew from the tops of sequence 2 reefs during a rapid rise of relative sea level. Growth was quick and localized, resulting in significant depositional relief but also significant constriction of reef diameter relative to the sequence 2 reefs on which they grew. Upward transition from *Tungussia* mounds to *Jurusania* sheets within the concentric-sheet bioherms reflects increasing water depth over the tops of the reefs, implying that the reefs failed to keep pace with rapidly rising sea level. Condensation at the tops of the reefs implies that reef growth was terminated by drowning ("give-up reefs" in the terminology of Neumann and Macintyre, 1985).

COMPARISONS AND PALEOECOLOGY

Proterozoic Comparisons

Although all of the stromatolite types in these early Neoproterozoic (Tonian) reefs range widely, they differ significantly from those that characterize older Mesoproterozoic reefs in northern and arctic Canada (Donaldson, 1976; Kerans and Donaldson, 1988; Narbonne and James, 1996), which are dominated by unbranched cylindrical stromatolites (*Kussiella* and *Colonella* in shallow-water facies; *Conophyton* in deeper-water facies) and stratiform stromatolites. This difference in stromatolite morphology exists despite close similarity in rock types and interpreted paleoenvironments between these Mesoproterozoic and early Neoproterozoic reefs, and serves to emphasize the broad temporal differences in stromatolite morphology that may reflect chemical (Grotzinger, 1989) and/or biological (Serebryakov, 1976) evolution of Proterozoic oceans.

Closer comparisons are possible with early Neoproterozoic stromatolite facies in the Bitter Springs Formation of Australia (Walter, 1972; Southgate, 1989) and the Little Dal Group of northwestern Canada (Turner et al., this volume), which contain most of the stromatolite types present in this study. Even so, the diversity of stromatolite facies in the Boot Inlet Formation is far lower than in either of these areas, key forms such as *Acaciella* apparently are absent, and the size of the individual stromatolite columns is considerably smaller. Significantly, despite intensive search, none of the distinctive calcimicrobial fabrics that characterize the deep-water reefs of the Little Dal Group (Aitken, 1988; Turner et al., 1993, 1997, this volume) have been observed in any of the samples from the Boot Inlet Formation of Victoria Island, nor have they been recorded from the reefs of the approximately coeval Bitter Springs Formation of Australia (Walter, 1972). This may be related to the deeper basinal setting of the Little Dal reefs, whereas the Boot Inlet and Bitter Springs successions were considerably shallower and extended only slightly into the outer ramp.

Paleoproterozoic and Mesoproterozoic reefs typically show a high degree of self-similarity that ranges through at least seven orders of magnitude from centimeter- to meter-scale features of lamination and growth form (Grotzinger and Rothman, 1996) to meter- to kilometer-scale reefal components (Narbonne and James, 1996, their fig. 9). This organization is absent from the early Neoproterozoic reefs of this study, which instead illustrate an organization more typical of Paleozoic, and especially Cambrian, reefs (see below).

Early Neoproterozoic Stromatolites and Sea Level

Studies of modern and fossil reefs have shown that growth of the main reef builders is affected by a multitude of environmental factors, such as temperature, illumination, turbidity, substrate, and nutrient levels. Many of these factors vary systematically with depth, and this has led to recognition of depth-related zonations of reef builders in rocks of Phanerozoic (e.g., Fagerstrom, 1987; James and Bourque, 1992) and Paleoproterozoic–Mesoproterozoic (Grotzinger, 1989, fig. 16) age. There have been fewer studies on conditions controlling the distribution of early Neoproterozoic stromatolites (but see Bertrand-Sarfati and Mousine-Pouchkine, 1988; Southgate, 1989; Sarkar and Bose, 1992; and Turner et al., this volume, for notable exceptions). The combination of reef types and sedimentary facies in the Boot Inlet Formation described above permits evaluation of some of the conditions under which the stromatolites grew.

Water depth and position on the ramp were first-order controls on reef growth and structure (Fig. 3). The current-oriented biostrome grew in the inner ramp, and table reefs and patch reefs grew in the brightly illuminated and relatively high-energy conditions of the transition from inner-ramp to mid-ramp. Concentric-sheet bioherms grew in the deeper, quieter, and presumably darker conditions of the outer ramp. Reefs did not grow well in the mid-ramp, perhaps because of periodic inundation by sediment during storms.

The rate of change in water depth (position in the sea-level cycle) was also critical to the development of reefs. As shown previously, the lower half of the Boot Inlet Formation records several higher-order sea-level cycles superimposed on an overall deepening trend, whereas in the upper half of the formation these sea-level cycles are superimposed on an overall shallowing trend. Reefs are thickest and most abundant in the lower half (especially lower quarter) of the formation, probably because of the greater accommodation space. Reefs are rare and typically thin above the midpoint of sequence 3 and, with the exception of a thin biostrome of pencil stromatolites marking the initial transgression of sequence 4, the meter-scale cycles of the uppermost sequence were too thin to provide sufficient accommodation space for reef growth.

Position in the largest-scale sea-level cycle also affected the shape and vertical development of the reefs. Reefs in the lower half of the formation are subcircular in plan view, reflecting mainly aggradational growth, whereas those in the upper half show a greater degree of progradational growth and current elongation. Multiple stacked meter-scale mounds grew in transgressive and early highstand systems tracts in the lower half of the formation and pass upward into the sheet stromatolites that cap the patch reefs and table reefs. Meter-scale mounds also grew in transgressive deposits at the bases of parasequences in the upper half of the formation (Fig. 2, unit 3.7) but invariably occur as isolated small bioherms, most likely because limited accommodation space did not permit full development of the patch-reef structure.

The combined effects of overall sea level and the rate of sea-level change on reef builders in the Boot Inlet Formation is summarized below:

Pencil Stromatolites (Jurusania).—These grew across the ramp during periods of rapid sea-level rise (especially marking flooding surfaces). Growth was particularly pronounced in outer-ramp settings, where pencil stromatolites seem to have been the only forms that could tolerate the inferred low light levels.

Meter-Scale mounds (Tungussia).—These characterize the inner- to mid-ramp transition zone, particularly during transgression and early highstand.

Smooth Meter-Scale Stromatolite Sheets (Baicalia).—These characterize the inner- to mid-ramp transition zone, especially during late highstand.

Current-Oriented Meter-Scale Stromatolite Sheets (Baicalia?).—The single occurrence of this structure is in late highstand deposits of the inner ramp.

Phanerozoic Comparisons

Phanerozoic reefs, because they are constructed by a skeletal metazoan–calcified algae/microbe consortium (James and Bourque, 1992), are not directly comparable to Proterozoic buildups. This is particularly so in this case, where Boot Inlet reefs are constructed solely by stromatolites, with no evidence of thrombolites or calcimicrobes. Thus, on a microscale they lack growth cavities, which allow for the accumulation of internal sediment, growth of coelobites, and abundant precipitation of synsedimentary cements. Instead the spaces between stromatolite digits is occupied by laminated lime mudstone or fragments of the stromatolites (stromaclasts). Yet, on a mesoscale and macroscale there are important similarities with Phanerozoic buildups.

The most striking is the meter-scale mound as a building block for bioherms. Most Early Cambrian reefs, although composed of calcimicrobes and archaeocyaths, are really aggregations of meter-scale mounds (James and Kobluk, 1978; James and Gravestock, 1990; Wood et al., 1993; Kruse et al., 1995). Such mounds are called "kalyptra" (Rowland and Gangloff, 1988) or just mounds (James and Kobluk, 1978). The Neoproterozoic seems to mark the first appearance of such structures, although wholly stromatolitic, and might reflect the first aggregation of a complex microbial reef-building consortia.

At the mesoscale, patch reefs and table reefs also have attributes similar to early Paleozoic structures in inner-ramp to mid-ramp settings where oolite was abundant. The transition upwards in shallowing successions from patch reefs to table reefs is exhibited in the metazoan–microbial Early Cambrian reefs of Labrador (James and Hiscott, 1982) and Middle Cambrian stromatolite–thrombolite reefs of the Appalachian Orogen (Kennard et al., 1988).

The deeper-water concentric-sheet bioherms, however, aside from their shape, have no obvious Phanerozoic analogs. Their composition, however, as a series of stacked concentric sheets is similar to that of modern deep-water lithoherms in the Straits of Florida (Neumann et al., 1977), composed of deep-water azooxanthellate corals and cemented sediment.

SUMMARY AND CONCLUSIONS

1. Early Neoproterozoic (Tonian) reefs of the Boot Inlet Formation, now exposed in the Minto Inlier on Victoria Island, grew in a storm-dominated carbonate ramp setting. Outer-ramp shales pass into mid-ramp parted dolosiltites, which in turn pass landward into inner-ramp shallow ooid shoals and leeward muddy lagoons.

2. The 500 m-thick Boot Inlet Formation is divisible into four stratigraphic sequences, reflecting lateral facies shifts in response to sea-level fluctuation and changes in carbonate-factory dynamics.

3. Reefs are built by meter-scale mounds and sheets generally composed of branching columnar stromatolites. Stacked meter-scale mounds of *Tungussia* are capped by concentric sheets of *Baicalia*, forming patch reefs and table reefs that typically reflect shallowing from mid-ramp to inner-ramp environments during sea-level highstand. Stacked concentric sheets of delicate "pencil" stromatolites (*Jurusania*) constituted large, deep-water reefs during early stages of sea-level rise.

4. The Boot Inlet reefs are typical of shallow-water Proterozoic reefs, especially those of the early Neoproterozoic Bitter Springs Formation of Australia, in their size, position in the reef spectrum, and stromatolitic composition. The development of meter-scale knobs in the lower facies of the Boot Inlet reefs has not previously been described from older Proterozoic reefs, but is similar and possibly ancestral to the "kalyptra" that characterize Cambrian and younger calcimicrobial–metazoan reefs.

ACKNOWLEDGMENTS

This research is funded by the Natural Sciences and Engineering Council of Canada (GMN and NPJ) and the Geological Survey of Canada (RHR and JM), with logistical support by the Polar Continental Shelf Project. We thank M.R. Walter, W.V. Preiss, and K. Grey for advice on stromatolite terminology and discussions about Proterozoic paleobiology, and C.W. Jefferson, G.M. Ross, E.C. Turner, and D. Winston for constructive reviews of the manuscript. This is Geological Survey of Canada (GSC) contribution number 1998264.

REFERENCES

AITKEN, J. D., 1981, Stratigraphy and sedimentology of the Upper Proterozoic Little Dal Group, Mackenzie Mountains, Northwest Territories, *in* Campbell, F. H. A., ed., Proterozoic Basins of Canada: Geological Survey of Canada, Paper 81-10, p. 47–71.

AITKEN, J. D., 1988, Giant "algal" reefs, middle/upper Proterozoic Little Dal Group (>770, <1200 Ma), Mackenzie Mountains, N.W.T., Canada, *in* Geldsetzer, H. H. J., James, N. P., and Tebbutt, G. E., eds., Reefs, Canada and Adjacent Areas: Canadian Society of Petroleum Geologists, Memoir 13, p. 13–23.

AITKEN, J. D., LONG, D. G. F., AND SEMIKHATOV, M. A., 1978, Correlation of Helikian strata, Mackenzie Mountains–Brock Inlier–Victoria Island: Geological Survey of Canada, Paper 78-1A, p. 485–486.

BERTRAND-SARFATI, J., AND MOUSSINE-POUCHKINE, A., 1988, Is cratonic sedimentation consistent with available models? An example from the Upper Proterozoic of the West African craton: Sedimentary Geology, v. 58, p. 255–276.

BURCHETTE, T. P., AND WRIGHT, V. P., 1992, Carbonate ramp depositional systems: Sedimentary Geology, v. 79, p. 3–58.

DONALDSON, J. A., 1976, Paleoecology of *Conophyton* and associated stromatolites in the Precambrian Dismal Lakes and Rae Groups, *in* Walter, M. R., ed., Amsterdam, Elsevier, Stromatolites: Developments in Sedimentology, v. 20, p. 523–534.

FAGERSTROM, J. A., 1987, The Evolution of Reef Communities: New York, Wiley. 592 p.

GREY, K., 1989, Handbook for the study of stromatolites (second draft): Stromatolite Newsletter, v. 14, p. 82–171.

GROTZINGER, J. P., 1989, Facies and evolution of Precambrian carbonate depositional systems: The emergence of the modern platform archetype, *in* Crevello, P. D.,Wilson, J. L., Sarg, J. F., and Read, J. F., eds., Controls on Carbonate Platform and Basin Development: SEPM, Special Publication 44, p. 79–106.

GROTZINGER, J. P., AND ROTHMAN, D. H., 1996, An abiotic model for stromatolite morphogenesis: Nature, v. 383, p. 423–425.

HEAMAN, L. M., LECHEMINANT, A. N., AND RAINBIRD, R. H., 1992, Nature and timing of Franklin igneous events, Canada: implications for a late Proterozoic mantle plume and the break-up of Laurentia: Earth and Planetary Science Letters, v. 109, 117–131.

JAMES, N. P., AND KOBLUK, D. R., 1978, Cambrian patch reefs and associated sediments, southern Labrador: Sedimentology, v. 25, p. 1–35.

JAMES, N. P., AND HISCOTT, R. N., 1982, Lower Cambrian bioherms and sandstones, southern Labrador: International Association of Sedimentologists, Congress, Hamilton, Ontario, Field Excursion 1A, 34 p.

JAMES, N. P., AND GRAVESTOCK, D. I., 1990, Lower Cambrian shelf and shelf margin buildups, Flinders Ranges, South Australia: Sedimentology, v. 37, p. 455–480.

JAMES, N. P., AND BOURQUE, P.-A., 1992, Reefs and mounds, in Walker, R.G., and James, N.P., eds., Facies Models: Response to Sea Level Change: St. John's, Newfoundland, Geological Association of Canada, p. 323–347.

JAMES, N. P., NARBONNE, G. M., AND SHERMAN, A. G., 1998, Molar-tooth carbonates: shallow subtidal facies of the Mid- to Late Proterozoic: Journal of Sedimentary Research, v. 68, p. 716–722.

JEFFERSON, C. W., AND YOUNG, G. M., 1988, Late Proterozoic orange-weathering stromatolite biostrome, western Mackenzie Mountains and Arctic Canada, in Geldsetzer, H. H. J., James, N. P., and Tebbutt, G. E., eds. Reefs, Canada and Adjacent Areas: Canadian Society of Petroleum Geologists, Memoir 13, p. 72–80.

KENNARD, J. M., CHOW, N., AND JAMES, N. P., 1988, Thrombolite–stromatolite bioherm, Middle Cambrian, Port-au-Port Peninsula, western Newfoundland. in Geldsetzer, H. H. J, James, N. P., and Tebbutt, G. E. eds. Reefs, Canada and Adjacent Areas; Canadian Society of Petroleum Geologists, Memoir 13, p. 151–155.

KERANS, C., AND DONALDSON, J. A., 1988, Deepwater conical stromatolite reef, Sulky Formation (Dismal Lakes Group), Middle Proterozoic, N.W.T. in Geldsetzer, H. H. J, James, N. P., and Tebbutt, G. E. eds. Reefs, Canada and Adjacent Areas; Canadian Society of Petroleum Geologists, Memoir 13, p. 81–88.

KRUSE, P. D., ZHURAVLEV, A. YU., AND JAMES, N. P., 1995, Primordial metazoan–calcimicrobial reefs: Tommotian (Early Cambrian) of the Siberian platform: Palaios, v. 10, p. 291–321.

MORIN, J., AND RAINBIRD, R. H., 1993, Sedimentology and sequence stratigraphy of the Neoproterozoic Reynolds Point Formation, Minto Inlier, Victoria Island, Northwest Territories: Geological Survey of Canada, Paper 93-1C, p. 7–18.

NARBONNE, G. M., AND JAMES, N. P., 1996, Mesoproterozoic deep-water reefs from Borden Peninsula, Arctic Canada: Sedimentology, v. 43, p. 827–848.

NEUMANN, A. C., KOFOED, J. W., AND KELLER, G. H., 1977, Lithoherms in the Straits of Florida: Geology, v. 5, p. 4–10.

NEUMANN, A. C., AND MACINTYRE, I. G., 1985, Reef response to sealevel rise: keep-up, catch-up or give-up: 5th International Coral Reef Symposium, Tahiti, Proceedings, v. 3, p. 105–110.

RAINBIRD, R. H., JEFFERSON, C. W., HILDEBRAND, R. S, AND WORTH, J. K., 1994a, The Shaler Supergroup and revision of Neoproterozoic stratigraphy in Amundsen Basin, Northwest Territories: Geological Survey of Canada, Paper 94-C, p. 61–70.

RAINBIRD, R. H., HODGSON, D. A., DARCH, W., AND LUSTWERK, R., 1994b, Bedrock and surficial geology of northeast Minto Inlier, Victoria Island, District of Franklin, Northwest Territories: Geological Survey of Canda, Open File 2781, scale 1:50,000.

RAINBIRD, R. H., JEFFERSON, C. W., AND YOUNG. G. M., 1996, The Early Neoproterozoic sedimentary succession B of northwestern Laurentia: Correlations and paleogeographic significance: Geological Society of America, Bulletin, v. 108, p. 454–470.

RAINBIRD, R. H., MCNICOLL, V. J., THÉRIAULT, R. J., HEAMAN, L. M., ABBOTT, J. G., LONG, D. G. F., AND THORKELSON, D. J., 1997, Pan-continental river system draining Grenville Orogen recorded by U–Pb and Sm–Nd geochronology of Neoproterozoic quartzarenites and mudrocks, northwestern Canada: Journal of Geology, v. 105, p. 1–18.

READ, J. F., 1985, Carbonate platform facies models: American Association of Petroleum Geologists, Bulletin, v. 69, p. 1–21.

ROWLAND, S. M., 1988, Structure and paleoecology of Lower Cambrian reefs: Palaios, v. 3, p. 111–135.

SARKAR, S., AND BOSE, P. K., 1992, Variations in Late Proterozoic stromatolites over a transition from basin plain to nearshore subtidal zone: Precambrian Research, v. 56, p. 139–157.

SEREBRYAKOV, S. N., 1976, Biotic and abiotic factors controlling the morphology of Riphean stromatolites, in Walter, M.R., ed., Amsterdam, Elsevier, Stromatolites: Developments in Sedimentology, v. 20, p. 321–336.

SOUTHGATE, P. N., 1989, Relationships between cyclicity and stromatolite form in the Proterozoic Bitter Springs Formation, Australia: Sedimentology, v. 36, p. 323–339.

THORSTEINSSON, R., AND TOZER, E. T., 1962, Banks, Victoria, and Stefansson Islands, Arctic Archipelago: Geological Survey of Canada, Memoir 330, 85 p.

TURNER, E. C., NARBONNE, G. M., AND JAMES, N. P., 1993, Neoproterozoic reef microstructures from the Little Dal Group, northwestern Canada: Geology, v. 21, p. 259–262.

TURNER, E. C., JAMES, N. P., AND NARBONNE, G. M., 1997, Growth dynamics of Neoproterozoic calcimicrobial reefs, Mackenzie Mountains, Northwest Canada: Journal of Sedimentary Research, v. 67, p. 437–450.

TURNER, E. C., NARBONNE, G. M., AND JAMES, N. P., in press, Framework composition of Early Neoproterozoic reefs and associated microbialites, Mackenzie Mountains, N.W.T., this volume.

WALTER, M. R., 1972, Stromatolites and the biostratigraphy of the Australian Precambrian and Cambrian: Palaeontological Association [London], Special Papers in Palaeontology, v. 11, 190 p.

WOOD, R. A., ZHURAVLEV, A. YU., AND CHIMED TSEREN, A., 1993, The ecology of Lower Cambrian buildups from Zuune Arts Mongolia: Implications for early metazoan evolution: Sedimentology, v. 40, p. 829–858.

YOUNG, G. M., 1981, The Amundsen Embayment, Northwest Territories: Relevance to the Upper Proterozic evolution of North America, in Campbell, F. H. A., ed., Proterozoic Basins of Canada: Geological Survey of Canada, Paper 81-10, p. 203–218.

YOUNG, G. M., AND LONG, D. G. F., 1977a, Carbonate sedimentation in a Late Precambrian shelf sea, Victoria Island, Canadian Arctic Archipelago: Journal of Sedimentary Petrology, v. 47, p. 943–955.

YOUNG, G. M., AND LONG, D. G. F., 1977b, A tide-influenced delta complex in the Upper Proterozoic Shaler Group, Victoria Island, Canada: Canadian Journal of Earth Sciences, v. 14, p. 2246–2261.

FRAMEWORK COMPOSITION OF EARLY NEOPROTEROZOIC CALCIMICROBIAL REEFS AND ASSOCIATED MICROBIALITES, MACKENZIE MOUNTAINS, N.W.T., CANADA

ELIZABETH C. TURNER, GUY M. NARBONNE, AND NOEL P. JAMES
Department of Geological Sciences, Queen's University, Kingston, Ontario, K7L 3N6, Canada

ABSTRACT: Giant reefs of the early Neoproterozoic Little Dal Group, Mackenzie Mountains, N.W.T., Canada, differ from most previously described Proterozoic buildups in containing a calcimicrobial and thrombolitic framework. Systematic vertical changes in composition permit the identification of five framework stages. Each stage contains a persistent community of calcimicrobes, yet the expression of element morphologies throughout the reefs is exceedingly varied, indicating that environment exerted the predominant control over framework attributes.

Framework development is correlated with extrinsic paleoenvironmental controls, namely change in relative sea level. Deepest-water intervals are characterized by accretion of dense, layered crusts (Stage IV), intermediate water depths are reflected by intricately anastomosing, morphologically diverse framework elements (Stages I and III), and shallowing on reef tops is expressed as thin successions of erect, well-ordered, columnar microbialites (Stages II and V).

Reef growth occurred in low- to moderate-energy regimes, within the photic zone, on hard substrates, and in the absence of significant settling of carbonate or terrigenous mud. The growth window is interpreted to have been delimited by the base of the photic zone at depth, and by excessive fragmentation near the water surface. Optimal growth occurred in moderate water depths, between fair-weather wave base and a limit determined by light attenuation at depth.

The Little Dal reefs record a major inflection point in the development of reefal ecosystems: although they display a combination of attributes from both Proterozoic and Paleozoic reef ecosystems, there is a preponderance of Phanerozoic-style features, including mineralized reef-building organisms, complex framework complete with growth cavities containing internal sediment and synsedimentary cement, vertical and lateral framework zonation, and large-scale accretion style that varies with relative-sea-level change. They are therefore the earliest known representatives of "modern"-style reef growth.

INTRODUCTION

Of all sedimentary deposits in the geologic record, reefs are among the most complex and the most informative. Fossil reefs built by calcareous algae and metazoans, like those growing in modern seas, are extensively documented and reasonably well understood (Fagerstrom, 1987; Geldsetzer et al., 1989; James and Bourque, 1992). The published record of ancestral reefs in the Archean and Proterozoic is, by comparison, minimal (Twenhofel, 1919; Bertrand-Sarfati, 1972; Hoffman, 1974; Cecile and Campbell, 1978; Beukes, 1987; Geldsetzer et al., 1989; Grotzinger, 1989a,1989b; Narbonne and James, 1996), and thus the origin and early evolution of this important marine ecosystem remain obscure.

Although buildups with the attributes of living reefs are found in earliest Cambrian rocks (James and Kobluk, 1979; Riding and Zhuravlev, 1995; Kruse et al., 1995), recent studies suggest that the "modern" reef prototype might have developed much earlier, in Neoproterozoic time (Turner et al., 1993, 1997a, 1997b; Saylor et al., 1995; Narbonne and James, 1996). Examples of this primordial reef ecosystem are especially well developed in the early Neoproterozoic Little Dal Group of northwestern Canada (Aitken, 1981, 1989). These reefs, built by microbes, but bearing all of the hallmarks of "modern" reef accretion style, provide a snapshot of the origin of complex framework and reef zonation. The purpose of this study is to describe the range of framework elements present, delineate their distribution throughout the reefs, integrate this with the history of reef growth and off-reef stratigraphy, and compare the framework types and framework stratigraphy to those of buildups from the Proterozoic and Phanerozoic. Detailed description and interpretation of microfabric and microstructure composition and preservation are the topic of a contribution to follow.

LOCATION, AGE, AND GEOLOGIC SETTING

Gigantic (ca. 400 m thick) early Neoproterozoic reefs occur in the unmetamorphosed Little Dal Group (<1083 Ma; >779 Ma; Heaman et al., 1992; Rainbird et al., 1996), a succession of carbonate, terrigenous clastic, and evaporitic rocks in the Mackenzie Mountains Supergroup, Northwest Territories, Canada (Figs. 1, 2, 3; Aitken, 1981, 1989). Reefs occur in strata that accumulated on the flat floor of an epicratonic basin at low latitude (Park, 1981; Aitken, 1981), some 100 to 200 km outboard of thick platform carbonates. They are underlain by cross-stratified oncoid packstones of the mudcracked formation (synaeresis cracks), overlain by the oolitic, intraclastic grainstone formation, and extend through the shale and lime mudstone of the basinal assemblage into the lowermost grainstone formation (Fig. 2).

Reefal framestone is constructed by calcimicrobes dominated by a filamentous form resembling Paleozoic *Girvanella*, and lesser numbers of a form resembling *Renalcis* (see Turner et al., 1993, for high-magnification photomicrographs of the calcimicrobes). The reefal framework is biogenic (in that it was formed by microbes), nonskeletal (dominated by non-enzymatic carbonate secretion), and partly chemical (synsedimentary cement volumetrically important in microfabric), and could thus be considered, texturally and compositionally, as a form of tufa (*sensu* Hofmann, 1973, fig. 5), although no relation to present-day tufa-forming environments is implied.

Buildups nucleated during transgression and died during shallowing at the end of deposition of the basinal assemblage (Turner et al., 1997a). Shale-dominated intervals in the mainly sub–storm wave base basinal strata reflect times of continuously rising relative sea level, whereas carbonate-mud-rich intervals are interpreted to reflect somewhat elevated paleo-salinities and enhanced precipitation of pelagic carbonate mud at times when relative-sea-level rise abated. This gives rise to four gradational shale-to-carbonate packages in the basinal assemblage (Fig. 4). Reefs aggraded or contracted during deposition of terrigenous mud on the basin floor, but prograded and shed talus during intervals of inter-reef pelagic carbonate deposition.

METHODS AND TERMS

These buildups conform to criteria defining "reefs" (e.g., Geldsetzer and James, 1989; James and Bourque, 1992; Webb,

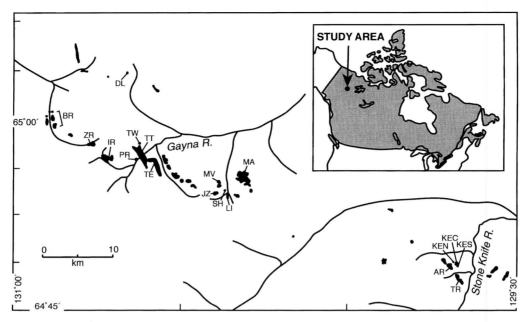

FIG. 1.—Location of Little Dal reef exposures (black). Reef abbreviations: AR = Apocryphal Reef; BR = Brouillard Reef; DL = Disneyland Reef; IR = Intrepid Reef; JZ = Jezebel Reef; KEC = Knife Edge Central Reef; KEN = Knife Edge North Reef; KES = Knife Edge South Reef; LI = Lilith Reef; MA = Medusa Reef; MV = Medb Reef; PR = Propitious Reef; SH = Sorhed Reef; TE = Table East Reef; TR = Tawuia Reef; TT = Table Top Reef; TW = Table West Reef; ZR = Zuviel Reef.

1996): (1) they existed in turbulent to quiescent conditions, and thrived in moderate-energy settings; (2) they were constructed in part by organisms; (3) they had syndepositional relief; (4) they were syndepositionally rigid. They cannot be reconciled with definitions of "mounds" ("built by smaller, commonly delicate and/or solitary elements in tranquil settings"; James and Bourque, 1992), or with those of mud mounds (e.g., Bosence and Bridges, 1995; Pratt, 1995), because they contain virtually no mud.

Reef framework distribution is described in "stages", closely corresponding to, but not identical to, reef-scale growth phases (Fig. 4) identified by Turner et al. (1997a). Framework composition was identified whenever possible in the field. Outcrop, however, is generally so "opaque" that field determination in many areas was not possible. In such areas, reefs were extensively sampled and framework composition determined from polished slabs and thin sections (Table 1). The nature of Stage III in particular was determined by cluster sampling throughout the reef core, where groups of ca. 20 samples were taken from areas 20 to 30 m², separated by 10 to 20 m of combined vertical and lateral distance; locations within the massive, gullied reef outcrops were recorded using photographs and an altimeter, permitting crude lateral and vertical comparison of the reef facies.

The extreme irregularity of many framework elements, and the lack of distinctive, reliable morphological characteristics defining end members, hamper adequate description of these structures. Wherever justifiable, however, the stromatolite description terminology of Grey (1989) has been used.

The term "framework" refers to the centimeter-scale structures that make up reef rocks at the hand sample to outcrop scale: stromatolitic, thrombolitic, and calcimicrobial categories

are recognized. The term "calcimicrobialite", as a subset of "microbialite" *sensu* Burne and Moore (1987), is used to encompass frameworks (including "porostromate" microstructure of Pia, 1927) that are composed predominantly of calcareous microfossils attributable to microbes ("calcimicrobes", *sensu* James and Gravestock, 1990). "Lamelliform" and "dendriform" framework elements are described by Aitken (1989) for stratiform and columnar microbialites having microfabrics not typical of stromatolites. "Fabric" refers to the microscopic internal structure of framework elements. "Laminar-reticulate fabric" is a microscopic calcimicrobial texture comprising diffuse alternating laminae of felted prostrate calcimicrobial filaments, and loosely packed, randomly to erectly oriented filaments (Turner et al., 1993), of which most reef framework elements are constructed. The term "ordering", as applied to framework, designates the degree of predictability in element morphology and distribution pattern.

All formation-rank stratigraphic divisions are informal and used as by Aitken (1981).

REEF ARCHITECTURE

Spatial association of stromatolite bioherms in the uppermost, oncolitic member of the mudcracked formation with lowest exposed reef rocks at two localities (Table 1) suggests that such topographic irregularities served as reef nucleation sites (Figs. 4, 5). Exposures of lowest reef rocks (Stage I), which are of talus margins rather than *in situ* reef core, are 20–30 m thick, and correspond to accumulation of basinal member 1 shale. A regional stromatolite biostrome is the carbonate part of basinal member 1: consisting of club-shaped bioherms 2 m thick in inter-reef areas, it occurs as layers up to 15 m thick adjacent to

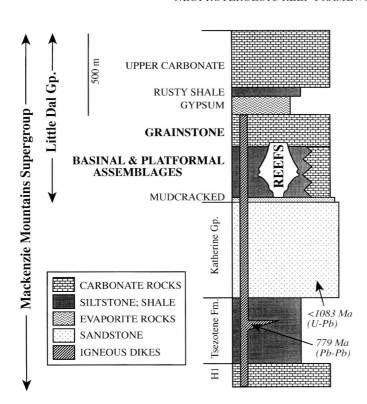

FIG. 2.—Generalized stratigraphic section for the Mackenzie Mountains Supergroup showing informal stratigraphic names (Aitken, 1981) for Little Dal Group, and radiometric dates from Heaman et al. (1992) and Rainbird et al. (1996). Reef growth interval extended from top of the mudcracked formation to partway into the grainstone formation.

FIG. 3.—Exhumed reefs of the Stone Knife River area: Tawuia Reef (TR), Apocryphal Reef (AR), and the Knife Edge Reefs (KEC, KES). Reef exposures are approximately 300 m high; distance from margin of TR in left foreground to KES is 2.5 km.

reefs. Stage II reef core corresponds to the upper part of the biostrome. It is ca. 15 m thick, and its margins are coated with layers of reef-flanking microbialites. Basinal members 2 and 3 correspond to gradual progradation and talus shedding at reef margins; equivalent core facies (Stage III; 150–200 m thick) are not stratigraphically differentiated. Basinal member 4 shale correlates to areal shrinkage of reef facies and a gradational but pronounced change in framework composition (Stage IV; 150–200 m thick). Member 4 carbonate grades upward into oolites of the overlying grainstone formation; the transitional interval

corresponds to reef framework Stage V (ca. 15 m), parts of which expand over reef-flanking sedimentary units (Figs. 4, 5). All changes in reef-core framework are gradational, except that separating Stages IV and V.

Links between off-reef, reef-margin, and core facies are provided by: (1) intercalation of Stage I talus boulders with basinal member 1 shale and with lower layers of the stromatolite biostrome; (2) presence of quartz sand and silt in (a) intercolumn sediments of the stromatolite biostrome, (b) thin layers in basinal strata of lowermost member 2, and (c) framework cavities

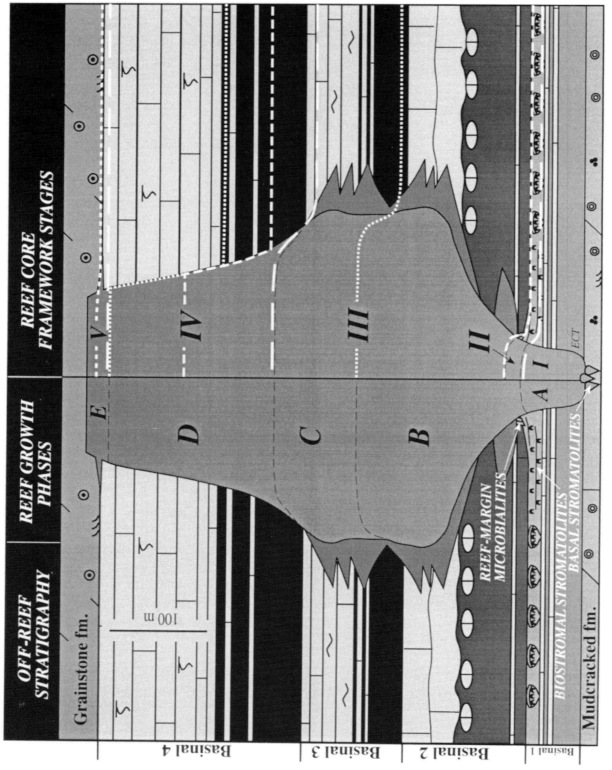

Fig. 4.—Relation of off-reef stratigraphy, reef growth phases, and reef-core-framework stages. Interpretive time lines (white) on right. Growth phases are in general linked to variation in framework facies, but not all events interpreted from reef external geometry are detected in framework composition. Basinal members 2 and 3 together probably record a single, subtle shallowing progression containing a smaller-scale carbonate-dominated interval (member 3). Details of basinal stratigraphy and sedimentology can be found in Turner et al. (1997a).

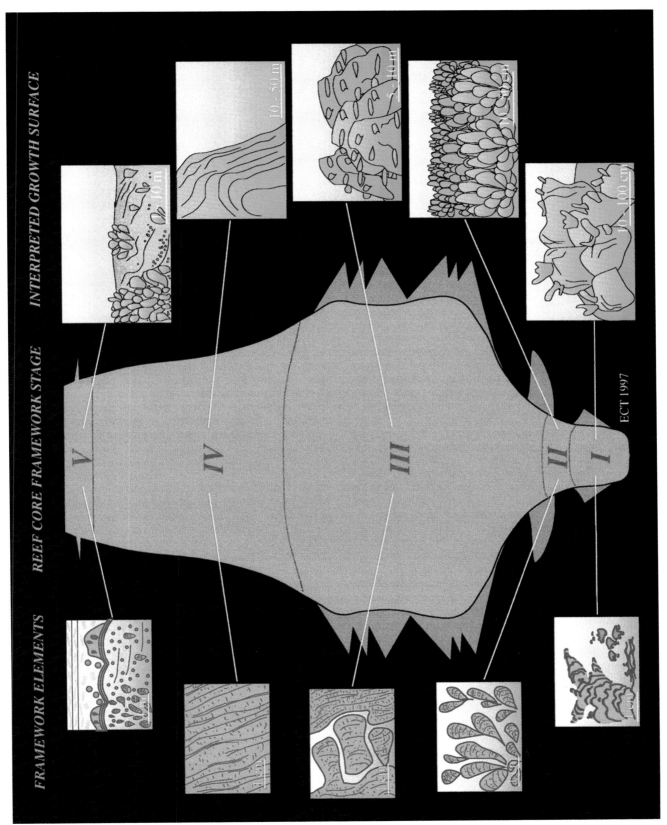

FIG. 5.—Reef-core-framework stages and interpretations of the active growth surfaces during each stage.

TABLE 1.—DATA SOURCES FOR FRAMEWORK IDENTIFICATION

Reef Core or Microbialite Stage	Reefs Examined	Samples Collected for Framework Identification	Field Exposure
V	**TT IR PR** ZR TE BR	(Identified in field; samples collected for corroboration and illustration.)	Good exposure at many creek-incised reef tops; also available in cores drilled for base metal exploration and abandoned in the field.
IV	**TT**	(Identified in field; samples collected for corroboration and illustration.)	Good exposure in water-washed canyons.
III	**MV** KEC	320(MV) + 85 (KEC)	Immense, lichen-covered pinnacles that rarely expose reef framework; transition to Stage IV exposed at MV.
II	**MV**	(Identified in field; samples collected for corroboration and illustration.)	Partially dolomitized; small extent.
I	**DL MV** MA KEN	38	Typically dolomized. Known exposures are of talus margins; samples provide framework of original position higher in Stage I reef core.
Reef Talus and Reef-Flank Sediment	**KEC** MV	119 (KEC) + 14 (MV) (Lower Phase B) 66 (KEC) Upper Phase B	Extensive bouldery flanks surround reefs exhumed to mid-levels; relations to off-reef strata locally exposed.
In Situ Reef-Margin Facies	**MV KEC**	(Identified in field; samples collected for corroboration and illustration.)	Limited field exposure; lack of geopetal structures prohibits certain distinction of *in situ* lamelliform framework from talus.
Reef-Margin Stromatolites	**KES MV DL** KEN JZ SH	(Identified in field; samples collected for corroboration and illustration.)	Limited exposure owing to small original extent of this stage.
Reef-Nucleating Stromatolite	**MV** MA	(Identified in field; samples collected for corroboration and illustration.)	Rubbly dolomitized outcrop <15 m below lowest reef rocks.

Reef abbreviations in bold print indicate main data source for framework identification; plain text indicates source of corroborative evidence.

of Stage II and lowermost Stage III, as compared to its dearth elsewhere in basinal and reefal rocks; (3) intercalation of talus wedges and off-reef strata, most notably in carbonate parts of members 2 and 3; and (4) off-reef expansion of parts of Stage V into strata of the basinal assemblage–grainstone formation transitional interval.

REEF CORE FACIES

Stage I—Diverse Calcimicrobial–Thrombolitic Framework

A variety of poorly ordered centimeter- to decimeter-scale framework components (Table 2; Fig. 6) includes elaborate, intergrown crustose (Fig. 6A), incipiently columnar (Fig. 6B, D), and thrombolitic (Fig. 6B, E) elements. Crustose structures arch gently on a decimeter scale (Fig. 6A); quasi-columnar elements are 1 to 3 cm in diameter (Fig. 6B, D). Microfabric is predominantly discontinuous, streaky micritic laminae and micritic clots, with local areas of filamentous calcimicrobial (Fig. 6C) fabric passing gradationally in all directions to the more obscure micritic fabric (Fig. 6B). Growth cavities are abundant, comparatively large (up to 2 cm), have complex morphologies, and are filled mainly by lime mudstone containing grumous to clotted textures suggestive of microbial influence (Fig. 6E). Cavity fills preserving geopetal indicators formed prior to redeposition as talus, indicating that synsedimentary cementation of cavity-filling lime mud by finely crystalline carbonate took place. Most cement in the pores is late-stage blocky calcite. This facies is characterized by: (1) wide variety and poor organization of mesoscopic framework elements; (2) predominance of clots and tufted micritic laminae rather than extensive calcimicrobial fabric; (3) delicacy and complexity of crusts and clots; (4) abundance of muddy interstitial sediment and paucity of cement; and (5) comparative dearth of fibrous marine cements.

Centimeter- to decimeter-scale structures indicate a loosely packed, porous framework. Framework ordering is poor: element shape is variable, and distribution is weakly organized.

Active growth surfaces would have been brittle, crustose, and porous irregular knobs of decimeter to meter scale, with a variety of irregular centimeter-scale digits, stratiform crusts, and bumps (Fig. 5). The active growth surface was at a depth above storm wave base, and was probably on the order of 10 meters above the surrounding flat sea floor, judging by the thickness of the equivalent off-reef succession (ca. 40 m), size of reef-margin talus boulders (meter-scale), and vertical extent of steep stromatolite biostrome layers at reef margins.

Stage II—Columnar Calcimicrobialite

In situ Stage II reef rock extends both up above Stage I outcrop (vertical thickness ca. 15 m) and out over the top of the regional stromatolite biostrome. Closely spaced, erratically branching small columns, locally defining decimeter-scale bushes, are 0.3–1 cm in diameter, up to 3–4 cm long, and vertical to slightly inclined (Fig. 7A, B; Table 2). Enveloping lamination is gently convex and consists of interlayered laminar-reticulate (i.e., calcimicrobial; Fig. 7D) and micritic laminae (Fig. 7C). Lamination is commonly asymmetric about the column axis: this orients the central, flattish part of laminae outward in inclined columns and in columns near bush margins. Growth cavities, filled with geopetal lime mudstone, local concentrations of quartz silt, and small amounts of fibrous cement (Fig. 7C), form an open honeycomb-like network among the columns. This framework type, with its well-defined and erect small columns and bush-like grouping of columns, is distinct from all other stages.

Framework is denser than that of Stage I, with more regularly dispersed voids between columns. The well-defined columns, loosely organized into bush-like patches, result in a comparatively well-ordered framework. Active growth surfaces were above storm wave base, and are envisaged as decimeter–scale shrubs of digitate columns giving rise to local reef-top topography on the scale of centimeters to decimeters (Fig. 5). Relief above the surrounding basin floor was probably on the order of

TABLE 2.—FRAMEWORK COMPOSITION OF LITTLE DAL REEFS

Framework or Stromatolite Stage	Dominant Framework Types	Fabric	Distribution	Associated Sediment	Framework Cavities	Internal Sediment	Cavity-Filling Cement
VIII	Erect columnar stromatolites	Muddy laminae	On apices of domal stromatolites	Oncoids, muddy intraclasts, molar tooth microspar clasts	(no framework cavities *sensu stricto*)	—	—
VII	Domal stromatolites	Spar–micrite couplets	Veneer over reef tops	Stromatolite intraclasts; giant oncoids	(no framework cavities *sensu stricto*)	—	—
VI	Erect columns	Calcimicrobial with trapped/bound cortoids	Meadows with oncoid/intraclast sheets	Calcimicrobial intraclasts, oncoids, catagraphs	(no framework cavities *sensu stricto*)	—	—
IV	Steeply encrusting layers ("lamelliform")	Calcimicrobial	Steep layers (45–75°) (dam–hm scale)	Rare lime mudstone	Few; isolated	Very rare; peloidal to muddy	Thick isopachous fibrous synsedimtary cement
III	Crustiform, nodular, and columnar; orientation variable	Calcimicrobial	Irregular knobs and shrubs (m–dam scale)	Lime mudstone; rare calcimicrobial intraclast grainstone	Irregular; commonly elongate parallel to element axis	Lime mudstone with rare quartz silt	Thick isopachous fibrous synsedimtary cement
II	Erect branching columns	Calcimicrobial	Bush-like clusters (dm scale)	Intraclast floatstone with quartz silt, sand	Honeycomb network of elongate voids	Lime mudstone with quartz silt and sand, intraclasts	Thick isopachous fibrous synsedimtary cement
I	Crustiform, columnar, and thrombolitic; orientation variable	Micritic laminae and clots; locally calcimicrobial	Irregular knobs and shrubs (m scale)	(unknown)	Irregular; abundant	Lime mudstone with quartz silt	Thick isopachous fibrous synsedimtary cement
Reef-Margin Microbialites	Columnar stromatolites, perpendicular to substrate	Micritic; weakly laminated	Steep to vertical layers encrusting reef margins	—	Honeycomb network of elongate voids	Intercolumn lime mudstone with quartz silt	Thick isopachous fibrous synsedimtary cement
Biostromal Stromatolites	Erect branching columnar stromatolites	Streaky micritic laminae	Biostrome of bioherms; stacked layers near reefs	Microbialite intraclast floatstone with quartz sand	(no framework cavities)	—	—
Sub-Reef Stromatolites	Erect branching columnar stromatolites	Weak micritic laminae	Clusters of bioherms; within oncolite member of Mudcracked fm	Quartz sandy oncolite with phosphatic clasts	(no framework cavities)	—	—

10 meters, judging from meter-scale size of equivalent talus boulders and vertical extent of individual layers within reef-margin encrusting microbialite facies.

Stage III—Diverse, Anastomosing Calcimicrobial Framework

Stage III begins approximately 15 m above the stromatolite biostrome (Table 2). Framework consists of an extreme variety of highly irregular, anastomosing, nodular, columnar, and crustose masses, most of which are gradational between columnar and lamelliform (*sensu* Aitken 1989), here arbitrarily divided into groups for the purpose of description (Fig. 8). All elements except thrombolites are composed of laminar-reticulate fabric (Fig. 8G), and many are encrusted by clotted to weakly layered micrite.

Dendriform Elements.—

Dendriform elements (Fig. 8A; Aitken, 1989) are columnar structures that anastomose irregularly, and have equant to oblate cross sections 0.5 to 1.5 cm in diameter. Axes are vertical to prostrate and locally slightly drooping, although inclined to prostrate orientations are most characteristic. Column length between branching is <1 cm to 3 cm, with exceptional unbranched prostrate columns extending for up to 20 cm. Laminar-reticulate fabric has gently to steeply convex lamination (Fig. 8E) and is variably enveloping. Element margins are smooth to ragged, depending on the degree of development of micritic clots (Fig. 8E). Inclined to prostrate elements are asymmetric: laminae envelop element margins more completely on the underside, and micritic selvages and clusters of clots are thickest on downward-facing element margins (Turner et al., 1993).

Dendriform elements occur throughout Stage III, but are most common and best-developed in lower Stage III (associated with the transition from Stage II to Stage III). They are also more abundant towards the margins of lower Stage III, such that they are common in the talus boulders at lower Stage III reef margins (just above the stromatolite biostrome). These observations suggest that dendriform elements grew best where reef margins were actively prograding and where space for element growth and cluster expansion was to be found laterally as well as vertically, such as at bush or reef margins.

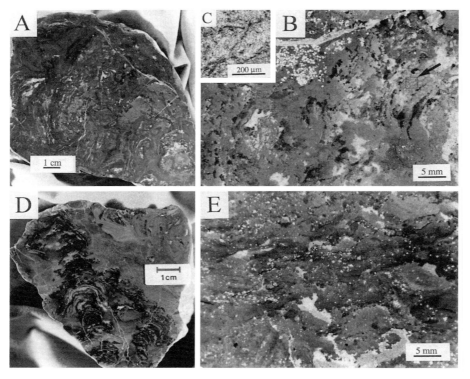

FIG. 6.—Framework types of reef Stage I. A) Polished slab of crustose framework of arched micritic laminae (dark). Note large volume of framework porosity filled with internal sediment (light gray). White areas contain both synsedimentary and late-stage cements. B) Thrombolitic and calcimicrobial fabric of arborescent framework element. Note grumous to clotted appearance of cavity-filling mud, and quartz sand in geopetal cavity fills. Same sample as (A). C) Filamentous calcimicrobes from boxed area in (B). D) Polished slab of irregular columnar framework element with ragged margins and significant, lime-mudstone-filled porosity. Microfabric is calcimicrobial with intercalated micritic laminae. E) Thrombolitic framework (dark gray clots) with grumous to micritic internal sediment (light gray) and cavity-filling cement (white). Larger white particles are diagenetic dolomite rhombs; smaller white particles are detrital quartz silt in sediment that fills framework pores. (A) and (D), polished slabs. (B), (C), and (E), thin-section photomicrographs in PPL. Samples from DL Stage I reef talus; samples are presented in presumed growth orientation, as derived from geopetal structures.

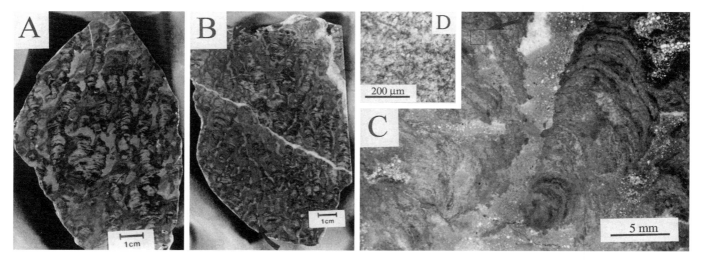

FIG. 7.—Oriented samples of Stage II reef core framework. A) Erect, sub-centimeter-scale columnar framework elements that branch erratically. Framework porosity is high. Column cores are dolomitized. B) Arrangement of columnar elements into irregular bushes; confluence of two bush margins is arrowed. C) Calcimicrobial composition of Stage II columnar framework elements. Note asymmetry of enveloping lamination, lack of micritic encrustations on column margins, presence of quartz silt in internal carbonate mudstone, and small geopetal structures. D) Filamentous calcimicrobes from boxed area in (C). (A) and (B), polished slabs. (C) and (D), thin-section photomicrographs in PPL. Samples from MV.

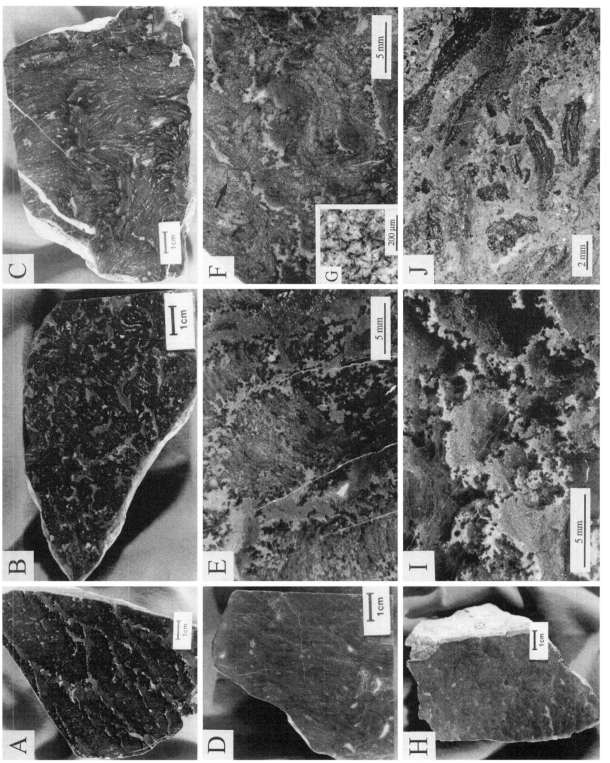

FIG. 8.—Oriented samples of selected framework types from Stage III reef cores. All but (H) and (I) are of calcimicrobial composition. A) Oblique, anastomosing dendriform elements. B) Oblique, anastomosing quasi-dendriform elements. (A) and (B) contain a high degree of framework porosity filled by geopetal lime mudstone and fibrous cements. C) Sideways-growing massive framework. D) Lamelliform elements. (C) and (D) contain lower volumes of framework porosity than the anastomosing framework types. E) Dendriform elements showing column core of laminar-reticulate fabric, with apical and marginal clusters of *Renalcis*-like micritic clots. F) Oblique to prostrate, irregularly nodular, anastomosing framework. G) Filamentous calcimicrobes from boxed area in (F). H, I) thrombolite framework elements. Note high degree of framework porosity, and geopetal structures. J) Reef-framework-clast rudstone with synsedimentary fibrous cement. (A)–(D), (H), polished slabs; (E)–(G), (I), (J), thin section photomicrographs in PPL. (A), (E)–(I) from KEC; (B)–(D), (J) from MV.

Quasi-Dendriform Elements.—

This group of structures (Fig. 8B) grades into dendriform elements, but members have one or more of the following distinctive characteristics: (1) more frequent anastomosing, such that proper columns never develop; (2) frequent coalescence to form massive bodies rather than well-defined columns; (3) greater widths than those typical for dendriform elements (to 2–3 cm), such that the elements resemble stout pillars; (4) lamination that ends abruptly at element margins without enveloping them; (5) lack of thick micritic selvages or clot encrustations that commonly define dendriform element margins; or (6) close packing of elements. These structures also grade into nodular and lamelliform types (below). They occur throughout Stage III; those that resemble broad columns of lamelliform elements, or interrupted lamelliform elements, are most abundant in uppermost Stage III.

Nodular to Massive Elements.—

These are common, lumpy to amorphous masses of calcimicrobial composition. Where significant framework porosity is present, the elements anastomose irregularly and resemble (a) centimeter-scale irregular nodules (Fig. 8F) or (b) irregular, platy crusts. Irregular nodules are a poorly ordered end member of the anastomosing framework types; platy crusts resemble contorted lamelliform elements. Where framework porosity is low, the framework is dense, > centimeter-scale masses of laminar-reticulate fabric with undulatory, irregularly oriented laminae (Fig. 8C). Lamination is usually weakly convex toward the growth direction, and partly enveloping to abruptly truncated at element margins (Fig. 8F).

Lamelliform Elements.—

Lamelliform elements (Aitken, 1989; Turner et al., 1993) are extensive layers of laminar-reticulate fabric up to tens of meters in extent. Lamelliform elements in Stage III are quite difficult to identify, even in hand sample, because of a homogeneous appearance that does not display the lamination evident in thin section (Fig. 8D). Orientation ranges from horizontal to vertical, with steeply inclined layers dominant. Lamelliform elements are found in close association with areas of other element types, suggesting that they encrust the margins of irregular masses of other growth forms (cf. Aitken, 1989), although there are no well-defined lamelliform-encrusted bioherms. Areas of lamelliform elements are increasingly abundant towards the top of Stage III.

Thrombolites and Clot-Dominated Framework.—

Entirely thrombolitic framework is rare. Where present, it consists of irregularly lobate to pendent, anastomosing micritic thromboids (Fig. 8H, I) 0.1 to 5 mm across, with profusely clotted margins. Grumous, prostrate thrombolitic framework from these reefs was described in Aitken and Narbonne (1989).

Areas of framework comprising exclusively sub-millimeter-scale clot-like structures analogous to *Renalcis* are likewise uncommon, but form diffuse to dense irregular clusters which grade in structure and size into the thromboids. Clusters and layers of renalcid clots encrust fracture surfaces and overhanging to partly enclosed areas on the margins of laminar-reticulate cored elements, or form nucleation sites for dendriform elements (Fig. 8E).

Framework cavities are not as abundant as in Stages I and II. They occur where elements are columnar to equant, and in framework dominated by clotted elements or thrombolites, or having clotted selvages on elements. They are filled with marine cement, commonly with minor geopetal lime mudstone. Walls of framework cavities are locally impregnated by phosphate or iron prior to precipitation of marine cements. Locally, areas of equant to columnar framework have calcimicrobial clasts in inter-element spaces.

Reef-surface sediment is moderately common. Sediment pockets, most of which are on a centimeter to decimeter scale are filled with lime mudstone that locally appears microbially bound or peloidal, and may contain millimeter-size clasts of calcimicrobial framestone. Some depressions contain millimeter- to centimeter-scale abraded calcimicrobialite intraclasts (Fig. 8J). Small fractures filled with sediment and cement crosscut *in situ* framework, but large-scale disruption, fragmentation, or rotation of reef-core areas is rare.

Stage III framework is moderately dense, and displays poor ordering because of its wide variety of irregular element shapes. Well-organized megascopic structures are absent, and the growth surface was probably composed of steep-sided dekameter-scale knobs with irregular to lumpy surfaces at a centimeter scale (Fig. 5); knobs would have had smoother surfaces in later parts of Stage III, as lamelliform elements began to dominate the structures. Synoptic relief of reef tops was probably on the order of several tens of meters to 100 meters, judging by vertical relief of tens of meters expressed in weak layering of sloping reef-margin talus deposits. Stage III, like Stage I, is distinctive because of its wide variety of irregular element morphologies, but it differs from Stage I because of the different framework types, denser structure, better preservation of calcimicrobes, and abundance of marine cements.

Stage IV—Lamelliform-Dominated Framework

Transition to this facies is gradational over tens of meters and is complete in reef core ca. 20–30 m higher than the last large talus wedge. This facies consists overwhelmingly of lamelliform elements (Table 2; Figs 9, 10; Aitken, 1989) made of laminae of filamentous calcimicrobes (Fig. 10D). Anastomosing structures are exceedingly rare, as are pockets of reef-surface detrital sediment. Mapping of lamelliform elements at outcrop scale some 140 m stratigraphically below one reef top and ca. 200 m inward from its reef margin (Fig. 9) shows this area to have been composed of steeply dipping (avg. 45° to 70°) layers of lamelliform elements, which encrusted one another over lateral distances of at least 100 m [in original orientation, prior to Laramide (Cretaceous to Tertiary) deformation; Figs. 9, 10A, B]. The orientation of the bulk of these encrustations is within 45° of the trend of the nearest reef margin (Fig. 9).

In two localities (ZR and PR–TT; Fig. 11), uppermost Stage IV outcrops are separated by several hundred meters of off-reef strata. In light of the contraction of reef margins through Stage IV, it is unlikely that these closely spaced exposures represent reefs that were independent throughout their entire growth history; instead, they probably indicate local partitioning and shrinkage of originally continuous reef growth surfaces into isolated bodies toward the end of Stage IV.

Microfabric is planar laminar-reticulate (Fig. 10C) and defines the steep encrustation orientation visible in outcrop. True

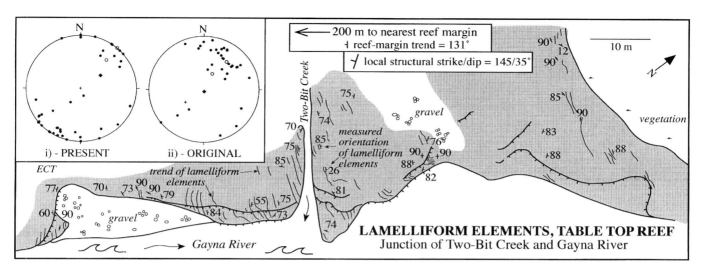

FIG. 9.—A map of the NW side of the Gayna River at TT, ca. 140 m stratigraphically below reef top, showing present-day orientation of lamelliform-dominated reef framework elements in Stage IV. Over the 100 m breadth of the exposure mapped, the outcrop trend of lamelliform elements is strikingly consistent. Stereonet (i) shows poles to a) measured orientation of lamelliform elements figured on map (dots); b) range of possible reef margin orientations (apparent dip between 60° and 90° (not directly measurable in outcrop; open circles); c) regional dip (diamond); and d) present-day horizontal (cross). When regional dip is removed, [stereonet (ii)] to show original orientation of lamelliform elements and reef margin before Laramide deformation, lamelliform elements are shown to have dipped steeply to the SW, i.e., toward the nearest reef margin.

framework cavities are scarce, irregular in shape, and filled with fibrous synsedimentary cements. Most cement-filled areas are millimeter-scale ovoid voids within the laminar-reticulate fabric, probably the result of gas bubbles in the microbial mat. Micro-unconformities within the laminar-reticulate fabric illustrate that millimeter- to centimeter-scale erosion subparallel to the lamination was followed by accretion of new encrusting layers.

Framework is dense and ordering is high, with only one element type, and highly predictable distribution. The few framework cavities present are not connected to one another. Outcrop-scale features indicate that megascopic structures must have been of 10 to 100 m scale and steep-sided, but are insufficient to determine the geometry and extent of these growth surfaces. Growth surfaces probably consisted of steep undulatory slopes or pinnacles, with local centimeter- to decimeter-scale knobs and protuberances (Fig. 5). Synoptic relief probably reached a maximum of ca. 100 meters, interpreted from calculated vertical extent (many tens of meters) of steeply dipping lamelliform layers, and from geometric correlation of interpreted deep-water facies in reef (lamelliform) and off-reef (basinal member 4 shale) settings.

Stage V—Columnar Calcimicrobialite, Stromatolite, and Oncoid Gravel

Terminal reef growth is characterized by a ca. 15 m thick succession of layered microbial facies markedly different from those in the stages below (Table 2; Figs. 11, 12). The contact with Stage IV is not well exposed, but in drillcore abruptly truncated lamelliform elements are overlain by intraclast–oncoid gravel and calcimicrobialite columns of Stage VI, interspersed with either large fragments of lamelliform framework or local regrowth of lamelliform framework (Fig. 11). Contacts among Stage V subunits are sharp but conformable, although

minor evidence of meteoric diagenesis in the form of dissolutional voids occurs locally.

Stage VI—Columnar Calcimicrobialite.—

This unit of robust columnar calcimicrobialites and oncolite–intraclast gravels is approximately 10 m thick (Figs. 11, 12B, C, E). Columns (2–3 cm wide, <10 cm long) are vertical, branch infrequently, and have strongly convex enveloping lamination consisting of laminar-reticulate fabric (Figs. 12C, D). They start at different levels, and are locally broken and toppled.

Column microfabric gradually changes upward to muddy, grumous, and peloidal lamination, with roughly the same column dimensions and morphology. Intraclast gravel with interparticle fibrous marine cement fills intercolumn spaces and is present as bedded strata between calcimicrobialite thickets. Allochems develop oncolitic cortices upwards through this stage.

This stage differs from columnar calcimicrobialite of Stage II in its larger column size, grainy associated sediments, partly muddy internal composition, and lack of true framebuilding.

Stage VII—Cement-Rich Stromatolite.—

This 2–4 m thick stromatolite unit consists of 1–3 m diameter low domes. Laminae are thick (1–3 mm) cement-rich grumous layers alternating with thin films (ca. 100 μm) of micrite (spar-micrite couplets) (Figs. 11, 12E, F, G). Laminae are even and regular, and show a high degree of inheritance. No calcimicrobes are present. Stromatolites are locally interlayered with and overlain by stromaclast rudstone; such clasts are locally recoated by stromatolite laminae, forming large oncoids (up to 6 cm diameter), or serve as nucleation sites for new stromatolite growth.

Stage VIII—Stromatolite–Intraclast.—

Cement-rich stromatolites are overlain by ca. 1 m of muddy-laminated columnar stromatolite (Stage VIII; Figs. 11, 12E, H,

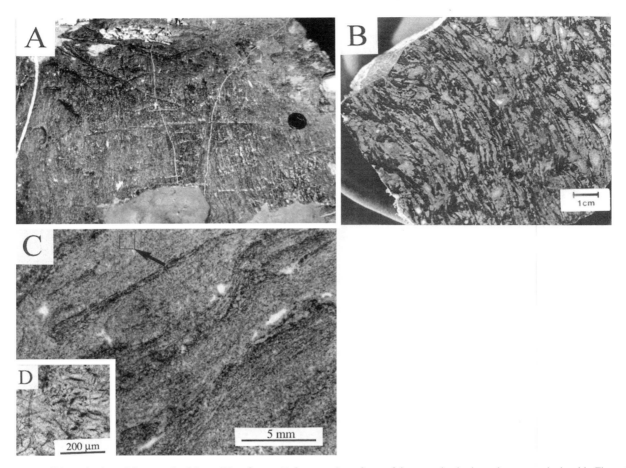

FIG. 10.—Lamelliform-dominated framework of Stage IV reef core. A) Outcrop view of part of the extensive horizontal exposure depicted in Figure 9. Note consistency of orientation. Lens cap 50 cm wide. B) Oriented, polished slab of lamelliform elements. Darker layers have denser accumulations of calcimicrobial filaments, whereas lighter areas are more cement-rich. C) Laminar-reticulate fabric of lamelliform framework elements, in growth orientation. Darker laminae have a denser population of calcimicrobial filaments than lighter, cement-rich laminae. Note paucity of framework cavities. D) Filamentous calcimicrobes from boxed area in (C). (C) and (D), thin-section photomicrographs in PPL. Samples from TT.

I, J) in uniform beds, or as bioherms atop stromatolite domes, with allochem accumulations between columns and bioherms. Microbialite intraclasts and flanking oncoid rudstones are interspersed upwards with tabular intraclasts of composition similar to that of molar-tooth crack fill (Fig. 12I; Furniss et al., 1998). Some localities exhibit yet a third, lenticular muddy-laminated columnar stromatolite facies (<0.5 m) with abundant tabular clasts and ooids. Above these facies are a succession of tabular intraclast rudstones to wackestones that pass upwards after 2–5 m to ooid-intraclast grainstones of the grainstone formation (Fig. 11).

Stage V microbialites have been documented within off-reef strata of the basinal assemblage–grainstone formation transition in the vicinity of some reef tops, locally with continuous exposure from reef to off-reef (Figs. 11, 12A). The peri-reefal microbialites vary slightly in stratigraphic position (on the order of meters), and thin away from reefs. At one location (Fig. 11), a prograded microbialite layer links two upper Stage IV outcrops that are separated by an expanse of basinal strata. The off-reef microbialites are usually dolomitized, and lack the abundant intraclastic and oncolitic intercolumn accumulations of reef-top microbialite. Domal stromatolites of Stage VII in

reef-top flanking strata locally display asymmetric dome shape, as if they accreted on a slight slope (Fig. 11).

Increments of Stage V are distinguished from all other phases of reef growth by: (1) robustness of framework elements; (2) well-organized framework; (3) distinct stratigraphic divisions; and (4) intimate association and interfingering with coarse-grained shallow-water deposits.

True framework is not present in Stage V. Throughout Stage V, a significant proportion of the rock volume is occupied by allochem grainstones and rudstones. Ordering of the microbialite structures is high, with elements of distinct morphology occurring in a predictable pattern within each of the Stage V increments. The reef-top growth surface during Stages VI and VIII would have consisted of thickets to meadows of microbial digits with intervening sheets and shoals of microbial intraclasts and oncoids; local relief was probably on the order of centimeters (Fig. 5). During the cement-rich stromatolite increment (Stage VII), a continuous biostromal veneer of domal structures with decimeter- to meter-scale relief was present across reef tops. Elevation of the reef tops above surrounding basinal areas was still significant enough (probably at least a few meters) to limit the lateral extent of reef-top facies, but was low enough

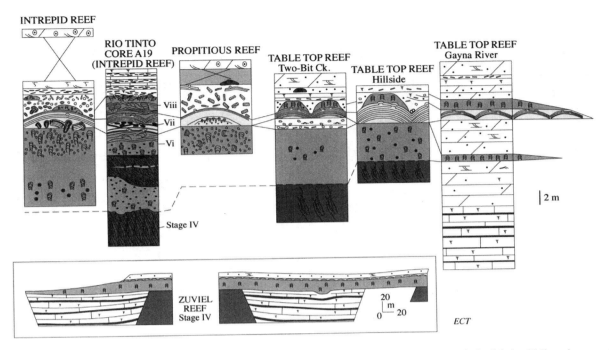

FIG. 11.—Distribution of Stage V facies across reef tops and adjacent off-reef settings. Stage VI is *in situ* or reworked calcimicrobialite columns and oncoid/intraclast rudstones; Stage VII is a uniform veneer of domal stromatolites; Stage VIII is developed on reef tops as patches of microbialite separated by accumulations of intraclasts and oncoids. All three stages are present locally as expansions into off-reef strata adjacent to reef tops. Prograded microbialite links tops of two upper Stage IV outcrops separated by an expanse of basinal strata.

that these facies could at times spread to immediately surrounding off-reef areas. Lack of intercolumn grainy accumulations in peri-reefal microbialite reflects slightly deeper conditions beyond the reef flanks.

REEF-RELATED MICROBIALITE FACIES

Basal Stromatolites

Clusters of closely packed meter-scale ellipsoid to upward-expanding cone-shaped bioherms are several tens of meters wide and up to 9 m thick, and have relief of several meters above the top of the surrounding draped oncolite beds (Tables 1, 2; Fig. 13A). Bioherms are founded on intraclastic dolo-packstone within the oncolite member. Sediment between bioherms and columns is quartzose dolostone with phosphatic clasts. Bioherms consist of vertical to inclined, erratically branching stromatolites (cf. *Baicalia*) (Fig. 13B), 1–2 cm in diameter, and up to 8 cm high, with spacing of approximately 0.5 cm. Laminae are gently convex, commonly with slight asymmetry in inclined columns, which exaggerates the upward-facing part of each lamina. Lamina microstructure consists of irregular bands and lenses of dark and light carbonate mud (Fig. 13C).

Reef-Flanking Microbialites

Stage II reef growth is accompanied by flanking stromatolites. The off-reef stromatolite biostrome, regionally consisting of 2-m-high club-shaped bioherms (Fig. 13D) of columnar stromatolites (Fig. 13E, F), thickens near reefs (within 100 m) to a

15-m-thick layer of bedded stromatolite columns (cf. *Baicalia, Inzeria, Acaciella*) (Table 2, Figs. 13G, H, I, 14); see also Aitken et al. (1978). Within several tens of meters of reef margins, it is expressed as domes and steeply arched to encrusting, sloped layers intercalated with isolated reef talus boulders or wedges of talus boulders (Fig. 14). Layer steepness increases upwards and towards reef margins. Lower layers of columnar stromatolites >1 cm wide (Fig. 13G, H) pass upward into layers of smaller, centimeter-wide stromatolites (Fig. 13I). Uppermost layers adhere to vertical reef core walls, and consist of a range of columnar (< centimeter scale) to stratiform stromatolites with diffuse layers of a weakly laminated to clotted micritic fabric (Figs. 14, 15). Stratiform stromatoids are roughly parallel to layer orientation (Fig. 15A, B); columnar stromatolites are perpendicular to layered increments, and show variable degrees of asymmetry in both column shape and lamina disposition (Fig. 15C–F). Some nearly vertical layers grade, over several vertical meters, from lower stratiform to upper columnar composition. Locally, the columnar stromatolites of these reef-encrusting layers become successively larger outwards. Sediment between columns is quartzose intraclastic wackestone to lime mudstone. Cement fills the remaining space in small geopetal structures within stratiform microbialites and shelter pores beneath inclined columns.

Reef Talus

Reef talus is abundant at reef margins of Stages I through III, and is particularly voluminous where associated with: (1) the flanking stromatolite biostrome of basal member 1; (2) lower basal member 2; and (3) carbonate parts of basinal

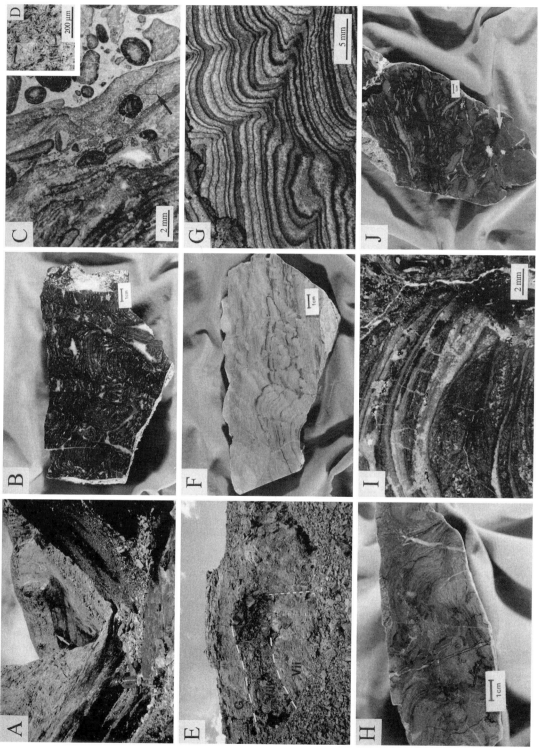

FIG. 12.—Outcrop photos and oriented samples of microbialite types from Stage V. A) Expansion of Stage VI microbialite (arrow) over basinal strata at reef tops. Photo taken looking outward from upper reef margin in an incised canyon. A bioherm is embedded within the expanded microbialite wedge. Laramide faulting brings the peri-reefal microbialite down on the left. B) Robust columnar calcimicrobialite of Stage VI with intercolumn calcimicrobialite clasts. C) Stage VI calcimicrobialite columns are locally walled by enveloping laminar-reticulate fabric. Note variety of intercolumn allochem types, and allochems incorporated into the microbialite body. Interparticle spaces are filled with synsedimentary fibrous cement. D) Filamentous calcimicrobes from boxed area in (C). E) Outcrop view of terminal reef stages: cement-rich domal stromatolites of Stage VII are conformably overlain by muddy stromatolites and flanking oncoid–intraclast accumulations of Stage VIII, followed by grainstone formation strata. Pole 1.5 m long. F) Part of a domal stromatolite from Stage VII, showing regularity of lamination. G) Spar–micrite couplets from the even lamination of the Stage VII stromatolites. Dark micritic laminae are thin, whereas sparry laminae are thicker, and commonly have peloidal texture. H) Muddy-laminated stromatolites of Stage VIII, with intraclast accumulations between columns. I) Lamination of Stage VIII stromatolite is irregular and texture is muddy to peloidal. Column margins are ragged, and intercolumn accumulations consist of intraclasts and oncoids. J) End of reef growth occurs where the Stage VIII muddy stromatolite unit is overlain by thin tabular intraclasts. Arrow indicates lightly iron-encrusted, but not significantly eroded, uppermost surface of Stage VIII stromatolite columns. (B), (F), (H), and (J), are oriented, polished slabs. (C), (D), (G), and (I) are thin-section photomicrographs in PPL. (A) from ZR; (B), (E), (I), (J) from TT; (C), (G) from IR outcrop.

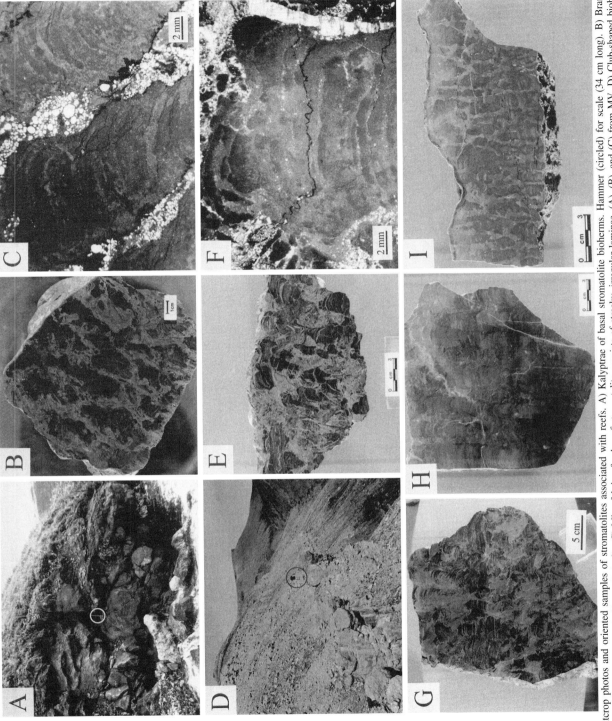

Fig. 13.—Outcrop photos and oriented samples of stromatolites associated with reefs. A) Kalyptrae of basal stromatolite bioherms. Hammer (circled) for scale (34 cm long). B) Branching columnar stromatolites of basal stromatolite, similar to *Baicalia*. C) Microfabric of sub-reef stromatolite consists of streaky, irregular laminae. (A), (B), and (C) from MV. D) Club-shaped bioherms of off-reef stromatolite biostrome (basinal member 1). Person (circled) atop stromatolite. E) Columnar stromatolites typical of the biostrome in the off-reef setting. F) Microfabric of biostromal stromatolites is irregularly, streakily laminated. (D), (E), and (F) from section approximately 300 m west of KEC and KES. G) Branching, columnar stromatolites from the lower part of the biostrome where it thickens in the vicinity of reefs. H) Unbranched, columnar stromatolites from the middle of the stromatolite biostrome near a reef. I) Smaller, dolomitized columns (cf. *Acaciella*) typical of the upper part of the stromatolite biostrome near reefs. (G), (H), and (I) from KEN; (B), (E), (G)–(I), polished slabs; (C), (F), thin-section photomicrographs in PPL.

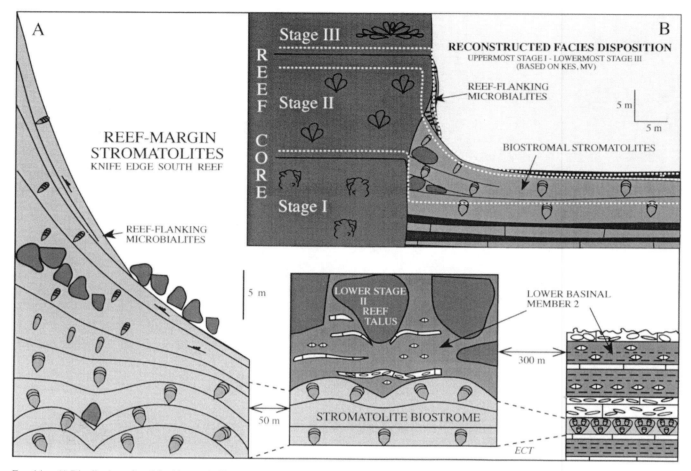

FIG. 14.—A) Distribution of reef-flanking and off-reef microbialites at KES. B) Reconstructed reef margin for uppermost Stage I to lowermost Stage III, with interpreted time lines (white) showing coeval reefal and off-reef facies (based on MV and KES).

members 2 and 3 (Table 2, Figs. 4, 16A). Composition and size of these clasts is as follows: (1) clasts immediately below and intercalated with layers of the stromatolite biostrome are of meter scale and are made of framework identical to that of Stage I and II reef core; (2) clasts at lower reef margins (above the stromatolite biostrome) are up to 10 m in diameter and identical in composition to lower reef core Stage III; (3) clasts at mid-reef margins are of 1 to 10 meter scale and consist of framework identical to that of reef core Stage III. Significant amounts of talus are not present at upper reef margins (Stages IV and V). In keeping with what is understood from growth dynamics (Turner et al. 1997a), this is because Stage IV represents high-relief aggradational growth with no opportunity for progradation, whereas facies of the low relief Stage V reef top were able to expand laterally without creating gravitationally unstable margins.

Geopetal cavity fillings in talus boulders record the orientation of framework prior to fragmentation and redeposition. Internal sediments are identical in composition and volume to those of analogous cavities of core facies. Fracturing in rocks now found in reef cores is scarce, but in talus boulders, sharply defined fractures encrusted by regrowth of similar or different fabrics developed prior to redeposition (Fig. 16A). No con-

vincing evidence for subaerial exposure or meteoric alteration is present in talus blocks. Well-ordered, originally erect columnar framework types like those of Stages II and IV are not present in any talus associated with mid-reef margins. These observations, together with the absence of erect columnar microbialite facies in Stage III, suggest that shallowing in Stage III was never pronounced enough to cause exposure or significant change in microbialite facies.

Reef-Margin Facies

Evidence for lateral variation of *in situ* framework is present at some stages of reef growth (Table 2, Fig. 16B). Talus-littered margins of lower Stage III contain significant volumes of lamelliform-dominated framework. Although the dearth of framework cavities and internal sediment in lamelliform framework renders it impossible to demonstrate that these reef-marginal lamelliform-dominated bodies are not talus clasts, the absence of extensive areas of such framework in lower and middle Stage III suggests that these areas represent *in situ* encrustations on reef flanks and talus boulders adjacent to, and topographically below, the active growth surface of the central reef core. Mid-reef talus margins of upper Stage III do not display these lamelliform encrustations.

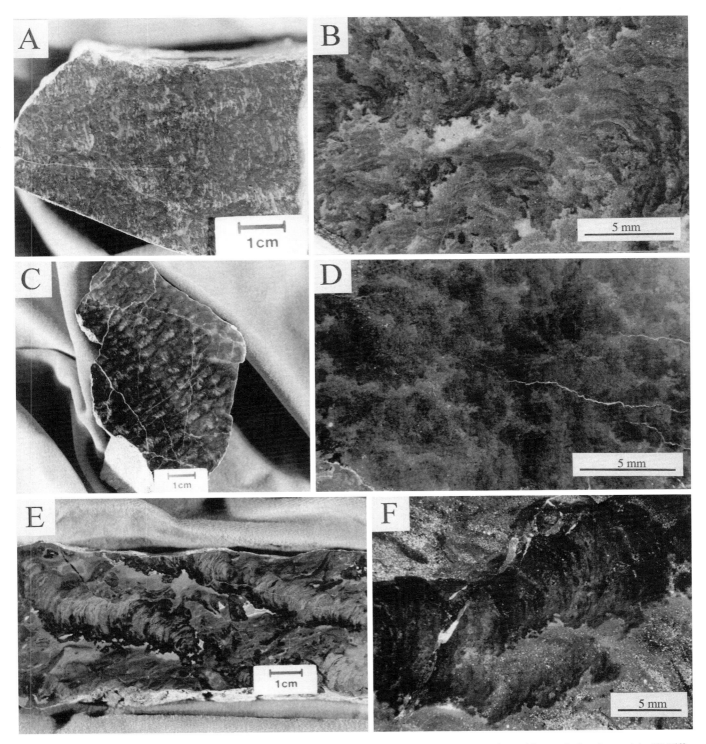

FIG. 15.—Oriented samples of microbialites adhering to margins of Stage II reef core. A) Filigreed encrustations with growth direction to right. B) Diffuse fabric of encrusting stromatolite such as in (A). C, D) Small oblique columns of encrusting microbialite. Internal fabric is micritic and poorly laminated; intercolumn material consists of cement, lime mudstone, and quartz silt particles. E, F) Larger, obliquely oriented stromatolite columns with slight upward growth vector and lamina asymmetry. Internal fabric (partly dolomitized) is weakly laminated and micritic; intercolumn material consists of quartzose lime mudstone with intraclasts. (A), (C), and (E), polished slabs; (B), (D), and (F), thin-section photomicrographs in PPL. (A) to (D) from KES; (E) and (F) from MV.

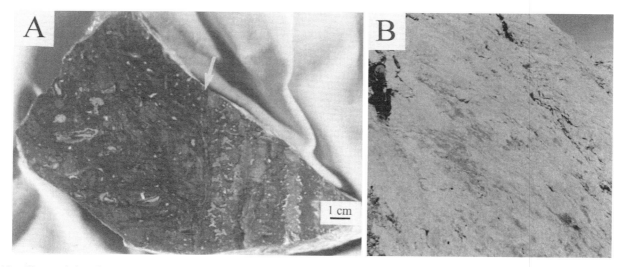

FIG. 16.—Characteristics of Stage III reef marginal facies. A) Talus boulders commonly display fracture surfaces (arrow) that were recolonized by microbial framework prior to being shed onto the talus pile. Polished slab from KEC. B) Some reef margins appear to be encrusted by steep lamelliform elements; person is standing upon such a surface, here exhumed at AR.

Cluster samples of Stage III reef core rock indicate, however, that lamelliform elements may be more volumetrically important toward the outer parts of reef cores. These relationships indicate either (a) a facies gradation from reef margin to reef interior, or, more probably (b) that sloping reef margins below the major growth surface were the sites of continued lamelliform framework accretion.

INTERPRETATION

Interpretation of these reefs is not straightforward. Physical sedimentary structures that would facilitate paleoenvironmental interpretation are few. The reefs are early Neoproterozoic, so there are no diagnostic metazoan or metaphyte body fossils to constrain paleoenvironment. They are constructed by microbes that are variably calcified, and have only equivocal modern and Phanerozoic counterparts. There are no close analogues for the reef framework elements.

The following interpretation is based upon the relative attributes of the rocks themselves, relating observed features to one another, to the few independent paleoenvironmental indicators present, to features of related off-reef strata, and to models derived from the study of stromatolites. The interpretations are tempered by the realization that these buildups and their components may be unique. Study of other such buildups is needed before a clear picture emerges—this is but a first-order analysis of these exceedingly complex structures.

Hydrodynamic Energy

Clues as to the energy regime at growing reef surfaces are provided by the type of sediment that accumulated in reef-top depressions, the degree of fragmentation of framework, the composition of internal sediments, framework morphology, and the expression of talus at reef margins.

Micro-unconformities within lamination (all stages), internal sediments (Stages I to III), abundant marine cements (Stages II to V), and local calcimicrobialite intraclasts (Stages II, III, and V), together indicate that water movement affected reef growth surfaces at most stages. The absence of significant areas of rotated or fragmented framework within reef core, however, suggests that although hydrodynamic energy was sufficient to produce micro-unconformities, to pump fine sediment into framework porosity, and to promote cementation, it was not strong enough to cause significant modification or destruction of growth surfaces. There was enough turbulence to keep fine sediment in suspension, such that no significant amount settled on the microbial mats; sediment was able to settle out of suspension only in protected depressions on reef tops, below storm wave base, or where it was pumped into framework porosity. Weak internal geopetal sediment lamination attests to episodic growth-cavity filling. Lack of any preferred areal orientation, elongation, or distribution of framework elements or clusters in the reef cores implies that subdued wave energy, with no single prevalent wave direction, was the dominant cause of water movement. Lamelliform core limestones were probably subject to gravitational spalling, as indicated by micro-unconformities within their constituent laminae.

These conclusions seem at odds with prolific talus shedding at reef margins in Stages I through III. Reef core and talus have been exhaustively examined at outcrop, hand-sample, and microscopic scales, but no clear evidence of paleokarst, calcrete, or meteoric precipitates has been found. Thus talus shedding does not appear to have been related to subaerial exposure of reef tops. Instead, it must have been an ongoing process during progradational and aggradational growth phases, largely the result of gravitational instability at margins of burgeoning reef tops. Some enhancement of the progradational and erosional processes might have occurred during slightly more hydrodynamically energetic times on reef tops during relative-sea-level stillstand associated with carbonate deposition in basinal members 1, 2, and 3. Rotated and transported blocks of reef core at reef margins, scarce within cores, attests to the need for significant gravitational potential in large-scale fragmentation of reef core material.

Morphology and Organization of Framework Elements

Morphology, size, and branching style of microbial structures are the subject of a vast literature, in which they have been related to hydrodynamics (e.g., Hoffman, 1967, 1976; Gebelein, 1969, 1974; Logan et al., 1974; Semikhatov, 1976; Horodyski, 1977; Cecile and Campbell, 1978; Southgate, 1989), sedimentation rate (e.g., Horodyski, 1977; Pratt and James, 1982; Grotzinger and Rothman, 1996), light intensity (e.g., Walter et al., 1976), water depth (Hoffman, 1976; Pratt and James, 1982; Southgate, 1989), and biotic composition (e.g., Raaben, 1969; Walter, 1972; Serebryakov, 1976; Walter et al., 1976; Awramik and Semikhatov, 1979; Beukes and Lowe, 1989; and many proponents of stromatolite biostratigraphy). It is generally accepted that both taxonomic composition and environmental variables contribute to microbialite morphogenesis, although the relative importance of their roles probably varies case by case.

Among those who have argued for the predominance of physical factors, Horodyski (1977) showed that (1) spacing of stromatolite nucleation sites could influence the degree of divergence of branched stromatolites; (2) stromatolite column diameters should be in "equilibrium" with environmental conditions, particularly scouring by intercolumn water movement; and (3) branching and changes in column width were best interpreted as responses to changing paleoenvironmental conditions.

Like stromatolites, the Little Dal framework elements are benthic microbial structures that grew in laminated increments. Although it is probable that the original microbial mat community consisted of a more diverse assemblage of microbes, the dominant, mineralized framework-building portion thereof is virtually monospecific, and there is little evidence in the form of voids or textural variation to suggest the former presence of other, less well-preserved community members that might have contributed to framebuilding. The filament-dominated community (Turner et al., 1993) of the bulk of basic framework types in the Little Dal reefs was roughly uniform throughout the structures, and therefore changes in biotic composition among the reef framework types are unlikely to have been the foremost influence on the changes in morphology of framework elements. Accumulation of detrital sediment on microbial growth surfaces was insignificant in the reefal microbialites. Therefore, it is most likely that, to a first approximation, other paleoenvironmental parameters controlled framework element morphology at a centimeter scale.

Reef framework stages are geometrically correlatable to off-reef strata that bear strong evidence of coeval changes in paleo–water depth (Turner et al., 1997a). Sedimentology of off-reef strata has already shown that most turbulent (and presumably shallowest) times in the basin are recorded in the carbonate part of basinal member 1 (stromatolite biostrome with intraclast rudstones and quartz sand grains), and the transition from basinal member 4 to the grainstone formation (cross-stratified oolitic and intraclastic dolograinstones): these are the only two basinal intervals that contain shallow-water allochems and sedimentary structures. These two comparatively high-energy units correspond to columnar calcimicrobialite framework stages II and V, respectively, as supported by: (1) presence of detrital quartz in intercolumn spaces of Stage II framework, biostromal upper basinal member 1, and lowermost member 2, in contrast with its relative dearth in other framework stages and off-reef strata; and (2) continuous outcrop of a layer of Stage VI calcimicrobialite from reef-top to off-reef where it is overlain and underlain by strata of the basinal assemblage–grainstone formation transition. Further corroboration that erect columnar elements represent the highest-energy framework type is presented by the varying degree of reef-surface fragmentation: reefal intraclasts are most abundant in Stages II and V. Diverse framework of Stage III accumulated in a protracted interval during which truly energetic conditions did not return to the basin floor; this correlation is indicated by interfingering of Stage III framework talus wedges with basinal members 2 and 3. The thick stratiform framework of Stage IV accumulated in quiet water during a time when regional deepening resulted in a carbonate-poor off-reef succession; this reef core interval is bracketed by links between reef and off-reef areas in Stages III and V.

If degree of column formation, branching, and anastomosis are directly related to hydrodynamics, mirrored in correlative off-reef units, then development of erect, robust, branching columns with comparatively coarse interstitial sediments in Stages II and V records highest-energy conditions on reef growth surfaces. More delicately and irregularly anastomosing frameworks of Stages I and III correspond to moderate energy levels, and stratiform framework with no impetus to branch (Stage IV) reflects the lowest hydrodynamic energy levels.

Although organization into distinct bioherms is generally absent, loose grouping of framework elements into cluster-like or bush-like domains spread across the growth surface is suggested in some stages (Fig. 17). These features are also likely related to factors controlling preferred orientation of growth vectors, and to depth of the growth surface. Expanding upon the model of Horodyski (1977), when accommodation space is abundant but nucleation sites are scarce, microbialites, once nucleated, can expand into large knobs, of which a significant part are elements growing obliquely or sideways at knob margins, and reef-surface sediments may accumulate in depressions between clusters (e.g., Stages I, III). Along reef margins, space for growth is available laterally, and sideways growth would be promoted. When accommodation space is limited, but both nucleation and growth are highly favored, element clusters are small and closely spaced, and have little room for lateral expansion and development of prostrate growth directions, or for significant accumulations of reef-surface sediment (Stage II; Fig. 17).

Inclination of the steep lamelliform layers in Stage IV would initially have been dictated by orientation of the founding substrate, and modified to steeper orientations by most favorable conditions, most prolific growth, and thickest lamination towards the most topographically elevated part of any given growth increment; growth conditions probably deteriorated down the depth profile in this zone owing to light attenuation. Framework morphology would have been controlled by hydrodynamic and/or illumination factors, and synoptic relief on the growth surface might have been maintained or increased by the ongoing creation of accommodation space.

Paleo–Water Depth of Growth Surfaces

Microbialite morphology, as a function of hydrodynamic energy, can serve as a proxy for relative water depth of the growth

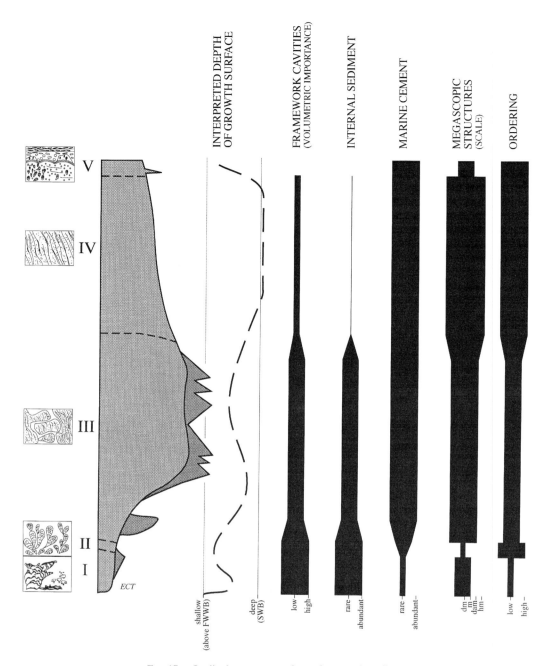

FIG. 17.—Qualitative summary of core framework attributes.

surface; this relationship has been exploited in studies by Hoffman (1976), Pratt and James (1982), and Southgate (1989). Following the argument above, in Little Dal reef core rocks, columnar, anastomosing, and steep stratiform framework types represent high-energy (shallow), moderate-energy (intermediate depth), and low-energy (deep water) incarnations of reef framework, respectively, within the bounds of the growth window for the constituent biota (Figs. 17, 18).

These data provide information only about the relative position of each growth stage within the growth window, but give no indication of why the growth surface varied in its relative position. Dynamics of reef growth can contribute to determining the relative importance of intrinsic (reef growth rate) versus extrinsic (eustatic or tectonic changes in relative sea level) factors in the changing paleo-depth of reef growth surfaces. The fact that both reef-surface and basin-floor depositional systems, though distinct and independent in their modes of accretion, show covarying changes, interpreted for each to be related ultimately to paleo-water depth, suggests that an extrinsic factor controlled both. It would then seem to be when externally driven changes in paleo–depth of the growth surface are imposed upon the system that framework facies changes occur.

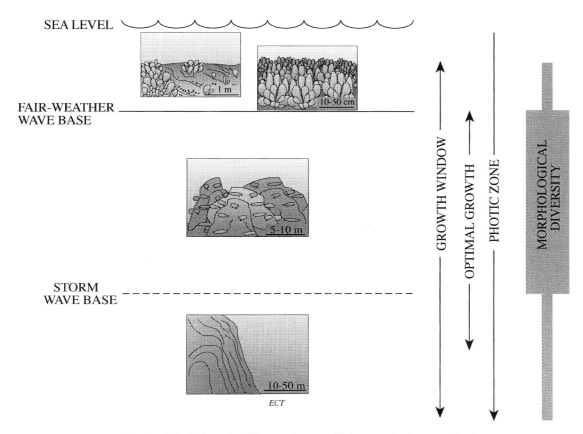

FIG. 18.—Distribution of reef framework types with interpreted paleo–water depth.

The reefal filamentous microstructures are probably related to modern oscillatoriacean cyanobacteria (Turner et al. 1993). Maximum depth for prolific growth of reefal calcareous green algae and for modern cyanobacteria is approximately 50–70 m in clear water (Brock, 1976; Saffo, 1987; James and Bourque, 1992). Many modern cyanobacteria are known to grow in low-light conditions (Fay, 1983), and ancient calcimicrobialites analogous to those of the Little Dal have been reported from paleo–water depths of >80 m (Playford, 1980). Given the interpreted origin of much of the basinal lime mud as water-column precipitate, it is possible that basinal waters were turbid, which might reduce the interpreted depth of the reef-growth surface to less than the depth possible in a clear water column. If episodic whitings were the source of basinal mud, however, it is plausible that the water column was clear most of the time, and that the cyanobacterial euphotic zone and reefal growth surfaces might have been up to 50–70 meters below the sea surface. This implies that all of the variability in framework expression was encompassed within a few tens of meters of water depth.

Microbialite Composition

The composition of framework elements at different reef levels gives some suggestion of the preferred conditions of different fabric types (Figs. 5, 18). Shallow-water framework is dominated by erect columnar microbialites made almost exclusively by laminar-reticulate fabric (Figs. 7, 12B, C). Deeper-water frameworks of Stages I and III also contain laminar-reticulate fabric, but display also development of micritic and renalcid encrustations, particularly on element margins, or as recolonization fabrics on fractured surfaces now found in talus boulders (Figs. 6B, 8E, F, 16A). Deep-water lamelliform framework of Stage IV (Fig. 10) and at talus-littered margins of lower Stage III (Fig. 16B) contain only laminar-reticulate fabric, and no significant volume of clotted fabrics. Reef-margin-encrusting microbialites at abandoned margins of Stage II reef are predominantly micritic. These characteristics suggest that whereas laminar-reticulate fabrics dominated most reef-growth surfaces, clotted and micritic structures encrusted surfaces in cavities, niches, and depressions on reef tops, and at lower, more protected, possibly darker sites along reef margins. This occurred particularly during times dominated by anastomosing framework: hydrodynamic energy was high enough to promote anastomosis, thus providing the appropriate microenvironments, but not so high as to cause a framework facies change to robust, columnar calcimicrobialite, or so low as to prohibit column formation or anastomosis. The increased diversity of the calcimicrobial community in Stage III (to include a greater proportion of renalcid clots and thromboids) is thus a result of increased diversity of framework growth habit, rather than its cause. Renalcid clots and micritic selvages are generally cryptic structures or surface encrustations that postdate the basic framework elements, and therefore could not have had a strong influence on their primary morphogenesis. Rather, they increased in volumetric importance because of greater availability of cryptic and protected niches presented by the anastomosing frameworks. Laminar-reticulate fabric also grew as lamelliform framework in deeper settings, but owing to the lack of turbulence necessary for the formation of anastomosing to columnar framework structures with significant centimeter-scale topography and cavity development, was unable to provide abundant protected sites where the clotted and micritic fabrics might grow.

Comparison with reef-associated microbialites provides clues as to the environmental requirements of the reef-building organisms. Sub-reef and biostromal stromatolites have muddy, streaky laminae. In addition to their possible trapping and binding of fine sediment, they are associated with flanking fine-grained sediment. Reef-marginal microbialite encrustations show little evidence for incorporation of detrital sediment, and are at most weakly laminated. Intercolumn spaces between these mainly columnar structures tend to be sediment-filled: the cavity network was open and readily plugged with sediment. In contrast, reef-core microbialites are associated with significantly smaller amounts of muddy sediment. These features suggest that settling of fine sediment on growth surfaces was less prominent in reef core calcimicrobialite than in sub-reef, off-reef, and possibly reef-marginal microbialites.

The setting in which biostromal stromatolites grew was not hydrodynamically significantly different from that in which Stages II and Vi calcimicrobialites grew: all contain allochems and structures indicative of relatively shallow, turbulent conditions. What differs in these settings is the relative abundance of lime mud. Settings where muddy sediment might accumulate on growth surfaces would seem to be inimical to the growth of reefal calcimicrobialite: at times when lime mud was comparatively abundant on the sea floor and in the water column, reef surfaces were elevated above the zone of settling, or were too steep to permit significant settling upon them. Reefs most likely nucleated on stromatolites, and despite rare presence of calcimicrobial laminae within basinal carbonate (Turner et al., 1997a), new reef growth was never initiated after this time, not even on top of the muddy biostromal stromatolite, which was surely within the calcimicrobial growth window. This would suggest that calcimicrobialite growth required not only a relatively mud-free setting (little mud in the water column, or turbulence at growth surfaces sufficient to prevent mud settling), but also hard substrate. Robust calcimicrobialite columns were able to grow even in turbulent and relatively low-relief conditions in Stage Vi, but no mud was present to accumulate on surfaces or in interstices.

Water Chemistry, Climate, and Illumination

Paleoenvironmental parameters that are related to the nutritional and energy requirements of cyanobacteria can be inferred from off-reef sedimentology and from reef-rock composition. Abundance of evaporites in strata above and below the basinal assemblage, widespread early phosphatic and hematitic replacement of framework cavity margins and internal sediments, and prevalence of carbonate deposition throughout the basin indicate that required nutrients (S, Na, K, P, Fe, Ca, Mg) were available. Together with the warm, hypersaline, carbonate-oversaturated, and possibly alkaline nature of basinal waters, combined attributes point to geochemical and climatic conditions ideal for the prolific growth and heavy calcification of cyanobacteria.

It is perplexing that the volume of basinal lime mud produced should display such marked variability throughout the basinal interval, whereas the reef biota appears to calcify more or less uniformly throughout the entire thickness of reefs. This implies that changing sea-water chemistry had less influence on the mineralization of the calcimicrobes than on water-column precipitation of lime mud. Calcimicrobes are generally viewed as organisms that indirectly induce precipitation of carbonate (Riding, 1991) in isotopic equilibrium with ambient sea water (Andrews et al., 1993); variable degrees of carbonate oversaturation might be insignificant in comparison to their own propensity to become calcified. $\delta^{13}C$ isotope data from Little Dal reef rocks [$\delta^{13}C$ (PDB) = 2.83 to 4.90, mean = 4.06, n = 14 (Stages I to IV); 2.43 to 6.02, mean = 4.32, n = 8 (Stage V)] do not differ significantly from those from off-reef limestones (3.30 to 5.18, mean = 4.33, n = 8), or from non-reefal limestones from age-equivalent strata in the Shaler Supergroup of Victoria Island (Kaufman and Knoll, 1995). These data portray normal Neoproterozoic marine C isotope values, and thus do not suggest any influence of nonmarine waters such as those from seeps or vents, as has been suggested for some fossil mounds (e.g., Beauchamp and Savard, 1992; Campbell et al., 1993), and so such a localized influx of fluids that might promote carbonate precipitation on these reefs is not likely.

Growth Window

The sum of observations indicate that reef-core calcimicrobialite required (1) a location in the photic zone; (2) little settling of fine sediment onto growth surfaces; and (3) a hard substrate. The upper depth limit for calcimicrobialite growth was probably above fair-weather wavebase, within several meters of the water surface (Fig. 18). The lower depth limit is unknown, but growth probably diminished down the illumination gradient, and was impossible on muddy basin floor substrates even when they were in the photic zone (Turner et al., 1997a). Other interpreted boundaries inside the growth window are fair-weather wavebase, the upper limit of the zone of diverse microbialite morphology, and storm wavebase, the upper limit of exclusively stratiform growth. The zone of optimal growth (Fig. 18) appears to have been in moderate water depths, and delimited by fair-weather wavebase (upper boundary) and light attenuation (lower boundary). Above the optimal growth zone, high-energy conditions limited morphology to robust columns, somewhat akin to the robust branching structures in shallowest parts of modern reefs.

It seems that facies composition in the zone of morphological diversity can remain roughly constant through a range of paleo–water depths. This is analogous to depth zonation of skeleton morphology on modern coral reefs, in which greatest diversity of growth habits occurs in moderate water depths on reef fronts (James and Ginsburg, 1979). Below this zone, where water movement is insignificant and light is attenuated, growth habits are less diverse and typically platy. The Little Dal depth-related growth habit zones are analogous to those of modern coral reefs, except that the modern reef zonation is based on examples where zonation is continuous along a depth gradient where all zones are contemporaneously expressed, as compared to the

Little Dal example, in which only one or two zones can be shown to have coexisted at any given time. They are also reminiscent of stromatolite zones defined by hydrodynamic stress in Shark Bay (Logan et al., 1974).

Reef Growth History

The following is an interpreted series of events envisaged to result in the observed distribution of facies in reefal and off-reef settings.

Stage I.—

Reefs nucleated during relative-sea-level rise, on topographic highs provided by stromatolite bioherms. Reef growth surfaces were in the zone of optimal growth, and morphologically diverse, poorly organized calcimicrobial and thrombolitic framework flourished.

Stage II.—

Shallowing led to: (1) elevation of the reef growth surface above fair-weather wavebase, limitation of accommodation space, and change to erect columnar calcimicrobialite framework; and (2) development of an off-reef stromatolite biostrome around and below the margins of the calcimicrobial reef. Biostromal layers overgrew talus boulders shed from the reef margin. Detrital quartz reached the basin as a result of relative-sea-level fall, accumulating in both off-reef areas and reef framework pores. Sheets of encrusting microbialite grew on the steep walls of the reef core.

Stage III.—

A rise in relative sea level submerged the reef growth surface into the zone of greatest morphological diversity for calcimicrobialites, and changed off-reef sediment from carbonate-rich to terrigenous-rich. Thin encrusting layers of tufted-mat microbialite continued to grow on the abandoned margins of Stage II core. Aggradation of the reef core was acompanied by talus shedding at reef margins and growth of lamelliform encrustations over talus-littered reef flanks low in the growth window. Reef relief was soon significant, and the lower reaches of the talus flanks descended below the growth window. Reefs continued to shed talus and gradually prograde. Reef-top growth surfaces were characterized by a spectrum of poorly organized framework-element growth forms, with muddy sediment accumulating in small reef-surface depressions; occasionally, storms fragmented core material into centimeter-scale calcimicrobial intraclasts. At the steep margins of the reef core, where storm wave energy was not as damped as at the central reef-core surface, framework elements grew in prostrate orientations, and reef-margin core was commonly fractured and redeposited as talus. Lower on the reef flanks, lamelliform elements made a final thick veneer before descending below the growth window and eventually being buried by inter-reef sediment. Gradual progradation continued and talus shedding increased as a subtle decrease in the rate of relative-sea-level rise led to increased carbonate content in off-reef muds of basinal members 2 and 3. Throughout this interval, the major reef growth surfaces remained within the zone of morphological diversity.

Stage IV.—

Renewed basin-wide deepening is recorded in off-reef shales and development of exclusively lamelliform framework across the entire growing surface of the reef. Growth surfaces were low in the growth window, and probably became steep-sided domes or pinnacles through preferential growth on elevated sites. Reefs contracted in areal extent and shed little talus.

Stage V.—

Pronounced shallowing led to increased precipitation of carbonate mud in the water column, and rapid accumulation of off-reef molar tooth lime mudstone reduced reef relief. Growth on reef tops ceased, and reef-core masses protruding into shallow water were eroded. Reef tops were then blanketed by sheets of oncoids containing thickets of robust columnar calcimicrobialite. Columns were episodically broken and toppled. Around some reef flanks, at slightly lower elevations than reef tops but higher than the inter-reef basin floor, microbialite meadows episodically expanded as haloes. Conditions on the basin floor became increasingly energetic, with the formation of ooids. Microbialite fabric changed from calcimicrobial to grumous, and eventually this facies was overgrown by domal, cement-rich stromatolites in very energetic waters. After a brief return to the muddy microbialite stage, reef tops were covered by intraclastic and oolitic sands and gravels of the grainstone formation, as all residual topographic relief was erased.

DISCUSSION

Growth Dynamics

Observation of large-scale (tens to hundreds of meters) attributes such as changes in reef areal extent, and relations between reef-margin areas and off-reef areas, led to the interpretation that reefs grew in increments linked to relative-sea-level change (Turner et al. 1997a). Observations at a scale several orders of magnitude smaller (centimeter- to meter-scale framework composition) permit refinement of this interpretation.

A predictable succession of deep to shallow facies and/or features should be expected in each phase of the reef core if each accreted under a similar succession of conditions. Whereas evidence is good for such a deep-to-shallow transition in Stages I–II facies, and at the end of reef growth (Stages IV–V), there is no such change (facies change, hiatus or exposure surfaces) that coincides with carbonate parts of basinal members 2 and 3 and the marked reef progradation and talus shedding in this interval. The vertical distribution of framework facies implies that reefs grew in two disparate increments, each of which was dominated by moderate-depth facies, and culminated in a thin and distinctive shallow-water facies. The expansion and talus shedding during Stage III, and the framework composition of reef-margin talus identical to that of adjacent reef core, however, negate any possibility that reefs grew in a single, exclusively deepening pulse through Stages III and IV. The framework patterns suggest instead that reefs flourished mainly in deeper water (Stages I, III, and IV), with shallowing reflected by progradation (if substrate was available), and by development of different microbialite facies (if shallowing was sufficient to bring reef tops to the upper limit of their growth window; Stages II and V). Gradual progradation during Stage III was therefore accomplished without emergence of reef tops into a truly shallow-water setting where changes in framework style or subaerial exposure would have occurred: relative depths of reef tops shallowed in a slow and subtle fashion, and never reached the limit evident in Stages II or V.

Comparison with Other Proterozoic Buildups

Paleoproterozoic and Mesoproterozoic reefs were composed of cement-rich or muddy-laminated stromatolites in which primary microbial structures are at best poorly preserved. Although these elements are present in the Neoproterozoic Little Dal reefs, they are rare and of little importance to reef growth. Instead, Little Dal reefs record the development of a new microbialite type: calcimicrobialites. Their microbiota was neither a microbial community passively exploiting a hard surface (abiotic view of stromatolite formation) nor an unlithified microbial mat preserved by the trapping, binding, or precipitation of sediment, but lacking obvious evidence of the former microbial constituents (traditional view of stromatolites). Instead, it was a prolific and visible component of the reef rock, essential to both mineral precipitation and microscopic fabric development, yet seemingly at the whim of environmental parameters as regards the centimeter-scale expression of framework morphology. The new frame-building capacity of such calcimicrobes permitted the development of complex framework comprising a wide spectrum of element morphologies and abundant framework porosity, zoned framework distribution, and enhanced ability to respond to changes in relative sea level. In light of this newly developed type of microbialite framestone, it is not to be expected that Little Dal framework elements will have close analogues in older Proterozoic buildups.

Composition.—

Calcimicrobial microstructures are known from the Neoproterozoic (filamentous, Srivastava, 1977; clotted, Kolosov, 1975 and Cloud et al., 1974), although widespread and complex structures of calcimicrobial composition have not been reported. Insofar as Little Dal reef framework is microbial, laminated, and forms discrete centimeter-scale structures, its stromatolitic heritage is readily apparent and useful in interpretation.

Erect calcimicrobial framework elements bear superficial morphological resemblance to known Proterozoic columnar stromatolite forms but differ in their internal composition. Anastomosing framework elements have no close morphological analogue among Proterozoic structures; the extreme degree of anastomosis together with the prevalence of drooping, horizontal, or inclined orientations are uncharacteristic of most stromatolites. Steep stratiform layers are uncommon in Proterozoic reefs, in which large structures tend to take the form of domes or horizontally layered stratiform structures. Thin sloping stratiform encrustations with distribution similar to those of reef-margin lamelliform layers were reported by Narbonne and James (1996). Buildups 10 to 100 m in size made entirely of steeply inclined stratiform structures are unique among Proterozoic microbial structures.

Thrombolitic framework is present in the Paleoproterozoic Rocknest Platform carbonates (Kah and Grotzinger, 1992).

These much older thrombolites are not in general similar to those of the Little Dal: they are measured in millimeters or less, are largely made of clear cement rather than micrite, are morphologically simpler, and come from meter-scale bioherms of dolomitic composition. Thrombolitic bioherms also occur in the terminal Neoproterozoic Nama Group (Saylor et al., 1995).

Stromatolites made of spar–micrite couplets similar to those of Little Dal Stage VII occur in the Wildbread Fm of the Paleoproterozoic Pethei Group (Hoffman, 1989; Sami and James, 1994, 1996). Evenly laminated, high-inheritance, cement-rich stromatolites are typical of the Paleoproterozoic, and so the appearance of such microstructure in Neoproterozoic rocks is anomalous.

Muddy-laminated stromatolite types from reef-nucleating bioherms and reef-margin biostromes are familiar from correlative Neoproterozoic strata in Australia (cf. *Acaciella*, *Baicalia*, *Inzeria*, *Jurusania*, *Kotuikania*, *Minjaria*; Walter, 1972; Grey, 1995).

Framework Architecture and Internal Stratigraphy.—

Vertical changes in biohermal and biostromal stromatolite morphology, concurrent with paleoenvironmental changes recorded in off-reef strata, are present in both older (Cecile and Campbell, 1978; Narbonne and James, 1996) and coeval (Southgate, 1989; Narbonne et al., this volume) rocks. Most Proterozoic buildups display construction by "self-similar" biohermal elements (Narbonne and James, 1996); this type of hierarchical composition is absent in the Little Dal reefs.

Comparison with Phanerozoic Buildups

Composition.—

Although microbial in composition, the Little Dal reefs invite extensive comparison to Paleozoic and younger structures. The reef framework contains virtually no mud and is not compositionally or texturally comparable to Paleozoic mud mounds (Lees and Miller, 1995; Pratt, 1995), except in rare examples. At the microscopic scale, calcimicrobial constituents are directly comparable to Paleozoic frame-building *Girvanella*, *Renalcis*, and thrombolites. Some aspects of comparative composition and texture have been presented by Turner et al. (1997a).

Texturally, parts of the filament-dominated framework of the Little Dal reefs resemble framework of Cambro-Ordovician platform margin boundstones in which loosely stacked arcuate *Girvanella* crusts form decimeter- to meter-scale mounds (James, 1981; Read and Pfeil, 1983). Most Paleozoic calcimicrobial bioherms are, however, either *Renalcis*-dominated [unlike the Little Dal reefs; Playford, 1980 (Devonian); Kruse et al., 1995 (Cambrian)], or are made by *Girvanella* clusters that do not form centimeter-scale framework elements with distinct morphological characteristics. Like *Renalcis* from Lower Cambrian buildups, clots in the Little Dal reefs are generally found on the undersides of framework elements (Turner et al., 1993), and only rarely exploit other niches, when clots are especially abundant (James and Kobluk, 1978; Kobluk and James, 1979).

The presence of Little Dal framework thromboids that are morphologically identical to those of Cambro-Ordovician examples (cf. Aitken and Narbonne, 1989), and their close relationship to calcimicrobial structures reinforces the closely related origin of calcimicrobialites and thrombolites (Kennard and James, 1986).

Element Morphology.—

Many of the columnar, anastomosing, nodular, and massive Little Dal framework elements are morphologically comparable to frame-building organisms from the Phanerozoic: the breadth of morphologies displayed by nodular, encrusting, and branching calcified algae, sponges, and colonial metazoans is mirrored to a large degree by the variety of morphologies adopted by Little Dal microbialites.

Comparison of Little Dal framework with Phanerozoic calcimicrobialite morphology is less rewarding. Paleozoic filamentous calcimicrobialites, although compositionally similar to those of the Little Dal, tend to have less distinctive and less elaborate morphological expression: massive heads or decimeter-scale irregular columns of *Girvanella* predominate (e.g., James, 1981), with few indications of sophisticated framework, branching, or anastomosis. Framework of clotted calcimicrobes (e.g., *Renalcis*) is more readily comparable to the Little Dal examples. *Renalcis* was commonly the dominant frame-builder of lower Paleozoic calcimicrobial bioherms (James and Debrenne, 1980; Playford, 1980; Rowland and Gangloff, 1988). Many examples of this calcimicrobe type occur, however, as encrustations on, or associations with, other framework components (e.g., archeocyathans), or in cryptic or protected settings (James and Kobluk, 1978; Kobluk and James, 1979), as in the the Little Dal examples.

Element Size.—

Size of framework elements in Phanerozoic reefs ranges from millimetric calcimicrobial bodies such as *Renalcis*, to meter-scale masses made by colonial metazoans. Many of the Little Dal framework elements fall into the same size range, but the large masses of encrusting lamelliform framework present, mainly in Stage IV, are not strictly comparable to framework in Phanerozoic reefs in that they represent massive bodies made by microscopic entities, and are not divisible into mesoscopic elements contributed by individual organisms or colonies. They are, however, reminiscent of deep-water stromatolites encrusting steep fore-reef slopes and drowned reef tops of the Devonian in the Canning Basin (Playford et al., 1976). As pointed out by Narbonne and James (1996), the size of microbial framework elements is not limited in the same sense as are most Phanerozoic framework organisms.

Framework Architecture and Internal Stratigraphy.—

Lower Cambrian buildups are the next youngest compositional analogues to the Little Dal reefs. They are formed largely by calcimicrobes, and, with the exception of the obvious presence of metazoan reef-builders and reef-dwelling and bioeroding organisms, show most of the same attributes. Ecological succession is minimal. Centimeter-scale areas defined by varying combinations of frame-building constituents make modular "domains" which, when assembled, make rather homogeneous meter-scale lenticular to lumpy structures ("kalyptrae"), which singly or in clusters make up the small bioherms (James and Kobluk, 1978; Kruse et al., 1995). This lack of well-organized subdivision of buildups into zoned bioherms, in contrast to the

architectural style of Proterozoic stromatolite reefs, is reminiscent of the heterogeneous, poorly ordered framework of much of the Little Dal reefs, and of other buildups throughout the Phanerozoic.

Ability to respond both in framework expression and in growth strategy is a familiar theme from many Phanerozoic buildups, and the framework stratigraphy in the Little Dal reefs is thematically allied to these structures.

SUMMARY AND CONCLUSIONS

(1) Morphology of calcimicrobial framework elements of the Little Dal reefs varies vertically throughout reef growth and can be divided into five stages. The predominant framework types are composed of filamentous and/or clotted calcimicrobes. The uniformity of biotic composition throughout the reefs indicates that framework morphology was a function of environmental parameters, most likely hydrodynamic energy, rather than biota.

(2) Covariance of framework change, large-scale reef growth patterns, and off-reef stratigraphic patterns implies an allogenic cause for all, probably relative-sea-level change. Shallow-water frameworks consisted of well-ordered erect columnar elements, whereas framework at intermediate depths comprised a spectrum of anastomosing and massive elements, and deepest-water framework was steeply inclined stratiform elements.

(3) Reef growth occurred in low- to moderate-energy regimes, within the photic zone, on hard substrates, and in the absence of significant settling of detrital mud. The growth window was delimited by the photic zone at depth and by excessive fragmentation near the water surface. Optimal growth occurred in moderate water depths, between fair-weather wave base and a limit determined by light attenuation at depth.

The Little Dal reefs record a major inflection point in the development of reefal ecosystems: they display a combination of attributes that were formerly considered the exclusive domain of either Proterozoic or Paleozoic reef ecosystems. Exclusively microbial frame-builders and laminated stromatolitic growth are predominantly motifs of the Proterozoic, whereas heavily calcified organisms forming complex framework, complete with growth cavities containing internal sediments and marine cements, and displaying well-developed vertical and lateral zonation and advanced adaptive responses at a variety of scales to changes in relative sea level, are attributes more commonly associated with the Phanerozoic reef archetype. The Little Dal reefs are the earliest known examples of "modern"-style reef growth.

Limitation of the frame-building organisms to a simple and persistent community provides a rare opportunity to inspect the effects on reefs of changes in paleoenvironmental conditions, without the usual complexity of extremely variable community composition. Although this reef system as a whole expresses the effects of factors other than relative-sea-level change, it appears that the latter was indeed the predominant control on framework expression. The complex interplay of biotic growth, hydrodynamics, cementation, and changes in relative sea level in these immense and fascinating structures is unprecedented from any Precambrian reefal ecosystem described to date.

ACKNOWLEDGMENTS

Deepest gratitude is owed to the field assistants who bore the all-too-literal burden of this study: J. Wiebe, S. Hooey, and B.

Macfarlane. H. Hofmann provided invaluable advice, particularly regarding stromatolite literature, and M. Walter (Macquarie University) generously helped with identification of some of the off-reef stromatolites. Isotope analyses were performed at Queen's University under the direction of K. Kyser. We gratefully acknowledge the reviews of P.-A. Bourque, H. Hofmann, and M. Walter. Access to the field area was made possible by the Northwest Territories government and local communities. Funding for this study is through the Northern Studies Training Program of the Department of Indian and Northern Affairs and Northern Development, Canada (ECT; 1994, 1996) and through Natural Sciences and Engineering Research Council (Canada) grants to NPJ and GMN. Funding was augmented by Geological Society of America Research Grants (1992, 1994), and an American Association of Petroleum Geologists Grant-in-Aid (1992) to ECT.

REFERENCES

AITKEN, J. D., 1981, Stratigraphy and sedimentology of the Upper Proterozoic Little Dal Group, Mackenzie Mountains, Northwest Territories, in Campbell, F. H. A., ed., Proterozoic Basins of Canada: Geological Survey of Canada, Paper 81-10, p. 47–71.

AITKEN, J. D., 1989, Giant "algal" reefs, Middle/Upper Proterozoic Little Dal group (> 770, < 1200 Ma), Mackenzie Mountains, N.W.T., Canada, in Geldsetzer, H. H. J., James, N. P., and Tebbut, G. E., eds., Reefs, Canada and Adjacent Areas: Canadian Society of Petroleum Geologists, Memoir 13, p. 13–23.

AITKEN, J. D., AND NARBONNE, G. M., 1989, Two occurrences of Precambrian thrombolites from the Mackenzie Mountains, Northwestern Canada: Palaios, v. 4, p. 384–388.

AITKEN, J. D., LONG, D. G. F., AND SEMIKHATOV, M. A., 1978, Correlation of Helikian strata, Mackenzie Mountains–Brock Inlier–Victoria Island: Geological Survey of Canada, Paper 78-1A, p. 485–486.

ANDREWS, J. E., RIDING, R., AND DENNIS, P.F., 1993, Stable isotope composition of Recent freshwater cyanobacterial carbonates from the British Isles: Local and regional environmental controls: Sedimentology, v. 40, p. 303–314.

AWRAMIK, S. M., AND SEMIKHATOV, M. A., 1979, The relationship between morphology, microstructure, and microbiota in three vertically intergrading stromatolites from the Gunflint Iron Formation: Canadian Journal of Earth Sciences, v. 16, p. 484–495.

BEAUCHAMP, B., AND SAVARD, M., 1992, Cretaceous chemosynthetic mounds in the Canadian Arctic: Palaios, v. 7, p. 434–450.

BERTRAND-SAFARTI, J., 1972, Paléoécologie de certains stromatolites en récifs des formations du Précambrien supérieur du Groupe d'Atar (Mauritanie, Sahara occidental): Création d'espèces nouvelles: Palaeogeography, Palaeoclimatology, Palaeoecology, v. 11, p. 33–63.

BEUKES, N. J., 1987, Facies relations, depositional environments and diagenesis in a major early Proterozoic stromatolitic carbonate platform to basinal sequence, Campbellrand Subgroup, Transvaal Supergroup, Southern Africa: Sedimentary Geology, v. 54, p. 1–46.

BEUKES, N. J., AND LOWE, D. R., 1989, Environmental control on diverse stromatolite morphologies in the 3000 Myr Pongola Supergroup, South Africa: Sedimentology, v. 36, p. 383–397.

BOSENCE, D. W. J., AND BRIDGES, P. H., 1995, A review of the origin and evolution of carbonate mud mounds, in Monty, C. L. V., Bosence, D. W. J., Bridges, P. H., and Pratt, B. R., eds., Carbonate Mud-Mounds: International Association of Sedimentologists, Special Publication 23, p. 3–9.

BROCK, T. D., 1976, Environmental microbiology of living stromatolites, in Walter, M. R., ed., Stromatolites: Amsterdam, Elsevier, Developments in Sedimentology 20, p. 141–148.

BURNE, R. V., AND MOORE, L. S., 1987, Microbialites: organosedimentary deposits of benthic microbial communities: Palaios, v. 2, p. 241–254.

CAMPBELL, K. A., CARLSON, C., AND BOTTJER, D. J., 1993, Fossil cold seep limestones and associated chemosymbiotic macroinvertebrate faunas, Jurassic–Cretaceous Great Valley Group, California, in Graham, S. A., and Lowe, D. R., eds., Advances in the Sedimentary Geology of the Great Valley Group, Sacramento Valley, California: SEPM, Pacific Section, Book no. 73, p. 37–50.

CECILE, M. P., AND CAMPBELL, F. H. A., 1978, Regressive stromatolite reefs and associated facies, middle Goulburn Group (lower Proterozoic) in Kilohigok Basin, N. W. T.: An example of environmental control of stromatolite form: Canadian Society of Petroleum Geologists, Bulletin, v. 26, p. 237–267.

CLOUD, P., WRIGHT, L. A., WILLIAMS, E. G., DIEHL, P., AND WALTER, M. R., 1974, Giant stromatolites and associated vertical tubes from the upper Proterozoic Noonday dolomite, Death Valley region, eastern California: Geological Society of America, Bulletin, v. 85, p. 1869–1882.

FAGERSTROM, J. A., 1987, The Evolution of Reef Communities: New York, Wiley, 600 p.

FAY, P., 1983, The Blue-Greens: London, Edward Arnold, Studies in Biology 160, 88 p.

FURNISS, G., RITTEL, J. F., AND WINSTON, D., 1998, Gas bubble and expansion crack origin of "molar-tooth" calcite structures in the middle Proterozoic Belt Supergroup, Western Montana: Journal of Sedimentary Research, v. 68, p. 104–114.

GEBELEIN, C. D., 1969, Distribution, morphology, and accretion rate of recent subtidal algal stromatolites, Bermuda: Journal of Sedimentary Petrology, v. 39, p. 49–69.

GEBELEIN, C. D., 1974, Biologic control of stromatolite microstructure: implications for Precambrian time stratigraphy: American Journal of Science, v. 274, p. 575–598.

GELDSETZER, H. H. J., AND JAMES, N. P., 1989, Introduction, in Geldsetzer, H. H. J., James, N. P., and Tebbut, G. E., eds., Reefs, Canada and Adjacent Areas: Canadian Society of Petroleum Geologists, Memoir 13, p. 1–7.

GELDSETZER, H. H. J., JAMES, N. P., AND TEBBUT, G. E., eds., 1989, Reefs, Canada and Adjacent Areas: Canadian Society of Petroleum Geologists, Memoir 13, 775 p.

GREY, K., 1995, Neoproterozoic stromatolites from the Skates Hill Fm., Savory Basin, Western Australia, and a review of the distribution of Acaciella australica: Australian Journal of Earth Sciences, v. 42, p. 123–132.

GREY, K., 1989, Handbook for the study of stromatolites and associated structures (second draft): Stromatolite Newsletter, no. 14, p. 82–171.

GROTZINGER, J. P., 1989a, Introduction to Precambrian reefs, in Geldsetzer, H. H. J., James, N. P., and Tebbut, G. E., eds., Reefs, Canada and Adjacent Areas: Canadian Society of Petroleum Geologists, Memoir 13, p. 9–12.

GROTZINGER, J. P., 1989b, Facies and evolution of Precambrian carbonate systems: Emergence of the modern platform archetype, in Crevello, P. D., Wilson, J. L., Sarg, J. F., and Read, J. F., eds., Controls on Carbonate Platform and Basin Development: SEPM, Special Publication 44, p. 79–106.

GROTZINGER, J. P., AND ROTHMAN, D. H., 1996, An abiotic model for stromatolite morphogenesis: Nature, v. 383, p. 423–425.

HEAMAN, L. M., LeCHEMINANT, A. N., AND RAINBIRD, R. H., 1992, Nature and timing of Franklin igneous events, Canada: Implications for a late Proterozoic mantle plume and the break-up of Laurentia: Earth and Planetary Science Letters, v. 109, p. 117–131.

HOFFMAN, P., 1967, Algal stromatolites: Use in stratigraphic correlation and paleocurrent determination: Science, v. 157, p. 1043–1045.

HOFFMAN, P., 1974, Shallow and deepwater stromatolites in lower Proterozoic platform-to-basin facies change, Great Slave Lake, Canada: American Association of Petroleum Geologists, Bulletin, v. 58, p. 856–867.

HOFFMAN, P., 1976, Stromatolite morphogenesis in Shark Bay, western Australia, in Walter, M. R., ed., Stromatolites: Amsterdam, Elsevier, Developments in Sedimentology 20, p. 261–271.

HOFFMAN, P., 1989, Pethei reef complex (1.9 Ga), Great Slave Lake, N. W. T., in Geldsetzer, H. H. J., James, N. P., and Tebbut, G. E., eds., Reefs, Canada and Adjacent Areas: Canadian Society of Petroleum Geologists, Memoir 13, p. 38–48.

HOFMANN, H. J., 1973, Stromatolites: Their characteristics and utility: Earth-Science Reviews, v. 9, p. 339–373.

HORODYSKI, R. J., 1977, Environmental influence on columnar stromatolite branching patterns: Examples from the middle Proterozoic Belt Supergroup, Glacier National Park, Montana: Journal of Paleontology, v. 51, p. 661–671.

JAMES, N. P., 1981, Megablocks of calcified algae in the Cow Head Breccia, western Newfoundland: Vestiges of a Cambro-Ordovician platform margin: Geological Society of America, Bulletin, v. 92, p. 799–811.

JAMES, N. P., AND BOURQUE, P.-A., 1992, Reefs and Mounds, in Walker, R. G., and James, N. P., eds., Facies Models: Response to Sea Level Change: Geological Association of Canada, p. 323–347.

JAMES, N. P., AND DEBRENNE, F., 1980, Lower Cambrian bioherms: Pioneer reefs of the Phanerozoic: Acta Palaeontologica Polonica, v. 25, p. 655–668.

JAMES, N. P., AND GINSBURG, R. N., 1979, The Seaward Margin of Belize Barrier and Atoll Reefs: International Association of Sedimentologists, Special Publication 3, 191 p.

JAMES, N. P., AND GRAVESTOCK, D. I., 1990, Lower Cambrian shelf and shelf margin buildups, Flinders Ranges, South Australia: Sedimentology, v. 37, p. 455–480.

JAMES, N. P., AND KOBLUK, D. R., 1978, Lower Cambrian patch reefs and associated sediments: southern Labrador, Canada: Sedimentology, v. 25, p. 1–35.

KAH, L. C., AND GROTZINGER, J. P., 1992, Early Proterozoic (1.9 Ga) thrombolites of the Rocknest Formation, Northwest Territories, Canada: Palaios, v. 7, p. 305–315.

KAUFMAN, A. J., AND KNOLL, A. H., 1995, Neoproterozoic variations in the C-isotopic composition of seawater: stratigraphic and biogeochemical implications: Precambrian Research, v. 73, p. 27–49.

KENNARD, J. M., AND JAMES, N. P., 1986, Thrombolites and stromatolites: Two distinct types of microbial structures: Palaios, v. 1, p. 492–503.

KOBLUK, D. R. AND JAMES, N. P., 1979, Cavity-dwelling organisms in Lower Cambrian patch reefs from southern Labrador: Lethaia, v.14, p. 193–218.

KOLOSOV, P. N., 1975, Upper Precambrian stratigraphy of southern Yakutia (in Russian): Academy of Science of the USSR, Geological Institute, Siberian Division, Yakutian Affairs, 155 p.

KRUSE, P. D., ZHURAVLEV, A. YU., AND JAMES, N. P., 1995, Primordial metazoan–calcimicrobe reefs: Tommotian (Early Cambrian) of the Siberian Platform: Palaios, v. 10, p. 291–321.

LEES, A., AND MILLER, J., 1995, Waulsortian banks, in Monty, C. L. V., Bosence, D. W. J., Bridges, P. H., and Pratt, B. R., eds., Carbonate Mud-Mounds: International Association of Sedimentologists, Special Publication 23, p. 191–271.

LOGAN, B. W., HOFFMAN, P., AND GEBELEIN, C. D., 1974, Algal mats, cryptalgal fabrics and structures, Hamelin Pool, Western Australia: American Association of Petroleum Geologists, Memoir 22, p. 140–194.

NARBONNE, G. M., AND JAMES, N. P., 1996, Mesoproterozoic deep-water reefs from Borden Peninsula, Arctic Canada: Sedimentology, v. 43, p. 827–848.

PARK, J. K., 1981, Analysis of the multicomponent magnetization of the Little Dal Group, Mackenzie Mountains, Northwest Territories, Canada: Journal of Geophysical Research, v. 86, p. 5134–5146.

PIA, J., 1927, Thallophyta, in Hirmer, M., ed., Handbuch der Paläobotanik, Bd. 1: Munich and Berlin, R. Oldenbourg, p. 31–136.

PLAYFORD, P. E., 1980, Devonian "Great Barrier Reef" of Canning Basin, Western Australia: American Association of Petroleum Geologists, Bulletin, v. 64, p. 814–840.

PLAYFORD, P. E., COCKBAIN, A. E., DRUCE, E. C., AND WRAY, J. L., 1976, Devonian stromatolites from the Canning Basin, Western Australia, in Walter, M. R., ed., Stromatolites: Amsterdam, Elsevier, Developments in Sedimentology 20, p. 543–563.

PRATT, B. R., 1995, The origin, biota, and evolution of deep-water mudmounds, in Monty, C. L. V., Bosence, D. W. J., Bridges, P. H., and Pratt, B. R., eds., Carbonate Mud-Mounds: International Association of Sedimentologists, Special Publication 23, p. 49–123.

PRATT, B. R., AND JAMES, N. P., 1982, Cryptalgal-metazoan bioherms of early Ordovician age in the St. George Group, western Newfoundland: Sedimentology, v. 29, p. 543–569.

RAABEN, M. E., 1969, Columnar stromatolites and late Precambrian stratigraphy: American Journal of Science, v. 267, p. 1–18.

RAINBIRD, R. H., JEFFERSON, C. W., AND YOUNG, G. M., 1996, The early Neoproterozoic sedimentary succession B of northwestern Laurentia: Correlations and paleogeographic significance: Geological Society of America, Bulletin, v. 108, p. 454–470.

READ, J. F., AND PFEIL, R. W., 1983, Fabrics of allochthonous reefal blocks, Shady Dolomite (Lower to Middle Cambrian), Virginia Appalachians: Journal of Sedimentary Petrology, v. 53, p. 761–778.

RIDING, R., 1991, Calcified cyanobacteria, in Riding, R., ed., Calcareous Algae and Stromatolites: Berlin, Springer-Verlag, p. 105–112.

RIDING, R., AND ZHURAVLEV, A. YU., 1995, Structure and diversity of oldest sponge–microbe reefs: Lower Cambrian, Aldan River, Siberia: Geology, v. 23, p. 649–652.

ROWLAND, S. M., AND GANGLOFF, R. A., 1988, Structure and paleoecology of Lower Cambrian reefs: Palaios, v. 3, p. 111–135.

SAFFO, M. B., 1987, New light on seaweeds: Bioscience, v. 37, p. 654–664.

SAMI, T. T., AND JAMES, N. P., 1994, Peritidal carbonate platform growth and cyclicity in an early Proterozoic foreland basin, upper Pethei Group, northwest Canada: Journal of Sedimentary Research, v. B64, p. 111–131.

SAMI, T. T., AND JAMES, N. P., 1996, Synsedimentary cements as Paleoproterozoic platform building blocks, Pethei Group, northwestern Canada: Journal of Sedimentary Research, v. 66, p. 209–222.

SAYLOR, B. Z., GROTZINGER, J. P., AND GERMS, G. J. B., 1995, Sequence stratigraphy and sedimentology of the Neoproterozoic Kuibis and Schwarzrand Subgroups (Nama Group), southern Namibia: Precambrian Research, v. 93, p. 153–171.

SEMIKHATOV, M. A., 1976, Experience in stromatolite studies in the U.S.S.R., in Walter, M. R., ed., Stromatolites: Amsterdam, Elsevier, Developments in Sedimentology 20, p. 337–357.

SEREBRYAKOV, S. N., 1976, Biotic and abiotic factors controlling the morphology of Riphean stromatolites, in Walter, M. R., ed., Stromatolites: Amsterdam, Elsevier, Developments in Sedimentology 20, p. 321–336.

SOUTHGATE, P. N., 1989, Relationships between cyclicity and stromatolite form in the Late Proterozoic Bitter Springs Formation, Australia: Sedimentology, v. 36, p. 323–339.

SRIVASTAVA, N. K., 1977, Sediment, petrographical, and geochemical studies of the late Precambrian stromatolites of India, in Flügel, E., ed., Fossil Algae: Berlin, Springer-Verlag, p. 105–112.

TURNER, E. C., NARBONNE, G. M., AND JAMES, N. P., 1993, Neoproterozoic reef microstructures from the Little Dal Group, northwestern Canada: Geology, v. 21, p. 259–262.

TURNER, E. C., JAMES, N. P., AND NARBONNE, G. M., 1997a, Growth dynamics of Neoproterozoic calcimicrobial reefs, Mackenzie Mountains, northwest Canada: Journal of Sedimentary Research, v. 67, p. 437–450.

TURNER, E. C., NARBONNE, G. M., AND JAMES, N. P., 1997b, Framework composition of Neoproterozoic reefs from northwestern Canada (abstract): Canadian Society of Petroleum Geologists–SEPM Joint Convention, Program with Abstracts, p. 279.

TWENHOFEL, W. H., 1919, Pre-Cambrian and Carboniferous algal deposits: American Journal of Science, v. 48, p. 339–352.

WALTER, M. R., 1972, Stromatolites and the biostratigraphy of the Australian Precambrian and Cambrian: The Palaeontological Association, Special Papers in Palaeontology No. 11, 190 p.

WALTER, M. R., BAULD, J., AND BROCK, T. D., 1976, Microbiology and morphogenesis of columnar stromatolites (Conophyton, Vacerrilla) from hot springs in Yellowstone National Park, in Walter, M. R., ed., Stromatolites: Amsterdam, Elsevier, Developments in Sedimentology 20, p. 273–310.

WEBB, G. E., 1996, Was Phanerozoic reef history controlled by the distribution of non-enzymatically secreted reef carbonates (microbial carbonate and biologically induced cement)?: Sedimentology, v. 43, p. 947–971.

PART IV
FACIES DYNAMICS

EVOLUTION OF THE NEOPROTEROZOIC KATAKTURUK DOLOMITE RAMP COMPLEX, NORTHEASTERN BROOKS RANGE, ALASKA

JAMES G. CLOUGH

Alaska Division of Geological & Geophysical Surveys, 794 University Ave., Suite 200, Fairbanks, AK 99709-3645, U.S.A.; and Department of Geology and Geophysics, University of Alaska Fairbanks, P.O. Box 755780, Fairbanks, AK 99775-5780, U.S.A.

AND

ROBERT K. GOLDHAMMER

Consulting Geologist, 1307 Constant Springs Drive, Austin, Texas 78746, U.S.A.

ABSTRACT: The Katakturuk Dolomite records an unsurpassed history of Neoproterozoic passive-margin cyclic sedimentation in Arctic Alaska and offers new insights into the evolution of Precambrian carbonate platforms in response to interpreted eustatic sea-level changes. The Katakturuk depicts a south-dipping, low-angle, distally steepened carbonate ramp complex with a complete spectrum of facies types, from proximal, updip tidal-flat complexes to distal, downdip, sub-wave-base allodapic turbidites, debrites, and rhythmites. The ramp margin is marked by thick stacks of amalgamated grainstone shoal complexes separating distally steepened downdip facies from ramp-interior facies. Using analysis of cycle stacking patterns, the 2500-m-thick Katakturuk can be subdivided into four second-order supersequences (of roughly equal thickness), each of which is made up of two to four third-order sequences (average a few hundred meters thick).

The high-frequency cyclic architecture of a single third-order depositional sequence (lower gray craggy dolomite member) provides an example of systems-tract development in the Katakturuk Dolomite. On the basis of physical bounding surfaces, two types of cycles are recognized: cycles bounded by marine flooding surfaces across which subfacies deepen, termed "subtidal cycles", and "peritidal cycles", that are bounded by subaerial exposure surfaces (e.g., peritidal laminites). The systematic vertical variation in cycle type (peritidal vs. subtidal) and cycle thickness, combined with vertical subfacies trends and the recognition of significant subaerial exposure surfaces (karsts, stacked tepees or peritidal breccias) define the transgressive and highstand systems tracts of thirteen third-order depositional sequences. The third-order sequences in turn stack to build larger second-order accommodation cycles. Coinciding second-order and third-order rises in relative sea level resulted in two major backstepping events, which were recorded in the deposition of outer-ramp slope facies directly on peritidal facies. The top of the Katakturuk is marked by a complete spectrum of karst facies, representing a supersequence lowstand superimposed on a third-order late highstand.

INTRODUCTION

Recognition and interpretation of shallowing-upward cycles is instrumental in reconstructing the depositional history of thick packages of platform carbonates. Studies of Phanerozoic shallow-platform cyclic carbonates rely on biostratigraphic and isotopic chronostratigraphy for correlation of depositional sequences and the timing of unconformities (Christie-Blick et al., 1988). Lacking bisostratigraphy, chronologic calibration of cycles and their duration is difficult for most Precambrian rocks, yet packages of cycles and their bounding flooding and exposure surfaces can provide a basis for establishing critical intrabasinal timelines. Although a lack of metazoan life in the Precambrian inhibits interpretations of paleoenvironments through depth- and environment-specific fauna and their burrowing and grazing activities, the complete absence of bioturbation allows for excellent preservation of primary sedimentary structures and the stratal interfaces that define cycle boundaries.

The Katakturuk Dolomite (Dutro, 1970) is the thickest, relatively conformable section (~2500 m) of Neoproterozoic rocks in Arctic Alaska, providing a nearly continuous record of carbonate sedimentation. Exposures of Katakturuk Dolomite in the Sadlerochit and Shublik Mountains (Fig. 1) afford a microcosm view of an apparently extensive carbonate depositional system. Although the lack of contiguous shoreline-to-basin exposure within these narrow outcrop belts precludes three-dimensional analysis of the lateral changes in depositional facies, examination of largely one-dimensional vertical changes in the patterns of cyclic sedimentation observed in widely spaced measured stratigraphic sections reveals the Katakturuk platform geologic history. This paper focuses on the evolution of the Katakturuk platform through time, and its response to eustatic sea-level change. We describe the systematic vertical variations in cycle type and cycle thickness and their organization into third-order and second-order depositional sequences. These are presented in a single schematic stratigraphic column and relative sea-level curve for the Katakturuk Dolomite. Our study is based on field studies conducted from 1985 though 1991 in the Sadlerochit and Shublik Mountains region. This field work consisted of: four stratigraphic sections that were measured and described through the complete Katakturuk succession (sections A, B, C, and D, Fig. 1); four very detailed stratigraphic sections were measured and described through a single unit in the middle part of the Katakturuk Dolomite (lower gray craggy dolomite member) (sections E, F, G, and H, Fig. 1); and paleocurrent measurements (where obtainable), observations of subfacies, and collections of hand samples that were taken at forty additional data stations throughout the study area (1–40, Fig. 1).

REGIONAL SETTING AND STRATIGRAPHY

Regional Geologic Setting

The Sadlerochit and Shublik Mountains are located in the northeast Brooks Range, a Cenozoic, north-vergent fold-and-thrust belt of the North American Cordilleran foldbelt. The Sadlerochit and Shublik Mountains, uplifted by north-vergent thrusting during the Cenozoic (Wallace and Hanks, 1990), contain a thick succession (up to 9000 m thick) of Precambrian through Cenozoic sedimentary, metamorphic, and igneous rocks that have undergone polyphase deformation since the Precambrian. The Katakturuk Dolomite generally strikes east–west and dips between 40° and 55° to the south, and is part of a competent structural package comprising Precambrian through lowermost Mississippian rocks that form the anticlinal cores of the Sadlerochit and Shublik mountain ranges (Wallace, 1993). Reed (1968) recognized at least two regional episodes of crustal shortening prior to Carboniferous onset of deposition over an angular unconformity.

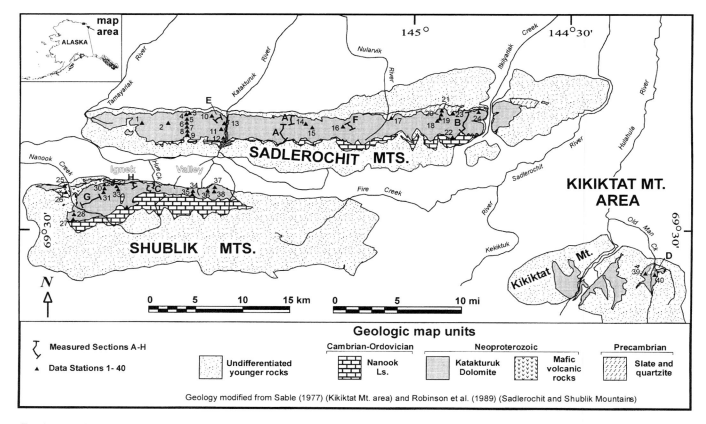

FIG. 1.—Location map of Katakturuk Dolomite, mafic volcanic rocks, and slate and quartzite outcrop belts in Sadlerochit and Shublik Mountains region. Inset map shows location of this map in northeastern Alaska.

Stratigraphic Overview

Dutro (1970) named the Katakturuk Dolomite after exposures in the Katakturuk River canyon in the Sadlerochit Mountains and subdivided the formation into nine informal members based on a composite type section in the western Shublik Mountains. Exposures of dolomite in the vicinity of Kikiktat Mountain (Fig. 1) were correlated with the Katakturuk Dolomite by Reiser (1970) and Sable (1977). The formation was later subdivided by Robinson et al. (1989) and Clough (1989) into sixteen informal lithostratigraphic members (Table 1), which are recognizable as distinct units throughout the study area.

In the western Shublik Mountains, the Katakturuk Dolomite overlies 450 m of mafic tholeiitic basalt flows that contain vesiculated and pillowed tholeiitic basalt and local pahoehoe structures (described in Moore, 1987). The relationship with the volcanic rocks is locally an erosional contact. The volcanic rocks and Katakturuk Dolomite succession constitute a distinct stratigraphic package (i.e., a megasequence) bounded by significant basal and upper "unconformities". The lower inferred unconformity is commonly a major detachment horizon in the eastern Sadlerochit Mountains and Kikiktat Mountain areas, locally juxtaposing the Katakturuk and volcanic megasequence above older polydeformed slate, quartzite, and dolomite. Along the north flank of the Sadlerochit and Shublik Mountains the megasequence is thrust over younger Paleozoic rocks. The upper boundary of the megasequence is a significant angular and erosional unconformity, with approximately 600 m of the uppermost Katakturuk Dolomite removed in the western Shublik Mountains prior to deposition of the Cambrian to Ordovician Nanook Limestone.

Age

The Katakturuk Dolomite is Late Proterozoic (Neoproterozoic) in age within these general limits: $<801 \pm 20$ Ma and >545 Ma (Clough and Goldhammer, 1995). The lower age limit is based on a Rb–Sr isotopic age date (Clough et al., 1990) from a diabase sill that intrudes older slate and quartzite in the eastern Sadlerochit Mountains. The diabase sill is considered to be coeval with the mafic volcanic flows exposed in the eastern Sadlerochit Mountains and western Shublik Mountains (Moore, 1987; Clough et al., 1990). The youngest detrital zircon age of 936 ± 3 Ma ($^{206}Pb/^{207}Pb$) obtained from the underlying slate and quartzite unit in the central Sadlerochit Mountains (McClelland, 1997) supports a similar minimum age for these older metasedimentary rocks. The upper age limit is likewise poorly constrained. Ichnogenera collected from the base of the overlying Nanook Limestone are Ediacaran or younger (G. M. Narbonne, personal communication, 1995). Trilobites collected ~950 m above the base of the Nanook Limestone have been identified as Late Cambrian (Blodgett et al., 1986).

Number (referred to in text)	Informal Member Name	Thickness
	Top of Katakturuk Dolomite	
(16)	Upper siliceous dolomite	150 m
(15)	Breccia dolomite	300 m
(14)	Horsetooth dolomite	75 m
(13)	Black laminated dolomite	75 m
(12)	Pink dolomite	170 m
(11)	Upper gray craggy dolomite	330 m
(10)	Thin-bedded algal dolomite	100 m
(9)	Lower gray craggy dolomite	90 m
(8)	Brown marker unit	40 m
(7)	White marker unit	45 m
(6)	Silicified oolite	450 m
(5)	Thin-laminated dolomite	60 m
(4)	Cobweb dolomite	50 m
(3)	Variegated dolomite	75 m
(2)	Zebra dolomite	80 m
(1)	Spire dolomite	450 m
	Base of Katakturuk Dolomite	

Correlation with Other Proterozoic Rocks of the Northern Cordillera

The connection between the Katakturuk Dolomite and other better understood Proterozoic carbonate successions in Canada is unclear. Rainbird et al. (1996) proposed placing the Katakturuk Dolomite within Proterozoic Sequence B rocks (~1.2 to ~0.78 Ga) of the northern Canadian Cordillera. Proterozoic Sequence B rocks include the lower Tindir Group (Ogilvie Mountains, Alaska and Yukon Territory), Shaler Supergroup (Amundsen Basin, Northwest Territory), Mackenzie Mountains Supergroup (Northwest Territory), Pinguicula Group (Wernecke Inlier, Yukon Territory), and Fifteenmile Group (Coal Creek Inlier, Yukon Territory). According to McClelland (1997), differences in detrital zircon ages from the Sadlerochit Mountains quartzite unit and those reported by Rainbird et al. (1992) for the Mackenzie Mountains and Shaler supergroups contradict the Proterozoic Sequence B stratigraphic correlations of Rainbird et al. (1996).

SUBFACIES AND FACIES ASSEMBLAGES

Katakturuk subfacies, the rock record of subenvironments, are combined into larger genetically linked sets of subfacies defined as facies assemblages, the rock record of an environment (Demicco and Hardie, 1994). Subfacies are the fundamental building blocks of cycles, and their recognition is crucial to reconstructing the evolutionary history of the Katakturuk platform. Modifying the usage of Demicco and Hardie (1994), we define Katakturuk Dolomite subfacies by (1) grain and sediment types, (2) depositional texture, (3) sedimentary structures, (4) biogenic structures, and (5) early diagenetic features. Grain and sediment types are summarized in Table 2. The most common sedimentary structures in the Katakturuk Dolomite are planar lamination, ripple cross-lamination, tabular cross-stratification, trough cross-stratification, hummocky cross-stratification, graded bedding, lumpy bedding, and wavy-lenticular bedding. Directional paleocurrent measurements (restored for tectonic tilt) taken from cross-bedding in the Katakturuk Dolomite (384 measurements, mainly trough and tabular cross-strata) are summarized in Figure 2A. Biogenic structures in the Katakturuk Dolomite are stromatolites, which often exhibit a preferred growth orientation and elongation that yields bidirectional paleocurrent information (146 measurements, summarized in Figure 2B). Early diagenetic features that disrupt bedding include diastasis cracks, mudcracks, prism cracks, sheet cracks, tepee antiforms, fenestrae, and dissolution surfaces and cavities.

Recognition of grain and sediment types, sedimentary structures, and sedimentary textures provides the diagnostic criteria for our paleoenvironmental reconstructions (discussed below). Subfacies are named after a textural or genetic classification preceded by one or more characteristic grain types and/or sedimentary structure(s), e.g., *trough cross-bedded ooid–pisoid grainstone*; *peritidal laminite*. We recognize five main, regionally correlative environments and associated facies assemblages in the Katakturuk Dolomite: (1) subaerial-exposure, (2) peritidal, (3) tide-dominated lagoon, (4) windward sand shoal, and (5) outer ramp and slope. These facies assemblages and their component subfacies extend laterally throughout the Katakturuk Dolomite outcrop belt except where their absence is stated specifically in text.

(1) Subaerial-Exposure Facies Assemblage

The subaerial-exposure facies assemblage records early to late vadose diagenetic events that altered and even obliterated original sedimentary textures. Component subfacies are: (1) dolocrete, (2) microspeleothem flowstone, (3) peritidal breccia and tepee, (4) collapse breccia, and (5) cave-fill karst breccia. Although most of these subaerial exposure subfacies result from diagenetic rather than depositional processes, we include them in this discussion because they play an important role in the evolution of the Katakturuk carbonate ramp. The vertical profile and diverse sedimentary textures and structures of this facies assemblage are determined by the host rock and the duration and magnitude of diagenetic alteration.

(1) Dolocrete Subfacies.—

Dolocrete (dolomitized calcrete) consists of up to 50-cm-thick layers of accretionary vadose pisoliths (vadoids of Peryt, 1983), chalky white laminar crusts, and sediment-filled and cement-filled cracks (Fig. 4A). The Katakturuk dolocrete profile generally consists of a thin laminar crust underlain by reverse-graded, polygonally fitted pisoliths. Cement and sediment infill cracks in the underlying host rock, which commonly is cross-bedded grainstone. Dolocrete subfacies are common in informal members 1, 3, and 6 (Table 1).
Subenvironment.—This subfacies represents soil alteration (paleosols) of subaerially exposed carbonate sediment. Accretionary pisoliths formed in the vadose zone by *in situ* precipitation of calcium carbonate percolating downward beneath a laminar hardpan. Cracks in the substrate are dissolution pathways that were later filled with sediment from above and carbonate cements. This type of subfacies was first described by Dunham (1969) in the Permian Capitan reef of New Mexico and Texas, and similar dolocretes have been documented in other Proterozoic rocks (cf. Bertrand-Sarfati and Moussine-Pouchkine, 1983; Pelechaty and James, 1991).

(2) Microspeleothem Flowstone Subfacies.—

This subfacies is composed of multilayered cements, micro-popcorn micrite, orbicular crusts, and pisoliths in layers up to 5 cm thick, and filling horizontal cavities and vertical cracks

TABLE 2.—TYPES OF KATAKTURUK DOLOMITE GRAINS AND SEDIMENT, BRIEF DESCRIPTIONS AND ORIGIN, AND KEY TO FIGURES

Grain and Sediment Types	Description and Origin	Figures
Coated grains: Ooids Pisoids Composite grains	Coated grains range in size from <2 mm in diameter (ooids) to up to 1 cm in diameter (pisoids and composite grains). Coatings are tangential-concentric and originate from inorganic carbonate precipitation during episodic tide- and wave-generated currents. Katakturuk pisoids are equivalent to "giant ooids" of Sumner and Grotzinger (1993). Grain shape has been attributed to frequency of bottom agitation (Wanless and Tedesco, 1993). Present in cross-stratified grainstones in predominantly shoal (ooids and pisoids), back shoal (composite grains), and tidal channels (ooids and pisoids).	Figs. 3A, 3B, 3C, and 10D
Peloids	Enigmatic; may represent both aggregates of flocculated aragonite particles sourced by whitings **and** neomorphic replacements of ooid, pisoid, and stromatolite fragments. Present in shallow to deep subtidal settings.	Figs. 3C and 3E
Intraclasts: Mudchips Stromaclasts Microbial sandchips	Fragmentation by current activity of penecontemporaneous lithified to semilithified sediment produces intraclasts. Mudchips represent reworked mechanically deposited (settle-out from suspension) mud. Current abrasion of stromatolites yields stromaclasts (Sami and James, 1994). Microbial sand chips (Pfluger and Gresse, 1996) represent eroded peritidal to subtidal filamentous mats. Present in peritidal to shallow subtidal settings.	Figs. 3D, 3F and 7E
Lime mud	Lime mud may be generated by both grain abrasion and inorganic precipitation of carbonate (i.e., "whitings"). May be present in peritidal to slope settings.	
Karst breccia	Formed by vadose–phreatic karst dissolution processes resulting in brecciation of host roof rock, which subsequently was redeposited in potholes, dissolution pipes, and laminar cavities.	Figs. 4E, 4F, 5B, 5C, and 5D
Allodapic sands	Shallow-platform-derived ooids, pisoids, peloids, and intraclasts, redeposited in a slope setting by sediment gravity flows. Includes dark gray to black chert spheroids and clasts that have undergone extensive late diagenetic silicification, which obliterated original internal coated grain fabric.	Fig. 11D
Peri-platform slope sediment	Tabular to angular dolomite clasts formed by erosion of slope substrate by turbidity-flow and debris-flow processes.	Figs. 10E, 10F, 11A, and 11B
Illite clays	Hemipelagic suspension settling of terrigenous mud that form fissile, graphitic shale beds. Present in turbidites of outer-ramp slope setting.	Figs. 11A and 11B.
Detrital quartz	Well-rounded, very fine silt-size quartz grains. Enigmatic origin; may be derived from extrabasinal source, suggesting transport and deposition by wind. Present as isolated grains within the uppermost branches of some stromatolites and as well-segregated layers in supratidal-flat sediments.	

(Fig. 4B, C). Microspeleothem flowstone is commonly associated with peritidal breccias and tepees (described below). Multilayered cements may exhibit over twelve generations of microsparite composed of acicular dolomite crystals oriented towards cavity centers. Micropopcorn micrite consists of arborescent micrite concretions fringing cavities. Microspeleothem flowstone is very abundant in the brown marker unit and less common in informal members 1, 6, 9, 10, 11, 13, and 15 (Table 1).

Subenvironment.—Microspeleothem flowstone records early vadose diagenesis of subaerially exposed carbonates, involving dissolution and reprecipitation of carbonate cement. Similar features are documented in Upper Proterozoic carbonates by Bertrand-Sarfati and Moussine-Pouchkine (1983) and in Holocene supratidal deposits of Fisherman Bay, South Australia (Ferguson et al., 1982). The Fisherman Bay microspeleothem flowstone is actively forming today beneath a megapolygon-dissected supratidal crust within which a confined aquifer emerges.

(3) Peritidal Breccia and Tepee Subfacies.—

This subfacies consists of disrupted, nontectonic, inverted-chevron slabs of peritidal laminite (mother rock composed of any of the laminite subfacies) that yield tepee structures and meter-scale breccias of peritidal laminite clasts (Fig. 4D, E). Microspeleothem flowstone commonly alternates with the peritidal breccia and tepee subfacies, particularly in the brown marker unit (Table 1). This subfacies is very abundant in the variegated dolomite member and brown maker units and is common in members 1, 6, 9, 10, 11, 13, 14, and 15 (Table 1).

Subenvironment.—This subfacies represents a peritidal complex that was overprinted with episodic subaerial and marine–vadose diagenesis. Peritidal breccias and tepees form by expansion of surface sediment through repeated wetting, desiccation and thermal contraction, and enlargement of fractures form by precipitation of carbonate cement (Assereto and Kendall, 1977).

(4) Collapse-Breccia Subfacies.—

This subfacies is composed of matrix-supported, angular and polymictic centimeter-scale breccia within circular and subhorizontal cavities, vertical cracks, and centimeter- to meter-scale continuous beds (Figs. 4F, 5B). The clasts have similar composition and commonly exhibit a "jigsaw puzzle" fit. Associated features include cement-filled cracks and fissures, microtepees, microspeleothem flowstone, cave popcorn, geopetal internal sediment, and scalloped karren surfaces (Figs. 4F, 5A). This subfacies is abundant in the brown marker unit and lower gray craggy dolomite. It is also common in members 3, 10, 11, 14, and 15 (Table 1).

Subenvironment.—These small-scale paleokarst features were formed by vadose–phreatic karst dissolution processes: alteration and collapse brecciation of host roof rock, which subsequently was redeposited in potholes, dissolution pipes, and laminar cavities. The collapse-breccia subfacies represents subaerial exposure diagenesis during sea-level lowstands of sufficient duration to form "local paleokarst" (Choquette and James, 1988). This subfacies is less pervasive and extensive than the cave-fill karst breccia subfacies described below.

(5) Cave-Fill Karst Breccia Subfacies.—

This subfacies is a thick unit (100 m to several hundreds of meters thick) composed of poorly sorted, matrix-supported

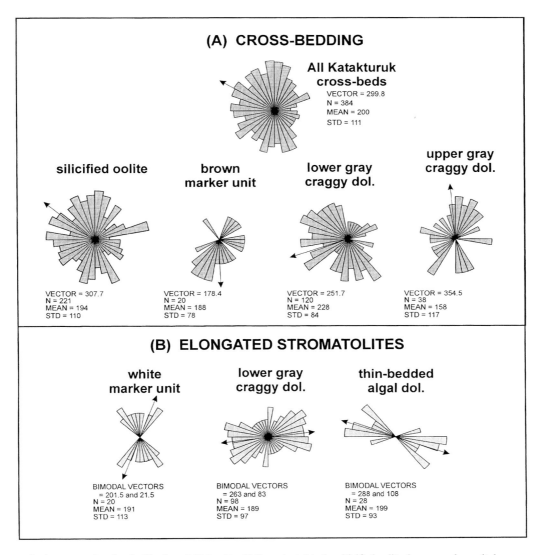

Fig. 2.—Summary of paleocurrent data for the Katakturuk Dolomite. A) Cross-bed data for silicified oolite, brown marker unit, lower gray craggy dolomite, and upper gray craggy dolomite members. B) Bimodal paleocurrent data for elongated stromatolites in white marker unit, lower gray craggy dolomite, and thin-bedded algal dolomite members. For stratigraphic position of members see table 1.

cave-fill breccia dominated by angular, polymict clasts (up to a meter in length) with larger clasts near the base of the subfacies (Fig. 5C, D). Slightly rotated mother rock (crackle breccia) grades upward into the top of unaltered Katakturuk roof rock composed of grainstone and laminite. The brecciated beds are locally laced with siliceous webs. Cave-fill karst breccia is present only in the upper four members of the Katakturuk Dolomite (members 13–16, Table 1) in the Sadlerochit Mountains.

Subenvironment.—The cave-fill karst breccia subfacies represents exposure of large areas of the carbonate ramp for sufficient duration to allow deep and extensive dissolution, alteration, and subsequent erosion of the host rock.

(2) Peritidal Facies Assemblage

Peritidal subfacies were deposited in and around a tidal-flat environment and include mechanically deposited sediment, or-

ganosedimentary features constructed by a benthic microbial community, and syngenetic chemically precipitated features. Burne and Moore (1987) introduced the term "microbialite" as a replacement for "cryptalgalaminated carbonate" (Aitken, 1967) to designate organosedimentary deposits formed as the result of trapping and binding of fine detrital sediment by microbial activity and biologically influenced calcification. Cryptmicrobialite is used herein since the microbial influence is inferred rather than directly observed. We retain "stromatolite" to designate organosedimentary structures forming discrete to laterally linked, thinly laminated masses with vertical relief, yet we recognize that they were also constructed by microbial activity. Direct evidence for the benthic microbial community in Katakturuk stromatolites is rare; however, degraded *Siphonophycus*-like tubular filaments are present in some specimens (identification by H.J. Hofmann, University of Montreal). Component subfacies are: (1) peritidal laminite, (2) tufa, (3) crystal

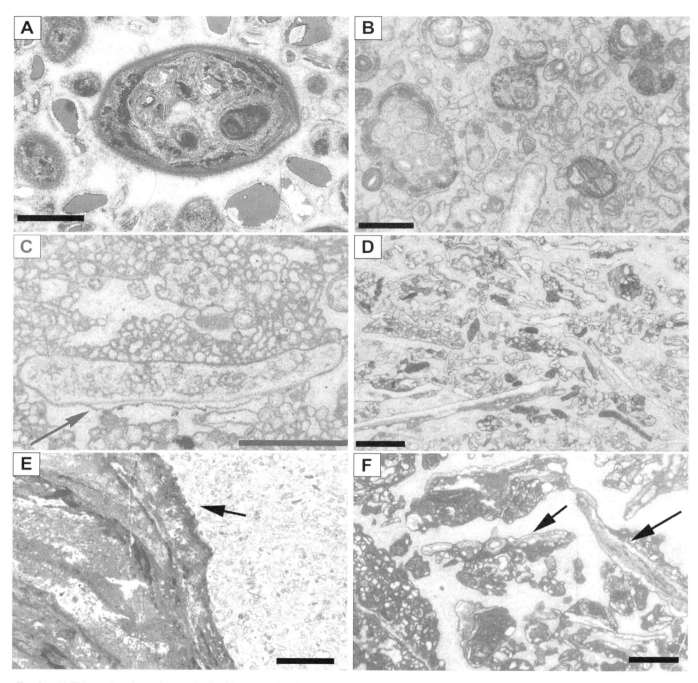

Fig. 3.—A) Thin-section photomicrograph of ooids, composite pisoid (center of figure), and with moldic porosity formed by leaching of ooid grains. Member 6, Section A. Scale bar equals 2 mm. B) Thin-section photomicrograph of composite-grain, ooid, and pisoid grainstone. Note thin superficial coatings around composite grains (hence pisoids). Recrystallized grains composed of sparry carbonate (now dolomite) suggests leaching of metastable carbonate phase and subsequent precipitation of sparry, mosaic cement in molds. Member 6, Section A. Scale bar equals 2 mm. C) Thin-section photomicrograph of poorly sorted composite grain–ooid grainstone with all grains recrystallized to sparry mosaic (now dolomite), suggesting extensive leaching. Pendant cement fabrics (arrow) and meniscus cements lining interparticle pores indicate early vadose diagenesis linked to subaerial exposure. Member 1, Section A. Scale bar equals 2 mm. D) Thin-section photomicrograph of poorly sorted intraclast–composite-grain grainstone. Intraclasts are eroded cryptmicrobialite. Member 9, Section G. Scale bar equals 2 mm. E) Thin-section photomicrograph of part of subtidal columnar stromatolite (left side of figure) and peloid grainstone (right side of figure). Interiors of peloids are completely leached and filled with micritic cement. Other peloids are incorporated into stromatolite laminae (arrow) by trapping and binding of microbial mat. Member 9, Section A. Scale bar equals 2 mm. F) Thin-section photomicrograph of intraclast–peloid grainstone. Intraclasts are predominantly stromaclasts (arrows) that are derived from erosion of subtidal stromatolites similar to those shown in Figure 3E. Member 9, Section A. Scale bar equals 2 mm.

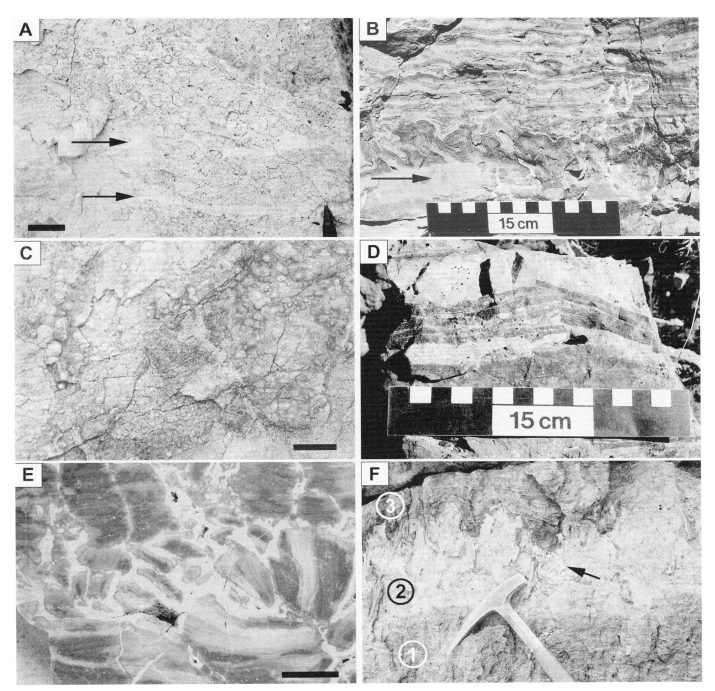

FIG. 4.—A) Dolocrete (dolomitized calcrete) consisting of chalky white laminar crusts (arrows) underlain by reverse-graded, polygonally fitted accretionary vadose pisoliths. Up to 50-cm-thick dolocrete profile at top of member 6, Section A. Scale bar equals 1 cm. B) Microspeleothem flowstone composed of multilayered cements. Multilayered cements were precipitated within a horizontal cavity beneath a megapolygon peritidal laminite. Irregular layer of flowstone (forming an orbicular crust) directly overlies peritidal laminite (arrow) at base of cavity. Member 8, Section A. C) Bedding-plane view of slab of microspeleothem flowstone exhibiting orbicular crusts and pisoliths. Member 8, Section A. Scale bar equals 1 cm. D) Tepee brecciation in peritidal laminite. Member 8, Section A. E) Brecciated peritidal laminite. Monomict composition (cryptmicrobialite) and *in situ* autobrecciated fabric suggests penecontemporaneous disruption of laminites associated with subaerial diagenesis during lowstand conditions. Polished hand specimen. Member 1, Section A. Scale bar equals 3 cm. F) Irregular subaerial exposure surface (karren) at top of light-colored peritidal laminite (layer 2). Small-scale collapse breccias (arrow) are common along this horizon. Peritidal laminite overlies darker cross-bedded grainstone (layer 1) and is overlain by tufa (layer 3). Member 9, Section A.

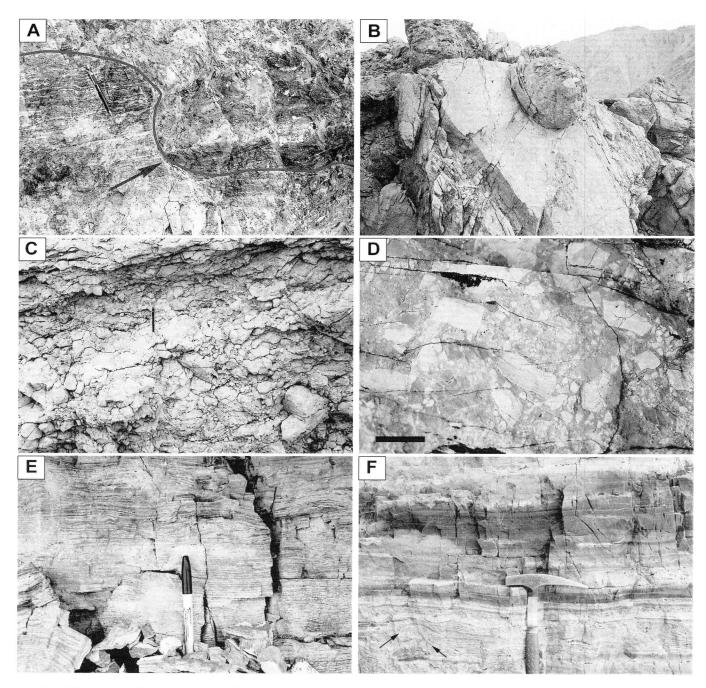

Fig. 5.—A) Sharp karstic dissolution cavity (outlined in black) within tufa subfacies. Irregular karstic hole (arrow) is infilled with angular monomict breccia composed of tufa clasts. This prominent karren is interpreted as a subaerial vadose dissolution surface related to subaerial exposure and leaching. Member 11, Section A. Pencil for scale equals 14 cm. B) Bedding-plane view of exhumed circular dissolution pit filled with collapse breccia. Collapse breccia is composed of angular clasts of intraclast–peloid grainstone. This laterally extensive horizon denotes a sea-level lowstand of duration sufficient to develop dissolution pits and collapse brecciation. Member 9, Section A. Pencil for scale (on solution pit) equals 14 cm. C) Outcrop photograph of top of karst breccia subfacies. The breccia consists largely of in-place, fractured, little rotated, monomict clasts of "mother rock". It is interpreted as in-place brecciated and veined "crackle breccia" representing the cavern-roof component of an extensive karst complex. Member 15, Station 9. Pencil for scale equals 14 cm. D) Outcrop photograph of poorly sorted, polymict, angular, matrix-supported karst breccia. This fabric is interpreted as the cave-fill component of the extensive karst complex. Member 15, Station 8, Scale bar equals 12 cm. E) Outcrop photograph of part of a thick stack of peritidal laminite composed of cryptmicrobialite. Member 3, Section A. Pen for scale equals 14 cm. F) Outcrop photograph of peritidal laminite. Light-colored carbonate below head of hammer is cryptmicrobialite, which is disrupted into tepee breccias (arrows). Dark-colored carbonate above hammer is parallel laminite composed of mechanically deposited, very fine-grained carbonate detritus. Member 8, Section E.

fan array, (4) laterally linked domal stromatolite, (5) intraclast flat-pebble conglomerate, and (6) wavy-lenticular ribbon rock.

(1) Peritidal Laminite Subfacies.—

This subfacies is characterized by continuous-bedded, millimeter-thick laminae consisting of (a) cryptmicrobialite and/or (b) parallel-laminated lime mud to very fine silt. Cryptmicrobialite is composed of sub-millimeter-scale white and gray micritic laminae couplets (Fig. 5E). Individual laminae exhibit high to moderate inheritance from underlying laminae and are generally planar but locally undulatory to tufted-crinkly. Associated sedimentary structures include fenestrae and desiccation mudcracks. Parallel laminite consists of millimeter-scale planar, wavy and very low-angle cross-stratified laminae composed of extremely well-sorted carbonate mud to very fine silt (Fig. 5F). Mudcracks (Fig. 6A) and fenestrae may also be present in this subfacies. Peritidal laminite is common throughout the Katakturuk Dolomite but absent from members 4 and 5 (Table 1).
Subenvironment.—This subfacies formed in an intertidal to supratidal setting in progradational tidal flat complexes that migrated either seaward from the landlocked, updip shoreline or landward from shoal crests. Fenestrae and mudcracks indicate episodic drying conditions in upper intertidal to supratidal settings. Tufted-crinkly cryptmicrobialite is similar in appearance to Holocene tufted mats of Hamelin Pool, Western Australia, which form in middle to upper intertidal areas where poor drainage conditions or high water table keep the mat and sediment permanently moist (Logan et al., 1974). Parallel laminite represents fairly rapid mechanical deposition by weak currents and settling of mud from suspension in an upper intertidal to supratidal setting. Wavy laminae result from mud draping of irregularities (Demicco and Hardie, 1994), which are commonly ripple cross-stratified (upper intertidal).

(2) Tufa Subfacies.—

This subfacies consists of medium to thick beds composed of irregular, wavy and tufted centimeter-scale cryptmicrobial-laminated mudstone alternating with thin (millimeter-scale) to thick (centimeter-scale) cement laminae (Fig. 6B–E). This is similar to tufa described by Grotzinger (1985, 1993), Hofmann and Jackson (1987), and Peryt et al. (1990). Cement laminae are continuous, smooth to undulatory, and colloform, locally forming irregular tufted microdigitate stromatolitic structures (millimeter-scale length and width) (Fig. 6D). Cement laminae are composed of a distinctive fibrous to radial fibrous microstructure. Internal fabric of cements is defined by bundled vertical arrays of acicular dolomite crystals, on average 25 mm thick and up to 5 mm tall. Fenestral fabric is common (Fig. 6E); microspeleothem features and karstic dissolution phenomena also are commonly associated with this subfacies (Fig. 5A). Tufa is most abundant in the thin-bedded algal dolomite member and is also present in members 3, 9, 11, 12, and 13 (Table 1). This subfacies occurs only in the Sadlerochit and Shublik Mountains.
Subenvironment.—The tufa subfacies is interpreted to have formed on tidal flats and in supratidal ponds where the influx of fine- to coarse-grained carbonate sediment was absent to extremely low, allowing the formation of cement crusts. The fibrous marine cements are inferred to have formed initially as

aragonite, which was later replaced by pseudomorphs of anhedral dolomitic neospar crystals (Grotzinger, 1985). Grotzinger (1993) attributed the genesis of this type of tufa to wind tides or storm tides pushing aragonite-supersaturated waters onto supratidal flats with subsequent evaporation and precipitation of cement crusts. Aragonite precipitation was apparently promoted by microbial photosynthesis, which lowered the pH of the water (Grotzinger, 1993).

(3) Crystal Fan Array Subfacies.—

This subfacies is characterized by botryoidal dolomite or silica crystals radiating upward from a single point, forming laterally continuous fan arrays up to 25 cm thick (Fig. 7A, B). Single crystal fans are inverted cones, circular in plan view. Individual crystals range from 2 to 8 mm in width and up to 25 cm in height. The matrix between crystal fans is carbonate mud to very fine silt. Crystal fan arrays are commonly associated with peritidal laminite (Fig. 7B) and may be truncated at their top by cross-bedded peloid–ooid packstone–grainstone. It is also closely associated with large tepee structures up to 0.35 m high. This subfacies is present only in the variegated dolomite member (Table 1) in the Sadlerochit and Shublik Mountains.
Subenvironment.—Crystal fan arrays formed in restricted hypersaline low-energy ponds to a shallow marine–lagoon setting. Similar crystal fans have been interpreted to have formed as upward authigenic crystal growth from the sea floor in the Lower Proterozoic Rocknest Formation of northwest Canada (Grotzinger and Read, 1983). Crystal fans originally formed as botryoidal aragonite through both authigenic and diagenetic processes and were later replaced by silica and dolomite (Grotzinger, 1986). Truncation by overlying bedding indicates that these fans are primary features and not late diagenetic phenomena.

(4) Laterally Linked Domal Stromatolite Subfacies.—

This subfacies embodies a variety of stromatolite morphologies including undulatory, pseudocolumnar, columnar, cumulate, bulbous, nodular, and domal forms (Fig. 7C, D). Laminae have continuous interconnections between stromatolites ("laterally linked"; Logan et al., 1964). Laminae exhibit moderate inheritance from underlying laminae. A vertical succession of stromatolite morphologies is common, from columnar to domal to elongated domal forms in beds up to 0.5 m thick (Fig. 7D). This subfacies is commonly present in members 6, 7, 9, 10, 11, 12, and 13 (Table 1).
Subenvironment.—The subfacies was deposited in a shallow subtidal to lower intertidal setting. Stromatolite morphologies reflect the environments in which they occur and result from physical processes (marine hydrodynamics) and chemical processes (inorganic carbonate precipitation and diagenesis). The vertical succession of stromatolite forms results in a reduction in stromatolite synoptic relief, attributed by Hoffman (1974) to shallowing of water depth due to relative sea-level fall and/or upward stromatolite construction. Stromatolite elongation is a product of wave erosion from a predominant direction, similar to Holocene examples in Shark Bay (Hamelin Pool), where elongation results from local prevailing trade-wind-driven wave erosion (Logan et al., 1974).

(5) Intraclast Flat-Pebble Conglomerate Subfacies.—

This subfacies consists of thin- to thick-bedded, well-sorted and mechanically stratified (parallel-stratified, low-angle, and

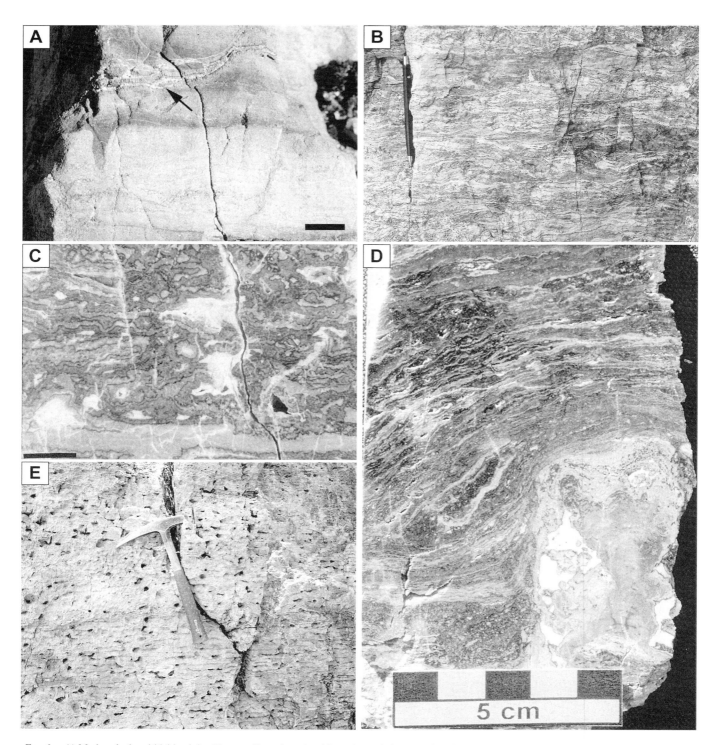

Fig. 6.—A) Mudcracked peritidal laminite. Note small autobrecciated layer (arrow) above mudcrack. Member 8, Section E. Scale bar equals 1 cm. B) Highly irregular-laminated tufa subfacies. Member 9, Section C. Pencil for scale equals 14 cm. C) Polished slab of dissolution-enlarged, non-fabric-selective porosity infilled with cement and internal sediment. Host rock is tufa and cryptmicrobialite (white layer). Member 11, Station 7. Scale bar equals 2 cm. D) Polished slab of tufa subfacies with microdigitate stromatolite in lower right corner. Member 10, Section G. E) Large-scale vuggy porosity developed in tufa subfacies. Tufa has a centimeter-thick lamination, which alternates with cryptmicrobialite. Member 11, Section A.

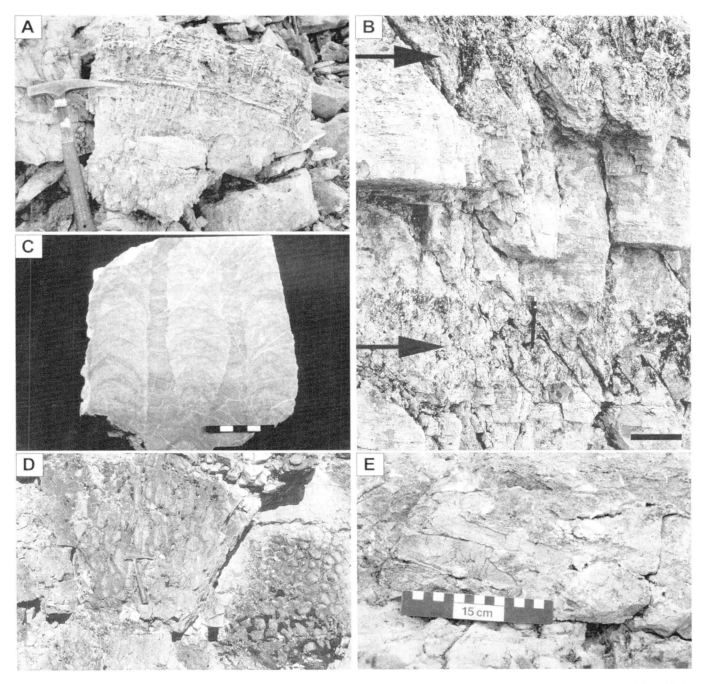

FIG. 7.—A) Silicified radiating crystalline fan. Member 3, Section A. B) Beds of crystal-fan-array subfacies (arrows) overlain by peritidal laminite subfacies. Member 3, Section A. Scale bar equals 10 cm. C) Columnar stromatolites that form the base of shoaling-upward cycles. Stromatolites were initially laterally linked with actual synoptic relief between columns no greater than 2 cm. Member 7, Station 6. Scale bar in centimeters. D) Bedding-plane view of laterally linked domal stromatolite subfacies. Elongated stromatolites (with hammer for scale) overlie domal stromatolites (lower right). Member 7, Station 13. E) Intraclast flat-pebble conglomerate subfacies. Large intraclasts are interpreted to represent eroded peritidal laminite deposited as imbricate storm lags. Member 9, Station 32.

imbricated) intraclasts (mudchips and microbial sandchips), and, depending upon available subtidal grain supply, ooids, pisoids, peloids, and composite grains may be present (Fig. 7E). Keystone vugs are locally present. The intraclast flat-pebble conglomerate subfacies is present in members 1, 2, 3, 6, 7, 8, 9, 10, 11, 12, and 13 (Table 1).

Subenvironment.—This subfacies formed in a shallow subtidal to intertidal grain flat with episodic high-energy deposition by storm-driven waves. Intraclasts represent eroded tidal-flat sediments (parallel laminite and cryptmicrobialite) with ooids, pisoids, peloids, and composite grains derived from shallow-marine sandbelt shoals. Keystone vugs delineate laminoid beach bubbles; imbricated flat-pebble breccias represent storm lag deposits.

(6) Wavy-Lenticular Ribbon Rock Subfacies.—

Thin beds of mudstone alternate with ripple cross-laminated sand or silt layers in this subfacies (Fig. 8A). Interbeds are commonly 3–5 cm thick. Discrete lenses of ripple cross-laminated sand or silt are also found within mudstone beds. Ripple cross-lamination usually is indistinct, because of the extremely well-sorted nature of the silt and sand. The wavy-lenticular ribbon rock subfacies is most abundant in members 2 and 3 and is present in members 6, 8, 9, and 13 (Table 1).
Subenvironment.—This subfacies formed in a shallow subtidal to lower intertidal setting. Current or wave action produces rippled sand and silt (fine abrasion detritus) on flooded tidal flats followed by slack-water conditions with suspension settle-out of muds, subsequently burying ripples (Reineck and Singh, 1980). The subfacies is similar to the dolomite ribbon rock described by Demicco (1983). Wavy-lenticular bedding is common to many mesotidal to macrotidal environments (Reineck and Singh, 1980; Demicco, 1983).

(3) Tide-Dominated Lagoon Facies Assemblage

This facies assemblage represents a predominantly tide-dominated, but temporally storm-influenced, shallow-water lagoon setting separated from the open ocean by a windward barrier of ooid–pisoid sand shoals (described below) that absorbed most of the wave energy. The lagoon was sufficiently broad (kilometers wide) that a low-energy peritidal complex developed on its landward edge. Within the lagoonal setting, linear tidal sand bars, oriented perpendicular to the platform strand line, migrated laterally, producing a sheet-like deposit of tabular cross-bedded grainstone. These flood-dominated tidal sand ridges were quite long (tens of kilometers in length) and covered with transverse sand waves oriented ~35° to the axes of the tidal bars (based on paleocurrent measurements). Ebb flow occurred in channels between the linear tidal sand ridges. During minor relative sea-level falls, peritidal facies were deposited directly on the tops of the tidal bars, and the onshore peritidal complex prograded seaward during extended relative sea-level falls. Grain types are predominantly peloids, stromaclasts, microbial sand chips, and composite grains. Ooids are notably rare to absent, and few coated peloids, stromaclasts, and composite grains are present. Component subfacies of the assemblage are: (1) wavy stromatolite, (2) branching columnar stromatolite, (3) coalesced stromatolite and grainstone, (4) stromatolite bioherm, (5) cross-bedded peloid–composite grainstone, and (6) cross-bedded intraclast–peloid grainstone.

(1) Wavy Stromatolite Subfacies.—

This subfacies is characterized by thin (millimeter- to centimeter-scale), laterally continuous to discontinuous beds composed of white to very light gray, sub-millimeter-scale, wavy to undulatory and planar laminae alternating with dark gray micritic laminae (Fig. 8C, D). Laminae exhibit moderate inheritance, with basal layers conforming to the underlying substrate, usually cross-bedded peloid–composite grainstone, imparting an undulatory nature to these stromatolites. This subfacies commonly overlies marine hardgrounds or subaerial

exposure karren and is locally dissected by channels filled with cross-stratified intraclast–peloid grainstone (Fig. 8D). Notably absent are desiccation phenomena such as fenestrae and mudcracks. The wavy stromatolite subfacies is present in members 9, 10, and 11 (Table 1).
Subenvironment.—In contrast to peritidal cryptmicrobialite, this subfacies was exclusively subtidal. The light-colored laminae represent microbial mats. The wavy stromatolite subfacies formed during relative sea-level rises of sufficient duration to allow microbial mat colonization of well-cemented substrate (hardgrounds or karren). We interpret this subfacies to represent the deepest water depth in the tide-dominated lagoon facies assemblage.

(2) Branching Columnar Stromatolite Subfacies.—

In this subfacies, columnar stromatolites range between 5 to 25 cm in height, commonly with divergent branches, and occur as discrete bodies within cross-bedded peloid–composite grainstone subfacies (Fig. 8E, F). Bases of adjacent stromatolites may be interconnected, particularly where formed from wavy stromatolite. Subfacies may be persistent laterally for tens of meters. In cross section, individual stromatolites are round to oval. Ovate columns and branches are oriented into the direction of the prevailing local paleocurrents (determined from paleocurrent data collected from cross-beds). Internal laminae consist of spar–micrite couplets. Stromatolite bases either form a sharp contact above hardgrounds of cross-bedded coarse grainstone or karren, or grew gradationally upward from wavy stromatolites. Tops of stromatolites are commonly truncated by overlying intraclastic grainstone composed of stromaclasts and the space between stromatolites is filled with coarse peloid–composite grainstone. This subfacies is present in members 9, 10, and 11 (Table 1).
Subenvironment.—These stromatolites are exclusively subtidal and grew in channels between linear tidal sand ridges and in deeper-water lagoon settings. Initial colonization by subtidal microbial mats occurred on stable substrate provided by well-cemented submarine hardgrounds and subaerial exposure surfaces (karren). Stromatolite tops were eroded by high-energy tidal currents and wave currents, which formed the overlying cross-bedded grainstone and inter-stromatolite sands. The setting was similar to the high-energy shoal environment of subtidal stromatolites reported by Dill and Shinn (1986) near Lee Stocking Island, Bahamas (Holocene) and Salem Limestone (Mississippian) of Indiana, described by Keith and Thompson (1994).

(3) Coalesced Stromatolite and Grainstone Subfacies.—

In this subfacies, white to light gray columnar stromatolites, rarely branching, coalesce to form biostromal layers between layers of cross-stratified intraclast–peloid grainstone and packstone (Fig. 9A). Layers of coalesced stromatolites are up to 0.25 m thick and display a polygonal-fitted fabric in transverse section. Basal layers of stromatolites are laterally linked cumulate forms. The grainstone is composed of stromaclasts and peloids in thin (millimeter-scale) to thick (tens of centimeters scale) beds that are commonly herringbone cross-stratified. This subfacies is present in members 9 and 10 (Table 1) in the western Shublik and Sadlerochit Mountains.

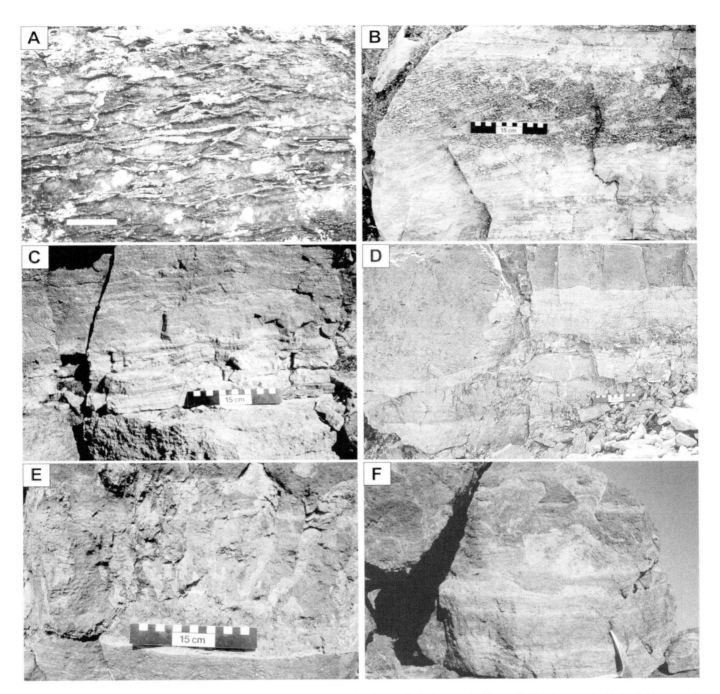

FIG. 8.—A) Silicified, wavy-lenticular ribbon rock subfacies. Member 2, Section A. Scale bar equals 10 cm. B) Tabular cross-bedded peloid–composite grainstone forming sigmoidal tidal bundles. Member 9, Station 16. C) Wavy stromatolite subfacies (light-colored laterally linked forms above scale). These subtidal stromatolites form the bases of lagoonal cycles. Cross-bedded grainstone (beneath scale) represents top of preceding cycle. Member 9, Section A. D) Erosional channel (left side of photo) in subtidal wavy stromatolite subfacies (lower right side of photo). Channel is filled with cross-bedded intraclast (stromaclasts)–peloid grainstone. Member 9, Section A. E) Wavy stromatolite growing upward into columnar forms marking the bases of subtidal lagoon cycles in middle of member 9, Section A. Cross-bedded intraclast–peloid grainstone (beneath scale) is the top of the preceding cycle. F) Branching columnar stromatolites (discrete to laterally linked forms). Member 9, Section A. Tip of hammer (lower right in photo) for scale.

Subenvironment.—This subfacies represents shallow marine banks of subtidal stromatolites with veneers of bidirectional thin sand waves deposited by flood and ebb tidal currents. This subfacies resembles the Holocene coalesced stromatolite "benches" forming in shallow subtidal depths (<1.5 m) near Bock Cay, Bahamas (Shapiro et al., 1990).

Fɪɢ. 9.—A) Light-colored benches of coalesced stromatolites marking the base of stromatolite-grainstone cycles. Member 9, Section G. B) Top of stromatolite bioherm (arrow points toward light-colored bioherm outlined with black line) encased in cross-bedded peloid–composite grainstone. Bidirectionally cross-bedded grainstone overlies bioherm. Member 9, Station 7.

(4) Stromatolite Bioherm Subfacies.—

Stromatolite bioherms are isolated and widely spaced irregular masses up to 2 m in height (Fig. 9B). They consist internally of multiple branching columns that are bound together by irregular laminae to form a single large bioherm. Spar–micrite couplets contain multiple generations of acicular cement, commonly black-colored, and commonly encasing peloids and intraclasts. Bioherms are closely associated with bidirectional ("herringbone") tabular cross-bedded peloidal grainstone, which is present beneath and above the stromatolite structures (Fig. 9B). This subfacies is present only in the lower gray craggy dolomite member (Table 1) in the central and western Sadlerochit and Shublik Mountains.
Subenvironment.—Stromatolite bioherms inhabited the deep channel environment between linear tidal sand ridges. Channels were generally kept clear of sand by tidal currents, but as the linear sand ridges migrated laterally, the bioherms became encased in cross-bedded grainstone. The large bioherms initially started as single branching columnar forms (described above). They appear to be analogous to the depositional setting of Holocene algal bryozoan reefs in intertidal channels near Joulters Cay, Bahamas, reported by Cuffey et al. (1977).

5) Cross-Bedded Peloid–Composite Grainstone Subfacies.—

This subfacies is characterized by laterally extensive to wedge-shaped cross-strata consisting of tabular, planar, and trough (less common) bedforms from 0.25 to 3 m thick (Fig. 8B). Inclination of internal foresets averages 20°. Thin foresets alternating with thicker foresets and bidirectional foresets ("herringbone" cross-strata) are common locally. Inclined discontinuity surfaces that often separate sets of cross-beds and ripple cross-lamination are common on the tops of these bedforms. Grain types are predominantly peloids and composite grains with lesser amounts of microbial sandchip intraclasts, stromaclasts and superficial ooids. The cross-bedded peloid–composite grainstone subfacies is most abundant in members 9 and 11 and is also present in members 6 and 12 (Table 1).
Subenvironment.—This subfacies represents linear tidal sand bars oriented normal to the strand line. The various forms of internal cross-stratification present within this subfacies indicates the actions of multiple depositional processes. The presence of tidal sand bars oriented parallel to the dominant flow direction (based on paleocurrent measurements) suggests that peak tidal currents exceeded 100 cm/s (cf. Halley et al., 1983). The large-scale cross-strata represent the internal foresets that advanced across the sea floor in response to flood tidal conditions. We interpret the wedge-shaped tabular cross-strata to represent transverse sand waves superimposed on the tidal bars. Numerous inclined discontinuity surfaces represent reactivation surfaces that reflect the time–velocity asymmetry of tidal currents (Klein, 1970). Alternating thin and thick foreset intervals are interpreted to represent tidal bundles. Large-scale trough cross-strata bedforms have been shown to result from major storm events that impart a cuspate orientation to megaripples in Bahamian ooid shoals (Hine, 1977). Planar stratification is the result of upper-flow-regime storm currents that destroyed the normal tidal bedforms. The small-scale ripple cross-lamination formed on the tops of tidal bars by wind-driven wave activity during slack tides.

(6) Cross-Bedded Intraclast–Peloid Grainstone Subfacies.—

This subfacies is characterized by thin- to medium-thick beds (1–10 cm thick) composed of cross-bedded stromaclasts and peloids (Fig. 8D). The subfacies occurs above or in channels cut into wavy stromatolite subfacies or as discrete beds between layers of cross-bedded peloid–composite grainstone. Intraclasts may be imbricated and segregated into distinct layers. This subfacies is most abundant in members 9, 10, and 11 and is also present in members 6 and 12 (Table 1).
Subenvironment.—This subfacies represents deposits of eroded benthic wavy irregular stromatolites. The channels cut into this subfacies suggest erosion by wind-driven currents and tidal currents. Discrete beds within tabular cross-bedded grainstone are remnants of completely eroded wavy irregular stromatolites.

(4) Windward Sand Shoal Facies Assemblage

The windward sand shoal facies assemblage formed on the Katakturuk ramp at the position where wave currents and tidal currents impinged upon the sea floor. These types of marine sand belts are oriented parallel to the strand line and, depending upon ramp paleobathymetry, form barrier or fringing shoals (Read, 1982). The genesis of coated grains was by normal tidal currents and waves, but the nature of the marine sand shoal was significantly altered by major storm events. The majority of ooid–pisoid grains were deposited as washover fans on the landward flanks of the marine sand belts. Assemblage subfacies components are: (1) trough cross-bedded ooid–pisoid grainstone, (2) composite ooid–pisoid packstone to wackestone, and (3) columnar stromatolite.

(1) Trough Cross-Bedded Ooid–Pisoid Grainstone Subfacies.—

Laterally extensive large-scale three-dimensional bedforms characterize this subfacies. The bedforms are typically 1 to 5 m thick and have curved festoon basal contacts or planar contacts (Fig. 10A–C). Internal foresets are generally concave upwards with truncated upper surfaces and form trough- to wedge-shaped bodies in grainstones composed of ooids, pisoids (Fig. 9D), and composite grains. Less common are tabular cross-beds. This subfacies is present in members 1, 2, 6, 11, 12, and 13 (Table 1).
Subenvironment.—This subfacies represents linear marine sand belts oriented parallel to depositional strike. Amalgamated sheet deposits of trough cross-bedded grainstone formed by aggradation and progradation. Trough cross-stratification resulted from downstream migration of curved, discontinuous-crested megaripples under uniform flow attributed to wave currents and tidal currents. Tabular cross-beds represent smaller-scale bedforms superimposed on a megaripple surface. Ooid–pisoid grain genesis occurred predominantly on the upcurrent, windward side of sand belts with the bulk of deposition on the shoal flanks.

(2) Composite Ooid–Pisoid Packstone to Wackestone Subfacies.—

This subfacies consists of laterally extensive thin to medium beds (typically 0.25 to 1 m thick) composed of composite ooid to pisoid grains within a matrix of finer-grained carbonate, in-

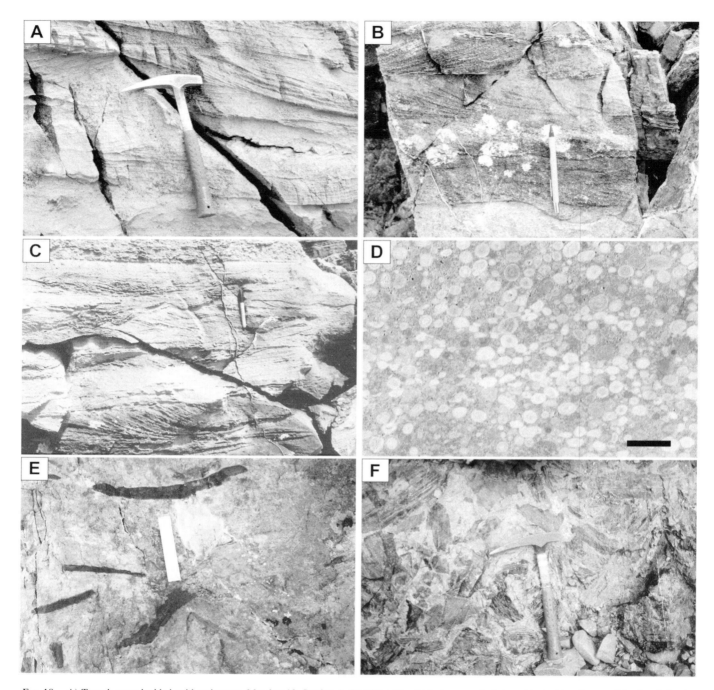

Fig. 10.—A) Trough cross-bedded ooid grainstone, Member 12, Section A. B) Bidirectional tabular cross-beds in ooid–pisoid grainstone. Member 6, Section C. Pencil for scale is 14 cm. C) Nested small-scale trough cross-stratification, current-ripple cross-lamination, and low-angle planar lamination. Overall this amalgamated unit fines upward to a prominent surface just above the pen, forming a high-frequency cycle. Member 6, Section A. Pen for scale equals 14 cm. D) Polished slab of cross-bedded pisoid grainstone. Member 1, Station 3. Scale bar equals 1 cm. E) Slump breccia occupying a channel in host rhythmite. Poorly sorted, matrix-supported breccias are interpreted as debris-flow deposits induced by slumping of up-dip, gravitationally unstable rhythmites and lime turbidites. Note chert clasts (black). Member 2, Section A. Ruler for scale is 15 cm long. F) Matrix-supported debris-flow deposit composed of poorly sorted angular clasts of rhythmite. Member 4, Section D.

cluding abrasion detritus. It locally contains low-angle planar to tangential cross-strata. This subfacies is present in members 1, 2, 6, 11, 12, and 13 (Table 1).

Subenvironment.—This subfacies formed in a backshoal envi-

ronment where periodic currents resulted in inorganic precipitation of concentrically coated compound grains but winnowing of fines was less pervasive than in the active part of the shoal. Cross-strata represent the distal margins of active shoal foresets.

(3) Columnar Stromatolite Subfacies.—

This subfacies consists of columnar stromatolites, ranging between 5 and 20 cm in height, occurring in channels between cross-bedded ooid–pisoid grainstone subfacies. These are similar to the stromatolites of the lagoon facies but they generally lack branches. Internal laminae consist of spar–micrite couplets. This subfacies is present in members 6, 11, 12, and 13 (Table 1).
Subenvironment.—These stromatolites inhabited current-swept channels between mobile ooid sand shoals. Stromatolite growth likely was initiated on stable, well-cemented submarine hardground substrate or subaerial exposure horizons. The stromatolites are similar to subtidal stromatolites reported by Dill and Shinn (1986) near Lee Stocking Island, Bahamas (Holocene) and in the Salem Limestone (Mississippian), Indiana described by Keith and Thompson (1994).

(5) Outer Ramp to Slope Facies Assemblage

The outer ramp to distally steepened slope setting extends from below storm wave base to many tens to hundreds of meters of water depth. Component subfacies are: (1) argillaceous cherty mudstone, (2) nodular limestone, dolomite, and chert, (3) matrix-supported debrite, (4) dolomite–shale rhythmite, and (5) graded ooid–pisoid grainstone.

(1) Argillaceous Cherty Mudstone Subfacies.—

This subfacies is composed of thin- to thick-bedded (10 cm to 0.5 m), light gray to gray peloidal mudstone with centimeter-scale bedding characterized by bedding-parallel white chert nodules. This subfacies is present only in the zebra dolomite member (Table 1).
Subenvironment.—This subfacies represents deep subtidal outer ramp muds deposited by suspension settling beneath storm wave base.

(2) Nodular Limestone, Dolomite, and Chert Subfacies.—

This subfacies consists of black to dark gray limestone in lumpy beds that average 2 cm thick but are up to 5 cm thick, black "palisades" crystal dolomite in beds up to 5 cm thick, and black chert and limestone nodules up to 4 cm in diameter. Intervals of this subfacies are 3 to 4 m thick. This subfacies is present only in the thin-laminated dolomite member (Table 1).
Subenvironment.—This subfacies represents suspension-settling deposition of predominantly platform-derived carbonate material. Hemipelagic terrigenous muds (see dolomitic mudstone–shale rhythmite subfacies) are notably absent, suggesting deposition in the upper-slope setting. Nodular to lumpy bedding resulted from localized sediment accumulation and prelithification compaction. Black "palisades" crystal dolomite may be deformed "cone-in-cone" compaction and dewatering structures. Black chert concretions resulted from early diagenetic silicification.

(3) Matrix–Supported Debrite Subfacies.—

This subfacies is characterized by massive-bedded, dark gray to black dolomite composed of chaotically oriented and poorly sorted tabular clasts of rhythmite floating in a mud to silt matrix (Fig. 10E, F). Rhythmite clasts are locally imbricated and may be chertified. The subfacies (present only in the cobweb dolomite member; Table 1) occurs throughout both mountain ranges and is thickest (65 m) in the Kikiktat Mountain area (Section D, stations 39 and 40; Fig. 1), where four distinct debris flows are recognized, each ranging between 10 and 20 m thick.
Subenvironment.—This subfacies represents debris-flow sheets deposited in the outer-ramp slope setting. These slope-derived, oligomictic rhythmite breccias may actually represent amalgamation of multiple flows, which are commonly difficult to distinguish (Coniglio and Dix, 1992). Clast imbrication is indicative of translational slope movement.

(4) Dolomite–Shale Rhythmite Subfacies.—

This subfacies consists of distinctive orangish-tan- to reddish-brown-weathering very fine silt-size dolomitic grainstone to mudstone in beds up to 10 cm thick, averaging 5 cm thick, alternating with fissile, graphitic siliceous shale in beds generally <2 cm thick (Fig. 11A, B). The subfacies is up to 60 m thick and composed of 90% dolomite beds and 10% shale beds. The composition of the shale is illite. Dolomite beds have sharp planar to undulatory erosional bases, with minor low-amplitude (<0.5 m) channels that pinch out laterally. Channels are filled with small centimeter-scale rhythmite clasts (debrite subfacies). Bouma *Tab*, *Tabe*, and *Tbde* turbidite divisions are recognized, and loading features and flute casts are present at the bases of some grainstone beds (Fig. 11C). This subfacies is present in members 2 and 5 (Table 1).
Subenvironment.—The dolomite part of the rhythmite represents sediment turbidity flow deposition as apron sheet flows on a distally steepened slope. The absence of allodapic grains indicates that the turbidites were sourced from the outer-ramp setting. The Bouma *Tab*, *Tabe*, and *Tbde* turbidite divisions suggest a proximal sediment source. Shale intervals were deposited by a continuous rain of hemipelagic terrigenous material that represents the off-ramp "natural background" suspension settling of clays and points to a source outside of the Katakturuk carbonate platform.

(5) Graded Ooid–Pisoid Grainstone Subfacies.—

In this subfacies, ooid and pisoid grainstone in upward-fining graded beds up to 0.5 m thick is overlain by laminated dolomitic mudstone (Fig. 11D). Bouma *Tab* and *Tcd* turbidite subdivisions are recognized. Ooids and pisoids locally form black chert spheroids. Conical stromatolites (*Conophyton*) also occur locally within this subfacies (Fig. 11E). This subfacies is present only in the lower 50 m of the silicified oolite member (Table 1).
Subenvironment.—The subfacies represents turbidity-flow deposition of ramp-edge allodapic sands (ooids and pisoids) in the uppermost slope setting. The Bouma *Tab* and *Tcd* turbidite subdivisions that are recognized suggest a proximal sediment source (i.e., ramp-edge shoals). Conical (*Conophyton*-like) stromatolites have been noted in other Precambrian deeper-water, carbonate settings (e.g., Grotzinger, 1986) and suggest deposition within the photic zone.

SEQUENCE STRATIGRAPHIC APPROACH

Early summaries of carbonate sequence stratigraphy emphasized seismic-scale geometries and recognition of "third-order" sequence boundaries and systems tracts at the seismic scale

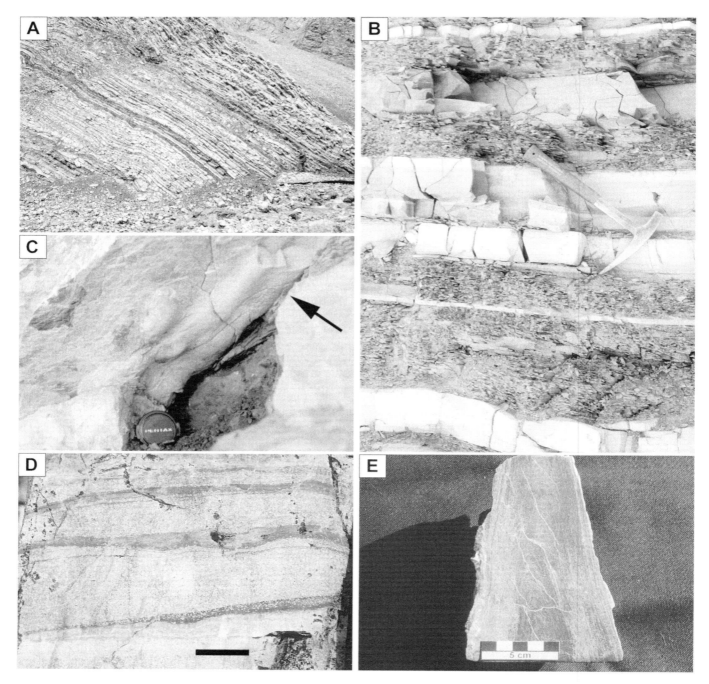

FIG. 11.—A) Dolomite–shale rhythmite (60-m-thick interval) interpreted to represent slope-apron turbidity-current deposits. Member 5, Section C. Overlain by gray-colored graded ooid grainstone (lowermost member 6) in upper right corner of photo (Fig. 10D). B) Close-up outcrop photograph of beds of dolomite–shale rhythmite. Member 5, Section C. C) Flute cast at base of grainstone bed in dolomite–shale rhythmite. Member 5, Section C. Camera lens for scale is 3.5 cm in diameter. D) Graded ooid–pisoid grainstone interpreted to represent turbidity-flow deposition of ramp-edge allodapic sands (ooids and pisoids) in the uppermost-slope setting. Member 5, Section C. Scale bar equals 2 cm. E) Polished-slab hand specimen of conical stromatolite (*Conophyton*?) associated with graded ooid–pisoid grainstone. Lowermost member 6, Station 5.

(e.g., Sarg, 1988; Tucker and Wright, 1990; Tucker et al., 1993). More recent work has attempted to integrate the generalized seismic-scale models with finer-scale well-log, core, and outcrop data. Methodology is now focused on the internal architecture of depositional sequences in well logs, cores, and outcrop data.

crop, with particular emphasis placed on the lateral continuity and vertical stacking patterns of reservoir-scale cycles within a systems-tract framework (e.g., Koershner and Read, 1989; Goldhammer et al., 1993; Grammer et al., 1996; Kerans, 1995; Kerans and Fitchen, 1995). The hierarchy of stratigraphic cyclicity approach to depositional sequences, "cyclostratigraphy" (Goldhammer et al., 1990; Goldhammer et al., 1991), can be invoked to interpret thick stacks of shelfal carbonates in which seismic-scale geometries are not visible, commonly the case in deformed terranes or in updip shelfal carbonate sections located landward of the shelf edge (i.e., the situation that confronts us within the Katakturuk). Cyclostratigraphy recognizes that the sedimentary record has stratigraphic cycles of different orders, which were originally classified on the basis of their duration (Table 3). Briefly stated, cycle-producing mechanisms (e.g., glacio-eustasy) yield rates of accommodation change that approximate shallow-water carbonate sedimentation rates and typically exceed tectonic subsidence rates (Goldhammer et al., 1993), resulting in superimposed orders of stratigraphic cyclicity (Read and Goldhammer, 1988; Koershner and Read, 1989; Grotzinger, 1989; Osleger, 1990; Goldhammer et al., 1991; Kerans, 1995).

Hierarchy of Stratigraphic Cycles

As in Paleozoic through Cenozoic carbonate platforms, the Katakturuk stratigraphic succession can be subdivided into a hierarchy of stratigraphic cycles that record the superimposed long-term and short-term changes in accommodation space. The duration of the Katakturuk Dolomite is unknown; thus, assigning different orders of stratigraphic cycles is somewhat arbitrary. Nevertheless it is essential to establish the relative hierarchy of stratigraphic cycles to provide a predictive framework for the evolutionary history of the Katakturuk Dolomite. A suitable hierarchy of sequence terminology is: high-frequency cycles = fifth-order, cycles = fourth-order, sequence = third-order, and supersequence = second-order) (Table 3). Cycles (meter-scale) and high-frequency cycles (on the scale of a few centimeters), equivalent to the parasequences of Van Wagoner et al. (1988), are the fundamental building blocks that stack to form third-order sequences. Third-order sequences in turn stack to build larger second-order accommodation cycles or supersequences. From widely spaced "one-dimensional" outcrop studies (Sections A, B, C, and D, Fig. 1) we reconstruct the two-dimensional stratigraphy that allows us to decipher the Katakturuk Dolomite depositional sequences.

Analysis of Cycle-Stacking Patterns

Using physical bounding surfaces as a basis, we recognize two types of cycles in the Katakturuk Dolomite: those bounded by marine flooding surfaces, across which subtidal subfacies deepen, termed "subtidal cycles", and those bounded by subaerial exposure surfaces (e.g., peritidal laminites), or "peritidal cycles". Analysis of cycle-stacking patterns examines the sys-

tematic vertical changes in cycle type (subtidal vs. peritidal), dominant cycle composition (subfacies trends), and cycle thickness (upward-thinning or upward-thickening trends). The stacking patterns of cycles provides the basis for our interpretations of Katakturuk deposition during relative-sea-level transgression (transgressive systems tract; TST), highstand (highstand systems tract; HST), and/or lowstand (lowstand systems tract; LST).

Sequence Boundaries

Within gently dipping carbonate ramps and flat-topped shelves of passive margins, not all third-order sequence boundaries are recognizable as distinct physical surfaces in outcrop (e.g., Goldhammer et al., 1993; Kerans and Fitchen, 1995) but instead are better represented as "zones" (Montañez and Osleger, 1993). Within the Katakturuk Dolomite, third-order sequence "boundaries" are distinguished by: (1) unconformities exhibiting karst surfaces (karren and collapse breccias) that present physical surfaces; (2) major shifts in depositional facies (e.g., peritidal facies overlain by shoal facies) as zones; (3) turnarounds from aggradational/progradational to retrogradational styles of cycle stacking as zones; and (4) patterns of cycle stacking thickness (upward shift from cycle thinning to cycle thickening), also as zones.

On the basis of cycle stacking patterns, we recognize at least four orders of superimposed stratigraphic cycles within the Katakturuk Dolomite succession, which are interpreted to depict superimposed long-term and short-term changes in accommodation space. The vertical stacking patterns of cycles define transgressive, highstand, and lowstand (where present) systems tracts of third-order depositional sequences, designated A to M, which are organized into four second-order supersequences, designated SSI to SSIV (Figs. 12, 13).

Katakturuk Cycles

Subtidal Cycles.—

Katakturuk subtidal cycles average 1.5 m in thickness and are upward-shallowing with cycle tops marked by an abrupt deepening of subfacies. Windward sand shoal cycles are composed of trough cross-bedded ooid–pisoid grainstone and ooid–pisoid packstone to wackestone (Fig. 14). In the tide-dominated lagoon setting, subtidal cycles are composed of wavy stromatolite to branching columnar stromatolite passing upward into cross-bedded peloid–composite grainstone (Fig. 15).

Peritidal Cycles.—

Katakturuk peritidal cycles average 0.5 m in thickness, and may be crystal-fan-array-based in the restricted lagoon setting

TABLE 3.—MODIFIED SEQUENCE STRATIGRAPHIC TERMINOLOGY USED IN THIS PAPER (MODIFIED FROM GOLDHAMMER ET AL., 1993, AND KERANS, 1995)

Sequence Stratigraphy Terminology[1]	Modified Terminology[2]	Eustatic Cycles (orders)	Duration	Amplitude (Meters)	Rise/Fall Rates (cm/1000 yr)
		First	> 100 myr		< 1
Supersequence	Supersequence	Second	10–100 myr	50–100	1–3
Sequence	Sequence	Third	1–10 myr	50–100	1–10
Sequence, Cycle	Cycles	Fourth	0.1–1 myr	1–150	40–500
Parasequence, Cycle	High Frequency Cycles (HFC)	Fifth	0.01–0.1 myr	1–150	60–700

[1] Terminology of Goldhammer et al. (1993).
[2] Modified terminology used in this paper.

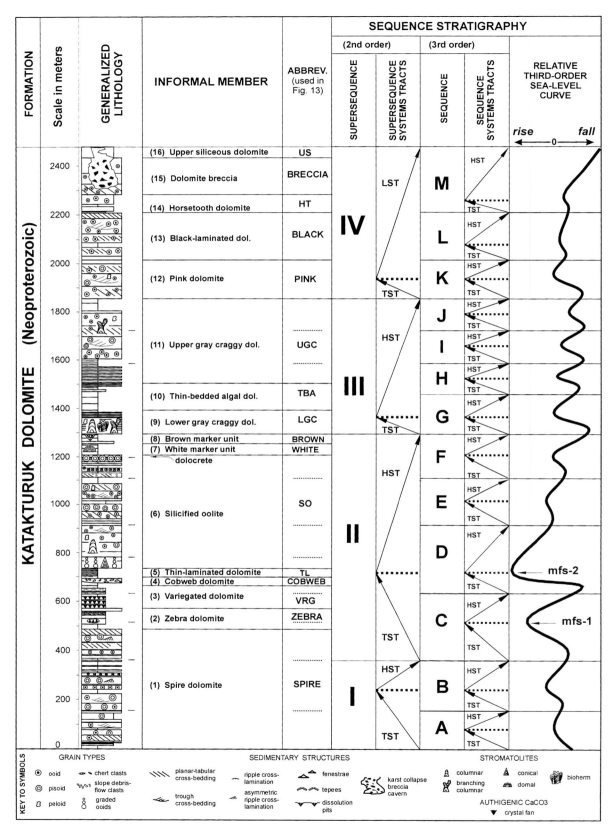

FIG. 12.—Composite stratigraphic column and sequence stratigraphic organization of Katakturuk Dolomite into systems tracts of second-order supersequences (SSI to SSIV) and third-order depositional sequences (A to M). Relative third-order sea-level curve is shown in right-hand column. Key to symbols also used in Figures 14–21 and 23–29.

KATAKTURUK DOLOMITE DEPOSITIONAL SEQUENCES

Katakturuk Dolomite informal members

Fig. 13.—Panorama of Katakturuk Dolomite along north-to-south ridge line in central Sadlerochit Mountains with subdivision into second-order supersequences (SSI to SSIV) and third-order depositional sequences (A to M). Informal member boundaries are shown in inset.

WINDWARD-SAND-SHOAL SUBTIDAL/PERITIDAL CYCLES

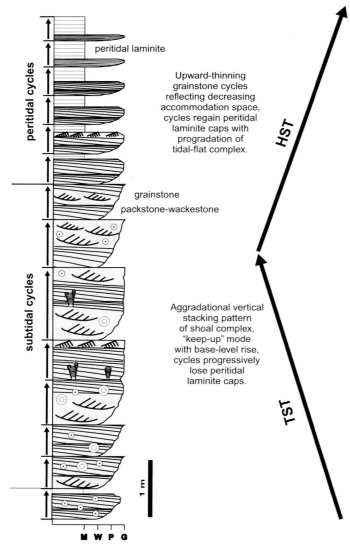

FIG. 14.—Windward sand shoal subtidal to peritidal cycles, idealized succession for sequences A, B, C, D, E, F, I, J, K, and L.

(Fig. 16) or subtidal-cross-bedded-grainstone-based in the windward sand shoal setting (Fig. 14), tidal flat setting (Fig. 17), and tide-dominated lagoon setting (Fig. 18). The tops of peritidal laminite cycles are commonly marked by exposure phenomena (mudcracks, fenestrae, tepee breccias, karren, and karsts).

Noncyclic Deep-Water Intervals.—

Outer-ramp to slope facies assemblages are noncyclic condensed intervals that show no apparent repetitions in their lithologies or sedimentary structures that provide evidence for small-scale eustatic sea-level fluctuations. Similar noncyclic deep-water intervals within successions of cyclic peritidal to shallow-subtidal cyclic carbonates are found in the Proterozoic (Grotzinger, 1986), Middle Cambrian (Montañez and Osleger,

1993), Upper Cambrian (Markello and Read, 1982), Upper Ordovician (Jennette and Pryor, 1993), Middle Devonian (Elrick, 1995), and Mississippian (Elrick and Read, 1991).

Development of Systems Tracts

As an example of systems-tract development in the Katakturuk Dolomite, we examine the systematic changes in high-frequency cycles (HFC) of a single third-order depositional sequence, the lower gray craggy dolomite member. This inner-ramp, high-energy, tide-dominated lagoon and peritidal flat complex contains: subtidal cycles that are characterized by thick cross-bedded peloid–composite grainstone with wavy to branching columnar stromatolites at cycle bases; and peritidal cycles consisting of a basal cross-bedded peloid–composite grainstone (± stromatolite bases) that are capped by peritidal laminite and tufa. Detailed analysis of a 97.5-m-thick section of the lower gray craggy dolomite member in the central Sadlerochit Mountains (Section A, Fig. 1) reveals 152 HFC that are organized into four fourth-order sequences. The cycles are shown diagrammatically in Figure 21, which illustrates five types of HFC (Fig. 21A), third-order and fourth-order systems tracts (Fig. 21B), and a Fischer accommodation plot for the measured section (Fig. 21C). Fischer plots (Fischer, 1964) can be used to tie cycle variations to changes in accommodation space (Read and Goldhammer, 1988).

TIDE-DOMINATED-LAGOON SUBTIDAL CYCLES

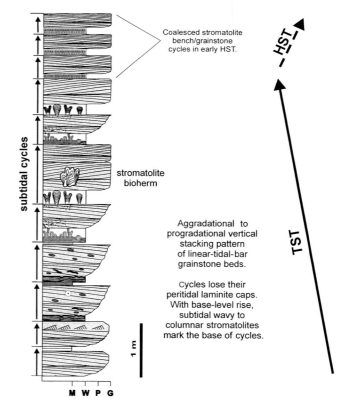

FIG. 15.—Stromatolite-based subtidal to peritidal cycles, idealized succession for sequence G.

CRYSTAL-FAN-ARRAY PERITIDAL CYCLES

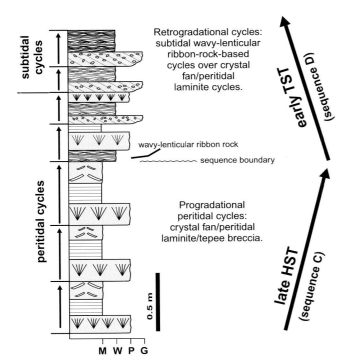

FIG. 16.—Peritidal cycles with crystal fan arrays, idealized succession for sequences C and D.

LATERALLY-LINKED-STROMATOLITE PERITIDAL CYCLES

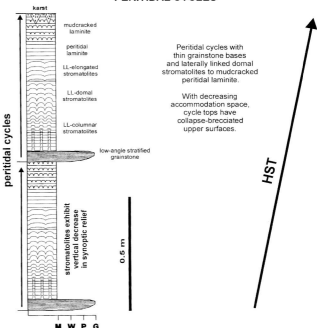

FIG. 17.—Peritidal cycles with laterally linked domal stromatolites, idealized succession for sequence F.

Type 1 HFC consist of subtidal cross-bedded peloid–composite grainstone with peritidal laminite caps. Types 2 and 3 HFC depict the development of wavy stromatolite subfacies at base of each HFC, indicating greater initial water depth allowing microbial mat colonization of the substrate. The grainstone parts of cycles increase in thickness upsection, and cycles eventually lose peritidal laminite caps, and they become exclusively subtidal type 3 HFC. Type 4 HFC exhibit an increase in the thickness of the subtidal stromatolite bases and a decrease in grainstone thickness and commonly develop dissolution surfaces (karren) at the tops of some HFC (arrows in Figure 21C). Peritidal laminite caps are generally missing from type 4 HFC, but abundant intraclasts in the cross-bedded intraclast–peloid grainstone part of the cycle suggest that laminite was deposited and then subsequently eroded. Type 5 HFC contain very thin grainstone bases and pass upward into tufa subfacies at the tops of cycles, where abundant karst phenomena (collapse breccias, solution pits, and karren) are present. Quartz silt, present at the tops of some peritidal HFC (Q in Fig. 21C), is interpreted to represent reworked windblown silt. Overall, the HFC systematically stack from upward-thickening subtidal HFC (transgressive systems tract), to upward-thinning subtidal HFC passing into peritidal HFC (early highstand systems tract), and finally to peritidal HFC with subaerial exposure phenomena (late highstand systems tract), reflecting progressive changes in third-order accommodation space with superimposed shifts in fourth-

LAGOON LAMINITE/TUFA PERITIDAL CYCLES

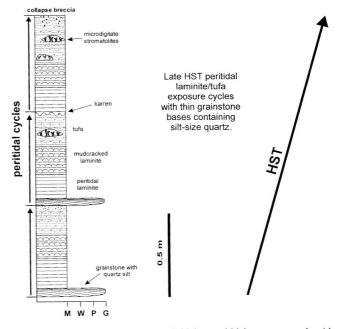

FIG. 18.—Tide-dominated lagoon subtidal to peritidal exposure cycles, idealized succession for sequences G, H, and I.

NONCYCLIC SLOPE TO OUTER RAMP, sequence C

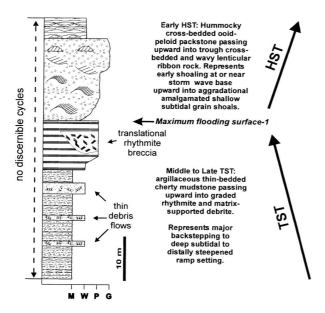

FIG. 19.—Noncyclic outer-ramp to slope subfacies, idealized succession for sequence C.

NONCYCLIC SLOPE TO OUTER RAMP, sequence D

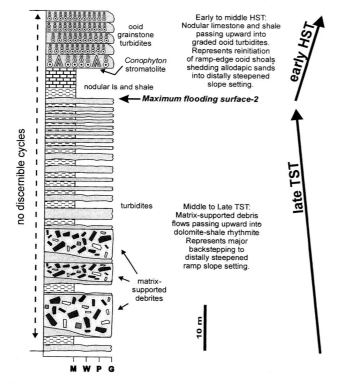

FIG. 20.—Noncyclic outer-ramp to slope subfacies, idealized succession for sequence D.

order and fifth-order accommodation space (i.e., karst horizon in the middle of the section; Fig. 21C). The fourth-order sequence "boundaries", which are actually zones and not physical surfaces, are placed at the point of maximum downward deflection in the accommodation plot.

EVOLUTION OF THE KATAKTURUK DOLOMITE

The paleotectonic setting of the volcanic rocks and Katakturuk Dolomite megasequence appears to be that of a thermally subsiding passive margin. The Late Proterozoic Rb–Sr isochron age of 801 ± 20 Ma (Clough et al., 1990) for the diabase sill in the western Sadlerochit Mountains approximates a 780 Ma rift event documented by Young et al. (1979) in the northern Canadian Cordillera. The tholeiitic volcanic rocks therefore delineate the rift stage of continental breakup, with the underlying slate and quartzite representing a Late Proterozoic precursor basin remnant (Fig. 22A). This event was followed by passive-margin drift and thermal cooling (Fig. 22B) prior to commencement of Katakturuk Dolomite carbonate-ramp deposition (Fig. 22C).

Our interpretation of a carbonate-ramp geometry for the Katakturuk Dolomite is based on (1) the paleotectonic setting (discussed above), (2) lateral variations observed in subfacies across the study area, (3) paleocurrent data, and (4) observations of the systematic vertical changes in shallow-water facies and their component subfacies. The matrix-supported debrite and dolomite–shale rhythmite subfacies of the outer-ramp to slope facies assemblage thicken southeastward towards Kikiktat Mountain (Section D and stations 39 and 40; Fig. 1). The cave-fill karst breccia subfacies is found only in the Sadlerochit Mountains, and the depth of the karst profile is greatest in the western end of the range. The combined paleocurrent data for all Katakturuk cross-beds have a mean vector of ~300° (Fig. 2), which is consistent with predominant onbank deposition to the northwest. These data suggest that the Katakturuk platform strandline was oriented northeast–southwest with its basin situated to the southeast (present-day). The peritidal to shallow-water carbonate facies, particularly the windward sand shoal facies assemblage, exhibit little variation laterally throughout the study area. The windward sand shoal facies form thick amalgamated and laterally extensive sheet deposits. Thick, laterally extensive deposits of shoal facies are common to many ramp settings and are rare in shelf environments, where they are localized over paleotopographic highs (Handford, 1988). The above observations suggest that the Katakturuk platform was a carbonate ramp with a low-gradient slope (typically <1°; Ahr, 1973) extending from shoreline to basin. Finally, ramps are more likely to evolve during geologic times that lack reef builders (James, 1979), such as the Precambrian.

Supersequence I (SSI)

Supersequence I (~250 m thick) (Fig. 12) marks the initiation of a carbonate-platform sedimentary regime on the passive margin. Supersequence I contains two third-order sequences (A and B).

Sequences A and B.—

Transgressive systems tracts of sequences A and B consist of aggradational, ramp-edge windward shoal complexes com-

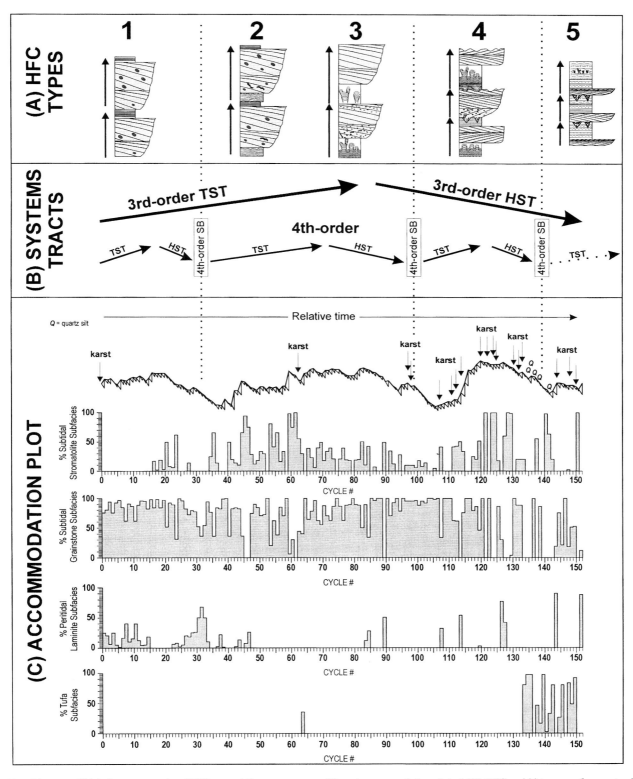

FIG. 21.—Diagram of high-frequency cycles (HFC) types (A), systems tracts (B), and accommodation plot of 152 HFC and histogram of percent subfacies type per individual cycle (C) in the lower gray craggy dolomite member. A) Subfacies composition of HFCs (examples 1–5) that typify changes in third-order accommodation space that are modified by higher-frequency (fourth- and fifth-order) changes in accommodation space (described in text). B) Organization of third-order and fourth-order systems tracts within the lower gray craggy dolomite member. C) Accommodation (Fischer) plot of 152 HFC. Histograms beneath accommodation plot show percentage of subfacies type per individual HFC, illustrating third-order and fourth-order accommodation control on subtidal stromatolite, subtidal grainstone, peritidal laminite, and tufa subfacies. Arrows show position of karsts at tops of cycles.

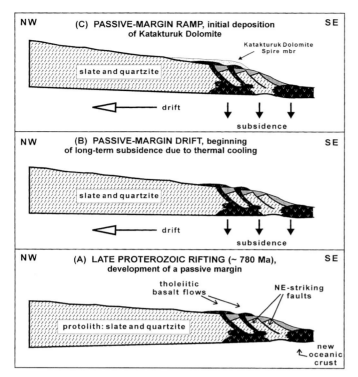

FIG. 22.—Model for development of Katakturuk Platform. A) Rifting event at 780 Ma in slate and quartzite protolith. Development of NE-striking normal faults, new oceanic crust, and related sill and dike system with tholeiitic basalt flows. B) Beginning of drift phase and associated thermal cooling and subsidence. C) Continued drift and subsidence with initiation of Katakturuk Dolomite deposition.

posed of trough cross-bedded ooid–pisoid grainstone (active shoal) to composite ooid–pisoid packstone to wackestone (backshoal) subfacies that are capped by peritidal laminite subfacies (Fig. 23). Individual cycle boundaries tend to be poorly defined unless the shoal tops are capped by peritidal laminite, resulting in ramp-edge tidal-flat islands (Strasser, 1988). Where well defined, the cycles are fairly symmetrical, averaging 1 to 5 m thick, and they progressively lose their peritidal laminite caps upsection (Fig. 14). At the turnaround in base level, HST shoal cycles begin to thin upward and develop peritidal laminite caps that thicken upsection. The highstand parts of both component third-order sequences consist of stacked aggradational, subtidal shoal cycles (3–6 m thick), deposited as a ramp-margin shoals. The late HST is marked by thinning-upward, seaward-progradational peritidal cycles with thick laminite caps and minor dolocrete (Fig. 14), indicating decreasing accommodation space. The upper boundary zone of SSI is placed within an interval of thick peritidal laminite caps near the top of the member 1 (Fig. 12), marking minimum accommodation.

Supersequence II (SS II)

Supersequence II, over 700 m thick, contains five third-order sequences (C to F; Fig. 12) that were identified using stacking-pattern analysis. Overall, the five third-order sequences thicken upward from the lower SSII boundary and then thin upward toward the top of SSI, indicative of a long-term increase and

then decrease in second-order accommodation. SS II is capped by a 1–3-m-thick karstic dissolution surface at the top of the thinnest third-order sequence (sequence F; Fig. 12) in the stack.

Sequence C.—

The transgressive systems tract of sequence C is characterized by retrogradationally stacked (i.e., upward-thickening) peritidal cycles that are abruptly terminated by deposition of noncyclic deep-water, off-ramp argillaceous cherty mudstone subfacies with matrix-supported debrite and highly silicified dolomite rhythmite (lacking shale) (Fig. 19). The top of the dolomite rhythmite subfacies approximates the third-order maximum flooding surface (mfs-1) (Figs. 13, 19).

The early HST of sequence C consists of hummocky cross-bedded ooid–peloid packstone (deposited at or near wave base), passing upward into a shallowing-upward mid-ramp, subtidal trough cross-bedded ooid–pisoid grainstone shoal complex capped by amalgamated subtidal cycles marked by wavy-lenticular ribbon rock subfacies (Figs. 19, 24). The late HST is marked by stacked thin supratidal cycles composed of alternating subtidal crystal fan array subfacies and peritidal laminites with peritidal breccia and tepees (Figs. 16, 25). The upper boundary (zone) of sequence C lies within a thick interval of disrupted peritidal tepees and autobrecciated laminites.

Sequence D.—

The transgressive systems tract of sequence D begins with an abrupt and major backstepping of the ramp edge that resulted in the deposition of over 100 m of noncyclic dolomite–shale rhythmite, matrix-supported debrite, and nodular limestone and shale on top of the previously shallow-water subfacies, suggesting that the Katakturuk ramp was distally steepened (Figs. 20, 24). The top of the dolomite–shale rhythmite subfacies approximates the third-order maximum flooding surface (mfs-2) for this sequence (Figs. 13, 20), where the transgressive systems tracts of SSII and sequence D coincide (Fig. 12).

The early HST of sequence D consists of graded ooid–pisoid grainstone representing allodapic turbidites sourced from the ramp-edge shoal complex, marking the reestablishment of shallow-water conditions across most of the Katakturuk platform. (Figs. 20, 26). An aggradational, ramp-edge shoal complex developed by mid-HST and is marked by stacked subtidal cycles (3–5 m thick) of trough cross-bedded ooid–pisoid grainstone with scattered columnar stromatolites and small stromatolite bioherms (Fig. 23). The late HST displays upward-thinning progradational, grainstone–laminite cycles.

Sequence E.—

Sequence E is a fairly symmetrical sequence characterized by a TST and early to middle HST composed of stacked, amalgamated, ramp-edge, aggradational subtidal shoal cycles (3–7 m thick) consisting of trough cross-bedded ooid–pisoid grainstone (Fig. 23). Similarly to sequence D above, the late HST displays upward-thinning progradational, grainstone–laminite cycles.

Sequence F.—

The early TST of sequence F also consists of stacked, amalgamated, ramp-edge, aggradational subtidal shoal cycles composed of trough cross-bedded ooid–pisoid grainstone (Fig. 23).

WINDWARD OOID-PISOID MARINE SAND BELT

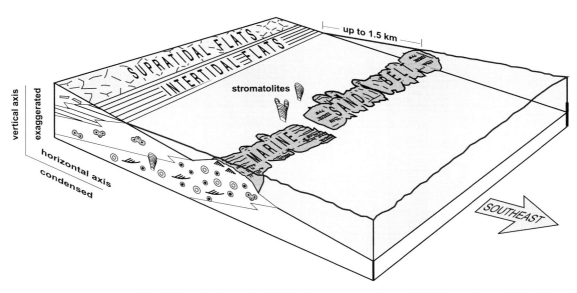

FIG. 23.—Model for windward marine ooid–pisoid sand belt complex. Small columnar stromatolites colonized the sea bottom behind the marine sand belts and in channels between them. Sequences A, B, C (TST), D (HST), E (early TST), F, I, J, K, L, and M. During HSTs the peritidal complex prograded over sandbelts.

DISTALLY STEEPENED RAMP

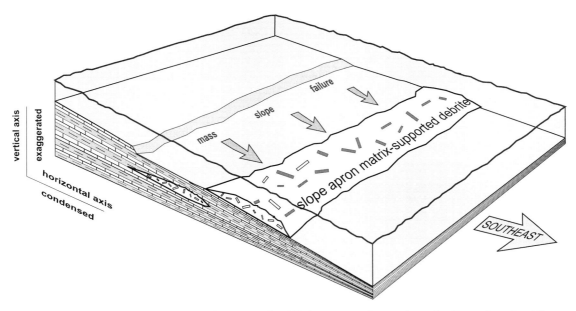

FIG. 24.—Model for distally steepened ramp. Late TSTs of sequences C and D that correspond to maximum flooding surfaces 1 and 2, respectively. Third-order sea-level rise is superimposed on second-order sea-level rise (TST of SSII), resulting in major backstepping and development of distally steepened ramp.

The late TST is marked by a distinctive inner-ramp shoal crest of stacked trough to tabular cross-bedded coarse-grained pisoid grainstone and dolocrete (Figs. 4A, 27). These pass upward into the early HST, which is composed of a thicker stack of upward-thinning peritidal cycles containing laterally linked domal stromatolite, peritidal laminite, and peritidal breccia and tepee sub-facies (Figs. 17, 27), indicative of more extensive seaward progradation of the inner-ramp tidal-flat complex than in the lower three sequences of SS II. The late HST of sequence F is the most regressive of all the sequences of SS II, with a very thin peritidal cycle composed of mechanically deposited parallel laminite with abundant tepees (Fig. 4D), microspeleothem

INNER-RAMP PERITIDAL COMPLEX

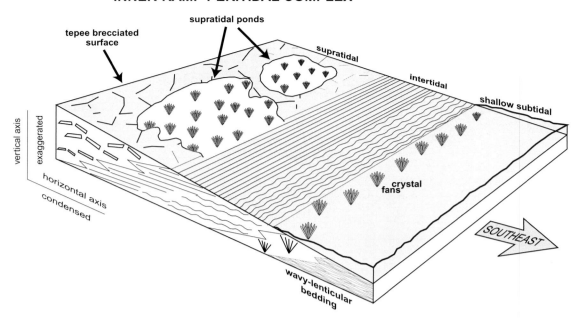

FIG. 25.—Model for peritidal complex (variegated dolomite member). Crystal fan arrays deposited in hypersaline lagoon and/or supratidal ponds. Intertidal zone represented by peritidal laminite (cryptmicrobialite and mechanically deposited parallel laminite). Supratidal setting, site of tepee brecciation and smaller-scale autobrecciated fabrics. Sequence C, late HST. Rate of third-order sea-level fall is much greater than second-order (SSII) sea-level rise.

flowstone (Fig. 4B), and karstic, polymictic, dissolution-collapse breccia marking the sequence boundary and the top of SS II (Fig. 12).

Supersequence III (SS III)

Supersequence III, approximately 500 m thick, incorporates four third-order sequences (G to J; Fig. 12) identified using stacking-pattern analysis. Overall, they thin upward, which is indicative of long-term second-order increase and then decrease in accommodation. The top of SS III is marked by a series of thin peritidal laminites, and the supersequence upper boundary is placed within this interval.

Sequence G.—

Sequence G contains an early TST of retrogradational, subtidal cycles composed of cross-bedded peloid–composite grainstone bases with peritidal laminite caps deposited on the inner ramp, a high-energy tide-dominated lagoon setting inboard of ramp-edge ooid shoals (Fig. 28). Cycles thicken upward into a middle to late TST consisting of wavy- to columnar-stromatolite-based cross-bedded grainstones arranged into amalgamated subtidal cycles 2–5 m thick (Fig. 15) that represent deposition by lateral migration of linear tidal bars (Fig. 28). Stromatolite bioherms up to 2 meters in height colonized channels between the linear tidal bars. The early to middle HST is marked by the appearance of coalesced stromatolite benches with thin veneers of cross-bedded peloid grainstone. The late HST is composed of progradational, upward-thinning grainstone–laminite–tufa cycles with collapse breccias (Fig. 18).

Sequence H.—

Sequence H is marked by an early TST of upward-thickening, laminite–tufa-capped peritidal cycles. These pass upward into a late TST consisting of inner-ramp, shallow subtidal thin stromatolite-based grainstone cycles capped by mudcracked laminite and tufa with subaerial exposure features (Figs. 18, 28). High-energy, inner-ramp, shoreface grainstones make up the early HST. The rest of the HST is characterized by a thick uninterrupted stack of monotonous tufa and peritidal laminite, which probably represents many thin condensed cycles. This late HST aggradation of supratidal flat deposition is capped by a karstic dissolution complex 1–3 m thick with notable collapse-breccia sinkholes and cavities suggestive of vadose–meteoric diagenesis at the third-order sequence boundary.

Sequences I and J.—

Sequence I contains a thin early TST of grainstone–tufa–laminite cycles that are overlain by a late TST of aggradationally stacked, subtidal grainstone cycles. These in turn pass upward into a second uninterrupted succession of tufa and peritidal laminite with microspeleothem fabrics and minor fenestral and vuggy porosity (Fig. 18). The upper boundary of this sequence is placed where tufa-capped cycles pass vertically into the TST of the succeeding sequence J. This TST consists of stacked, amalgamated, inner-ramp, high-energy shoal-water grainstones (Fig. 23). The grainstones are arranged into thick amalgamated subtidal cycles with abundant mechanical cross-stratification. The late HST of this last sequence within SS III is composed of a series of upward-thinning, laminite-capped, progradational cycles.

Supersequence IV (SS IV)

Supersequence IV is from 400 m to over 820 m thick, in part dependent upon the thickness of cave-fill karst breccia, as well

DISTALLY STEEPENED RAMP WITH RAMP-EDGE SHOAL AND ALLODAPIC TURBIDITES

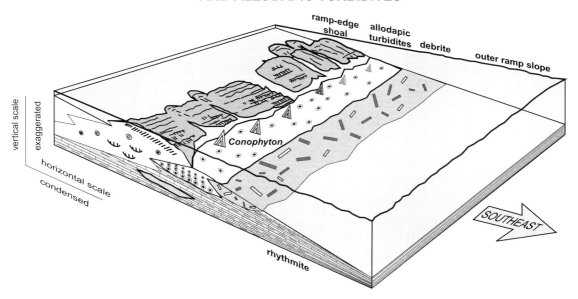

FIG. 26.—Model for distally steepened ramp with ramp-edge shoal complex and allodapic sand turbidites. Ramp-edge shoals are kilometers from shoreline and developed during relative sea-level fall. Conical stromatolites (*Conophyton*) occur within the allodapic sands. Early HST of sequence D, third-order sea-level fall allows development of ramp-edge shoal and shedding of ooids into slope setting.

as structural relations, at the top of the supersequence (Fig. 12). There are three third-order sequences within SS IV (K to M; Fig. 12). The uppermost sequence (M) consists of up to 500 m of karst breccia (Clough, 1989) and thus might in fact incorporate more than a single third-order sequence, with additional third-order sequences "hidden" within the karst breccia diagenetic overprint.

Sequence K.—

The TST of sequence K consists of a thick, uninterrupted stack of porous, trough cross-bedded ooid grainstones like those typical of TSTs in sequences E and F below. These grainstones are arranged into aggradational, thick, fining-upward, subtidal cycles reflecting a return to a high-energy, ramp-edge shoal complex of shallow subtidal to lower intertidal subfacies (Figs. 14, 23). The HST contains a lower interval of stacked subtidal grainstone cycles and an upper interval of upward-thinning grainstone–peritidal laminite cycles. The third-order sequence boundary is placed within an interval of repeating relatively thin cycles.

Sequence L.—

The TST of sequence L contains high-energy, cross-bedded grainstones representing deposition in an inner-ramp, shoreface setting. These grainstones pass vertically upward into a HST marked by successively thinner and increasingly regressive peritidal cycles with laminite caps disrupted by subaerial exposure features. The third-order sequence boundary is placed within an interval of repeating relatively thin cycles.

Sequence M.—

The final third-order sequence of SS IV is somewhat arbitrary and includes the complex cave-fill karst breccia complex that

caps the Katakturuk Dolomite (Fig. 29). Shallow-water depositional facies recognized within the stratigraphically intact part of sequence M represent a TST of thin-bedded, grainstone-based cycles. The thicker HST consists of a monotonous stack of highly fractured, vuggy, silicified thin peritidal cycles. The peritidal laminite caps overall thicken upward at the expense of the fine-grained grainstone bases. The pervasive dissolution and brecciation associated with the coincidence of second-order lowstand and third-order late highstand (Fig. 12) also affected the underlying members 13 and 14 of sequence L, which are highly fractured and silicified locally.

The top of SSIV is the angular and erosional unconformity with the overlying Nanook Limestone. This surface marks the end of Neoproterozoic carbonate deposition on the Katakturuk ramp.

DISCUSSION

Our work suggests that, in the absence of precise geochronologic calibration, the creation of a sequence stratigraphic hierarchy through stacking-pattern analysis of high-frequency (fifth-order and fourth-order) cycles provides a rational methodology for resolving the evolutionary history of thick packages of Proterozoic shallow-water carbonate rocks. In addition, where two-dimensional dip profiles of carbonate platforms are lacking, as is the case in the structurally deformed terrane of the northeast Brooks Range, such analysis is the only plausible means of deciphering long-term patterns of stratigraphic evolution. Within the Katakturuk Dolomite succession, we have identified thirteen larger third-order sequences, which are assembled into four second-order supersequences, by evaluating systematic changes in such attributes as facies proportions, thickness, and early diagenetic features within the high-fre-

PERITIDAL COMPLEX WITH COLLAPSE BRECCIA AND MICROSPELEOTHEMS

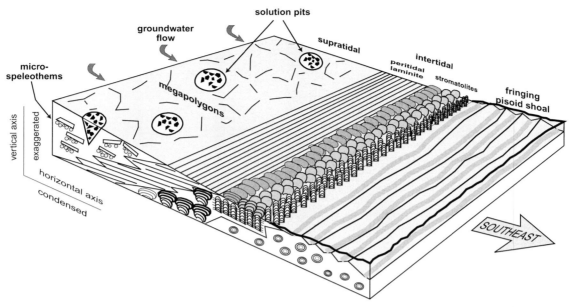

FIG. 27.—Model for peritidal complex with fringing pisoid shoal, laterally linked stromatolites, and megapolygon supratidal flat with dissolution pits and microspeleothems. Sequence F, late TST to LST. Third-order relative sea-level fall superimposed on second-order (SSII) relative sea-level fall.

TIDE-DOMINATED LAGOON COMPLEX

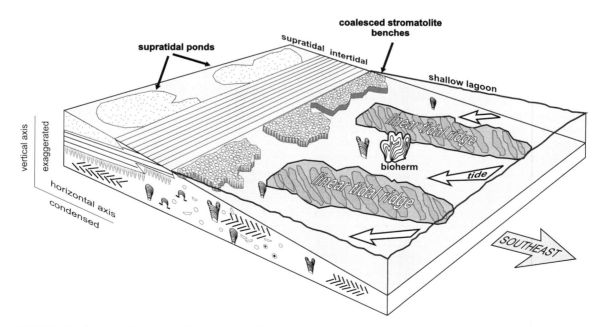

FIG. 28.—Model for tide-dominated lagoon complex, sequences G, H, and I. Kilometers-wide lagoon separated from open ocean by ramp-edge shoals (not shown). Linear tidal ridges responded to dominant flood tide direction and were altered significantly by normal and storm-wind-driven currents. Stromatolite bioherms and smaller, columnar stromatolites colonized the sea bottom between the linear sand ridges. Shoreward, columnar stromatolites coalesced to form laterally extensive benches. The intertidal and supratidal setting was the site of deposition of cryptmicrobialite and tufa.

CAVE-FILL KARST BRECCIA

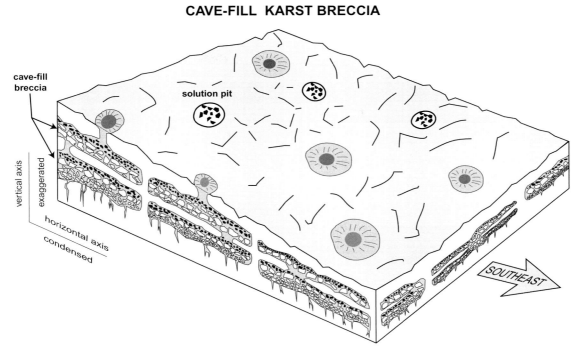

FIG. 29.—Model for cave-fill karst with pervasive dissolution and extensive brecciation, sequence M. Major sea-level fall occurring when LST of SSIV coincides with Late HST of sequence M.

quency fifth-order and fourth-order cycles, the fundamental "building blocks" of the Katakturuk system. Vertical trends in cycle types and sequences (i.e., retrogradational, aggradational, and progradational) reflect the interaction between sediment supply, sea-level oscillations, and platform subsidence rates. The considerable thickness of the Katakturuk Dolomite and lack of internal unconformities or evidence for substantial erosion suggest a moderate to high subsidence rate, consistent with the early drift phase of a rifted continental margin. Additionally, if high-frequency eustasy was operant, amplitudes were apparently fairly low.

We have presented the details of our stacking-pattern analysis of the lower gray craggy dolomite member, which demonstrates the central theme that emerges from the Katakturuk succession. In this example, fifth-order cycles are nested into fourth-order cycles, the architecture of which defines the third-order transgressive to highstand system tracts of sequence G, interpreted here as a tide-dominated lagoon complex. The majority of third-order systems tracts in the Katakturuk Dolomite are symmetrical and are characterized by windward sand shoal to peritidal complexes (sequences A, B, D, E, F, I, J, K, and L), which formed from inherently high rates of sediment supply sufficient to keep up with sea-level rise coupled with subsidence. Where long-term (second-order) and shorter-term (third-order) relative sea-level rise coincides we document evidence for two major backstepping events (sequences C and D) during which the Katakturuk platform evolved into a distally steepened ramp with deposition of deep-water noncyclic carbonate and clastic sediment.

As the Katakturuk platform approached "middle age," a midramp, tide-dominated lagoon complex developed landward of

the barrier shoal. This setting was a mixed-energy environment, an interplay between tidal and wave-current depositional forces. During fair-weather periods, tidal currents strongly influenced the orientation and migration of subtidal to intertidal sand waves. Normal wave-current and episodic storm-wave activity reshaped the configuration and nature of these sand bodies. Constructional and destructional aspects of these forces resulted in amalgamation of linear tidal sand bars to form a continuous sheet of cross-bedded grainstone. Inner-ramp peritidal complexes prograded seaward during most Katakturuk third-order sea-level highstands, capping mid-ramp lagoon and outer-ramp shoal deposits. Where second-order and third-order sea-level falls were coincident (sequence M of SSIV) a major subaerial exposure event occurred, resulting in extensive dissolution and the development of a karst-breccia cave-fill system and the termination of Katakturuk Dolomite deposition.

ACKNOWLEDGMENTS

This manuscript has benefited immensely from the careful and thoughtful reviews by David Osleger (University of California, Davis), Maurice Tucker (Durham University), Wes Wallace and Mike Whalen (University of Alaska Fairbanks), Keith Watts (formerly with the University of Alaska Fairbanks), and John Southard (Massachusetts Institute of Technology). This report is part of the first author's dissertation research at the University of Alaska Fairbanks, Department of Geology and Geophysics as well as work conducted for the Alaska Division of Geological & Geophysical Surveys (ADGGS). Funding for this study was provided by ADGGS, and the Tectonics and Sedimentation Research Group, Geophysical Institute, University of Alaska Fairbanks through grants from Amoco Production Company, ARCO Alaska, Inc., BP Exploration (Alaska) Inc., Chevron USA, Inc., Conoco Inc., Elf Exploration, Inc., Exxon Company USA, Japan National Oil Corporation, Mobil Exploration and Producing U.S. Inc., Murphy Exploration and Production Company, Phillips Petroleum Company, Shell Western Exploration & Production Inc., Texaco Inc., and Union Oil Company of California. The first author gratefully acknowledges the advice and support of John Decker (formerly with ADGGS and currently with UNOCAL), Mark Robinson (formerly with ADGGS), Gil Mull (ADGGS), and Keith Crowder (formerly with the University of Alaska Fairbanks). Assistance in portions of the field work was cheerfully provided by Eugene Pavia and Tim Ryherd. Jim Clough is also greatly indebted to the late Conrad Gebelein for granting the opportunity to study modern carbonates on the Great Bahama Bank in 1976.

REFERENCES

AHR, W. M., 1973, The carbonate ramp—an alternative to the shelf model: Gulf Coast Association of Geological Societies, Transactions, v. 23, p. 221–225.

AITKEN, J. D., 1967, Classification and environmental significance of cryptalgal limestones and dolomites, with illustrations from the Cambrian and Ordovician of southwestern Alberta: Journal of Sedimentary Petrology, v. 37, p. 1163–1178.

ASSERETO, R. L., AND KENDALL, C. G. ST. C., 1977, Nature, origin and classification of peritidal tepee structures and related breccias: Sedimentology, v. 24, p. 153–210.

BERTRAND-SARFATI, J., AND MOUSSINE-POUCHKINE, A., 1983, Pedogenetic and diagenetic fabrics in the Upper Proterozoic Sarnyéré Formation (Gourma, Mali): Precambrian Research, v. 20, p. 225–242.

BLODGETT, R. B., CLOUGH, J. G., DUTRO, J. T., JR., ORMISTON, A. R., PALMER, A. R., AND TAYLOR, M. E., 1986, Age revisions of the Nanook Limestone and Katakturuk Dolomite, northeastern Brooks Range, Alaska, in Bartsch-Winkler, S., and Reed, K. M., eds., Geologic Studies in Alaska by the U.S. Geological Survey during 1985: U.S. Geological Survey, Circular 978, p. 5–10.

BURNE, R. V., AND MOORE, L. S., 1987, Microbialites; organosedimentary deposits of benthic microbial communities: Palaios, v. 2, p. 241–254.

CHOQUETTE, P. W., AND JAMES, N. P., 1988, Introduction, in James, N. P., and Choquette, P. W., eds. Paleokarst: New York, Springer-Verlag, p. 1–21.

CHRISTIE-BLICK, N., GROTZINGER, J. P., AND VON DER BORCH, C. C., 1988, Sequence stratigraphy in Proterozoic successions: Geology, v. 16, p. 100–104.

CLOUGH, J. G., 1989, General stratigraphy of the Katakturuk Dolomite in the Sadlerochit and Shublik Mountains, Arctic National Wildlife Refuge, northeastern Alaska: Alaska Division of Geological & Geophysical Surveys, Public-Data File 89-4a, 11 p., 1 in. = 100 m, 1 sheet.

CLOUGH, J. G., AND GOLDHAMMER, R. K., 1994, Stromatolite cyclicity on a Late Proterozoic high-energy carbonate ramp system, Katakturuk Dolomite, northeastern Brooks Range, Alaska (abstract), in Awramik, S. M., ed., Death Valley International Stromatolite Symposium, Laughlin, Nevada, p. 20–21.

CLOUGH, J. G., AND GOLDHAMMER, R. K., 1995, Deposition on a Late Proterozoic carbonate ramp, Katakturuk Dolomite, northeast Brooks Range, Alaska (abstract): Geological Society of America, Cordilleran Section, Abstracts with Programs, v. 27, p. 10.

CLOUGH, J. G., ROBINSON, M. S., PESSEL, G. H., IMM, T. A., BLODGETT, R. B., HARRIS, A. G., BERGMAN, S. C., AND FOLAND, K. A., 1990, Geology and age of Franklinian and older rocks in the Sadlerochit and Shublik Mountains, Arctic National Wildlife Refuge, Alaska (abstract): Geological Association of Canada and Mineralogical Association of Canada, Annual Meeting, Program with Abstracts, v. 15, p. A25.

CONIGLIO, M., AND DIX, G. R., 1992, Carbonate slopes, in Walker, R. G., and James, N. P., eds., Facies Models, Response to Sea Level Change: St. Johns, Newfoundland, Geological Association of Canada, p. 349–373.

CUFFEY, R. J., GEBELEIN, C. D., FONDA, S. S., BLIEFNICK, D. M., KOSICH, D. F., AND SOROKA, L. G., 1977, Modern tidal-channel bryozoan reefs at Joulters Cays (Bahamas), in Third International Coral Reef Symposium, Miami, Florida, Proceedings, part 2, Geology, p. 339–345.

DEMICCO, R. V., 1983, Wavy and lenticular-bedded carbonate ribbon rocks of the Upper Cambrian Conococheague Limestone, central Appalachians: Journal of Sedimentary Petrology, v. 53, p. 1–22.

DEMICCO, R. V., AND HARDIE, L. A., 1994, Sedimentary Structures and Early Diagenetic Features of Shallow Marine Carbonate Deposits: SEPM, Atlas Series No. 1, 265 p.

DILL, R. F., AND SHINN, E. A., 1986, Giant stromatolites in subtidal channels of the Bahamas provide new insight to ancient counterparts (abstract): Geological Society of America, 1986 Annual Meeting, Abstracts with Programs, v. 18, p. 585.

DUNHAM, R. J., 1969, Vadose pisolite in the Capitan reef (Permian), New Mexico and Texas, in Friedman, G. M., ed., Depositional Environments in Carbonate Rocks: Society of Economic Paleontologists and Mineralogists, Special Publication 14, p. 182–190.

DUTRO, J. T., JR., 1970, Pre-Carboniferous carbonate rocks, northeastern Alaska, in Adkison, W. L., and Brosge, W. M., eds., Proceedings of the Geological Seminar on the North Slope of Alaska: Los Angeles, American Association of Petroleum Geologists, Pacific Section, p. M1–M8.

ELRICK, M., 1995, Cyclostratigraphy of Middle Devonian carbonates of the eastern Great Basin: Journal of Sedimentary Research, v. B65, p. 61–79.

ELRICK, M., AND READ, J. F., 1991, Cyclic ramp-to-basin carbonate deposits, Lower Mississippian, Wyoming and Montana: a combined field and computer modeling study: Journal of Sedimentary Petrology, v. 61, p. 1194–1224.

FISCHER, A. G., 1964, The Lofer Cyclothems of the Alpine Triassic, in Merriam, D. F., ed., Symposium on Cyclic Sedimentation: Kansas State Geological Survey, Bulletin 169, v. 1, p. 107–149.

FERGUSON, J., BURNE, R. V., AND CHAMBERS, L. A., 1982, Lithification of peritidal carbonates by continental brines at Fisherman Bay, South Australia, to form megapolygon/spelean limestone association: Journal of Sedimentary Petrology, v. 52, p. 1127–1147.

GOLDHAMMER, R. K., DUNN, P. A., AND HARDIE, L. A., 1990, Depositional cycles, composite sea-level changes, cycle stacking patterns, and the hierarchy of stratigraphic forcing: examples from Alpine Triassic platform carbonates: Geological Society of America, Bulletin, v. 102, p. 535–562.

GOLDHAMMER, R. K., LEHMAN, P. J., TODD, R. G., WILSON, J. L., WARD, W. C., AND JOHNSON, C. R., 1991, Sequence stratigraphy and cyclostratigraphy of the Mesozoic of the Sierra Madre Oriental, northeast Mexico: A Field Guidebook: Austin, Texas, SEPM, Gulf Coast Section, Foundation, 85 p., 1 plate.

GOLDHAMMER, R. K., LEHMANN, P. J., AND DUNN, P. A., 1993, The origin of high-frequency platform carbonate cycles and third-order sequences (Lower Ordovician El Paso Gp, west Texas): Constraints from outcrop data, inverse and forward stratigraphic modeling: Journal of Sedimentary Petrology, v. 63, p. 318–359.

GRAMMER, G. M., EBERLI, G. P., VAN BUCHEM, F. S., STEVENSON, G. M., AND HOMEWOOD, P., 1996, Application of high-resolution sequence stratigraphy to evaluate lateral variability in outcrop and subsurface—Desert Creek and Ismay intervals, Paradox Basin, in Longman, M. W., and Sonnenfeld, M. D., eds., Paleozoic Systems of the Rocky Mountain Region: SEPM, Rocky Mountain Section, p. 235–266.

GROTZINGER, J. P., 1985, Evolution of Early Proterozoic passive-margin carbonate platform, Rocknest Formation, Wopmay Orogen, N.W.T., Canada [Ph.D. thesis]: Virginia Polytechnic Institute, Blacksburg, Virginia, 224 p.

GROTZINGER, J. P., 1986, Cyclicity and paleoenvironmental dynamics, Rocknest platform, northwest Canada: Geological Society of America, Bulletin, v. 96, p. 1208–1231.

GROTZINGER, J. P., 1989, Facies and evolution of Precambrian carbonate depositional systems: Emergence of the modern platform archetype, in Crevello, P. D., Wilson, J. L., Sarg, J. F., and Read, J. F., eds., Controls on Carbonate Platform and Basin Development: SEPM, Special Publication 44, p. 79–106.

GROTZINGER, J. P., 1993, New views of old carbonate sediments: Geotimes, September, p. 12–15.

GROTZINGER, J. P., AND READ, J. F., 1983, Evidence for primary aragonite precipitation, lower Proterozoic (1.9 Ga) Rocknest dolomite, Wopmay orogen, northwest Canada: Geology, v. 11, p. 710–713.

HANDFORD, C. R., 1988, Review of carbonate sand-belt deposition of ooid grainstones and application to Mississippian reservoir, Damme Field, Southwestern Kansas: American Association of Petroleum Geologists, Bulletin, v. 72, p. 1184–1199.

HALLEY, R. B., HARRIS, P. M., AND HINE, A. C., 1983, Bank margin environment, in Scholle, P. A., Bebout, D. G., and Moore, C. H., eds., Carbonate Depositional Environments: American Association of Petroleum Geologists, Memoir 33, p. 463–506.

HINE, A. C., 1977, Lily Bank, Bahamas: history of an active sand shoal: Journal of Sedimentary Petrology, v. 47, p. 1554–1581.

HOFFMAN, P. F., 1974, Shallow and deepwater stromatolites in Lower Proterozoic facies change, Great Slave Lake, Canada: American Association of Petroleum Geologists, Bulletin, v. 58, p. 856–867.

HOFMANN, H. J., AND JACKSON, G. D., 1987, Proterozoic ministromatolites with radial-fibrous fabric: Sedimentology, v. 34, p. 963–971.

JAMES, N. P., 1979, Facies models 11, Reefs, *in* Walker, R. G., ed., Facies Models: Geoscience Canada, Reprint Series 1, p. 121–132.

JENNETTE, D. C., AND PRYOR, W. A., 1993, Cyclic alteration of proximal and distal storm facies: Kope and Fairview formations (Upper Ordovician), Ohio and Kentucky: Journal of Sedimentary Petrology, v. 63, p. 183–203.

KEITH, B. D., AND THOMPSON, T. A., 1994, Mississippian subtidal stromatolites in a high-energy shoal setting, Salem Limestone, Indiana: an analog for modern stromatolites (abstract): American Association of Petroleum Geologists, Annual Convention, Official Program, v. 3, p. 184.

KERANS, C., 1995, Use of one- and two-dimensional cycle analysis in establishing high-frequency sequence frameworks, *in* Read, J., Kerans, C., Weber, J. L., Sarg, J. F., and Wright, F. M., eds., Milankovitch Sea-Level Changes, Cycles, and Reservoirs on Carbonate Platforms in Greenhouse and Ice-House Worlds: SEPM, Short Course Notes no. 35, Part 2, 20 p.

KERANS, C., AND FITCHEN, W. M., 1995, Sequence hierarchy and facies architecture of a carbonate-ramp system: San Andres Formation of Algerita Escarpment and Western Guadalupe Mountains, west Texas and New Mexico: University of Texas, Bureau of Economic Geology, Report of Investigations no. 235, 86 p.

KLEIN, G. D., 1970, Depositional and dispersal dynamics of intertidal sand bars: Journal of Sedimentary Petrology, v. 40, p. 1095–1127.

KOERSHNER, W. F., AND READ, J. F., 1989, Field and modeling studies of Cambrian carbonate cycles, Virginia Appalachians: Journal of Sedimentary Petrology, v. 59, p. 654–687.

LOGAN, B. W., REZAK, R., AND GINSBURG, R. N., 1964, Classification and environmental significance of algal stromatolites: Journal of Geology, v. 72, p. 68–83.

LOGAN, B. W., HOFFMAN, P. F., AND GEBELEIN, C. D., 1974, Algal mats, cryptalgal fabrics, and structures, Hamelin Pool, Western Australia, *in* Logan, B. W., Read, J. F., Hagan, G. M., Hoffman, P., Brown, R. G., Woods, P. J., and Gebelein, C. D., eds., Evolution and Diagenesis of Quaternary Carbonate Sequences, Shark Bay, Western Australia: American Association of Petroleum Geologists, Memoir 22, p. 140–194.

MARKELLO, J. R., AND READ, J. F., 1982, Upper Cambrian intrashelf basin, Nolichucky Formation, Southwest Virginia Appalachians: American Association of Petroleum Geologists, Bulletin, v. 66, p. 860–878.

MCCLELLAND, W. C., 1997, Detrital zircon studies of the Proterozoic Neruokpuk Formation, Sadlerochit and Franklin Mountains, northeastern Alaska (abstract): Geological Society of America, Cordilleran Section, 93rd Annual Meeting, Abstracts with Programs, v. 29, p. 28.

MONTAÑEZ, I. P., AND OSLEGER, D. A., 1993, Parasequence stacking patterns, third-order accommodation events, and sequence stratigraphy of Middle to Upper Cambrian platform carbonates, Bonanza King Formation, southern Great Basin, *in* Loucks, R. G., and Sarg, J. F., eds., Carbonate Sequence Stratigraphy; Recent Developments and Applications: American Association of Petroleum Geologists, Memoir 57, p. 305–326.

MOORE, T. E., 1987, Geochemistry and tectonic setting of some volcanic rocks of the Franklinian assemblage, central and eastern Brooks Range, *in* Tailleur, I., and Weimer, P., eds., Alaskan North Slope Geology, Volume II: SEPM, Pacific Section, California and Alaska Geological Society, Alaska, p. 691–710.

OSLEGER, D. A., 1990, Cyclostratigraphy of Late Cambrian cyclic carbonates: an interbasinal and modeling study, U.S.A. [Ph.D. thesis]: Virginia Polytechnic Institute and State University, Blacksburg, Virginia, 303 p.

PELECHATY, S. M., AND JAMES, N. P., 1991, Dolomitized middle Proterozoic calcretes, Bathurst Inlet, Northwest Territories, Canada: Journal of Sedimentary Petrology, v. 61, p. 988–1001.

PERYT, T. M., 1983, Classification of coated grains, *in* Peryt, T. M. ed., Coated Grains: Berlin, Springer-Verlag, p. 3–6.

PERYT, T. M., HOPPE, A., BECHSTAEDT, T., KOESTER, J., PIERRE, C., AND RICHTER, D. K., 1990, Late Proterozoic aragonitic cement crusts, Bambui Group, Minas Gerais, Brazil: Sedimentology, v. 37, p. 279–286.

PFLUGER, F., AND GRESSE, P. G., 1996, Microbial sand chips a non-actualistic sedimentary structure: Sedimentary Geology, v. 102, p. 263–274.

RAINBIRD, R. H., HEAMAN, L. M., AND YOUNG, G. M., 1992, Sampling Laurentia; detrital zircon geochronology offers evidence for an extensive Neo-

proterozoic river system originating from the Grenville Orogen: Geology, v. 20, p. 351–354.

RAINBIRD, R. H., JEFFERSON, C. W., AND YOUNG, G. M., 1996, The early Neoproterozoic sedimentary Succession B of northwestern Laurentia: Correlations and paleogeographic significance: Geological Society of America, Bulletin, v. 108, p. 454–470.

READ, J. F., 1982, Carbonate platforms of passive (extensional) continental margins—types, characteristics and evolution: Tectonophysics, v. 81, p. 195–212.

READ, J. F., AND GOLDHAMMER, R. K., 1988, Use of Fischer plots to define third-order sea-level curves in Ordovician peritidal cyclic carbonates, Appalachians: Geology, v. 14, p. 107–110.

REED, B. L., 1968, Geology of the Lake Peters area, northeastern Brooks range, Alaska: U.S. Geological Survey, Bulletin 1236, 132 p.

REINECK, H.-E., AND SINGH, I. B., 1980, Depositional Sedimentary Environments, 2nd Edition: New York, Springer-Verlag, 549 p.

REISER, H. N., 1970, Northeastern Brooks Range—a surface expression of the Prudhoe Bay section, *in* Adkison, W. L., and Brosge, M. M., eds., Proceedings of the Geological Seminar on the North Slope of Alaska: Los Angeles, American Association of Petroleum Geologists, Pacific Section, p. K1–K14.

ROBINSON, M. S., DECKER, J., CLOUGH, J. G., REIFENSTUHL, R. R., BAKKE, A., DILLON, J. T., COMBELLICK, R. A., AND RAWLINSON, S. E., 1989, Geology of the Sadlerochit and Shublik Mountains, Arctic National Wildlife Refuge, northeastern Alaska: Alaska Division of Geological & Geophysical Surveys, Professional Report 100, 1:63,360 scale map.

SABLE, E. G., 1977, Geology of the western Romanzof Mountains, Brooks Range, northeastern Alaska: U.S. Geological Survey, Professional Paper 897, 84 p

SAMI, T. T., AND JAMES, N. P., 1994, Peritidal carbonate platform growth and cyclicity in an early Proterozoic foreland basin, upper Pethei Group, Northwest Canada: Journal of Sedimentary Research, v. B64, p. 111–131.

SARG, J. F., 1988, Carbonate sequence stratigraphy, *in* Wilgus, C. K., Hastings, B. S., Ross, C. A., Posamentier, H., Van Wagoner, J., and Kendall, C. G. St. C., eds., Sea Level Changes—An Integrated Approach: SEPM, Special Publication 43, p. 155–181.

SHAPIRO, R. S., AALTO, K. R., AND DILL, R. F., 1990, Physical control of distribution and morphology of subtidal stromatolites, Exumas, Bahamas (abstract): Geological Society of America, 1990 Annual Meeting, Abstracts with Programs, v. 22, p. A93.

STRASSER, J. A., 1988, Shallowing-upward sequences in Purbeckian peritidal carbonates (lowermost Cretaceous, Swill and French Jura Mountains): Sedimentology, v. 35, p. 369–383.

SUMNER, D. Y., AND GROTZINGER, J. P., 1993, Numerical modeling of ooid size and the problem of Neoproterozoic giant ooids: Journal of Sedimentary Petrology, v. 63, p. 974–982.

TUCKER, M. E., AND WRIGHT, V. P., 1990, Carbonate depositional systems; I, Marine shallow-water and lacustrine carbonates, *in* Tucker, M. E., Wright, V. P., and Dickson, J. A. D., eds., Carbonate Sedimentology: Blackwell Scientific Publications, p. 101–227.

TUCKER, M. E., CALVET, F., AND HUNT, D., 1993, Sequence stratigraphy of carbonate ramps: systems tracts, models and application to the Muschelkalk carbonate platforms of eastern Spain, *in* Posamentier, H. W., Summerhayes, C. P., and Haq, B. U., eds., Sequence Stratigraphy and Facies Associations: International Association of Sedimentologists, Special Publication 18, p. 397–415.

VAN WAGONER, J. C., POSAMENTIER, H. W., MITCHUM, R.M., VAIL, P. R., SARG, J. F., LOUTIT, T. S., AND HARDENBOL, J., 1988, An overview of the fundamentals of sequence stratigraphy and key definitions, *in* Wilgus, C. K., Hastings, B. S., Ross, C. A., Posamentier, H., Van Wagoner, J., and Kendall, C. G. St. C., eds., Sea-Level Changes: An Integrated Approach: SEPM, Special Publication 42, p. 39–45.

WALLACE, W. K., 1993, Detachment folds and a passive roof duplex: examples from the northeastern Brooks Range, Alaska, *in* Solie, D., and Tannian, F., eds., Short Notes on Alaskan Geology 1993: Alaska Division of Geological & Geophysical Surveys, Professional Report 113, p. 81–99.

WALLACE, W. K., AND HANKS, C. R., 1990, Structural provinces of the northeastern Brooks Range, Arctic National Wildlife Refuge, Alaska: American Association of Petroleum Geologists, Bulletin, v. 74, p. 1100–1118.

WANLESS, H. R., AND TEDESCO, L. O., 1993, Comparison of oolitic sand bodies generated by tidal vs. wind-wave agitation, *in* Keith, B. D., and Zuppann, C. W., eds., Mississippian Oolites and Modern Analogs: American Association of Petroleum Geologists, Studies in Geology no. 35, p. 199–225.

YOUNG, G. M., JEFFERSON, C. W., DELANEY, G. D., AND YEO, G. M., 1979, Middle and late Proterozoic evolution of the northern Canadian Cordillera and Shield: Geology, v. 7, p. 125–128.

EVOLUTION OF LATE PALEOPROTEROZOIC RAMP SYSTEMS, LOWER McNAMARA GROUP, NORTHEASTERN AUSTRALIA

TERRY T. SAMI,* NOEL P. JAMES, AND T. KURTIS KYSER

Department of Geological Sciences, Queen's University, Kingston, Ontario K7L 3N6, Canada

AND

PETER N. SOUTHGATE, M. JIM JACKSON, AND ROD W. PAGE

Australian Geological Survey Organisation, PO Box 378, Canberra, ACT 2601, Australia

ABSTRACT: Rocks of the lower McNamara Group (including the Torpedo Creek, Gunpowder Creek, Paradise Creek, and Esperanza formations) form part of the extensive late Paleoproterozoic sedimentary cover in northwestern Queensland. The succession varies in thickness from 450 to 1250 m and consists largely of dolomite, chert, and siliciclastic rocks deposited in nonmarine, marginal marine, and marine environments. The package is divisible into two distinct basin-filling supersequences (second-order sequences): Prize, a lower suite of fault-bounded, storm-dominated siliciclastic ramps; and the overlying Gun, a regionally extensive, southeast-facing, storm-dominated mixed carbonate/siliciclastic ramp. A regionally correlative unconformity in the lower to middle Gunpowder Formation, representing a depositional hiatus of over 28 My, records the boundary between these two supersequences. Combining facies architecture with gamma-ray logs derived from hand-held spectrometers enables further subdivision into three third-order depositional sequences, (1) Prize 2, Torpedo Creek–lower Gunpowder Creek, (2) Gun 1, upper Gunpowder Creek–Paradise Creek, and (3) Gun 2, upper Paradise Creek–Esperanza, each of which is bounded by regionally correlative disconformities.

The Prize 2 depositional sequence consists largely of siliciclastic storm-dominated ramp sediments deposited in locally fault-controlled depocenters. The overlying Gun 1 sequence marks the transition from a siliciclastic to a carbonate ramp as storm-dominated shallow-water carbonate facies prograded east/southeastward over the underlying siliciclastics. Storm processes continued to dominate sedimentation. Formation of stromatolitic rim complexes had a significant hydrodynamic effect on this second ramp and promoted flattening of the inner ramp and steepening of the outer ramp to form a distally steepened ramp to rimmed platform. Unlike the underlying succession, the Gun 1 depositional sequence represents a regionally continuous depositional system with only minor thickness variations. The Gun 2 depositional sequence similarly represents a storm-dominated siliciclastic/carbonate ramp. The most striking difference between the Gun 1 and 2 sequences is the relatively abrupt shift from micrite-rich domal–columnar stromatolites to spar-rich microdigitate and digitate columnar stromatolites.

Unlike most other Paleoproterozoic carbonate successions documented to date, the lower McNamara platform was dominated by storm-deposited and reworked sediments, predominantly intraclasts, quartz and peloid silt, and muds, rather than precipitated carbonate cements. The preponderance of silt-size grains, rather than mud-size, differentiates this succession from most other detrital Proterozoic platforms. The internal architecture and evolution of the succession is instead similar to sediment-rich Phanerozoic carbonate ramps.

INTRODUCTION

For carbonate depositional systems the Mesoproterozoic (1650 to 900 Ma) marks a period of transition (see discussions in Grotzinger, 1989; Knoll and Swett, 1990; Sami and James, 1996; Kah and Knoll, 1996) from precipitate-dominated platforms (Paleoproterozoic, 2500 to 1650 Ma) to largely detrital platforms (Neoproterozoic, 900 to 544 Ma, and Phanerozoic). As such, many Mesoproterozoic carbonate platforms are commonly a complex amalgamation of these two styles of deposition. This study concentrates on lower McNamara Group carbonate-rich strata (about 1700 to 1650 Ma) of the Lawn Hill Platform. The late Paleoproterozoic to Mesoproterozoic Lawn Hill Platform is located in western Queensland, Australia, and covers an area of about 20,000 square kilometers (Fig. 1). The succession varies in thickness from 2500 m to about 8500 m. Lower McNamara strata crop out in the southeast parts of this belt and comprise about 450 m to 1250 m of strata at the base of the platform. Carbonate rocks are mainly a mixture of precipitated stromatolites and fine- to coarse-grained detrital carbonates.

Among the difficulties faced by workers studying early to middle Proterozoic successions is the lack of effective biostratigraphic control. This deficiency is felt most acutely when attempting to determine detailed basin architecture and the geometry of basin fills. Thus, sequence stratigraphic interpretations of Proterozoic successions have largely been worked out by inference from facies architecture. The difficulty in establishing time-stratigraphic units, particularly in structurally complex basins, has commonly led to the use of lithostratigraphic correlation methods in these successions, to the detriment of sequence stratigraphic frameworks.

This study forms part of a project designed to construct structural and time-stratigraphic frameworks for sedimentary basins in northern Australia. The required time-stratigraphic dissection of the Proterozoic succession in northern Australia has been attempted by complementing detailed outcrop and core studies with zircon-derived SHRIMP dates generated from felsic tuffaceous beds and gamma-ray curves generated from drillcore, by hand-held spectrometers, and wireline logs (see Jackson et al., this volume). In this context a predictive tectono-stratigraphic framework can be reconstructed with the use of established sequence stratigraphic techniques. This paper provides an example, using the lower McNamara Group, of how traditional techniques of facies architecture analysis are complemented by the addition of easily collected gamma-log data.

Thus, the goals of this study are twofold: firstly, to examine the facies dynamics and evolution of a carbonate platform at a critical period in Earth's history in an effort to better understand how the carbonate system was changing; and secondly, to demonstrate that a high-resolution sequence stratigraphical framework, within which basin geometry and evolution can be explored, can be generated for Proterozoic successions.

REGIONAL SETTING AND STRATIGRAPHIC FRAMEWORK

The Australian Bureau of Mineral Resources, Geology and Geophysics, in cooperation with the Northern Territory and Queensland geological surveys, conducted much of the previous work in the region from the 1960s through to the 1980s. Results of geochronological, geochemical, and petrologic stud-

*Present address: Wascana Energy Inc., P.O. Box 2727, Station M, 2900-240-4th Ave., Rm. 28089, Calgary, Alberta, T2P 5C1, Canada

Carbonate Sedimentation and Diagenesis in the Evolving Precambrian World
Copyright © 2000, SEPM (Society for Sedimentary Geology) Special Publication 67, ISBN 1-56576-072-7

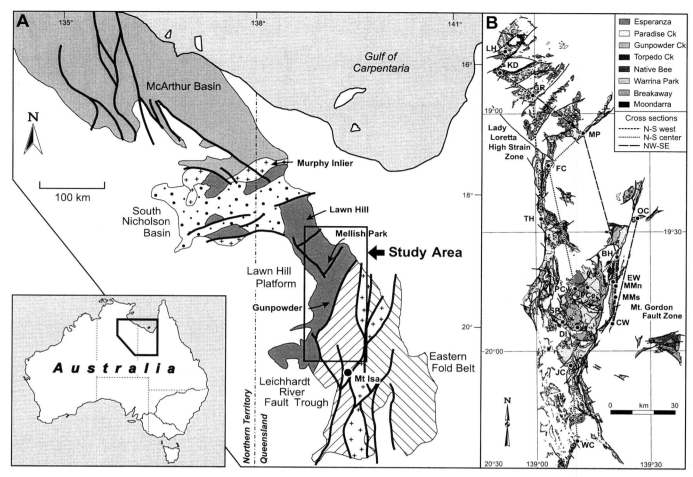

FIG. 1.—Map of North Australian Proterozoic basins and main structural elements: A) location of study area; B) Extent of outcrop belt of studied formations. Labeled sites refer to location of composite sections and cores: LH, Lawn Hill (core); KD, Kamarga Dome; GR, Gregory River; TH, Thorntonia; MP, Mellish park; FC, Police Creek; PCw, Paradise Creek West; PCe, Paradise Creek East; BH, Barr hole; EW, Esperanza Waters; SP, AASP 1A (core); DI, AADi 1 (Core); JC, Judenan Creek; WC, Wilfred Creek; MMn, Mammoth Mines North; MMs, Mammoth Mines South; CW, Crocodile Waterhole, OC, Oxide Creek. Broken lines indicate location of cross sections in Figures 3 and 7.

ies and regional mapping are synthesized in Plumb et al. (1980), Plumb et al. (1981), Hutton and Sweet (1982), and Plumb et al. (1990). SHRIMP zircon data collected by Page and Sweet (1998) indicates that deposition of sediments of the Isa Superbasin, comprising the McArthur Basin and the Lawn Hill Platform (Fig. 1), began about 1698 Ma following the decay of regional volcanism, and was terminated about 1575 Ma in response to regional uplift and metamorphism associated with the Isan Orogeny (Fig. 2). Regional fault zones controlled the accumulation of Isan Superbasin sediments, which vary regionally from 1500 to 15,000 m thick.

Nine unconformity-bounded, second-order supersequences can be recognized in the Isa Superbasin (Fig. 2). In the southern McArthur and Murphy Inlier regions (Fig. 1) reduced accommodation rates resulted in regional incision surfaces at each supersequence boundary, whereas in more basinward areas to the southeast (Lawn Hill and Mt Isa), many of the regionally correlative boundaries show little or no interruption of sedimentation. Supersequences range from 10 to 20 My in duration and comprise third- and fourth-order sequences (Fig. 3) and

higher-order parasequences. Second-order supersequences are 1000–3000 m thick, third- and fourth-order sequences are hundreds and tens of meters thick, respectively, and parasequences vary from a few meters to several tens of meters.

SHRIMP dating has helped assign geologic ages to the sedimentary fill within these packages (Fig. 2) and gives some indication of the duration of nondepositional and/or erosional events (Page, 1997; Page and Sweet, 1998). This study focuses on the Prize and Gun supersequences in the Lawn Hill–Gunpowder area and encompasses the Torpedo Creek, Gunpowder Creek, Paradise Creek, and Esperanza formations and their correlatives in the Mt Isa region: the Warrina Park, Moondarra, Breakaway, Native Bee, and Urquhart formations (Figs. 1, 2). In the study area carbonate sediments are largely restricted to the Prize, Gun, and Loretta supersequences. Prize supersequence sediments were deposited at paleolatitudes of 10 to 15° (hemisphere not determined) whereas those of the Gun supersequence accumulated at paleolatitudes of about 20 to 30° (M. Idnurm, personal communication, 1997).

The McNamara Group (includes Prize, Gun, Loretta, River, Term, Lawn, Wide, and Doom supersequences in the Lawn Hill

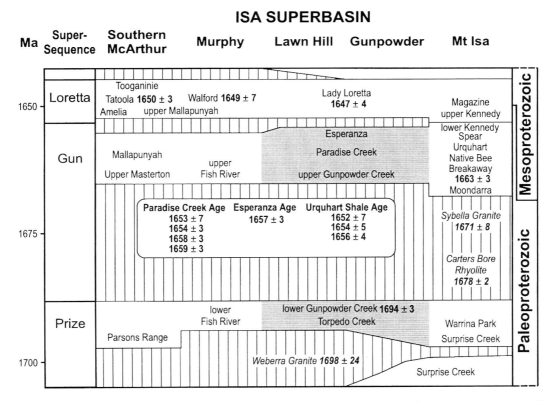

FIG. 2.—Regional stratigraphic framework of North Australian Paleoproterozoic to Mesoproterozoic basins. Supersequences are separated by regional unconformities and their correlative conformities and are named after the formation in which maximum flooding of the basin is recorded. Numbers refer to rock ages determined from SHRIMP dating of strata within studied formations. Time scale is constructed from these ages. Vertical hatching indicates periods of nondeposition and/or erosion. Shaded boxes indicate strata examined in this study.

and Gunpowder regions) rests unconformably (Prize Supersequence boundary in Figure 2) on felsic volcanics of the Fiery Creek Formation (1709 ± 3 Ma). These volcanics are interpreted (D. Scott, personal communication, 1998) to represent a period of rift/extension, which was ultimately responsible for basin formation sometime after 1698 Ma. The basin in turn rests on a deep-seated graben system that was reactivated by major thermal events between 1710 and 1730 Ma. Decay of these thermal events drove the extensional pulses responsible for initiation of subsidence. The Esperanza Formation is overlain by basal breccias of the Lady Loretta Formation, a problematic unit variously attributed to exposure, solution collapse, or diagenetic alteration (Hutton and Sweet, 1982) of marine carbonates. This brecciated unit is, in turn, covered by marine carbonates and siliciclastics of the Lady Loretta Formation (about 1647 Ma) and nonmarine and marine siliciclastics of the upper McNamara Group. Thus, lower McNamara deposition occurred over a period of less than 51 My (1698 Ma to 1647 Ma), including extensive intervals of nondeposition (Fig. 2). Throughout the study area, the southeast-thickening McNamara Group is characterized by extensional or transtensional faults and is currently thought to have accumulated in an intracratonic rift basin (Scott et al., 1997). Interpretation of continuous, high- to moderate-amplitude seismic profiles suggests that the lower McNamara Group represents a regionally extensive siliciclastic/carbonate ramp (Scott and Bradshaw, 1997). Deposition was interrupted by periods of NNW–SSE extension or strike-slip

tectonism, which broke the basin into small, localized depocenters (Bradshaw and Scott, 1997). Postdepositional folding and faulting has complicated stratigraphic correlation and partially obscured paleogeographic relationships. Several paleotopographic highs intermittently influenced deposition during lower McNamara time: the Mount Gordon Fault Zone to the southeast, and parallel structures, such as the Lady Loretta High Strain Zone, to the north and west (Figs. 1, 3).

METHODS

The 18 composite sections used in Figure 3 are based on detailed examination of 56 outcrop sections and five subsurface cores. Petrographic descriptions of lower McNamara rock types are based on study of 100 polished thin sections. Samples were obtained from all localities and from all stratigraphic levels throughout the study area. Facies are defined by sedimentary structures, component grains and fabrics, and where present, stromatolite types and morphologies. Depositional environments are based on interpretations of facies dynamics, geometry, and stratigraphic and geographic interrelationships (cf. Hardie and Shinn, 1986; Walker and James, 1992).

The gamma-ray logs were generated with the use of handheld Scintrex spectrometers. Readings were taken at 50 cm intervals of true thickness and used to generate total count (K–Th–U) curves (Fig. 3). Data represent average total gamma-ray counts per second over a ten-second interval. The spectrometer was placed in contact with the sample for three successive ten-second periods in order to permit stabilization of the counts and eliminate inter-sample effects. The resultant curves permitted correlation with subsurface datasets. Cycles were identified at a variety of scales on the basis of curve shape and recurring patterns. Because gamma-ray readings are affected by diagenetic alteration of the original sediments (e.g., silicification, calcretization), the curves were always interpreted in conjunction with detailed lithologic and petrographic information. Excellent corroboration between curves generated with the hand-held instruments from core and wireline logs from the same hole helped provide strong validation for this method of gamma-ray log generation. In order to increase legibility and emphasize lower-order patterns, the figures in this paper use gamma-ray curves that have undergone time-series smoothing. All interpretations and correlations are based on the original, unsmoothed curves.

LITHOFACIES AND DEPOSITIONAL SETTINGS

Table 1 summarizes the petrographic and lithologic characteristics of the eleven distinct rock types that, in variable combination, make up lithofacies of the lower McNamara Group (Fig. 3). Three cross sections have been constructed in order to best represent sedimentological and tectonic variations across the basin (see Figure 1 for locations). The first (Fig. 3A) includes sections located adjacent to, and to the west of, the Lady Loretta High Strain Zone (Fig. 1). The second (Fig. 3B) covers sections located between the Lady Loretta High Strain Zone, to the west, and the Mount Gordon Fault Zone, to the east. The

third (Fig 3C) transects these two north–south oriented cross sections and includes sections affected by the two tectonically active zones as well as one section (Oxide Creek) to the east of the Mount Gordon Fault Zone.

Three main lithofacies belts are identified, corresponding to the three third-order depositional sequences (Fig. 4): (1) Torpedo Creek–lower Gunpowder Creek; (2) upper Gunpowder Creek–Paradise Creek; and (3) upper Paradise Creek–Esperanza. Stacking patterns of higher-order sequences within each third-order sequence indicate initial backstepping during transgression, followed by aggradation and progradation as highstand accommodation rates slowed. Lithofacies represent environments ranging from nonmarine through shallow marine to deep marine.

Torpedo Creek–Lower Gunpowder Creek Lithofacies

This package is composed largely of siliciclastic rocks with minor carbonate content locally. The overall thickness of this interval is highly variable, suggesting that the basin was segmented by block faulting into local sediment sources and depocenters (Fig. 3). Four main lithofacies (Fig. 4A) are identified, and they are organized into stacked shallowing-upward packages.

Siliciclastic Nonmarine–Shoreface.—This facies is composed of clean, white quartz arenite, quartz siltstone–wacke, and local concentrations of coarse lithic conglomerate (Table 1). Strata are typically medium- to thick-bedded and are arranged in fining- and thinning-upward packages. Sedimentary structures in-

TABLE 1.—SUMMARY OF LOWER McNAMARA GROUP ROCK TYPES

Rock Types	Description
Lithic conglomerate	pebble to cobble conglomerate, subrounded to subangular clasts of quartz arenite, quartz siltstone/wacke, and chert; weak grading, matrix of quartz arenite and quartz siltstone/wacke
Quartz arenite	medium to coarse quartz sand, subspherical, very well rounded, well sorted, minor polycrystalline quartz; minor fine muscovite sand, poor lamination, quartz overgrowth cement, minor dolomite cement
Quartz siltstone–wacke	silt to fine quartz sand, subspherical, angular to subrounded, well sorted; fine to very fine muscovite sand, variable clay mineral content, very well laminated, quartz overgrowth cement, minor dolomite cement
Mudstone–shale	minor quartz and muscovite silt, angular to subrounded, moderately sorted; abundant clay mineral content, very well laminated, dolomite and clay-mineral cement
Dolomudstone	dololutite as microspar; rare quartz silt, angular to subangular, well sorted; irregular organic-rich films, dissolution seams, locally fenestral or with clotted fabric, local molar-tooth structure, poorly laminated, largely featureless,
Quartz–peloid grainstone	silt- to very fine sand-size micritic peloids, well rounded, well sorted; silt to very fine quartz sand, subspherical, angular to subangular, well sorted, quartz content variable (up to 50%), quartz well disseminated or concentrated in lenses one to two grains thick; variable intraclast content; minor muscovite silt, generally well laminated, minor dolomicrite matrix, pore-filling carbonate cement
Ooid grainstone	medium to very coarse sand-size concentric (common), radial (rare), and mixed ooids (radial core, concentric rind) moderate to very well sorted, fine to coarse quartz sand, peloids, and micritic intraclasts as nuclei; isopachous and pore-filling carbonate cements (commonly silicified), locally spalled, locally multigenerational
Intraclast grainstone	very fine sand to gravel-size intraclasts; clasts include dolomudstone, quartz–peloid grainstone, microbial laminite, domal–columnar microbialite, intraclast grainstone, ooid grainstone; clasts are subspherical to elongate to oblate, subangular to well rounded, poorly sorted; silt to very fine sand-size micritic peloids, well rounded, well sorted; silt to coarse quartz sand, subspherical, subangular to subrounded, moderately to well sorted, quartz content variable (up to 30%); rare medium to very coarse sand-size concentric (common), radial (rare), and mixed ooids (radial core, concentric rind); minor dolomicrite content variable (up to 10%), locally keystone vugs, locally development of coated grains, isopachous and pore-filling carbonate cement
Microbial laminite	irregular to slightly cuspate laminae (mm scale), filamentous microbial elements (0.025 mm diameter), high micrite content, clotted fabric, organic-rich films, spar-filled fenestrae, some microcrystalline spar with fibrous remnants, minor to moderate quartz silt and peloid content, grains largely concentrated in discrete layers and lenses
Domal–columnar microbialite	planar to irregular laminae (0.2–5 mm thick) spar-rich at base and micritic at top, clotted fabric, organic-rich films, spar-filled smooth-walled fenestrae, some microcrystalline spar with fibrous remnants, minor quartz silt and peloid content, moderate to high micrite content, grains largely concentrated in discrete layers and lenses, intraclast grainstone, quartz-peloid grainstone, and dolomudstone between domes and columns
Digitate columnar microbialite	irregular internal structure, laminae 0.1 to 0.5 mm thick, clotted fabric, low micrite content, minor quartz silt, peloid, and intraclast content, intraclast grainstone and quartz-peloid grainstone between columns, largely microcrystalline and fibrous silica

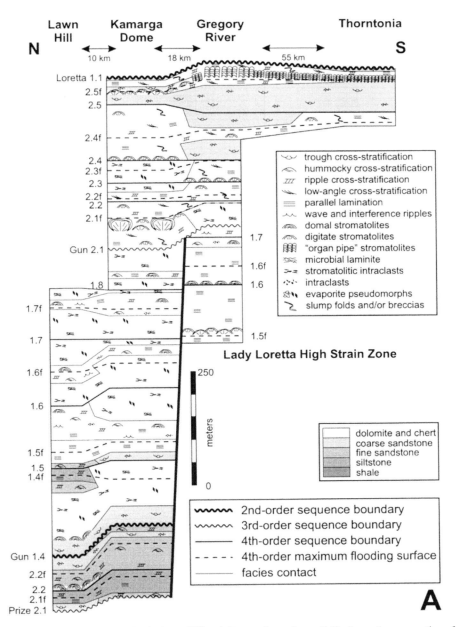

FIG. 3.—Correlation of lower McNamara Group facies in the Lawn Hill and Gunpowder regions. A) North–south cross section of sub-basin located to West of Lady Loretta High Strain Zone. B) North–south cross section of sub-basin located between Lady Loretta High Strain Zone to West and Mount Gordon Fault Zone to East. C) Northwest–southeast cross section transecting Lady Loretta High Strain Zone, Mount Gordon Fault Zone, and sub-basins. Second-, third-, and fourth-order sequence boundaries are overlain on facies correlations and are indicated by heavy wavy lines, light wavy lines, and heavy straight lines, respectively. Labels refer to fourth-order sequence boundaries (e.g., Prize 2.2, Gun 1.6) and maximum flooding surfaces (e.g., Gun 1.5f, Gun 2.2f) described in text. Thus Gun 1.7 refers to the basal bounding unconformity of the fourth-order Gun 1.7 depositional sequence and Gun 1.7f refers to its fourth-order maximum flooding surface. All locations are from Figure 1. Symbols in Figure 3A apply to 3B and 3C as well.

clude asymmetrical current ripples and large-scale trough cross-stratification. Sandstones tend to be very well sorted and rounded and cemented by silica. Conglomerates are poorly sorted and contain pebbles and cobbles of underlying rocks, mostly sandstone. Discontinuous brecciated horizons in which abundant iron-rich coated clasts occur in a heavily altered groundmass are present to the northwest, at Kamarga Dome, and to the Southeast, at Barr Hole, Esperanza Waters, and Crocodile Waterhole (Fig. 3).

Proximal Tempestite.—Medium- to coarse-grained quartz arenite, quartz siltstone–wacke, and mudstone–shale are arranged in decimeter-scale fining-upward beds (Table 1). Quartz–peloid grainstone (Fig. 5A), dolomudstone, and intraclast grainstone (Fig. 5B) are locally important. Siltstones are the volumetrically dominant constituent rock type. Beds are medium- to thick-bedded, commonly amalgamated, and arranged in decimeter-scale coarsening- and thickening-upward packages. Strata are characterized by symmetrical ripples, megaripples, trough and

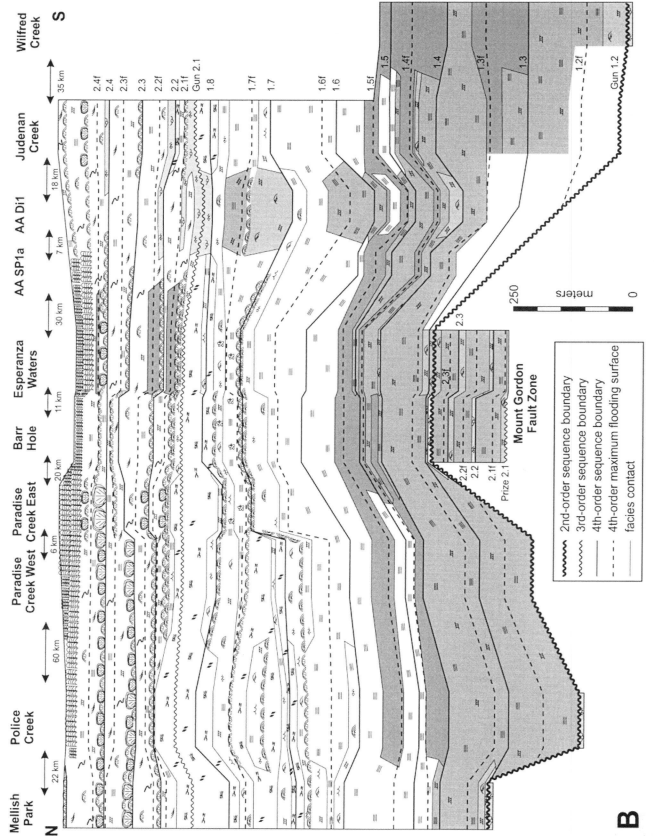

FIG. 3.—Continued.

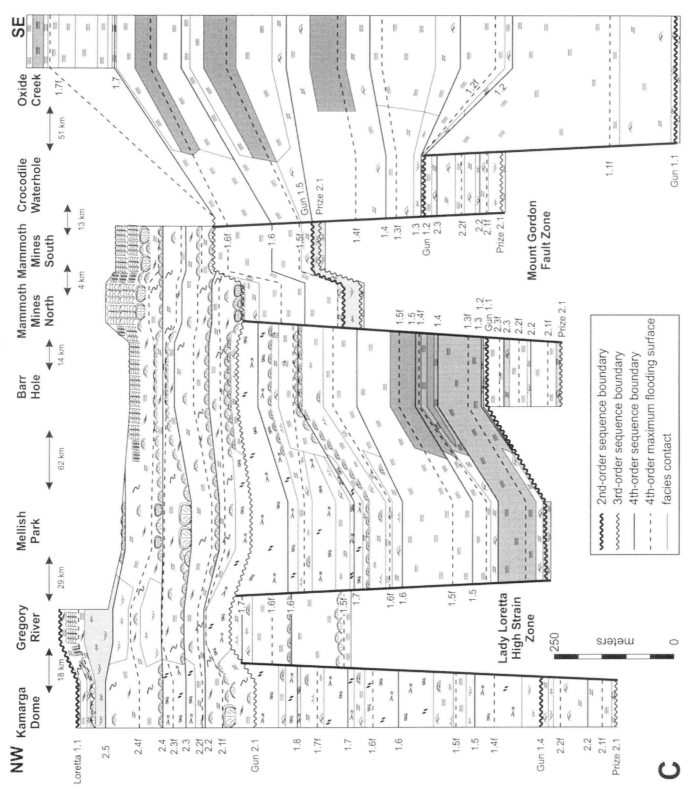

FIG. 3.—Continued.

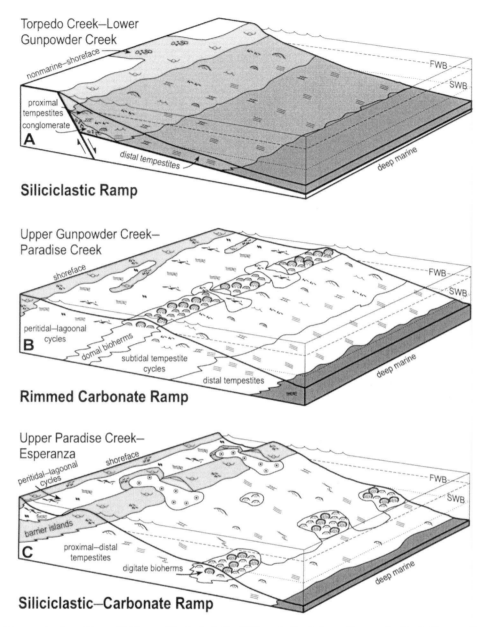

FIG. 4.—Environmental reconstruction of lower McNamara lithofacies belts: A) Torpedo Creek–lower Gunpowder Creek; B) upper Gunpowder Creek–Paradise Creek; and C) upper Paradise Creek–Esperanza. FWB, fair-weather wave base; SWB, storm wave base. See Figure 3 for identification of symbols and fills.

planar cross-stratification, hummocky cross-stratification, ball-and-pillow structures, scour surfaces, and graded bedding. Small to medium (5–20 cm diameter) domal stromatolites and thin dolomite intraclast lenses are present locally.

Distal Tempestite.—This lithofacies is similar in composition to the proximal tempestites, but with a greater abundance of fine-grained rock types such as quartz siltstone–wacke and mudstone–shale. Minor amounts of quartz–peloid grainstone and dolomudstone are present locally. Beds are predominantly thin- to medium-bedded and typically have a wavy appearance. Units are arranged into decameter-scale coarsening- and thickening-upward packages. Common sedimentary structures include interference ripples, parallel and planar cross-stratification, hum-

mocky cross-stratification, ball-and-pillow structures, scour surfaces, and slumped beds. Beds are typically graded and topped by mudstone–shale.

Deep Marine.—This facies is largely mudstone–shale with minor amounts of quartz siltstone–wacke and dolomudstone (Table 1). Strata are characterized by thin wavy bedding and parallel internal stratification and are organized into thickening- and coarsening-upward packages. Siltstone beds are commonly graded but lack any cross-stratification.

Interpretation.—Lateral correlations show that coarser lithofacies grade laterally into finer ones and vertical transitions are likewise gradational. Such gradual transitions and the presence of broad facies belts is indicative (cf. Reading, 1986) of deposition on a predominantly siliciclastic ramp (Fig. 4A). The presence of well-developed tempestite beds suggests that the ramp was strongly influenced by storm depositional processes. The well-stratified, fining-upward sandstones of the Torpedo Creek Formation are interpreted as primarily fluvial, possibly extending into nearshore beach environments (cf. Miall, 1992). The abundance of angular quartz silt in many rocks implies a significant source of eolian quartz on land. Thickness of this depositional package is highly variable regionally, ranging from 3 to 250 m. Brecciated, iron-rich horizons (in both siliciclastic and carbonate rocks) proximal to ancient topographic highs (Kamarga Dome to the northwest and the Mount Gordon Fault Zone to the southeast) are interpreted to represent intervals of regolith formation during periods of extended exposure. Lateral facies patterns show deepening away from these features but do not exhibit any strong regional orientation (deepened to the south-southeast at Kamarga Dome and to the west-southwest at the Mount Gordon Fault Zone). This trend is interpreted as the development of local depocenters resulting from extensive syndepositional block faulting. During periods of decreased siliciclastic sediment supply, precipitation of carbonate sediments occurred in marginal marine environments to produce domal stromatolites, dolomudstones, quartz–peloid grainstones, and intraclast grainstones in proximal and distal tempestite lithofacies. No peritidal carbonate facies are preserved in this package. Such carbonate sediments were subsequently reworked and redistributed by fair-weather and storm processes onto deeper parts of the ramp, in much the same way as the siliciclastic sediments. The presence of slump folds and scours in deepwater lithofacies points to either the effects of synsedimentary tectonics or an unstable depositional slope. Some of the coarser beds may have been deposited by turbidity currents resulting from this slope instability.

Upper Gunpowder Creek–Paradise Creek Lithofacies

The upper Gunpowder Creek–Paradise Creek third-order depositional sequence records the transition from dominantly siliciclastic to carbonate deposition and the development of regionally uniform accommodation rates. The resulting depositional architecture is characterized by broad, regionally extensive (tens of kilometers) facies belts and minor thickness variations (Fig. 3). Seven main lithofacies types are recognized, some similar to those found in the underlying sequence. Similarly, they are organized into a suite of shallowing-upward packages (Fig. 4B).

Shoreface–Barrier Island.—This volumetrically minor lithofacies is a combination of well-sorted and rounded coarse-grained quartz arenite and sand-size intraclast grainstone (Fig. 5C) in subequal quantities (Table 1). Such rocks are most abundant in the western parts of the study area, and the relative proportion of quartz sand increases westward. Carbonate grains include micritized ooids, peloids, and intraclasts of quartz–peloid grainstone, dolomudstone, microbial laminite, and reworked intraclast grainstone. Beds are largely thick-bedded and show well-defined high-angle trough cross-stratification, herringbone cross-stratification, and symmetrical wave ripples. This lithofacies commonly grades upward with decreasing thickness into peritidal cycles or subtidal tempestite cycles.

Peritidal–Lagoonal Cycles.—Thin- to thick-bedded units of microbial laminite (Fig. 5D), dolomudstone, intraclast grainstone (Fig. 5B), isolated small (5–20 cm diameter), low-relief domal stromatolites and quartz–peloid grainstone (Fig. 5A) are arranged, in descending order, into cycles 0.5–5.0 m thick (Table 1). Cycles are poorly defined overall and cannot be correlated laterally over more than a few tens of meters. Volumetrically, intraclast grainstone makes up the largest proportion of this lithofacies, followed by microbial laminite and dolomudstone. Intraclasts are derived from all the different rock types present in this lithofacies. Intraclast grainstones locally preserve keystone vugs and contain isopachous cement rinds as well as radiating cement fans. Ooid grainstone (Fig. 5E) is locally present in minor quantities. The various rock types are intimately interstratified at a millimeter to centimeter scale. Preservation of microbial fabric is moderate to poor overall, but remnants of vertical and horizontal filamentous tubules are present within some micritic microbial laminae (Fig. 5F). Beds contain largely parallel or planar cross-stratification, wave ripples, tepee structures, normal grading, hummocky cross-stratification, and low-angle erosional truncations. Pseudomorphs of gypsum are locally abundant and commonly displace carbonate sediments although small rosettes or bushes are present locally on some bedding surfaces. Halite pseudomorphs, molar-tooth structures, and conical columnar stromatolites (5–15 cm diameter) occur in western localities.

Domal–Columnar Stromatolite Bioherms and Biostromes.—This lithofacies is composed of isolated domal–columnar stromatolite and microbial laminite bioherms and laterally continuous complexes of coalesced bioherms (Table 1). Bioherms are composed of small to large (10–50 cm diameter) moderate-relief domal and columnar stromatolites (Fig. 5G). Stromatolite diameter and relief decrease upward within individual bioherms. Columns are locally inclined up to 45°. Domal forms pass upward into columns and ultimately into prone microbial laminite. Individual bioherms vary from 1 to 15 m diameter and from 1 to 5 m relief. Stromatolites are composed of micrite-rich and spar-rich laminae. They can contain some peloid-rich lenses but rarely any volumetrically important quantities of coarse sediment. There is no apparent regional asymmetry or orientation to the bioherms. Interbioherm areas are filled by intraclast grainstone, quartz–peloid grainstone, dolomudstone, and ooid grainstone. Most intraclasts are composed of tabular to platy stromatolitic laminae that form rosettes between stromatolite heads. The overall quartz silt content of both the bioherms and intervening sediment is minor. These deposits contain parallel and planar cross-stratification, hummocky cross-stratification, erosional scours, and normal grading.

Digitate Stromatolite Bioherms and Biostromes.—Digitate stromatolites are not volumetrically significant below the Esperanza Formation but are present at specific horizons in the Paradise Creek Formation (e.g., mid-stromatolite marker bed in Figure 6). They are always silicified. Where present they tend to overlie or drape domal stromatolite bioherms and preserve the same general bioherm morphology and scale. They are composed of interbedded small (1–3 cm diameter) low-relief digitate columns and microbial laminite forming radiating bioherms (Fig. 5H). Intermound depressions are filled by bridging microbial laminite and quartz–peloid grainstone. Columns are commonly spherical in cross section but can be locally elliptical.

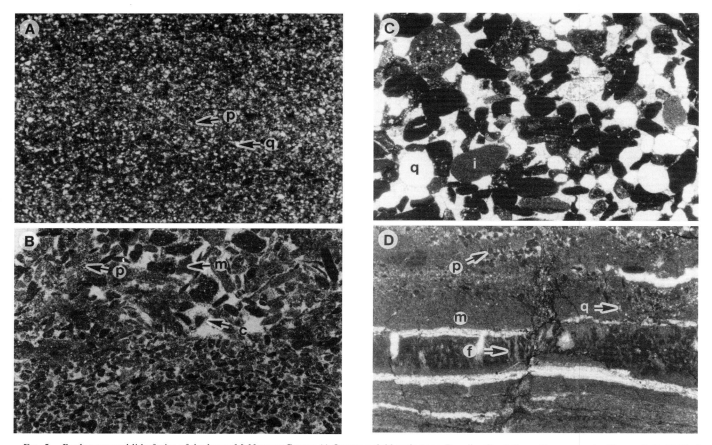

FIG. 5.—Rock types and lithofacies of the lower McNamara Group: A) Quartz–peloid grainstone, Paradise Creek Formation. q, quartz silt; p, peloid. Field of view is 7.6 mm across. B) Intraclast grainstone, Paradise Creek Formation. p, quartz–peloid grainstone; m, dolomudstone; c, synsedimentary isopachous cement. Field of view is 7.6 mm across. C) Quartz arenite–intraclast grainstone, Paradise Creek Formation. q, quartz sand; i, intraclast. Field of view is 7.6 mm across. D) Microbial laminite, Paradise Creek Formation. m, micrite; f, filamentous microbial element; p, peloid; q, quartz silt. Field of view is 7.6 mm across.

Internal fabric is typically poorly preserved owing to pervasive, late-stage silicification. Where preservation is good, a clotted, sparry fabric with vague lamination is visible.

Subtidal Tempestite Cycles.—These 1–10 m thick shallowing-upward cycles contain a basal portion of proximal quartz–peloid grainstone (Fig. 5A) and dolomudstone tempestite and an upper portion of domal stromatolite, microbial laminite, and intraclast grainstone. Individual beds vary from thin- to thick-bedded and contain interference and symmetrical wave ripples, parallel and planar cross-stratification, hummocky cross-stratification, erosional scours, and normal grading. Domal–columnar stromatolites are small to medium (10–50 cm diameter) and organized into moderate-relief bioherms and biostromes. In the upper Paradise Creek Formation evaporite pseudomorphs (cauliflower chert) appear to have grown displacively within the tempestite beds.

Distal Tempestites.—Distal tempestites are represented by both carbonate and siliciclastic beds. Carbonate beds are composed of quartz–peloid grainstone and dolomudstone, whereas siliciclastic tempestites contain fine quartz arenite, quartz siltstone–wacke, and mudstone–shale. Both show the same range of sedimentary structures: thin to medium wavy bedding, interference ripples, parallel and planar cross-stratification, ball-and-pillow structures, scour surfaces, graded bedding, slump folds and

scars, and rarely hummocky cross-stratification. The carbonate tempestites also contain gutters and grooves and isolated, small (5–10 cm diameter) domal stromatolites with associated microbial intraclast lenses and rosettes. Both are arranged in decameter-scale upward-thickening and -coarsening packages.

Deep Marine.—These rocks are largely carbonaceous mudstone–shale and quartz siltstone–wacke with minor amounts of dolomudstone and quartz–peloid grainstone. Phosphatic crusts and pavements are present locally. Strata are thinly bedded, contain parallel lamination, and are arranged in decameter-scale upward-thickening packages.

Interpretation.—Environments in the upper Gunpowder Creek–Paradise Creek depositional sequence range from shoreface–peritidal to deep, possibly euxinic, subtidal. The minor regional variation in sequence thickness and gradual lateral lithofacies transitions are indicative (cf. Burchette and Wright, 1992; Reading, 1986) of ramp-style deposition (Fig. 4B). In the upper Gunpowder Creek Formation the east-southeast-facing ramp was predominantly siliciclastic but passed gradationally into a similarly oriented carbonate ramp. As with the underlying ramp, sedimentation was strongly influenced by storm depositional processes. Peritidal and shallow subtidal lithofacies all show evidence of storm activity: intraclast generation, interference ripples, abundant scours, graded tempestite beds, and

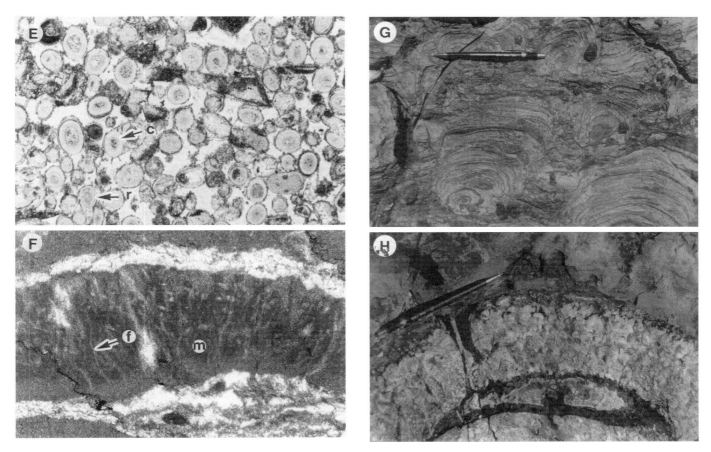

Fig. 5.—E) Ooid grainstone, Esperanza Formation. c, concentric ooid; r, radial ooid. Field of view is 7.6 mm across. F) Microbial laminite with filaments, Paradise Creek Formation. f, filament; m, micrite. Field of view is 3.8 mm across. G) Inclined domal stromatolite columns with inter-column quartz–peloid grainstone and dolomudstone from the upper meter of a domal–columnar stromatolite bioherm, Paradise Creek Formation. Pencil is 15 cm long. H) Small digitate stromatolite dome and overlying dolomudstone from the top of a digitate columnar stromatolite bioherm, Esperanza Formation. Pencil is 15 cm long.

hummocky cross-stratification. Nearshore environments varied from high-energy (quartz and intraclast sands) to low-energy (microbial laminites and dolomuds) at different locations and stratigraphic intervals. Poor lateral exposure of the coarse quartz–intraclast sand lithofacies prevents determination of sand-body geometry, and thus it has not been possible to ascertain whether these sandstones were true barrier bars or attached shoreface deposits (cf. Reading, 1986). Shallow-water carbonate facies contain only minor amounts of primary evaporite pseudomorphs and few desiccation features (primarily to the west, near Kamarga Dome; see Figures 1 and 3), suggesting that although supratidal conditions were present, platform-wide exposure was not widespread. Abundance of carbonate mud, paucity of high-energy structures, and the low relief of microbial laminites all suggest an overall very low-energy environment. The abundance of intraclasts indicates that high-energy events, most likely storms, regularly affected peritidal and lagoonal environments. Paucity of ooid grainstone suggests that shallow subtidal environments were either not energetic enough, too turbid for good ooid development, or lacked significant tidal currents. Peritidal facies grade laterally into domal stromatolite bioherms and proximal tempestite cycles, both of which are interpreted to have developed in shallow subtidal

environments subject to fair-weather wave processes. Thick, high-relief wave-resistant biohermal complexes could have formed an effective wave-energy barrier on the inner to mid-ramp and allowed the growth of an areally extensive inboard peritidal complex in the upper Paradise Creek Formation. Channel-fills between stromatolitic mounds tends to be coarse-grained and thick, and contain high-angle cross-stratification. Such channels would have fed the outlying ramp, where the resultant allochthonous sediments were extensively reworked by storm processes. The abundance of intraclasts and the lack of ooids associated with this barrier system reflects the dominance of intermittent, storm-generated sediment transport and suggests that tidal currents were of only minor importance (cf. Hine, 1983). With increasing water depth, such lithofacies grade into distal tempestites and deep-water fine-grained sediments. Organic-rich shales and phosphatic precipitates, restricted to the top of the Gunpowder Creek Formation, indicate deposition during a period of reduced siliciclastic influx and carbonate production and are interpreted to represent condensed sedimentation (Loutit et al., 1988). Lithofacies relationships indicate that the carbonate ramp prograded east-southeastward over the underlying siliciclastic ramp. Coarse-grained siliciclastics likely had localized provenance, mostly in the west.

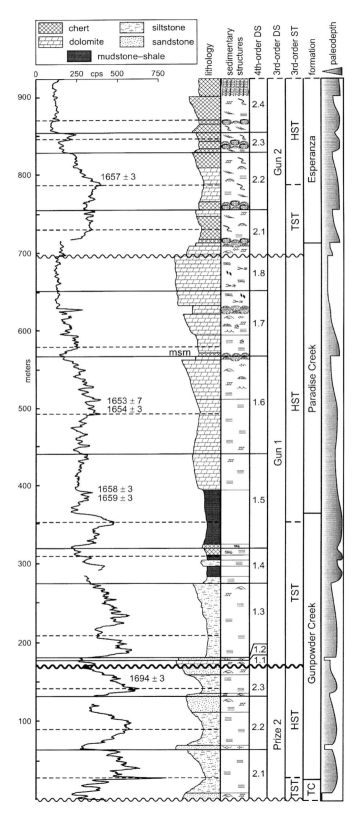

Upper Paradise Creek–Esperanza Lithofacies

The most conspicuous difference between the second and third depositional sequences is the change in abundance from largely domal to predominantly digitate stromatolite forms and the resumption of significant siliciclastic sedimentation. As below, facies belts are regionally extensive, but localized influxes of siliciclastic sediment resulted in marked local thickness variations (Fig. 3). Much of this interval has been extensively silicified. The six component lithofacies are organized in stacked, upward-shallowing lithofacies (Fig. 4C).

Shoreface–Barrier Island.—This lithofacies is largely restricted to western sections and represents a significant proportion of the basin fill in these areas (Fig. 4). It includes intermixed quartz arenite and quartz–peloid grainstone (Fig. 5A). Beds commonly contain low-angle and ripple cross-stratification, hummocky cross-stratification, and small (3–5 cm wavelength) straight-crested symmetrical to asymmetrical ripples.

Peritidal–Lagoonal Cycles.—Peritidal and lagoonal lithofacies are composed of dolomudstone, microbial laminite (Fig. 5D), ooid grainstone (Fig. 5E), intraclast grainstone (Fig. 5B), and quartz–peloid grainstone (Fig. 5A) arranged in poorly defined cycles (<1 m thick). Dolomudstone beds commonly contain spar-filled fenestrae and molar-tooth structure. Ooid grainstone beds vary from thin sheets up to beds a meter thick with well-developed cross-stratification. Small (<30 cm diameter) isolated domal–columnar stromatolites are present locally, generally associated with quartz–peloid grainstone beds. Intraclast grainstones contain reworked fragments of all rock types present in this lithofacies, locally with oncolitic coatings. Evaporite pseudomorphs and desiccation features are rare but locally present.

Proximal–Distal Tempestites.—These strata are dominated by quartz–peloid grainstone (Fig. 5A) and dolomudstone arranged in normally graded beds. Beds are tabular to lenticular and their thickness varies from thin (<5 cm) to thick (>50 cm). Common sedimentary structures include hummocky cross-stratification, parallel and planar cross-stratification, ball-and-pillow structures, slump folds and breccias, and abundant scour surfaces. Isolated, small (5–10 cm) digitate columnar stromatolites and digitate crusts are prevalent, particularly common on slump folds and breccias.

Digitate Stromatolite Bioherms and Biostromes.—These buildups are bioherms and biostromes of digitate columnar stromatolites and microbial laminite (Fig. 5H). Columns generally range in diameter from 1 to 5 cm and have low synoptic relief. Columns can be inclined up to 45° and are locally elongate. In a distinctive variant, referred to as "organ pipes", the columns can be as large as 10 cm in diameter. At larger diameters, col-

---

Fig. 6.—(left) Sequence stratigraphic framework of lower McNamara Group as represented by the Barr Hole composite lithologic section and its gamma-ray log generated from outcrop. Second-, third-, and fourth-order sequence boundaries and fourth-order maximum flooding surfaces are indicated by heavy wavy lines, light wavy lines, heavy straight lines, and heavy broken lines, respectively. Rock ages indicate stratigraphic level of samples used in SHRIMP dating of strata. Paleodepth curve is based on lithofacies interpretations and deepens to right. TST, transgressive systems tract; HST, highstand systems tract; msm, mid-stromatolite marker; TC, Torpedo Creek Formation; cps, total gamma-ray counts per second; DS, depositional sequence; ST, systems tract. See Figure 3 for identification of sedimentary structure symbols.

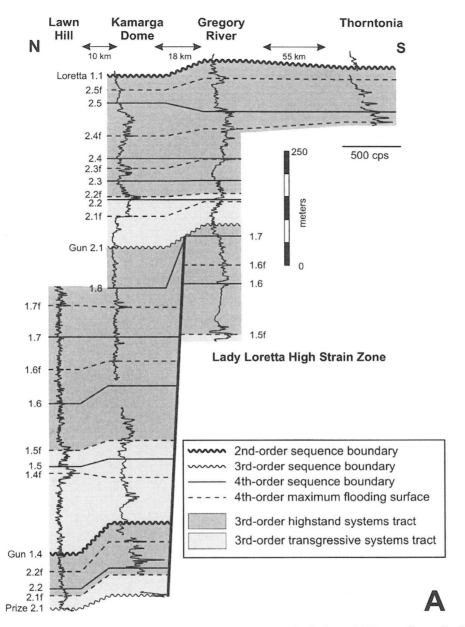

FIG. 7.—Gamma-ray log correlation and architecture of third- and fourth-order sequences in the lower McNamara Group. Shading indicates third-order transgressive and highstand systems tracts. cps, total gamma-ray counts per second. Labels refer to fourth-order sequence boundaries (e.g., Prize 2.2, Gun 1.6) and maximum flooding surfaces (e.g., Gun 1.5f, Gun 2.2f) described in text. Cross section locations are as described in Figure 3.

umns are not contiguous and inter-column spaces are filled with sediment. Columns in this case are connected by bridges and locally have a star shape in plan view. Stromatolite column diameter and relief decrease upward within individual bioherms. Mounds are composed of interbedded microbial laminite and digitate columnar stromatolites. Bioherms vary in size from 1 to 50 m diameter and have depositional relief of 1 to 15 m. These structures coalesce to form complexes up to 25 m thick. Spacing between mounds is from 1 to 20 m. Inter-mound areas are filled by microbial laminite, quartz–peloid grainstone, and intraclast grainstone. These beds typically contain parallel, trough, and hummocky cross-stratification. Stromatolites con-

tain little identifiable sediment and digitate columnar forms are always silicified.

Deep Marine.—As in the underlying depositional sequences, the deep-water environment is dominated by dolomudstone and argillaceous mudstone–shale rock types (Table 1). In the upper Paradise–Esperanza depositional sequence the deep marine lithofacies also includes isolated digitate columnar stromatolite mounds and crusts. Beds are generally thin and homogeneous or contain faint parallel lamination.

Interpretation.—Facies transitions in the upper Paradise–Esperanza are on the whole more abrupt than underlying strata. Subtidal sediments contain abundant synsedimentary defor-

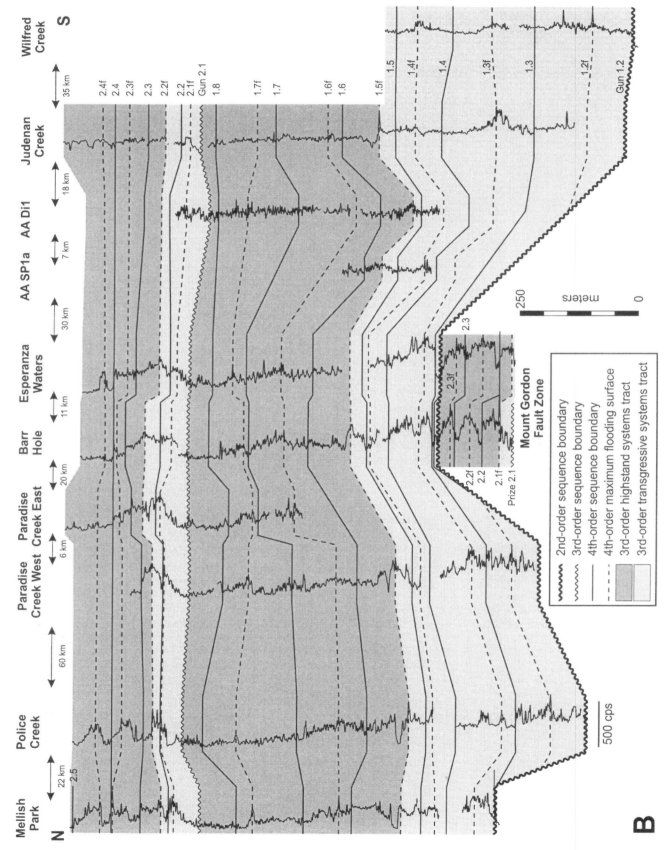

Fig. 7.—Continued.

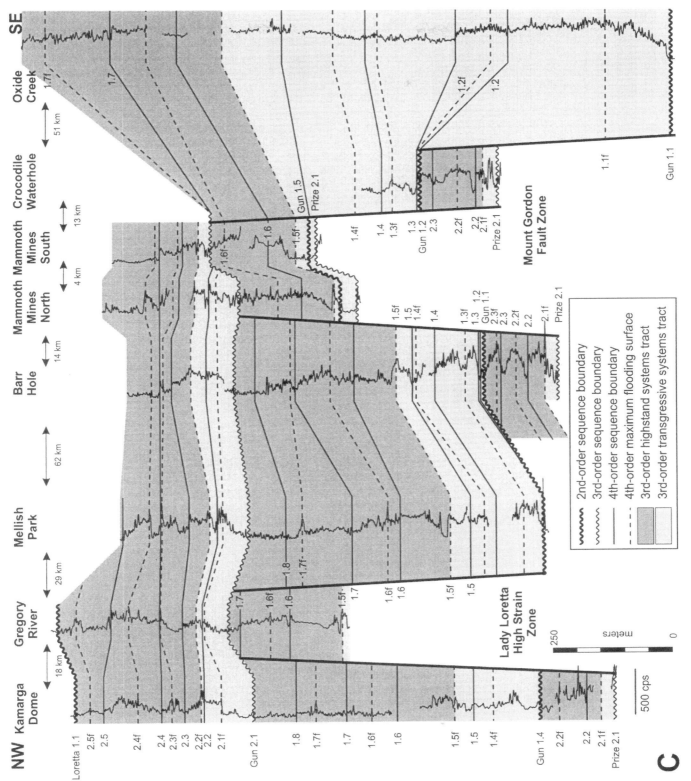

FIG. 7.—Continued.

TABLE 2.—SUMMARY OF CRITERIA USED TO DEFINE FOURTH-ORDER SEQUENCES AND THEIR BOUNDING SURFACES

	Criteria	Lawn Hill	Kamarga Dome	Gregory River	Thorntonia	Mellish Park	Police Creek	Paradise Creek
Gun 2.5	Basal bounding surface:	No outcrop	Erosional	Erosional	Erosional	Erosional	No outcrop	No outcrop
	Incision:		?	Yes	?	?		
	Facies base RW:		Shoreface-barrier	Shoreface-barrier	Shoreface-barrier	Not present		
	Facies base TST:		Digitate bioherms	Proximal-distal temp.	Digitate bioherms	Digitate bioherms		
	Facies base HST:		Digitate bioherms	Proximal-distal temp.	Proximal-distal temp.	No outcrop		
	Facies top HST:		Shoreface-barrier	Dig. bioh. & organ pipes	Shoreface-barrier	No outcrop		
	Stratigraphic architecture:		A/B/P	P/B/P-A	P/B/P	No outcrop		
	Principal lithology:		70 Silici, 30 Carb	50 Carb, 50 Silici	Siliciclastic	Carbonate		
	Quartz sand in:		RW & HST	RW	RW & HST	Nil		
Gun 2.4	Basal bounding surface:	No outcrop	Erosional	Erosional	No outcrop	Erosional	Erosional	Erosional
	Incision:		?	Yes, >10 m		No	No	No
	Facies base RW:		Not present	Shoreface-barrier		Not present	Not present	Not present
	Facies base TST:		Digitate bioherms	Proximal-distal temp.		Digitate bioherms	Digitate bioherms	Digitate bioherms
	Facies base HST:		Proximal-distal temp.	Proximal-distal temp.		Proximal-distal temp.	Proximal-distal temp.	Proximal-distal temp.
	Facies top HST:		Proximal-distal temp.	Shoreface-barrier		Dig. bioh. & organ pipes	Organ pipes	Organ pipes
	Stratigraphic architecture:		X/B/P	P/B/P		X/A-B/P-A	X/A-B/P-A	X/A-B/P-A
	Principal lithology:		Carbonate	Carbonate		Carbonate	Carbonate	Carbonate
	Quartz sand in:		HST	RW & HST		Nil	Nil	Nil
Gun 2.3	Basal bounding surface:	No outcrop	Erosional	Erosional	No outcrop	Erosional	Erosional	Erosional
	Incision:		No	No		No	No	No
	Facies base RW:		Not present	Not present		Not present	Not present	Not present
	Facies base TST:		Peritidal-lagoonal	Digitate bioherms		Digitate bioherms	Digitate bioherms	Digitate bioherms
	Facies base HST:		Peritidal-lagoonal	Proximal-distal temp.		Proximal-distal temp.	Proximal-distal temp.	Proximal-distal temp.
	Facies top HST:		Peritidal-lagoonal	Truncated		Proximal-distal temp.	Proximal-distal temp.	Proximal-distal temp.
	Stratigraphic architecture:		X/B/P	X/A-B/T		X/A-B/C	X/A-B/P	X/A-B/P
	Principal lithology:		Carbonate	Carbonate		Carbonate	Carbonate	Carbonate
	Quartz sand in:		Nil	Nil		Nil	Nil	Nil
Gun 2.2	Basal bounding surface:	No outcrop	Erosional	Erosional	No outcrop	Erosional	Erosional	Erosional
	Incision:		No	No		No	No	No
	Facies base RW:		Not present	Not present		Not present	Not present	Not present
	Facies base TST:		Proximal-distal temp.	Digitate bioherms		Digitate bioherms	Digitate bioherms	Deep marine
	Facies base HST:		Peritidal-lagoonal	Proximal-distal temp.		Proximal-distal temp.	Proximal-distal temp.	Proximal-distal temp.
	Facies top HST:		Peritidal-lagoonal	Proximal-distal temp.		Proximal-distal temp.	Proximal-distal temp.	Proximal-distal temp.
	Stratigraphic architecture:		X/B/P	X/B/P		X/B/A	X/B/P	X/B/P
	Principal lithology:		Carbonate	Carbonate		Carbonate	Carbonate	Carbonate
	Quartz sand in:		Nil	Nil		Nil	Nil	Nil
Gun 2.1	Basal bounding surface:	No outcrop	Erosional	Erosional	No outcrop	Erosional	Erosional	Erosional
	Incision:		Yes	Yes >50m		Yes	Yes	Yes, 20 m
	Facies base RW:		Not present	Not present		Not present	Not present	Not present
	Facies base TST:		Digitate bioherms	Peritidal-lagoonal		Peritidal-lagoonal	Peritidal-lagoonal	Peritidal-lagoonal
	Facies base HST:		Proximal-distal temp.	Proximal-distal temp.		Proximal-distal temp.	Proximal-distal temp.	Proximal-distal temp.
	Facies top HST:		Peritidal-lagoonal	Proximal-distal temp.		Proximal-distal temp.	Proximal-distal temp.	Proximal-distal temp.
	Stratigraphic architecture:		X/A-B/P	X/A-B/P		X/A-B/P	X/B/P	X/B/P-A
	Principal lithology:		Carbonate	Carbonate		Carbonate	Carbonate	Carbonate
	Quartz sand in:		Nil	Nil		Nil	Nil	Nil
Gun 1.8	Basal bounding surface:	No outcrop	Erosional	Truncated	No outcrop	Conformable	Conformable	Conformable
	Incision:		?			No	No	No
	Facies base RW:		Not present			Not present	Not present	Not present
	Facies base TST:		Peritidal-lagoonal			Peritidal-lagoonal	Peritidal-lagoonal	Subtidal temp. cycles
	Facies base HST:		Subtidal temp. cycles			Peritidal-lagoonal	Peritidal-lagoonal	Subtidal temp. cycles
	Facies top HST:		Peritidal-lagoonal			Peritidal-lagoonal	Peritidal-lagoonal	Peritidal-lagoonal
	Stratigraphic architecture:		X/A/A			X/A/A	X/A-B/P-A	X/B/P-A
	Principal lithology:		Carbonate			Carbonate	Carbonate	Carbonate
	Quartz sand in:		Nil			Nil	Nil	Nil

Gun 1.7

Field	1	2	3	4	5	6	7
Basal bounding surface:	Erosional	Erosional	Erosional	No outcrop	Erosional	Erosional	Erosional
Incision:	?	?	No		No	No	No
Facies base RW:	Peritidal-lagoonal	Peritidal-lagoonal	Subtidal temp. cycles		Peritidal-lagoonal	Peritidal-lagoonal	Peritidal-lagoonal
Facies base TST:	Peritidal-lagoonal	Peritidal-lagoonal	Truncated		Peritidal-lagoonal	Peritidal-lagoonal	Digitate bioherms
Facies base HST:	Subtidal temp. cycles	Subtidal temp. cycles	Truncated		Subtidal temp. cycles	Subtidal temp. cycles	Distal tempestites
Facies top HST:	No outcrop	Peritidal-lagoonal	Truncated		Peritidal-lagoonal	Peritidal-lagoonal	Subtidal temp. cycles
Stratigraphic architecture:	A/B/A-P	A/B/P-A	P/X/X		A/B/P-A	P/B/P-A	P/B/P
Principal lithology:	Carbonate	Carbonate	Carbonate		Carbonate	Carbonate	Carbonate
Quartz sand in:	RW	RW	RW		RW	RW	RW

Gun 1.6

Field	1	2	3	4	5	6	7
Basal bounding surface:	Conformable	Conformable	Conformable	No outcrop	Conformable	Conformable	Conformable
Incision:	No	No	No		No	No	No
Facies base RW:	Peritidal-lagoonal	Peritidal-lagoonal	Domal bioherms		Distal tempestites	Distal tempestites	Distal tempestites
Facies base TST:	Peritidal-lagoonal	Peritidal-lagoonal	Distal tempestites		Subtidal temp. cycles	Distal tempestites	Distal tempestites
Facies base HST:	Subtidal temp. cycles	Subtidal temp. cycles	Subtidal temp. cycles		Distal tempestites	Distal tempestites	Distal tempestites
Facies top HST:	Peritidal-lagoonal	Peritidal-lagoonal			Peritidal-lagoonal	Peritidal-lagoonal	Subtidal temp. cycles
Stratigraphic architecture:	A/B/A-P	X/A/A	P/B/A-P		P/B/P-A	A/B/P	P/B/A-P
Principal lithology:	Carbonate	Carbonate	Carbonate		Carbonate	Carbonate	Carbonate
Quartz sand in:	Nil	Nil	Nil		Nil	Nil	Nil

Gun 1.5

Field	1	2	3	4	5	6	7
Basal bounding surface:	Erosional	Erosional	No outcrop	No outcrop	Conformable	Conformable	Conformable
Incision:	Yes	Yes	No outcrop		No	No	No
Facies base RW:	Not present	Nonmarine-shoreface	No outcrop		Not present	Not Present	Not present
Facies base TST:	Proximal tempestites	Nonmarine-shoreface	Distal tempestites		Distal tempestites	Distal tempestites	Distal tempestites
Facies base HST:	Distal tempestites	Distal tempestites	Distal tempestites		Distal tempestites	Deep marine	Deep marine
Facies top HST:	Subtidal temp. cycles	Peritidal-lagoonal			Distal tempestites	Distal tempestites	Distal tempestites
Stratigraphic architecture:	X/B/P	X/B/P	X/B/A		X/B/A	X/A/A-P	X/B/A
Principal lithology:	Carbonate	Carbonate	Carbonate		Carbonate	40 Silici, 60 Carb	40 Silici, 60 Carb
Quartz sand in:	TST	RW	Nil		Nil	Nil	Nil

Gun 1.4

Field	1	2	3	4	5	6	7
Basal bounding surface:	Erosional	Erosional	No outcrop	No outcrop	No outcrop	No outcrop	No outcrop
Incision:	Yes	Yes			No outcrop	No outcrop	No outcrop
Facies base RW:	Nonmarine-shoreface	Nonmarine-shoreface			Not present	No outcrop	No outcrop
Facies base TST:	Domal bioherms	Nonmarine-shoreface			Distal tempestites	No outcrop	No outcrop
Facies base HST:	Distal tempestites	Peritidal-lagoonal			Distal tempestites	Distal tempestites	Distal tempestites
Facies top HST:	Distal tempestites	Peritidal-lagoonal			Distal tempestites	Distal tempestites	Distal tempestites
Stratigraphic architecture:	P/A-B/A	P/A-B/P			X/B/P	X/X/A	X/X/A
Principal lithology:	50 Carb, 50 Silici	30 Silici, 70 Carb			30 Silici, 70 Carb	70 Silici, 30 Carb	50 Carb, 50 Silici
Quartz sand in:	RW, TST, & HST	RW			Nil	Nil	Nil

Gun 1.3

Field	1	2	3	4	5	6	7
Basal bounding surface:	Onlapped	Onlapped	No outcrop	No outcrop	Erosional	Erosional	No outcrop
Incision:					Yes	No	No outcrop
Facies base RW:					Nonmarine-shoreface	Distal tempestites	No outcrop
Facies base TST:					Proximal tempestites	Distal tempestites	No outcrop
Facies base HST:					Proximal tempestites	Distal tempestites	Distal tempestites
Facies top HST:					Proximal tempestites	Distal tempestites	Distal tempestites
Stratigraphic architecture:					P/B/P	A/B/P	X/A/P
Principal lithology:					Siliciclastic	Siliciclastic	Siliciclastic
Quartz sand in:					RW	Nil	Nil

Gun 1.2

Field	1	2	3	4	5	6	7
Basal bounding surface:	Onlapped	Onlapped	No outcrop	No outcrop	Onlapped	Erosional	Erosional
Incision:						Yes	Yes
Facies base RW:						Not present	Not present
Facies base TST:						Distal tempestites	Distal tempestites
Facies base HST:						Distal tempestites	Distal tempestites
Facies top HST:						Distal tempestites	Distal tempestites
Stratigraphic architecture:						X/B/P	X/B/P
Principal lithology:						Siliciclastic	Siliciclastic
Quartz sand in:						Nil	Nil

TABLE 2.—(Continued) SUMMARY OF CRITERIA USED TO DEFINE FOURTH-ORDER SEQUENCES AND THEIR BOUNDING SURFACES

Criteria	Lawn Hill	Kamarga Dome	Gregory River	Thorntonia	Mellish Park	Police Creek	Paradise Creek
Gun 1.1							
Basal bounding surface:	Onlapped	Onlapped	No outcrop	No outcrop	Onlapped	Onlapped	Onlapped
Incision:							
Facies base RW:							
Facies base TST:							
Facies base HST							
Facies top HST:							
Stratigraphic architecture:							
Principal lithology:							
Quartz sand in:							
Prize 2.3							
Basal bounding surface:	Truncated	Truncated	No outcrop	No outcrop	Truncated	Truncated	Truncated
Incision:							
Facies base RW:							
Facies base TST:							
Facies base HST							
Facies top HST:							
Stratigraphic architecture:							
Principal lithology:							
Quartz sand in:							
Prize 2.2							
Basal bounding surface:	Erosional	Erosional	No outcrop	No outcrop	Truncated	Truncated	Truncated
Incision:	Yes	Yes					
Facies base RW:	Nonmarine-shoreface	Proximal tempestites					
Facies base TST:	Proximal tempestites	Proximal tempestites					
Facies base HST	Proximal tempestites	Proximal tempestites					
Facies top HST:	Nonmarine-shoreface	Proximal tempestites					
Stratigraphic architecture:	P/B/P	P/B/P					
Principal lithology:	Siliciclastic	Siliciclastic					
Quartz sand in:	RW, TST & HST	RW, TST & HST					
Price 2.1							
Basal bounding surface:	Erosional	Erosional	No outcrop	No outcrop	Truncated	Truncated	Truncated
Incision:	Yes	Yes					
Facies base RW:	Nonmarine-shoreface	Proximal tempestites					
Facies base TST:	Distal tempestites	Not present					
Facies base HST	Distal tempestites	Not present					
Facies top HST:	Distal tempestites	Distal tempestites					
Stratigraphic architecture:	P/B/P	P/X/P					
Principal lithology:	Siliciclastic	Siliciclastic					
Quartz sand in:	RW	RW					

Gun	Criteria	Barr Hole	Esperanza Waters	AASp 1 & AADi 1	Judenan Creek	Wilfred Creek	Mammoth Mines	Crocodile WH	Oxide Creek
Gun 2.5	Basal bounding surface:	No outcrop	No outcrop	No core	No outcrop	No outcrop	No outcrop	No outcrop	No outcrop
	Incision:								
	Facies base RW:								
	Facies base TST:								
	Facies base HST:								
	Facies top HST:								
	Stratigraphic architecture:								
	Principal lithology:								
	Quartz sand in:								
Gun 2.4	Basal bounding surface:	Erosional	Erosional	No core	Erosional	No outcrop	Erosional	No outcrop	No outcrop
	Incision:	No	No		No		No		
	Facies base RW:	Not present	Not present		Shoreface-barrier		Not present		
	Facies base TST:	Digitate bioherms	Digitate bioherms		Proximal-distal temp.		Digitate bioherms		
	Facies base HST:	Proximal-distal temp.	Deep marine		Proximal-distal temp.		Proximal-distal temp.		
	Facies top HST:	Proximal-distal temp.	Organ pipes		Digitate bioherms		Proximal-distal temp.		
	Stratigraphic architecture:	Organ pipes / X/A-B/A	X/B/P-A		P/B/A-P		Organ pipes / X/B/P-A		
	Principal lithology:	Carbonate	Carbonate		Carbonate		Carbonate		
	Quartz sand in:	Nil	Nil		RW		Nil		
Gun 2.3	Basal bounding surface:	Erosional	Conformable	No core	Erosional	No outcrop	No outcrop	No outcrop	No outcrop
	Incision:	No	No		No		No		
	Facies base RW:	Not present	Not present		Not present		Not present		
	Facies base TST:	Proximal-distal temp.	Digitate Bioherms		Digitate bioherms		Proximal-distal temp.		
	Facies base HST:	Proximal-distal temp.	Proximal-distal temp.		Proximal-distal temp.		Proximal-distal temp.		
	Facies top HST:	Proximal-distal temp.	Proximal-distal temp.		Proximal-distal temp.		Proximal-distal temp.		
	Stratigraphic architecture:	X/B/P	X/B/P		X/B/P		X/B/P		
	Principal lithology:	Carbonate	Carbonate		Carbonate		Carbonate		
	Quartz sand in:	Nil	Nil		Nil		Nil		
Gun 2.2	Basal bounding surface:	Erosional	Erosional	No core	Erosional	No outcrop	Erosional	No outcrop	No outcrop
	Incision:	No	Yes		No		No		
	Facies base RW:	Not present	Not present		Shoreface-barrier		Not present		
	Facies base TST:	Proximal-distal temp.	Digitate bioherms		Proximal-distal temp.		Digitate bioherms		
	Facies base HST:	Proximal-distal temp.	Deep marine		Proximal-distal temp.		Proximal-distal temp.		
	Facies top HST:	Proximal-distal temp.	Proximal-distal temp.		Proximal-distal temp.		Proximal-distal temp.		
	Stratigraphic architecture:	X/B/P	X/B/P		A/B/P		X/B/P		
	Principal lithology:	Carbonate	Carbonate		70 Silici, 30 Carb		Carbonate		
	Quartz sand in:	Nil	Nil		Nil		Nil		
Gun 2.1	Basal bounding surface:	Erosional	Erosional	Erosional	Erosional	No outcrop	Erosional	No outcrop	No outcrop
	Incision:	Yes	Yes	Yes	Yes		Yes		
	Facies base RW:	Not present	Not present	Shoreface-barrier	Shoreface-barrier		Shoreface-barrier		
	Facies base TST:	Subtidal temp. cycles	Subtidal temp. cycles	Proximal-distal temp.	Digitate bioherms		Digitate bioherms		
	Facies base HST:	Proximal-distal temp.	Deep marine	Proximal-distal temp.	Proximal-distal temp.		Proximal-distal temp.		
	Facies top HST:	Proximal-distal temp.	Proximal-distal temp.		Peritidal-lagoonal		Proximal-distal temp.		
	Stratigraphic architecture:	X/B/P	X/B/P	A/B/P	A/B/P		X/B/P		
	Principal lithology:	Carbonate	50 Carb, 50 Silici	50 Carb, 50 Silici	50 Carb, 50 Silici		Carbonate		
	Quartz sand in:	Nil	Nil	RW	RW		Nil		
Gun 1.8	Basal bounding surface:	Conformable	Conformable	Erosional	Erosional	No outcrop	Truncated	No outcrop	No outcrop
	Incision:	No	No	No	No				
	Facies base RW:	Not present	Not present	Shoreface-barrier	Peritidal-lagoonal				
	Facies base TST:	Peritidal-lagoonal	Subtidal temp. cycles	Shoreface-barrier	Peritidal-lagoonal				
	Facies base HST:	Peritidal-lagoonal	Peritidal-lagoonal	Shoreface-barrier	Peritidal-lagoonal				
	Facies top HST:	Peritidal-lagoonal	Peritidal-lagoonal	Shoreface-barrier	Shoreface-barrier				
	Stratigraphic architecture:	X/A/A	B/P-A	A/A/A	P/B/P				
	Principal lithology:	Carbonate	Carbonate	Siliciclastic	Carbonate				
	Quartz sand in:	Nil	Nil	RW & HST	RW & HST				

TABLE 2.—(Continued) SUMMARY OF CRITERIA USED TO DEFINE FOURTH-ORDER SEQUENCES AND THEIR BOUNDING SURFACES

Unit	Criteria	Barr Hole	Esperanza Waters	AASp 1 & AADi 1	Judenan Creek	Wilfred Creek	Mammoth Mines	Crocodile WH	Oxide Creek
Gun 1.7	Basal bounding surface:	Erosional	Erosional	Erosional	Erosional	No outcrop	Truncated	No outcrop	Erosional
	Incision:	Yes, 1–15 m	Yes, 1–2 m	?	Yes				?
	Facies base RW:	Not present	Not present	Proximal tempestites	Proximal tempestites				Distal tempestites
	Facies base TST:	Digitate bioherms	Digitate bioherms	Subtidal temp. cycles	Subtidal temp. cycles				Distal tempestites
	Facies base HST:	Distal tempestites	Distal tempestites	Distal tempestites	Subtidal temp. cycles				Distal tempestites
	Facies top HST:	Peritidal-lagoonal	Subtidal temp. cycles	Subtidal temp. cycles	Peritidal-lagoonal				No outcrop
	Stratigraphic architecture:	X/B/P-A	P/B/P	P/B/P	P/B/P				P/B/A-P
	Principal lithology:	Carbonate	Carbonate	Siliciclastic	Carbonate				50 Carb, 50 Silici
	Quartz sand in:	Nil	Nil	RW	RW				Nil
Gun 1.6	Basal bounding surface:	Conformable	Conformable	Conformable	Conformable	No outcrop	Conformable	No outcrop	Conformable
	Incision:	No	No	No	No		No		No
	Facies base RW:	Distal tempestites	Distal tempestites	Distal tempestites	Distal tempestites		Distal tempestites		Distal tempestites
	Facies base TST:	Distal tempestites	Distal tempestites	Distal tempestites	Distal tempestites		Distal tempestites		Distal tempestites
	Facies base HST:	Distal tempestites	Distal tempestites	Distal tempestites	Distal tempestites		Distal tempestites		Deep marine
	Facies top HST:	Domal bioherms	Subtidal temp. cycles	Distal tempestites	Distal tempestites		Proximal tempestites		Distal tempestites
	Stratigraphic architecture:	P/B/P	P/B/A-P	A/B/A	A/B/A		P-A/B/A-P		P-A/B/A-P
	Principal lithology:	Carbonate	Carbonate	50 Carb, 50 Silici	Carbonate		Carbonate		siliciclastic
	Quartz sand in:	Nil	Nil	Nil	Nil		Nil		Nil
Gun 1.5	Basal bounding surface:	Conformable	No outcrop	Conformable	Conformable	Conformable	No outcrop	Conformable	
	Incision:	No	?	No	No	No		No	
	Facies base RW:	Not present	No outcrop	Not present	Not present	Not present		Proximal tempestites	
	Facies base TST:	Deep marine	No outcrop	Distal tempestites	Distal tempestites	Deep marine		Distal tempestites	
	Facies base HST:	Deep marine	Deep marine	Deep marine	Deep marine	No outcrop		Deep marine	
	Facies top HST:	Distal tempestites	Distal tempestites	Distal tempestites	Distal tempestites	No outcrop		Distal tempestites	
	Stratigraphic architecture:	X/B/A	X/X/A	X/B/A	X/B/A	X/B/X		P/B/A	
	Principal lithology:	40 Silici, 60 Carb	40 Silici, 60 Carb	70 Silici, 30 Carb	30 Silici, 70 Carb	Siliciclastic		Siliciclastic	
	Quartz sand in:	Nil	Nil	Nil	Nil	Nil		RW	
Gun 1.4	Basal bounding surface:	Conformable	Conformable	Erosional	Erosional	Erosional	Onlapped	Erosional	Conformable
	Incision:	No	No	?	No	No		No	No
	Facies base RW:	Distal tempestites	Proximal tempestites	Proximal tempestites	Distal tempestites	Deep marine		Proximal tempestites	Proximal tempestites
	Facies base TST:	Deep marine	Distal tempestites	Distal tempestites	Distal tempestites	Deep marine		Not present	Deep marine
	Facies base HST:	Deep marine	No outcrop	Distal tempestites	Deep marine	Deep marine		Not present	Deep marine
	Facies top HST:	Deep marine	No outcrop	Distal tempestites	Distal tempestites	Deep marine		Proximal tempestites	Proximal tempestites
	Stratigraphic architecture:	B/B/P	B/B/X	P/B/A	B/B/A	B/B/A		P/X/X	P/B/A
	Principal lithology:	Siliciclastic	Siliciclastic	Siliciclastic	Siliciclastic	Siliciclastic		Siliciclastic	siliciclastic
	Quartz sand in:	Nil	RW	RW	Nil	Nil		RW	RW
Gun 1.3	Basal bounding surface:	Erosional	Erosional	No core	Erosional	Erosional	Onlapped	Erosional	Erosional
	Incision:	Yes	Yes		No	No		Yes	No
	Facies base RW:	Not present	Not present		Distal tempestites	Not present		Nonmarine-shoreface	Proximal tempestites
	Facies base TST:	Distal tempestites	Proximal tempestites		Distal tempestites	Deep marine		Proximal tempestites	Distal tempestites
	Facies base HST:	Distal tempestites	Distal tempestites		Deep marine	Deep marine		Proximal tempestites	Distal tempestites
	Facies top HST:	Distal tempestites	Distal tempestites		Distal tempestites	Distal tempestites		Proximal tempestites	
	Stratigraphic architecture:	X/B/P	X/B/P		P/B/P-A	X/B/P-A		P/B/P	P/B/P
	Principal lithology:	Siliciclastic	Siliciclastic		Siliciclastic	Siliciclastic		Siliciclastic	Siliciclastic
	Quartz sand in:	TST	TST		Nil	Nil		RW	RW
Gun 1.2	Basal bounding surface:	Erosional	Erosional	No core	No outcrop	Erosional	Onlapped	Erosional	Erosional
	Incision:	Yes	Yes		No outcrop	Yes		Yes	?
	Facies base RW:	Not present	Not present		No outcrop	Not present		Not present	Not present
	Facies base TST:	Nonmarine-shoreface	Proximal tempestites		Distal tempestites	Proximal tempestites		Nonmarine-shoreface	Proximal tempestites
	Facies base HST:	Not present	Not present		Distal tempestites	Distal tempestites		Not present	Distal tempestites
	Facies top HST:	Not present	Not present			Distal tempestites		Not present	Distal tempestites
	Stratigraphic architecture:	Not Applicable	Not Applicable		X/B/P	X/B/P		Not Applicable	X/B/P
	Principal lithology:	Siliciclastic	Siliciclastic		Siliciclastic	Siliciclastic		Siliciclastic	Siliciclastic
	Quartz sand in:	TST	TST		Nil	TST		TST	TST

Gun 1.1

Basal bounding surface: Erosional	Onlapped	No core	No outcrop	Onlapped	Onlapped	Onlapped	Erosional
Incision: Yes							Yes
Facies base RW: Not present							Nonmarine-shoreface
Facies base TST: Proximal tempestites							Proximal tempestites
Facies base HST: Not present							Distal tempestites
Facies top HST: Not present							Distal tempestites
Stratigraphic architecture: X/P/X							P/B/A
Principal lithology: Carbonate							Siliciclastic
Quartz sand in: TST							RW & TST

Prize 2.3

Basal bounding surface: Erosional	Erosional	No core	No outcrop	Truncated	Truncated	Erosional	Truncated
Incision: Yes	Yes					Yes	
Facies base RW: Not present	Not present					Not present	
Facies base TST: Distal tempestites	Distal tempestites					Proximal tempestites	
Facies base HST: Distal tempestites	Distal tempestites					Distal tempestites	
Facies top HST: Not present	Proximal tempestites					Not present	
Stratigraphic architecture: X/B/P	X/B/P					X/B/X	
Principal lithology: Siliciclastic	Siliciclastic					Siliciclastic	
Quartz sand in: Nil	HST					TST	

Prize 2.2

Basal bounding surface: Erosional	Erosional	No core	No outcrop	Truncated	Truncated	Erosional	Truncated
Incision: Yes	Yes					Yes	
Facies base RW: Nonmarine-shoreface	Proximal tempestites					Nonmarine-shoreface	
Facies base TST: Distal tempestites	Distal tempestites					Proximal tempestites	
Facies base HST: Distal tempestites	Distal tempestites					Distal tempestites	
Facies top HST: Proximal tempestites	Proximal tempestites					Proximal tempestites	
Stratigraphic architecture: P/B/P	P/B/P					P/B/P	
Principal lithology: Siliciclastic	Siliciclastic					Siliciclastic	
Quartz sand in: RW & HST	RW & HST					RW & TST & HST	

Prize 2.1

Basal bounding surface: Erosional	Erosional	No core	No outcrop	Truncated	Erosional	Erosional	Truncated
Incision: Yes	Yes				Yes	Yes	
Facies base RW: Proximal tempestites	Proximal tempestites				Nonmarine-shoreface	Nonmarine-shoreface	
Facies base TST: Distal tempestites	Distal tempestites				Not present	Nonmarine-shoreface	
Facies base HST: Distal tempestites	Distal tempestites				Not present	Proximal tempestites	
Facies top HST: Distal tempestites	Distal tempestites				Not present	Proximal tempestites	
Stratigraphic architecture: P/B/P	P/B/P				P/X/X	P/B/P	
Principal lithology: Siliciclastic	Siliciclastic				Siliciclastic	Siliciclastic	
Quartz sand in: RW	RW				RW	RW, TST & HSt	

Notes: RW, regressive wedge; TST, transgressive systems tract; HST, highstand systems tract
For stratigraphic architecture X/X/X represents regressive wedge/transgressive systems tract/highstand systems tract (X, not applicable; B, backstepping; A, aggradational; P, progradational)
For principal lithology Silici, siliciclastic; Carb, carbonate

mation features indicating resumption of syndepositional tectonics or that depositional gradients were higher than in the underlying succession, although the lack of high-energy rim facies suggests that a ramp profile still existed (Fig. 4C). Nearshore and shallow subtidal environments have a significant siliciclastic component and appear to have been more energetic, with less dolomudstone and more ooids. The presence of significant ooid accumulations (unlike the underlying depositional sequences) implies that tidal currents may have played a more important role (cf. Hine, 1983). Domal–columnar stromatolites are rare and the lack of significant shallow-water stromatolite bioherms, to function as an energy barrier, may have been responsible for the generally higher nearshore energy levels interpreted for this interval. Interstratification of shoreface sands with lagoonal carbonates suggests that a barrier-island system may have formed outboard of shoreface sands, although outcrop restrictions prevent determination of sand-body geometry. The abundance of tempestite beds once again attests to the strong influence of storms on subtidal sediment dispersal and deposition. Unlike domal–columnar bioherms, digitate columnar bioherms had high depositional relief (up to 15 m) and were not surrounded by high-energy facies, suggesting that they likely accreted in lower-energy environments. Although internal textures are poorly preserved, it does not appear that detrital sediment was important in their construction. Such stromatolites are interpreted to have formed largely by precipitation of micrite and fibrous calcite, on and within microbial structures, during periods of decreased carbonate sediment production and accumulation, in both deep and shallow subtidal, low-energy environments (see discussion below). This is most evident in the case of the "organ pipe" stromatolites that blanketed a large part of the platform in upper Esperanza Formation time, locally forming buildups with a cumulative thickness of up to 80 m.

SEQUENCE STRATIGRAPHY AND PLATFORM EVOLUTION

The gamma logs generated from core and outcrop, when combined with detailed facies descriptions and architecture and constrained by radiometric dating, have proved extremely effective in identifying high-resolution sequence stratigraphic surfaces (Figs. 6, 7). The three cross sections of Figure 7 (A, B, and C) correspond to the cross sections of Figure 3. Rocks of the lower McNamara Group (Torpedo Creek Quartzite, Gunpowder Creek, Paradise Creek, and Esperanza Formations) are grouped into the Prize and Gun Supersequences (Fig. 2) and cut by three regionally correlatable disconformities (Figs. 3, 6, 7). Each supersequence is named after the stratigraphic unit that hosts the supersequence maximum flooding surface. Both supersequences comprise two third-order sequences (Prize 1 and 2, Gun 1 and 2). This study considers the upper Prize third-order sequence and both Gun third-order sequences. This subdivision reflects the three main depositional sequences described above. The Prize 2 sequence comprises three fourth-order sequences (Prize 2.1, Prize 2.2, and Prize 2.3), the Gun 1 sequence is made up of eight fourth-order sequences (Gun 1.1, Gun 1.2, Gun 1.3, Gun 1.4, Gun 1.5, Gun 1.6, Gun 1.7, Gun 1.8), and the Gun 2 sequence contains five fourth-order sequences (Gun 2.1, Gun 2.2, Gun 2.3, Gun 2.4, Gun 2.5).

Enough detail can be derived from the gamma logs to identify both parasequences and parasequence sets, which in turn

facilitate correlation and in many cases the recognition of systems tracts. On a regional scale, both the third- and fourth-order sequences show excellent correlation (Figs. 6, 7) over several hundred kilometers, whereas correlation of individual parasequences and parasequence sets is more problematic. Sequence stratigraphic surfaces were identified through a combination of: (1) gamma-ray log response and pattern; (2) sedimentological interpretation of facies; (3) architectural stacking patterns; (4) nature of facies transitions; (5) evidence of regional incision; and (6) radiometric ages (see Table 2 for a summary of fourth-order sequence boundary characteristics).

Taken in combination, the third-and fourth-order sequences were the most useful in reconstructing the sedimentology and evolution of the lower McNamara platform. Facies belts within the sequences are highly variable and reflect the interplay of siliciclastic and carbonate sediment supply and changing rates of accommodation. In response to interpreted tectonic events, variations in accommodation rate, and inherent depositional heterogeneities in carbonate production and accumulation, the lower McNamara platform evolved through a series of distinct depositional geometries.

Torpedo Creek–Lower Gunpowder Creek Depositional Sequence (Prize 2.1–2.3)

Transgressive Systems Tract.—Sandstones of the Torpedo Creek Quartzite, the oldest stratigraphic unit considered in this study, comprise early transgressive deposits at the base of the upper third-order Prize Sequence (Prize 2.1 in Figure 7). In parts of the Mount Gordon Fault Zone and Leichhardt River Fault Trough, alluvial-fan conglomerates overlie this sequence boundary and are interpreted to imply tectonic enhancement of the unconformity. The sandstones comprise thick to thin accumulations of nonmarine and nearshore facies. Abrupt thickness variations throughout the study area imply highly localized sediment sources and discrete depocenters. An increase in accommodation rates caused retrogradation of fluvial to shallow marine sandstones and the subsequent deposition of subtidal, storm-dominated fine-grained sandstones, siltstones, and shales of the lower Gunpowder Creek Formation (Figs. 7, 8A). Basin geometry consisted of a series of east-southeast-facing ramps deepening away from structurally controlled highs (e.g., Mount Gordon Fault Zone).

Highstand Systems Tract.—As accommodation rates decreased, shallow to deep subtidal ramp sediments were deposited in three fourth-order progradational sequences (Fig. 7). The basal sequence is capped by coarse-grained shoreface sandstones (Prize 2.1), whereas the two overlying ones shallow up into proximal siliciclastic and carbonate tempestites (Prize 2.1 and 2.3). Each of these sequences is characterized by high-energy nearshore environments and storm-dominated subtidal sedimentation (Fig. 8B). Syndepositional tectonic movement, likely related to basin tilting, produced coarse conglomerates and regolith horizons adjacent to local topographic highs (e.g., Kamarga Dome, Mount Gordon Fault Zone; Figs. 1, 3). This contemporaneous faulting was active throughout Prize 2 sequence deposition. The source of both siliciclastic and carbonate sediments in the southern area appears to have been largely to the

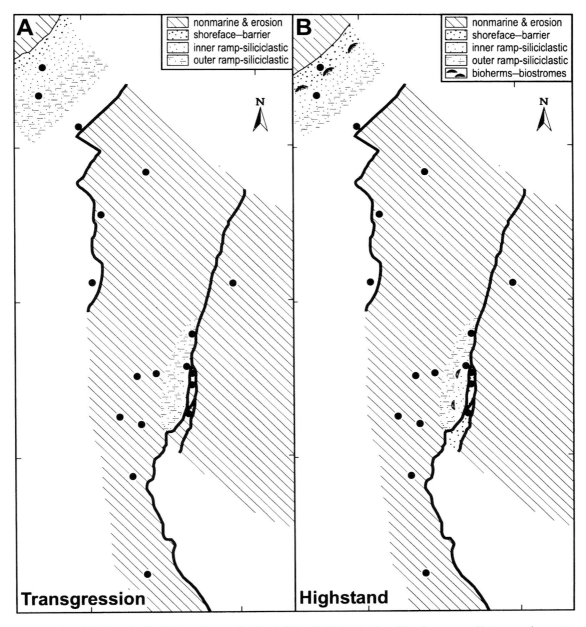

Fig. 8.—Paleogeography of the Torpedo Creek–lower Gunpowder Creek (Prize 2) third-order depositional sequence: A) transgressive systems tract, and B) highstand systems tracts. Black circles represent locations of sections and cores (identification as in Figure 1). Bold black lines represent syndepositional and postdepositional Lady Loretta High Strain Zone (to northwest) and Mount Gordon Fault Zone (to southeast).

south–southwest, whereas in the north they were derived from the north–northwest. Deposition of this sequence was terminated by long-term (>28 My) regional exposure and regolith formation (Gun Supersequence boundary; Figs. 2, 3, 6, and 7).

Local incision at the base of the Gun Supersequence has removed both highstand and transgressive deposits of the upper third-order sequence in the Prize Supersequence. At Mellish Park and in the Leichhardt River Fault Trough, Gun Supersequence sediments overlie sandstones of the Torpedo Creek and Warrina Park Quartzites. North and south of Gunpowder (Mount Gordon Fault Zone) highstand deposits are preserved in the lower Gunpowder Creek Formation (Fig. 7).

Upper Gunpowder Creek–Paradise Creek Depositional Sequence (Gun 1.1–1.8)

Transgressive Systems Tract.—Four and a half fourth-order sequences (Gun 1.1–1.5) are recognized in the transgressive systems tract of this third-order sequence (Fig. 7). Terrigenous clastic sediments dominate the first three sequences, and in the upper two sequences carbonate sediments largely replaced the terrigenous clastics, reflecting the progressive transgression of provenance areas (Fig. 3). The fourth-order sequences display gradually deepening, progradational facies patterns, and a back-stepping gamma-ray log motif. Successive sequences thin upward.

The lower two sequences (Gun 1.1 and 1.2) are best developed to the south-southeast in the Leichhardt River Fault Trough. Renewed subsidence to the east and west of the Mount Gordon Fault Zone initiated deposition of the Moondarra Siltstone and upper Gunpowder Creek Formation on a siliciclastic ramp. In the vicinity of the Mount Gordon Fault Zone a thin package of nonmarine conglomerates, nearshore siliciclastic sands, and shallow-water carbonates accumulated in areas of minor accommodation (Fig. 9A). These thin intervals probably mark zones of sediment bypass as material was transported from northern and western provenance areas and depocenters were shifted to the south–southeast.

At Barr Hole and Esperanza Waters, an increase in accommodation rates along the western parts of the Mount Gordon Fault Zone created space for micaceous siltstones and shales of the Gun 1.3 sequence in an area of previous sediment bypass (Fig 7). During the Gun 1.4 and 1.5 sequences a south- to southeast-facing, mixed carbonate and siliciclastic ramp developed. Progressive onlap to the north and west inundated the clastic provenance areas and created space for evaporite-rich peritidal carbonates and quartz sand deposition in nearshore environments. In the south, concomitant subtidal sedimentation passed from storm-dominated siliciclastic to carbonate sands and silts. As accommodation rates continued to increase and rates of sed-

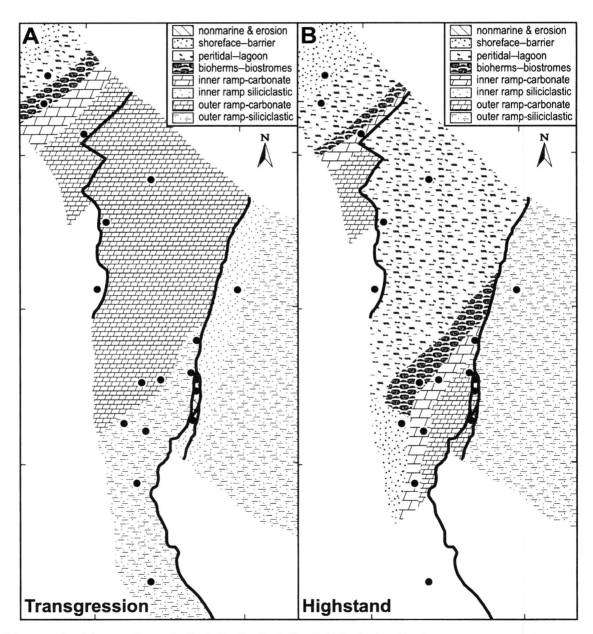

FIG. 9.—Paleogeography of the upper Gunpowder Creek–Paradise Creek (Gun 1) third-order depositional sequence: A) transgressive systems tract, and B) highstand systems tracts. Black circles represent locations of sections and cores (identification as in Figure 1). Bold black lines represent syndepositional and postdepositional Lady Loretta High Strain Zone (to northwest) and Mount Gordon Fault Zone (to southeast).

iment supply decreased, deep-water sediments, including a suite of carbonaceous shales, bituminous carbonates, phosphatic crusts, stromatolites, and hardgrounds were deposited. In the upper Gunpowder Formation this condensed interval contains the maximum flooding for the Gun supersequence (Figs. 3, 6, 7). By the beginning of Paradise Creek deposition, the Mount Gordon Fault Zone appears to have had a decreased influence on sedimentation in the southeast and a true regional ramp system developed (Figs. 3, 7, 9A).

Highstand Systems Tract.—A gradual decline in accommodation rates during lower Paradise Creek time, combined with a severe reduction of siliciclastic sediment influx, enabled carbonate facies progradation from the west–northwest (Figs. 7, 9B). Three and a half fourth-order sequences (Gun 1.5–1.8) are recognized in the highstand systems tract of the Gun 1 third-order cycle. In the south, where deeper-water facies prevailed, the lower one and a half sequences are dominated by aggradational stacking patterns. Farther north, where shallower facies first appeared, aggradational to progradational stacking patterns occur. In the upper two sequences progradational stacking patterns were gradually replaced by aggradational peritidal facies.

Both the Gun 1.6 and 1.7 sequence boundaries are characterized by a basinward shift in facies (Figs. 7, 10A). At the 1.6 surface aggradational distal tempestite facies locally shallow into progradational proximal tempestite cycles prior to returning to aggradational distal tempestites. In highstand deposits of the Gun 1.5 and 1.6 sequences the inner- to middle-ramp proximal carbonate storm beds and small domal stromatolites are interbedded to form meter-scale cycles. These grade, with increased water depth, into distal carbonate and ultimately siliciclastic tempestites on the outer ramp.

A tectonic event is recorded at the base of the Gun 1.7 sequence boundary (Fig. 10A). At Paradise Creek, Police Creek, Kamarga Dome, and Mellish Park an influx of medium to grit-grade quartz sand occurs above the sequence boundary, suggesting rejuvenation of clastic provenance areas to the west. At Barr Hole and Esperanza Waters the 40–60 m thick package of progradational sandy carbonates is absent. In its place an incision surface with 1–2 m of local relief attests to coeval fault rejuvenation along the Mount Gordon Fault Zone (Fig 10A). A rapid increase in subsidence rates followed and transgression arrested the supply of quartz sand and carbonate clasts, facilitating the accretion of digitate stromatolite bioherms of the mid-stromatolite marker (Fig. 6).

The platform maintained a ramp profile as long as accommodation rates remained elevated. Decreases in accommodation rates midway through the Paradise Creek Formation (Gun 1.7 highstand) were followed by extensive progradation of shallow-water carbonate depocenters (Fig. 10A). Along the Mount Gordon Fault Zone reduced accommodation rates during the Gun 1.7 highstand promoted the development of a high-energy barrier composed of domal to columnar stromatolite biostromes and bioherms tens of meters in diameter and with several meters of relief (Fig. 10A). Coalescence of these bioherms resulted in the formation of rim complexes that had significant hydrodynamic effect on the ramp and promoted flattening of the inner ramp and steepening of the outer ramp to form a distally steepened ramp to rimmed shelf (Figs. 9B, 10A). These bioherms pass laterally into intraclast grainstones (stromatolite-derived) and amalgamated, cross-bedded dolosiltstones. Absorption of

wave energy by this rim favored the formation of extensive low-energy peritidal and lagoonal inner-ramp environments. In the uppermost fourth-order sequence (Gun 1.8) very low accommodation rates permitted progradation of peritidal environments across the entire platform and increased modification of the ramp profile (Fig. 10A). Unlike the underlying succession, the upper Gunpowder–Paradise Creek accommodation package represents a regionally continuous depositional system with some incision and local facies control in tectonically active areas such as the Lady Loretta High Strain Zone and the Mount Gordon Fault Zone (Figs. 3, 7, 10A). The upper Gunpowder to Paradise Creek third-order depositional package was terminated by a depositional hiatus at the Gun 2.1 sequence boundary (Figs. 2, 3, 6, 7). Along the Mount Gordon Fault and Lady Loretta High Strain zones incision at the Gun 2.1 sequence boundary (Mammoth Mines and Gregory River sections) provides evidence for tectonic activity at this boundary. In the south, reduced accommodation rates facilitated the accumulation of nearshore siliciclastic sands.

Upper Paradise Creek–Esperanza Depositional Sequence (Gun 2.1–2.5)

Transgressive Systems Tract.—One and a half fourth-order sequences (Gun 2.1–2.2) are recognized in the third-order Gun 2 transgressive systems tract (Figs. 6, 7). An abrupt return to high accommodation rates resulted in the pronounced backstepping of peritidal and shallow marine carbonates and the deposition of digitate stromatolite bioherms and biostromes similar to those found at the mid-stromatolite marker at the base of the Gun 1.7 sequence (Fig. 11A). As increasing areas of the platform were drowned, dolosilt production increased and these sediments were transported basinward to be deposited as proximal–distal tempestite facies (Gun 2.1 terminal transgressive and highstand systems tracts). A decline in the production of dolosilt, possibly related to increased rates of transgression (Gun 2.2), facilitated a return to the formation of digitate stromatolite bioherms and biostromes. Stromatolite accretion was unable to keep pace with the elevated rate of transgression, and this resulted in the accumulation of shale-dominated sediments of the condensed interval of maximum flooding in the lower Esperanza Formation (Gun 2.2; Figs. 3, 6, 7, 11A). Decreased sediment supply to the basin subsequently permitted these largely precipitated digitate buildups to blanket significant portions of the platform.

Highstand Systems Tract.—Three and a half fourth-order sequences (Gun 2.2, 2.3, 2.4, and 2.5) are recognized in this largely progradational third-order Gun 2 highstand (Figs. 6, 7). In the Gun 2.2 and 2.3 sequences, slightly lowered accommodation rates in middle- and outer-ramp settings permitted accumulation of thick, prograding packages of extensively slumped and brecciated carbonate tempestites, and growth of isolated bioherms of small digitate columnar stromatolites and stratiform microbial laminite (Figs. 3, 6). The abundance of slump features is interpreted to reflect increased depositional gradients inherited from the underlying distally steepened ramps to rimmed shelves of the Upper Paradise Creek Formation and a possible reactivation of syndepositional tectonics.

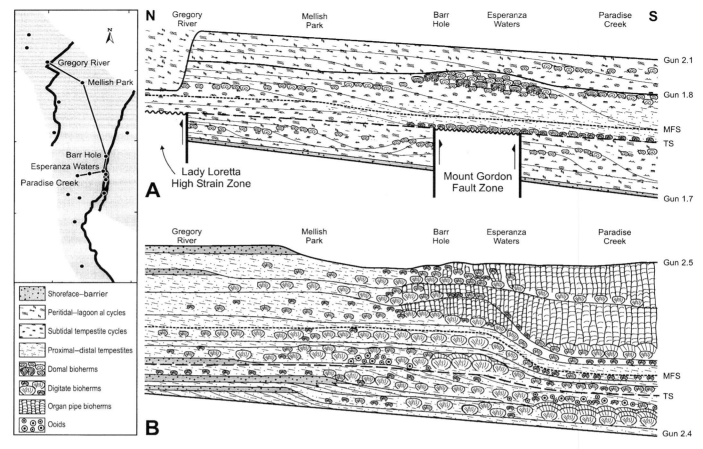

FIG. 10.—Evolutionary reconstructions of selected fourth-order depositional sequences formed during third-order highstand deposition: A) Gun 1.7 and Gun 1.8 depositional sequences; B) Gun 2.4 depositional sequence. MFS, fourth-order maximum flooding surface; TS, fourth-order transgressive surface. Inset map from Figure 1 indicates location of measured sections used to construct cross sections.

Bioherms generally nucleated on synsedimentary, slump-fold crests, lenses of intraclasts, or ooid-rich sands, indicating a substrate preference. Inner-ramp and peritidal facies are similar to those of the Paradise Creek Formation, with the addition of dolomudstone-hosted molar-tooth structures. During periods of reduced sediment influx (times of rapid relative sea-level rise at fourth-order transgressions), coalesced mounds of digitate stromatolites formed aggrading biohermal complexes tens of meters in diameter and with up to tens of meters of relief on the mid to outer ramp.

At the Gun 2.4 sequence boundary a basinward shift in facies introduced locally sourced, nearshore siliciclastic accumulations in the upper Esperanza Formation in the Kamarga Dome and Gregory River regions (Figs. 10B, 11B). The associated decrease in accommodation rates resulted in severe restriction of carbonate production and produced a basinward progradation of these marginal marine quartz sands (Figs. 3, 10B). In more basinward positions (e.g., Esperanza Waters) digitate bioherms and biostromes and ooid shoals developed in areas where the supply of dolosilt was limited (Fig. 10B). Following this relative fall in sea level, a combination of platform geometry and rapid relative sea-level rise facilitated a backstepping suite of digitate stromatolite parasequences and retreat of the siliciclas-

tic facies belt (Fig. 10B). In basinward locations (e.g., Esperanza Waters), the carbonate sediment supply was reduced and shales of the condensed section accumulated. In the northwest, at Kamarga Dome, Gregory River, and Thorntonia, siliciclastic facies belts prograded southeastward (Fig. 10B). An influx of terrigenous clastic sediment arrested dolosilt production on the inner to middle ramp so that proximal tempestite facies belts were restricted. These factors combined to restrict the supply of carbonate and siliciclastic sediment to the outer ramp, permitting the accretion of extensive "organ pipe" stromatolite bioherms and biostromes in deeper-water environments (Figs. 3, 6, 10B). Aggradation of "organ pipe" stromatolites filled much of the available space in the previously deep-water environments and contributed to a gradual decrease in the depositional gradient. This infilling permitted the widespread progradation of siliciclastic and shallow-water carbonate facies of the Gun 2.5 sequence (Fig. 3)

In the upper parts of the third-order Gun 2 sequence, shallow-water facies belts provide evidence for decreasing accommodation and widespread progradation. At Kamarga Dome and the Gregory River the basal breccia of the overlying Lady Loretta Formation has a sharp contact with mixed carbonates and siliciclastics of the upper Esperanza Formation. Elsewhere the

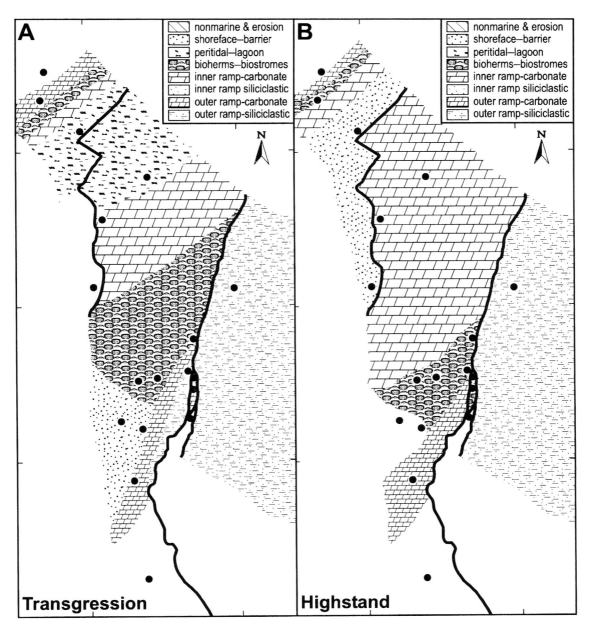

FIG. 11.—Paleogeography of the upper Paradise Creek-Esperanza (Gun 2) third-order depositional sequence: A) transgressive systems tract, and B) highstand systems tracts. Black circles represent locations of sections and cores (identification as in Figure 1). Bold black lines represent syndepositional and postdepositional Lady Loretta High Strain Zone (to northwest) and Mount Gordon Fault Zone (to southeast).

contact crops out poorly. On seismic sections, an erosion surface with up to 1700 m of incision occurs at the base of the Loretta Supersequence and a sediment wedge thickens basinward away from this surface (Bradshaw et al. 1998). In the Lawn Hill region, Sweet and Hutton (1982) mapped a ferruginous chert breccia near the base of the Lady Loretta Formation and suggested a Tertiary origin for it. However, in areas of good outcrop the breccia is conformable with the regional dip, suggesting a Paleoproterozoic origin. We correlate this breccia with the erosion surface identified on seismic sections. Poor outcrop beneath the breccia inhibits the documentation of incision beneath this surface.

DISCUSSION

Lower McNamara Deposition

The lower McNamara succession is best interpreted as an arid, carbonate–siliciclastic–evaporite ramp (cf. Read, 1985; Handford and Loucks, 1993). The ramp was dominated, alternately, by detrital carbonate and siliciclastic sediment. The tectonic setting (intracratonic extensional basin) with its attendant block and strike-slip faulting (D. Scott, personal communication) dominated the depositional history of the basin, controlling the regional extent of the ramp and the creation of sub-basins throughout formation of the Lawn Hill Platform.

Several topographic highs were active during lower McNamara time. The Mount Gordon Fault Zone and parallel structures to the west (e.g., Lady Loretta High Strain Zone) played a significant role in modifying depositional systems. In many areas, incision at the base of the Gun Supersequence has removed sediments of the lower Gunpowder Creek Formation, so that the unconformity rests on sands of the Torpedo Creek Quartzite. However, at Barr Hole and Esperanza Waters these sediments are locally preserved. A few kilometers south of Esperanza Waters the Gun Supersequence boundary incises to sediments of the much older Myally Sub Group. Clearly the Mount Gordon Fault Zone was tectonically active during the hiatus at the base of the Gun Supersequence with variable rates and degrees of displacement taking place along this fault. The fault zone remained episodically active during deposition of the Gun Supersequence. Incision at the basal boundaries of the Gun 1.7 and 2.1 sequences records uplift along this zone. Initial onlap of Gun Supersequence transgressive deposits at sequences 1.3 and 1.5 along the Mount Gordon Fault Zone provides evidence for variable and comparatively late subsidence along the fault zone. The appearance of quartz sand at the Gun 1.7, 2.4, and 2.5 sequence boundaries may have resulted from tectonic activity along parallel north–south structures near Lady Loretta and farther west. The absence of Gun 1.1–1.3 sequences from the Kamarga Dome region suggests that this area was a topographic high at this time. Sediments in the Gun 1.4 and 1.5 sequences are quartz-rich, consistent with a clastic provenance proximal to the Kamarga Dome. A return to terrigenous clastic deposition late in the Esperanza Formation (Gun 2.4 and 2.5) suggests that tectonism in the region of Kamarga Dome rejuvenated the provenance areas.

As regional tectonism abated (following the Gun supersequence boundary), the overall gentle gradients on the ramp served to moderate the effect of relative sea-level fluctuations. Such gentle profiles permitted entire facies belts to gradually shift back and forth across the study area. Coastal to nearshore (inner ramp) environments tended to be mixed siliciclastic–carbonate–evaporite systems and reacted most to the influence of relative sea-level variations through fluctuations in siliciclastic sediment supply. Periods of high siliciclastic influx were characterized by high-energy shoreline systems (beaches and barrier bars), whereas periods of low siliciclastic influx saw the development of extensive low-energy peritidal–lagoonal carbonates and evaporites. A key factor that permitted the progradation of these peritidal–lagoonal complexes was the formation of nearshore stromatolitic rim barriers that effectively subdued inner-ramp energy levels. Offshore (middle) ramp environments were dominated by storm processes during both siliciclastic and carbonate regimes. Outer ramp and slope environments were characterized by gravity processes, low-energy stromatolitic buildups, and organic-rich hemipelagic sedimentation. Overall, carbonate production, and the resultant platform geometry, appears to have been more affected by tectonically controlled siliciclastic supply and rates of creation of accommodation space than by eustatic sea-level changes.

The most conspicuous feature of many Proterozoic carbonate platforms is the prevalence of significant volumes of seafloor carbonate cements (Grotzinger, 1986, 1989; Sami and James, 1993, 1994, 1996; Grotzinger and Knoll, 1995). Although present in lower McNamara strata (predominantly in stromatolites

of the Esperanza Formation), such early marine precipitates are a relatively minor component in most of these ramp systems. Significantly, they are conspicuously absent in lower McNamara peritidal lithofacies.

The other main type of carbonate system common in the Proterozoic (particularly in the Mesoproterozoic and Neoproterozoic) is the carbonate-mud-rich platform. Examples of this type of platform include the 1800 Ma old Belcher Group (Ricketts and Donaldson, 1989), the 1700 Ma old Hornby Bay Group (Ross and Donaldson, 1989), the 1450 to 1250 Ma old Belt Supergroup (O'Connor, 1972; Horodyski, 1983; Winston, 1990; Winston and Link, 1993), the 1200 Ma old Society Cliffs Formation (Kah and Knoll, 1996; Kah, 1997), and the 1200 Ma old Victor Bay Formation (Sherman et al., 1997; Sherman et al., this volume). Such platforms tend to be dominated by carbonate muds, commonly with abundant molar-tooth structure, but they can also contain early marine precipitates (Kah and Knoll, 1996). Although the precise origin of the carbonate mud has not been conclusively determined, it is commonly believed to be a combination of water-column precipitates and reworked internal (produced within stromatolitic laminae) micritic cements (Knoll and Swett, 1990; Sami and James, 1993, 1994, 1996; Kah and Knoll, 1996). High-energy subtidal environments typically include stromatolites, ooids, and intraclasts (micritic and stromatolitic). Thus an apparent dichotomy exists between the bulk of Paleoproterozoic platforms, which contain abundant precipitates but few detrital carbonates other than intraclasts, and Mesoproterozoic–Neoproterozoic platforms, which have abundant carbonate muds and sands (cf. Grotzinger, 1989; Knoll and Swett, 1990; Kah and Knoll, 1996). The lower McNamara platform appears to occupy a transitional position between these two end members. Precipitate-rich digitate columnar stromatolites bear an affinity to Paleoproterozoic forms, whereas mud-rich domal–columnar stromatolites are more characteristic of late Mesoproterozoic–Neoproterozoic platforms. Intertidal mudstones with molar-tooth structures, outerramp muddy tempestites, and the abundance of micritic intraclasts in lower McNamara strata all indicate that carbonate muds were important in low-energy environments.

One element that is conspicuously absent in many Proterozoic platforms, but found in most Phanerozoic carbonate systems (cf. Burchette and Wright, 1992), is a significant volume of carbonate silt. This is largely due to the lack of skeletal metazoan particles, a ready source of silt-size material in the Phanerozoic, in the early to middle Proterozoic. Yet, despite the many similarities with the above-mentioned Proterozoic platforms, subtidal lower McNamara ramp environments are characterized by an abundance of carbonate silt. Seafloor precipitates and muddy facies are present, but the most volumetrically important lithofacies are largely composed of silt-size carbonate grains. Thus, the lower McNamara succession has more in common with texturally graded, storm-dominated Phanerozoic ramps (Burchette and Wright, 1992; Jones and Desrochers, 1992; Reid and Dorobek, 1993) than with precipitate- or mud-rich Paleoproterozoic ramps. Such an abundance of carbonate silts is not due to the high volume of siliciclastics present in the system, because many Proterozoic platforms are similarly mixed (O'Connor, 1972; Horodyski, 1983; Ricketts and Donaldson, 1989; Ross and Donaldson, 1989; Winston, 1990; Winston and Link, 1993; Sherman et al., 1997). Neither is this discrepancy due to the presence of unique depositional environments or platform geometry. Lower McNamara lithofacies reflect the full spectrum of peritidal to deep subtidal environments, both high- and low-energy, and represent deposition on both open and rimmed ramps. Similar conditions were present on many of the above-mentioned platforms. Three possible scenarios can therefore be advanced to account for such a disparity: (1) a source of carbonate silt absent in other Proterozoic systems exists in the lower McNamara platform, (2) distinct tectonic and depositional setting and water chemistry favored silt production, or (3) sedimentary and/or diagenetic factors are obscuring the contribution of silts to these other platforms. The first alternative appears unlikely inasmuch as the mechanisms envisioned for carbonate silt generation (see below) are interpreted to have been relatively common on most Proterozoic platforms. Similarly, there is no evidence that the lower McNamara platform grew in a basin that incorporated any unique or aberrant environmental conditions. Carbonate ramps forming in shallow cratonic seas were not unusual in the Proterozoic, and preliminary geochemical investigation does not suggest that the chemistry of lower McNamara seas were extraordinary (J. Lindsay, personal communication, 1997). The very nature of micritic peloids (the main contributor to silt-size grains in the lower McNamara) makes them difficult to identify in Proterozoic rocks. Unless lithified early they are very susceptible to compaction and diagenetic alteration during burial (Tucker and Wright, 1990), such that grainstones composed of poorly lithified peloids are generally difficult to distinguish from mudstones. The complete replacement of micrite by microcrystalline dolomite in many Proterozoic successions further hampers the identification of peloid-rich grainstones. Whether the abundance of carbonate silts in the lower McNamara succession is due largely to preferential preservation or to the existence of unique initial conditions remains undetermined. Yet, despite this uncertainty, the lower McNamara succession remains one of the oldest carbonate platforms to show definite sedimentological affinities to both late Proterozoic and Phanerozoic systems.

Controls on Stromatolite Growth

Domal–columnar stromatolites (the dominant form in the Gunpowder Creek and Paradise Creek formations) and digitate columnar stromatolites (abundant in the Esperanza Formation) appear to be largely mutually exclusive, indicating that specific factors exist which would favor the development of one form over the other. Both are found in close association with subtidal sediments, but their different internal and external characteristics likely reflect different origins.

Domal–columnar stromatolites are generally restricted to shallow subtidal and peritidal environments (Figs. 3, 4). Where domal–columnar stromatolites are intimately associated with microbial laminites they show the same internal structure of alternating (0.1–1.0 mm thick) micrite-spar laminae (Fig. 5D). Couplets are separated by thin, organic-rich wisps, commonly accentuated by pressure solution. Laminae tend to be convex and well defined. Spar-rich laminae are formed largely of blocky to drusy dolomite, with only minor remnants of fibrous precursors. Other spar-rich laminae preserve remnants of sac-like and irregular bodies (0.10–0.35 mm diameter) in micro-

crystalline spar surrounded by blocky spar. The bulk of the laminae are micrite-rich. Micritic laminae are either dense and unlaminated or have a clotted texture. Spar-filled tubules and filaments are present in well-preserved samples (Fig. 5F). These filaments are commonly less than 0.25 mm diameter and are arranged in vertical or radiating bundles suggestive of tufted mats. The most volumetrically important laminae, however, are those of clotted micrite with interstitial blocky spar. Clots tend to be spherical and relatively uniform in size, about 0.05–0.1 mm diameter. Thin single-grain-thick laminae and lenses of quartz–peloid grainstone are common in microbial laminites but relatively rare in domal–columnar stromatolites. Microbial laminites also commonly preserve tepees and spar-filled irregular fenestrae (the latter particularly in micrite-rich laminae). Intraclasts of all three types of laminae are abundant and intimately associated with these stromatolites. Domal–columnar stromatolites are found on most substrate types, from loose sediment to well-cemented hardgrounds.

Digitate columnar stromatolites and their associated microbial laminites are invariably silicified by late-stage diagenetic processes, and thus fine microstructure preservation is not generally good. Poorly defined laminae (<0.5 mm thick) are made up of clotted fibrous and microcrystalline silica. There does not appear to be the same organization of repeating couplets seen in domal–columnar stromatolites. No evidence of original microorganisms is preserved. Laminae are convex but can locally be conical. Microbial laminites contain many laminae composed of microdigitate columns (<5 mm diameter). Most columns tend to be smaller (commonly 1–3 cm diameter) and have less vertical continuity than the domal–columnar forms. These columns are arranged in a three-dimensional, branching fabric with dolomudstone, micrite intraclasts, and quartz–peloid grainstone between columns. Intraclasts composed of eroded fragments of digitate columnar stromatolite are rare. "Organ pipes" can reach up to 10 cm diameter and form domal biostromes with the exclusion of all other lithofacies. Such stromatolites appear to have effectively excluded sediment from their laminae. Even when formed in dominantly siliciclastic environments, these stromatolitic mounds were able to grow with negligible amounts of incorporated sediment. Digitate columnar stromatolites favored firm or stable substrates, such as early-cemented ooid or intraclast grainstones, domal–columnar stromatolites, slump folds and breccias, or erosional hardgrounds. Bioherms and biostromes of digitate columnar stromatolite and microbial laminite tend to be larger in scale than domal–columnar ones, as low rates of sediment influx permitted uninterrupted growth.

These differences all point to specific controlling factors: substrate, general energy levels, sediment influx rates, and mechanism of formation. Digitate columnar stromatolites, in the lower McNamara succession, were more sensitive to substrate conditions and so were less opportunistic. On the other hand, once conditions were suitable, such as during Esperanza time, they tended to proliferate. Associated sedimentary structures, sediment types, and generally delicate growth forms all suggest that digitate columnar stromatolites were favored in lower-energy environments, but not necessarily deeper-water ones. In the Esperanza Formation, isolated digitate and conical forms present in what appear to be lagoonal facies argues against restriction to deep-water environments. Abundant accommodation space did permit construction of immense bio-hermal complexes in the Esperanza Formation. Internal micro-fabrics of digitate columnar stromatolites point to carbonate precipitation, both as micrite and fibrous calcite, as the dominant mechanism of accretion, whereas domal–columnar stromatolites likely grew by a combination of micrite precipitation and the trapping of fine carbonate sediment (predominantly muds and silts). Stratigraphically, domal–columnar stromatolites flourished during periods of high carbonate productivity, particularly of fine-grained mud. Conversely, digitate columnar stromatolites appear to have done best during periods of decreased carbonate production and deposition, perhaps benefiting from decreased water turbidity, higher carbonate saturation levels, or simply lower-energy conditions. Lack of significant generation of digitate stromatolite intraclasts is either: (1) a result of growth in generally lower-energy environments; (2) related to the absence of an easily eroded couplet-based microstructure; or (3) due to possibly early silicification. Digitate stromatolites appear to have been more pervasively cemented than domal stromatolites, whose heterogeneity likely made them particularly susceptible to plucking and erosion of laminae during storms.

The abrupt shift from domal to largely digitate stromatolites between Gun 1 and Gun 2 depositional sequences can thus be attributed to a combination of these factors. In general, environments in the Esperanza sequence: (1) were less muddy; (2) had an increased siliciclastic supply which was beginning to restrict the size of the shallow-water carbonate factory; and (3) had greater rates of creation of accommodation space than during previous sequences. All these factors would have favored the growth of digitate columnar stromatolites over domal–columnar forms.

Origin of Sedimentary Grains

The bulk of the lower McNamara succession is composed of a handful of different sedimentary grains. By far the most abundant grain types are quartz and peloid silt. These grains are ubiquitous, and sediments can vary from pure quartz silt to pure peloids, but they are usually mixed in subequal proportions (Table 1). The peloids are marginally coarser-grained, but the lack of grading in mixed populations suggests that these grains were effectively hydraulically equivalent. A regionally extensive eolian source for very fine quartz sand and silt is suggested by their widespread occurrence, grain size, angularity, and well-sorted population. The quartz silt population is discrete from the more locally distributed coarse quartz sands. These well-rounded, well-sorted grains are interpreted to have been derived from fluvial processes working on a low-relief stable craton. These supermature sands were subsequently reworked in high-energy shoreface and nearshore environments. Finer-grained siliciclastics, containing abundant micas and clay minerals, are similarly fluvially derived, but lack extensive reworking prior to deposition.

The origin of the peloids is more problematic, because little information can be gleaned from petrographic examination. They are micritic, largely microcrystalline dolomite, featureless and spherical to subspherical. As with the quartz silt, the entire population is remarkably well sorted, suggesting a source control. Micritic intraclasts have a wide range of grain sizes, but

for the most part the grain sizes of peloids and intraclasts do not overlap, indicating that it is unlikely that a significant proportion of peloids are derived from the mechanical breakdown of dolomudstone beds. There are only two other probable sources of micritic material: organically mediated water-column precipitates and clotted micritic cements within stromatolite laminae. The former would require clumping or flocculation of carbonate mud as it settled in the water column. It is questionable whether this process would produce cohesive sedimentary grains of uniform size and shape in the volumes observed in the lower McNamara succession. It is more likely that these precipitates would contribute to mud-size sediments rather than silt-size ones (cf. Robbins and Blackwelder, 1992). A better choice would be some form of internal precipitate or calcified element within microbial laminites and stromatolites. The lower McNamara succession contains a significant volume of stromatolitic material, much of it already accounting for the abundant intraclast grains. The observed clotted laminae are an ideal candidate for peloid generation. The clots are of comparable size and shape, and probably were sufficiently cohesive. The process of calcifying benthic cyanobacteria requires increased calcium carbonate saturation levels, a condition believed to have existed for Proterozoic oceans (Grotzinger, 1989; Grotzinger and Knoll, 1995). Disintegration of these partially lithified mats would be a ready source of micritic peloids and micrite (cf. Kazmierczak et al., 1996; Kazmierczak and Iryu, 1997).

The next most abundant grain types are intraclasts. These grains occur across a wide range of grain sizes and represent reworking of all the carbonate rock types present in the succession (with the exception of digitate columnar stromatolites). The most common are quartz–peloid grainstone, microbial laminite, and domal–columnar stromatolite clasts (stromaclasts). The abundance of intraclasts suggests widespread early lithification, both of stromatolitic and detrital sediments. Intraclasts occur as platy, angular fragments representing storm transport with minor reworking, and as well-rounded to coated grains (often with several generations) that represent extensive fair-weather reworking and reactivation. As such, they range from the supratidal to the limit of storm-wave influence on the seafloor. Intraclast rosettes and flat-pebble conglomerates are fairly common in the succession, particularly near biohermal complexes, the result of extensive reworking by strong currents, possibly tidal (cf. Wilson, 1975; Ricketts and Donaldson, 1989; Tucker and Wright, 1990). Yet, despite the prevalence of intraclasts, subtidal early marine cements are not ubiquitous, attested to by the widespread resedimentation of sediment from the inner ramp to the middle and outer ramps. Most grainstones (intraclast, quartz–peloid, and particularly ooid) lack any evidence of early marine cements (Figs. 5A, B, E). The bulk of intraclasts were generated in peritidal–lagoonal settings or proximal to stromatolitic laminae and subsequently resedimented onto mid- and outer-ramp environments, resulting in a platform that remained blanketed largely by loose sediment.

SUMMARY

1. The lower McNamara succession is composed of a suite of carbonate, siliciclastic, and evaporitic lithofacies deposited in nonmarine, shallow marine, and deep marine environ-

ments. The predominant lithofacies types are detrital and were deposited on storm-dominated ramps. Volumetrically, the most important grain types are eolian quartz silt, microbially derived micritic peloids, and storm-generated intraclasts. Nonmarine and high-energy shoreface systems are predominantly siliciclastic. Low-energy peritidal and lagoonal lithofacies chiefly contain carbonates and evaporites. Shallow subtidal depositional environments were initially siliciclastic (Gunpowder Creek Formation) and subsequently largely carbonate (Paradise Creek and Esperanza formations). Deep-water lithofacies are a mixture of fine-grained siliciclastic and carbonate sediments.

2. By combining detailed facies architecture with gamma logs derived from hand-held spectrometers the succession can be divided into three main third-order depositional sequences by four regionally correlatable erosional and/or nondepositional surfaces of varying duration. These include: (i) Torpedo Creek–lower Gunpowder depositional sequence (Prize 2); (ii) upper Gunpowder Creek–Paradise Creek depositional sequence (Gun 1); and (iii) upper Paradise Creek–Esperanza depositional sequence (Gun 2). These sequences can be further subdivided into a suite of correlatable fourth-order sequences

3. During the Prize 2 depositional sequence, sediments accumulated in a series of segmented, fault-controlled siliciclastic depocenters, deepening away from local tectonic highs. Following a marked depositional hiatus, the Gun 1 depositional sequence recorded the development of a regionally extensive, east- to southeast-deepening homoclinal carbonate ramp. Prograding rim facies drove the ramp to adopt a distally steepened profile. During the Gun 2 depositional sequence a ramp geometry was once again created, although depositional gradients appear to have been higher and overall environments deeper in the study area.

4. Differences in lithofacies between Gun 1 and Gun 2 depositional sequences reflect increased tectonic activity and resultant increased rates of creation of accommodation space. The main results of these changes include: (1) increased siliciclastic supply rates; (2) generally higher inner-ramp energy levels (thus less carbonate mud), (3) increased tidal influence (more ooids); and (4) a transition from largely domal–columnar stromatolites to digitate columnar stromatolites, reflecting a shift from mixed precipitate/trapping strategies to largely precipitate stromatolite growth processes.

5. On the basis of its sequence stratigraphic framework and facies architecture the lower McNamara Group can best be described as a storm-dominated arid carbonate–evaporite–siliciclastic ramp formed in a tectonically active intracratonic basin. Facies belts and evolutionary history bear a stronger affinity to models proposed for Phanerozoic mixed ramps than to precipitate-dominated Paleoproterozoic or mud-dominated Neoproterozoic systems.

ACKNOWLEDGMENTS

This project benefited from the extensive experience and kind help of the many geologists and technicians involved in the North Australian Basins Resource Evaluation (NABRE) project. Particular thanks go to D. Scott and B. Bradshaw for help with the structural and tectonic history of the basin, M. Idnurm for paleomagnetic reconstructions, J. Lindsay for geochemical trends, and I. Zeilinger for generation of maps. Logistics and all field operating funds were provided by the Australian Geological Survey Organisation. The Natural Science and Engineering Research Council of Canada provided operating grants for TTS, NPJ, and KK. Thank you to the Geological Survey of Queensland in Brisbane for providing access to, and support with, drillcore. Andrew, Garth, Kevin, and Scotty provided able and occasionally enthusiastic assistance in the field. Heartfelt thanks go to the people of Mt. Isa and northwestern Queensland for their warm welcome and irrepressible good humor. Special thanks to the station personnel who provided information and access on remote locations. Three cheers for sweat bees, spinnifex, and Land Rovers. P.N. Southgate, M.J. Jackson, and R.W. Page publish with permission of the Executive Director, AGSO.

REFERENCES

BRADSHAW, B., AND SCOTT, D., 1997, McNamara and Fickling group correlations: implications for tectonostratigraphic history, Mount Isa basin (abstract):Australian Geological Survey Organisation Record 1997/12.

BRADSHAW, B. E., SCOTT, D. L., KRASSAY, A. K., AND SOUTHGATE, P. N., 1998, Elizabeth Creek Prospect: Buried mineral play in Century equivalent strata, northern Lawn Hill Platform, Queensland: Australian Geological Survey Organisation Record 1998/4, 26 p., 39 plates.

BURCHETTE, T. P., AND WRIGHT, V. P., 1992, Carbonate ramp depositional systems: Sedimentary Geology, v. 79, p. 3–57.

GROTZINGER, J. P., 1986, Cyclicity and paleoenvironmental dynamics, Rocknest platform, northwest Canada: Geological Society of America, Bulletin, v. 97, p. 1208–1231.

GROTZINGER, J. P., 1989, Facies and evolution of Precambrian carbonate depositional systems: emergence of the modern platform archetype: in Crevello, P. D., Wilson, J. L., Sarg, J. F., and Read, J. F., eds., Controls on Carbonate Platform and Basin Development: SEPM, Special Publication 44, p. 79–106.

GROTZINGER, J. P., AND KNOLL, A. H., 1995, Anomalous carbonate precipitates: Is the Precambrian key to the Permian?: Palaios, v. 10, p. 578–596.

HANDFORD, C. R., AND LOUCKS, R. G., 1993, Carbonate depositional sequences and systems tracts—Responses of carbonate platforms to relative sea-level changes, in Loucks, R. G., and Sarg, J. F., eds., Carbonate Sequence Stratigraphy: Recent Developments and Applications: American Association of Petroleum Geologists, Memoir 57, p. 3–41.

HARDIE, L. A., AND SHINN, E. A., 1986, Carbonate Depositional Environments; Part 3: Tidal Flats: Colorado School of Mines Quarterly, v. 81, 74 p.

HINE, A. C., 1983, Modern shallow water carbonate platform margins, in Cook, H. E., Hine. A. C., and Mullins, H. T., eds., Platform Margin and Deep Water Carbonates: Society of Economic Paleontologists and Mineralogists, Short Course Notes 12, p. 3.1–3.100.

HORODYSKI, R. J., 1983, Sedimentary geology and stromatolites of the middle Proterozoic Belt Supergroup, Glacier National Park, Montana: Precambrian Research, v. 20, p. 391–425.

HUTTON, L. J., AND SWEET, I. P., 1982, Geological evolution, tectonic style, and economic potential of the Lawn Hill Platform cover, northwest Queensland: BMR Journal of Australian Geology and Geophysics, v. 7, p. 125–134.

JONES, B., AND DESROCHERS, A., 1992, Shallow platform carbonates, in Walker, R.G., and James, N.P., eds., Facies Models: Response to Sea Level Change: St. John's, Newfoundland, Geological Association of Canada, p. 277–301.

KAH, L. C., 1997, Styles of carbonate deposition in Mesoproterozoic successions: a balance of environmental and biogeochemical processes (abstract): Canadian Society of Petroleum Geologists–SEPM Joint Convention, Program with Abstracts, p. 149.

KAH, L. C., AND KNOLL, A. H., 1996, Microbenthic distribution of Proterozoic tidal flats: environmental and taphonomic considerations: Geology, v. 24, p. 79–82.

KAZMIERCZAK, J., AND IRYU, Y., 1997, Cyanobacterial origin of syngenetic microcrystalline cements from Pleistocene corallinacean crusts and rhodoliths of Okierabu-Jima (Ryukyu Islands, Japan) (abstract): 18th Regional European meeting of Sedimentology, p. 188.

KAZMIERCZAK, J., COLEMAN, M. L., GRUSZCZYNSKI, M., AND KEMPE, S., 1996, Cyanobacterial key to the genesis of micritic and peloidal limestones in ancient seas: Acta Palaeontologica Polonica, v. 41, p. 319–338.

KNOLL, A. H., AND SWETT, K., 1990, Carbonate deposition during the late Proterozoic Era: An example from Spitzbergen: American Journal of Science, v. 290-A, p. 104–132.

LOUTIT, T. S., HARDENBOL, J., VAIL, P. R., AND BAUM, G. R., 1988, Condensed sections: the key to age dating and correlation of continental margin sequences, in Wilgus, C. K., Hastings, B. S., Ross, C. A., Posamentier, H., Van Wagoner, J., and Kendall, C. G. St. C., eds., Sea-Level Changes: An Integrated Approach: SEPM, Special Publication 42, p. 183–213.

MIALL, A. D., 1992, Alluvial deposits, in Walker, R. G., and James, N. P., eds., Facies Models: Response to Sea Level Change: St. John's, Newfoundland, Geological Association of Canada, p. 119–142.

O'CONNOR, M. P., 1972, Classification and environmental interpretation of the cryptalgal organosedimentary "molar-tooth" structure from the late Precambrian Belt–Purcell Supergroup: Journal of Geology, v. 80, p. 592–610.

PAGE, R. W., 1997, Geological constraints provided by U–Pb Zircon dating of basin phases in the Lawn Hill and McArthur basins (abstract): Australian Geological Survey Organisation Record 1997/12.

PAGE, R. W., AND SWEET. I. P., 1998, Geochronology of basin phases in the western Mt. Isa Inlier, and correlation with the McArthur Basin: Australian Journal of Earth Sciences, v. 45, p. 219–232.

PLUMB, K. A., DERRICK, G. M., AND WILSON, I. H., 1980, Precambrian geology of the McArthur River–Mount Isa region, northern Australia, in Henderson, R. A., and Stevenson, P. J., eds., The Geology and Geophysics of Northeastern Australia: Brisbane, Geological Society of Australia, Queensland Division, p. 71–88.

PLUMB, K. A., DERRICK, G. M., NEEDHAM, R. S., AND SHAW, R. D., 1981, The Proterozoic of northern Australia, in Hunter, D. R., ed., Precambrian of the Southern Hemisphere: Amsterdam, Elsevier, Developments in Precambrian Geology 2, p. 205–307.

PLUMB, K. A., AHMAD, M., AND WYGRALAK, A. S., 1990, Mid-Proterozoic basins of the north Australian craton—regional geology and mineralization, in Hughes, F. E., ed., Geology of the Mineral Deposits of Australia and Papua–New Guinea: Melbourne, The Australasian Institute of Mining and metallurgy, p. 881–902.

READ, J. F., 1985, Carbonate platform facies models: American Association of Petroleum Geologists, Bulletin, v. 69, p. 1–21.

READING, H. G., 1986, Sedimentary Environments and Facies, 2nd edition: Oxford, U.K., Blackwell, 615 p.

REID, S. K., AND DOROBEK, S. L., 1993, Sequence stratigraphy and evolution of a progradational, foreland carbonate ramp, lower Mississippian Mission Canyon Formation and stratigraphic equivalents, Montana and Idaho, in Loucks, R. G., and Sarg, J. F., eds., Carbonate Sequence Stratigraphy: Recent Developments and Applications: American Association of Petroleum Geologists, Memoir 57, p. 327–352.

RICKETTS, B. D., AND DONALDSON, J. A., 1989, Stromatolite reef development on a mud-dominated platform in the middle Precambrian Belcher group of Hudson Bay, in Geldsetzer, H. H. J., James, N. P., and Tebbutt, G. E., eds., Reefs, Canada and Adjacent Areas: Canadian Society of Petroleum Geologists, Memoir 13, p. 113–119.

ROBBINS, L. L., AND BLACKWELDER, P. L., 1992, Biochemical and ultrastructural evidence for the origin of whitings: a biologically induced calcium carbonate precipitation mechanism: Geology, v. 20, p. 464–468.

ROSS, G. M., AND DONALDSON, J. A., 1989, Reef development and facies geometry on a high-energy early Proterozoic carbonate shelf (Hornby Bay Group, Northwest Territories, Canada), in Geldsetzer, H. H. J., James, N. P., and Tebbutt, G. E., eds., Reefs, Canada and Adjacent Areas: Canadian Society of Petroleum Geologists, Memoir 13, p. 120–128.

SAMI, T. T., AND JAMES, N. P., 1993, Evolution of an early Proterozoic foreland basin carbonate platform, lower Pethei Group, Great Slave Lake, northwest Canada: Sedimentology, v. 40, p. 403–430.

SAMI, T. T., AND JAMES, N. P., 1994, Peritidal carbonate platform growth and cyclicity in an early Proterozoic foreland basin, upper Pethei group, northwest Canada: Journal of Sedimentary Research, v. B64, p. 111–131.

SAMI, T. T., AND JAMES, N. P., 1996, Synsedimentary cements as Paleoproterozoic platform building blocks, Pethei group, northwestern Canada: Journal of Sedimentary Research, v. 66, p. 209–222.

SCOTT, D., AND BRADSHAW, B., 1997, Seismic interpretation of tectonostratigraphic packages within the northern Mt. Isa basin (abstract): Australian Geological Survey Organisation Record 1997/12.

SCOTT, D., TARLOWSKI, C. LEVEN, J., AND MARTIN, S., 1997, Basement Studies: current status of models and dataset integration (abstract): Australian Geological Survey Organisation Record 1997/12.

SHERMAN, A. G., NARBONNE, G. M., AND JAMES, N. P., 1997, Facies model for a Mesoproterozoic carbonate ramp, Victor Bay Formation, Borden Peninsula, northern Canada (abstract): Canadian Society of Petroleum Geologists–SEPM Joint Convention, Program with Abstracts, p. 254.

SWEET, I. P., AND HUTTON, L. J., 1982, Lawn Hill Region: Queensland 1:100,000 Map Commentary: Australia, Bureau of Mineral Resources Geology and Geophysics, 36 p.

TUCKER, M. E., AND WRIGHT, V. P., 1990, Carbonate Sedimentology: Oxford, U.K., Blackwell, 482 p.

WALKER, R. G., AND JAMES, N. P., 1992, Facies Models: Response to Sea Level Change: St. John's, Newfoundland, Geological Association of Canada, 454 p.

WILSON, J. L., 1975, Carbonate Facies in Geologic History: New York, Springer-Verlag, 471 p.

WINSTON, D., 1990, Evidence for intracratonic, fluvial and lacustrine settings of middle to late Proterozoic basins of western U.S.A., in Gower, C. F., Rivers, T., and Ryan, B., eds., Mid-Proterozoic Laurentia–Baltica: Geological Association of Canada, Special Paper 38, p. 535–564.

WINSTON, D., AND LINK, P. K., 1993, Middle Proterozoic rocks of Montana, Idaho and eastern Washington: the Belt Supergroup, in Reed, J. C. Jr. et al., eds., Precambrian: Conterminous U.S.: Boulder, Colorado, Geological Society of America, The Geology of North America, v. C-2, p. 487–517.

SEDIMENTOLOGY OF A LATE MESOPROTEROZOIC MUDDY CARBONATE RAMP, NORTHERN BAFFIN ISLAND, ARCTIC CANADA

ANNE G. SHERMAN, NOEL P. JAMES, AND GUY M. NARBONNE

Department of Geological Sciences, Queen's University, Kingston, Ontario, K7L 3N6, Canada

ABSTRACT: The ~1200 Ga Victor Bay Formation is a muddy, predominantly subtidal carbonate ramp succession that crops out in the Borden Basin of northern Baffin Island. The ~ 400-m-thick upper member is dominated by a variety of lime mudstone facies representing supratidal to deep subtidal environments. The lateral transition between shallow-water and deep-water environments is best exposed in cliff sections along the northeast margin of the Milne Inlet Trough, the major graben in the Borden Basin.

The upper Victor Bay Formation is interpreted as a ramp with well-defined inner-ramp facies (red shale facies, dololaminite facies, molar-tooth calcarenite facies), mid-ramp facies (molar-tooth mudstone facies), and outer-ramp facies (nodular limestone facies, ribbon and parted limestone facies, carbonaceous rhythmite facies). Episodic storms are considered to have been the main depositional influence on an otherwise low-energy ramp.

The principal controls on the style of deposition on the Victor Bay ramp are (1) production of lime mud, interpreted to have taken place in the water column, and (2) redistribution of the mud and mudstone-derived grains during storms. Grainstones in the shallow subtidal and nearshore environments are composed of subtidal molar-tooth crack-fill grains and intraclasts of peritidal dololaminite facies, with only minor amounts of ooids. Microbialites form large stromatolitic buildups that accreted during times of rapid increase in accommodation space and/or times of decreased lime mud production.

Comparison with other Proterozoic carbonate platforms indicates that the Victor Bay ramp represents an end member where production of clastic lime mud far exceeded seafloor cementation by inorganic precipitates or growth of microbialites. It is therefore more similar to mud- and grain-dominated Phanerozoic ramps than to cement- and stromatolite-dominated Paleoproterozoic carbonate systems. The close temporal association of the muddy Victor Bay ramp with the underlying Society Cliffs Formation, which has attributes more typical of early Paleoproterozoic carbonates, attests to the wide spectrum of carbonate depositional systems that had evolved by the late Mesoproterozoic.

INTRODUCTION

Although different in detail, the main themes of carbonate sedimentation have remained roughly similar throughout much of geologic history (Wilson, 1975). There appears, however, to be an evolution in the style of carbonate platforms and ramps as well as in their constituent particle composition though Proterozoic time (Grotzinger, 1989). Older platforms are dominated by various kinds of benthic precipitates, whereas late Mesoproterozoic and Neoproterozoic ramps have many of the attributes ascribed to skeletal-rich Phanerozoic successions. Nevertheless, these younger Proterozoic carbonate platforms are constructed by elements in some ways peculiar to this geological interval, a time of rapid and dramatic change in tectonic plate configuration and ocean composition (Grotzinger, 1990; Knoll and Swett, 1990).

Sedimentary rocks of the late Mesoproterozoic Victor Bay Formation in Arctic Canada record carbonate sedimentation in a ramp-to-basin setting within the Borden Basin on northern Baffin Island (Fig. 1). The strata are unmetamorphosed, flat-lying, and well-exposed along extensive cliff faces. Shallow-water to deep-water facies transitions can be walked out or traced laterally over comparatively short, kilometer-scale distances, allowing temporal and spatial facies relationships to be discerned both parallel and perpendicular to depositional strike. The rocks are mainly limestone and have excellent fabric preservation. Thus, these strata are an exceptional example of a late Proterozoic carbonate depositional system.

The purpose of this paper is (1) to describe the facies attributes of the rocks, (2) to determine the origin of the sediments, and (3) to interpret the depositional nature of the system. The sediments are then compared to those on other carbonate ramps to determine their place in the carbonate depositional spectrum.

GEOLOGICAL SETTING

Age and Structural Setting of the Bylot Supergroup

Rifting of Archean and Paleoproterozoic crystalline rocks in northern Laurentia *ca.* 1270 Ma created several Mesoprotero-

zoic basins exposed in the present-day Arctic (Jackson and Iannelli, 1981; Galley et al., 1983; Fahrig, 1987). The Borden Basin rocks (Christie et al., 1972) are broadly contemporaneous to strata of the Fury and Hecla Basin of northwest Baffin Island (Chandler, 1988), the Thule Basin of Ellesmere Island and Western Greenland (Dawes, 1976), and the Aston–Hunting succession of Somerset Island (Blackadar, 1967; Reinson et al., 1976; Stewart, 1987). Lithostratigraphic correlation between Bylot, Thule, and Aston–Hunting strata is reinforced by recent $\delta^{13}C$ chemostratigraphy (Kah et al., 1999).

Of these successions, the Bylot Supergroup in the Borden Basin is the thickest (Lemon and Blackadar, 1963; Blackadar, 1970). Most of the 6 km of strata (Fig. 2) is flat-lying and undeformed. Basal sedimentary rocks of the Bylot Supergroup locally reach sub-greenschist facies (Jackson and Morgan, 1978; Galley et al., 1983; Dostal et al., 1989), but all overlying units including the rocks of this study are unmetamorphosed (Knight and Jackson, 1994). The Bylot Supergroup is divided into three groups (Blackadar, 1956). The sandstones, shales, and subaerially deposited basalts of the Eqalulik Group reflect initial rifting (Galley et al., 1983; Dostal et al., 1989). Limestones and dolostones of the overlying Uluksan Group accumulated during a subsequent interval of relative tectonic quiescence (Jackson and Iannelli, 1981, 1989). Overlying sandstones, siltstones, shales, and minor carbonate rocks of the Nunatsiaq Group represent sedimentation in a variety of fluvial and marine environments that developed during renewed rifting and eventual post-rift subsidence (Jackson and Iannelli, 1981, 1989). An unconformity separates the Bylot Supergroup from overlying lower Paleozoic Admiralty Group strata.

Rocks of the Bylot Supergroup are exposed in three principal grabens (Fig. 1A): the Milne Inlet, Eclipse, and North Bylot troughs (Jackson et al., 1975). The graben margins are defined by major fault zones that separate the sedimentary rocks from horsts of crystalline basement (Jackson et al., 1975). The study area is located in the central to southeastern part of the NW–

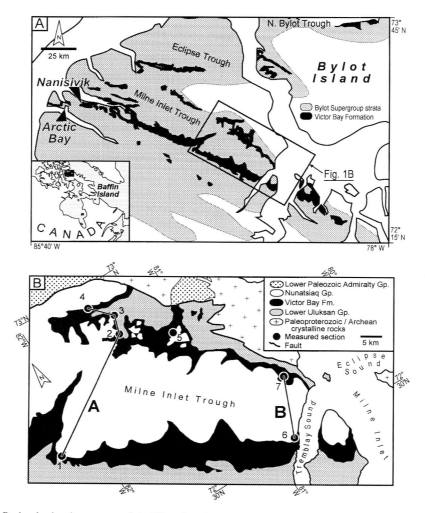

Fig. 1.—A) Map of Borden Peninsula showing outcrop of the Victor Bay Formation and location of the major grabens (troughs) in the Borden Basin. The study area is outlined and enlarged in Figure 1B. After Jackson and Ianelli (1981) and Jackson and Sangster (1987). B) Location of measured sections in the study area: 1, Adams River; 2, Pingo Valley South; 3, Pingo Valley North; 4, Mala River; 5, Camp Prozac; 6, Alfred Point; 7, Tremblay Sound. Lines A and B refer to cross sections in Figure 3.

SE-oriented Milne Inlet Trough, the largest of the grabens (Fig. 1B). Strata on either side of the trough dip gently towards the center, forming a broad synclinal structure that plunges to the NW.

Although paleontological data cannot be used to date Bylot Supergroup rocks precisely (Hofmann and Jackson, 1991, 1994), paleomagnetic studies and isotope geochemistry imply a late Mesoproterozoic age. Basalts of the Nauyat Formation are paleomagnetically indistinguishable (Fahrig et al., 1981) from the 1267 ± 2 Ma Mackenzie dike swarm (U–Pb badde-leyite age; LeCheminant and Heaman, 1989), providing a maximum age. Minimum U–Pb baddeleyite ages for the basin of 723 +4/−2 Ma (Heaman et al., 1992) and ca. 725 Ma (Pehrsson and Buchan, 1994) have been obtained from analyses of Franklin diabase dikes on Baffin Island that intrude all formations of the Bylot Supergroup. Paleomagnetic data suggest that the entire Bylot Supergroup was deposited prior to 1.21–1.19 Ga (see discussion in Knight and Jackson, 1994). A late Mesoproterozoic age for the succession is further implied by two

recent Pb–Pb dates from carbonates of the Uluksan Group and lowermost Nunatsiak Group (L.C. Kah, personal communication, 1998). Samples from the Society Cliffs Formation and lowermost Victor Bay Formation yield an age of 1199 ± 24 Ma, and an age of 1204 ± 22 Ma has been obtained for a suite taken across the entire Uluksan group and into the lowermost Athole Point Formation (Nunatsiak Group). Paleomagnetic studies suggest that the paleolatitude of the Borden Basin was equatorial at the time of deposition of the lower Bylot Supergroup, and had reached 10° N when the upper Bylot strata were deposited (Fahrig et al., 1981).

The Uluksan Group

The carbonate platform phase, represented by the Uluksan Group (Fig. 2), is divided into two major packages: (1) dolostones, minor limestones, and siliciclastic rocks of the Society Cliffs Formation (see Kah, this volume) and, along the southern margin of the basin, laterally equivalent siliciclastic conglom-

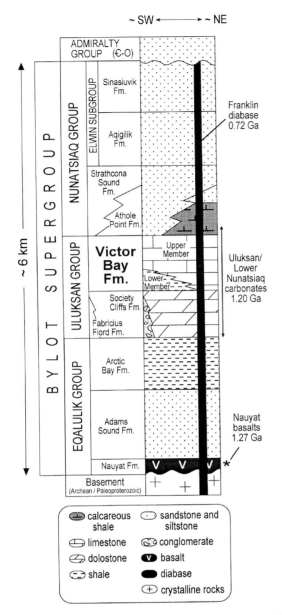

FIG. 2.—Generalized stratigraphic section of the Bylot Supergroup. Modified from Hofmann and Jackson (1991) and Iannelli (1992). Nauyat basalt age from LeCheminant and Heaman (1989); Uluksan Group age from L. C. Kah (personal communication, 1998); and Franklin dike age from Heaman et al. (1992) and Pehrsson and Buchan (1994).

erates and breccias of the Fabricius Fiord Formation; and (2) the Victor Bay Formation, comprising a lower member of dolomitic shales (VB$_1$ of Jackson and Iannelli, 1981) and an upper member of limestones, dolostones, and siliciclastic rocks (VB$_2$ of Jackson and Iannelli, 1981). In most of the Milne Inlet Trough the contact between the peritidal to shallow subtidal Society Cliffs Formation and basinal shales of the lower Victor Bay member is conformable and either abrupt or gradational (Jackson and Iannelli, 1981). In the Eclipse Trough and northwestern Milne Inlet Trough, the lower Victor Bay member is absent and the Society Cliffs Formation is directly overlain by

upper Victor Bay member carbonates. Limestones and dolostones of the upper member of the Victor Bay include tidal flat, shallow to deep subtidal, and inner to outer slope facies. Deepwater settings host extensive stromatolitic reef complexes (Geldsetzer, 1973; Jackson and Iannelli, 1981; Narbonne and James, 1996). In central and eastern Milne Inlet Trough the upper member is in conformable contact with overlying calcareous shales of the Athole Point Formation. In the Eclipse Trough and in the western part of the Milne Inlet Trough, the Athole Point Formation is absent and the Victor Bay Formation is unconformably overlain by siltstones, sandstones, conglomerates, and minor dolostones of the lower Strathcona Sound Formation (Jackson and Iannelli, 1981; Narbonne and James, 1996).

METHODS

This study is based on cliff sections and stream sections measured in the Victor Bay Formation east of the communities of Arctic Bay and Nanisivik (Fig. 1A). Stratigraphic sections at Nanisivik and seven other localities (Fig. 1B) were examined during two six-week field seasons in 1994 and 1995. Facies descriptions are based on field observations, photographs, slabbed lithological samples, and thin sections. Cyclic packaging of these facies and regional correlations of Victor Bay strata will be addressed in future work.

FACIES OF THE VICTOR BAY FORMATION

Lower Victor Bay Member

Brown, black, and dark gray dolomitic shale and minor dolosiltite–shale turbidites overlie Society Cliffs Formation dolostones conformably to locally disconformably (Jackson and Iannelli, 1981). Shale is a maximum of 370 m thick on central Borden Peninsula (Iannelli, 1992) but averages 100 to 150 m thick in the study area (Fig. 3). The basal 15 to 25 m are black, bituminous shales containing nodular and disseminated pyrite. At intervals of 0.5 to 1 m, the shale contains centimeter-thick beds of buff-weathering microcrystalline dolostone. There is an upward increase in bed thickness, abundance of T_{de} (Bouma, 1962) calciturbidites, and number of coarse conglomerates with nodular and ribbon limestone clasts through the lower member. Transition into carbonates of the upper Victor Bay is marked by 15 to 25 m of interlayered nodular limestone and small bioherms of columnar stromatolites.

The sharp transition from shallow-water carbonate rocks of the Society Cliffs Formation to deep-water shales of the Victor Bay Formation has been interpreted as a rapid drowning event, possibly tectonically driven (Jackson and Iannelli, 1981; Iannelli, 1992). The gradual upward increase in carbonate content, more numerous carbonate turbidites, and the transition into upper carbonate member rock types is interpreted as reflecting progradation and restoration of the Uluksan carbonate platform (Jackson and Iannelli, 1981; Iannelli 1992).

Upper Victor Bay Member

In contrast to the lower member, which is lithologically uniform at the regional scale, the limestones, dolostones, and minor siliciclastic rocks of the upper Victor Bay member suggest a significant shallowing from SW to NE. Where measured along the southwestern edge of the study area, upper-member facies are predominantly deep-water, consisting of dolomitic shale, nodular limestone, and ribbon limestone (Fig. 3). In the northeast, however, shallow-water facies dominate the succession, and include peritidal carbonate mudstone, coarse intraclast limestone, and stromatolitic carbonate.

Stromatolite buildups up to 275 m thick and up to 1 km wide occur in the upper member of the Victor Bay Formation (Geldsetzer, 1973; Jackson and Iannelli, 1989; Narbonne and James, 1996). In the eastern part of the Milne Inlet Trough, including the study area, they are present only on the northern margin of the Trough (Fig. 3). To the west, where the Milne Inlet Trough and the Eclipse Trough meet, the reef outcrop stretches almost to the southern margin. The upper member attains a maximum thickness of 702 m in eastern Borden Basin (Jackson and Iannelli, 1981) and ranges between 350 and 450 m in the study area. Late dolomitization of the upper member in North Bylot Trough, Eclipse Trough, and southeastern Milne Inlet Trough has resulted in finely crystalline, pink, gray, or white dolospar that locally contains vugs filled with saddle dolomite. With the exception of the largest stromatolite reef (Section 2, Fig. 1B) and almost all facies at the easternmost locality (Section 7, Fig. 1B), limestone in the study area did not undergo this late dolomitization and retains excellent fabric detail.

Upper Victor Bay rocks are packaged into shallowing-upwards cycles 20 to 50 m thick (Fig. 3). Where they are exposed on the northeast margin of the Milne Inlet Trough (Fig. 4), shallow-water facies thin to the southwest and are replaced by deeper-water equivalents (Fig. 5). This transition can be traced visually in continuous outcrop over the 6.5 km distance separating Sections 2 and 3 (Fig. 5). Upper Victor Bay lithofacies are described and interpreted below, and summarized in Table 1.

Red Shale Facies.—

Weakly laminated red shale forms units less than 1 m thick with desiccation cracks, rare discoid sulfate molds up to a centimeter long, and thin layers of scattered gypsum nodules. Evaporite minerals and molds make up an estimated 10% of the rock volume. Thin layers of fine to coarse sand-size particles consist of rounded microcline, quartz, and granitic gneiss. These shales are commonly interlayered with dolomitic mudstone, and locally with green shale, carbonaceous shale, and thinly bedded limestone.

Desiccation cracks, sulfate molds, and nodular gypsum indicate an environment that was subjected to subaerial exposure in a hypersaline setting (Kendall and Skipwith, 1969). Laminated to massive red mudstones with layers of coarse sand and evaporites are known from modern mud flats associated with playas, salinas, or coastal sabkhas (Wright, 1984; Kendall, 1992). Interlayering with laminated dolomitic mudstones of marine character (dololaminite facies; see below) suggests proximity to tidewater, in the form of coastal salina or sabkha environments. The nodular and matrix-dominated style of the evaporite-bearing layers more specifically suggests a high supratidal, coastal sabkha mud flat environment (Pratt et al., 1992). The discoid evaporite molds are typical of displacive intra-sediment growth (Kendall, 1992), and the preservation of nodular sulfate testifies to the aridity and high temperature at

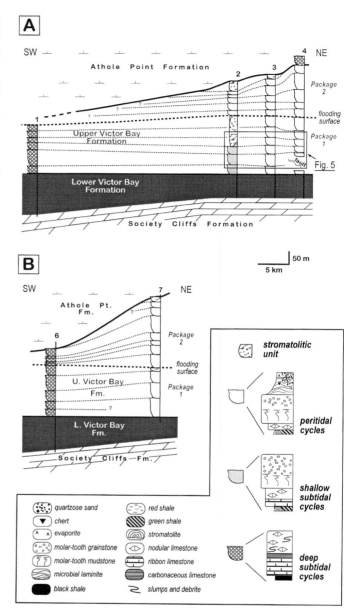

FIG. 3.—Regional correlation of sections in the study area from southwest to northeast. Section numbers refer to locations in Figure 1B. Northeastern sections (2, 3, 4, 7) are dominated by shallow-subtidal to supratidal cycles, whereas cycles are exclusively deep-water in the southwestern sections (1, 6). Idealized cycles in the legend illustrate lateral facies changes from shallow to deep water. The outlined part of cross section A is enlarged in Figure 5. Rocks at Section 7, located in the easternmost part of the study area, have undergone regional dolomitization. Shallow-water equivalents to the northwest remain predominantly limestone.

the time of deposition (Kinsman, 1976). Coarse siliciclastic interlayers of gneiss pebbles and other siliciclastic material indicate a nearby terrigenous source, possibly crystalline rocks from uplifted rift blocks of Paleoproterozoic basement.

Dololaminite Facies.—

The dololaminite facies includes two principal rock types: (1) thin- to medium-bedded laminated dolomitic mudstone and

FIG. 4.—Cyclically packaged carbonates in the upper member of the Victor Bay Formation 2.5 km NNE of Section 2. Recessive deep-water facies alternate with resistant shallow-water molar-tooth mudstone, molar-tooth calcarenite, and pale-weathering peritidal dolostone. Dolomitic shales of the lower Victor Bay member form the recessive slope below the cliffs. Scale bar = 50 m.

(2) intraclast packstone to rudstone with terrigenous sand. The mudstone crops out recessively and is buff in color, whereas fresh surfaces range from medium to dark gray with increasing organic content. Millimeter-scale laminae are predominantly smooth, locally tufted and crinkled, and bounded by thin, black organic-rich layers. Small stromatolitic domes under 10 cm in height, microbial mat roll-ups, wave ripples, fenestral pores, desiccation cracks, and tepee structures (Fig. 6A) are present locally. Lenses of blue to black displacive nodular chert 3 to 10 cm wide and 1 to 2 cm thick are relatively rare. Massive to crudely layered packstone to rudstone beds are 10 to 50 cm thick, with basal lags of dolomitic mudstone intraclasts up to 10 cm long (Fig. 6B). Laminated and cross-stratified medium to coarse quartzose sand constitutes up to 20% of the intraclast beds, and locally forms cross-bedded layers up to 0.5 m thick.

Although Precambrian stratiform microbial fabrics are interpreted to have formed in quiet environments in both shallow and deep water (Serebryakov and Semikhatov, 1974; Southgate, 1989; Sami and James, 1993) a quiet subtidal origin for this facies is discounted because of associated mudcracks and tepee structures (Shinn, 1986; Kendall and Warren, 1987) as well as abundant intraclasts and cross-bedded sandstone. Furthermore, smooth and tufted cryptomicrobial laminites are abundant in modern carbonate tidal flats (Shinn, 1986) and commonly recognized in ancient peritidal successions (Fischer, 1964; Grotzinger, 1986a; Pratt et al., 1992). The association of evaporites, dololaminites, and dolomudstone intraclasts is similar to that in Holocene shallowing-upwards sequences of the Persian Gulf (Purser and Evans, 1973). A low supratidal to high intertidal environment is therefore inferred for the dololaminite facies. Furthermore, the alternating microbial layers and thick, graded beds of mud and intraclasts resemble facies on unprotected tidal levees and beach ridges where microbial mats briefly reestablish themselves between episodes of storm deposition in modern supratidal environments (Shinn, 1986; Wanless et al., 1988).

The interpretation of a low supratidal to high intertidal environment is also supported by the interbedding of dololaminites with calcitic mudstones and grainstones, implying early fabric-specific or facies-specific dolomitization of carbonate mud in the supratidal subsurface (e.g., Persian Gulf; Patterson and Kinsman, 1982). Preservation of primary sedimentary structures is good, and coarse dolospar associated with later burial dolomitization is absent. The abundance of quartz and microcline sand further suggests proximity to a terrestrial source.

Molar-Tooth Mudstone Facies.—

The term "molar-tooth limestone" was first coined by Bauerman (1885) for lime mudstone in the Mesoproterozoic Belt–Purcell Supergroup, which contains sinuous vertical and horizontal sheet cracks and bubble-like pods, all filled with fine calcite spar. Molar-tooth structure in the upper Victor Bay Formation is dominated by ptygmatically folded synsedimentary fractures but pods are relatively rare (Fig. 7A–C). White- to medium-gray-weathering microspar crack-fill dissects a matrix of pale yellow to brownish-gray, argillaceous to dolomitic lime mudstone. Most cracks are subvertical, 1 to 10 mm wide, up to 50 cm deep, and commonly reach the top of the bed. Subhorizontal, microspar-filled sheet cracks are less common, and tend to be restricted to the muddy tops of graded beds. They locally account for up to 10% of beds by volume. As much as 75% by volume of beds can be composed of densely packed convoluted cracks; at the other end of the spectrum, short and simple spindle-shaped cracks make up less than 5% of some layers. Cracks occur in beds that are either (1) uniformly muddy, or (2) graded from a rudstone or packstone base to a mudstone top. Basal rudstone and packstone are composed of reworked particles of microspar identical to the molar-tooth crack-fill, with small amounts of quartzose sand and fine dololaminite clasts. Imbrication, compaction, and undulose shape of the microspar clasts

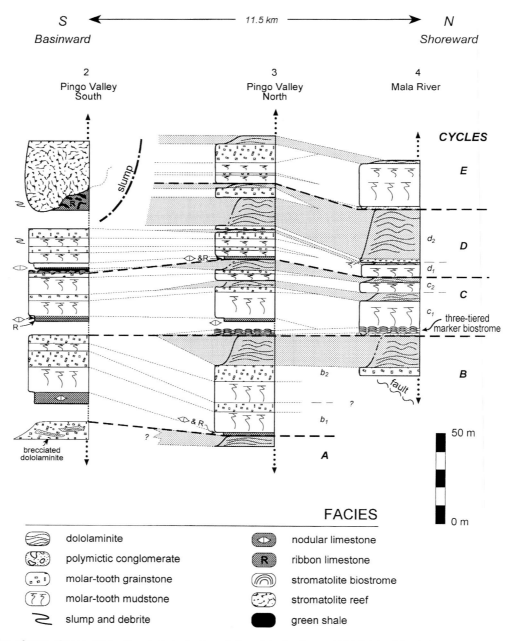

FIG. 5.—Correlation of parts of upper Victor Bay strata in Sections 2, 3, and 4, showing peritidal dololaminite facies (shaded) thinning to the south. See Figures 1B and 3 for regional context.

bestow a "welded" appearance to the coarser layers. Layers of finer, more equant fragments are locally cross-stratified. Bed bases range from planar to locally undulose where scours and small calcarenite dunes create relief on the order of 2 to 5 cm. Crack-fills can be truncated at scour surfaces, or protrude into the basal lag of the overlying bed. Bedding-plane expression of the cracks includes evenly spaced subparallel arrangements (Fig. 7D) to pseudo-polygonal networks. Polygonal networks are most common at the bases of molar-tooth mudstone packages, whereas subparallel cracks tend to occur towards the tops of the units. Where measured at Sections 2 and 3, subparallel

cracks have a consistent NW–SE orientation, parallel to the interpreted paleostrike of the platform. In the Victor Bay Formation, molar-tooth mudstone is consistently underlain by nodular limestone facies and overlain by molar-tooth calcarenite facies above (Sherman et al., 1997; James et al., 1998).

The depositional environment of molar-tooth mudstone is interpreted to be subtidal (James et al., 1998) on the basis of the shape of the cracks and their depositional context within the graded beds. Inclusion of crack-fill intraclasts in the molar-tooth storm beds, and truncated crack-fill, point to early precipitation of microspar in the fissures. Despite a variety of forms, molar-

TABLE 1.—SUMMARY OF LITHOFACIES AND INTERPRETED ENVIRONMENTS

Facies	Constituents	Bedding	Sedimentary Structures	Interpretation
Red shale	Red argillaceous mudstone, coarse quartz–microcline sand	Very thin to thin, weakly laminated	Desiccation cracks, gypsum nodules, sulfate moulds	High supratidal (coastal sabkha)
Dololaminite	Laminated dolomitic mudstone, sandy intraclast packstone to rudstone, layers of fine to coarse quartzose sand	Thin to medium; laminae 1–3 mm, smooth to crinkled, organic material concentrated in laminae; grading in intraclast packstone to rudstone	Tepee cracks and associated folds, desiccation cracks, small domal stromatolites, chert nodules, fenestral pores, roll-ups, wave ripples, cross-stratification in sandy layers	Low supratidal to intertidal (coastal sabkha to proximal inner ramp)
Molar-tooth calcarenite	Microspar intraclasts of medium sand to pebble size, fine to coarse quartzose sand, rare ooids, sparry cement	Thin to medium, 4–20 cm, locally lenticular	Planar lamination, scours, wave and ripple cross-lamination, HCS	Shallow subtidal (shoreface to foreshore; inner ramp)
Molar-tooth mudstone	Lime mudstone to dolomitic lime mudstone with ptygmatically folded microspar-filled cracks, rudstone to packstone of reworked crack-fill intraclasts	Thin to medium, up to 50 cm, bases planar to scoured and irregular, graded bedding in rudstone-to-mudstone couplets	Density of horizontal and vertical cracks 5–75%; local scours, rare cross-stratification and imbrication of microspar intraclasts in storm beds	Shallow subtidal (between storm and fair-weather wave base; mid-ramp)
Sandy polymictic conglomerate	Medium to coarse sand-size matrix of quartz, microcline and calcarenite, pebble- to cobble-size fragments of dololaminite intraclasts, stromatolites, and molar-tooth microspar	Medium beds up to 50 cm thick, with planar to scalloped, broadly scoured bases	Cross-stratification, scours, crude grading of clasts	Shallow subtidal (shoreface; inner ramp)
Nodular limestone	Calcite nodules in an argillaceous to dolomitic limestone matrix, debrites of nodular limestone.	Thin to medium, planar to undulose upper and lower surfaces of bed	Slumps, distorted beds	Deep subtidal (below storm wave base; proximal outer ramp)
Ribbon limestone	Couplets of lime mudstone and subequal layers (ribbon limestone) to thin seams (parted limestone) of argillaceous to dolomitic mudstone; debrites and breccias of ribbon limestone.	Thin, 2–4 cm couplets, microlamination in lime mudstone	Slump folds, synsedimentary breccias	Deep subtidal (below storm wave base; intermediate outer ramp)
Carbonaceous rhythmite	Dolospar/calcispar–carbonaceous shale couplets, bitumen-rich	Laminae 1–2 mm thick, beds 2–20 cm, locally undulose	Doming and warping of beds by creep, synsedimentary breccias	Deep subtidal (below storm wave base; intermediate outer ramp)
Dolomitic shale	Fissile black and dark gray shale, rare thin limestone flake breccias	Thin, with weak lamination	—	Deep subtidal (below storm wave base; distal outer ramp to basin)
Stromatolite biostrome	Columnar limestone stromatolites 1–5 cm wide, up to 50 cm tall, with gently to steeply convex laminae; inter-columnar sediment of stromaclasts, lime mud, quartzose sand, mudstone intraclasts; green shale cap	0.5–1.5 m thick biostromes with planar to undulose upper surface, mm-scale stromatolitic laminae, synoptic relief 1–4 cm	Elongation and inclination of columns	Shallow subtidal (inner ramp to mid-ramp)
Stromatolite reef	Columnar limestone to dolostone stromatolites 3–10 cm wide, up to 1 m tall with linked hemispherical to conical laminae; domal stromatolites 1–10 m in diameter	Bioherms up to 275 m thick, 1–2 km wide with flat to sloping upper surfaces	Elongation of columns on upper surface; talus blocks up to 40 m in height adjacent to southern (basinward) margin	Initial development in deep subtidal (usually outer ramp). Growth of largest reefs is maintained into shallow subtidal.

tooth structure never defines closed polygons on the surface of beds as do desiccation cracks. They are not diastasis cracks (Cowan and James, 1992), because they do not (1) have a brittle or fragmented appearance or (2) involve the overlying bed. Although molar-tooth cracks are morphologically similar to spindle-shaped synaeresis cracks, they do not contain detrital material as do fissures created by desiccation, diastasis, or synaeresis. Absence of cryptomicrobial fabrics and fenestrae, which are common in intertidal and supratidal facies, further supports an interpretation of subtidal deposition. Rudstone lags and scoured bases of graded beds are typical of tempestites and

point to deposition above storm wave base (Aigner, 1982). Predominance of mud in the tops of tempestite layers suggests that they are distal storm beds deposited below fair-weather wave base (Aigner, 1982; Dott and Bourgeois, 1982; Aigner, 1985).

Much debate has surrounded the origin of molar-tooth structure, and proposed mechanisms have included subaqueous shrinkage (Horodyski, 1976; Knoll and Swett, 1990), microbial action (Smith, 1968; O'Connor, 1972; Furniss et al., 1998), evaporite replacement (Eby, 1975), and seismicity (Fairchild et al., 1997; Pratt, 1998). Experimental work by Furniss et al. (1998) strongly suggests that coupled dewatering and gas es-

FIG. 6.—Field photographs of dololaminite facies, upper member of the Victor Bay Formation. A) Laminated dolomitic mudstone with tepee cracks overlain by bed of carbonate mudstone intraclast rudstone. Lens cap = 5.5 cm in diameter. B) Quartzose lag of dolomudstone intraclasts (dark with light clasts) overlain by laminated dolomitic mudstone (light). Lens cap = 5.5 cm in diameter.

cape in lime mud could account for vertical and horizontal sheet cracks in molar-tooth carbonates. In a $\delta^{13}C$ study of molar-tooth microspar, Frank and Lyons (1998) identify CO_2 degassing as a possible mechanism for seafloor precipitation of the microspar, and suggest that changes in salinity, temperature, water depth, and microbial uptake of CO_2 could have been responsible.

Molar-Tooth Calcarenite Facies.—

This facies consists of thin- to medium-bedded, massive to fining-upward molar-tooth-fragment rudstone, packstone, and grainstone with grain size ranging from 0.5 mm to 4 cm and averaging 1 to 2 mm. It is similar to the coarse lags at the bases of molar-tooth mudstone tempestites, but grains are better sorted and generally finer. Weathering color is medium to dark gray and fresh surfaces are dark gray. Particles are equant to platy microspar fragments with minor quartz sand and dolomitic mudstone intraclasts. Thin interlayers and lenses of lime mudstone (Fig. 8A) are similar to those associated with modern storm-current reactivation of subaqueous dunes (Shinn et al., 1993). Although generally rare, ooids are locally important and can represent from 5 to 35% of some beds (Harrington, 1995).

Physical sedimentary structures are wave ripples (Fig. 8B), dune and ripple cross-lamination, and rare hummocky cross-stratification (HCS; Harms et al., 1975; Harms, 1979). Diastasis cracks developed in the thin mudstone interlayers (Fig. 8A) often have a curlicue shape in plan view (Fig. 8C; cf. fig. 6D in Cowan and James, 1992). In rare cases, early cementation of calcarenite beds was followed by erosion, resulting in irregularly scoured surfaces with relief of up to 30 cm. These erosional surfaces bear a thin, centimeter-thick layer of laminated cement which is microstalactitic where it encrusts the underside of overhangs.

Wave- and storm-generated bedforms, coarse grain size, and low mud content of this lithofacies suggest that the sediments accumulated as proximal tempestites well above fair-weather wave base (Aigner, 1982; Dott and Bourgeois, 1982). Beds maintain constant thickness laterally and do not have lenticular shapes, large subaqueous dunes, or herringbone cross-bedding, features associated with tidal channels or migrating shoals. Grains have a mixed provenance, some transported from subtidal molar-tooth mudstone facies and the rest from intertidal to supratidal quartz-rich dololaminite facies. Abundant planar lamination is consistent with high-energy regime of modern storm-dominated shoreface settings (Greenwood and Sherman, 1986). Rare beds of early cemented, eroded, and subsequently encrusted calcarenite resemble beachrock (Ginsburg, 1953; Stoddart and Cann, 1965; and others) and suggest episodic subaerial exposure at the strandline.

Sandy Polymictic Conglomerate Facies.—

This conglomerate consists of pebble- to cobble-size dololaminite intraclasts, fragments of columnar stromatolites, and pieces of molar-tooth microspar (Fig. 8D). The matrix is (1) medium to coarse sand-size quartz and microcline, and (2) sand-size carbonate particles of molar-tooth microspar, dolomitic mudstone, and minor ooids. Beds are up to 50 cm thick, have planar to scalloped bases, and exhibit varying degrees of crude grading, planar lamination, cross-stratification, and convolute bedding.

The wide range of sources represented by different clast types suggests that the conglomeratic material was derived from erosion of all of the shallow-water facies described herein. The absence of mud and the high proportion of quartz and microcline suggest a high-energy depositional environment close to a terrestrial source of siliciclastic material. The conglomerate exhibits characteristics of both shoreface beach deposition (cross-stratification, planar lamination) and proximal tempestite accumulation (convolute bed tops, grading). The interpreted environment for this facies is a series of nearshore channels with rapid deposition of material.

Nodular Limestone Facies.—

This facies consists of dark-gray-weathering limestone nodules in a matrix of buff to brownish-gray dolomite, dolomitic limestone, or, rarely, dolomitic shale. Nodules are either (1) large and smooth-sided or (2) small and irregularly shaped (Fig. 9A). In cross section, smooth nodules have subcircular to elliptical shapes with sharply defined margins. They attain diameters of several tens of centimeters and have cross-sectional aspect ratios of up to 1:10. Irregular nodules are much smaller, with diameters of 1 to 2 cm and sharp to diffuse margins, giving the

FIG. 7.—Molar-tooth mudstone facies, upper member of the Victor Bay Formation. A) Sparse millimeter-scale crenulated cracks and small pods in mudstone bed. Note basal lag of crack-fill intraclast rudstone above sharp erosional surface (lower left, at fingertip). Scale bar = 5 cm. B) Cross-sectional view of large molar-tooth fractures creating a dense pattern in the mudstone matrix. Some cracks reach 50 cm in depth. Hammer = 35 cm long. C) Thin- to medium-bedded molar-tooth mudstone-to-rudstone tempestites. Note angular, scoured bases and numerous graded beds. Hammer (in vertical fracture at left) = 35 cm long. D) Bedding-plane view of molar-tooth cracks in dolomitic lime mudstone. A set of well-developed parallel fractures is associated with smaller perpendicular spindle-shaped cracks. Hammer = 35 cm long.

limestone a mottled appearance. Smooth-sided nodules are present everywhere, but irregular nodules occur only in shallow-water cycles. Nodules are included in muddy debrites up to 1 m thick, attesting to an early diagenetic origin for the nodules prior to transport. Slumped and dislocated nodular beds are common in the north of the study area and ubiquitous in the south.

It is generally agreed that suspension settling of lime mud swept offshore by storm or wave action creates fine-grained carbonate deposits in deep subtidal waters on the proximal outer slope, below storm wave base (Bathurst, 1975; Mullins et al., 1980; Müller and Kvingan, 1988). Early cementation of this lime mud results in partial to complete layer lithification. The preponderance of mud to the exclusion of other grain sizes and lack of wave- or storm-generated sedimentary structures in this Victor Bay lithofacies also suggests subtidal deposition below storm wave base. Slumping and accumulation of nodule-bearing debrite sheets indicate a slope and the accommodation afforded by deep subtidal slope environments, as in Holocene slope nodular periplatform ooze (Mullins et al., 1980) and ancient slope nodular limestones (Cook and Mullins, 1983; Müller and Kvingan, 1988).

Ribbon and Parted Limestone Facies.—

A ribbon-like appearance is imparted to this facies by subequal couplets of limestone and argillaceous carbonate. Thin, continuous layers of dark gray lime mudstone 1 to 2 cm thick are separated by equal thicknesses of less resistant buff-weathering argillaceous to dolomitic limestone. Also included in this facies is parted limestone (Coniglio and Dix, 1992) in which lime mudstone layers are thicker than the argillaceous layers by a factor of 2:1. Locally beds can be traced into slump folds and/or mosaic to rubble floatbreccia (Morrow, 1982) with clasts of lime mud derived from the ribbon limestone (Fig. 9B). T_{c-e} and T_{de} calciturbidites (Bouma, 1962) occur as rare interbeds, and dolosiltite with HCS fabric is present at one locality. This facies is also associated with columnar stromatolite bioherms, and can be traced laterally into the flanks of these carbonate buildups.

Alternation of limy and argillaceous beds as in ribbon or parted limestone arises from the combination of the primary sedimentation signal and late cementation of carbonate layers (Hallam, 1986; Coniglio and James, 1990). Plate-like ribbon limestone clasts in upper Victor Bay debrites attest to early cementation of lime mud layers in an environment prone to

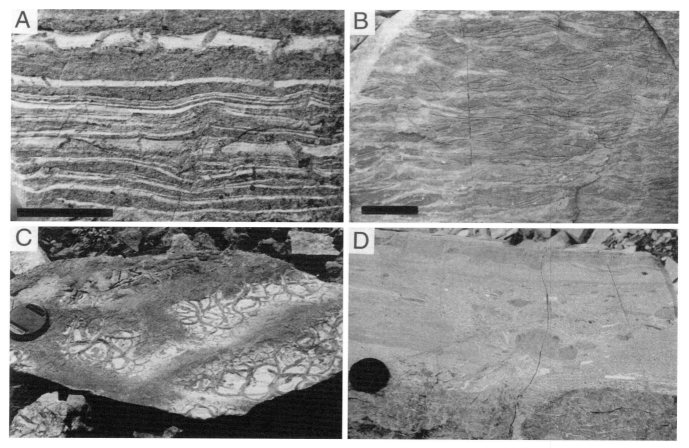

FIG. 8.—Molar-tooth calcarenite facies and sandy polymictic conglomerate facies, upper member, Victor Bay Formation. A) Diastasis cracks in lime mudstone (light) between thin beds of molar-tooth calcarenite (dark). Scale bar = 5 cm. B) Thick package of wave ripples in molar-tooth calcarenite. Scale bar = 5 cm. C) Bedding-plane view of rippled molar-tooth intraclast grainstone to packstone. Mud drapes in ripple troughs display curlicue diastasis cracks. Lens cap = 5.5 cm in diameter. D) Sandy polymictic conglomerate facies with large columnar stromatolite fragments. Lens cap = 5.5 cm in diameter.

resedimentation, as do the turbidites. Influence of waves or storms is not evident. This ribbon limestone is likely the deeper, more completely cemented equivalent of the nodular limestone facies (Bathurst, 1975; Mullins et al., 1980). Similar rock types in modern and ancient deposits are interpreted as hemipelagic periplatform deposits, common in slope environments below storm wave base and which represent fallout deposits of distal slope origin (Cook and Mullins, 1983; Coniglio and Dix, 1992).

Carbonaceous Rhythmite Facies.—

A "pinstriped" appearance is imparted to this lithofacies by alternating millimeter-scale layers of limestone/dolostone and carbonaceous shale. Weathering colors are dark brown and buff; fresh surfaces are black and gray and have a strong bituminous odor. Brittle and soft-sediment deformation is apparent in the form of abundant slump features and pinch-and-swell structures (Fig. 9C). Carbonaceous rhythmite units are generally less than 1 m thick and usually intercalated with ribbon and nodular limestone. These rhythmites occur almost exclusively in the southern part of the study area.

Synsedimentary deformation and fracturing of the laminae in the carbonaceous rhythmite indicate the presence of a slope, whereas the absence of wave- or current-formed sedimentary

structures suggests deposition in a zone of deep water. The millimeter-scale laminae record periodic alternation between organic-matter-dominated and carbonate-mud-dominated sedimentation, and likely represent higher-frequency events (Wetzel, 1991) than the centimeter-scale ribbon limestone couplets. It is inferred that, as a whole, the carbonaceous rhythmite facies represents deposition during a time of high organic productivity. Periodic, perhaps seasonal, decreases in productivity are defined by laminae of relatively organic-poor carbonate mud derived from suspension settling of storm-borne platformal mud (Bathurst, 1975; Mullins et al., 1980; Müller and Kvingan, 1988).

Dolomitic Shale Facies.—

This greenish-gray to buff-gray weathering dolomitic shale crops out as units less than a few meters thick and is a minor constituent by volume of the upper member. It is fissile to platy and recessively weathering, with a weak lamination visible on black to dark gray fresh surfaces. It is interlayered with nodular and ribbon carbonate, and at some localities with thin debrites containing millimeter-thick ribbon limestone and shale clasts.

The environment of deposition was quiet, and either received or accumulated very little carbonate sediment. Unlike the car-

FIG. 9.—Deep-water and stromatolitic facies, upper member of the Victor Bay Formation. A) Irregular nodular limestone interbedded with thin ribbon limestone and beds of smooth, elongate nodules. Hammer = 35 cm. B) Ribbon and parted limestone beds showing synsedimentary slumping and brecciation of some beds (right side of photograph). Lens cap = 5.5 cm in diameter. C) Carbonaceous rhythmite showing soft-sediment deformation and brittle synsedimentary fracturing. Scale graduated in millimeters. D–F) Stromatolitic facies. D) Small upright to inclined columnar stromatolites with gently to steeply convex laminae. Lens cap = 5.5 cm in diameter. E) Stromatolites in D have developed on a bed of sandy intraclast rudstone to form a three-tiered biostrome 1.5 m thick and with a lateral extent of at least 20 km. Person for scale (circled at right). F) Stromatolite reef facies in the lower 170-m-thick biostrome (top and base indicated by arrows) at Section 2 (see Figure 1B), composed of laminated domes 1–10 m in diameter, and columnar stromatolites 3–10 cm in diameter with conical to convex laminae. Scale bar = 100 m.

bonaceous rhythmites, no regular millimeter-scale laminae are discernible and the relative proportion of organic material is much lower. A basinal to distal slope environment is suggested by the lack of shallow-water sedimentary structures, and by its association with other deep-water facies (Potter et al., 1980). This interpretation is supported by the high degree of similarity between this facies and the deep-water shales of the lower Victor Bay member (Jackson and Iannelli, 1981; Iannelli, 1992).

Stromatolitic Facies.—

Apart from smooth laminae in the dololaminite facies, microbial structures are relatively rare in the upper member. They occur in two principal guises: (1) as columnar forms in thin, meter-scale biostromes and (2) as columns and large domal stromatolites in large decameter- to hectometer-scale reefs.

*Meter-Scale Biostrome Facies.—*These limestone biostromes are 0.5 to 1.5 m thick and composed of columnar stromatolites with gently to steeply convex laminae (Fig. 9D). Columns, typically 5 to 15 cm tall, are nucleated on shallow-water deposits of dololaminite intraclast conglomerate, sandy polymictic conglomerate facies, or molar-tooth calcarenite facies. Carbonate mudstone intraclasts, quartzose sand, and molar-tooth microspar clasts are present as coarse intercolumnar sediment. Rarely, stromatolite biostromes can be traced laterally into coarse polymictic conglomerate composed of cobbles of columnar stromatolites and other shallow-water lithoclasts. The most extensive and thickest biostrome is a distinctive three-tiered marker unit up to 3 m thick (Fig. 9E). It is composed of inclined to vertical nonbranching columnar stromatolites 3 to 5 cm wide and 5 to 20 cm long. In the basal tier, the stromatolites define domes 1 to 1.5 m wide with surface relief of 0.3 to 0.5 m. The stromatolite columns become narrower and more uniformly vertical in the upper tiers, although they collectively preserve the domal shape. In plan view, stromatolite columns at the top of the biostrome are elongated roughly perpendicular to the inferred paleostrike of the ramp. Elongation is most pronounced on the flanks of domes and less distinct on the crests. Coarse intercolumnar sediment consists of stromaclasts (*sensu* Sami and James, 1994), molar-tooth microspar clasts, and fine quartzose sand. Unlaminated green dolomitic shale is present as thin drapes on some biostrome tops where it is locally interlayered with nodular limestone and/or dolomitic shale facies.

Modern stromatolites accrete in the photic zone, and this is also assumed to be the case in most ancient successions. Coarse intercolumnar sediment in meter-scale biostromes and elongation of columns suggest presence of a persistent current (Hoffman, 1976; Horodyski, 1976). A shallow subtidal environment is therefore interpreted for the stromatolites. The abrupt transition into the overlying deep-water facies indicates that deepening to below storm wave base had occurred by the time shale and nodular limestone facies were deposited.

*Stromatolite Reefs.—*Stromatolite buildups up to 275 m in thickness (Geldsetzer, 1973; Jackson and Ianelli, 1989; Narbonne and James, 1996) occur over several tens of kilometers of outcrop length. In the study area, intervals of reef growth are associated with two deepening events, and define the tops of the two stratigraphic packages (Fig. 3A). In the northwest of the study area (Section 2), the lower buildup is 170 m thick (Fig. 9F) and the upper buildup is 60 m thick. The composition of the reefs varies from dolostone to limestone, and two principal fabrics are recognized: domes 1–10 m in diameter with smooth to crinkled stratiform laminae, and columnar forms 3–10 cm in width with hemispherical to conical laminae. Columnar stromatolites on the uppermost surface of the lower reef have a strongly elongate shape in transverse section, suggesting that they were constructed under the influence of currents that flowed roughly perpendicular to the inferred ramp paleostrike. In the study area, these reefs occur in a narrow, 1–2 km strip where they separate shallow-water strata to the NE from deep-water strata to the SW. This reef-tract zone contains evidence of slope instability: an olistostrome several tens of meters thick extends for at least a kilometer at the base of the reefs and contains blocks several tens of cubic meters in volume. The reef appears to have nucleated on the blocks, and the stromatolites at the base of the reef can be followed laterally into ribbon limestone facies. In the east of the study area (Section 7; Fig. 1B), the dolomitized upper buildup is flanked by overturned, decameter-scale reef blocks, suggesting that the reef had developed substantial vertical relief before it was mantled by deep-water strata of the overlying Athole Point Formation.

It appears that the stromatolite reefs developed at least initially in deep water, coevally with deposition of deep subtidal ribbon limestone facies. Current-elongation of stromatolites at the top of the reef at Section 2, however, suggests that it must have eventually built up into shallow water (Hoffman, 1976; Horodyski, 1976).

DEPOSITIONAL ATTRIBUTES OF THE VICTOR BAY FORMATION

Regional Stratigraphy and Correlations within the Upper Member

Correlation of Victor Bay strata in the study area indicates thinning of the carbonate upper member to the southwest together with slight thickening of the shaly lower member (Fig. 3). Upper member lithofacies are packaged into shallowing-upwards cycles 20 to 50 m thick that are classified on the basis of the capping lithofacies (idealized cycles of Fig. 3): (1) peritidal cycles, capped by dololaminite or red shale, and containing molar-tooth calcarenite and molar-tooth mudstone; (2) shallow subtidal cycles topped by molar-tooth calcarenite and dominated by molar-tooth mudstone; and (3) deep-water cycles dominated by nodular and ribbon limestone facies. The upper member is divided into two main packages that can be correlated across the axis of the Milne Inlet Trough (Fig. 3). The base of the lower package contains peritidal cycles in the north that gradually deepen southward into subtidal cycles (Fig. 5) and eventually deep-water cycles in the south. In the upper half of the package, the 170-m-thick stromatolite bioherm occupies the transition between peritidal and deep-water cycles. This buildup is capped by current-elongated stromatolites that pass laterally into a sandy polymictic conglomerate above the peritidal cycles to the north. Deep-water dolomitic shale overlies the reef and the conglomerate, defining a flooding event at the base of the second package. This upper package consists everywhere of peritidal cycles, and is capped by a 60-m-thick stromatolite reef and its laterally equivalent deep-water strata.

The lower package is analogous to sequences identified in the upper Victor Bay Formation by Narbonne and James (1996) in the Strathcona River reef complex, located 60 km NW of the study area. There, a mid-ramp, subreef sequence is overlain by a wedge-shaped stromatolite biostrome (first reefal sequence). This biostrome is capped by a karst surface and overlain by a second reefal sequence. The morphology of the wedge-shaped reef and the abundance of grainstones in the subreef sequence are similar to the lower package of Section 2 (Fig. 3). The first reefal sequence at Strathcona River, however, is coeval with deep-water lithofacies and ends at a karst surface. The lack of shallow-water lithofacies in off-reef strata, together with karsting of the Strathcona reefs, point to a tectonic mechanism for rapid exposure and flooding events (Narbonne and James, 1996). The regional differences in the character of sequences across the Borden Peninsula suggest that local block tectonics might have been important (Jackson and Iannelli, 1981; Iannelli, 1992).

Carbonate Platform Architecture

The distribution and geometry of upper Victor Bay lithofacies indicate deposition on a ramp rather than a platform or shelf, because there is no sharp declivity or platform margin, and shallow-water facies pass gradually offshore into outer-slope and basinal strata (Ahr, 1973; Burchette and Wright, 1992). Gradual thinning of shallow-water strata can be walked out and traced visually in outcrop. This exceptional transect from NE to SW, through the transition from inner ramp to mid-ramp, clearly shows wedges of peritidal dololaminite facies passing basinward into laterally equivalent subtidal molar-tooth calcarenite facies (Fig. 5).

Muddy, tempestite-bearing ramps are considered to be low-wave-energy, microtidal, storm-dominated settings (Burchette and Wright, 1992). Because the influence of tides and waves is negligible, waters on these ramps are calm, except during episodic storm events that remobilize fine material and fragment lithified units into intraclasts. As a whole, the upper Victor Bay carbonate ramp consists by volume of 60 to 90% lime mudstone facies. Virtually mud-free molar-tooth calcarenite facies, however, attests to efficient winnowing in the inner ramp, perhaps by breaking waves in the littoral zone. All Victor Bay peritidal cycles contain at least a few meters of molar-tooth calcarenite facies, which inevitably separate subtidal molar-tooth mudstone tempestites from the peritidal dololaminites. The slight topographic relief afforded by sheets of brecciated carbonate might have protected an inner-ramp tidal flat (e.g., Fairchild et al., 1997). In the study area, however, such a thin bank or accumulation of molar-tooth calcarenite facies was insufficient to protect the intertidal and supratidal zones against storm waves (Fig. 10).

The relationship between reefs and platformal strata in the study area gives insight into the effect of the reefs on inshore sedimentation. Storm bedding is no less abundant in shallow-water strata that are coeval with reef growth than it is in those strata deposited at a time when no reefs were present. This suggests that these bioherms did not form a barrier complex and that they were ineffective in damping waves or storms to the shallow inshore waters. These buildups are nucleated on slumps and deep-water strata in a context similar to that of the reefs in the Strathcona River area (Narbonne and James, 1996).

Ramps are traditionally subdivided into inner, middle, and outer ramp, where the mid-ramp is bracketed by fair-weather wave base inshore and storm wave base offshore (Burchette and Wright, 1992). On the Victor Bay ramp, interpreted inner-ramp facies include molar-tooth calcarenite, dololaminite, and red shale facies. Molar-tooth mudstone distal tempestites occupy the mid-ramp, whereas nodular limestone, ribbon and parted limestone, and carbonaceous rhythmite constitute facies on the sloping outer ramp. Deposition of dolomitic shale is interpreted to have occurred at the transition from distal outer ramp to basin. Geographic distribution of these facies suggests a minimum width for the inner ramp of 10 km, a mid-ramp of approximately 5 km, and an outer ramp more than 20 km wide (Fig. 10).

Clasts in thick debrites of the upper Victor Bay generally belong to outer-ramp facies, suggesting distal steepening in the outer ramp (Read, 1982, 1985). The inflection might have been (1) created by rapid aggradation of the upper Victor Bay ramp, (2) partly inherited from the underlying Society Cliffs Formation, or (3) caused by synsedimentary block faulting at the transition from mid-ramp to outer ramp. Previous workers (Jackson and Ianelli, 1981; Jackson and Sangster, 1987; Ianelli, 1992) mapped a zone of southwest-dipping normal faults which coincides with the position of the reef tract and which might have been the locus of synsedimentary faulting. Alternatively, instability of the outer ramp could have been related to rapid accumulation of lime mud exported to deep water by storm currents, especially during times of high carbonate productivity (Droxler and Schlager, 1985; Milliman et al., 1993).

Controls on the Distribution of Carbonate Sediment Particles

The proportion and type of sedimentary components in the inner-ramp, mid-ramp, and outer-ramp environments of the Victor Bay Formation reflect hydrodynamic conditions (Fig. 10). In tidal flats and calcarenite banks, the inner ramp contains an overall volume of mud (~50%) similar to mid-ramp molar-tooth tempestites, but the types of grains are quite different. Molar-tooth microspar intraclasts are the only significant component in the mid-ramp, whereas dololaminite intraclasts, terrigenous sand, and, to a lesser degree, molar-tooth spar intraclasts and ooids are all significant in the coarse fraction of inner-ramp lithofacies. The molar-tooth calcarenite facies, as a subset of the inner-ramp environment, contains little mud, usually in the form of thin drapes, and is interpreted to represent high-energy shoreface and shallow subtidal deposition above fair-weather wave base. Below fair-weather wave base, the proportion of gravel- and sand-size grains decreases rapidly. With the exception of the stromatolite bioherm facies, lime mud and debrites of early lithified lime mudstone make up almost all outer-ramp facies.

Lime Mud.—

*Distribution.—*Lime mud is the principal carbonate sediment in all ramp lithofacies except molar-tooth calcarenite. The high intertidal–low supratidal zone of the inner ramp (dololaminite facies), and the shallow to deep subtidal mid- to outer ramp are at least 50% lime mud. On the inner-ramp tidal flats, the fine sediment settled out after storm events. In the mid-ramp, degassing, dewatering, and stiffening of muds (Furniss et al., 1998) might have prevented to some degree the erosion of fine-grained carbonate by waves or storms. Storm suspension and offshore transport into deep water probably contributed mud to the outer ramp.

*Origin.—*Production of lime mud in the Proterozoic most likely arises from direct precipitation of $CaCO_3$ in the water column (Grotzinger, 1989, 1990; Knoll and Swett, 1990) in a manner analogous to modern-day marine whitings (Shinn et al., 1989; Robbins and Blackwelder, 1992). Metabolic and degradational processes involving microbes and organic matter in the water

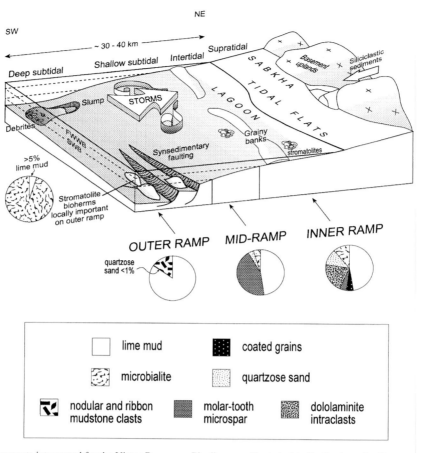

FIG. 10.—Depositional environments interpreted for the Victor Bay ramp. Pie diagrams illustrate the distribution of sediment components on the inner, middle, and outer ramp. Abundance of lime mud remains roughly the same in the inner and mid-ramp but increases below storm wave base in the outer ramp. Lime mud and mud-generated intraclasts together form no less than 75% and as much as 100% of sediment components across the ramp. An exception is the locally important accumulation of microbialites in large deep-water stromatolite buildups. Abundances of sedimentary particles, represented in the pie diagrams, are based on a visual estimate of the composition of each lithofacies; this estimate is used to derive an average abundance, which is weighted on (1) the total lithofacies thickness in the study area, and (2) its volumetric importance in each of the three ramp zones. FWWB = fair-weather wave base, SWB = storm wave base.

column can promote micrite precipitation (Robbins and Black-welder, 1992), and this mechanism has been postulated to generate vast amounts of lime mud in today's oceans. On Great Bahama Bank, the volume of mud suspended in modern whitings can account for almost three times the bank-top accumulation (Robbins et al., 1997). Furthermore, whitings occur today in seas that are less saturated in $CaCO_3$ than Proterozoic oceans, suggesting that a similar source of micrite was of great importance in Precambrian carbonate systems (Grotzinger, 1989; Knoll and Swett, 1990; Grotzinger and Kasting, 1993). Once formed, this detrital micrite was deposited in low-energy peritidal areas or was swept offshore by storms, accumulating in slope and basinal environments (e.g., Sami and James, 1996). It is conceivable that at a time of relatively high carbonate saturation in marine waters (Grotzinger, 1989; Herrington and Fairchild, 1989) this mechanism could have supplied most of the lime mud to all upper Victor Bay ramp facies, from inner ramp to distal outer ramp. The inner-ramp and mid-ramp waters adjacent to an arid, evaporitic margin at low latitude must have been a zone of high precipitation of lime mud, in view of the warm water temperatures and the added effect of prolific or-

ganic productivity associated with those warm waters. In contrast, presumably colder offshore water above the outer ramp might not have fostered as high a rate of precipitation. The rhythmic packaging of carbonate mud in those deeper-water lithofacies (e.g., nodular and ribbon limestone) might therefore reflect episodic storm influx of hemipelagic mud to the outer ramp, rather than fluctuations in the rate of carbonate mud production on the ramp. In shallow subtidal environments, lime mud was deposited in the zone of carbonate production as caps on molar-tooth tempestites, perhaps locally bound by microbial films. Mudstone intraclasts are not found in tempestite lags, suggesting that in the molar-tooth mudstone facies early lithification of microspar crack-fill and did not extend to the muddy matrix.

Grains.—

Distribution.—The grainiest deposits in the Victor Bay ramp occur in inner-ramp facies that were most affected by fair-weather and storm wave conditions. Grain types are diverse, including dololaminite intraclasts, molar-tooth microspar, quartzose sand, and rare ooids. The diversity and abundance of coarse particles tapers off towards the mid-ramp. There, grains are almost exclusively molar-tooth microspar and are restricted to the bases of molar-tooth tempestites. Coarse slope-derived conglomerates of remobilized, early lithified nodular, ribbon, and parted limestone facies occur well below storm wave base on the outer ramp.

Origin.—The shallow-water agitated zone acted as a repository for clasts produced and brought shoreward by storms, but was not a zone of production of grains such as ooids. All three types of coarse carbonate material—molar-tooth grains, dololaminite intraclasts and slope conglomerate fragments—are derived from reworked muddy lithofacies. Early lithified dololaminite tidal-flat facies provided the material for storm-generated intraclasts (cf. Shinn, 1983). Whereas these clasts were formed by storm erosion of existing bedding-parallel crusts, molar-tooth grains were released from a casing of unlithified mud during storm events. This is analogous to winnowed coarse skeletal grains from a packstone or muddy rudstone matrix (James et al., 1998). According to Furniss et al. (1998), molar-tooth-like cracks are produced in modern sediments, and early microspar precipitation in the synsedimentary cracks is the key to their preservation in late Proterozoic strata (James et al., 1998). Thus, were it not for microspar precipitation with such shallow subtidal molar-tooth mudstone facies, carbonate grains on the Victor Bay ramp would be limited to mostly dololaminite intraclasts and deep-water debrite clasts, with some ooids.

The scarcity of ooids in shallow-water facies supports a microtidal model for the Victor Bay ramp. In modern carbonate platforms and ramps, strong tidal currents and fair-weather waves rework sediments and lead to the formation of ooid-filled tidal channels and bars (e.g., Persian Gulf; Purser and Evans, 1973). Ooids are rare on the Victor Bay ramp, despite an ample supply of suitable nuclei such as molar-tooth calcarenite grains. Interestingly, they are locally abundant in calcarenite units underlying equally rare stromatolitic intervals, or in units of polymictic conglomerate that also contain stromatolite clasts. The association of ooids and stromatolites in shallow-water facies of the Victor Bay ramp indicates that they require a common set of environmental conditions to develop. Experimental work points to the significant influence of microbial films on the formation and continued growth of ooids (Davies et al., 1978; Ferguson et al., 1978). Perhaps episodic decreases in micrite production in the shallow subtidal environment of the Victor Bay ramp fostered the development of microbial films and led to an increase in benthic precipitates in the form of ooids and stromatolites.

Microbialites and Cements.—

Distribution.—Microbial structures on the Victor Bay ramp are neither abundant nor consistently present in shallow-water cycles. Crinkly stratiform microbialites of the dololaminite facies are an important exception, but they are usually overlain by thick beds of intraclast- and sand-rich tempestites. Where present, columnar and domal stromatolites are associated with rapid creation of accommodation space and with a hard or grainy substrate suitable for nucleation. Small columnar stromatolites nucleated on shallow-water grainstones or rudstones at the tops of a few cycles, and grew as space was made available by rapid rises in sea level. The extensive mid-ramp bioherms are also an anomalous facies, because they are the by-product of slope failure at the mid- to outer-ramp slope break. The deep amphitheaters of slump scars provided growth space, and lithified slump blocks were suitable for nucleation of stromatolites. The only other thick bioherms in the upper member developed as water depth increased rapidly at the contact with the deep-water shale of the Athole Point Formation. In either case, whether by slope failure or by relative sea-level rise, stromatolite bioherms grew to significant thicknesses only when accommodation space was rapidly increasing.

Origin.—Stromatolites, lithified supratidal mats, and inorganically precipitated crusts and fans are classic components of early Paleoproterozoic platformal successions. The decline of stromatolite abundance throughout the Proterozoic (Awramik, 1971; Walter and Heys, 1985; Grotzinger, 1990) was well underway by Mesoproterozoic time, as the conditions favorable to microbial benthic precipitation became less widespread. In the Victor Bay Formation these conditions were rare in shallow environments but did occur in deeper water where they fostered the development of impressive stromatolitic reefs.

Growth of Victor Bay stromatolites always coincided with a rapid increase in depth, and nucleated on hard or grainy substrates. For example, the three-tiered marker biostrome (Fig. 9E) is nucleated on planar-bedded shallow-water conglomerates and achieved synoptic relief of a few decimeters. It is directly overlain by subtidal facies, either calcareous shale and nodular limestone, or by argillaceous molar-tooth mudstone. Similarly, the largest stromatolitic reefs accumulated on lithified slump blocks of deep-water ribbon limestones and are mantled by dolomitic shale or more ribbon limestone. Judging from the development of thick reefs in the upper member, once stromatolites gained a toehold they had the potential to maintain their growth and coexist with muddy mid- to inner-ramp facies, as demonstrated by the interfingering of mid-ramp reefs with molar-tooth mudstone, molar-tooth grainstone, and dololaminite facies. The reef complex might have, by virtue of its sheer size, provided patches of firm substrate even at times of abundant mud production. It is possible that in shallow water the generally high rate of water-column mud production might have limited benthic microbial cementation either by blocking the penetration of light onto the seafloor or by maintaining a soft, inhospitable substrate, thus preventing the nucleation of columnar stromatolites. The benthic microbialites tend therefore to occur when water-column mud production decreased across the entire ramp with the influx of transgressive waters. Such carbonate-starved waters (Berger et al., 1981) might have promoted a decrease in turbidity, fostering blooms of benthic photosynthetic microbes where sunlight penetration to the seafloor was increased. Alternatively, a differing chemistry of the transgressive waters could have initiated a shift between benthic and water-column precipitation. For example, the presence of inhibitors such as Fe^{2+} could have inhibited water-column precipitation of calcite and promoted the growth of benthic carbonate, as Sumner and Grotzinger (1996) have proposed for the Archean and early Proterozoic.

A Mud-Dominated Carbonate Factory.—

Primary and secondary carbonate production on the Victor Bay ramp was entirely controlled by the production and distribution of lime mud on the ramp. Most lithofacies were mud-dominated, and by virtue of its stiffening and early lithification in the inner ramp and mid-ramp, lime mud was the source of essentially all carbonate grains, including outer-ramp resedimented limestones. The only carbonate lithofacies not dominated by either mud or grains are stromatolitic, and these are volumetrically minor. Abundance of clastic carbonate mud and development of shallow-water stromatolite–ooid associations appear to be mutually exclusive. This suggests that if carbonate mud production had been much less important on the Victor Bay ramp, not only would molar-tooth mudstones and molar-tooth calcarenite facies have been absent, but subtidal stromatolites and ooids would have been ubiquitous.

DISCUSSION

Comparison with Ancient and Modern Carbonate Platforms

Archean and Paleoproterozoic.—

The record of Archean carbonate deposition is relatively sparse, but evidence from preserved remnants suggests that extensive platforms had evolved by late Archean time (Grotzinger, 1989). Paleoproterozoic carbonate platforms developed a range of profiles, from ramps to rimmed platforms (Grotzinger, 1989). What characterizes both Archean and Paleoproterozoic carbonate platforms of all types is an overall abundance of *in situ* cement textures and stromatolites. Microbially mediated and inorganically precipitated cements are ubiquitous, occur in various forms (Grotzinger and Read, 1983; Hofmann and Jackson, 1987; Sami and James, 1996), and span the entire facies spectrum across both ramps and platforms. Carbonate mud derived from the water column was a significant sedimentary component only below storm wave base or in peritidal complexes in the Paleoproterozoic (e.g., Pethei Platform; Sami and James, 1994, 1996), and was deposited contemporaneously with microbialites. Carbonate mud is the principal sedimentary component across the Victor Bay ramp (Fig. 10), but its occurrence is antithetical to that of stromatolitic facies. Extrinsic factors such as the postulated secular decrease in seawater carbonate concentration (Grotzinger, 1990; Knoll and Swett, 1990) might have impeded the development of microbialites on the Victor Bay ramp.

Mesoproterozoic and Neoproterozoic.—

The apparent global decline in stromatolites in the Mesoproterozoic and Neoproterozoic (Awramik, 1971; Grotzinger, 1990) has been explained as resulting from lower concentrations of carbonate in sea water. The relegation of benthic carbonate precipitates to restricted intertidal to supratidal environments was well under way by late Mesoproterozoic time (Kah and Knoll, 1996). Low ramp profile, abundance of lime mud, and presence of molar-tooth mudstone facies are features shared by other mid- and late Proterozoic carbonate platforms. Neoproterozoic carbonate platforms with abundant molar-tooth limestone and ramp tempestites, such as the Shaler Group (Young, 1974, 1981), Akademikerbreen Group (Knoll and Swett, 1990); Canyon Formation (Fairchild, 1989; Fairchild and Herrington, 1989; Herrington and Fairchild, 1989), Xinmincun Formation of China (Fairchild et al., 1997), and Wonoka Formation of Australia (Haines, 1988; James et al., 1998) all attest to the overall shift from cement-rich rimmed platforms to muddy storm-dominated ramps, a trend that began in the latest Paleoproterozoic and early Mesoproterozoic. Stromatolite-poor cyclic successions in the Wallace (Grotzinger, 1986b) and correlative Helena–Siyeh formations of the Belt–Purcell Supergroup (O'Connor, 1972; Winston and Lyons, 1993) indicate that by 1.4–1.3 Ga the conditions on muddy ramps rich in molar-tooth lithofacies were not conducive to extensive stromatolite accumulation in shallow subtidal waters.

Society Cliffs Formation.—

A great contrast in facies exists even within the Uluksan Group, between the shallow-water Society Cliffs Formation and the upper Victor Bay member. Both ramp types encompass roughly similar marine environments and are interpreted to have developed in arid climates (Jackson and Iannelli, 1981; Kah, 1997), but the proportion of sedimentary components is quite different (Kah, 1997; Sherman et al., 1997).

Society Cliffs facies associations range from marine shoreline to mid-ramp environments (Kah, 1997; Kah, this volume). Microbialites and isopachous cements dominate the inner ramp, which is separated from laminated and nodular dolostones of the mid-ramp by ooid and intraclast shoals. Inner-ramp facies interfinger shoreward with gypsum-bearing redbeds. In the study area, similar redbeds in the Victor Bay Formation (the red shale facies) interfinger with dololaminite facies and are not traceable into isopachous cement facies typical of the Society Cliffs inner ramp. Stromatolite-bearing ooid shoals in the Society Cliffs Formation were deposited under higher energy than the molar-tooth calcarenite banks or sand sheets of the Victor Bay ramp (Kah, 1997). The common presence of small columnar stromatolite bioherms in the Society Cliffs mid-ramp and inner ramp contrasts with their rarity in the same zones on the Victor Bay ramp. Conversely, the large deep-water reefs of the Victor Bay Formation have no equivalent in the Society Cliffs ramp.

In both Society Cliffs and upper Victor Bay Formations, stromatolites are associated with ooids, and formed at the bases of cycles at a time when the rate of increase in accommodation space was high. The relatively high abundance of stromatolites in the Society Cliffs Formation, however, suggests that conditions were favorable for the development and preservation of subtidal benthic precipitates (Kah and Knoll, 1996). Tellingly, Society Cliffs mid-ramp facies do not exhibit significant storm-controlled facies, perhaps because of a higher degree of seafloor cementation than on the Victor Bay ramp. In this sense, the Society Cliffs ramp is Paleoproterozoic in style, as further evidenced by the early-Proterozoic-style taphonomic conditions (Kah and Knoll, 1996) that dominated the high-intertidal to supratidal environments in the Society Cliffs ramp. That these two ramps were deposited in succession and under similar paleogeographic conditions and yet differ so strongly in carbonate constituents suggests that the late Mesoproterozoic was a time of carbonate platform diversity, where the spectrum had broadened to include both Paleoproterozoic-style and Phanerozoic-style carbonate depositional systems.

Phanerozoic.—

The absence of molar-tooth facies in the Phanerozoic is attributed to the lack of early microspar precipitation in voids created by dewatering and degassing of muds, and to the destruction of cracks by burrowing macrobiota (Furniss et al.,

1998). Nonetheless, sediment dynamics in the upper member of the Victor Bay are more similar to those of muddy Phanerozoic ramps than they are to those of most Paleoproterozoic carbonate platforms. Despite the absence of shelly macrofossils in the late Proterozoic, molar-tooth crack-fill grains can be considered analogous to skeletal allochems in that they form the coarse fraction of molar-tooth tempestites (James et al., 1998). Low-energy, storm-affected, and muddy, the Victor Bay Formation shares features with carbonate ramps that accreted when development of skeletal reefs was at an ebb in the Phanerozoic (see review in Burchette and Wright, 1992).

SYNTHESIS

The distribution of Victor Bay carbonate facies and their principal components hinges on the abundance of lime mud in the water column and its early diagenesis on the seafloor. Turbidity, substrate availability and consistency, and formation of carbonate grains are all governed by the presence or absence of micrite in the water column. The microtidal nature of the Victor Bay ramp and the strong influence of storms on sedimentation in the middle to inner ramp ultimately dictated the distribution of mud and therefore the production of grains. The transfer of most carbonate production from the seafloor to the water column in the Mesoproterozoic and Neoproterozoic drastically reduced the ability of microbial benthos to contribute to early cementation of the substrate. The surplus $CaCO_3$ eventually precipitated as the distinctive molar-tooth crack fill (James et al., 1998; Frank and Lyons, 1998).

The influence of water-column carbonate precipitation is understated in Phanerozoic carbonate systems, where it is overshadowed by metaphyte and metazoan carbonate production. In today's oceans, a significant volume of micrite forms in the water column (Robbins et al., 1997), but this contribution to the overall carbonate sediment budget pales in comparison to that of the late Precambrian water-column factory. Better understanding of the mechanisms that drive carbonate precipitation in the modern oceans will yield greater insight into the relationship between water-column micrite and the decline of microbialites in the Mesoproterozoic and Neoproterozoic.

SUMMARY

1) Abundance of mudstone-based lithofacies, and the distribution of tempestites and resedimented deep-water facies in the Victor Bay Formation, suggest that deposition occurred on a low-energy, microtidal, storm-dominated, distally steepened ramp.

2) Lime mud constitutes 50% to 90% by volume of upper Victor Bay lithofacies and is by far the primary sediment component from inner to outer ramp. It accumulated on the inner ramp as peritidal dololaminite facies, on the mid-ramp as molar-tooth mudstone facies, and on the outer ramp as nodular, ribbon, and parted limestone facies.

3) Storm-reworked muddy lithofacies were the principal source of grains in the inner ramp and mid-ramp, such as dololaminite intraclasts and molar-tooth microspar grains. Early cementation of mud in nodular and ribbon limestones provided clasts that were incorporated into slope debrites on the outer ramp.

4) The correlation of stromatolites to periods of decreased carbonate production and rapid creation of accommodation space points to an antithetical relationship between deposition of benthic microbial carbonate and precipitation of lime mud in the water column. Increased turbidity related to mud suspended in the water column, and the predominance of soft, muddy substrates, might have been inimical to nucleation and development of stromatolites.

5) The distribution of lithofacies in the Victor Bay ramp is recognized in rocks of similar age, which are also interpreted as low-energy, storm-dominated ramps with strong similarities to Phanerozoic ramps. Whereas the Victor Bay Formation lacks abundant ooids and shallow-water stromatolites, the underlying, lithologically contrasting Society Cliffs Formation is similar to older cement-, stromatolite-, and ooid-rich carbonate platforms of the Paleoproterozoic. This provides an example of the broadening spectrum of carbonate platform types in the late Mesoproterozoic.

ACKNOWLEDGMENTS

We thank P. N. Southgate, J. P. Grotzinger, E. C. Turner, R. B. MacNaughton, and an anonymous reviewer for constructive comments that greatly improved this manuscript. Excellent field assistance was provided by J. E. M. Harrington in 1994 and 1995. Financial support was provided through research grants to N. P. James and G. M. Narbonne from the Natural Sciences and Engineering Research Council of Canada, a Geological Society of America Research Grant and a Queen's Doctoral Travel Grant to A. G. Sherman, as well as Northern Studies Training Program grants to A. G. Sherman and J. E. M. Harrington. Logistical support from Breakwater Resources Ltd.–Nanisivik Mines and the Polar Continental Shelf Project was essential to the success of this research (PCSP publication no. 00299).

REFERENCES

AHR, W. M., 1973, The carbonate ramp: An alternative to the shelf model: Gulf Coast Association of Geological Societies, Transactions, 23rd Annual Convention, p. 221–225.

AIGNER, T., 1982, Calcareous tempestites: Storm dominated stratification in Upper Muschelkalk limestones (M. Trias, SW Germany), in Einsele, G., and Seilacher, A., eds., Cyclic and Event Stratigraphy: Berlin, Springer-Verlag, p. 180–198.

AIGNER, T., 1985, Storm Depositional Systems: Dynamic Stratigraphy in Modern and Ancient Shallow-Marine Sequences: Berlin, Springer-Verlag, 174 p.

AWRAMIK, S. M., 1971, Precambrian columnar stromatolite diversity: Reflection of metazoan appearance: Science, v. 147, p. 825–827.

BATHURST, R. G. C., 1975, Carbonate Sediments and Their Diagenesis, 2nd Edition: New York, Elsevier, 658 p.

BAUERMAN, H., 1885, Report on the geology of the country near the forty-ninth parallel of north latitude west of the Rocky Mountains: Geological Survey of Canada, Report on Progress 1882–1884, Part B, p. 1–42.

BERGER, W. H., VINCENT, E., AND THIERSTEIN, H. R., 1981, The deep-sea record: Major steps in Cenozoic ocean evolution, in Warme, J. E., Douglas, R. G., and Winterer, E. L., eds., The Deep Sea Drilling Project: A Decade of Progress: Society of Economic Paleontologists and Mineralogists, Special Publication 32, p. 489–504.

BLACKADAR, R. G., 1956, Geological reconnaissance of Admiralty Inlet, Baffin Island, Arctic Archipelago, Northwest Territories: Geological Survey of Canada, Paper 55-6, 25 p.

BLACKADAR, R. G., 1967, Precambrian geology of Boothia Peninsula, Somerset Island and Prince of Wales Island, District of Franklin (with maps): Geological Survey of Canada, Bulletin 151, 62 p.

BLACKADAR, R. G., 1970, Precambrian geology, northwestern Baffin Island, District of Franklin: Geological Survey of Canada, Bulletin 191, 89 p.

BOUMA, A. H., 1962, Sedimentology of Some Flysch Deposits: Amsterdam, Elsevier, 168 p.

BURCHETTE, T. P., AND WRIGHT, V. P., 1992, Carbonate ramp depositional systems: Sedimentary Geology, v. 79, p. 3–57.

CHANDLER, F. W., 1988, Geology of the late Precambrian Fury and Hecla Group, northwest Baffin Island, District of Franklin: Geological Survey of Canada, Bulletin 370, 30 p.

CHRISTIE, R. K. L., COOK, D. G., NASSICHUK, W. W., TRETTIN, H. P., AND YORATH, C. J., 1972, The Canadian Arctic Islands and the Mackenzie Region: 24th International Geological Congress, Guidebook for Excursion A-66, 146 p.

CONIGLIO, M., AND DIX, G. R., 1992, Carbonate Slopes, in Walker, R. G., and James, N. P., eds., Facies Models: Response to Sea Level Change: St. John's, Newfoundland, Geological Association of Canada, p. 349–373.

CONIGLIO, M., AND JAMES, N. P., 1990, Origin of fine-grained carbonate and siliciclastic sediments in an early Palaeozoic slope sequence, Cow Head Group, western Newfoundland: Sedimentology, v. 37, p. 215–230.

COOK, H. E., AND MULLINS, H. T., 1983, Basin margin environment, in Scholle, P. A., Bebout, D. G., and Moore, C. H., eds., Carbonate Depositional Environments: American Association of Petroleum Geologists, Memoir 33, p. 539–617.

COWAN, C. A., AND JAMES, N. P., 1992, Diastasis cracks: Mechanically generated synaeresis-like cracks in Upper Cambrian shallow water oolite and ribbon carbonates: Sedimentology, v. 39, p. 1101–1118.

DAVIES, P. J., BUBELA, B., AND FERGUSON, J., 1978, The formation of ooids: Sedimentology, v. 25, p. 703–730.

DAWES, P. R., 1976, Precambrian to Tertiary of northern Greenland, in Escher, A. E., and Watt, W. S., eds., The Geology of Greenland: Geological Survey of Greenland, p. 248–303.

DOSTAL, J., JACKSON, G. D., AND GALLEY, A., 1989, Geochemistry of Neohelikian Nauyat plateau basalts, Borden rift basin, northwestern Baffin Island, Canada: Canadian Journal of Earth Sciences, v. 26, p. 2214–2223.

DOTT, R. H., JR., AND BOURGEOIS, J., 1982, Hummocky stratification: Significance of its variable bedding sequences: Geological Society of America, Bulletin, v. 93, p. 663–680.

DROXLER, A. W., AND SCHLAGER, W., 1985, Glacial versus interglacial sedimentation rates and turbidite frequency in the Bahamas: Geology, v. 13, p. 799–802.

EBY, D. E., 1975, Carbonate sedimentation under elevated salinities and implications for the origin of "molar-tooth" structure in the middle Belt carbonate interval (late Precambrian), northwestern Montana (abstract): Geological Society of America, Abstracts with Program, v. 7, p. 1063.

FAHRIG, W. F., 1987, The tectonic setting of continental mafic dyke swarms: Failed arm and early passive margin, in Halls, H. C., and Fahrig, W. F., eds., Mafic Dyke Swarms: Geological Association of Canada, Special Paper 34, p. 331–348.

FAHRIG, W. F., CHRISTIE, K. W., AND JONES, D. L., 1981, Paleomagnetism of the Bylot basins: Evidence for Mackenzie continental tensional tectonics, in Campbell, F. H. A., ed., Proterozoic Basins of Canada: Geological Survey of Canada, Paper 81-10, p. 303–312.

FAIRCHILD, I. J., 1989, Dolomitic stromatolite-bearing units with storm deposits from the Vendian of East Greenland and Scotland: A case of facies equivalence, in Gayer, R. A., ed., The Caledonide Geology of Scandinavia: London, Graham & Trotman, p. 275–283.

FAIRCHILD, I. J., AND HERRINGTON, P. M., 1989, A tempestite–stromatolite–evaporite association (Late Vendian, East Greenland): A shoreface–lagoon model: Precambrian Research, v. 43, p. 101–127.

FAIRCHILD, I. J., EINSELE, G., AND SONG, T., 1997, Possible seismic origin of molar tooth structures in Neoproterozoic carbonate ramp deposits, north China: Sedimentology, v. 44, p. 611–636.

FERGUSON, J., BUBELA, B., AND DAVIES, P. J., 1978, Synthesis and possible mechanisms of formation of radial carbonate ooids: Chemical Geology, v. 72, p. 63–76.

FISCHER, A. G., 1964, The Lofer cyclothems of the Alpine Triassic, in Merriam, D. F., ed., Symposium on Cyclic Sedimentation: Kansas Geological Survey, Bulletin 169, p. 107–149.

FRANK, T. D., AND LYONS, T. W., 1998, "Molar-tooth" structures: A geochemical perspective on a Proterozoic enigma: Geology, v. 26, p. 683–686.

FURNISS, G., RITTEL, J. F., AND WINSTON, D., 1998, Gas bubble and expansion crack origin of "molar-tooth" calcite structures in the Middle Proterozoic Belt Supergroup, western Montana: Journal of Sedimentary Research, v. 68, p. 104–114.

GALLEY, A. G., JACKSON, G. D., AND IANELLI, T. R., 1983, Neohelikian subaerial basalts with ocean floor-type chemistry, northwestern Baffin Island (abstract): Geological Association of Canada, Program with Abstracts, v. 8, p. A25.

GINSBURG, R. N., 1953, Beachrock in South Florida: Journal of Sedimentary Petrology, v. 23, p. 85–92.

GELDSETZER, H., 1973, The tectono-sedimentary development of an algal-dominated Helikian succession on northern Baffin Island, N.W.T., in Aitken, J. D., and Glass, D. J., eds., Symposium on Arctic Geology: Geological Association of Canada, Memoir 19, p. 99–126.

GREENWOOD, B., AND SHERMAN, D. J., 1986, Hummocky cross-stratification in the surf zone: Flow parameters and bedding genesis: Sedimentology, v. 33, p. 33–45.

GROTZINGER, J. P., 1986a, Cyclicity and paleoenvironmental dynamics, Rocknest Platform, northwest Canada: Geological Society of America, Bulletin, v. 97, p. 1208–1231.

GROTZINGER, J. P., 1986b, Shallowing-upwards cycles of the Wallace Formation, Belt Supergroup, northwestern Montana and northern Idaho, in Roberts, S. M., ed., Belt Supergroup: A Guide to Proterozoic Rocks of Western Montana and Adjacent Areas: Montana Bureau of Mines and Geology, Special Publication 94, p. 143–160.

GROTZINGER, J. P., 1989, Facies and evolution of Precambrian depositional systems: Emergence of a modern carbonate platform archetype, in Crevello, P. D., Wilson, J. L., Sarg, J. F., and Read, J. F., eds., Controls on Carbonate Platform and Basin Development: SEPM, Special Publication 44, p. 79–106.

GROTZINGER, J. P., 1990, Geochemical model for Proterozoic stromatolite decline: American Journal of Science, v. 290-A, p. 80–103.

GROTZINGER, J. P., AND KASTING, J. F., 1993, New constraints on Precambrian ocean composition: Journal of Geology, v. 101, p. 235–243.

GROTZINGER, J. P., AND READ, J. F., 1983, Evidence for primary aragonite precipitation, lower Proterozoic (1.9 Ga) dolomite, Wopmay orogen, northwest Canada: Geology, v. 11, p. 710–713.

HAINES, P. W., 1988, Storm-dominated mixed carbonate/siliciclastic shelf sequence displaying cycles of hummocky cross-stratification, late Proterozoic Wonoka Formation, South Australia: Sedimentary Geology, v. 58, p. 237–254.

HALLAM, A., 1986, Origin of minor limestone–shale cycles: Climatically induced or diagenetic?: Geology, v. 14, p. 609–612.

HARMS, J. C., 1979, Primary sedimentary structures: Annual Review of Earth and Planetary Sciences, v. 7, p. 227–248.

HARMS, J. C., SOUTHARD, J. B., SPEARING, D. R., AND WALKER, R. G., 1975, Depositional environments as interpreted from primary sedimentary structures and stratification sequences: Society of Economic Paleontologists and Mineralogists, Short Course Notes 2, 161 p.

HARRINGTON, J. E. M., 1995, The Origin and Diagenesis of Neohelikian Grainstones in the Victor Bay Formation, Northwestern Baffin Island, Canada [unpublished B.Sc. thesis]: Queen's University, Kingston, Ontario, 41 p.

HEAMAN, L. M., LECHEMINANT, A. N., AND RAINBIRD, R. H., 1992, Nature and timing of Franklin igneous events, Canada: Implications for Late Proterozoic mantle plume and the break-up of Laurentia: Earth and Planetary Science Letters, v. 109, p. 117–131.

HERRINGTON, P. M., AND FAIRCHILD, I. J., 1989, Carbonate shelf and slope facies evolution prior to Vendian glaciation, central East Greenland, in Gayer, R. A., ed., The Caledonide Geology of Scandinavia: London, Graham & Trotman, p. 275–283.

HOFFMAN, P., 1976, Environmental Diversity of Middle Precambrian stromatolites, in Walter, M. R., ed., Stromatolites: New York, Elsevier, Developments in Sedimentology, v. 20, p. 599–611.

HOFMANN, H. J., AND JACKSON, G. D. 1987, Proterozoic ministromatolites with radial-fibrous fabric: Sedimentology, v. 34, p. 963–971.

HOFMANN, H. J., AND JACKSON, G. D., 1991, Shelf-facies microfossils from the Uluksan Group (Proterozoic Bylot Supergroup), Baffin Island, Canada: Journal of Paleontology, v. 65, p. 361–382.

HOFMANN, H. J., AND JACKSON, G. D., 1994, Shale-facies microfossils from the Proterozoic Bylot Supergroup, Baffin Island, Canada: Journal of Paleontology, v. 68, no. 4, supp., 35 p.

HORODYSKI, R. J., 1976, Stromatolites of the upper Siyeh Limestone (Middle Proterozoic), Belt Supergroup, Glacier National Park, Montana: Precambrian Research, v. 3, p. 517–536.

IANNELLI, T. R., 1992, Revised Stratigraphy of the Late Proterozoic Bylot Supergroup, Northern Baffin Island, Arctic Canada: Implications for the Evolution of Borden Basin [unpublished Ph.D. dissertation]: University of Western Ontario, London, Ontario, 412 p.

JACKSON, G. D., AND IANNELLI, T. R., 1981, Rift-related cyclic sedimentation in the Neohelikian Borden Basin, northern Baffin Island, in Campbell, F. H. A., ed., Proterozoic Basins of Canada: Geological Survey of Canada, Paper 81-10, p. 269–302.

JACKSON, G. D., AND IANNELLI, T. R., 1989, Neohelikian reef complexes, Borden Rift Basin, northwestern Baffin Island, *in* Geldsetzer, H. H. J., James, N. P., and Tebbutt, G. E., eds., Reefs, Canada and Adjacent Area: Canadian Society of Petroleum Geologists, Memoir 13, p. 55–63.

JACKSON, G. D., AND MORGAN, W. C., 1978, Precambrian metamorphism on Baffin and Bylot islands, *in* Fraser, J. A., and Heywood, W., eds., Metamorphism in the Canadian Shield: Geological Survey of Canada, Paper 78-10, p. 249–267.

JACKSON, G. D., AND SANGSTER, D. F., 1987, Geology and resource potential of a proposed national park, Bylot Island and N.W. Baffin Island: Geological Survey of Canada, Paper 87-17, 31 p.

JACKSON, G. D., DAVIDSON, A., AND MORGAN, W. C., 1975, Geology of the Pond Inlet map-area, Baffin Island, District of Franklin: Geological Survey of Canada, Paper 74-25, 33 p.

JAMES, N. P., NARBONNE, G. M., AND SHERMAN, A. G., 1998, Molar-tooth carbonates: Shallow subtidal facies of the mid- to late Proterozoic: Journal of Sedimentary Research, v. 68, p. 716–722.

KAH, L. C., 1997, Sedimentological, Geochemical and Paleobiological Interactions on a Mesoproterozoic Carbonate Platform: Society Cliffs Formation, Northern Baffin Island, Arctic Canada [unpublished Ph.D. dissertation]: Harvard University, Cambridge, Massachusetts, 292 p.

KAH, L. C., AND KNOLL, A. H., 1996, Microbenthic distribution of Proterozoic tidal flats: Environmental and taphonomic considerations: Geology, v. 24, p. 79–82.

KAH, L. C., SHERMAN, A. G., NARBONNE, G. M., KNOLL, A. H., AND KAUFMAN, A. J., 1999, δ¹³C isotope stratigraphy of the Proterozoic Bylot Supergroup, northern Baffin Island: Implications for regional lithostratigraphic correlations: Canadian Journal of Earth Sciences, v. 36, p. 313–332.

KENDALL, A. C., 1992, Evaporites, *in* Walker, R. G., and James, N. P., eds., Facies Models: Response to Sea Level Change: St. John's, Newfoundland, Geological Association of Canada, p. 375–409.

KENDALL, C. G. ST. C., AND SKIPWITH, P. A. D., 1969, Holocene shallow-water carbonate and evaporite sediments of Khor al Bazam, Abu Dhabi, southwest Persian Gulf: American Association of Petroleum Geologists, Bulletin, v. 53, p. 841–869.

KENDALL, C. G. ST. C., AND WARREN, J., 1987, A review of the origin and setting of tepees and their associated fabrics: Sedimentology, v. 34, p. 1007–1027.

KINSMAN, D. J. J., 1976, Evaporites: Relative humidity control on primary mineral facies: Journal of Sedimentary Petrology, v. 46, p. 273–279.

KNIGHT, R. D., AND JACKSON, G. D., 1994, Sedimentology and stratigraphy of the Mesoproterozoic Elwin Subgroup (Aqigilik and Sinasiuvik Formations), uppermost Bylot Supergroup, Borden rift basin, northern Baffin Island: Geological Survey of Canada, Bulletin 455, 43 p.

KNOLL, A. H., AND SWETT, K., 1990, Carbonate deposition during the Late Proterozoic Era: An example from Spitsbergen: American Journal of Science, v. 290-A, p. 104–132.

LECHEMINANT, A. N., AND HEAMAN, L. M., 1989, Mackenzie igneous events, Canada: Middle Proterozoic hotspot magmatism associated with ocean opening: Earth and Planetary Science Letters, v. 96, p. 38–48.

LEMON, R. R. H., AND BLACKADAR, R. G., 1963, Admiralty Inlet area, Baffin Island, District of Franklin: Geological Survey of Canada, Memoir 328, 84 p.

MILLIMAN, J. D., FREILE, D., STEINEN, R. P., AND WILBER, R. J., 1993, Great Bahama Bank aragonitic muds: Mostly inorganically precipitated, mostly exported: Journal of Sedimentary Petrology, v. 63, p. 589–595.

MÜLLER, N. K., AND KVINGAN, K., 1988, The genesis of nodular limestones in the Ordovician and Silurian of the Oslo region (Norway): Sedimentology, v. 35, p. 405–420.

MORROW, D. W., 1982, Descriptive field classification of sedimentary and diagenetic breccia fabrics in carbonate rocks: Canadian Society of Petroleum Geologists, Bulletin, v. 30, p. 227–229.

MULLINS, H. T., NEUMANN, A. C., WILBER, R. J., AND BOARDMAN, M. R., 1980, Nodular carbonate sediment on Bahamian slopes: Possible precursors to nodular limestones: Journal of Sedimentary Petrology, v. 50, p. 117–131.

NARBONNE, G. M., AND JAMES, N. P., 1996, Mesoproterozoic deep-water reefs from Borden Peninsula, Arctic Canada: Sedimentology, v. 43, p. 827–848.

O'CONNOR, M. P., 1972, Classification and environmental interpretation of the cryptalgal organosedimentary "molar-tooth" structure from the Late Precambrian Belt–Purcell Supergroup: Journal of Geology, v. 80, p. 592–610.

PATTERSON, R. J., AND KINSMAN, D. J. J., 1982, Formation of diagenetic dolomite in coastal sabkha along Arabian (Persian) Gulf: American Association of Petroleum Geologists, Bulletin, v. 66, p. 28–43.

PEHRSSON, S. J., AND BUCHAN, K. L., 1994, Borden dykes interpreted as remagnetized Franklin dykes based on U–Pb baddeleyite geochronology and paleomagnetic re-interpretation (abstract): Geological Association of Canada, Program with Abstracts, v. 19, p. A87.

POTTER, P. E., MAYNARD, J. B., AND PRYOR, W. A., 1980, Sedimentology of Shale: Berlin, Springer-Verlag, 306 p.

PRATT, B. R., 1998, Molar-tooth structure in Proterozoic carbonate rocks: Origin from synsedimentary earthquakes and implications for the nature and evolution of basins and marine sediments: Geological Society of America, Bulletin, v. 110, p. 1028–1045.

PRATT, B. R., JAMES, N. P., AND COWAN, C. A., 1992, Peritidal Carbonates, *in* Walker, R. G., and James, N. P., eds., Facies Models: Response to Sea Level Change: St. John's, Newfoundland, Geological Association of Canada, p. 303–322.

PURSER, B. H., AND EVANS, G., 1973, Regional sedimentation along the Trucial Coast, southeast Persian Gulf, *in* Purser, B. H., ed., The Persian Gulf: Berlin, Springer-Verlag, p. 211–231.

READ, J. F., 1982, Carbonate platforms of passive (extensional) continental margins: Types, characteristics and evolution: Tectonophysics, v. 81, p. 195–212.

READ, J. F., 1985, Carbonate platform facies models: American Association of Petroleum Geologists, Bulletin, v. 69, p. 1–21.

REINSON, G. E., KERR, J. W., AND STEWART, W. D., 1976, Stratigraphic field studies, Somerset Island, District of Franklin: Geological Survey of Canada, Paper 76-1A, p. 497–499.

ROBBINS, L. L., AND BLACKWELDER, P. L., 1992, Biochemical and ultrastructural evidence of the origin of whitings: A biologically induced calcium carbonate precipitation mechanism: Geology, v. 20, p. 464–468.

ROBBINS, L. L., TAO, Y., AND EVANS, C. A., 1997, Temporal and spatial distribution of whitings on Great Bahama Bank and a new lime mud budget: Geology, v. 25, p. 947–950.

SAMI, T. T., AND JAMES, N. P., 1993, Evolution of an early Proterozoic foreland basin carbonate platform, lower Pethei Group, Great Slave Lake, north-west Canada: Sedimentology, v. 40, p. 403–430.

SAMI, T. T., AND JAMES, N. P., 1994, Peritidal carbonate platform growth and cyclicity in an Early Proterozoic foreland basin, upper Pethei Group, northwest Canada: Journal of Sedimentary Research, v. B64, p. 111–131.

SAMI, T. T., AND JAMES, N. P., 1996, Synsedimentary cements as Paleoproterozoic platform building blocks, Pethei Group, northwestern Canada: Journal of Sedimentary Research, v. 66, p. 209–222.

SEREBRYAKOV, S. N., AND SEMIKHATOV, M. A., 1974, Riphean and Recent stromatolites: A comparison: American Journal of Science, v. 274, p. 556–574.

SHERMAN, A. G., NARBONNE, G. M., AND JAMES, N. P., 1997, Facies model for a Mesoproterozoic carbonate ramp, Victor Bay Formation, Borden Peninsula, northern Canada (abstract): SEPM–Canadian Society of Petroleum Geologists Joint Meeting, Abstracts, p. 254.

SHINN, E. A., 1983, Tidal flat environment, *in* Scholle, P. A., Bebout, D., and Moore, C. H., eds., Carbonate Depositional Environments: American Association of Petroleum Geologists, Memoir 33, p. 172–210.

SHINN, E. A., 1986, Modern carbonate tidal flats: Their diagnostic features, *in* Hardie, L. A., and Shinn, E. A., eds., Carbonate Depositional Environments, Modern and Ancient. Part 3: Tidal Flats: Colorado School of Mines Quarterly, v. 81, p. 7–35.

SHINN, E. A., STEINEN, R. P., LIDZ, B. H., AND SWART, P. K., 1989, Whitings, a sedimentologic dilemma: Journal of Sedimentary Petrology, v. 59, p. 147–161.

SHINN, E. A., STEINEN, R. P., DILL, R. F., AND MAJOR, R., 1993, Lime-mud layers in high-energy tidal channels: A record of hurricane deposition: Geology, v. 21, p. 603–606.

SMITH, A. G., 1968, The origin and deformation of some "molar-tooth" structures in the Precambrian Belt–Purcell Supergroup: Journal of Geology, v. 76, p. 426–443.

SOUTHGATE, P. N., 1989, Relationships between cyclicity and stromatolite form in the Late Proterozoic Bitter Springs Formation, Australia: Sedimentology, v. 36, p. 323–339.

STEWART, W. D., 1987, Late Proterozoic to Early Tertiary stratigraphy of Somerset Island and Northern Boothia Peninsula, District of Franklin, N.W.T.: Geological Survey of Canada, Paper 83-26, 78 p.

STODDART, D. R., AND CANN, J. R., 1965, Nature and origin of beachrock: Journal of Sedimentary Petrology, v. 35, p. 243–273.

SUMNER, D. Y., AND GROTZINGER, J. P., 1996, Were kinetics of Archean calcium carbonate precipitation related to oxygen concentration?: Geology, v. 24, p. 119–122.

WALTER, M. R., AND HEYS, G. R., 1985, Links between the rise of the metazoa and the decline of stromatolites: Precambrian Research, v. 29, p. 149–174.

WANLESS, H. R., TYRELL, K. M., TEDESCO, L. P., AND DRAVIS, J. J., 1988, Tidal-flat sedimentation from Hurricane Kate, Caicos Platform, British West Indies: Journal of Sedimentary Petrology, v. 58, p. 724–738.

WETZEL, A., 1991, Stratification in black shales: Depositional models and timing—An overview, *in* Einsele, G., Ricken, W., and Seilacher, A., eds., Cycles and Events in Stratigraphy: Berlin, Springer-Verlag, p. 508–523.

WILSON, J. L., 1975, Carbonate Facies in Geologic History: Berlin, Springer-Verlag, 471 p.

WINSTON, D., AND LYONS, T., 1993, Sedimentary cycles in the St. Regis, Empire and Helena formations of the Middle Proterozoic Belt Supergroup, northwestern Montana, *in* Link, P.K., ed., Geologic Guidebook to the Belt–Purcell Supergroup, Glacier National Park and Vicinity, Montana and Adjacent Canada: Whitefish, Montana, Belt Symposium III Field Trip, p. 21–51.

WRIGHT, V. P., 1984, Peritidal carbonate facies models: A review: Geological Journal, v. 19, p. 309–325.

YOUNG, G. M., 1974, Stratigraphy, paleocurrents and stromatolites of Hadrynian (Upper Precambrian) rocks of Victoria Island, Arctic Archipelago, Canada: Precambrian Research, v. 1, p. 13–41.

YOUNG, G. M., 1981, The Amundsen Embayment, Northwest Territories; Relevance to the Upper Proterozoic evolution of North America, *in* Campbell, F. H. A., ed., Proterozoic Basins of Canada: Geological Survey of Canada, Paper 81-10, p. 203–218.

PART V
DIAGENESIS AND GEOCHEMISTRY

CONTROLS ON Sr AND C ISOTOPE COMPOSITIONS OF NEOPROTEROZOIC Sr-RICH LIMESTONES OF EAST GREENLAND AND NORTH CHINA

IAN J. FAIRCHILD
Department of Earth Sciences, Keele University, Keele, Staffs ST5 5BG, U.K.
BARUCH SPIRO
NERC Isotope Geosciences Laboratory, Keyworth, Nottingham NG12 5GG, U.K.
PAUL M. HERRINGTON
Enterprise Oil plc, Grand Buildings Trafalgar Square, London WC2N 5EJ, U.K.
AND
TIANRUI SONG
Institute of Geology, Chinese Academy of Geological Sciences, 26 Baiwanzhuang Road, Beijing 100037, China

ABSTRACT: The Sr and C isotope compositions of Neoproterozoic carbonates have been argued to provide important constraints on the timing and origin of depositional events, including ice ages. We investigated the geochemical signatures of immediately preglacial Sr-rich limestones from an unusually complete section in E Greenland and compared with limestones in an analogous position in the basin stratigraphy from N China.

In some Greenland sections, slope facies grade upwards into glacimarine deposits, whereas in others slope facies are overlain by platform carbonates, then terrestrial eolian or glacial deposits without signs of erosion. The slope facies are mixed carbonate (ferroan dolomite and siderite)–siliciclastic (berthierine–quartz) shales with local limestone beds, variably disrupted by synsedimentary slumping. The shelf facies consists of mostly massive limestones with local molar-tooth structure. High Sr contents and poor fabric preservation indicate a primary mineralogy dominated by aragonite. Carbon isotopic values are negative in the slope facies whereas the overlying platform facies are isotopically positive, with mean $\delta^{13}C$ values rising from $+4.3$ to $+7.5\%$ upwards. The current paradigm is that such a negative-to-positive anomaly reflects the termination of a glacial event elsewhere. We prefer the alternative that deposition occurred across a stratified narrow ocean basin in which $\delta^{13}C$ decreases significantly at depth. Samples from the platform facies with over 2000 ppm Sr and negligible Mn have $^{87}Sr/^{86}Sr$ ratios around 0.70635. These are rather lower than previously reported values in preglacial platformal sediments in the basin, and consistent with no increase in continental erosion prior to glacial deposition.

The Dalian area of the North China block contains a 4-km-thick, tectonically deformed Neoproterozoic shallow marine succession, at the top of which are 80 m of storm-dominated limestone facies with abundant molar-tooth structures passing up into thin peritidal and dolomitic units below an erosion surface thought to correlate with glaciation elsewhere. Sr isotope ratios correlate with Mn, Fe, and insoluble residue and inversely with Sr, indicating the diagenetic addition of heavy Sr by interaction with silicate phases. Apparently unaltered signals are found in samples with Sr > 500 ppm and Mn < 100 ppm, with $^{87}Sr/^{86}Sr$ ratios decreasing upward from 0.7069 to 0.7063 from 70 m to 20 m below the top of the limestones. Nearly all $\delta^{13}C$ analyses lie between $+1.7$ and $+3.3\%$. These limestones correlate with preglacial carbonate-platform facies in the E Greenland–NE Svalbard basin, but cannot be tied to a specific horizon.

Whereas a Mn/Sr ratio of <2 is commonly taken to be a sufficient screening criterion for Sr Proterozoic isotope stratigraphy, increases in $^{87}Sr/^{86}Sr$ were found at Mn/Sr ratios as low as 0.2 in both regions. Availability of suitable lithologies is currently a major limitation on Sr isotope chemostratigraphic studies. However, Sr-rich Neoproterozoic limestones may achieve a $^{87}Sr/^{86}Sr$ resolution of (±0.0002. Deposition of such limestones bearing molar-tooth-type cracks ceased at around the time of a glaciation traditionally regarded as Varangian (c. 600 Ma), but which could conceivably be Sturtian (c. 740 Ma).

INTRODUCTION

Neoproterozoic sedimentary rocks record a period in Earth history in which important evolutionary events, such as the diversification of animals, were set against a backdrop of wide fluctuations in earth-surface elemental cycling and climate (Knoll and Walter, 1992; Knoll, 1993). In many regions, there is evidence for at least two phases of glaciation, which in some regions interrupted tropical conditions (Fairchild, 1993) and/or occurred in low paleolatitudes (Schmidt and Williams, 1995). Table 1 illustrates the extent of disagreement about Neoproterozoic events by contrasting two current and mutually incompatible syntheses. Jacobsen and Kaufman's (1999) synthesis is a development of earlier studies (e.g., Asmerom et al., 1991; Derry et al., 1992; Kaufman et al., 1993; Kaufman and Knoll, 1995; Kaufman et al., 1997) in which data from several sections are combined by adding model ages based on subsidence models to the sparse radiometric database. This synthesis postulates the existence of at least four major glacial events (two older Sturtian and two younger Varangian) represented in a given section either by glacial deposits, or a hiatus, or a negative $\delta^{13}C$ anomaly. Sr isotope ratios show a distinct rise at the end of both the Sturtian and Varangian events, with a dip in between. In contrast, Kennedy et al. (1998) argue that there is evidence for only two glacial events (an older Sturtian and a younger Marinoan). On this basis, in sections where authors discuss two supposedly Varangian glacial deposits (e.g., Fairchild and Hambrey, 1995; Saylor et al., 1998), the lower one is actually Sturtian, whereas where two supposedly Sturtian glaciations are represented (e.g., Hoffman et al., 1998), the upper one is really Marinoan (i.e., Varangian). The space for such a major disagreement arises because only two glacial formations are present in a given section and the age of a given section is constrained only by a reliable Neoproterozoic radiometric date at the base or the top (or neither), never both. Hence, the study of carbonate rocks has an important part to play in resolving Neoproterozoic geoscience problems, not only in characterizing depositional environments but also in constraining paleoclimates and providing independent data on age through Sr and C chemostratigraphy (e.g., Derry et al., 1989; Jacobsen and Kaufman, 1999).

Reconstructed Neoproterozoic carbonate facies tracts show much of the variation of their Phanerozoic counterparts (James et al., 1998). Carbonate sediment is inferred to have precipitated as carbonate mud in whitings and stromatolites and on tidal flats (Knoll and Swett, 1990), as ooids (Swett and Knoll, 1989), and as early diagenetic cements (e.g., Fairchild et al., 1990).

TABLE 1.—NEOPROTEROZOIC CHRONOLOGY AND CHRONOSTRATIGRAPHY. ALL Sr AND C ISOTOPE SIGNALS REFER TO PERIODS BEFORE OR AFTER GLACIATIONS AND ARE APPROXIMATED FROM THE PUBLICATIONS CITED. THE TERMS RISING AND FALLING REFER TO TRENDS UP-SECTION

Age (Ma)	Cowie et al. (1989)	Saylor et al. (1998)	Jacobsen and Kaufman (1999) $^{87}Sr/^{86}Sr$ signal	Jacobsen and Kaufman (1999) $\delta^{13}C$ signal	Kennedy et al. (1999) $^{87}Sr/^{86}Sr$ signal	Kennedy et al. (1999) $\delta^{13}C$ signal
544[1]	Cambrian		0.7087			
	—	—	0.7085	−4[3]		
		Post-Varangian		Up to +5		+5
						+2
		— (562 Ma)	0.7081	−5	0.7079	−2, falling to −5
			V1 ice age (575–580 Ma)		Ice Age (Marinoan)	
	Neoproterozoic III	Varangian	0.7068	+4	0.7072	
			0.7068	−5		Falling to +2
			V2 ice age (590–595 Ma)			
		— (592 Ma)	0.7068	+4		
		Pre-Varangian	0.7072			
650[2]	—	—	0.7066	+8 ± 2		+8
			0.7072			
			0.7075	−5		−2, rising rapidly to +4
			S1 ice age (720–725 Ma)			
	Cryogenian		0.7066–0.7068	−5, rising to +8	0.7070	
			S2 ice age (740–750 Ma)		Ice Age (Sturtian)	
			0.7068	+6		Positive, falling near glacial[4]
			0.7056	+4		
850[2]	—					
	Tonian					
1000[2]						

[1] Grotzinger et al. (1995)
[2] by definition, Cowie et al. (1989)
[3] glaciation around this time according to Bertrand-Sarfati et al. (1995)
[4] data of Hoffman et al. (1998)

Early diagenesis and reworking led to abundant intraclastic and peloidal allochems, which together with micrite were widely dispersed by agents such as storms and tides (e.g., Fairchild and Herrington 1989; Fairchild et al., 1991). The absence of a skeletal calcareous biota would have enhanced the saturation state of oceans for calcium carbonates compared with Phanerozoic times, although there is evidence of a decrease in saturation compared with early eras (Grotzinger, 1989; Knoll and Swett, 1990).

Both Mg-calcite and aragonite, sometimes mixed, formed the primary precipitates in ooids (e.g., Fairchild et al., 1991) and stromatolites (e.g., Fairchild et al., 1990); there is no equivalent in geochemical terms to the low-Mg calcite of many Phanerozoic skeletons. Knoll et al. (1993) argued that a high proportion of carbonate was originally precipitated in peritidal environments, where it was highly susceptible to dolomitization. Complete dolomitization within a meter of the surfaces of tidal flats can sometimes be demonstrated (Fairchild et al., 1991).

Glacial facies commonly contain a high proportion of erosional products of carbonate platforms. A difference from carbonate in Quaternary glacial deposits is that these detrital carbonates were young and susceptible to further diagenesis in glacial environments. For example, there is evidence of glacimarine recrystallization of dolomite; also dissolution of carbonate debris enabled the precipitation of primary low-Mg calcite and dolomite in glacilacustrine environments (Fairchild et al., 1989; Fairchild, 1993). The common presence of a "cap carbonate" on glacial deposits attests to the enhanced precipitation of carbonates immediately following glaciation (Kennedy, 1996).

The vast bulk of Neoproterozoic chemostratigraphic data has been obtained from relatively pure carbonate facies. Diagenetic modification of a primary marine signal is much less likely in such facies than in calcareous shales, although there are some occurrences of isotopically light C in limestones affected by meteoric diagenesis (e.g., Fairchild et al., 1990), which show the need for vigilance in this respect. Nevertheless, a number of lines of evidence indicate that the carbonate carbon isotope signatures of carbonate rocks are typically close that of the original marine carbonate: the similarity of results from dolomites and limestones, the covariation with $\delta^{13}C$ signatures of organic carbon, and the lack of a demonstrable vital effect in stromatolites (Knoll et al., 1986; Fairchild, 1991; Kaufman and Knoll, 1995). As a result $\delta^{13}C$ chemostratigraphy of Neoproterozoic rocks has blossomed and a paradigm has become established that negative anomalies reflect the global impact of glacial events, regardless of whether glacial facies are represented in the studied sections (Knoll et al., 1986; Kaufman and Knoll, 1995; Kaufman et al., 1997). Given the minor role of diagenetic alteration, there are two factors that limit this approach, in addition to the paucity of independent radiometric dating control mentioned above. The first is stratigraphic incompleteness. This can be mitigated by combining the $\delta^{13}C$ analysis of rocks from several correlated sections in conjunction with sequence stratigraphic analysis (e.g., Hoffman et al., 1998; Saylor et al., 1998). The second is the possibility of paleoceanographic variability in $\delta^{13}C$ (Kennedy, 1996; Shields et al., 1997), which is particularly acute given that a stratified ocean, with a ^{13}C-depleted reservoir at depth, has been postulated to exist through much of Neoproterozoic times (Kaufman and Knoll, 1995; Knoll et al., 1996). In this paper we present evidence for a negative $\delta^{13}C$ stratigraphic anomaly that is interpretable in terms of depth-related $\delta^{13}C$ variations and hence casts doubt on the universal validity of the glacial paradigm for such anomalies.

Sr isotope analysis, like that of C isotopes, is most reliable on pure carbonate facies, but the $^{87}Sr/^{86}Sr$ ratio is more susceptible to being reset postdepositionally than the $\delta^{13}C$ value

(Kaufman et al., 1993; Jacobsen and Kaufman, 1999). As mentioned above, the primary phases are not preserved in Neoproterozoic nonglacial carbonates, and during the mineral replacement processes there will typically be a significant net loss of Sr, and gain of other elements, such as Mn, present in diagenetic fluids. If a more radiogenic (^{87}Sr-rich) source of Sr, typically from silicate diagenesis, is available during carbonate precipitation, a modified signature will result. As a result, geochemical screening criteria are commonly adopted for Sr isotope studies (e.g., Kaufman et al., 1993; Brasier et al., 1996). The latest compilation by Jacobsen and Kaufman (1999) uses an acceptability criterion of Mn/Sr < 2, which removes much of the small-scale variability of the Sr isotope stratigraphic records. Such variability is not expected to be a genuine primary marine feature because of the long oceanic residence time of Sr (4.1 Myr today; Kaufman et al., 1993). The maximal rate of change in the Neogene was 0.0001 per Myr for a brief period around 20 Ma (Richter et al., 1992), several times the mean Neogene value, which itself is much higher than normal in earth history. In the Neoproterozoic, the best documented rapid change is that of Shields et al. (1997), who record a unidirectional rise of 0.0005 in a 50 m Neoproterozoic postglacial shaly carbonate section. In this paper we present new ^{87}Sr/^{86}Sr data on some Sr-rich limestone facies and combine results with previously published information to show that even more stringent screening criteria are required than those used by Jacobsen and Kaufman (1999) to eliminate postdepositional effects.

The limestones chosen for analysis are in an intriguing stratigraphic position in that they are the last Neoproterozoic representatives of pure marine micritic limestones in sections in E Greenland and N China. Both contain abundant molar-tooth structures, which represent early-cemented fractures in subtidal sediments. The fracturing reflects distinctive physical properties of these micrites, which were inferred to be originally bound by microbial mats (James et al., 1998). Our new chemostratigraphic data on the local last occurrences of such limestones are consistent with a correlation of the two sections and illustrate that such Sr-rich facies could potentially generate a highly precise Sr isotope curve for at least part of Neoproterozoic time.

METHODS

Samples for geochemical analysis were prepared as powders drilled from cut surfaces corresponding to areas that had been thin-sectioned, or from thick thin sections. In several cases on the Chinese material there was insufficient powder to carry out all analyses. Cation analyses were carried out by inductively coupled atomic emission spectrometry (ICP-AES) on solutes resulting from dissolution of approximately 10 mg sample powder in 8 ml Aristar-grade HCl at a strength of 10% (v/v) for Greenland samples and 5% for Chinese samples. Standardization was by a series of matrix-matched standards and results on British Chemical Society (BCS) dolomite and calcite standards agreed closely with reported values. Analytical precisions on the most concentrated standard were ($\pm$2, 2, 6, 8, and 1% for Ca, Mg, Fe, Mn, and Sr, respectively, for Greenland samples and similar values for Chinese samples. All values presented are more than 10 times the detection limits calculated from BCS standards using the methods of Thompson and Walsh (1983).

X-ray diffraction was carried out on Greenland sample powders containing significant insoluble residue. Carbonate-free

samples displayed significant cation yields (mainly from berthierine) in acid leachates, and so no trace-element data are presented from Greenland samples with significant insoluble residue. Percent insoluble residue (with errors of $\pm$5 absolute %) was estimated for Chinese samples as the deviations from 100% analytical totals.

Stable-isotope analysis was carried on 10 mg aliquots of sample powders prepared as mentioned using the method of McCrea (1950). Calcites were reacted at 25(C and other carbonates at 55°C. Results are presented relative to (V-)PDB with an overall analytical reproducibility of $\pm$0.05‰.

Samples were prepared for Sr isotope analysis by leaching powder aliquots in 10% (v/v) acetic acid for 8 hours at room temperature. ^{87}Sr/^{86}Sr ratios were determined in a Finnigan MAT262 TIMS with a within-run precision better than 0.000002 (2σ). The NBS 987 standard gave a ^{87}Sr/^{86}Sr ratio of 0.710201 at the time of the analytical program.

We have not carried out Rb analysis to correct the measured isotopic values to true initial values, because we sought primary marine signals in samples with least radiogenic Sr. We use screening criteria (introduced later) of Mn < 100 ppm and Sr > 500 ppm for acceptable marine Sr isotopic values. Results of Derry et al. (1989), Derry et al. (1992), and Kaufman et al. (1993) on carbonates from the Greenland–Svalbard sections indicate that samples meeting such criteria required corrections of 0.00000 to -0.00004 to convert measured to initial values.

EAST GREENLAND SECTION

The East Greenland interval studied is at the top of a carbonate-dominated succession and immediately below the lower of two glacial formations. Palaeontological evidence for age of the carbonate succession, mainly in the form of long-ranging acritarch assemblages, indicates a Late Riphean age (Knoll and Swett, 1990), which conservatively confirms only that the strata are Neoproterozoic and preglacial. The strata formed part of the same sedimentary basin as NE Svalbard; there are numerous lithostratigraphic tie points between the two areas (Knoll et al., 1986; Fairchild and Hambrey, 1995). The East Greenland–NE Svalbard basin of the Laurentian block has been matched, by means of the glacial units, with the classic Varanger tillites of northern Norway in adjacent Baltica, but there are no good radiometric constraints on any of these "Varangian" glacial deposits of the North Atlantic area. Kennedy et al. (1998) postulate that the first glacial in NE Svalbard (and by extension, E Greenland) is actually Sturtian. There is evidence for accelerated subsidence (development of carbonate slope deposits) immediately prior to glaciation in E Greenland (Herrington and Fairchild, 1989), which implies that a relatively complete chemostratigraphic record is present.

Stratigraphy

The stratigraphic relationships in East Greenland are described by Herrington and Fairchild (1989), who also compared the section with the co-basinal section of NE Spitsbergen (part of Svalbard). More detailed comparisons in the light of new data and sequence stratigraphic concepts were made by Fairchild and Hambrey (1995). The "bed-groups" of the stratigraphy should be understood as formations (Sønderholm and Tirsgaard, 1993), but given the absence of formal stratigraphic definitions, the original names are retained here. Our interest centers on bed-groups 19 and 20.

Figure 1 summarizes the stratigraphy at two localities, representative (at formation level) of the fjord region of central East Greenland. Although other sections have been described (summarized by Hambrey and Spencer, 1987, and Fairchild and Hambrey, 1995), there are no other useful member-level descriptions of these formations. The bases of the sections are correlated by means of a regional marker: a 20–25 m thick, thinly interlaminated dolostone–limestone, the top member of bed-group 18. Bed-group 19 was divided by Herrington and Fairchild (1989) into 7 members (19.1 to 19.7), which were correlatable across the 50 km distance between Ella Ø and Kap Weber. However, they cautioned that the definition of member 19.6, reflecting in part a collection of carbonate horizons showing variable synsedimentary brecciation, was somewhat arbitrary.

The boundary between bed-group 19 and the glacigenic Ulvesø Formation is known to be conformable at several sections studied by Hambrey and Spencer (1987). Coarse glacial debris is introduced gradationally over intervals varying from 1 cm to 2 m at different localities. At the sampled Ella Ø section, the contact is also conformable, but sharp. Here Moncrieff (1988) regarded the thin basal bed of the Ulvesø Formation as a debris flow, overlain by other glacimarine strata.

At Kap Weber (and other northern localities), bed-group 19 shales pass upward into the limestone-dominated bed-group 20. The sections at Kap Weber are variably affected by thrust faulting that locally removes member 20.2 and 20.3. However, apart from in the immediate vicinity of thrusts, the sediments are uncleaved. A thickness of 130 m was measured at the least disturbed section, with an apparently conformable contact to eolian sandstones and overlying glacial deposits, both of the Ulvesø Formation (Moncrieff and Hambrey, 1990).

Sedimentology and Sedimentary Petrology

A summary sedimentological interpretation was given by Herrington and Fairchild (1989). Member 19.1 consists of peritidal limestones and dolostones whereas the rest of bed-group 19 is dominated by mixed carbonate–siliciclastic shales. The presence of slump folds, and interbedding of inferred turbidites and debris-flow deposits with the shales (Fig. 1), indicates a slope apron environment throughout members 19.2 to 19.7. The sediment gravity flows are particularly thick and carbonate-rich in members 19.3 and 19.6, probably representing periods of deepening of the lysocline. Whereas in member 19.3 they are predominantly dolostones (turbidites with Bouma B to E divisions), in member 19.6 there are several beds of dolomitic limestone or limestone, interpreted as debris-flow units of local derivation. In some cases, discrete calcareous nodules formed in the host sediments around which some compaction of the (now dolomitic) sediments occurred. In other cases, particularly at Ella Ø, pure laminated limestones occurred with molar-tooth-type cracks filled with pure and equicrystalline (10–15 μm) calcite microspar. Both nodular limestones and (uncompacted) molar-tooth crack fills are truncated and incorporated into debris flows, indicating that both nodules and molar-tooth cements were generated within a few meters of the sediment surface.

Members 19.2, 19.4, 19.5, and 19.7 are dominated by less carbonate-rich lithologies, which Herrington (1989) inferred to reflect a fall in the lysocline rather than a change in water depth. In these rocks, x-ray diffraction analysis demonstrates that the dominant clay mineral is berthierine. There is a consistent occurrence of disseminated 1–10 μm pyrite crystals, regardless of carbonate content. Where carbonate minerals are present they are finely crystalline and composed of either (Fe-rich) dolomite or siderite or both. The association of berthierine with iron carbonates in organic-rich shales is an authigenic assemblage common in marine ironstones (e.g., Taylor and Curtis, 1995).

Bed-group 20 consists predominantly of 10–30 cm beds of massive or laminated dark-colored limestones. Shaly limestone horizons, 3–10 cm thick, are variably developed between beds and contain abundant pressure-solution seams. The limestones are predominantly inequicrystalline microspars with local traces of silt- to sand-grade allochems marked by variations in crystal size or (organic) impurity content, cross-lamination, and/or grading preserved. The carbonate-rich nature of the bulk of the facies suggests a broadly shelfal environment (Herrington and Fairchild, 1989). Member 20.2 represents a return to berthierine–Fe-dolomite–rich shales, whereas member 20.3 reverts to pure carbonates including (at different levels) intraclastic rocks and molar-tooth-bearing laminated limestones and dolostones.

Overall, the succession of members 19.2 to 19.7 is interpreted to represent the most significant deepening event in the 6.5 km preglacial sedimentary record of the basin, where otherwise no marine slope facies are recorded. The combination of tilting and deepening is interpreted as tectonic in origin and probably triggered by rifting (Herrington and Fairchild, 1989; Fairchild and Hambrey, 1995). Synsedimentary faulting accords with a seismic origin of the original "molar-tooth" fractures as proposed by Fairchild et al. (1997). Locally, shelfal limestone facies were able to prograde over the slope (parts of member 19.6 at Ella Ø), but were able to become firmly established only at Kap Weber, forming bed-group 20. At Ella Ø the slope-facies shales are overlain by glacimarine diamictites, reflecting the basinal setting of this section. By contrast, at Kap Weber, the shallower-water member 20.3 is overlain by Ulvesø Formation eolianites (Moncrieff and Hambrey, 1990), presumably reflecting glacioeustatic sea-level fall. Although regionally there may be a small hiatus here (the only sequence boundary in the section; Fairchild and Hambrey, 1995), the existence of a basal eolian sandstone makes significant erosion unlikely.

Geochemistry and Chemostratigraphy

Data Presentation.—

Figures 2 to 6 summarize relevant geochemical data from the sections studied, and Table 2 presents data for all carbonate-rich samples for which isotope data have been obtained (other data are listed in Herrington, 1989). Sr elemental data (Fig. 2) illustrate mean values in excess of 1000 ppm (locally up to 2700 ppm), with large variations in individual members. These results were used to screen samples for Sr isotope analysis: two samples from member 20.1 with in excess of 2000 ppm yielded $^{87}Sr/^{86}Sr$ ratios between 0.7063 and 0.7064 (Table 2, Fig. 2). A sample from the top of the formation with 680 ppm Sr gave a value of 0.70660.

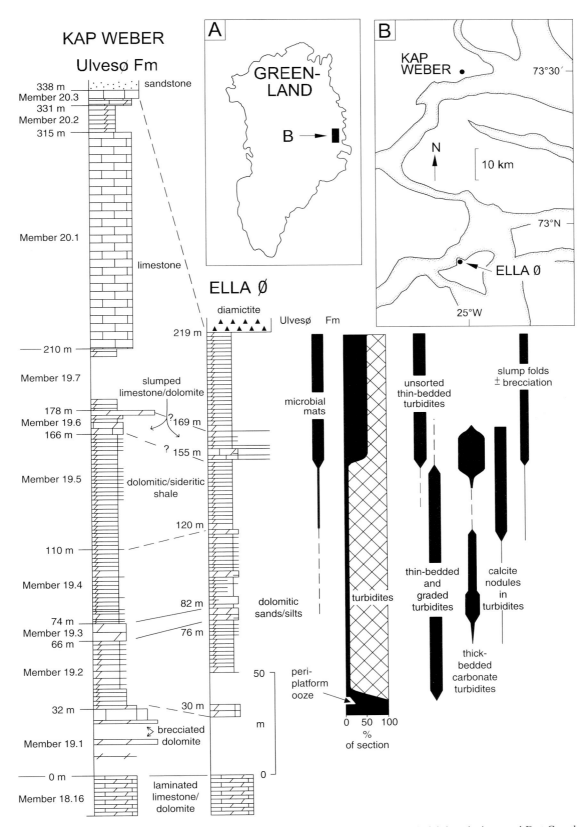

FIG. 1.—Location and stratal profiles of carbonates immediately underlying the older Neoproterozoic glacial deposits in central East Greenland. Carbonate slope facies of bed-group 19 (log after Herrington and Fairchild, 1989) underlie the shelfal bed-group 20 (log after Herrington, 1989) at Kap Weber, thought to be time-equivalent to uppermost bed-group 19 deposits at Ella Ø.

TABLE 2.—CHEMISTRY (ELEMENTAL AND ISOTOPIC) OF BED-GROUP 19 AND 20 ISOTOPIC SAMPLES, CENTRAL EAST GREENLAND

Sample	Member	Height (m)[1]	Description	Fe, ppm	Mn, ppm	Sr, ppm	CaCO$_3$ mol%	MgCO$_3$ mol %	FeCO$_3$ mol%	δ^{18}O, ‰	δ^{13}C, ‰	^{87}Sr/^{86}Sr[2]
Kap Weber												
43	20.3	335.4	Intraclastic grainstone	5100	420	680	97.4	1.5	0.9	−7.09	7.22	0.70660
045i	20.3	333.4	Dolomicrospar band	66600	2100	270	49.0	39.2	11.4	−0.76	5.55	
045ii	20.3	333.4	Molar tooth cement	5200	630	980	97.6	1.3	0.9	−8.28	8.93	
40ii	20.3	333.4	Microsparry limestone	4950	310	680	96.5	2.5	0.9	−6.73	7.1	
39ii	20.3	333.4	Microsparry limestone	4450	590	755	97.6	1.5	0.8	−5.89	6.79	
37	20.1	271.8	Microsparry limestone	760	24	1925	98.8	0.9	0.1	−3.49	7.03	
36	20.1	259.4	Microsparry limestone	1010	31	2750	98.4	1.1	0.2	−4.35	6.77	**0.70634**
35	20.1	254.5	Microsparry limestone	3550	37	2050	97.9	1.2	0.6	−6.35	6.54	
34	20.1	229.5	Microsparry limestone	4350	37	2400	97.9	1.0	0.8	−5.76	5.24	**0.70638**
33	20.1	222.3	Microsparry limestone	1950	25	1300	98.5	1.0	0.4	−3.27	5.3	
32	20.1	219.4	Microsparry limestone	5050	160	900	98.1	0.9	0.9	−3.59	2.98	
31	20.1	219.4	Microsparry limestone	3350	77	980	98.4	0.9	0.6	−3.56	3.76	
25	19.5	163.6	Nodular microspar	4800	675	1150	97.2	1.7	0.9	−5.93	−3.8	
18	19.3	71.3	Nodular microspar	1950	455	350	94.8	4.7	0.3	0.02	−5.95	
Ella Ø												
459i	19.6	167	Molar-tooth cement	2700	320	1750	98.7	0.6	0.5	−3.51	−1.48	
459ii	19.6	167	Molar-tooth cement	2100	290	1700	98.9	0.5	0.4	−6.13	−1.46	
459iii	19.6	167	Slump clast (microspar)	2350	285	1950	98.9	0.4	0.4	−6.6	−1.73	
458i	19.6	166.4	Molar-tooth cement	610	190	19a50	99.0	0.6	0.1	−7.24	−1.38	
458ii	19.6	166.4	Slump clast (microspar)	1650	240	2650	98.3	1.1	0.3	−4.95	−1.64	
383ii	19.6	165.9	Molar-tooth cement	1400	180	1700	98.9	0.6	0.1	−5.44	−1.42	
374i	19.6	165.5	Slump clast (microspar)	2950	320	1800	96.0	3.2	0.5	−7.48	−4.87	
385	19.6	164.1	Slump clast (microspar)	4500	315	975	98.5	0.5	0.8	−4.21	−1.99	
365	19.6	162.7	Nodular microspar	5650	360	995	96.8	2.0	1.0	−5.58	−2.63	
364	19.6	159.8	Slump clast (microspar)	3550	500	2050	97.5	1.6	0.6	−6.65	−3.87	
364ii	19.6	159.8	Molar-tooth cement	1600	240	1800	98.5	1.0	0.3	−0.17	−2.46	
364iii	19.6	159.8	Slump matrix	22000	930	1070	86.6	9.2	3.9	−9.25	−2.53	
362	19.6	155.8	Slump clast (microspar)	2000	710	1550	97.9	1.4	0.4	−6.65	−3.09	

[1] Height refers to stratigraphic position with respect to the base of bed-group 19.
[2] Sr isotope values in bold pass the criterion of Mn/Sr < 0.2.

Figure 3 illustrates carbon-isotope data showing that bed-group 19 samples, including samples from both study localities, are isotopically negative, whereas bed-group 20 samples are isotopically positive. The heaviest values are from the top of bed-group 20 (average of four calcite samples from member 20.3 is +7.5‰), whereas values at the base of bed-group 20 are significantly lower (average of four lowest samples is +4.3‰). Pure limestone facies of member 19.6 show a range from −1.4 to −4.9‰, but in the 166–167 m interval six samples display a much lower dispersion (range −1.4 to −1.7‰, Table 2). The heaviest four of these are all 100% pure molar-tooth cement samples all lying within 0.1‰ of each other. The ferruginous carbonates from bed-group 19 shales are also plotted in Figure 3 for comparison and display a range of δ^{13}C values from −1.1 to −10.2‰.

Figure 4 demonstrates that the difference in δ^{13}C values between bed-groups 19 and 20 limestones and dolomitic limestones occurs independently of a similar wide range of δ^{18}O values, and there is no correlation between the two parameters. Figure 5 illustrates that the observation made above for δ^{18}O applies also to Mn, although the lowest Mn values are found only in bed-group 20. The data of Table 1 illustrate that Fe shows a similar lack of correlation with δ^{13}C. Figure 6 demonstrates the tendency for Sr and Mn to be inversely related in concentration, although a large range in bed-group 20 limestones at Kap Weber is found at constant low Mn concentrations. The difference between most Kap Weber and Ella Ø samples is likely related to their different stratigraphic sampling horizons (cf. Fig. 2). No relationship was observed between δ^{18}O or δ^{13}C with Sr or other parameters.

Discussion.—The pure limestone lithologies were originally aragonite-dominated, judging by their high mean Sr content and poorly preserved primary textures (Tucker, 1986; Swett and Knoll, 1989). The distinctive equigranular microspar cements filling molar-tooth structures may have had an origin similar to Paleozoic and modern Bahamian microspars described by Munnecke et al. (1997), which were interpreted to have grown simultaneously with the dissolution of initial needle aragonite cements. Simultaneous growth of microspar crystals is also consistent with the cathodoluminescence observations of Fairchild and Spiro (1987) on molar-tooth cements. The wide range in Sr content may reflect either varying proportions of Mg-calcite in the original sediment or varying conditions of conversion to calcite. The heaviest δ^{18}O values may be the most ^{18}O-rich Precambrian limestone values recorded and can be used to extend the arguments of Fairchild and Spiro (1987) that Neoproterozoic sea water was no lighter in δ^{18}O than the modern ocean. Thus, the predominantly light δ^{18}O signature of Precambrian carbonates is due to their metastable primary mineralogy. The wide range of δ^{18}O compositions, independent of Sr or δ^{13}C composition, reflects a variety of timings of stabilization, but with relatively low water–rock ratios, allowing relatively good conservation of species other than oxygen. The tendency for Sr-poor limestones to have higher Mn (Fig. 6) and Fe reflects secondary incorporation of these elements accompanying diagenetic crystal growth, in this case probably during burial diagenesis; some Mn and Fe may also have been derived from silicates during sample leaching.

The constancy of pyrite occurrence in the carbonate-poor facies suggests that it was the first Fe-bearing phase to form. The generation of authigenic berthierine, siderite, and Fe-bearing dolomite indicates that significant microbially mediated redox reactions occurred during early diagenesis. The wide range of δ^{13}C values is expected from such ferruginous facies given

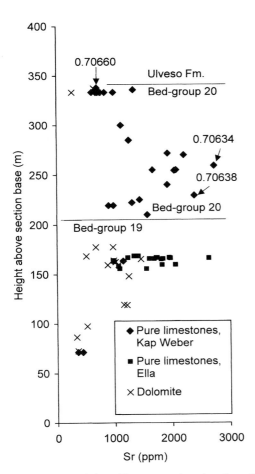

FIG. 2.—Stratigraphic variation of Sr concentrations (together with three Sr isotopic determinations at arrowed points) from bed-groups 19 and 20 from limestones and variably dolomitized limestones (referred to as dolomite in the key).

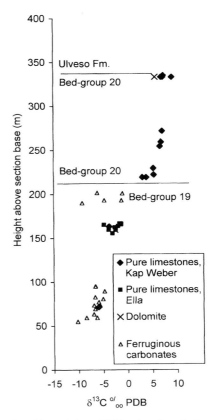

FIG. 3.—Stratigraphic variation of $\delta^{13}C$ values from bed-groups 19 and 20 from limestones, mixed dolomite/limestone lithologies, and ferruginous carbonates (ferroan dolomite and/or siderite within berthierine-bearing shales).

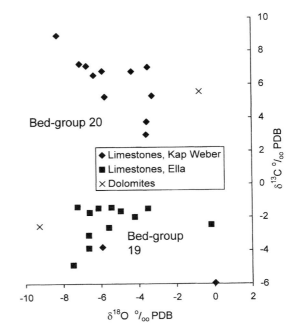

FIG. 4.—Cross-plot of $\delta^{13}C$ versus $\delta^{18}O$ for limestone and dolomitic limestone lithologies of bed-groups 19 and 20. Significant variation in $\delta^{18}O$ occurs independently of the stratigraphically related change in $\delta^{13}C$.

the potential sources of carbon from marine carbonate, oxidation, and methanogenesis. The source of iron could have been terrigenous iron oxides or Fe^{2+} from the water column. A land source of iron is feasible, in spite of the purity of adjacent carbonate platforms, because of the along-strike dispersal of sediment in the basin (Herrington and Fairchild, 1989). In this case berthierine can originate by alteration of a kaolinite substrate, as in the Phanerozoic model (Taylor and Curtis, 1995). However, anoxic bottom waters bearing Fe^{2+} also cannot be ruled out. Ferruginous deposits associated with such waters are regarded as typically associated with Sturtian rather than younger glacial deposits by Kennedy et al. (1998).

A crucial question in any study of carbon-isotope chemostratigraphy is whether a primary marine signature is preserved. The marine signal itself can be variable at any one time. Depositional factors on carbonate platforms can impart variations of up to several per mil (Patterson and Walter, 1994a) and in basins with good circulation a systematic negative shift by up to 2‰ is expected at depth because of oxidation of sinking organic matter (Berger and Vincent, 1986). This would be more substantial in stratified seas (Keith, 1982). Additionally, all the facies described bear significant organic carbon (are dark-col-

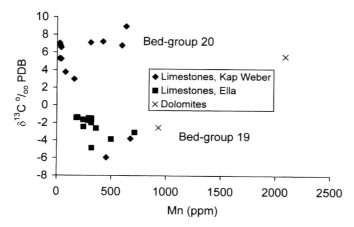

FIG. 5.—Cross-plot of δ¹³C and Mn variations in limestones and dolomitic limestones from bed-groups 19 and 20. Significant Mn variation occurs independently of the stratigraphically related change in δ¹³C, although the lowest Mn values are restricted to bed-group 20.

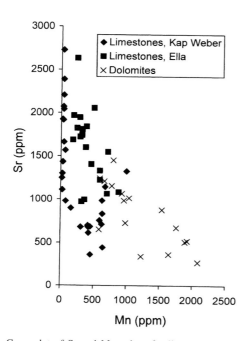

FIG. 6.—Cross-plot of Sr and Mn values for limestones and mixed dolomites–limestones from bed-groups 19 and 20. Dolomites tend to be higher in Mn and lower in Sr. At Kap Weber, very large variations in Sr are found without increase in Mn. Differences between Kap Weber and Ella Ø samples appear to relate to stratigraphic level of samples (cf. Fig. 2).

ored) and are therefore considered to have undergone early diagenetic microbial mediation. In modern calcareous facies, small negative carbon-isotope shifts have been described in relation to early microbial activity (Patterson and Walter, 1994b). In other Neoproterozoic examples of organic-rich limestone facies, variations in content of organic carbon either cause no dispersion of δ¹³C analyses (Tucker, 1983) or a mean depletion in ¹³C of 0.5‰ in organic-rich laminae (Pelechaty et al., 1996). Significantly, in the Greenland samples there is no relation of δ¹³C with the redox-sensitive elements Mn and Fe, and therefore no positive evidence of significant difference in δ¹³C be-

tween pore waters and depositional waters in pure limestone facies. Another supporting line of evidence is that carbon-isotope data from several carbonate–organic carbon pairs of Knoll et al. (1986) show the same fractionation in bed-group 19 as in other formations in the basin. To ascribe a secondary origin for the isotopic shift across the bed-group 19–20 boundary would require a large excess of organically derived carbon to have been present in the pore waters of the limestones of member 19.6. However, the member 19.6 limestones (allowing for synsedimentary brecciation) are similar to those found in member 20.3, where the carbon-isotope signature is completely different. The evidence of reworking of nodular limestones and molar-tooth cements demonstrates that diagenesis occurred near the sea bed where chemical diagenesis was unaffected by diffusion from underlying shales. The very small variation of δ¹³C in molar-tooth cements from member 19.6 also supports the primary marine origin of this signature.

If a signature close to primary marine carbonate is accepted, the origin of the carbon isotope trend within the section (Fig. 2) can be interpreted in two ways: either it reflects a secular excursion of the isotopic composition of Neoproterozoic ocean water, or it is evidence for a stratification of water in the depositional basin. This is discussed later in the Further Implications section.

The geographic variations in marine Sr isotope ratios today affect only the sixth decimal place (McArthur, 1994). The much longer residence time of Sr than C means that significant change in ⁸⁷Sr/⁸⁶Sr is not to be expected over short stratigraphic intervals, particularly in the Greenland section, which is inferred to have been deposited relatively rapidly (Fairchild and Hambrey, 1995). Although addition of nonradiogenic Sr from volcanic sources could in principle lower the ⁸⁷Sr/⁸⁶Sr ratio (Veizer, 1989), there is no evidence of volcaniclastic material in the basin. The more normal problem is addition of radiogenic Sr from clay minerals during diagenesis or sample preparation. The Sr isotope signature of bed-group 20 is quite well constrained from the three data obtained. The most reliable figures should be the two with the highest Sr (and negligible Mn) concentrations, which yielded values of 0.70634 and 0.70638, which are significantly lower than expected from previous studies (Derry et al., 1989, Derry et al., 1992; Kaufman et al., 1993). These values confirm that no increase in continental erosion, with its high ⁸⁷Sr/⁸⁶Sr signature, occurred prior to glaciation. They also place more severe constraints on the proposed "snowball" model of Neoproterozoic glaciations (Kirschvink, 1992; Hoffman et al., 1998). This implies a shutdown of continental erosion during glaciation and hence a tendency for ⁸⁷Sr/⁸⁶Sr ratios to fall towards ⁸⁷Sr-poor mantle values, although the fall would have been negligible if the glaciation was short as implied by the modeling of Jacobsen and Kaufman (1999). On current data, however, the ⁸⁷Sr/⁸⁶Sr isotope signature was around 0.7068 after glaciation (Jacobsen and Kaufman, 1999).

LIAONING SECTION, NORTH CHINA

Our N China section also lies at the top of a carbonate-dominated succession, but is truncated above by an erosional surface that is separated from Lower Cambrian marine strata by two thin marginal-marine to continental formations (Qiao et al., 1996; Fairchild et al., 1997). Similar carbonate successions are capped by Luoquan glacial deposits on the southern margin of the North China block (Lu et al., 1985; Brookfield, 1994), 1500 km SW of our section in Liaoning province (Figs. 7, 8). These deposits were thought at the time to be either uppermost Sinian to lower Cambrian (somewhere in the range 640–580 Ma), but on the basis of whole-rock radiometric data and a 590 Ma age for the Precambrian–Cambrian boundary, neither of which would now be accepted. It is probable that the Luoquan glaciation was Neoproterozoic and that it happened during the interval occupied by the erosion surface in our section. Acritarch assemblages in the carbonate succession are again fairly undistinctive long-ranging Upper Riphean forms (Qiao et al., 1996).

Most authors do not show the North China Block (the NCB) in Precambrian continental reconstructions. An exception is the 720 Ma reconstruction of Li et al. (1996), which makes use of the judged overall tectonostratigraphic similarities between the NCB, Siberia, and North Greenland in the Proterozoic. This reconstruction positions the NCB between Siberia and Baltica (which in turn abutted Greenland at the tip of Laurentia) within the supercontinent of Rodinia (Fig. 8A). Li et al. (1996) suggested that these blocks remained together until after the early Vendian (580 Ma), but by the Cambrian were widely separated (Greenland and N. China lay in different trilobite provinces by this time; McKerrow et al., 1992).

Stratigraphy, Sedimentology and Sedimentary Petrology

The stratigraphy of the section at Golden Stone Beach (Fig. 7C) is shown in Figure 9. It has recently been described by Fairchild et al. (1997) and is an excellent representative of the region (Qiao et al., 1996). Overlying 4 km of Neoproterozoic siliciclastic and carbonate formations is the 150-m-thick Xinmincun Formation, composed predominantly of subtidal limestones. The upper 80 m of this was logged by Fairchild et al. (1997) and interpreted to be dominated by storm deposits with inter-storm muds. There is an overall regressive tendency upwards from thick-bedded storm units to thin-bedded and laminated shoreface limestones, to partly to completely dolomitized peritidal laminites (Fig. 9). Most of the limestones bear molar-tooth structures, which have been interpreted as modified originally seismically triggered fractures (Qiao et al., 1996; Fairchild et al., 1997). The upper boundary of the Xinmincun Formation is erosional and interpreted as a sequence boundary, overprinted by a marine transgressive surface. The overlying Gejiatun Formation (approximately 33 m thick) consists of interbedded sandstones and carbonaceous mudrocks, above a basal conglomerate, and is interpreted as lagoonal. A gradational boundary with the overlying 92-m-thick Dalinzi Formation (red and green calcreted sandstones, mudstones, and dolostones with tepee structures) marks the transition to a playa lake or salina complex. This in turn is overlain by the Lower Cambrian Jiangchang Formation (with *Redlichia*) with a basal marine transgressive erosion surface. It is not known whether the Dalinzi and Gejiatun Formations are Neoproterozoic or Cambrian.

The strata suffered two periods of Mesozoic deformation, the second giving rise to tight folds and thrusts, and cleavage formation, and representing a collisional orogeny between North and South China blocks (Li, 1994). Carbonate rocks developed a spaced pressure-solution cleavage, which increases in inten-

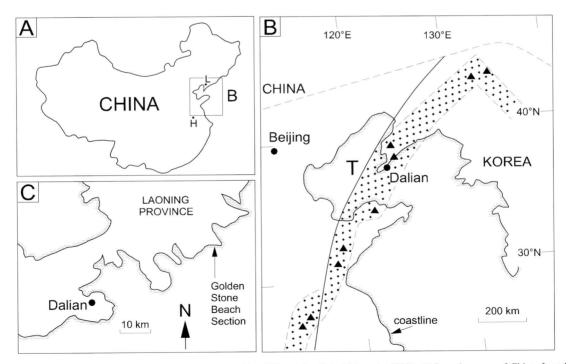

FIG. 7.—Location maps for studied section, 50 km NE of Dalian City, China (after Fairchild et al., 1997). A) Location map of China. L and H refer to the generalized Neoproterozoic sections shown in Figure 8B. B) locations of outcrops (black triangles) of Neoproterozoic successions with seismogenic sedimentary structures including molar-tooth structures (black triangles) within an interpreted fault-bounded palaeoseismic zone, the paleo–Tanlu Zone (stippled). The present-day Tanlu (Tancheng–Lujiang) Fault (T) defines the western edge of the zone, except in the south, where Neoproterozoic deposits have been displaced westwards by Mesozoic thrusting (Li, 1994; Qiao et al., 1996). C) Part of southern Liaoning province showing Golden Stone Beach location.

sity in relation to the abundance of clay impurities. Sedimentary structures are strongly flattened in the cleavage but appear undeformed on cleavage surfaces (Fairchild et al., 1997). Recrystallization during burial and deformation has rendered unrecognizable allochems finer than coarse silt to very fine sand size.

Petrological study of the Xinmincun Formation (Fairchild et al., 1997) indicates that the primary sediment was carbonate mud, which was prone to sea-floor cementation. Storms caused erosion to form intraclasts, which were often abraded to peloids. There are myriad tempestite horizons, which, where best developed, display grading from intraclast breccia through sand to coarse-silt-sized peloidal limestones to micrites. Beds of intraclast breccia up to 2 m thick may represent tidally reworked banks. Peritidal facies consist of interlaminated micrite and coarse silt- to gravel-size higher-energy sediments, and desiccation cracks and laminoid fenestrae are common. The content of siliciclastic silt and clay, presumably derived from a nearby

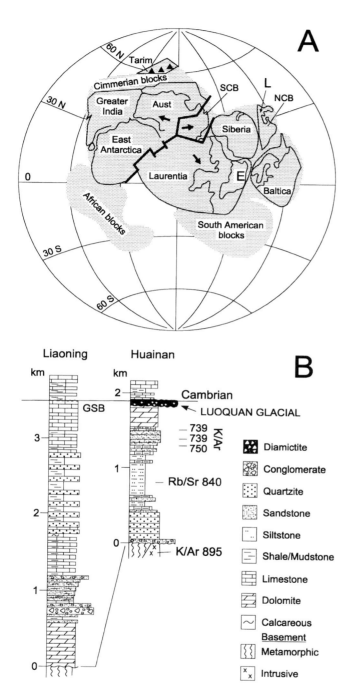

FIG. 8.—A) Paleogeographic reconstruction of the initial stages of break-up of the supercontinent Rodinia based on palaeomagnetic data at around 720 Ma (after Li et al., 1996). L represents the Liaoning region within the North China Block (NCB) and E represents the East Greenland locality. SCB = South China Block. Arrows indicate directions of plate movements. B) Comparative summary Neoproterozoic sections (after Brookfield, 1994) in Liaoning province (GSB = horizon of Golden Stone Beach section) and Huainan (H in Figure 7A) 1500 km farther SW near the southern margin of the North China Block. The Luoquan glacial deposits are inferred to postdate the unconformity at the top of the Xinmincun Formation of the Golden Stone beach section.

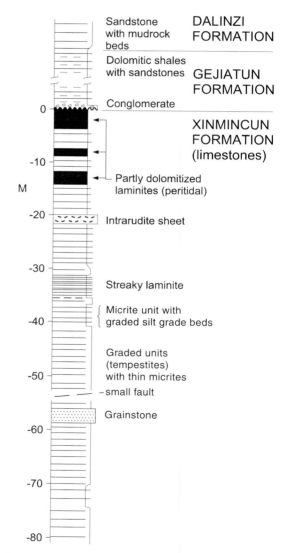

FIG. 9.—Summary section of uppermost Neoproterozoic limestone facies in Golden Stone Beach section, Dalian, North China block (summarized from Fairchild et al., 1997).

landmass, tends to increase upwards in the Xinmincun Formation.

Larger early diagenetic pore spaces in the Xinmincun Formation were filled by equant, equigranular (10–15 μm) microspar, interpreted as marine cements after aragonite (cf. Munnecke et al., 1997), as in the East Greenland case described above. The initial pores were developed in intraclastic grainstones as intergranular porosity, as laminoid fenestrae, and as fillings of "molar-tooth" cracks.

Three samples were taken for analysis at other stratigraphic levels: a columnar stromatolitic limestone just below the Xinmincun Formation, avoiding inter-columnar dolomitized areas; a lagoonal mudrock sample from the Gejiatun Formation with subequal amounts of siliciclastic silt/clay and dolomicrite; and a sandstone from near the base of the Dalinzi Formation displaying displacive calcrete growth textures as cements of calcite, with some dolomite.

Geochemistry and Chemostratigraphy

Data Presentation.—

Stratigraphic variation in Sr and C isotopes and Sr abundance are illustrated in Figure 10, and data for all samples for which isotope data have been obtained are listed in Table 3. Sr isotope values all lie at or below 0.710 in the main part of the section, but rise to high and very variable values in the upper part, where Sr abundances also fall. In contrast, $\delta^{13}C$ signatures up to the top of the Xinmincun Formation, apart from two outlying values, lie between +1.7 and +3.3‰, with no stratigraphic trend. Figure 11 illustrates that there is a wide dispersion in $\delta^{18}O$, with no relationship to $\delta^{13}C$ data. There is also no correlation between $\delta^{18}O$ and $^{87}Sr/^{86}Sr$ for the seven limestones for which both parameters are available.

The Sr isotope signatures co-vary with Mn, Fe, and inferred insoluble residue (IR) content, and all these parameters show antipathetic variation with Sr. Figures 12 and 13 illustrate that there is a wide dispersion in Sr contents at relatively low Mn and $^{87}Sr/^{86}Sr$ values. Fe shows a particularly simple relationship with $^{87}Sr/^{86}Sr$ ratios (Fig. 14), and it is notable that the lowest Fe content of 570 ppm corresponds with the lowest Sr isotope ratio measured at 0.70630. Figure 15 demonstrates the relationship between Mn/Sr (the geochemical screening criterion) and $^{87}Sr/^{86}Sr$. Isotope values increase above a Mn/Sr value of 0.2.

Geochemistry appears to be related largely to the content of insoluble residue rather than the petrological types listed in Table 3. Microspar cements tend to be particularly pure, and to have relatively high Sr, and low Fe, Mn, and $^{87}Sr/^{86}Sr$ values. Bulk limestones towards the top of the Xinmincun Formation have more mineralogical impurities and yield higher Fe, Mn, and $^{87}Sr/^{86}Sr$ signatures. The $^{87}Sr/^{86}Sr$ isotopic values in the Gejiatun and Dalinzi Formations are not primary.

Interpretation.—

The large variations in Sr isotope signature at any one level indicate that the bulk of the values are not representative of original marine waters. Even in the lower part of the Xinmincun Formation, local variations of nearly 0.004 are an order of magnitude larger than possible in a short continuous section. The relationships illustrated in Figures 12–14 demonstrate an association of increased $^{87}Sr/^{86}Sr$ values with indicators (Fe, Mn,

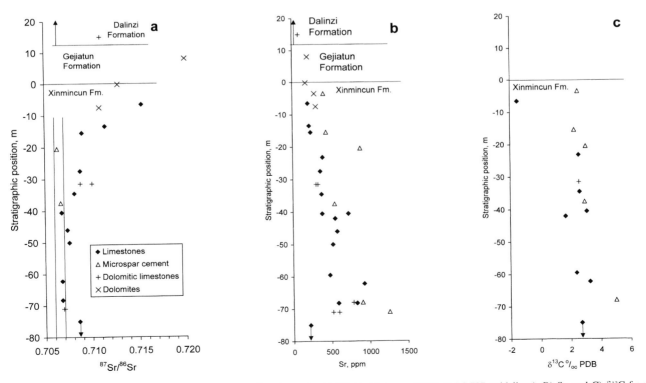

FIG. 10.—Stratigraphic variations in A) $^{87}Sr/^{86}Sr$ (with least altered samples highlighted between 0.706 and 0.707 guidelines), B) Sr, and C) $\delta^{13}C$ from the Golden Stone Beach section.

TABLE 3.—CHEMISTRY (ELEMENTAL AND ISOTOPIC) OF GOLDEN STONE BEACH ISOTOPIC SAMPLES, NORTH CHINA

Sample	Height (m)[1]	Description	Fe, ppm	Mn, ppm	Sr, ppm	CaCO$_3$ mol %	MgCO$_3$ mol %	FeCO$_3$ mol %	δ^{18}O, ‰	δ^{13}C, ‰	^{87}Sr/^{86}Sr[2]	% IR[3]
DL45	15	Dolomicrite (dolocreted sandstone)	31500	2900	82	83.9	10.0	5.6			0.71097	34
DL44	8	Dolomicrite	36000	2250	200	45.5	48.0	6.1			0.71996	47
DL28	0	Black dolomicrite	22500	750	175	51.2	44.9	3.7			0.71282	19
DL27b	−3.5	Microspar cement in fenestrae	5300	410	410	94.0	4.9	1.0	−10.54	2.50		2
DL29	−6.5	Micrite with terrigenous silt/clay	15100	320	200	93.0	4.3	2.7	−9.87	−1.52	0.71532	42
DL30	−7.5	Dolomitized silt-grade limestone	15500	390	310	66.7	30.6	2.6			0.71085	18
DL32	−13.5	Laminated silt-grade and micritic limestone	12200	350	220	94.6	3.2	2.2			0.71143	19
DL34a	−15.5	Molar-tooth cement	990	86	440	99.2	0.6	0.2	−8.45	2.26		0
DL34b	−15.5	Micritic limestone	9200	250	240	95.0	3.3	1.6			0.70896	15
DL23	−20.5	Microspar cement of intraclast breccia	570	87	880	99.0	0.8	0.1	−10.59	3.03	**0.70630**	4
DL35	−23.2	Laminated silt-grade and black micritic limestone	3550	125	395	96.2	3.1	0.6	−10.87	2.56		13
DL20	−27.5	Black (micritic) limestone	5000	135	360	95.4	3.7	0.9			0.70874	14
DL18a	−31.5	Silt-grade limestone	7350	170	330	92.1	6.6	1.3	−12.42	2.58	0.70875	18
DL18b	−31.5	Black (micritic) limestone	9000	170	305	90.0	8.3	1.6			0.71000	23
DL15	−34.5	Black laminated (micritic) limestone	4200	110	380	97.9	1.3	0.8	−10.03	2.62	0.70811	13
DL10	−37.5	Molar-tooth cement	960	60	550	99.2	0.5	0.2	−10.25	2.95	**0.70665**	0
DL41b	−40.5	Silt-grade limestone	2550	140	730	98.3	1.2	0.5	−8.16	3.09	0.70675	8
DL42	−42	Silt-grade limestone	4000	190	550	98.0	1.2	0.7	−8.61	1.67		12
DL52	−46	Black (micritic) limestone	3350	130	580	98.2	1.1	0.6				11
DL51	−50	Massive micritic limestone	2850	130	520	98.3	1.1	0.5			0.70754	11
DL55	−59.5	Silt-grade limestone	5300	130	480	97.3	1.7	1.0	−6.81	2.39		18
DL58	−62.2	Intraclastic grainstone	3570	160	930	98.5	0.7	0.6	−6.97	3.29	0.70735	14
DL54b	−68	Molar-tooth cement	640	40	910	98.6	1.2	0.1	−11.79	5.02		2
DL62a	−68.2	Black (micritic) limestone	2000	60	830	97.1	2.4	0.4			**0.70677**	6
DL67a	−71	Black (micritic) limestone	5900	125	520	75.3	23.6	1.0			0.70702	9
DL67b	−71	Silt-grade limestone	4950	92	600	80.7	18.3	0.9			**0.70690**	8
DL69	−80	Stromatolitic limestone	2300	186	220	97.7	1.8	0.4	−15.15	2.73	0.70857	11
DL67d	(−71)	Vein calcite	1400	89	260	99.1	0.6	0.3	−18.87	2.01		2

[1] Height refers to stratigraphic position with respect to the top of the Xinmincun Formation.
[2] Sr isotope values in bold type pass the criteria of Mn/Sr < 0.2, Mn < 100 ppm, and Sr > 500 ppm.
[3] Insoluble residue.

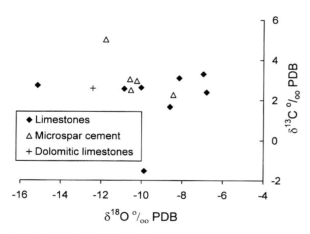

FIG. 11.—Cross-plot of δ^{13}C and δ^{18}O of Xinmincun Formation carbonates from the Golden Stone Beach section.

IR content) of either postdepositional recrystallization, or leaching from noncarbonate phases during sample preparation, or both. Evidence that partial recrystallization during tectonic deformation is likely to be an important factor is supported by data of Spiro and Fairchild (1996), who subjected limestone powders to repeated water leaching at low water–rock ratios. Sample DL15 (Table 2) yielded significantly higher ^{87}Sr/^{86}Sr ratios during five successive water leaches (0.7098 to 0.7090) than the acetic acid leach value of 0.7081 reported in Table 2. An impure limestone sample from another tectonically deformed geological locality behaved similarly. If we assume that exchangeable ions on silicates are absent by the fourth and fifth

leaches, these data are consistent with a model of regrowth of the outer parts of calcite crystals parallel to a developing pressure-solution cleavage, and incorporation of excess ^{87}Sr derived from silicates. Vein calcite, with a δ^{18}O signature of −18.9‰ illustrates the tectonic δ^{18}O signal, but this is much lighter than any of the limestone samples, illustrating that total recrystallization did not occur. Indeed, the lack of correlation between ^{87}Sr/^{86}Sr and δ^{18}O for limestones (Table 2) in the δ^{18}O range −6 to −11‰ indicates that significant variations in oxygen-isotope composition between samples may previously have been established during marine burial diagenesis (as in the Neoproterozoic I-5 limestones from Mauritania of Fairchild et al., 1990). The uniformity of δ^{13}C values reflects the resistance of

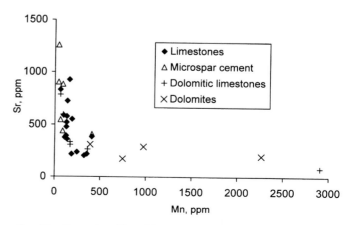

FIG. 12.—Cross-plot of Sr and Mn in carbonates of the Golden Stone Beach section.

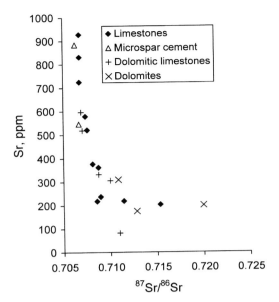

FIG. 13.—Cross-plot of Sr and $^{87}Sr/^{86}Sr$ in carbonates of the Golden Stone Beach section.

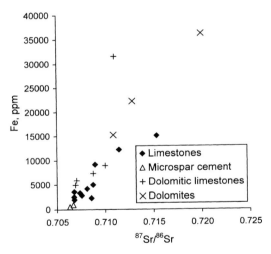

FIG. 14.—Cross-plot of Fe and $^{87}Sr/^{86}Sr$ in carbonates of the Golden Stone Beach section demonstrating strong covariation.

this parameter to secondary alteration, although the two carbon-isotope values lying outside the main band are unexplained.

The foregoing arguments indicate that the chemical trends up-section are likely to be related to increased content of terrigenous impurities in the carbonates. More impurities are associated with stronger cleavage development and a hence a greater tendency to recrystallize during tectonic deformation, leading to compositional change.

The sample suite as a whole displays lighter $\delta^{18}O$ signatures than "best preserved" samples in Svalbard and Greenland (Derry et al., 1992), but there is no evidence of any systematic relationship between Sr and O isotope values in the Chinese section. Hence $\delta^{18}O$ is not used as a screening criterion (cf. Kaufman et al., 1993; Kennedy et al., 1998). Mn/Sr is used more universally as a criterion, with a maximum in the range

1 to 3 being acceptable by different authors (Kaufman et al., 1993; Brasier et al., 1996; Kennedy et al., 1998; Jacobsen and Kaufman, 1999). On this basis, values of up to 0.7085 would be accepted from the Xinmincun Formation. However, Figure 15 shows that a much more stringent criterion of 0.2 is required. The range of $^{87}Sr/^{86}Sr$ is reduced slightly to 0.7063 to 0.7069 if additional >100 ppm Mn and < 500 ppm Sr are imposed. These Sr isotope values are associated with $\delta^{13}C$ values between +2 and +4‰. These are our best estimates of primary marine carbonate at the close of deposition of limestones with molar-tooth structures in the North China block.

FURTHER IMPLICATIONS

Greenland Carbon-Isotope Anomaly

The Greenland data display a contrast between negative $\delta^{13}C$ values in the upper part of bed-group 19, specifically limestones of member 19.6, and positive values of bed-group 20. This difference was argued, earlier in the text, to be primary in origin. The marked ^{13}C enrichment of Neoproterozoic limestones has been argued to reflect the development of a stratified ocean (Kaufman et al., 1991; Derry et al., 1992; Knoll et al., 1996), with a lower anoxic layer, depleted in ^{13}C. Did the preserved Greenland sediments intersect the lower boundary of such an ocean? This can be evaluated by several tests:

1. Is the magnitude of the change greater than normally expected with depth in a well-mixed ocean? The difference of around 9‰ is clearly much greater than the 2‰ expected from the open ocean (Berger and Vincent, 1986).
2. Are the changes consistent with estimated paleobathymetry? The lowering of $\delta^{13}C$ isotope values at the base of bed-group 20, close to the boundary with shales, and the co-occurrence of slump folds and turbidites with isotopically negative limestones, are consistent relationships. The latter could certainly have been deposited at depths greater than the typical 75 m thickness of the mixed layer of the modern ocean.
3. Is the basin geometry consistent with good development of anoxic facies? Inferred deflections of turbidites indicate that

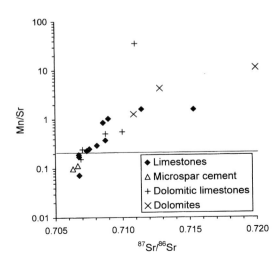

FIG. 15.—Cross-plot of Mn/Sr versus $^{87}Sr/^{86}Sr$ in carbonates of the Golden Stone Beach section.

bed-group 19 was deposited in an elongated basin (Herrington and Fairchild, 1989), which may therefore have been particularly prone to have restricted water circulation promoting stratification. There is also no evidence for strong wave action or tidal currents to deepen the effective surface layer. The pronounced development of Fe minerals in bed-group 19 is also consistent with an anoxic environment.

4. Is there evidence that the organic carbon at depth was not predominantly produced in the surface layer? Evidence of deepwater organic production is in the form of discrete organic-rich laminae, interpreted as microbial mats, found in the upper part of bed-group 19 (Fig. 1; Herrington and Fairchild, 1989). Also the data and models of Keith (1982), Logan et al. (1995), Ross et al. (1995), and Knoll et al. (1996) indicate that bacterial activity at depth (e.g., by sulfate reduction) should be the dominant source of organic carbon below the surface ocean.

The alternative interpretation of the carbon-isotope anomaly is the existing paradigm (Kaufman and Knoll, 1995) that it reflects a sequential change in global seawater chemistry. A test would be to find a negative-to-positive isotopic trend, as found in bed-groups 19 to 20, in coeval sections elsewhere. Correlative shallow-water strata in Spitsbergen lack isotopically negative values. The uppermost 20 m of strata below the first glacial unit have low positive values (Fairchild and Spiro, 1987), but are dolomites with unusual (possibly biologically mediated) textures, and the section probably contains hiati (Fairchild and Hambrey, 1995). The only preglacial negative anomaly known to us is from the top 20 m of carbonates below Sturtian glacial deposits on the Congo craton (Hoffman et al., 1998), whose negative $\delta^{13}C$ values are interpreted as a decrease in organic productivity relative to carbonate deposition.

In summary, we feel that the balance of evidence suggests that the $\delta^{13}C$ variations reflect bathymetric changes in a stratified basin. Deep-water ^{13}C-depleted carbonates are known from the Paleoproterozoic but have yet to be recorded from the Neoproterozoic (Kaufman and Knoll, 1995), apart from in the glacigenic (Sturtian) Rapitan Group iron formation, which was interpreted as being deposited during a time of low global $\delta^{13}C$ values (Klein and Beukes, 1993). This implies that significant oceanic mixing had not occurred prior to glaciation (cf. Kaufman et al., 1997). More generally, we would concur with Shields et al. (1997) that a close similarity in $\delta^{13}C$ signatures is not to be expected in geographically separate sections. It is highly likely that the prolonged Neoproterozoic enrichment in ^{13}C in shallow-water carbonates is a global phenomenon, reflecting an excess burial over weathering of organic carbon in relation to carbonate carbon (Knoll et al., 1986). However, because various authors have argued for the mechanism of stratification as a key controlling factor, spatial variations in the degree of ^{13}C enrichment are to be expected. This is because the deep-marine ^{13}C-depleted reservoirs may upwell or mix with more enriched waters to varying extents. For example, systematic variations of up to 6‰ were found between coeval shallow-water Permo-Carboniferous sections in western and northern Canada and attributed to variable mixing of shallow and deep reservoirs (Beauchamp et al., 1987).

Procedures in Sr-Isotope Stratigraphy

Although the large-scale features of the Neoproterozoic Sr isotope record are recognizable to the third decimal place of the

ratios, the variations in the period between Varangian and Sturtian tillites and distinction of V1 versus S1 and V2 versus S2 ice ages (Table 1; interpretation of Jacobsen and Kaufman, 1999) are more subtle and are readily confused by even small degrees of introduction of radiogenic Sr. Inspection of available data from the Greenland–NE Svalbard basin (Derry et al., 1989, Derry et al., 1992; Kaufman et al., 1993; herein) indicate that a more rigorous screening of samples to eliminate points with much higher $^{87}Sr/^{86}Sr$ ratios than adjoining samples is required to clarify the record. Only by eliminating all dolomites and samples with Mn/Sr > 0.2 is this objective achieved (Fig. 16). Figure 17 is a plot of surviving data from this procedure for strata within 1600 m of the lower glacial unit. Two separate periods of gradually falling $^{87}Sr/^{86}Sr$ ratios are apparent, separated by a poorly sampled interval that includes the dolomitic Draken Formation (Fairchild et al., 1991). The falling trends can be approximated as smooth curves given an uncertainty in the values of ± 0.0002. This small degree of error is encouraging for the use of formerly aragonitic limestones in Neoproterozoic Sr isotope stratigraphy in that it should be possible to find in such facies samples that meet even the stringent screening criteria adopted here. In particular, pure early diagenetic molar-tooth-type cements proved particularly resistant to secondary alteration even in the deformed Chinese section.

Conversely, many Neoproterozoic sections lack appropriate lithologies that would satisfy the geochemical screening criteria used here. Nevertheless, Figure 14 illustrates that it may be possible to extrapolate along linear alteration trends to find primary ratios, as was done by Fairchild et al. (1990) for carbon isotopes. This is most likely to be successful where 1) there is one principal mechanism for ^{87}Sr enrichment and 2) micro-analytical studies can demonstrate the siting of this excess ^{87}Sr.

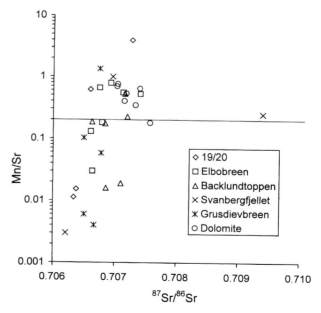

FIG. 16.—Cross-plot of Mn/Sr versus $^{87}Sr/^{86}Sr$ in carbonates from the NE Spitsbergen–E Greenland basin using data from Derry et al. (1989), Derry et al. (1992), Kaufman et al., (1993), and herein. Names in key are Svalbard formation names in stratigraphic order apart from 19/20 (Greenland) and dolomite (which refers to samples from several formations).

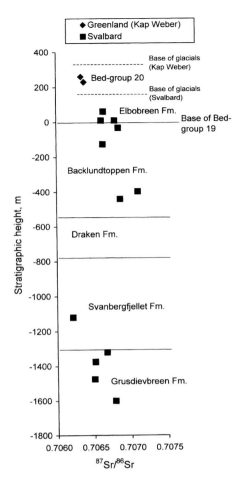

FIG. 17.—Stratigraphic plot of [87]Sr/[86]Sr isotope signatures of best preserved samples (limestones with Mn < 100 ppm and Sr > 500 ppm) from data of Figure 16. Fairchild and Hambrey (1995) correlated the base of bed-group 19 with the Backlundtoppen–Elbobreen boundary of NE Svalbard. Onset of glaciation is thought to be synchronous in the two areas. Two periods of falling [87]Sr/[86]Sr are visible.

New solid-source mass spectrometric techniques are also becoming available which will help in isolating micro-environments of samples where primary [87]Sr/[86]Sr ratios are retained.

Correlation of Greenland and Chinese Sections

As discussed earlier, only by applying a rigorous Mn/Sr criterion to the Chinese dataset, and eliminating samples with >100 ppm Mn or <500 ppm Sr, are striking outliers in [87]Sr/[86]Sr eliminated. The remaining four [87]Sr/[86]Sr data (with depths below the top of the Xinmincun Formation) are: 0.7069 (71 m), 0.7068 (68 m), 0.7067 (38 m), and 0.7063 (21 m). Comparison with Figure 16 indicates a correlation with either of the two falling trends in the E Greenland–NE Svalbard basin is possible, although the latter took place over rather greater stratigraphic thicknesses. Carbon-isotope signatures lie between +1.7 and +3.3‰ in the Chinese section whereas a negative carbon-isotope anomaly occurs in the strata 100 m either side of the Svanbergfjellet–Grusdievbreen formational boundary of Figure 16. However, this is an insufficient restraint to rule out

correlation of the Chinese section with strata lower in the Grusdievbreen Formation. It has already been argued that correlations need not be expected on the basis of slightly different δ^{13}C values, given the variable geometry and oceanic connections of different basins. However, an overall chemostratigraphic correlation of carbonate platform sediments in the two areas is established. The coeval development of these facies is consistent with the reconstruction of Li et al. (1996), who position our Chinese section within 30° of latitude of the E Greenland one (Fig. 8A), as part of the same supercontinent.

Cessation of Molar-Tooth Limestone Formation in Relation to Neoproterozoic Events

James et al. (1998) have drawn attention to the time-limited occurrence of molar-tooth limestones. The peculiar physical properties of calcareous sediments that are required to form molar-tooth cracks (Fairchild et al., 1997) might have been restricted to periods of negligible disturbance of subtidal microbial mats by animals (James et al., 1998). Hence, the cessation of formation of such facies could have global significance. In fact, they are practically unknown after a glaciation traditionally assumed to be Varangian (Table 1), but which would be Sturtian on the arguments of Kennedy et al. (1998). Our chemostratigraphic data are supportive both of the broad correlation of the Chinese and Greenland occurrences and the suggestion that the Luoquan glaciation of the North China Block postdated deposition of the section studied. In fact, we are not aware of the occurrence of molar-tooth carbonates stratigraphically higher than glacial deposits in any Neoproterozoic section. This implies that after glaciation, as after a decisive war, things were never the same again: a combination of tectonic, paleoceanographic, and biotic factors had moved the world on to a new phase of evolution. Eyles (1993) and Young (1995) argued for a relationship between sequential Sturtian and Varangian phases of glaciation and two phases of supercontinent rifting. In contrast, the reductionist interpretation of Neoproterozoic glaciations of Kennedy et al. (1998) would imply a link between one Sturtian phase of glaciation and the demise of molar-tooth structure, perhaps coincident with the supercontinental rift phase depicted in Figure 8A (modified from Li et al., 1996).

CONCLUSIONS

1) Formerly aragonitic subtidal limestones, commonly displaying cemented early diagenetic fractures (molar-tooth structures) are a characteristic feature of several Neoproterozoic basins and appear to be time-restricted (James et al., 1998). Examples from E Greenland and the N China block show comparable Sr isotope signatures consistent with roughly coeval deposition of the two platforms. In E Greenland, Sr isotope values fall to around 0.70635 immediately prior to the first of two Neoproterozoic glaciations, traditionally regarded as Varangian (c. 600 Ma), but which would be Sturtian (c. 740 Ma) on the correlation of Kennedy et al. (1998). There is therefore no evidence for increased continental erosion prior to glaciation, and the low values further constrain the "snowball" glaciation model of Hoffman et al. (1998).

2) Studies of geochemical patterns of alteration of Neoproterozoic limestones confirms the usefulness of Mn/Sr as an in-

dicator of diagenetic alteration, but demonstrates that only samples with Mn/Sr values of less than 0.2 show no sign of alteration. Sr-rich, formerly aragonitic limestones can potentially be used for chemostratigraphic purposes with an uncertainty of around (± 0.0002 in $^{87}Sr/^{86}Sr$ ratio. Carbon-isotope ratios show no sign of alteration even in the Chinese limestones with a strong pressure-solution cleavage.

3) a negative-to-positive carbon-isotope anomaly in an upwards-shallowing slope to shelf succession immediately prior to glaciation in E Greenland is interpreted as primary in origin. The strata with negative $\delta^{13}C$ values are interpreted to have been originally deposited as sediments deposited beneath the ^{13}C-depleted deep waters of a stratified ocean, which has been previously invoked to explain the prolonged period of high $\delta^{13}C$ values in shallow-water Neoproterozoic strata. This example may have been influenced by restricted circulation in an elongated, probably fault-bounded basin. The new data strengthen concerns about the global applicability and relationship to glaciations of negative carbon-isotope anomalies.

Note added after submission of revised manuscript

New carbon-isotope results on organic C separates from the top of the Ella section of bedgroup 19 (equivalent to bed-group 20), with distance below the base of the glacial deposits, are: $-27.3‰$ (0 m), $-28.3‰$ (14.6 m), and $-22.8‰$ (17.9 m). Knoll et al. (1986) obtained results of $-30.0‰$ and $-34.8‰$ from the main part of bed-group 19, which differed by 25.8 and 28.1‰, respectively, between organic and carbonate carbon fractions. The new results imply a carbonate $\delta^{13}C$ value around zero, which in comparison to the negative-to-positive upward trend at Kap Weber could be explained by a combination of marine stratification and a secular increase in carbon isotope signals immediately prior to glaciation.

ACKNOWLEDGMENTS

Greenland samples were collected in 1985 under grant GR3/5438 to Brian Harland on an expedition led by Michael Hambrey. Chinese samples were collected in 1993 with the aid of a Royal Society scientific exchange grant and considerable help from personnel in the Golden Stone Beach administrative district. Dr. N. Walsh and Ms. J. Harris are thanked for assistance with use of ICP facilities at the University of London and Birmingham, respectively, and Mrs. P. F. Derbyshire for assistance with Sr isotope analyses at the NIGL, and we are grateful to Graham Shields, Robert Rainbird, Grant Young, Jay Kaufman, and editor Noel James for suggested improvements to the manuscript.

REFERENCES

ASMEROM, Y., JACOBSEN, S. B., KNOLL, A. H., BUTTERFIELD, N. J., AND SWETT, K., 1991, Strontium isotopic variations of Neoproterozoic seawater: Implications for crustal evolution: Geochimica et Cosmochimica Acta, v. 55, p. 2883–2894.

BEAUCHAMP, B., OLDERSHAW, A. E., AND KROUSE, H. R., 1987, Upper Carboniferous to Upper Permian ^{13}C-enriched primary carbonates in the Sverdrup Basin, Canadian Arctic: Comparisons to coeval western North American ocean margins: Chemical Geology, v. 65, p. 391–413.

BERGER, W. H., AND VINCENT, E., 1986, Deep-sea carbonates: Reading the carbon-isotope signal: Geologische Rundschau, v. 75, p. 249–269.

BERTRAND-SARFATI, J., MOUSSINE-POUCHKINE, A., ARNARD, B., AND AÏT KACI AHMED, A., 1995, First Ediacaran fauna found in western Africa and evidence for an Early Cambrian glaciation: Geology, v. 23, p. 133–136.

BRASIER, M. D., SHIELDS, G., KULESHOV, V. N., AND ZHEGALLO, E. A., 1996, Integrated chemo- and biostratigraphic calibration of early animal evolution: Neoproterozoic–early Cambrian of southwest Mongolia: Geological Magazine, v. 133, p. 445–485.

BROOKFIELD, M. E., 1994, Problems in applying preservation, facies and sequence models to Sinian (Neoproterozoic) glacial sequences in Australia and Asia: Precambrian Research, v. 70, p. 113–143.

COWIE, J. W., ZIEGLER, W., AND REMANE, J., 1989, Stratigraphic commission accelerates progress, 1984–1989: Episodes, v. 12, p. 79–80.

DERRY, L. A., KETO, L. S., JACOBSEN, S. B., KNOLL, A. H., AND SWETT, K., 1989, Sr isotopic variations in Upper Proterozoic carbonates from Svalbard and East Greenland: Geochimica et Cosmochimica Acta, v. 53, p. 2331–2339.

DERRY, L. A., KAUFMAN, A. J., AND JACOBSEN, S. B., 1992, Sedimentary cycling and environmental change in the Late Proterozoic: evidence from stable and radiogenic isotopes: Geochimica et Cosmochimica Acta, v. 56, p. 1317–1329.

EYLES, N., 1993, Earth's glacial record and its tectonic setting: Earth-Science Reviews, v. 35, p. 1–248.

FAIRCHILD, I. J., 1991, Origins of carbonate in Neoproterozoic stromatolites and the identification of modern analogues: Precambrian Research, v. 53, p. 281–299.

FAIRCHILD, I. J., 1993, Balmy shores and icy wastes: the paradox of carbonates associated with glacial deposits in Neoproterozoic times: Sedimentology Review, v. 1, p. 1–17.

FAIRCHILD, I. J., AND HAMBREY, M. J., 1995, Vendian basin evolution in East Greenland and NE Svalbard: Precambrian Research, v. 73, p. 217–233.

FAIRCHILD, I. J., AND HERRINGTON, P. M., 1989, A tempestite–evaporite–stromatolite association (late Vendian, East Greenland): a shoreface–lagoon model: Precambrian Research, v. 43, p. 101–127.

FAIRCHILD, I. J., AND SPIRO, B., 1987, Petrological and isotopic implications of some contrasting Late Precambrian carbonates, NE Spitsbergen: Sedimentology, v. 34, p. 973–989.

FAIRCHILD, I. J., HAMBREY, M. J., JEFFERSON, T. H., AND SPIRO, B., 1989, Late Proterozoic glacial carbonates in NE Spitsbergen: new insights into the carbonate–tillite association: Geological Magazine, v. 126, p. 469–490.

FAIRCHILD, I. J., MARSHALL, J. D. AND BERTRAND-SARFATI, J., 1990, Stratigraphic shifts in carbon isotopes from Proterozoic stromatolitic carbonates (Mauritania): influences of primary mineralogy and diagenesis: American Journal of Science, v. 290-A, p. 46–79.

FAIRCHILD, I. J., KNOLL, A. H., AND SWETT, K., 1991, Coastal lithofacies and biofacies associated with syn-depositional dolomitization and silicification (Draken Formation, Upper Riphean, Svalbard): Precambrian Research, v. 53, p. 165–197.

FAIRCHILD, I. J., EINSELE, G., AND SONG, T., 1997, Possible seismic origin of molar-tooth structures in Neoproterozoic carbonate ramp deposits, north China: Sedimentology, v. 44, p. 611–636.

GROTZINGER, J. P., 1989, Facies and evolution of Precambrian carbonate depositional systems: The emergence of the modern platform archetype, *in* Crevello, P. D., Wilson, J. L., Sarg, J. F., and Read, J. F., eds., Controls on Carbonate Platform and Basin Development: SEPM, Special Publication 44, p. 79–106.

GROTZINGER, J. P., BOWRING, S. A., SAYLOR, B. Z., AND KAUFMAN, A. J., 1995, Biostratigraphic and geochronologic constraints on early animal evolution: Science, v. 270, p. 598–604.

HAMBREY, M. J., AND SPENCER, A. M., 1987, Late Precambrian glaciation of central east Greenland: Meddelser om Grønland, v. 19, p. 1–50.

HERRINGTON, P. M., 1989, Stratigraphy, sedimentology, and diagenesis of Late Precambrian Carbonates from the Upper Limestone-Dolomite "Series", central East Greenland (unpublished Ph.D. thesis): University of Birmingham, 226 p.

HERRINGTON, P. M., AND FAIRCHILD, I. J., 1989, Carbonate shelf and slope facies evolution prior to Vendian glaciation, central east Greenland, *in* Gayer, R. A., ed., The Caledonide Geology of Scandinavia: London, Graham & Trotman, p. 263–273.

HOFFMAN, P. F., KAUFMAN, A. J., HALVERSON, G. P., AND SCHRAG, D. P., 1998, A Neoproterozoic snowball Earth: Science, v. 281, p. 1342–1346.

JACOBSEN, S. B., AND KAUFMAN, A. J., 1999, The Sr, C and O isotopic evolution of Neoproterozoic seawater: Chemical Geology, v. 161, p. 37–57.

JAMES, N. P., NARBONNE, G. M. AND SHERMAN, A. G., 1998, Molar-tooth carbonates: Shallow subtidal facies of the Mid- to Late Proterozoic: Journal of Sedimentary Research, v. 68, p. 716–722.

KAUFMAN, A. J., AND KNOLL, A. H., 1995, Neoproterozoic variations in the C-isotopic composition of seawater: stratigraphic and biogeochemical implications: Precambrian Research, v. 73, p. 27–49.

KAUFMAN, A. J., HAYES, J. M, KNOLL, A. H., AND GERMS, G. J. B., 1991, Isotopic compositions of carbonates and organic carbon from upper Proterozoic successions in Namibia: stratigraphic variation and the effects of diagenesis and metamorphism: Precambrian Research, v. 49, p. 301–327.

KAUFMAN, A. J., JACOBSEN, S. B., AND KNOLL, A. H., 1993, The Vendian record of Sr and C isotopic variations in seawater: Implications for tectonics and paleoclimate: Earth and Planetary Science Letters, v. 120, p. 409–430.

KAUFMAN, A. J., KNOLL, A. H., AND NARBONNE, G. M., 1997, Isotopes, ice ages, and terminal Proterozoic earth history: National Academy of Sciences, [U.S.A.], Proceedings, v. 94, p. 6600–6605.

KEITH, M. L., 1982, Violent volcanism, stagnant oceans and some inferences regarding petroleum, strata-bound ores and mass extinctions: Geochimica et Comochimica Acta, v. 46, p. 2621–2637.

KENNEDY, M. J., 1996, Stratigraphy, sedimentology, and isotopic geochemistry of Australian Neoproterozoic postglacial cap dolostones: deglaciation, δ^{13}C excursions, and carbonate precipitation: Journal of Sedimentary Research, v. 66, p. 1050–1064.

KENNEDY, M. J., RUNNEGAR, B., PRAVE, A. R., HOFFMANN, K.-H., and ARTHUR, M. A., 1998, Two or four Neoproterozoic glaciations?: Geology, v. 26, p. 1059–1063.

KIRSCHVINK, J. L, 1992, Late Proterozoic low-latitude global glaciation: the snowball Earth, *in* Schopf, J. W., and Klein, C., eds., The Proterozoic Biosphere: Cambridge, U.K., Cambridge University Press, p. 51–52.

KLEIN, C., AND BEUKES, N. J., 1993, Sedimentology and geochemistry of the glaciogenic Late Proterozoic Rapitan iron-formation in Canada: Economic Geology, v. 88, p. 542–565.

KNOLL, A. H., 1993, Neoproterozoic evolution and environmental change, *in* Bengtston, S., ed., Early Life on Earth: New York, Columbia University Press, Nobel Symposium 84, p. 439–449.

KNOLL, A. H., AND SWETT, K., 1990, Carbonate deposition during the Late Proterozoic era: an example from Spitsbergen: American Journal of Science, v. 290-A, p.104–131.

KNOLL, A. H., AND WALTER, M. R., 1992, Latest Proterozoic stratigraphy and Earth history: Nature, v. 356, p. 673–678.

KNOLL, A. H., HAYES, J. M., KAUFMAN, A. J., SWETT, K., AND LAMBERT, I. B., 1986, Secular variation in carbon isotope ratios from Upper Proterozoic successions of Svalbard and East Greenland: Nature, v. 321, p. 832–839.

KNOLL, A. H., FAIRCHILD, I. J., AND SWETT, K., 1993, Calcified microbes in Neoproterozoic carbonates: implications for our understanding of the Proterozoic/Cambrian transition: Palaios, v. 8, p. 512–525.

KNOLL, A. H., BAMBACH, R. K., CANFIELD, D. E., AND GROTZINGER, J. P., 1996, Comparative Earth history and Late Permian mass extinction: Science, v. 273, p. 452–457.

LI, Z. X., 1994, Collision between the North and South China blocks: a crustal-detachment model for suturing in the region east of the Tanlu fault: Geology, v. 22, p. 739–742.

LI, Z. X., ZHANG, L., AND POWELL, C. MCA., 1996, Positions of the East Asian cratons in the Neoproterozoic supercontinent Rodinia: Australian Journal of Earth Sciences, v. 43, p. 593–604.

LU, S., MA, G., GA, Z., AND LIN, W., 1985, Sinian ice ages and glacial sedimentary facies-areas in China: Precambrian Research, v. 29, p. 53–63.

LOGAN, G. A., HAYES, J. M., HIESHIMA, G. B., AND SUMMONS, R., 1995, Terminal Proterozoic reorganization of biogeochemical cycles: Nature, v. 376, p. 53–56.

MCARTHUR, J. M., 1994, Recent trends in Sr isotope stratigraphy: Terra Nova, v. 6, p. 33–358.

MCKERROW, W. S., SCOTESE, C. R., AND BRASIER, M. D., 1992, Early Cambrian continental reconstructions: Geological Society Journal, London, v. 149, p. 599–606.

MCCREA, J. M., 1950, The isotope chemistry of carbonates and a paleotemperature scale: Journal of Chemical Physics, v. 18, p. 849–857.

MONCRIEFF, A. C. M., 1988, The Vendian Stratigraphy and Sedimentology of East Greenland: (unpublished Ph.D. dissertation), University of Cambridge.

MONCRIEFF, A. C. M., AND HAMBREY, M. J., 1990, Marginal-marine glacial sedimentation in the late Precambrian succession of East Greenland, *in* Dowdeswell, J. A., and Scourse, J. D., eds., Glacimarine Environments: Processes and Sediments: Geological Society of London, Special Publication 53, p. 387–410.

MUNNECKE, A., WESTPHAL, H., REIJMER, J. J. G., AND SAMTLEBEN, C., 1997, Microspar development during early marine burial diagenesis: a comparison of Pliocene carbonates from the Bahamas with Silurian limestones from Gotland (Sweden): Sedimentology, v. 44, p. 977–990.

PATTERSON, W. P., AND WALTER, L. M., 1994a, Syndepositional diagenesis of modern platform carbonates: Evidence from isotopic and minor element data: Geology, v. 22, p. 127–130.

PATTERSON, W. P., AND WALTER, L. M., 1994b, Depletion in ^{13}C in seawater CO_2 on modern carbonate platforms: Significance for the carbon isotopic record of carbonates: Geology, v. 22, p. 885–888.

PELECHATY, S. M., KAUFMAN, A. J., AND GROTZINGER, J. P., 1996, Evaluation of δ^{13}C chemostratigraphy for intrabasinal correlation: Vendian strata of northeast Siberia: Geological Society of America, Bulletin, v. 108, p. 992–1003.

QIAO X., SONG T., LI, H., AND GAO L., 1996, Genetic stratigraphy of the Sinian and Lower Cambrian strata in south Liaoning province: Beijing, Science Press, 174 p. + 24 pl.

RICHTER, F. M., ROWLEY, D. B., AND DEPAOLO, D. J., 1992, Sr isotope evolution of seawater: the role of tectonics: Earth and Planetary Science Letters, v. 109, p. 11–23.

ROSS, G. M., BLOCH, J. D., AND KROUSE, H. R., 1995, Neoproterozoic strata of the southern Canadian Cordillera and the isotopic evolution of seawater sulfate: Precambrian Research, v. 73, p. 71–99.

SAYLOR, B. Z., KAUFMAN, A. J., GROTZINGER, J. P., AND URBAN, F., 1998, A composite reference section for terminal Proterozoic strata of southern Namibia: Journal of Sedimentary Research, v. 68, p. 1223–1235.

SCHMIDT, P. W., AND WILLIAMS, G. E., 1995, The Neoproterozoic climatic paradox: Equatorial palaeolatitude for Marinoan glaciation near sea level in South Australia: Earth and Planetary Science Letters, v. 134, p. 107–124.

SHIELDS, G., STILLE, P., BRASIER, M. D., AND ATUDOREI, N. V., 1997, Stratified oceans and oxygenation of the late Precambrian environment: a postglacial geochemical record from the Neoproterozoic of W. Mongolia: Terra Nova, v. 9, p. 218–222.

SØNDERHOLM, M., AND TIRSGAARD, H., 1993, Lithostratigraphic framework of the Upper Proterozoic Eleonore Bay Supergroup of East and North-east Greenland: Grønlands Geologische Undersøgelse, Bulletin, v. 167, 38 p.

SPIRO, B., AND FAIRCHILD, I. J., 1996, Strontium isotope ratios in water leachates of calcareous rocks and their significance, *in* Bottrell, S. ed., Fourth International Symposium on the Geochemistry of the Earth's Surface, Proceedings, Ilkley, Yorkshire, July 1996: Leeds, University of Leeds, p. 672–676.

SWETT, K., AND KNOLL, A., 1989, Marine pisolites from Upper Proterozoic carbonates of East Greenland and Spitsbergen: Sedimentology, v. 36, p. 75–93.

TAYLOR, K. G., AND CURTIS, C. D., 1995, Stability and facies association of early diagenetic mineral assemblages: an example from a Jurassic ironstone–mudstone succession, UK: Journal of Sedimentary Research, v. A65, p. 358–368.

THOMPSON, M., AND WALSH, J. N., 1983, A Handbook of Inductively-Coupled Plasma Spectrometry: London, Blackie.

TUCKER, M. E., 1983, Sedimentation of organic-rich limestones in the Late Precambrian of southern Norway: Precambrian Research, v. 22, p. 295–315.

TUCKER, M. E., 1986, Formerly aragonitic limestones associated with tillites in the Late Proterozoic of Death Valley, California: Journal of Sedimentary Petrology, v. 56, p. 818–830.

VEIZER, J., 1989, Strontium isotopes in seawater through time: Annual Review of Earth and Planetary Sciences, v. 17, p. 141–167.

YOUNG, G. M., 1995, Are Neoproterozoic glacial deposits preserved on the margins of Laurentia related to the fragmentation of two supercontinents?: Geology, v. 23, p. 153–156.

THE INTEGRITY OF δ^{18}O RECORDS IN PRECAMBRIAN CARBONATES: A MESOPROTEROZOIC CASE STUDY

TRACY D. FRANK

Department of Earth Sciences, University of Queensland, Brisbane, Queensland 4072, Australia

AND

TIMOTHY W. LYONS

Department of Geological Sciences, University of Missouri, Columbia, Missouri 65211, U.S.A.

ABSTRACT: A high-resolution, integrated approach was used to assess the integrity of the oxygen-isotope record derived from carbonates of the Helena Formation of the Mesoproterozoic Belt Supergroup, western Montana. Paired stable-isotope and minor-element analyses were performed on multiple microsamples from the full range of petrographic components, including ooids, intergranular cements, molar-tooth calcite, dolomitic mudstone, stromatolites, and late-stage diagenetic cements in crosscutting fractures. Data were examined within a context of sedimentologic and petrographic constraints to assess temporal and spatial effects on isotopic compositions. Petrographic and isotopic constraints demonstrate that δ^{18}O values that best approximate primary oxygen-isotope compositions occur in syndepositional and early diagenetic intergranular cements within oolitic grainstones that occur in the upper part of the Helena Formation. While cautious in our interpretation, we also recognize fundamental patterns in isotopic and geochemical data which indicate that oxygen-isotope compositions of other petrographic components in the Helena Formation have not been completely homogenized and reset during diagenesis. These include: (1) stratigraphic and facies-specific trends in isotopic compositions that are consistent with inferred depositional conditions, (2) compositional heterogeneities within and among individual petrographic components on small spatial scales, and (3) retention of the expected oxygen-isotope fractionation between early-formed calcite and associated dolomite pairs. Although diagenetic overprints are significant, these relationships argue against wholesale diagenetic resetting of primary compositions and suggest that with careful examination, general depositional controls can be discerned in oxygen-isotope data from the Helena Formation.

INTRODUCTION

Whereas numerous investigations have demonstrated the value of oxygen isotopes as indicators of ocean chemistry and paleoenvironment in studies of Phanerozoic marine carbonates, the utility of oxygen isotopes in Precambrian reconstructions remains ambiguous. This ambiguity stems mainly from the paucity of unaltered limestone in Precambrian strata that could serve as a basis for comparison. While oxygen-isotope studies of marine cherts, phosphates, and carbonates have yielded some insight into Precambrian ocean chemistry (e.g., Perry and Tan, 1972; Knauth and Lowe, 1978; Perry and Ahmad, 1983; Karhu and Epstein, 1986; Burdett et al., 1990; Veizer et al., 1992a; Veizer et al., 1992b), a preponderance of extremely negative δ^{18}O values has fostered a heated debate concerning the relative influences of diagenetic overprints, ocean temperature, and ocean chemistry on the oxygen-isotope compositions of Precambrian marine sediments (e.g., Muehlenbachs and Clayton, 1976; Veizer and Hoefs, 1976; Gregory and Taylor, 1981; Walker and Lohmann, 1989; Holmden and Muehlenbachs, 1993). Because of the inferred extremes in either Precambrian ocean temperature or composition necessary to account for exceedingly low δ^{18}O values (Anderson and Arthur, 1983), oxygen-isotope data derived from Precambrian carbonates are commonly neglected under the assumption that primary signatures have been obliterated during burial and prolonged exposure to isotopically light diagenetic fluids. Few workers, however, have attempted to assess the robustness of the Precambrian oxygen isotope record by considering data in a rigorous context of regional depositional facies patterns, paragenetic relations, and possible diagenetic and metamorphic overprints on original isoopic compositions. Notable exceptions include studies by Zempolich et al. (1988) on the Neoproterozoic Beck Spring Dolomite in eastern California and Burdett et al. (1990) on the Paleoproterozoic Rocknest Formation in northwestern Canada.

In this paper, we examine an extensive suite of oxygen-isotope data that were generated in conjunction with a detailed evaluation of carbon-isotope trends in the Helena Formation of the Mesoproterozoic Belt Supergroup (Frank et al., 1997). A marine to restricted-marine depositional setting for the Helena Formation has been inferred previously on the basis of carbon-isotope data (Frank et al., 1997) and the widespread occurrence of molar-tooth structures in fine-grained Helena lithologies (Frank and Lyons, 1998). The intent of the present study is to assess the quality of the oxygen-isotope record in the Helena Formation and, in a broader sense, the potential for recognizing primary signals in Precambrian carbonates. Rather than relying on bulk sampling methods, we employed the rigorous style of integrated geochemistry routinely applied in diagenetic studies of Phanerozoic sequences, which emphasizes microsampling of individual petrographic components and evaluating the resulting data within a strict stratigraphic, sedimentologic, and petrographic context. Such an approach eliminates questions of wholesale diagenetic resetting of primary isotopic compositions and, ultimately, allows for better discrimination between primary and secondary isotopic signatures.

GEOLOGIC FRAMEWORK

Age and Tectonic Setting

The rocks of the Belt Supergroup of the western United States and the correlative Purcell Supergroup of Canada are the most extensive Mesoproterozoic succession in western North America (Fig. 1; Winston, 1990). Radiometric dating suggests that Belt deposition began 1450 Ma (Harrison, 1984; Ross et al., 1992). Estimates for the age of the upper contact range from 900 to 1250 Ma (Elston and Bressler, 1980; Elston, 1984; Harrison, 1984; Ross et al., 1992). U–Pb$_{zir}$ dating of a bentonite bed in the upper part of the Helena Formation, however, has recently yielded an age of 1449 Ma (Aleinikoff et al., 1996), thus highlighting the remaining uncertainty in age control. During the Mesoproterozoic, the eastern and southern limits of the Belt basin were defined by the North American craton and the Dillon Block of the Wyoming Province (Hoffman, 1989; Win-

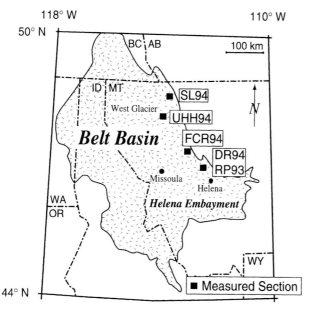

FIG. 1.—Map of field area showing the approximate limit of Belt Supergroup and age-equivalent strata (stippled area), and locations of measured sections. After Harrison (1972).

Formation is the eastern facies of the middle Belt carbonate interval and grades westward into more argillaceous beds of the Wallace Formation (Winston, 1990). Along the eastern margin of the Belt basin, where samples for the present study were collected (Fig. 1), the Helena Formation reaches a maximum thickness of 100–200 m. Here, the lower part of the Helena Formation consists of a series of 1–10 m thick cyclic intervals of fine-grained, siliciclastic-rich sediment that grades upward into variably dolomitized, microlaminated mudstone (Fig. 2). The middle part of the Helena Formation in this part of the basin is dominated by domal stromatolites associated with high-energy facies, including oolites and intraclastites (Fig. 2; Winston, 1998). This stromatolite-dominated interval corresponds to the stromatolitic *Baicalia–Conophyton* horizon of Winston and Lyons (1993), which provides a distinct lithostratigraphic marker that aids in correlation of the Helena and Wallace Formations over broad regions of the eastern and central Belt basin. Above the stromatolite-rich interval, microlaminated mudstones dominate in sections in the eastern part of the basin, although interbeds of cryptalgal laminites, domal stromatolites, oolites, and intraclastites also occur (Fig. 2). Mudstones become increasingly dolomitic toward the top of the section and, in the uppermost part of the Helena Formation, show evidence of desiccation and subaerial exposure (Winston and Lyons, 1993; Winston, 1998).

SEDIMENTOLOGY AND PETROGRAPHY

Fine-Grained Cyclic Intervals

Within the study area, significant portions of the lower Helena Formation consist of a series of 1–10-m-thick cyclic intervals separated by coarse lag deposits. Cycles consist of fine-grained, siliciclastic-rich calcisilitites that grade upward into dolomitized microlaminated mudstones. Calcareous mudstones that cap individual cycles commonly contain a range of sheet-like and bleb-like features filled with microcrystalline calcite that weather recessively into the surrounding dolomitized mudstone (Fig. 3). Sedimentologic relations indicate that these features, known collectively as "molar-tooth" structures, formed prior to significant lithification and compaction of the surrounding sediment. For example, initially continuous laminae that intersect molar-tooth structures are now truncated at the boundaries of these features, whereas sedimentary laminae above and below molar-tooth structures are compactionally draped around them (Furniss et al., 1998). Molar-tooth structures have commonly been folded, broken, and offset because of later compaction of the sediment around them (Smith, 1968). Concentrations of reworked fragments of molar-tooth structures form the lag deposits that mark the bases of fine-grained cyclic intervals. At such surfaces, the eroded tops of *in situ* molar-tooth structures extend upward into lag deposits, which occur as lenses or thin, continuous layers. Considered as a whole, these petrographic and sedimentologic characteristics indicate that molar-tooth calcite precipitated at shallow burial depths and within reach of erosive currents (Winston and Lyons, 1993).

The petrographic and geochemical attributes of molar-tooth structures suggest that they reflect rapid precipitation of calcite into early diagenetic gas-generated voids in cohesive muds during early diagenesis (Frank and Lyons, 1998; Furniss et al.,

ston, 1990). A recent geochronological study indicates that the western margin of the Belt basin, as long inferred on the basis of sedimentologic observations and plate-tectonic reconstructions (Winston, 1986, 1989; Dalziel, 1991; Moores, 1991; Young, 1995), was bounded by the North Australian craton (McDonald et al., 1997). Uncertainties regarding the northern and northwestern margins of the basin have left open the long-lived debate regarding marine versus nonmarine depositional conditions (Winston and Link, 1993; and references therein). Whereas stratigraphic and sedimentologic relationships are relatively ambiguous, geochemically based paleoenvironmental reconstructions favor deposition under marine to restricted marine conditions within a shallow, semi-enclosed basin that was intermittently connected to the open Mesoproterozoic ocean (Frank et al., 1997; Lyons et al., in press).

Belt strata thicken from about 5 km in the Helena Embayment, an eastward-extending projection of the Belt basin, to a maximum of about 18 km in the western part of the basin (Winston, 1990). Oxygen-isotope geothermometry, studies of illite transformation, and previous oxygen-isotope studies of Belt carbonates have documented an overprint on the western and deeper part of Belt section that is consistent with low-grade metamorphism (Maxwell and Hower, 1967; Eslinger and Savin, 1973; Hall and Veizer, 1996). Consequently, samples used in the present study were collected from five measured sections located along the eastern margin of the Belt basin, where burial conditions were less extreme and the Helena Formation has not been metamorphosed (Fig. 1; Harrison, 1972; Schieber, 1989).

Stratigraphy

The Belt Supergroup is subdivided informally from bottom to top into the lower Belt Group, the Ravalli Group, the middle Belt carbonate interval, and the Missoula Group. The Helena

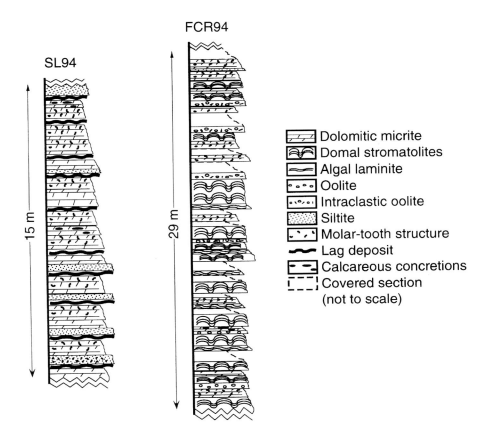

FIG. 2.—Measured sections from within the lower (SL94) and middle to upper (FCR94) Helena Formation illustrating the character and stratigraphic distribution of lithofacies along the eastern margin of the Belt Basin. Fine-grained cyclic intervals dominate in the lower Helena Formation (SL94). The middle to upper part of the formation is more variable lithologically and dominated by domal stromatolites associated with high-energy facies, including oolites and intraclastites (FCR94); the abundance of microlaminated mudstone interbeds increases in the uppermost part of the section.

1998). These attributes include the microcrystalline nature of molar-tooth calcite, the restriction of molar-tooth structures to fine-grained lithologies, a lack of detrital infill, the ovoid to nearly spherical shape of some structures, and the formation of molar-tooth structures proximal to the sediment–water interface within unlithified sediment. In some cases, precipitation of molar-tooth-related calcite extended into the surrounding sediment to form calcitic rims that project 1–5 mm beyond the sharp walls of molar-tooth structures and into the host sediment, which is otherwise variably replaced by fine-grained dolomite (Frank et al., 1997). These paragenetic relationships and the inclusion of clasts of dolomitized mudstone into lag concentrations suggest that Helena mudstones were dolomitized soon after the precipitation of molar-tooth calcite and prior to the erosion and deposition of lag concentrations of reworked molar-tooth fragments. Considered as a whole, these associations imply geochemical conditions that promoted widespread and rapid calcite precipitation into early formed sedimentary voids and near synsedimentary dolomitization of these shallow-water sediments.

Stromatolites

The Helena Formation is noted for the occurrence of decimeter- to meter-scale, variably dolomitized stromatolites with exceptionally well-preserved microtextures (Horodyski, 1989).

Stromatolites are most prominent within two cyclic, stratigraphic horizons in the middle part of the formation (the *Baicalia–Conophyton* cycles of Winston, 1993; Winston, 1998). *Baicalia* and *Conophyton* are poorly developed along the eastern margin of the Belt basin (Winston, 1998), where samples for the present study were collected. In this part of the basin, the cyclic *Baicalia–Conophyton* marker horizons are supplanted by domal stromatolites that are surrounded by and interbedded with oolitic and intraclastic lithologies, indicating deposition under high-energy, shallow water conditions. By contrast, the development of two cycles of biohermal, branched *Baicalia* overlain by *Conophyton* forms in the western part of the basin may reflect cycles of deepening or expansion of the water column not experienced to the east (Winston, 1998). Throughout the Belt basin, algal facies become less frequent above the *Baicalia–Conophyton* stratigraphic horizon. Where they occur along the eastern margin of the basin, they are typically associated with oolites, intraclastites, and microlaminated, dolomitic mudstones, which become desiccated and mudcracked in the uppermost part of the section.

Oolitic Grainstone

Oolitic beds ranging from approximately 0.03 to 0.1 m in thickness are common along the eastern margin of the Belt basin in the middle to upper part of the Helena Formation. Al-

FIG. 3.—Field photograph of dolomitized mudstone that constitutes the upper halves of meter-scale siliciclastic-to-carbonate cycles in the Helena Formation (Measured Section SL94). Abundant *in situ* molar-tooth structures are visible as dark wrinkled ribbons and blebs on the outcrop surface. Reworked fragments of molar-tooth occur in a 3-cm-thick lag concentration (dark layer in the middle to upper part of the photographed area). In outcrop, the dolomitic host sediment weathers to a yellowish or buff color, whereas calcitic molar-tooth structures are uniformly gray.

though ooids are now composed of low-Mg calcite (LMC), ooid fabrics suggest that they represent the neomorphosed products of originally aragonite, high-Mg calcite, and bimineralic ooids (Eby, 1977; Tucker, 1984). Owing to excellent retention of primary radial fabrics, the present study focuses on former high-Mg calcite ooids as inferred from the presence of microdolomite inclusions (Lohmann and Meyers, 1977). Helena oolites contain two generations of cement. The first generation occurs as a 0.1–0.3 mm thick isopachous coating of bladed to prismatic calcite on ooid cortices (Fig. 4). On the basis of petrographic constraints, including its restriction to primary intergranular pore space, its isopachous nature and its morphological resemblance to Phanerozoic marine cements, this phase has been interpreted as the calcitized product of a synsedimentary cement (Frank et al., 1997). Under cathodoluminescence (CL) the isopachous cement appears either zoned or to consist of irregular intergrowths of luminescent and nonluminescent calcite. In either case, nonluminescent areas are concentrated in crystal interiors, whereas luminescent areas tend to occur along crystal margins and at crystal terminations. If not completely occluded by the synsedimentary cement, the remaining pore space in Helena oolites is filled with CL zoned, equant calcite spar (Fig. 4). Petrographic relations suggest that this phase was emplaced prior to compaction (Frank et al., 1997). Isopachous and equant cements predate dully luminescent, blocky cements, which fill late-stage subvertical fractures that crosscut Helena lithologies.

The retention of CL zones in equant cement and in some examples of isopachous cement suggests that these phases have not been altered or replaced since formation, chiefly because it would be difficult to either preserve or create CL zones during the dissolution–precipitation reactions attendant to carbonate diagenesis. By contrast, the disruption of CL zones in radial ooid cortices and in some samples of isopachous cement indicates that these components have been recrystallized or variably replaced during diagenesis (Fig. 4; e.g., Given and Lohmann, 1985; Frank and Lohmann, 1996).

METHODS

Microsamples for geochemical (200–300 μg) and isotopic (20–30 μg) analysis were drilled from polished slabs and from the same thin sections used for petrographic analysis using a microscope-mounted drilling assembly and dental drill bits with 20 to 500 μm tip diameters. Microsamples were roasted under vacuum at 380°C for one hour to remove volatile contaminants. Microsamples for carbon and oxygen isotopic analysis, including splits from samples designated for geochemical analysis, were reacted at 73°C with anhydrous phosphoric acid in individual reaction vessels of an on-line, automated Kiel device coupled to a Finnigan–MAT 251 mass spectrometer. Oxygen-isotope ratios were corrected for ^{17}O contribution (Craig, 1957) and are reported in permil (‰) relative to the VPDB standard. Precision is better than 0.1‰ for $\delta^{13}C$ and $\delta^{18}O$ values and was monitored through daily analyses of NBS 19 ($\delta^{18}O$ = −2.19‰) and other powdered calcite standards; the fractionation factor used to calculate the $\delta^{18}O$ value of carbonate is 1.00867. Data are available in Frank et al. (1997).

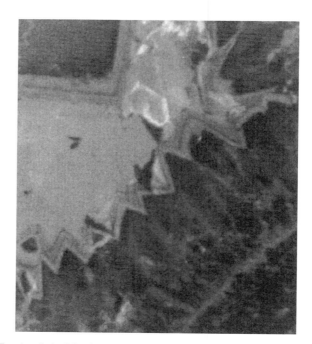

FIG. 4.—Cathodoluminescence photomicrograph of intergranular cements in oolitic grainstone (Measured Section FCR94). The first generation of cement has a bladed to prismatic morphology and forms isopachous coatings on radial–concentric ooid cortices. Early parts of overlying equant cement crystals contain luminescent subzones that mimic adjacent crystal terminations, whereas later parts are uniformly luminescent. Width of photomicrograph is approximately 300 μm.

Concentrations of Ca, Mg, Sr, Mn, and Fe were determined by inductively coupled plasma–atomic emission spectrometry (ICP-AES) using a Leeman Labs Plasma-Spec III (Table 1). Analytical precision, determined using gravimetric standards, was ±2% for Ca, ±3% for Mg and Sr, ±4% for Mn, and ±5% for Fe. Where small sample size precluded analysis by ICP-AES, concentrations of Ca, Mg, Mn, and Fe were measured by electron microprobe analysis (EMPA); Sr concentrations were not measured using this method because EMPA detection limits for Sr in carbonates exceed Sr contents in Helena carbonates. Microprobe analyses were conducted on a Cameca Camebax microprobe with a beam current of 15 nA, a spot size of 6–10 μm, and an accelerating voltage of 15 kV for Mg and Ca and 30 kV for Mn and Fe. Counting time was 30 s, and analytical precision was monitored through five replicate analyses at each spot. Raw cation contents were converted to weights of $MeCO_3$, and total weights of the collective $MeCO_3$ species were used to convert to ppm (where Me is the minor element in question). Detection limits were 270 ppm for Ca, 180 ppm for Mg, 200 ppm for Mn, and 160 ppm for Fe.

RESULTS

Stratigraphic Trends

Preservation of primary δ¹³C values in eastern sections of the Helena Formation has been demonstrated previously by a correspondence in carbon-isotope compositions among the full array of petrographic components distributed over a broad stratigraphic range and among five measured sections located along the eastern margin of the Belt basin (Fig. 5; Frank et al., 1997). In the eastern part of the basin, the Helena Formation is marked by a distinct stratigraphic increase in δ¹³C values, from an average of −0.2‰ at the bottom of the formation to an average of +1.4‰ near the top (Fig. 5). Stratigraphically, this progression to more positive δ¹³C values begins just below the transition from fine-grained facies characteristic of the lower part of the Helena Formation to interbedded fine-grained lithologies, stromatolitic facies and oolites characteristic of the middle and upper parts of the section. Although a global change in the carbon cycle cannot be entirely ruled out (e.g., Knoll et al., 1995), the correspondence between isotopic and sedimentologic data suggests that the stratigraphic shift in δ¹³C values is more likely related to a temporal change in local conditions. Sedimentologic features within and above the lateral equivalent of the *Baicalia–Conophyton* stratigraphic horizon along the eastern margin of the Belt basin are consistent with increasing restriction, including mixed-mineralogy ooids and evidence for their synsedimentary deformation (e.g., Eby, 1977; Tucker, 1984), occasional molds and casts after halite (Eby, 1977), a gradual increase in the dolomite content of calcareous mudstones (Winston and Lyons, 1993), and the occurrence of desiccation and subaerial exposure features in the uppermost part of the section (Winston, 1998). In light of these constraints, the increase in δ¹³C values has been interpreted previously to reflect a basin-wide increase in biologic productivity and, ultimately, gradual restriction of the eastern part of the Belt basin (Frank et al., 1997). Furthermore, the associated increase in salinity could have contributed to a rise in the rate of CO_2 outgassing with a corresponding carbon-isotope effect (i.e., Stiller et al., 1985).

TABLE 1.—Mg, Sr, Mn, AND Fe CONCENTRATIONS IN SELECTED PETROGRAPHIC COMPONENTS OF THE HELENA FORMATION.

Component	Sample #	Mg (ppm)	Sr (ppm)	Mn (ppm)	Fe (ppm)	Method
Equant cement	FCR94-14	518		872	365	EMPA
Equant cement	FCR94-14	373		857	383	EMPA
Equant cement	FCR94-14	435		728	364	EMPA
Equant cement	FCR94-14	705		1226	347	EMPA
Equant cement	FCR94-14	447		894	325	EMPA
Equant cement	FCR94-3	794		332	241	EMPA
Equant cement	FCR94-3	786		343	433	EMPA
Equant cement	FCR94-3	995		493	292	EMPA
Equant cement	FCR94-3	744		292	191	EMPA
Equant cement	FCR94-3	821		365	152	EMPA
Equant cement	FCR94-3	773		432	321	EMPA
Equant cement	RP93-26	1004		477	368	EMPA
Equant cement	RP93-26	3228		761	629	EMPA
Equant cement	RP93-26	3324		1023	831	EMPA
Equant cement	RP93-26	3617		980	899	EMPA
Isopachous cement	FCR94-14	1732		260	1081	EMPA
Isopachous cement	FCR94-14	2561		343	1240	EMPA
Isopachous cement	FCR94-14	1981		424	1506	EMPA
Isopachous cement	FCR94-14	1934		428	998	EMPA
Isopachous cement	FCR94-14	1082		1082	526	EMPA
Isopachous cement	FCR94-14	2105		458	1108	EMPA
Isopachous cement	FCR94-14	1929		426	1441	EMPA
Isopachous cement	FCR94-14	1267		493	724	EMPA
Isopachous cement	FCR94-14	1861		409	1779	EMPA
Isopachous cement	FCR94-3	2677		150	479	EMPA
Isopachous cement	FCR94-3	2630		301	311	EMPA
Isopachous cement	FCR94-3	2348		140	569	EMPA
Isopachous cement	FCR94-3	1820		232	435	EMPA
Isopachous cement	FCR94-3	1838		192	363	EMPA
Radial ooid	FCR94-11	3251		460	390	EMPA
Radial ooid	FCR94-11	2507		473	322	EMPA
Radial ooid	FCR94-11	2725		498	366	EMPA
Radial ooid	FCR94-11	2855		479	571	EMPA
Radial ooid	FCR94-11	2080		434	242	EMPA
Radial ooid	FCR94-11	2900		449	316	EMPA
Radial ooid	FCR94-11	2742		496	334	EMPA
Radial ooid	RP93-15	3922		281	1073	EMPA
Molar-tooth calcite	RP93-1	3680	121	540	188	ICP-AES
Molar-tooth calcite	RP93-11	18400	139	3020	377	ICP-AES
Molar-tooth calcite	RP93-11	17000	140	2840	379	ICP-AES
Molar-tooth calcite	RP93-11	20400	133	4100	368	ICP-AES
Molar-tooth calcite	RP93-11	18200	137	3550	375	ICP-AES
Molar-tooth calcite	RP93-21	1610	125	470	239	ICP-AES
Molar-tooth calcite	RP93-21	1610	135	490	210	ICP-AES
Molar-tooth calcite	RP93-22	980	139	350	182	ICP-AES
Molar-tooth calcite	RP93-22	1150	148	400	239	ICP-AES
Molar-tooth calcite	RP93-28	660	107	430	182	ICP-AES
Molar-tooth calcite	RP93-5	1470	161	290	110	ICP-AES
Molar-tooth calcite	RP93-8	890	158	440	152	ICP-AES
Molar-tooth calcite	UHH94-107	1700	81	620	277	ICP-AES
Molar-tooth calcite	UHH94-107	2190	137	900	257	ICP-AES
Molar-tooth calcite	UHH94-107	2150	109	970	294	ICP-AES
Molar-tooth calcite	UHH94-109	4960	179	2390	633	ICP-AES
Molar-tooth calcite	UHH94-112	9220	151	2620	432	ICP-AES
Molar-tooth calcite	UHH94-118	2000	101	820	160	ICP-AES
Molar-tooth calcite	UHH94-119	1150	77	540	178	ICP-AES
Molar-tooth calcite	UHH94-127	3070	124	1190	221	ICP-AES
Molar-tooth calcite	UHH94-127	1180	105	540	200	ICP-AES
Molar-tooth calcite	UHH94-95	15300	161	6860	484	ICP-AES
Molar-tooth calcite	UHH94-95	7690	176	2580	504	ICP-AES
Molar-tooth calcite	UHH94-96	3700	161	2190	335	ICP-AES
Dolomitized mudstone	RP93-1	101000	131	1150	52500	ICP-AES
Dolomitized mudstone	RP93-1	91200	113	748	10600	ICP-AES
Dolomitized mudstone	RP93-11	106000	103	815	18700	ICP-AES
Dolomitized mudstone	RP93-21	57000	110	537	13700	ICP-AES
Dolomitized mudstone	RP93-22	46900	135	617	7860	ICP-AES
Dolomitized mudstone	RP93-5	105000	120	549	14900	ICP-AES
Dolomitized mudstone	UHH94-112	137000	150	899	31900	ICP-AES
Dolomitized mudstone	UHH94-118	84700	165	728	19500	ICP-AES
Dolomitized mudstone	UHH94-119	116000	159	796	26700	ICP-AES
Dolomitized mudstone	UHH94-95	137000	156	1470	50300	ICP-AES

Continued

TABLE 1.—(Continued)

Component	Sample #	Mg (ppm)	Sr (ppm)	Mn (ppm)	Fe (ppm)	Method
Stromatolite transect						
Distance (mm)						
0.0	DR91-7	62700			12180	ICP-AES
1.0	DR91-7	17800			5860	ICP-AES
3.0	DR91-7	9900			2170	ICP-AES
4.0	DR91-7	7100			2130	ICP-AES
5.0	DR91-7	17700			3420	ICP-AES
6.0	DR91-7	7200			1630	ICP-AES
10.5	DR91-7	15300			379	ICP-AES
13.5	DR91-7	3800			1180	ICP-AES
16.5	DR91-7	5700			1470	ICP-AES
21.0	DR91-7	6600			2310	ICP-AES
27.0	DR91-7	6500			2450	ICP-AES
30.5	DR91-7	5800			1420	ICP-AES
35.0	DR91-7	6200			1800	ICP-AES
39.5	DR91-7	7100			1570	ICP-AES
40.5	DR91-7	6400			1760	ICP-AES
42.0	DR91-7	6100			1910	ICP-AES
43.0	DR91-7	5600			1630	ICP-AES
44.0	DR91-7	6000			1370	ICP-AES
46.5	DR91-7	8300			1700	ICP-AES
46.5	DR91-7	8300			1700	ICP-AES
46.5	DR91-7	8300			1700	ICP-AES
46.5	DR91-7	8300			1700	ICP-AES
53.5	DR91-7	4500			1470	ICP-AES

EMPA = Electron microprobe analysis
ICP–AES = Inductively coupled plasma–atomic emission spectrometry

The range in $\delta^{18}O$ values (-13.0 to $-4.0‰$) in Helena samples (excluding cements in late-stage fractures) greatly exceeds the spread in $\delta^{13}C$ values ($+2.2$ to $-1.3‰$; Fig. 5). The lower half of the section, dominated by cycles of fine-grained, siliciclastic-rich sediment grading into carbonate mudstone, is marked by a uniform increase in $\delta^{18}O$ values from the base of the section; at any given horizon, the spread in $\delta^{18}O$ values rarely exceeds 4‰ (Fig. 5). By contrast, the overlying part of the section is more heterogeneous isotopically, with $\delta^{18}O$ values ranging from $-13‰$ to $-4‰$ (Fig. 5). The most positive $\delta^{18}O$ values obtained from individual components that are present throughout the full extent of the Helena Formation (e.g., molar-tooth calcite, dolomitic mudstone) increase by nearly 3‰ from the bottom to the top of the section. Given that the isotopic fractionation between calcite and water decreases with increasing temperature according to the equation of Friedman and O'Neil (1977) and assuming a maximum stratigraphic thickness of 100–200 m and a normal geothermal gradient (30°C km^{-1}), this 3‰ stratigraphic shift in the Helena Formation exceeds the expected burial gradient by 1.5 to 2.5‰. As such, the stratigraphic increase in Helena $\delta^{18}O$ values cannot be attributed solely to greater effects of burial diagenesis with depth in the section. In this context, the stratigraphic increase in the magnitude and degree of variation in $\delta^{18}O$ values from the Helena Formation is consistent with increasingly restrictive deposi-

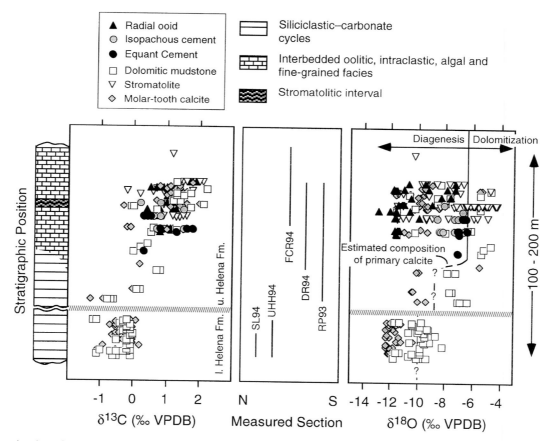

FIG. 5.—Composite plots of carbon (left) and oxygen (right) isotope data from all measured sections versus stratigraphic position according to stratigraphic correlations of Winston (modified from Frank et al., 1997). Also shown are the general stratigraphic facies progression, the stratigraphic ranges of measured sections, and the estimated starting $\delta^{18}O$ value of Helena calcite.

tional conditions along the eastern margin of the Belt basin, which have been inferred previously on the basis of sedimentology and carbon-isotope data (Frank et al., 1997). Several lines of evidence, however, indicate that this primary signal has been partially obscured during diagenesis. A strong facies control on diagenesis is suggested by the correspondence between the increase in compositional heterogeneity toward the top of the section and the lithologic change from a relatively uniform succession of fine-grained, cyclic facies in the lower part of the section to a more varied mixture of oolites, intraclastites, stromatolitic intervals, and cryptalgal laminites interbedded with the fine-grained, cyclic facies in the upper part (Figs. 2, 5). Owing to the greater variation in porosity, grain size, and original mineralogy, diagenetic conditions were likely more diverse in the upper part of the Helena Formation relative to the lower part, accounting, at least in part, for the increased range in δ¹⁸O values.

Facies-Related Trends

Fine-Grained Facies.—

Within any particular stratigraphic horizon, components in the fine-grained facies of the Helena Formation have relatively uniform carbon and highly variable oxygen-isotope compositions (Fig. 6). Much of the heterogeneity in oxygen-isotope composition is exhibited in δ¹⁸O values from the dolomitized mudstones (Fig. 6). Whereas at a given stratigraphic level δ¹⁸O values of molar-tooth calcite typically vary by less than 1‰, δ¹⁸O values from dolomitized mudstones range by several permil to values as much as 4‰ more positive than those of co-occurring molar-tooth calcite. Mg concentrations determined by ICP–AES in the dolomitized mudstone range to 52 mole % $MgCO_3$; concentrations in molar-tooth calcite are generally less than 4 mole % $MgCO_3$ (Table 1). Although a contribution of Mg from sources other than dolomite cannot be ruled out because measurements were made on whole-rock samples, the range of Mg concentrations in mudstones are interpreted to re-

flect widespread replacement by fine-grained dolomite that was observed petrographically. This interpretation is further supported by the 3–4‰ spread in δ¹⁸O values between lower, relatively invariant δ¹⁸O values from molar-tooth calcite and higher, more variable values surrounding dolomitized mudstone (Fig. 6). These relationships are consistent with the oxygen-isotope fractionation factor for cogenetic dolomite and calcite (Δ_{dol-cc} = 3 ± 1‰) determined by Land (1980).

Stromatolites.—

Microsamples for isotopic and geochemical analysis were collected along growth transects within individual decimeter-scale domal stromatolites. Elevated Mg (>10⁵ ppm) and Fe contents suggest that most stromatolites have suffered partial to complete dolomitization (Frank et al., 1997); δ¹⁸O values in these stromatolites range from approximately −8 to −4‰. By contrast, low and invariant Mg and Fe contents measured across a few growth transects suggest that a limited number of stromatolites have escaped dolomitization (Table 1). In these stromatolites, δ¹⁸O values vary between −12 and −7‰ (Fig. 7). We attribute the differences in the magnitude of δ¹⁸O values among dolomitic and calcitic stromatolites to reflect preferential incorporation of ¹⁸O into dolomite relative to calcite (Land, 1980). Along growth transects, δ¹⁸O and δ¹³C values tend to covary, such that positive shifts in δ¹⁸O values are matched by positive shifts in δ¹³C values; these patterns are best developed in calcitic stromatolites (Fig. 7). In dolomitized stromatolites, positive fluctuations in δ¹⁸O values along growth transects correspond to large increases in Mg and Fe contents. As such, we attribute oxygen-isotope variations in these stromatolites to variable dolomitization. By contrast, because shifts in δ¹⁸O values in calcitic stromatolites cannot be attributed to dolomitization, the cause of isotopic variability in these stromatolites is less clear. Variability in δ¹⁸O values may, in part, be related to variable interaction with diagenetic fluids at the scale of individual laminae. Alternatively, the cyclic nature of shifts in δ¹⁸O and δ¹³C values (Fig. 7) suggests that a record of fluctuations in primary depositional conditions may have been retained in select stromatolites. This possibility is addressed in a later section of this paper.

Oolitic Grainstone.—

Ooids and intergranular cements in oolitic grainstones have nearly identical carbon isotope compositions, whereas δ¹⁸O values of these components vary over a range of nearly 7‰ (Fig. 8). Of these components, ooids are the most isotopically heterogeneous and have δ¹⁸O values that vary between −13 and −7.5‰. δ¹⁸O values for the isopachous synsedimentary cements exhibit slightly less variation and range from approximately −9 to −6.5‰. Equant cements are the most uniform isotopically and exhibit the most positive δ¹⁸O values (−6.1‰). Small sample size precluded paired minor-element and isotopic analyses of individual drilled microsamples from ooids and cements. Instead, minor-element contents were determined by EMPA on the same polished thick sections from which microsamples were drilled. Mn and Fe concentrations in ooids and cements are consistent with their CL characteristics (Fig. 9; Table 1). Equant cement is characterized by generally low Fe (average 310 ± 120 ppm) and variable Mn contents (~300 to 1000 ppm). By contrast, ooids and isopachous ce-

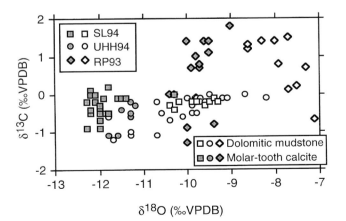

Fig. 6.—Carbon and oxygen isotope compositions of molar-tooth calcite (filled symbols) and dolomitic calcareous mudstone (open symbols) from measured sections SL94 and UHH94 (lower Helena Formation) and RP93 (middle to upper Helena Formation). Note that the 2.5‰ difference in δ¹³C values of samples among different measured sections reflects the stratigraphic shift in δ¹³C (Fig. 5); within any given stratigraphic horizon, δ¹³C values are relatively uniform.

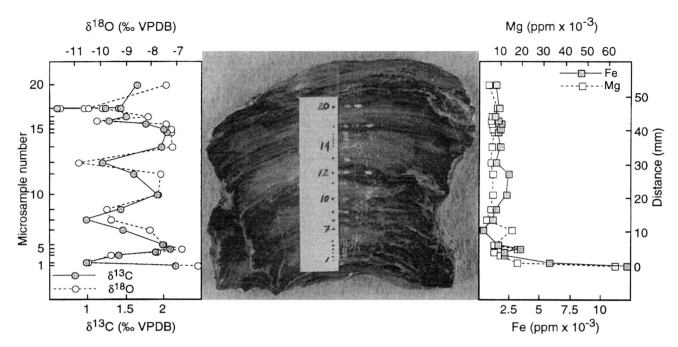

FIG. 7.—Isotopic (left) and elemental (Mg and Fe, right) variations along a vertical transect across a single domal stromatolite (middle photograph) from measured section DR94.

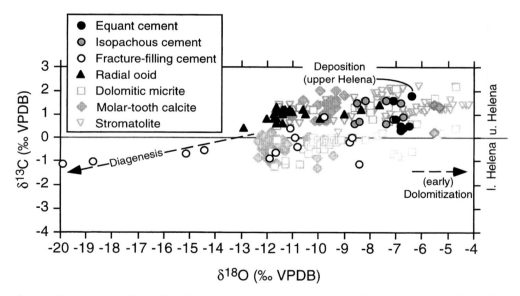

FIG. 8.—Carbon and oxygen isotope compositions of ooids, intergranular cements, and fracture-filling cements in the Helena Formation. Arrows denote expected changes in isotopic composition resulting from dolomitization and interaction with late-stage diagenetic fluids. Also shown is the inferred primary composition of Helena calcite, estimated from the compositions of intergranular cements in oolites. Isotopic compositions of other components are shown for comparison (light gray symbols).

ments have Mn contents generally less than 500 ppm, whereas Fe concentrations range up to 1780 ppm.

Although analytical methods do not facilitate direct comparison of minor-element concentrations (determined by EMPA on polished sections) and isotopic compositions (measured on drilled powders) of ooids and intergranular cements, the general trends within each data set can be considered simultaneously.

Given that diagenetically least-altered carbonate phases have the most positive $\delta^{18}O$ values and relatively low concentrations of Fe (Brand and Veizer, 1980; Banner and Hanson, 1990), isotopic and geochemical data from Helena oolites are generally consistent with inferences made on the basis of petrographic constraints. Samples of equant cement inferred as unaltered on the basis of CL zoning have the lowest Fe contents and are the

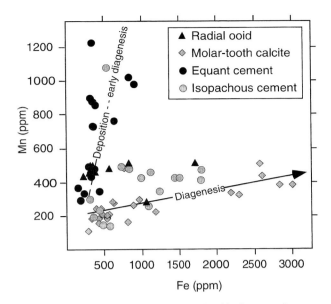

FIG. 9.—Mn and Fe concentrations in radial ooids, intergranular cements, and molar-tooth calcite in the Helena Formation.

most enriched in ^{18}O, whereas isopachous cements and ooids that exhibit a patchy luminescence under CL have generally higher Fe contents and more variable oxygen-isotope compositions that are relatively depleted in ^{18}O (Figs. 8, 9). In contrast to this generalized scenario, the nonluminescent interiors of some isopachous cements have Fe concentrations as high as 1500 ppm (Fig. 9; Table 1). If these samples are indeed unaltered, as suggested by the retention of CL zones, elevated Fe contents may reflect redox conditions that allowed for significant amounts of Fe^{2+} in ambient depositional and/or early diagenetic pore fluids.

Late-Stage Cement in Crosscutting Fractures.—

Subvertical fractures, possibly related to Mesozoic and Cenozoic tectonism, crosscut Helena lithologies. $\delta^{18}O$ values from this late cement phase range from ~ -20 to $-8‰$, whereas $\delta^{13}C$ values are relatively uniform and vary from -2 to $+1‰$ (Fig. 8; Frank et al., 1997). This pattern is typical for late-stage diagenetic carbonates (Choquette and James, 1990). The large range in $\delta^{18}O$ values reflects either: (1) calcite precipitation over a range of water–rock ratios, such that more negative values reflect precipitation at high water–rock ratios and more closely resemble the composition of the diagenetic fluid, and/or (2) precipitation over a range of burial temperatures, such that more negative $\delta^{18}O$ values reflect precipitation at higher temperatures. Carbon-isotope data from late-stage cements appear to be most consistent with variable water–rock ratios during diagenesis. Lower $\delta^{13}C$ values are typically coupled with more negative $\delta^{18}O$ values and are interpreted to reflect a water-dominated diagenetic system. By contrast, higher $\delta^{13}C$ values coupled with higher $\delta^{18}O$ values may reflect a diagenetic fluid–rock system that was buffered by the carbon-isotope composition of the host rock because of the large amount of inorganic carbon in the carbonate rock relative to the water reservoir (Algeo et al., 1992).

DISCUSSION

Detailed sampling reveals differences in oxygen-isotope composition within and among disparate petrographic components. With the exception of intergranular cements in oolites, petrographic components sampled in the Helena Formation are compositionally heterogeneous and have $\delta^{18}O$ values that vary over a range of at least 6‰. This isotopic variability is evident both at the scale of the formation as a whole and at the scale of individual hand samples. Such heterogeneity indicates that original oxygen-isotope compositions in Helena carbonates have not been completely reset and homogenized, despite a long postdepositional history. Rather, the present oxygen-isotope compositions of ooids, molar-tooth structures, algal lithologies, and mudstones form a mixing trend that reflects diagenesis under variable conditions that ranged between two end-member settings. At one end of the spectrum under closed or rock-dominated conditions, low water–rock ratios enabled the diagenetic system to be buffered by the composition of the host rock, such that near-primary compositions were retained in diagenetic phases. By contrast, diagenesis under open or water-dominated conditions resulted in the loss of geochemical and isotopic signatures that better reflect depositional conditions.

Because the way in which diagenesis proceeds within a given suite of carbonate rocks is heavily influenced by local conditions, the diagenetic component of such mixing trends must be defined expressly for the sequence of rocks under study. In the Helena Formation, the $\delta^{18}O$ value of the late-stage diagenetic end-member is interpreted as the most negative $\delta^{18}O$ value from late diagenetic fracture-filling cements ($-20‰$). Isotopic data from other petrographic components lie along the trend defined by data from fracture-filling cements, suggesting that all components have been affected by a late-stage diagenetic fluid of similar composition. The subtle bimodal distribution of $\delta^{13}C$ values about this diagenetic trend reflects the stratigraphic increase in $\delta^{13}C$ values from the bottom to the top of the Helena Formation (Fig. 6); components from the lower part of the section have $\delta^{13}C$ values that tend to fall at or below the trend defined by data from late-stage cement, whereas components from the upper part of the section have $\delta^{13}C$ values that tend to fall above the trend (Frank et al., 1997). As such, this distribution reflects the higher water–rock ratios at which $\delta^{13}C$ values of diagenetic carbonate is buffered by the original $\delta^{13}C$ value of the host rock relative to those required for original $\delta^{18}O$ values to be retained in secondary phases (Lohmann, 1988; Banner and Hanson, 1990).

Estimating a starting oxygen-isotope composition for diagenetically altered carbonates is hampered by the possibility of secular variation in the isotopic composition of marine calcite (Lohmann, 1988). Whereas secular variation in the $\delta^{18}O$ value of marine calcite during the Phanerozoic has been relatively well constrained (e.g., Popp et al., 1986; Veizer et al., 1986; Lohmann and Walker, 1989; Bruckschen and Veizer, 1997), a lack of detailed isotopic studies and a general absence of components from which original marine calcite isotopic compositions could be more easily discerned (e.g., skeletal grains, abiotic marine cements) has led to much controversy regarding the oxygen-isotope composition of the Precambrian oceans. An additional factor that hinders estimation of primary marine calcite $\delta^{18}O$ values is the often pervasive dolomitization of Precambrian strata in general and the associated oxygen-isotope fractionation (e.g., Veizer, 1992b). As such, the starting $\delta^{18}O$ value Precambrian marine carbonates is best determined in the context of the "best-preserved" calcitic component for the suite of carbonate rocks under study as defined petrographically and geochemically. In the Helena Formation, CL petrography indicates that zoned examples of intergranular cement phases in oolitic grainstones have remained unaltered; paragenetic relationships suggest that these cements are synsedimentary (isopachous phase) and early diagenetic (equant phase). Moreover, of all the calcitic components in the Helena Formation, these phases are the most enriched in ^{18}O. In this context, the most positive $\delta^{18}O$ value from these cements ($-6.1‰$) is interpreted to provide the most conservative (minimum) proxy estimate of the composition of calcite precipitating from waters in the Belt basin during deposition of the Helena Formation (Fig. 8; Frank et al., 1997). Because stratigraphic trends in $\delta^{13}C$ (Frank et al., 1997) and $\delta^{18}O$ values suggest that conditions became increasingly restricted in the eastern part of the Belt basin during deposition of the Helena Formation, caution must be used when using interpreting oxygen-isotope data derived from Helena cements in the context of Mesoproterozoic ocean chemistry. Given the restriction of oolitic grainstones to the upper part of the Helena Formation, $\delta^{18}O$ values from intergranular cements in these facies likely overestimate the $\delta^{18}O$ value of the Mesoproterozoic marine calcite and instead reflect precipitation from modified (e.g., evaporated, pre–evaporite precipitation) marine water. Primary $\delta^{18}O$ values from the lower part of the Helena Formation are relatively poorly constrained. However, the magnitude of the stratigraphic increase in $\delta^{18}O$ values from coexisting molar-tooth calcite and dolomitic mudstone, the only components to occur throughout the stratigraphic extent of the Helena Formation, suggests that primary carbonate values were on the order of 1–2‰ more negative during deposition of the lower part of the section (Fig. 5).

Facies-Related and Component-Related Trends

Given estimates for end-member primary ($-6.1‰$) and diagenetic ($-20‰$) $\delta^{18}O$ values for Helena Formation calcite, the distribution of $\delta^{18}O$ values for ooids, molar-tooth calcite, stromatolites, and mudstones suggests that near-original oxygen-isotope compositions have been retained only in limited samples. Within this context, however, we recognize patterns in the isotopic and geochemical data from selected components that may provide higher-resolution insight into aspects of depositional and early diagenetic conditions as recorded in Helena lithologies.

Stromatolites.—

Microsampling transects in calcitic stromatolites exhibit cyclic shifts in $\delta^{18}O$ and $\delta^{13}C$ values that cannot be attributed to selective dolomitization of individual growth laminae (Fig. 7; microsamples 2–20). The most positive $\delta^{18}O$ values ($-7.0‰$) from such transects are similar to $\delta^{18}O$ values of equant and isopachous cements (Fig. 8), which have been interpreted to provide the best estimate for the primary $\delta^{18}O$ value of calcite during deposition of the upper part of the Helena Formation. Cyclic variations documented in calcitic stromatolites are consistent with the character and magnitude of isotopic variations linked to cycles of flooding and evaporation that have been

documented in African lacustrine stromatolites and marine stromatolites in Shark Bay, Australia (Casanova and Hillaire-Marcel, 1993; Chivas et al., 1990). If reflecting primary conditions, such isotopic records are compatible with growth in a restricted, shallow Belt basin that was subject to periodic perturbations in the hydrologic balance (Frank et al., 1997). However, recognizing (1) that stratigraphic and sedimentologic constraints indicate a possible deepening or expansion of the water column in the central and western parts of the Belt basin in the stratigraphic interval dominated by stromatolite growth (Winston, 1998) and (2) that low-grade metamorphism precludes any comparison of stromatolite data from the central and western parts of the Belt basin, caution must be used when extrapolating the significance of isotopic data from these apparently well-preserved stromatolites beyond the limits of the eastern margin of the Belt basin.

Fine-Grained Facies.—

Given the oxygen-isotope fractionation factor for co-occurring dolomite and calcite ($\Delta_{dol-cc} = 3 \pm 1‰$; Land, 1980), the nearly ubiquitous several permil range in $\delta^{18}O$ values between variably dolomitized mudstones and coexisting molar-tooth calcite suggests that the dolomite and calcite in mudstones and the calcite in molar-tooth structures formed in a fluid of similar oxygen-isotope composition (Figs. 6, 8). As such, retention of the expected oxygen-isotope fractionation between calcite and associated dolomite pairs is consistent with sedimentologic and petrographic constraints that suggest (1) that molar-tooth calcite is an early diagenetic phase (Frank and Lyons, 1998; Furniss et al., 1998) and (2) that calcareous mudstones in the Helena Formation were dolomitized soon after deposition (Frank et al., 1997).

The fine-grained nature of the early-formed dolomite in mudstone and the calcite in molar-tooth structures, the retention of original mineralogical differences, and the preservation of the expected oxygen-isotope fractionation between associated calcitic and dolomitic pairs suggests that dissolution–precipitation reactions associated with diagenesis must have proceeded at a microscale. Under such conditions, diagenetic alteration can occur in isolation from effective exchange with ambient diagenetic pore fluids, such that diagenetic precipitates inherit the geochemical characteristics of the dissolving phase (Given and Lohmann, 1985; Frank and Lohmann, 1996). Evidence for retention of primary $\delta^{13}C$ values in Helena lithologies indicates that the diagenetic system was generally rock-dominated or closed with respect to carbon-isotope composition. The absence of synsedimentary and early diagenetic intergranular cements in the lower part of the Helena Formation and a corresponding lack of constraint on primary calcite $\delta^{18}O$ values in that part of the section makes it difficult to discern to what degree original oxygen-isotope compositions of molar-tooth calcite and dolomitized mudstone may have been shifted during diagenesis.

CONCLUSIONS

While diagenetic overprints may be significant, petrographic, isotopic, and geochemical relationships argue against wholesale diagenetic resetting and homogenization of primary isotopic compositions and suggest that general depositional controls can still be discerned in oxygen-isotope data from the Helena Formation. Early formed intergranular cements in oolitic grainstones provide the most reliable estimates of the primary $\delta^{18}O$ value of calcite ($-6.1‰$). Partial rather than complete resetting of $\delta^{18}O$ values in other components appears to have been the product of widespread early cementation, including molar-tooth formation and the nearly complete occlusion of primary pore space in oolites by syndepositional and early diagenetic cements. In conjunction with generally low initial porosities in the dominant fine-grained lithologies, widespread cementation apparently facilitated alteration at small spatial scales under relatively closed-system conditions during late-stage diagenesis. Stratigraphic variation in the degree of heterogeneity in $\delta^{18}O$ values appears reflect a facies control on diagenesis (e.g., mineralogy and porosity differences). However, the overall stratigraphic increase in $\delta^{18}O$ values exceeds that expected due to the geothermal gradient and is therefore consistent with increasingly restricted conditions along the eastern margin of the Belt basin inferred previously on the basis of carbon-isotope data (Frank et al., 1997). Data from select stromatolites, which exhibit cyclic shifts in $\delta^{18}O$ and $\delta^{13}C$ values along growth transects that cannot be attributed to selective dolomitization, are also consistent with a depositional model that implies growth in a closed body of water.

In a broader sense, the present study reveals the potential for recognizing primary depositional controls in oxygen-isotope data derived from Precambrian carbonates. However, discrimination between primary and secondary oxygen-isotope signatures requires a detailed approach, which emphasizes microsampling to document the degree of compositional heterogeneity within and among coexisting petrographic components. Where heterogeneity is significant, questions of wholesale diagenetic resetting of original isotopic compositions are eliminated and end-member oxygen-isotope signatures related to primary and diagenetic influences can be estimated within the context of regional depositional facies patterns and paragenetic relations. Ultimately, the routine application of this high-resolution approach has the potential to provide important constraints for understanding Precambrian depositional environments and ocean chemistry and, furthermore, may provide a compromise in the highly polarized debate over the integrity of Precambrian $\delta^{18}O$ records.

ACKNOWLEDGMENTS

Supported by National Science Foundation Grant #EAR-9596079 (Lyons, Lohmann, and Walter) and grants from the Belt Association, Inc. (Frank) and the Scott Turner Awards in Earth Sciences program at the University of Michigan (Frank and Lyons). This manuscript benefited from reviews by Kurt Kyser and Martine Savard and numerous discussions with Kacey Lohmann. Roberta Hotinski reviewed an early version. We are grateful to Don Winston for introducing us to the Belt Supergroup and for sharing his insight regarding the stratigraphy and sedimentology of this classic succession. In addition, we are grateful to Nate Hathaway for his help with field collection and Lora Wingate and Ted Huston for their assistance with laboratory analyses.

REFERENCES

ALEINIKOFF, J. N., EVANS, K. V., FANNING, C. M., OBRADOVICH, J. D., RUPPEL, E. T., ZIEG, J. A., AND STEINMETZ, J. C., 1996, Shrimp U–Pb ages of felsic igneous rocks, Belt Supergroup, Western Montana (abstract): Geological Society of America, Abstracts with Programs, v. 28, p. A-376.

ALGEO, T. J., WILKINSON, B. H., AND LOHMANN, K. C, 1992, Meteoric-burial diagenesis of Middle Pennsylvanian limestones in the Orogrande Basin, New Mexico: water/rock interactions and basin geothermics: Journal of Sedimentary Petrology, v. 62, p. 652–670.

ANDERSON, T. F., AND ARTHUR, M. A., 1983, Stable isotopes of oxygen and carbon and their application to sedimentologic and paleoenvironmental problems, in Arthur, M. A., Anderson, T. F., Kaplan, I. R., Veizer, J., and Land, L. S., eds., Stable Isotopes in Sedimentary Geology: SEPM Short Course 10, p. 1.1–1.151.

BANNER, J. L., AND HANSON, G. N., 1990, Calculation of simultaneous isotopic and trace element variations during water–rock interaction with application to carbonate diagenesis: Geochimica et Cosmochimica Acta, v. 54, p. 3123–2137.

BRAND, U., AND VEIZER, J., 1980, Chemical diagenesis of a multicomponent carbonate system 1: Trace elements: Journal of Sedimentary Petrology, v. 50, p. 1219–1236.

BRUCKSCHEN, P., AND VEIZER, J., 1997, Oxygen and carbon isotopic composition of Dinantian brachiopods: paleoenvironmental implications for the Lower Carboniferous of western Europe: Palaeogeography, Palaeoclimatology, Palaeoecology, v. 132, p. 243–264.

BURDETT, J. W., GROTZINGER, J. P., AND ARTHUR, M. A., 1990, Did major changes in the stable-isotope composition of Proterozoic seawater occur?: Geology, v. 18, p. 227–230.

CASANOVA, J., AND HILLAIRE-MARCEL, C., 1993, Carbon and oxygen isotopes in African lacustrine stromatolites: palaeohydrological interpretation, in Swart, P. K., Lohmann, K. C., McKenzie, J. A., and Savin, S., eds., Climate Change in Continental Isotopic Records: American Geographical Union, Geophysical Monograph 78, p. 123–133.

CHIVAS, A. R., TORGERSON, T., AND POLACH, H. A., 1990, Growth rates and Holocene development of stromatolites from Shark Bay, Western Australia: Australian Journal of Earth Sciences, v. 37, p. 113–121.

CHOQUETTE, P. W., AND JAMES, N. P., 1990, Limestones—the burial diagenetic environment, in McIlreath, I. A., and Morrow, D. W., eds., Diagenesis: Geoscience Canada, Reprint Series 4, p. 75–111.

CRAIG, H., 1957, Isotopic standards for carbon and oxygen and correction factors for mass spectrometric analysis of carbon dioxide: Geochimica et Cosmochimica Acta, v. 12, p. 133–149.

DALZIEL, I. W. D., 1991, Pacific margins of Laurentia and East Antarctica—Australia as a conjugate rift pair: evidence and implications for an Eocambrian supercontinent: Geology, v. 19, p. 598–601.

EBY, D. E., 1977, Sedimentation and early diagenesis within eastern portions of the "middle Belt carbonate interval" (Helena Formation), Belt Supergroup (Precambrian-Y), western Montana [unpublished Ph.D. dissertation]: State University of New York at Stony Brook, Stony Brook, New York, 712 p.

ELSTON, D. P., 1984, Magnetostratigraphy of the Belt Supergroup—a synopsis, in Hobbs, S. W., ed., The Belt: Abstracts with Summaries, Belt Symposium II, Montana Bureau of Mines and Geology Special Publication 90, p. 88–90.

ELSTON, D. P., AND BRESSLER, S. L., 1980, Paleomagnetic poles and polarity zonation from the Mesoproterozoic Belt Supergroup, Montana and Idaho: Journal of Geophysical Research, v. 85, p. 339–355.

ESLINGER, E. V., AND SAVIN, S. M., 1973, Oxygen isotope geothermometry of the burial metamorphic rocks of the Precambrian Belt Supergroup, Glacier National Park, Montana: Geological Society of America, Bulletin, v. 84, p. 2549–2560.

FRANK, T. D., AND LOHMANN, K. C, 1996, Diagenesis of fibrous magnesian calcite marine cement: implications for the interpretation of $\delta^{18}O$ and $\delta^{13}C$ values from ancient equivalents: Geochimica et Cosmochimica Acta, v. 60, p. 2427–2436.

FRANK, T. D., AND LYONS, T. W., 1998, "Molar-tooth" calcite: a geochemical perspective on a Proterozoic enigma: Geology, v. 26, p. 683–686.

FRANK, T. D., LYONS, T. W., AND LOHMANN, K. C, 1997, Isotopic evidence for the paleoenvironmental evolution of the Mesoproterozoic Helena Formation, Belt Supergroup, Montana: Geochimica et Cosmochimica Acta, v. 61, p. 5023–5041.

FRIEDMAN, I., AND O'NEIL, J.R., 1977, Compilation of stable isotope fractionation factors of geochemical interest, in Fleischer, M., ed., Data of Geochemistry, 6th Edition, Chapter KK: United States Geological Survey, Professional Paper 440-KK, 12 p. + figures.

FURNISS, G., RITTEL, J. F., AND WINSTON, D., 1998, Gas bubble and expansion crack origin of "molar-tooth" calcite structures in the Middle Proterozoic

Belt Supergroup, western Montana: Journal of Sedimentary Research, v. 68, p. 104–114.

GIVEN, R. K., AND LOHMANN, K. C, 1985, Derivation of the original isotopic composition of Permian marine cements: Journal of Sedimentary Petrology, v. 55, p. 430–439.

GREGORY, R. T., AND TAYLOR, H. P., 1981, An oxygen isotope profile in a section of Cretaceous oceanic crust, Samail ophiolite, Oman: evidence for $\delta^{18}O$ buffering of the oceans by deep (>5 km) seawater-hydrothermal circulation at mid-ocean ridges: Journal of Geophysical Research, v. 86, p. 2737–2755.

HALL, S. M., AND VEIZER, J., 1996, Geochemistry of Precambrian carbonates: VII. Belt Supergroup, Montana and Idaho, USA: Geochimica et Cosmochimica Acta, v. 60, p. 667–677.

HARRISON, J. E., 1972, Precambrian Belt basin of northwestern United States— its geometry, sedimentation, and copper occurrences: Geological Society of America, Bulletin, v. 83, p. 1215–1240.

HARRISON, J. E., 1984, Session on geochronology and geophysics, summary, in Hobbs, S.W., ed., The Belt: Abstracts with Summaries, Belt Symposium II, Montana Bureau of Mines and Geology, Special Publication 90, p. 98–100.

HOFFMAN, P. F., 1989, Precambrian geology and tectonic history of North America, in Bally, A. W., and Palmer, A. R., eds., The Geology of North America—An Overview: Geological Society of America, The Geology of North America, vol. A, p. 447–512.

HOLMDEN, C., AND MUEHLENBACHS, K., 1993, The $^{18}O/^{16}O$ ratio of 2-billion-year-old seawater inferred from ancient oceanic crust: Science, v. 259, p. 1733–1736.

HORODYSKI, R. J., 1989, Stromatolites of the Belt Supergroup, Glacier National Park, Montana, in Winston, D., Horodyski, R. J., and Whipple, J. W., eds., Mesoproterozoic Belt Supergroup, Western Montana: 28th International Geological Congress, Field Trip Guidebook T334, American Geophysical Union, p. 27–42.

KARHU, J., AND EPSTEIN, S., 1986, The implication of the oxygen isotope records in coexisting cherts and phosphates: Geochimica et Cosmochimica Acta, v. 50, p. 1745–1756.

KNAUTH, L. P., AND LOWE, D. R., 1978, Oxygen isotope geochemistry of cherts from the Onverwacht Group (3.4 billion years), Transvaal, South Africa, with implications for secular variations in the isotopic composition of cherts: Earth and Planetary Science Letters, v. 41, p. 209–222.

KNOLL, A. H., KAUFMAN, A. J., AND SEMIKHATOV, M. A., 1995, The carbon-isotope composition of Proterozoic carbonates: Riphean successions from northwestern Siberia (Anabar Massif, Turukhansk uplift): American Journal of Science, v. 295, p. 823–850.

LAND, L. S., 1980, The isotopic and trace element geochemistry of dolomite: the state of the art, in Zenger, D. H., Dunham, J. B., and Ethington, R. L., eds., Concepts and Models of Dolomitization: Society of Economic Paleontologists and Mineralogists, Special Publication 28, p. 87–110.

LOHMANN, K. C., 1988, Geochemical patterns of meteoric diagenetic systems and their application to studies of paleokarst, in James, N. P., and Choquette, P. W., eds., Paleokarst: New York, Springer-Verlag, p. 58–80.

LOHMANN, K. C., AND MEYERS, W. J., 1977, Microdolomite inclusions in cloudy prismatic calcites: A proposed criterion for former high magnesium calcites: Journal of Sedimentary Petrology, v. 47, p. 1078–1088.

LOHMANN, K.C, AND WALKER, J. C. G., 1989, The $\delta^{18}O$ record of Phanerozoic abiotic marine calcite cements: Geophysical Research Letters, v. 16, p. 319–322.

LYONS, T. W., LUEPKE, J. J., SCHREIBER, M. E., AND ZIEG, G. A., in press, A geochemical model for Mesoproterozoic marine deposition: Lower Belt Supergroup, northwestern US: Geochimica et Cosmochimica Acta.

MAXWELL, D. T., AND HOWER, J., 1967, High-grade diagenesis and low-grade metamorphism of illite in the Precambrian Belt series: American Mineralogist, v. 52, p. 843-857.

McDONALD, G. D., COLLERSON, K. D., AND KINNY, P. D., 1997, Late Archean and Early Proterozoic crustal evolution of the Mount Isa block, northwest Queensland, Australia: Geology, v. 25, p. 1095–1098.

MOORES, E. M., 1991, Southwest US–East Antarctic SWEAT connection: a hypothesis: Geology, v. 19, p. 425–428.

MUEHLENBACHS, K., AND CLAYTON, R. N., 1976, Oxygen isotope composition of the oceanic crust and its bearing on seawater: Journal of Geophysical Research, v. 81, p. 4365–4369.

PERRY, E. C., JR., AND AHMAD, S. N., 1983, Oxygen isotope geochemistry of Proterozoic chemical sediments, in Medaris, L. G., Jr., Byers, C. W., and Mickelson, D., eds., Proterozoic Geology; Selected Papers from an International Proterozoic Symposium: Geological Society of America, Memoir 161, p. 253–263.

PERRY, E. C., JR., AND TAN, F. C., 1972, Significance of oxygen and carbon isotope variation in Early Precambrian cherts and carbonate rocks of southern Africa: Geological Society of America, Bulletin, v. 83, p. 467–664.

POPP, B. N., ANDERSON, F. T., AND SANDBERG, P. A., 1986, Brachiopods as indicators of original isotopic compositions in Paleozoic limestones: Geological Society of America, Bulletin, v. 97, p. 1262–1269.

ROSS, G. M., PARRISH, R. R., AND WINSTON, D., 1992, Provenance and U–Pb chronology of the Mesoproterozoic Belt Supergroup (northwestern United States): implications for the age of deposition and pre-Panthalassa plate reconstructions: Earth and Planetary Science Letters, v. 113, p. 57–76.

SCHIEBER, J., 1989, Facies and origin of shales from the Mid-Proterozoic Newland Formation, Belt basin, Montana, USA: Sedimentology, v. 36, p. 203–219.

SMITH, A. G., 1968, The origin and deformation of some molar-tooth structures in the Precambrian Belt–Purcell Supergroup: Journal of Geology, v. 76, p. 426–443.

STILLER, M., ROUNICK, J. S., AND SHASHA, S., 1985, Extreme carbon-isotope enrichments in evaporating brines: Nature, v. 316, p. 434–435.

TUCKER, M. E., 1984, Calcitic, aragonitic and mixed calcitic–aragonitic ooids from the mid-Proterozoic Belt Supergroup, Montana: Sedimentology, v. 31, p. 627–644.

VEIZER, J., AND HOEFS, J., 1976, The nature of O^{18}/O^{16} and C^{13}/C^{12} secular trends in sedimentary carbonate rocks: Geochimica et Cosmochimica Acta, v. 40, p. 1387–1395.

VEIZER, J., FRITZ, P., AND JONES, B., 1986, Geochemistry of brachiopods: oxygen and carbon isotopic records of Paleozoic oceans: Geochimica et Cosmochimica Acta, v. 50, p. 1679-1696.

VEIZER, J., CLAYTON, R. N., AND HINTON, R. W., 1992a, Geochemistry of Precambrian carbonates: IV. Early Early Proterozoic (2.25 ± 0.25 Ga) seawater: Geochimica et Cosmochimica Acta, v. 56, p. 875–885.

VEIZER, J., PLUMB, K. A., CLAYTON, R. N., HINTON, R. W., AND GROTZINGER, J. P., 1992b, Geochemistry of Precambrian carbonates: Late Early Proterozoic seawater: Geochimica et Cosmochimica Acta, v. 56, p. 2487–2501.

WALKER, J. C. G., AND LOHMANN, K. C, 1989, Why the oxygen isotopic compositon of sea water changes with time: Geophysical Research Letters, v. 16, p. 323–326.

WINSTON, D., 1986, Sedimentation and tectonics of the Mesoproterozoic Belt basin and their influence on Phanerozoic compression and extension in western Montana and northern Idaho, in Peterson, J. A., ed., Paleotectonics and Sedimentation in the Rocky Mountain Region, United States: American Association of Petroleum Geologists, Memoir 41, p. 87–118.

WINSTON, D., 1989, Introduction to the Belt, in Winston, D., Horodyski, R. J., and Whipple, J. W., eds., Mesoproterozoic Belt Supergroup, Western Montana: 28th International Geological Congress, Field Trip Guidebook T334, American Geophysical Union, p. 1–6.

WINSTON, D., 1990, Evidence for intracratonic, fluvial and lacustrine settings of Middle and Late Proterozoic basins of western USA, in Gower, C. F., Rivers, T., and Ryan, B., eds., Mid-Proterozoic Laurentia–Baltica: Geological Association of Canada, Special Paper, 38, p. 535–564.

WINSTON, D., 1993, Cycles of the upper Helena Formation, Mesoproterozoic Belt Supergroup, Montana, in Pearson, R. C., ed., Belt Symposium III Abstracts, Montana Bureau of Mines and Geology.

WINSTON, D., 1999, Lacustrine cycles in the Helena and Wallace Formations, Middle Proterozoic Belt Supergroup, Western Montana, in Berg, R. B., ed., Proceedings of Belt Symposium III: Montana Bureau of Mines and Geology, Special Publication, p. 70–88.

WINSTON, D., AND LINK, P. K., 1993, Mesoproterozoic rocks of Montana, Idaho and eastern Washington: the Belt Supergroup, in Reed, J. C., Jr., Bickford, M. E., Houston, R. S., Link, P. K., Rankin, R. W., Sims, P. K., and VanSchmus, W. R., eds., Precambrian: Conterminous US, Geology of North America C-2, Decade of North American Geology, Geological Society of America, p. 487–517.

WINSTON, D., AND LYONS, T. W., 1993, Sedimentary cycles in the St. Regis, Empire and Helena Formations of the Mesoproterozoic Belt Supergroup, northwestern Montana, in Link, P. K., ed., Geologic Guidebook to the Belt–Purcell Supergroup, Glacier National Park and Vicinity, Montana and Adjacent Canada: Belt Symposium III Field Trip Guidebook, Belt Association, Spokane, Washington, p. 21–51.

YOUNG, G. M., 1995, Are Neoproterozoic glacial deposits preserved on the margins of Laurentia related to the fragmentation of two supercontinents?: Geology, v. 23, p. 153–156.

ZEMPOLICH, W. G., WILKINSON, B. H., AND LOHMANN, K. C, 1988, Diagenesis of Late Proterozoic carbonates: the Beck Spring Dolomite of eastern California: Journal of Sedimentary Petrology, v. 58, p. 656–672.

GEOCHEMISTRY OF MARINE AND NONMARINE ENVIRONMENTS OF A NEOPROTEROZOIC CRATONIC CARBONATE/EVAPORITE: THE BITTER SPRINGS FORMATION, CENTRAL AUSTRALIA

A. C. HILL, K. AROURI, P. GORJAN, AND M. R. WALTER[1]

Department of Earth and Planetary Sciences, Macquarie University, Sydney NSW 2109, Australia

ABSTRACT: The Bitter Springs Formation constitutes the upper part of Supersequence 1, an 830 Ma carbonate succession deposited in the intracratonic Centralian Superbasin. The Superbasin covered 2 million km^2 of the Australian continent during Neoproterozoic times. We have integrated new carbon, oxygen, sulfur, and strontium isotopic information, and new biomarker information, with existing results, to test and extend previous studies of the formation.

The Gillen Member of the Bitter Springs Formation was deposited in a marine environment. The evidence for this interpretation includes isotopes of strontium, carbon, and sulfur, and biomarkers. $^{87}Sr/^{86}Sr$ ratios in the Gillen Member are comparable to the lowest ever recorded from the Shaler Supergroup of Canada, of similar age. These low strontium isotopic ratios are associated with comparable secular change in seawater $\delta^{13}C_{carb}$. Steroidal hydrocarbon biomarker assemblages, seawater $\delta^{34}S_{sulfate}$ values, and low $\delta^{34}S_{pyrite}$ values further indicate a marine origin.

The lower part of the Loves Creek Member (Units 1 and 2) was also deposited in a marine environment. Facies-independent secular change in seawater $\delta^{13}C_{carb}$ and low $^{87}Sr/^{86}Sr$ ratios are comparable to those in the upper Shaler Supergroup of Canada. Seawater $\delta^{34}S_{sulfate}$ values, low $\delta^{34}S_{pyrite}$, and evidence for algal biomarkers are also consistent with marine deposition.

The upper part of the Loves Creek Member (Unit 3), and lower part of Unit 2, is nonmarine. Rare pyrite, heavy $\delta^{34}S_{pyrite}$, abundant irregularly branched C_{25} and C_{30} isoprenoids from methanogens, and abundant pseudomorphs after halite indicate carbonate precipitation in sulfate-poor hypersaline lakes. Heavy and variable $\delta^{13}C_{carb}$ and $\delta^{18}O$ indicate that continental groundwater brines, which were low in dissolved carbonate, drained into the lakes. Evaporation of the lake waters increased the concentration of dissolved carbonate, and increased still more the $\delta^{18}O$ values, and may have had a small positive effect on $\delta^{13}C_{carb}$. Dolomitization of the continental redbeds occurred by the evaporative reflux of groundwater. Cyanobacteria formed mats on the lake margins, where they were quickly silicified. Domical and irregular stromatolites formed within the lakes. The occasional presence of C_{30} desmethyl steranes and 4-methylsteranes in the lower parts of Unit 3 indicates that either there were marine incursions or that marine algae were transported to the lakes, possibly by winds. Nonmarine Neoproterozoic algae may have synthesized these sterols.

INTRODUCTION

This study presents new geochemical data that place constraints on depositional (marine and nonmarine) and diagenetic environments. These include stable (C, O, and S) and radiogenic (Sr) isotopes, trace elements (Sr, Mn, and Fe) and biomarkers. In this paper we have added to previous paleobiological and sedimentological studies to attempt a comprehensive documentation of a Neoproterozoic carbonate. We consider that it shows how an integrated sedimentological, geochemical, and paleobiological approach can allow confident recognition of paleoenvironments at a time when the fossil record is sparse.

"Most studies of Precambrian carbonates have not been comprehensive, instead tending to focus on specific, usually biological, aspects of carbonate occurrences" (Grotzinger, 1989). For example, stromatolites of the Bitter Springs Formation are amongst the most intensively studied anywhere. They were first described by Chewings (1914) and Howchin (1914), and more forms were found and described by Mawson and Madigan (1930) and Madigan (1932a, 1932b, 1935). Glaessner et al. (1969), Cloud and Semikhatov (1969), and Walter (1972) described nine different forms of distinctive columnar branching stromatolites from the formation, and Walter et al. (1979) provided some additional taxonomic information. Microfossils discovered in stromatolitic cherts in the formation by Barghoorn and Schopf (1965) were subsequently studied in great detail by Schopf (1968), Schopf and Blacic (1971), Oehler (1976, 1977), Oehler et al. (1979), Knoll and Golubic (1979), and Knoll (1981), shedding considerable light on the evolution of bacteria. A sedimentological study of the upper (Loves Creek) member by Southgate (1986, 1989, 1991) revealed marine and nonmarine facies, and showed that the taxonomically described stromatolites are confined to the marine facies, and the microfossils to the nonmarine facies.

Studies of the evolution of the composition of seawater have utilized the strontium isotopic composition of the Bitter Springs Formation (Veizer and Compston, 1976) and the composition of its evaporites (Holland, 1984). The formation has also received significant interest from organic geochemists, initiated by McKirdy's (1976) work on stromatolites, followed by detailed biomarker studies by Summons and Walter (1990), Summons and Powell (1991), Summons (1992), and Logan et al. (1997) on the Gillen Member. The formation has been examined as a source rock for petroleum (Summons and Powell, 1991) and has been a target for exploration for base metals and petroleum.

GEOLOGICAL SETTING

The areal extent of the first Neoproterozoic carbonate and evaporite accumulation in the Centralian Superbasin is shown in Figure 1 (Walter et al., 1995; Walter and Veevers, 1997). The Bitter Springs Formation was deposited in the Amadeus Basin (boxed area in Figure 1), one of several structural basins later developed during uplift of parts of the Superbasin at 540–600 Ma (Petermann Ranges Orogeny) and 320 Ma (Alice Springs Orogeny) (Walter et al., 1995). Within the Superbasin four distinct sedimentary units, or supersequences, are recognized, on the basis of sequence analysis, lithostratigraphy, and biostratigraphy (Fig. 2); Supersequence 1 comprises the Bitter Springs Formation and underlying Heavitree Quartzite (Walter et al., 1995). A U–Pb zircon date of 827 ± 6 Ma for the Gairdner Dyke Swarm (Wingate et al., 1998), which is correlated by strong similarities in geochemical and isotopic data with volcanics present throughout the Bitter Springs Formation (Zhao et al., 1994), provides the best estimate of the age of the Bitter Springs Formation. It also provides a minimum age for the commence-

[1]To whom correspondence should be addressed: Malcolm.Walter@mq.edu.au

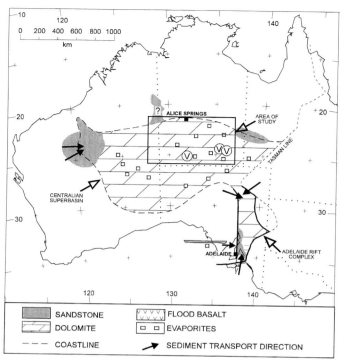

Fig. 1.—Areal extent of carbonate and evaporite deposition in the Centralian Superbasin at 830 Ma, with the area of study (Amadeus Basin) shown (after Walter and Veevers, 1997).

ment of Neoproterozoic sedimentation in the Centralian Superbasin and Adelaide Rift Complex to the southeast. Sediments on the developing plate margin of the Adelaide Rift Complex are some five times thicker than equivalents in the Centralian Superbasin. A 170 My gap separates the base of the Centralian Superbasin and associated Adelaide Rift Complex from latest Mesoproterozoic (1 Ga) metamorphic rocks and mafic volcanics (Fig. 2).

METHODOLOGY

Sections in drillcore and outcrop, selected for geographic spread and preservation of outcrop, were systematically logged and sampled for geochemical analysis. The sampling interval was 10 m, in places shorter to ensure comprehensive facies coverage. Samples were selected for isotopic analysis on the basis of fabric preservation, fineness of grain, and textural uniformity, as seen in thin section by transmitted light (cf. Tucker, 1983; Kaufman and Knoll, 1995). Terminology for dolomite petrography is after Sibley and Gregg (1987). All dolomite samples exhibit uniform orange cathodoluminescence (CL), so CL did not influence selection for isotopic analysis. Primary texture was the main selection criterion. Two nodular anhydrite samples in the Wallara-1 core yielded low $^{87}Sr/^{86}Sr$ ratios of use in the global seawater curve.

Eleven samples from Wallara-1 with the highest total organic carbon content were chosen for biomarker analysis. Bitumen, or solvent-extractable organic matter, was extracted using established procedures (Strauss et al., 1992; Summons and Strauss, 1992a, 1992b). The saturated hydrocarbon fractions were analyzed on a MD 800 (Fisons Instruments) GC-MS fitted with a Carlo Erba GC 8000, and controlled by a MassLab data system. A DB-1 (60 m × 0.32 mm i.d.; 0.1 μm film thickness) capillary column with H_2 carrier gas was used. The GC was

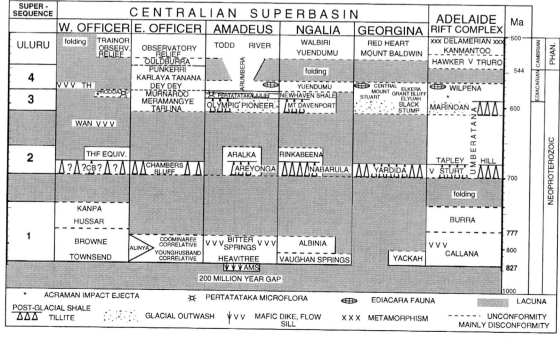

Fig. 2.—Neoproterozoic stratigraphy of the Centralian Superbasin, and Adelaide Rift Complex (after Walter and Veevers, 1997; Morton, 1997).

programmed from 50 to 100°C at 15°C min^{-1} and then to 310°C at 3°C min^{-1}. Ions were generated by 70 eV electron impact (E1+) with an accelerating voltage of 8 kV. The MS was used in full-scan mode (m/z 50–500) and the total analysis time was 90 minutes with a cycle time of 1.82 seconds.

Carbon, oxygen, and strontium isotopic analyses were undertaken at the Center for Isotope Studies (CIS), CSIRO, Sydney. Stable-isotope analysis of carbonates used the traditional method of phosphorolysis (McCrea, 1950). Organic carbon isotopes were carried out by sealed-tube combustion (see Strauss et al., 1992). Sulfur-isotope analyses were performed on pyrite and kerogen (Canfield et al., 1986), and sulfate. CO_2 and SO_2 generated in these reactions were analyzed on a Finnigan MAT 252 mass spectrometer. $\delta^{18}O$ values were corrected for CO_2-H_2O equilibration at 25°C using a fractionation factor of 1.0412 for calcite (Freidman and O'Neil, 1977). The $\delta^{18}O$ value for dolomite was corrected relative to calcite by +0.67‰ (Rosenbaum and Sheppard, 1986). Both $\delta^{13}C$ and $\delta^{18}O$ are reported relative to PDB with a precision of ± 0.2‰. $\delta^{34}S$ values are reported relative to CDT; precision for pyrite was ± 0.5‰ and ± 0.2‰ for sulfate. The two nodular anhydrite samples were dissolved in de-ionized water, strontium was separated using cation exchange columns, and the isotopic determination was carried out on a thermal ionization mass spectrometer. $^{87}Sr/^{86}Sr$ ratios are normalized to $^{86}Sr/^{88}Sr = 0.1194$ and to a Standard Reference Material 987 value of 0.710241 (Asmerom et al., 1991; Derry et al., 1992). Twenty-nine carbonates were analyzed for minor (Fe, Mn, Sr) elements by ICP-AES at the CSIRO. Instrument precision is 1%. All sample repeats were within 3.5%.

BITTER SPRINGS FORMATION

The Bitter Springs Formation comprises the 400 m thick Gillen Member of halite and gypsum and minor carbonate, overlain by the 600 m thick Loves Creek Member of stromatolitic dolomite and interbedded dolomitic siltstone and carbonate. Thin basic volcanics occur sporadically throughout both members. To ensure complete coverage, the Bitter Springs Formation was sampled in drillcore (AS-3, Wallara-1, AS-27, AS-28) and outcrop (Dump and Bluebush field sections), the locations of which are shown in Figure 3. In stratigraphic order, the Gillen Member is exposed in the Dump field section, which shows the contact with the Heavitree Quartzite; the AS-3 drillcore; and the Bluebush Field section, which shows the contact with the Loves Creek Member. Southgate (1991) divided the Loves Creek Member into three units, each representing a distinctive depositional environment. The lower unit (1) of the Loves Creek Member is exposed in the Bluebush field section. Unit 2 is exposed in the Bluebush field section, Wallara-1, AS-27, and AS-28 drillcores. Unit 3 is exposed in the Wallara-1, AS-27, and AS-28 drillcores. There is extensive outcrop of all units except the evaporites, and even these crop out locally.

To allow compilation of a comprehensive record of isotope stratigraphy of the formation, a composite column was compiled (see Fig. 4) from the base upward, from (a) the Dump field section, (b) the AS-3 drillcore, (c) the Bluebush field section, and (d) the Wallara-1 drillcore. For this reason, sample depths for these individual sections are shown relative to the base of the Dump field section. Sample depths in AS-27 and

AS-28 are shown as depths below the top of the drillcore. Wallara-1 was used in preference to AS-27 and AS-28 in the composite column because it probably overlaps with the Bluebush field section in Unit 2 of the Loves Creek Member, and records about 100 m of additional Unit 3 sediments not found in outcrop or AS-27 and AS-28. There are several reasons for postulating this overlap. Extensive mapping (see discussion in Southgate, 1991) indicates that Unit 2 has a maximum thickness of about 200 m, which is the approximate thickness in Wallara-1. Also, the presence of the redbed facies in the lowermost parts of Wallara-1 and in the Bluebush field section, concomitant with a gradual shift in $\delta^{13}C_{carb}$ and $\delta^{18}O$ in both sections, suggest synchronicity. However, the appearance of this facies may have been diachronous across the basin.

Gillen Member

Sedimentology and Petrography.—

The contact of the Gillen Member with the Heavitree Quartzite is exposed in the Dump field section (Figs. 3, 4). Here, the Gillen member consists of black shale overlain by interbedded gray–black shale, minor sandstone, and thin-bedded dolomite with small amounts of detrital quartz silt and clay minerals. Columnar stromatolites form biostromes 70 cm thick in the uppermost parts of ~4 m thick dolomite units (Walter, 1972). At an unknown height above the basal shale and dolomite, as seen in drill holes and on seismic records, are the characteristic evaporite facies of laminated sulfate and dolomite, and a 40 m thick middle halite unit (Fig. 4), beneath which occur several other thin halite units. Siltstone, shale, and sandstone occur as thin, interbedded and graded units (Lindsay, 1987). Shale and dolomite are black, as seen at the base of the formation. Stewart (1979) described five facies within the AS-3 core. Two of these predominate: a bituminous dolomite facies and a dolomite–gypsum breccia facies. Bituminous dolomite characterizes the lower half of the core and consists of dark gray to black, massive and laminated dolomite. Laminae are commonly wispy and consist of rounded quartz silt, clay, disseminated pyrite, and dark brown organic matter. Color lamination is common, dark laminae being finer grained than pale laminae. This facies is commonly brecciated by veins of anhydrite and gypsum and contains laminae of pale brown, very fine-grained chalcedonic silica preserving filamentous microbial fossils, considered to be cyanobacteria (Oehler et al., 1979). The dolomite–gypsum breccia facies, which forms up to 50% of the core, predominates in the upper half of AS-3 (Fig. 4). This facies has rhythmically interlaminated dolomite and gypsum. The laminae are often broken and contorted in a matrix of white gypsum. In thin section, the gypsum is medium to coarse grained. Just below the Loves Creek Member contact occurs laminated dolomite with microbial lamination.

Dolomite petrography of the Gillen Member sections is shown in Table 1.

Isotopes.—

Carbon, oxygen, and sulfur isotopic data for the Gillen Member are shown in Table 2. Strontium isotopic data are shown in Table 3. All isotopic data are shown in Figure 4. Carbon-isotope data in AS-3 seem to be facies-controlled. $\delta^{13}C_{carb}$ values of the bituminous dolomite facies, mostly from the lower half of AS-3, are between 1.6 and 5.6‰ (average 4.2 ± 1.1‰), and $\delta^{18}O$

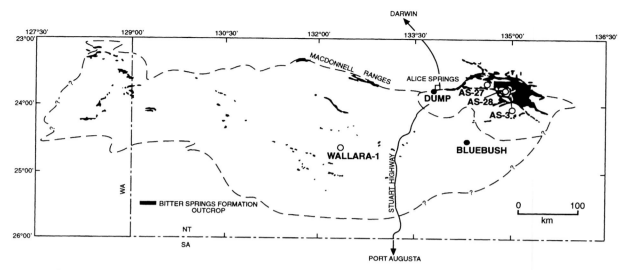

FIG. 3.—Bitter Springs Formation drillcore and field sampling locations, Amadeus Basin (adapted from Southgate, 1991).

between -5.4 and $-3.0\%o$ (average $-3.6 \pm 0.7\%o$). $\delta^{13}C_{carb}$ values of the dolomite–gypsum breccia facies (all samples from the upper half of AS-3) are between 0.3 and 2.2‰ (average 1.7 $\pm 0.8\%o$), and $\delta^{18}O$ between -7.4 and $-3.1\%o$ (average $-5.5 \pm 1.2\%o$).

Molecular Fossils and Microfossils.—

The distribution of biomarkers and microfossils in the Gillen Member is shown in Figure 5. Biomarker maturity parameters indicate a mild thermal history for the Gillen Member (refer to Peters and Moldowan, 1993, for key to parameters listed in Figure 5). All biomarker data were derived from other drillcores so their distributions in Figure 5 are arbitrary. The microfossils are from AS-3 (Oehler et al., 1979). Additionally, Logan et al. (1997) found that hydrocarbon biomarker patterns are consistent with known sedimentary environments, further testimony that the hydrocarbons in the Gillen Member are indigenous.

Low-diversity microbial communities consisting of predominantly filamentous, probably cyanobacterial, microfossils, many in mat-like masses, have been described (Oehler et al., 1979; Zang and Walter, 1992). Walter (1972) described one form of columnar stromatolite. Zang and Walter (1992) described some spheroidal and small acanthomorph acritarchs, presumed to be algae. Disseminated pyrite depleted in ^{34}S indicates the action of sulfate-reducing bacteria.

Biomarkers reported by Summons and Walter (1990), Summons and Powell (1991), Summons (1992), and Logan et al. (1997) are consistent with the described microfossils. These include abundant acyclic isoprenoids derived mostly from halophilic Archaea, abundant algal steroidal biomarkers, and monomethyl alkanes and hopanes, both probably derived from cyanobacteria and other bacteria, C_{30} desmethyl steranes, 4-methyl steranes, and dinosterane. The detection of dinosterane, which is known only to be produced by dinoflagellates, led Summons and Walter (1990) to suggest that dinoflagellates and other desmethylsterane-producing marine algae probably had ancestors in the Neoproterozoic.

Sedimentary and Diagenetic History.—

Stewart (1979) interpreted the Gillen Member evaporites as having formed in a barred basin cut off from the ocean by a stromatolite barrier reef. As circulation became restricted, bituminous dolomite accumulated in the lagoon behind the reef. With continued evaporation, brine concentration increased and gypsum and halite precipitated. However, Lindsay (1987) favored formation of the evaporites in poorly circulating anoxic sub-basins within a basin of considerable areal extent. He suggested that the evaporites were deposited in a shallow marine setting at a time of relative sea-level highstand. Laminated carbonates and sulfates developed around basin margins and later-stage halite was deposited in sub-basin centers. The apparent sea-level high may relate to basin dynamics, whereas the cyclicity of the evaporites may be due to eustatic sea-level controls, which resulted in the repeated opening and closing of the Centralian Superbasin to the ocean. A similar distribution of evaporite facies is seen in the Upper Carboniferous Otto Fiord Formation of the Sverdrup Basin (Beauchamp et al., 1987). Sedimentation was on a scale similar to the Centralian Superbasin, and paleontological data show that the Sverdrup sea remained interconnected with the Paleopacific ocean throughout most of the late Paleozoic except for episodic closure at the time of deposition of the Otto Fiord evaporites.

The acritarchs and molecular fossils suggest a marine origin. Zang and Walter (1992) considered the presence of acritarchs to be consistent with deposition on an open marine shelf, though given the little information available on the paleoenvironmental distribution of Proterozoic acritarchs, this can be only tentative. Steroidal hydrocarbon compositions are consistent with deposition in an evaporitic marine environment (e.g., Logan et al., 1997).

Carbon and sulfur isotopic data from this study, and a reinterpretation of available strontium isotopic data, indicate marine deposition for the Gillen Member. $\delta^{34}S_{sulfate}$ values (Table 2) are typical of Neoproterozoic seawater (Holser et al., 1988), and low $\delta^{34}S_{pyrite}$ values (Table 2) are consistent with bacterial sulfate reduction in sediment that was constantly replenished with

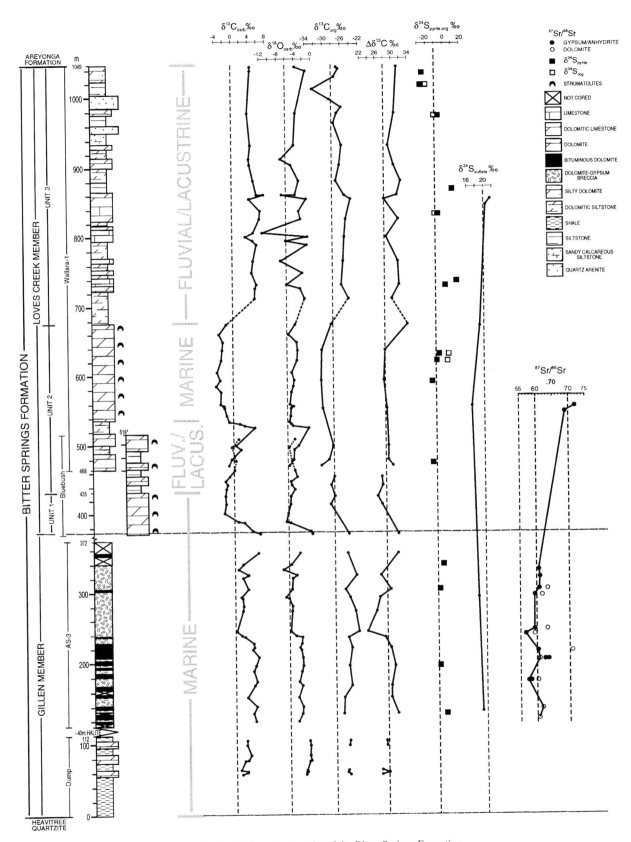

FIG. 4.—Isotope stratigraphy of the Bitter Springs Formation.

TABLE 1.—DOLOMITE PETROGRAPHY, GILLEN MEMBER

Section	Facies	Fabric	Crystal shape	Crystal size (μm)	Crystal size distribution
Dump	thin-bedded dolomite	poor preservation of beds/laminae	nonplanar	1-100	polymodal
AS-3	bituminous dolomite and dolomite–gypsum breccia	well-preserved laminae	nonplanar	1-15	polymodal
Bluebush	thin-bedded dolomite	well-preserved laminae	nonplanar	1-25	polymodal

TABLE 2.—CARBON, OXYGEN, AND SULFUR ISOTOPIC DATA, GILLEN MEMBER

Location	Sample	Height above base (m)	Facies	$\delta^{18}O$ (‰ PDB)	$\delta^{13}C_{carb}$ (‰ PDB)	$\delta^{13}C_{org}$ (‰ PDB)	$\Delta\delta^{13}C$ (‰ PDB)	TOC (%C)	$\Delta^{34}S_{sulfate}$ (‰ CDT)	$\delta^{34}S_{pyrite}$ (‰ CDT)
Bluebush dam	950701.01	376	thin-bedded dolomite	−0.4	6.1	−24.8	31.0	0.02	—	—
AS-3 core	960429.01	355	bituminous dolomite	−3.4	5.6	−25.2	30.8	0.10	—	—
AS-3 core	960429.02	339	dolomite–gypsum breccia	−5.5	1.9	—	—	—	—	−3.0
AS-3 core	960429.04	332	dolomite–gypsum breccia	−7.4	0.8	—	—	—	—	—
AS-3 core	960429.06	324	dolomite–gypsum breccia	−4.2	3.2	−23.2	26.5	0.04	—	—
AS-3 core	960429.07	320	dolomite–gypsum breccia	−5.2	1.9	—	—	—	—	—
AS-3 core	960429.11	304	bituminous dolomite	−5.4	3.1	−25.7	28.9	0.23	—	−7.7
AS-3 core	960429.13	293	dolomite–gypsum breccia	−6.8	1.4	−24.8	26.2	0.02	18.2	—
AS-3 core	960429.14	291	dolomite–gypsum breccia	−6.1	1.7	—	—	—	—	—
AS-3 core	960430.02	280	dolomite–gypsum breccia	−5.3	2.0	—	—	—	—	—
AS-3 core	960430.03	273	dolomite–gypsum breccia	−5.4	1.8	−23.5	25.3	0.02	—	—
AS-3 core	960430.45	245	dolomite–gypsum breccia	−5.8	0.3	−22.7	23.0	0.04	—	—
AS-3 core	960430.48	239	bituminous dolomite	−4.5	1.5	—	—	—	—	—
AS-3 core	960430.49	237	dolomite–gypsum breccia	−3.1	2.2	−25.1	27.4	0.04	—	—
AS-3 core	960430.52	228	bituminous dolomite	−3.2	4.3	—	—	—	—	—
AS-3 core	960430.53	222	bituminous dolomite	−3.7	4.4	−24.4	28.8	0.05	—	—
AS-3 core	960430.54	219	bituminous dolomite	−3.3	4.0	—	—	—	—	—
AS-3 core	960430.55	208	bituminous dolomite	−3.0	5.5	—	—	—	—	—
AS-3 core	960431.01	196	bituminous dolomite	−2.9	4.8	−25.0	29.8	0.07	—	−8.1
AS-3 core	960431.02	187	bituminous dolomite	−3.2	4.2	—	—	—	—	—
AS-3 core	960431.04	173	bituminous dolomite	−3.9	5.1	—	—	—	—	—
AS-3 core	960431.06	168	bituminous dolomite	−3.1	4.4	−24.5	28.9	0.25	—	—
AS-3 core	960431.09	152	bituminous dolomite	−4.0	2.7	−26.2	28.9	0.29	—	—
AS-3 core	960431.12	139	bituminous dolomite	−3.0	5.0	—	—	—	—	—
AS-3 core	960431.13	132	dolomite–gypsum breccia	—	—	—	—	—	19.1	—
AS-3 core	960431.14	129	bituminous dolomite	−3.2	4.1	−26.3	30.5	0.10	—	−0.3
AS-3 core	960431.17	118	bituminous dolomite	−4.0	4.7	—	—	—	—	—
Alice Springs dump	950716.10	103	thin-bedded dolomite	−1.6	2.5	−25.0	27.5	0.02	—	—
Alice Springs dump	950716.09	97	thin-bedded dolomite	−1.4	2.5	−25.2	27.6	0.01	—	—
Alice Springs dump	950716.08	83	thin-bedded dolomite	−1.5	3.4	—	—	—	—	—
Alice Springs dump	950716.07	76	thin-bedded dolomite	−1.3	2.8	—	—	—	—	—
Alice Springs dump	950716.06	75	thin-bedded dolomite	−1.5	2.0	—	—	—	—	—
Alice Springs dump	950716.04	62	thin-bedded dolomite	−2.2	1.0	−25.4	26.4	0.04	—	—
Alice Springs dump	950716.03	60	thin-bedded dolomite	−2.1	2.6	—	—	—	—	—
Alice Springs dump	950716.02	59	thin-bedded dolomite	−2.3	2.6	—	—	—	—	—
Alice Springs dump	950716.01	56	thin-bedded dolomite	−2.4	1.4	−25.0	26.4	0.02	—	—

TABLE 3.—STRONTIUM ISOTOPIC DATA, AS-3, GILLEN MEMBER (FANNING, 1986)

Sample type	Height above base (m)	$^{87}Sr/^{86}Sr$
gypsum	332	0.70606 ± 0.00010
gypsum	322	0.70610 ± 0.00009
gypsum	305	0.70607 ± 0.00008
gypsum	295	0.70595 ± 0.00010
gypsum	247	0.70593 ± 0.00008
gypsum	241	0.70568 ± 0.00009
gypsum	216	0.70601 ± 0.00006
vein gypsum	204	0.70626 ± 0.00005
gypsum	204	0.70636 ± 0.00009
anhydrite	174	0.70581 ± 0.00010
gypsum	173	0.70574 ± 0.00011
anhydrite	173	0.70625 ± 0.00006
dolomite	305	0.70633 ± 0.00008
dolomite	295	0.70618 ± 0.00007
dolomite	247	0.70631 ± 0.00007
dolomite	241	0.70592 ± 0.00011
dolomite	216	0.70708 ± 0.00013
dolomite	204	0.70608 ± 0.00006
dolomite	173	0.70601 ± 0.00013
dolomite	135	0.70617 ± 0.00006
dolomite	121	0.70605 ± 0.00008

SO_4^{2-} (Goldhaber and Kaplan, 1974), that is, seawater. The lowest known seawater $^{87}Sr/^{86}Sr$ values were first reported by Asmerom et al. (1991) in shallow subtidal to intertidal carbonates (Young, 1981) of the upper Shaler Supergroup of Canada, an approximate correlative of the Bitter Springs Formation. The samples show smooth and systematic variation between 0.70561 and 0.70676. A ratio of 0.70621 from the lower Akademikerbreen Group of Svalbard, an approximate correlative of the upper Shaler Supergroup, matches these remarkably low values (Derry et al., 1989; Derry et al., 1992). In the AS-3 drillcore, Fanning (1986) determined twelve $^{87}Sr/^{86}Sr$ ratios from gypsum/anhydrite of between 0.70568 and 0.70636 (Table 3, Fig. 4). Nine dolomites were also analyzed with $^{87}Sr/^{86}Sr$ ratios between 0.70592 and 0.70780. These values support global correlation between Australia, Canada, and Spitsbergen at about 830 Ma (Zhao et al., 1994; Wingate et al., 1998), a time when an unprecedented flux of Sr from basalts occurred.

A shift in $\delta^{13}C_{carb}$ from about 6‰ to −4‰ in the uppermost Shaler Supergroup (Kaufman and Knoll, 1995), accompanied

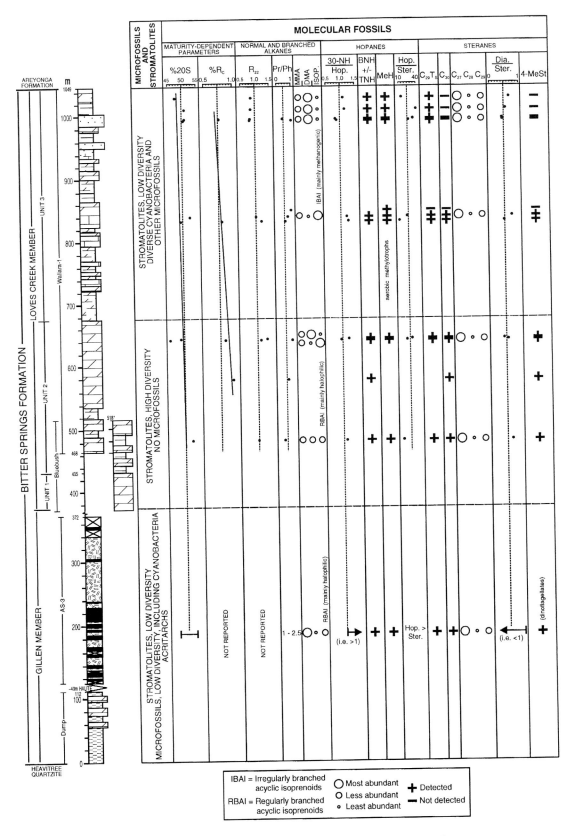

FIG. 5.—Biomarker and fossil occurrence in the Bitter Springs Formation.

by an increase in $^{87}Sr/^{86}Sr$ from 0.7058 to 0.7067, is matched in Australia. A $\delta^{13}C_{carb}$ shift from around 6‰ in the upper Gillen Member (Bluebush field section and AS-3) to about $-4‰$ in Unit 2 of the lower Loves Creek Member, accompanied by an increase in $^{87}Sr/^{86}Sr$ from 0.7060 in the upper Gillen Member to 0.7069 in Unit 2 of the lower Loves Creek Member, supports correlation with Canada. The $\delta^{13}C_{carb}$ value of 6.1‰ just below the Loves Creek Member contact is part of a facies-independent $\delta^{13}C_{carb}$ shift that occurs in Unit 1 of the Loves Creek Member (see discussion below). Although $\delta^{13}C_{carb}$ values in AS-3 are facies-dependent, the heaviest values, which occur in the bituminous dolomite facies, are between 3‰ and 6‰, which is within the range of values in the upper Shaler Supergroup.

This integrated sedimentological and geochemical approach has made it possible to show that the Gillen Member was deposited in a marine environment. In intracratonic, evaporitic settings this can often be difficult to prove, particularly without the aid of an informative fossil record (e.g., Frank et al., 1997).

Well-preserved, fine-grained textures in dolomite near the contact with the Loves Creek Member, and heavy $\delta^{18}O$, suggest early dolomitization in evaporated seawater (Gaines, 1968, 1980; Tucker, 1983; Land, 1985; Fairchild and Spiro, 1987; Zenger and Dunham, 1988; Gregg and Shelton, 1990; Gao and Land, 1991; Montañez and Read, 1992). Nonplanar polymodal texture probably indicates later recrystallization events (Sibley and Gregg, 1987; Gregg and Shelton, 1990). A similar depositional and diagenetic history is envisaged for dolomites near the Heavitree Quartzite contact, although fabrics are poorly preserved. An alternative is dolomitization in a marine–meteoric mixing zone (e.g., Allan and Matthews, 1982; Zempolich et al., 1988; Meyers et al., 1997). However, the mixing-zone dolomitization model has received much criticism because dolomite is not being precipitated in modern mixing zones to the extent inferred for ancient successions (e.g., Land, 1985; Machel and Mountjoy, 1986, 1987; Hardie, 1987; Sun, 1994).

Figure 6 clearly demonstrates lighter and more variable $\delta^{13}C_{carb}$ and $\delta^{18}O$ values for the dolomite–gypsum breccia facies, in contrast to the bituminous dolomite facies. There is also $\delta^{18}O-\delta^{13}C_{carb}$ covariation in the dolomite–gypsum breccia facies, which may partly be a result of secular $\delta^{13}C_{carb}$ variation. The presence of evaporites with dolomite should rule out any freshwater-influenced carbonate diagenesis because under those conditions the evaporites would have dissolved. However, all evidence indicates that gypsum in the dolomite–gypsum breccia

facies is secondary, formed from preexisting anhydrite (Stewart, 1979). Hydration of anhydrite to gypsum in freshwater fluids, and inherent mineralogical expansion, would explain both *in situ* brecciation of the dolomite–gypsum breccia facies and depleted $\delta^{18}O$ values. Depleted $\delta^{13}C_{carb}$ values might indicate the presence of carbon derived from a soil microbiota. The small volume of dolomite in the dolomite–gypsum breccia facies would render it more susceptible to carbon isotopic alteration (e.g., Land, 1992). Organic-matter diagenesis can be ruled out as the cause of ^{13}C-depletion in the dolomite because of the low total organic carbon contents in the Gillen Member.

Loves Creek Member

Unit 1.—

Sedimentology and Petrography.—Southgate (1991) described three facies in Unit 1 (lower Loves Creek Member), all dolomitic. The lowermost 0.1–5 m consists of intraclast and peloid grainstone. Angular to rounded dolomite clasts are locally derived and set in a coarse-grained matrix of quartz sand and dolomite. Overlying the grainstone is a stromatolitic unit indicative of a deepening-upward water body. Irregular and bulbous stromatolites initially grow from the irregular conglomeratic surface, gradually passing into parallel to slightly divergent columnar stromatolites that broaden to form the internal parts of expanding domes. Domes extend both outward and upward to produce forms 4–5 m in diameter. The uppermost domes reach 15–20 m in diameter and have up to 2 m of relief. The larger domes are composed internally of pseudo-columnar stromatolites. Peloids, intraclasts, and quartz grit fill the intercolumnar and interdomal areas. Overlying the stromatolitic unit is 20 to 30 m of thinly bedded dolo-mudstone, which passes upwards into Unit 2.

The dolomite petrography of Unit 1 facies is shown in Table 4.

Isotopes.—Carbon and oxygen isotopic data for Unit 1 are shown in Table 5 and in Figure 4.

Sedimentary and Diagenetic History.—Southgate (1991) considered that Unit 1 was deposited as a result of gradual marine transgression. Intraclast and peloid grainstone were deposited as relative sea level gradually rose at the start of the transgression. Further deepening of the water body is represented by gradually expanding domal stromatolites. The onset of comparatively deep, quiet-water conditions resulted in deposition of the uppermost dolo-mudstone unit, which Southgate (1991) suggested represents a maximum flooding surface.

Carbon and oxygen isotopic data are consistent with Southgate's (1991) interpretation that Unit 1 was deposited as a result of marine transgression because the negative $\delta^{13}C_{carb}$ and $\delta^{18}O$ shifts are independent of facies. The $\delta^{13}C_{carb}$ values are thus part of secular change in global seawater, which, as discussed earlier, is supported by correlation with the similar-aged upper Shaler Supergroup of Canada. A $\delta^{18}O$ value of $-0.4‰$ in well-preserved dolomite just below the Loves Creek Member contact, which precedes a $\delta^{18}O$ shift to $-6.4‰$ in Unit 1, suggests mixing of two waters: an ^{18}O-enriched brine (Gillen Member) and normal seawater associated with marine transgression (Unit 1). Intermittent closure of the Centralian Superbasin to the global ocean during evaporite deposition in the Gillen Member probably caused seawater $\delta^{18}O$ to increase in the Superbasin.

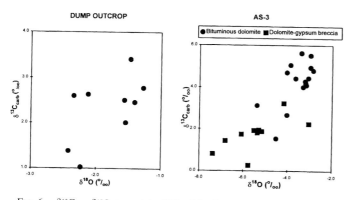

FIG. 6.—$\delta^{13}C_{carb}$–$\delta^{18}O$ crossplots, Gillen Member.

TABLE 4.—DOLOMITE PETROGRAPHY, UNIT 1, LOVES CREEK MEMBER

Facies	Fabric	Crystal shape	Crystal size (μm)	Crystal size distribution
stromatolite	1st dolomite phase: interlaminated fine and coarse stromatolite laminae	nonplanar	1–25	polymodal
	2nd dolomite phase: patchy growth of fabric-destructive dolospar	nonplanar	1–60	polymodal
dolo-mudstone	bedding planes poorly preserved	nonplanar	1–30	polymodal

TABLE 5.—CARBON AND OXYGEN ISOTOPIC DATA, BLUEBUSH FIELD SECTION AND WALLARA-1, LOVES CREEK MEMBER

Location	Sample	Height above base (m)	Facies	Mineralogy	$\delta^{18}O$ (‰ PDB)	$\delta^{13}C_{carb}$ (‰ PDB)	$\delta^{13}C_{org}$ (‰ PDB)	$\Delta\delta^{13}C$ (‰ PDB)	TOC (‰ C)
Wallara-1, Unit 3	950703.03	1044	thin-bedded	dolomite	−3.7	4.5	−26.9	31.4	0.15
Wallara-1, Unit 3	950703.05	1041	thin-bedded	dolomite	—	—	−26.5	—	0.35
Wallara-1, Unit 3	950703.06	1040	thin-bedded	dolomite	−1.3	4.5	—	—	—
Wallara-1, Unit 3	950703.14	1031	thin-bedded	dolomite	—	—	−27.5	—	0.38
Wallara-1, Unit 3	950703.22	1013	redbeds	dolomite	—	—	−32.4	—	0.65
Wallara-1, Unit 3	950704.02	1000	redbeds	dolomite	—	—	−28.5	—	0.57
Wallara-1, Unit 3	950704.08	988	redbeds	dolomite	—	—	−25.9	—	0.06
Wallara-1, Unit 3	950704.12	979	thin-bedded	dolomite	−3.7	3.8	−26.9	30.7	0.12
Wallara-1, Unit 3	950704.15	966	redbeds	dolomite	—	—	−27.6	—	0.06
Wallara-1, Unit 3	950705.01	935	thin-bedded	dolomite	−4.2	4.5	−25.9	29.1	0.02
Wallara-1, Unit 3	950705.09	914	thin-bedded	dolomite	−7.2	4.1	—	—	—
Wallara-1, Unit 3	950705.12	906	thin-bedded	dolomite	−4.9	4.2	−26.4	30.5	0.06
Wallara-1, Unit 3	950705.18	883	thin-bedded	dolomite	−3.0	5.1	−27.2	32.2	0.03
Wallara-1, Unit 3	950705.22	865	ribboned	calcite	−7.0	7.5	—	—	—
Wallara-1, Unit 3	950705.23	863	ribboned	dolomite	−3.9	5.9	−25.3	31.2	0.08
Wallara-1, Unit 3	950705.26	858	redbeds	dolomite	−1.3	4.1	−23.9	28.0	0.07
Wallara-1, Unit 3	950706.03	853	thin-bedded	siltstone	—	—	−21.2	—	10.6
Wallara-1, Unit 3	950706.10	842	thin-bedded	dolomite	−3.0	6.7	—	—	—
Wallara-1, Unit 3	950706.15	831	ribboned	dolomite	−2.7	6.5	−25.1	31.6	0.01
Wallara-1, Unit 3	950706.19	809	ribboned	calcite	−11.5	5.0	—	—	—
Wallara-1, Unit 3	950706.20	806	redbeds	dolomite	−1.1	3.1	−25.4	28.5	0.01
Wallara-1, Unit 3	950706.22	799	ribboned	calcite	−6.1	4.9	—	—	—
Wallara-1, Unit 3	950706.23	792	redbeds	dolomite	−1.2	5.7	—	—	—
Wallara-1, Unit 3	950706.24	770	ribboned	calcite	−7.3	4.9	−25.7	31.4	0.01
Wallara-1, Unit 3	950709.02	754	thin-bedded	dolomite	−2.3	4.6	—	—	—
Wallara-1, Unit 3	950709.08	736	ribboned	calcite	−6.0	5.7	−26.1	31.7	0.03
Wallara-1, Unit 3	950709.11	731	redbeds	dolomite	−2.8	5.3	—	—	—
Wallara-1, Unit 3	950709.12a	717	redbeds	dolomite	−1.8	5.2	−24.5	29.8	0.06
Wallara-1, Unit 2	950709.16	679	mudstone	dolomite	−4.1	−1.6	−28.5	33.7	0.01
Wallara-1, Unit 2	950710.03	666	mudstone	dolomite	−5.7	−3.3	—	—	—
Wallara-1, Unit 2	950710.09	655	stromatolite	dolomite	−3.8	−2.4	—	—	—
Wallara-1, Unit 2	950710.21	642	stromatolite	dolomite	−3.6	−2.6	−30.6	28.0	0.04
Wallara-1, Unit 2	950710.30	628	stromatolite	dolomite	−3.7	−2.8	—	—	—
Wallara-1, Unit 2	950711.05	611	stromatolite	dolomite	−5.0	−3.8	—	—	—
Wallara-1, Unit 2	950711.10	602	stromatolite	dolomite	−4.4	−3.1	−30.8	27.7	0.08
Wallara-1, Unit 2	950711.15	593	mudstone	dolomite	−4.6	−4.0	—	—	—
Wallara-1, Unit 2	950711.17	584	mudstone	dolomite	−5.0	−2.8	—	—	—
Wallara-1, Unit 2	950711.29a	567	mudstone	dolomite	−5.4	−3.0	—	—	—
Wallara-1, Unit 2	950711.30	565	mudstone	dolomite	−4.9	−2.3	—	—	—
Wallara-1, Unit 2	950712.01	563	mudstone	dolomite	−4.6	−2.2	—	—	—
Wallara-1, Unit 2	950712.03	561	mudstone	dolomite	−5.2	−2.1	−30.5	28.4	0.07
Wallara-1, Unit 2	950712.11	548	grainstone	dolomite	−5.3	−1.6	—	—	—
Wallara-1, Unit 2	950712.15	542	redbeds	dolomite	−5.5	−1.0	—	—	—
Wallara-1, Unit 2	950712.20	537	redbeds	dolomite	−5.2	1.6	—	—	—
Wallara-1, Unit 2	950712.23Ba	535	thin-bedded	dolomite	−4.8	2.7	—	—	—
Wallara-1, Unit 2	950712.24a	532	redbeds	dolomite	−1.1	5.0	—	—	—
Wallara-1, Unit 2	950712.38	508	redbeds	dolomite	−3.5	0.5	−28.2	28.7	0.03
Wallara-1, Unit 2	950712.43	501	stromatolite	dolomite	−4.5	1.7	—	—	—
Wallara-1, Unit 2	950713.08	486	stromatolite	dolomite	−4.7	−0.5	−29.1	28.7	0.14
Wallara-1, Unit 2	950713.14	478	mudstone	dolomite	−5.7	−1.2	−30.9	29.8	0.05
Bluebush dam, Unit 2	950701.15	513*	stromatolite	dolomite	−4.3	1.3	—	—	—
Bluebush dam, Unit 2	950701.14	499*	stromatolite	dolomite	−5.7	−0.4	—	—	—
Bluebush dam, Unit 2	950701.13	480*	stromatolite	dolomite	−5.1	0.6	—	—	—
Bluebush dam, Unit 2	950701.12	468	grainstone	dolomite	−4.4	0.2	—	—	—
Bluebush dam, Unit 2	950701.11	457	stromatolite	dolomite	−3.9	−1.0	−28.0	27.0	0.01
Bluebush dam, Unit 2	950701.10	450	grainstone	dolomite	−5.4	−2.0	—	—	—
Bluebush dam, Unit 2	950701.09	445	stromatolite	dolomite	−5.2	−1.6	−28.7	27.2	0.01
Bluebush dam, Unit 2	950701.08	439	thin-bedded	dolomite	−4.4	−1.9	—	—	—
Bluebush dam, Unit 1	950701.07	429	mudstone	dolomite	−5.4	−2.0	−27.9	25.9	0.01
Bluebush dam, Unit 1	950701.06	418	mudstone	dolomite	−5.5	−1.9	−28.9	26.9	0.01
Bluebush dam, Unit 1	950701.05	405	mudstone	dolomite	−6.1	−2.3	—	—	—
Bluebush dam, Unit 1	950701.04	393	stromatolite	dolomite	−6.4	0.9	—	—	—
Bluebush dam, Unit 1	950701.03	391	stromatolite	dolomite	−5.5	2.4	—	—	—
Bluebush dam, Unit 1	950701.02	380	grainstone	dolomite	−0.8	4.3	—	—	—

*Asterisked depths from the Bluebush Dam field section lie above the (postulated) overlapping Unit 2 contact in Wallara-1.

The retention of fine-grained dolomite in some fabrics suggests that syndepositional dolomitization occurred in seawater, probably after initial $CaCO_3$ precipitation (Gaines, 1968, 1980; Tucker, 1983; Land, 1985; Fairchild and Spiro, 1987; Zenger and Dunham, 1988; Gregg and Shelton, 1990; Gao and Land, 1991; Montañez and Read, 1992). Nonplanar polymodal texture and the presence of fabric-destructive, pervasive and patchy dolospar in most fabrics probably suggests that later burial recrystallization took place (Zenger, 1983; Land, 1985; Sibley and Gregg, 1987; Zenger and Dunham, 1988; Gregg and Shelton, 1990; Kupecz and Land, 1991; Gao and Land, 1991; Montañez and Read, 1992). The homogenization of $\delta^{18}O$ values ($-6.4‰$ and $-5.4‰$) above the facies-independent negative $\delta^{18}O$ shift may support burial recrystallization (e.g., Zenger and Dunham, 1988). An alternative is dolomitization in a marine–meteoric mixing zone (e.g., Allan and Matthews, 1982; Zempolich et al., 1988; Meyers et al., 1997).

Unit 2.—

Sedimentology and Petrography.—The central stromatolite-dominant unit of the Loves Creek Member comprises a series of laterally continuous shallowing-upward stromatolite cycles that mark a period of gradual marine regression (Southgate, 1991). A complete cycle, as seen in the field, comprises a lower grainstone facies, a middle domical and columnar stromatolite facies, and an upper thin-bedded stratiform stromatolite dolomite facies. However, part-cycles are more common. Glaessner et al. (1969), Cloud and Semikhatov (1969), Walter (1972), and Walter et al. (1979) document the stromatolites of this unit. In the lower parts of Unit 2 there is a redbed facies, comparable with those in Unit 3, interbedded with the Unit 2 facies.

The grainstone facies consist mainly of ooid grainstone and packstone, and peloid–intraclast grainstone (Southgate, 1991). The stromatolite facies commences with small stromatolites that accrete vertically and merge laterally to produce domes that expand progressively upwards and outwards to form larger domes (Walter, 1972; Southgate, 1991). In thicker cycles (up to 12 m thick), domes have a diameter of 4–10 m with synoptic relief of 1–2 m. Farther up the cycle, columns radiate perpendicular to the curved dome surface, and branch to form smaller and smaller columns. The columns become pseudocolumnar and pass gradually into continuous sheets of stratiform stromatolites. Capping the shallowing-upward cycle is a thin-bedded dolomite facies consisting of thin-bedded dolo-mudstone, stratiform stromatolites, and peloid–intraclast grainstone and packstone (Southgate, 1991). Desiccation cracks and cauliflower chert nodules occur in the dolo-mudstone. Carbonate mineralogy varies between dolomite and calcite in stromatolite fabrics, but in Wallara-1 Unit 2 is entirely dolomitic. Silicification of all facies is common.

The dolomite petrography of Unit 2 is shown in Table 6; limestone petrography is comparable to dolomite petrography. *Isotopes and Trace Elements.*—Wallara-1 carbon and oxygen isotopic data are shown in Table 5. Carbon and oxygen isotopic data for AS-27 and AS-28 are shown in Appendix 1. Sulfur and strontium isotopic data are shown in Table 7, and elemental data in Table 8. Dolomites in AS-27 have a mean $\delta^{13}C_{carb}$ of $-2.1 \pm 0.6‰$ and $\delta^{18}O$ of $-6.1 \pm 0.8‰$. In Wallara-1 the mean $\delta^{13}C_{carb}$ above the positive excursion (Fig. 4) is $-2.8 \pm 0.7‰$, and $\delta^{18}O$ $-4.3 \pm 0.7‰$. There is no correlation of $\delta^{13}C_{carb}$ or $\delta^{18}O$ with facies, stromatolite type, or crystal size. There are also no correlations between trace-element abundances and isotopic composition. There is a carbon and oxygen isotopic difference between dolomite and calcite: dolomite is about 1‰ heavier in $\delta^{13}C_{carb}$ and 4–5‰ heavier in $\delta^{18}O$ than calcite (Fig. 7). These differences are consistent with fractionation between calcite and dolomite precipitated from a fluid with the same geochemical composition (Sheppard and Schwarcz, 1970; Land, 1980).

$\delta^{34}S_{org}$ is heavier than $\delta^{34}S_{pyrite}$, which is consistent with dissolved sulfide (H_2S) reacting quickly with available iron to form pyrite (Pyzik and Sommer, 1981) but more slowly with organic matter to produce organosulfur compounds (Francois, 1987). H_2S, formed initially during sulfate reduction, is depleted in ^{34}S relative to that formed during later stages of the reduction process.

Molecular Fossils and Microfossils.—The distribution of biomarkers and microfossils in Unit 2 of the Loves Creek Member is shown in Figure 5. Biomarker maturity parameters (refer to Peters and Moldowan, 1993 for key to parameters listed in Figure 5), including calculated vitrinite reflectance derived from methylphenanthrene index measurements (Radke and Welte, 1983), indicate a relatively mild thermal history, consistent with the biomarkers being indigenous.

Some of the columnar stromatolites contain chert nodules, but none of an extensive collection of these made some years ago is fossiliferous (Walter, unpublished observations). Despite the lack of direct microfossil evidence, the dominance of hopanes over steranes, and the abundance of monomethyl (MMAs; see Figure 5) and dimethyl branched alkanes (DMAs), indicates that cyanobacteria were the main contributor to organic matter. This is consistent with the conventional interpretation of stromatolites, which are abundant in this unit. The dimethylalkanes are composed almost exclusively of 3,7-dimethyl alkanes in the range C_{15}–C_{35}, which have been reported only from Proterozoic sulfides (Mycke et al., 1987) and Holocene cyanobacterial mats (Kenig et al., 1995). The presence of disseminated pyrite with a light isotopic signature indicates the activity of sulfate-reducing bacteria. The detection of C_{30} desmethyl steranes and 4-methylsteranes (probably including dinosteranes) indicates algal input, albeit minimal. The presence of abundant regular extended acyclic isoprenoids is consistent with the former occurrence of Archaea (which thrive in hypersaline conditions; cf. Waples et al., 1974), perhaps extreme halophiles.

Sedimentary and Diagenetic History.—Early during the deposition of Unit 2 there was a positive $\delta^{13}C_{carb}$ and $\delta^{18}O$ shift not far above the appearance of a new facies: red dolomitic siltstone and red siltstone (redbeds), comparable with those in Unit 3. Interbedded with the redbeds are the characteristic facies described for Unit 2: stromatolite, thin-bedded and grainstone facies. The rise in both $\delta^{13}C_{carb}$ and $\delta^{18}O$ with a change in depositional environment has implications for paleoenvironmental interpretations and is discussed below under the Unit 3 heading.

Southgate (1991) interpreted facies of Unit 2 to represent a series of shallowing-upward cycles. The grainstone facies accumulated during an initial deepening phase in semi-emergent to submerged environments. Following the transgression, quiet, deeper-water conditions permitted accretion of gradually expanding domal stromatolites that mark commencement of the

TABLE 6.—DOLOMITE PETROGRAPHY, UNIT 2, LOVES CREEK MEMBER

Facies	Fabric	Crystal shape	Crystal size (μm)	Crystal size distribution
grainstone	well-preserved peloid–intraclast grainstone	nonplanar mostly nonplanar	clasts: 1–25 matrix: 1–80	polymodal polymodal
stromatolite	ooid grainstone silicified 1st dolomite phase: interlaminated fine and coarse stromatolite laminae	nonplanar	fine: 1–25 coarse: 1–80	polymodal
dolo-mudstone	2nd dolomite phase: patchy growth of fabric-destructive dolospar 1st dolomite phase: most bedding planes preserved 2nd dolomite phase: coarse, patchy growths	mostly nonplanar nonplanar mostly nonplanar	1–150 1–25 1–60	polymodal polymodal polymodal

TABLE 7.—SULFUR AND STRONTIUM ISOTOPIC DATA, WALLARA-1, LOVES CREEK MEMBER

Unit	Sample	Height above base (m)	$\delta^{34}S_{sulfate}$ (‰ CDT)	$\delta^{34}S_{pyrite}$ (‰ CDT)	$\delta^{34}S_{org}$ (‰ CDT)	$^{87}Sr/^{86}Sr$
3	950703.03	1044	—	−23.9	—	—
3	950703.16	1028	—	−27	−25.4	—
3	950704.09	986	—	−6.3	−10.5	—
3	950704.18	937	—	—	—	—
3	950705.01	935	21.7	—	—	—
3	950705.06	924	20.5	—	—	—
3	950705.18	883	—	10.5	—	—
3	950706.07	845	—	3.4	2.4	—
3	950709.03	746	—	15.4	—	—
3	950709.06	740	—	1.8	—	—
2	950709.18	677	19.1	—	—	—
2	950710.23	640	—	−7.2	6.2	—
2	950710.28	634	—	−9.8	4.4	—
2	950711.09	604	—	−14	—	—
2	950711.30	565	—	—	—	0.7072 ± 0.0003
2	950712.01	563	17.3	—	—	0.7069 ± 0.0003
2	950713.15	477	—	−15.1	—	—

TABLE 8.—ELEMENTAL DATA, WALLARA-1, AS-27, AND AS-28, LOVES CREEK MEMBER

Location	Sample	Height above base (m)	Mineralogy	Fe (ppm)	Mn (ppm)	Sr (ppm)	Mg/Ca (mole ratio)
Wallara-1, Unit 3	950703.03	1044	dolomite	5689	786	45	1.1
Wallara-1, Unit 3	950704.12	979	dolomite	9065	918	32	1.1
Wallara-1, Unit 3	950705.23	863	dolomite	1771	202	81	1.6
Wallara-1, Unit 3	950706.15	831	dolomite	2365	247	<2	1.4
Wallara-1, Unit 3	950706.24	770	calcite	46	368	22	—
Wallara-1, Unit 3	950709.12a	717	dolomite	1423	692	69	1.3
Wallara-1, Unit 3	950712.03	561	dolomite	2323	158	40	1.1
Wallara-1, Unit 2	950713.08	486	dolomite	1226	106	<2	1.1
AS-27, Unit 3	950315.16	138	dolomite	1617	1061	15	1.2
AS-27, Unit 3	950316.05	143	dolomite	779	551	174	—
AS-27, Unit 3	960506.03	226	dolomite	2650	439	19	1.2
AS-27, Unit 2	960506.07	237	calcite	225	147	89	—
AS-27, Unit 2	960507.03	258	dolomite	1200	198	<2	1.1
AS-27, Unit 2	960507.10	274	dolomite	2942	423	<2	1.2
AS-27, Unit 2	960508.09	306	dolomite	2397	298	<2	1.1
AS-28, Unit 3	950316.15	43	dolomite	3362	1282	62	1.4
AS-28, Unit 3	950316.17	71	dolomite	2939	634	50	2.6
AS-28, Unit 3	950317.05b	99	calcite	437	849	43	—
AS-28, Unit 2	960509.17	197	calcite	198	128	84	—
AS-28, Unit 2	960509.19a	207	dolomite	2022	262	11	1.2

shallowing portion of the cycle. Thin-bedded dolomite was deposited at the tops of the cycles in semi-emergent to emergent conditions. The appearance of sulfate evaporites and desiccation features at the tops of shallowing-upward stromatolite cycles indicates the environment often evaporated to dryness.

The isotopic and biomarker data are consistent with a marine origin. $\delta^{13}C_{carb}$ values are facies-independent, correlatable across the Amadeus Basin, and comparable with those in the similar-aged uppermost Shaler Supergroup of Canada (Kauf-man and Knoll, 1995). As discussed earlier, correlation with Canada is also possible with $^{87}Sr/^{86}Sr$ ratios, which, along with $\delta^{13}C_{carb}$ values, reflect secular change in the global ocean. $\delta^{34}S_{sulfate}$ values (Table 7) are typical of Neoproterozoic seawater (Holser et al., 1988), and are similar to Gillen Member values (Table 2). Low $\delta^{34}S_{pyrite}$ values (Table 7) are consistent with bacterial sulfate reduction in marine sediment (Goldhaber and Kaplan, 1974). The detection of C_{30} desmethyl steranes and 4-methylsteranes is also consistent with marine deposition, and the presence of regular extended acyclic isoprenoids (consistent with the former occurrence of Archaea) suggest that the conditions were hypersaline.

Concentrations of Fe and Mn in dolomite are greater, and Sr concentrations lower, than those in calcite. These differences are greater than predicted by calcite–dolomite distribution coefficients (Kretz, 1982), suggesting that dolomitization occurred in reducing conditions (Land, 1985). The preservation of calcite with carbon and oxygen isotopic compositions lighter than coeval dolomite indicates penecontemporaneous equilibrium fractionation (Land, 1980), that is, crystallization of dolomite from a water body with similar isotopic composition. Accepting that the environment of deposition for Unit 2 was oxygenated above the sediment–water interface, because of the abundance of photosynthesizing cyanobacteria in a shallow (2 m) water body, then dolomite must have formed below the sediment–water interface, in marine water little altered in isotopic composition after initial calcite precipitation. The presence of disseminated pyrite with light $\delta^{34}S$ values indicates that sediments during diagenesis were not only anoxic but also open to diffusion of marine water saturated with SO_4^{2-} (Goldhaber and Kaplan, 1974) and Mg^{2+}. Gebelein and Hoffman (1973) found that decaying cyanobacteria can provide a significant source of Mg^{2+} for dolomitization, as can the precipitation of primary calcite (Gaines, 1968, 1980; Folk and Land, 1975; Land, 1985). Initial dolomitization was probably a diffusion-controlled process by which Mg-saturated marine fluids circulated through calcitic sediment just below the sediment surface. This first phase of dolomitization in saline, Mg-saturated marine fluids retained the fine-grained, laminated microstructure. The retention of some fine-grained calcite in the deeper-water facies indicates varying salinities, and probably supports the empirical observation by Knoll and Swett (1990) and Sun (1994) that Neoproterozoic intertidal to supratidal sediments are commonly dolomitized whereas deeper-water sediments show less dolomitization.

Above the isotope excursions in the lower part of Unit 2, dolomite $\delta^{18}O$ values are invariant (−5.7‰ to −3.6‰) in all facies, and all different carbonate components (laminated dolomicrospar, peloids, stromatolite laminae, and intercolumnar

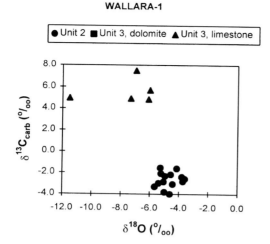

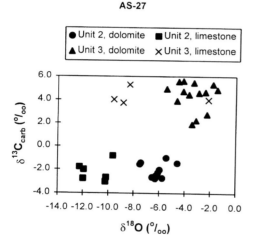

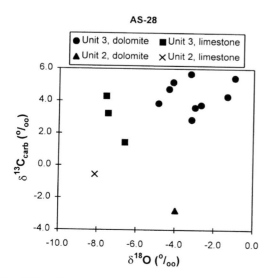

FIG. 7.—$\delta^{13}C_{carb}$–$\delta^{18}O$ crossplots, Loves Creek Member.

stromatolite fillings). If it is accepted that heavier $\delta^{18}O$ values should occur in the shallower facies (e.g., McKenzie et al., 1980; Kah, this volume), then a second dolomitization event occurred. The homogenization of $\delta^{18}O$ values probably indicates burial recrystallization (e.g., Zenger and Dunham, 1988), also suggested by nonplanar textures (Sibley and Gregg, 1987), patchy dolospar growths (e.g., Zenger, 1983; Land, 1985; Sibley and Gregg, 1987; Kupecz and Land, 1991; Gao and Land, 1991), and low Sr concentrations (Land, 1980, 1985). However, Vahrenkamp and Swart (1990) suggested that low Sr concentrations in ancient dolomite could be primary, on the basis of their calculation of a low dolomite distribution coefficient for Sr. The presence of meteoric fluids during burial could also explain low Sr and low $\delta^{18}O$ values, and the replacement of many sulfate nodules with chert.

Unit 3.—

Sedimentology and Petrography.—The uppermost unit of the Loves Creek Member consists of two sub-units, red dolomitic siltstone and red siltstone (redbeds), interbedded with dolomite, limestone, and dolomitic limestone. Each carbonate unit represents the lower part of a shallowing-upward parasequence beginning with a ribboned facies then a thin-bedded facies and ending in the redbeds (Southgate, 1991). The lowermost carbonate units consist of both the ribboned and thin-bedded facies; the uppermost units consist of only the thin-bedded facies. The carbonate units become thinner upwards. The redbeds are mostly red dolomitic siltstone in the lower parts, with red siltstone predominating in the upper parts. Collectively, these observations are consistent with continued regression throughout the deposition of Unit 3. About 100 m of interbedded white quartz arenite, silty quartzite, silty dolomite, and siltstone appear at the top of Unit 3 in Wall-ara-1.

In outcrop the ribboned facies often has in its lower parts beds of bulbous to pseudocolumnar stromatolites (Walter, 1972; Southgate, 1991). The stromatolites pass both vertically and laterally into characteristic alternating thin beds of blue-gray limestone and tan-colored dolomite. The limestone occurs either as thin beds, lenses, or pods in an anastomosing network of tan dolomite. Overlying this sub-facies is a combination of flake intraclast conglomerate and peloid grainstone. Another feature of the ribboned facies is the occurrence of molar-tooth structures, which have been described from shallow-water carbonate successions that range in age from Mesoproterozoic to Neoproterozoic (e.g., Smith, 1968; Aitken, 1981; Bertrand-Sarfati and Moussine-Pouchkine, 1988; Calver and Baillie, 1990; Sarkar and Bose, 1992; Fairchild et al., 1997).

Overlying the ribboned facies is thin-bedded to laminated dolo-mudstone and cross-laminated, peloid, intraclast packstone and grainstone. Stratiform and pseudocolumnar stromatolites form laterally discontinuous sheet-like bodies up to 2 m thick. A distinctive suite of early diagenetic silica structures characterize this facies, such as concentrically banded chert concretions, chert-replaced skeletal halite, rare cauliflower cherts, and thin chert lenses and beds.

The redbeds consist of a homogeneous mixture of dolomite, quartz silt, and clay minerals. The only discernible structures are laterally discontinuous graded laminae between 2 to 6 mm thick. Each lamina overlies an erosion surface and is capped by a discontinuous veneer of dark red mudstone.

The petrography of Unit 3 facies is shown in Table 9.

Isotopes and Trace Elements.—Wallara-1 carbon and oxygen isotopic data are shown in Table 5, and AS-27 and AS-28 data in Appendix 1. Sulfur-isotope data are shown in Table 7, and elemental data in Table 8. For all facies $\delta^{13}C_{carb}$ falls between 1.9‰ and 8.4‰, and $\delta^{18}O$ between $-11.5‰$ and 0.4‰. Heavier and highly variable $\delta^{13}C_{carb}$ and $\delta^{18}O$ values distinguish Unit 3 from Units 1 and 2. In contrast to Unit 2, there is some $\delta^{18}O$ variation between facies. As in Unit 2, dolomite $\delta^{18}O$ is 2.2‰ to 3.8‰ heavier than coeval calcite, and $^{13}C_{carb}$ is 0.5‰ to 1.1‰ heavier (see Fig. 7). Therefore, isotopic comparisons between facies have been made on dolomite samples. There are no correlations between $\delta^{18}O$, Fe, and Mn in any facies.

$\delta^{34}S_{org}$ is not always heavier than $\delta^{34}S_{pyrite}$, which suggests that pyrite may have formed later than organosulfur compounds, possibly from residual H_2S produced in the sediment during diagenesis (Tuttle and Goldhaber, 1993).

Molecular Fossils and Microfossils.—The distribution of biomarkers and microfossils in Unit 3 of the Loves Creek Member are shown in Figure 5. As for Unit 2, biomarker maturity parameters indicate a relatively mild thermal history (refer to Peters and Moldowan, 1993 for key to parameters listed in Figure 5).

The microfossils of this unit have been described by Barghoorn and Schopf (1965), Schopf (1968), Schopf and Blacic (1971), Oehler (1976, 1977), Oehler et al. (1979), Knoll and Golubic (1979), and Knoll (1981). Knoll (1981) recognized at least five microbial associations, which include filamentous and coccoid cyanobacterial mats. The abundant presence of monomethyl and dimethyl branched alkanes supports previous interpretations that the assemblages are dominated by cyanobacteria. Most of Unit 3 contains abundant isoprenoids, including the irregularly branched C_{25} (2,6,10,15,19-pentamethyleicosane) and C_{30} (2,6,10,15,19,23-hexamethyltetracosane or squalane) isoprenoids. These biomarkers are sourced exclusively from methanogens (Brassell et al., 1981; Brassell et al., 1987). In the lower parts of Unit 3, C_{30} desmethyl steranes and 4-methylsteranes were detected, which are known from Phanerozoic marine algae (e.g., Moldowan et al., 1985).

Sedimentary and Diagenetic History.—Southgate (1991) interpreted rocks of the ribboned facies as having accumulated in shallow submerged conditions whereas those of the thin-bedded facies represent semi-emergent to emergent conditions. The redbeds accumulated on broad, low-relief siltflats and mudflats marginal to the environment of the thin-bedded facies. Southgate (1991) found a predominance of sulfate pseudomorphs in Unit 2 and a dominance of a dolomite–halite–chert suite of synsedimentary diagenetic minerals in Unit 3. Coupled with the observation that rocks of the thin-bedded facies form laterally discontinuous units that intertongue with the redbeds across sharp erosional contacts, this suggests that the carbonate units of Unit 3 were deposited in a series of shallow, hypersaline lakes and ponds. Groundwaters feeding the lakes and ponds contained dissolved Na^+, Cl^-, Si^{4+}, Mg^{2+}, and CO_3^{2-}/HCO_3^- ions, which upon evaporation and early dolomite precipitation were concentrated to form a silica–sodium–chlorine brine.

Isotopic, elemental, and biomarker data indicate a nonmarine origin for Unit 3, consistent with the sedimentology. Considerable variability in both $\delta^{13}C_{carb}$ and $\delta^{18}O$ indicate deposition from a nonmarine water body. The tendency for $\delta^{18}O$ values to increase from the ribboned facies to the more evaporitic thin-bedded dolomite and redbed facies (Table 10) suggests that deposition occurred in a restricted, shallowing-upward water body. Although not as strong as facies variations described by Kah (this volume) in shoaling Mesoproterozoic marine environments or increasing $\delta^{18}O$ trends from subtidal to supratidal environments in the Persian Gulf (McKenzie et al., 1980), there is a tendency for heavier values with increasing evaporation. The preservation of $\delta^{18}O$ structure in dolomite of the Unit 3 facies suggests syndepositional dolomitization. Later dolomite neomorphism, which produced polymodal nonplanar textures (Sibley and Gregg, 1987; Gregg and Shelton, 1990), retained this structure even though bulk values were probably depleted.

A paucity of sulfate evaporites in Unit 3 (Southgate, 1991), rarity of pyrite, heavy $\delta^{34}S_{pyrite}$, and biomarker evidence for methanogens indicate a nonmarine origin. Heavy $\delta^{34}S_{pyrite}$ is consistent with bacterial sulfate reduction in sediment not being constantly replenished with sulfate, where the isotopic composition of reduced sulfide approaches that of the starting sulfate (Goldhaber and Kaplan, 1974). Irwin et al. (1977) found that archael methanogenesis begins as soon as sulfate reduction stops, hence the low sulfate-reducing biomass in Unit 3 would have allowed methanogens to thrive. Carbon dioxide formed during biogenic methane production is ^{13}C-enriched, because methane is depleted in ^{13}C by 30 to 50‰ (Games and Hayes, 1976; Whiticar et al., 1986). Methane does not exchange with carbon dioxide (Sackett and Chung, 1979), rather it escapes to the atmosphere while CO_2 is transformed into ^{13}C-enriched dissolved CO_3^{2-}; Irwin et al. (1977) estimated a fractionation in CO_2 by up to $+15‰$. However, there is evidence that the biogenic recapture of methane carbon has been responsible for the ^{13}C depletion of sedimentary TOC relative to primary inputs (Freeman et al., 1990). Hayes (1983) hypothesized biogenic methane recapture was at least partly responsible for $\delta^{13}C$ values as light as $-59‰$ in the Neoarchean, and Hayes et al. (1987) argued that this process was responsible for $\delta^{13}C_{org}$ values being depleted in ^{13}C by 8δ in the Eocene Messel Shale.

TABLE 9.—PETROGRAPHIC DATA, UNIT 3, LOVES CREEK MEMBER

Facies	Fabric	Crystal shape	Crystal size (μm)	Crystal size distribution
ribboned	interbedded, dolomite and calcite	mostly nonplanar	1–30, some up to 150	polymodal
		nonplanar	5–16	unimodal
	molar tooth (dolomite and calcite)	nonplanar	1–16	dolomite-polymodal
				calcite-unimodal
thin-bedded	good preservation of laminae/beds	nonplanar	1–20, some micrite patches	polymodal
redbeds	excellent preservation	nonplanar,	1–25	polymodal
		some planar	1–50	polymodal

TABLE 10.—SUMMARY OF CARBON AND OXYGEN ISOTOPIC DATA, UNIT 3,
LOVES CREEK MEMBER

| | | Isotopic data (‰ PDB) | | | |
| | | $\delta^{13}C_{dol}$ | | $\delta^{18}O_{dol}$ | |
Facies	Core	range	mean	range	mean
Ribboned	Wallara-1	5.9 to 8.4	6.8 ± 0.9	−6.4 to −2.7	−5.1 ± 1.8
	AS-27	4.7 to 5.6	5.3 ± 0.3	−5.6 to −2.9	−3.9 ± 0.8
	AS-28	4.9 to 5.2	5.0 ± 0.2	−5.2 to −3.8	−4.4 ± 0.7
Thin-bedded	Wallara-1	3.1 to 6.8	4.5 ± 1.1	−7.2 to −0.4	−3.5 ± 1.6
	AS-27	2.8 to 4.9	3.9 ± 0.7	−4.9 to −2.0	−2.8 ± 0.8
	AS-28	3.6 to 4.6	4.1 ± 0.4	−4.2 to −2.2	−3.3 ± 0.8
Redbeds	Wallara-1	3.1 to 5.7	4.9 ± 1.0	−4.6 to −1.1	−2.0 ± 0.3
	AS-27	1.9 to 5.5	4.0 ± 1.2	−5.5 to −1.5	−3.2 ± 1.2
	AS-28	2.6 to 5.7	4.3 ± 1.1	−4.9 to −1.0	−2.8 ± 1.4

($\delta^{13}C$ values are up to 2‰ greater in Unit 3, in contrast to Unit 2. This suggests that biogenic methane production has either contributed a small volume of ^{13}C-depleted methane carbon to organic matter, or a small volume of ^{13}C-enriched CO_2 to lake waters, or both.

There were probably additional causes of ^{13}C enrichment. Burial of organic matter in the lakes could increase the ^{13}C content of the residual lake water. Although the organic carbon content is low in most of the sediments, there is a 5 cm thick bed in Wallara-1 with a TOC of 10.6% (950706.03, Table 5), which suggests that some lakes were accumulating significant amounts of organic matter. Evaporation of groundwaters feeding the lakes could also have led to enrichment in both ^{18}O and ^{13}C (Stiller et al., 1985; Beauchamp et al., 1987), and the lack of terrestrial plants would have emphasized the effects by minimizing organic input to the groundwater.

The step in carbon and oxygen isotopic curves across the erosion surface that separates Unit 2 (marine) and Unit 3 (nonmarine) might suggest that these two environments were not coeval (see Figure 4). However, no sequence boundary is recognized within the Loves Creek Member (Southgate, 1991), which suggests that the erosion surface is only locally significant. The appearance of the nonmarine redbed facies in the lower part of the otherwise marine Unit 2, accompanied by a

APPENDIX 1.—CARBON AND OXYGEN ISOTOPIC DATA, AS-27 AND AS-28, LOVES CREEK MEMBER

Location	Sample	Stratigraphy (m)	Facies	Mineralogy	$\delta^{18}O$ (‰DB)	$\delta^{13}C_{carb}$ (‰DB)	$\delta^{13}C_{org}$ (‰DB)	$\Delta\delta^{13}C$ (‰DB)	TOC (%C)
AS-27, Unit 3	950313.11	93	redbeds	dolomite	−4.6	3.9	—	—	—
AS-27, Unit 3	950313.12	96	thinly bedded	dolomite	−2.4	4.7	−24.7	29.4	0.03
AS-27, Unit 3	950314.03	98	thinly bedded	dolomite	−3.7	4.5	−24.5	29.1	0.03
AS-27, Unit 3	950314.05	107	ribboned	calcite	−8.9	3.8	−23.8	27.6	0.03
AS-27, Unit 3	950315.02	109	redbeds	dolomite	−1.5	4.9	−24.3	29.2	0.01
AS-27, Unit 3	950315.03	118	redbeds	dolomite	−2.9	4.6	—	—	—
AS-27, Unit 3	950315.04	120	thinly bedded	dolomite	−2.3	2.8	—	—	—
AS-27, Unit 3	950315.08	124	redbeds	calcite	−2.2	4.0	−25.6	29.6	0.01
AS-27, Unit 3	950315.10	129	ribboned	calcite	−9.6	4.0	−23.1	27.1	0.01
AS-27, Unit 3	950315.13a	134	ribboned	dolomite	−4.2	5.6	−23.6	29.2	0.01
AS-27, Unit 3	950315.14	137	ribboned	calcite	−8.4	5.3	−24.9	30.2	0.02
AS-27, Unit 3	950315.16	138	ribboned	dolomite	−4.5	5.6	—	—	—
AS-27, Unit 3	950316.05	143	ribboned	dolomite	−4.2	4.7	−24.9	29.7	0.01
AS-27, Unit 3	950316.03	144	redbeds	dolomite	−1.8	5.3	—	—	—
AS-27, Unit 3	960431.18	171	redbeds	dolomite	−5.5	4.9	—	—	—
AS-27, Unit 3	960431.19	200	redbeds	dolomite	−3.3	5.5	—	—	—
AS-27, Unit 3	960506.01	220	redbeds	dolomite	−3.5	1.9	—	—	—
AS-27, Unit 3	960506.03	226	redbeds	dolomite	−3.1	2.2	−27.9	30.1	0.01
AS-27, Unit 2	960506.04b	229	stromatolite	calcite	−9.6	−0.8	—	—	—
AS-27, Unit 2	960506.05	231	stromatolite	calcite	−12.3	−1.8	—	—	—
AS-27, Unit 2	960506.06a	233	mudstone	dolomite	−5.4	−1.0	−27.7	25.9	0.03
AS-27, Unit 2	960506.07	237	stromatolite	calcite	−10.2	−3.0	−30.5	27.4	0.04
AS-27, Unit 2	960506.08	238	mudstone	dolomite	−6.1	−2.3	—	—	—
AS-27, Unit 2	960506.09	242	stromatolite	calcite	−10.2	−2.7	—	—	—
AS-27, Unit 2	960506.10b	242	grainstone	dolomite	−7.4	−1.4	—	—	—
AS-27, Unit 2	960506.11	247	stromatolite	calcite	−11.9	−2.0	−30.3	28.3	0.07
AS-27, Unit 2	960507.03	258	stromatolite	dolomite	−4.6	−1.5	−27.8	26.3	0.04
AS-27, Unit 2	960507.07	270	mudstone	dolomite	−6.0	−2.0	−30.5	28.5	0.05
AS-27, Unit 2	960507.10	274	mudstone	dolomite	−6.3	−2.8	−32.1	29.3	0.24
AS-27, Unit 2	960507.11	276	stromatolite	calcite	−12.0	−2.8	—	—	—
AS-27, Unit 2	960508.03	286	stromatolite	dolomite	−7.5	−1.5	−30.0	28.4	0.06
AS-27, Unit 2	960508.05	295	mudstone	dolomite	−6.2	−2.5	−30.8	28.3	0.06
AS-27, Unit 2	960508.09	306	mudstone	dolomite	−5.7	−2.7	−30.4	27.7	0.09
AS-27, Unit 2	960509.02	315	stromatolite	dolomite	−6.3	−2.6	−30.1	27.5	0.05
AS-27, Unit 2	960509.10	319	stromatolite	dolomite	−6.5	−2.7	−29.8	27.2	0.04
AS-28, Unit 3	950316.15	43	thinly bedded	dolomite	−3.0	3.6	−24.4	27.9	0.03
AS-28, Unit 3	950316.17	71	redbeds	dolomite	−4.9	3.9	—	—	—
AS-28, Unit 3	950316.21	74	redbeds	dolomite	−1.3	4.3	−23.6	27.9	0.01
AS-28, Unit 3	950316.22b	81	ribboned	calcite	−7.5	3.2	—	—	—
AS-28, Unit 3	950317.04	96	thinly bedded	dolomite	−2.7	3.7	−25.5	29.0	0.01
AS-28, Unit 3	950317.05b	99	ribboned	calcite	−6.6	1.4	−24.8	26.2	0.02
AS-28, Unit 3	950317.06	106	ribboned	dolomite	−4.1	5.2	−24.5	29.6	0.01
AS-28, Unit 3	950317.08	107	ribboned	calcite	−7.6	4.3	−24.7	29.0	0.01
AS-28, Unit 3	960509.11	110	redbeds	dolomite	−1.0	5.4	−25.5	31.0	0.02
AS-28, Unit 3	960509.12	141	redbeds	olomite	−4.3	4.7	—	—	—
AS-28, Unit 3	960509.13	162	redbeds	dolomite	−3.2	5.7	—	—	—
AS-28, Unit 3	960509.15	192	redbeds	dolomite	−3.2	2.8	−27.3	30.1	0.01
AS-28, Unit 2	960509.17	197	stromatolite	calcite	−8.1	−0.6	−29.0	28.5	0.02
AS-28, Unit 2	960509.19a	207	mudstone	dolomite	−4.0	−2.8	−30.6	33.3	0.03

gradual shift in $\delta^{13}C_{carb}$ and $\delta^{18}O$, also suggests that the facies were coeval. The gradual isotopic shifts in Unit 2 suggest the mixing of seawater with another fluid that had a much heavier $\delta^{13}C_{carb}$ and $\delta^{18}O$ composition, most likely a groundwater brine (Fig. 8).

Concentration of inflowing continental freshwater probably occurred by evaporative reflux (Fig. 8) in a way similar to that described by McKenzie et al. (1980) for Persian Gulf sabkhas and by Ferguson and Skyring (1995) for sabkhas in Hamelin Pool, Shark Bay. The pervasive dolomitization and occurrence of some early diagenetic anhydrite growths in the redbeds supports this interpretation. Reflux of the groundwater brine through the redbeds above the water table probably caused dolomitization of the redbeds and would explain why redbed dolomites generally have the heaviest $\delta^{18}O$ values. The Mg/Ca ratio of the brine must have been high. The absence of tepee structures suggests that no carbonate crusts were forming near the lake margins, probably because the outcropping groundwater brines were not high in dissolved carbonate. The redbeds toward the top of Unit 3 lack carbonate, which suggests that they formed farther inland, before the groundwater became concentrated enough to precipitate carbonate during reflux. This supports the sedimentological evidence for continuing regression through Unit 3.

The occurrence of marine algal biomarkers (C_{30} desmethyl steranes and 4-methylsteranes) in the dominantly lacustrine lower part of Unit 3 suggests either occasional marine incursions, or that algae were transported to the lakes, possibly by winds. However, the possibility that nonmarine Neoproterozoic algae synthesized these sterols cannot be ruled out.

Carbon and oxygen isotopes have previously been used to distinguish between marine and lacustrine environments, for example the Mesoproterozoic Helena Formation of the Belt Supergroup (Frank et al., 1997). This study has extended that geochemical approach to include biomarkers and sulfur isotopes, making the interpretations even more convincing.

CONCLUSIONS

It is difficult to distinguish marine and lacustrine environments in Neoproterozoic intracratonic settings. We show that an integrated geochemical, paleobiological, and sedimentological approach can make the distinction. The use of biomarker and sulfur isotope geochemistry, in conjunction with analysis of C, O, and Sr isotopes, all in a sedimentological and paleobiological framework, can substantially improve our understanding of Proterozoic carbonates.

The Gillen Member of the Bitter Springs Formation was deposited in a marine environment. The evidence for this interpretation includes isotopes of strontium, carbon, and sulfur, and biomarkers. $^{87}Sr/^{86}Sr$ ratios in the Gillen Member are comparable to the lowest ever recorded, from the similar-aged Shaler Supergroup of Canada. These low strontium isotopic ratios are associated with comparable secular change in seawater $\delta^{13}C_{carb}$. Steroidal hydrocarbon biomarker assemblages, seawater $\delta^{34}S_{sulfate}$ values (Holser et al., 1988), and low $\delta^{34}S_{pyrite}$ values further indicate a marine origin. The distribution of evaporite facies in the Gillen Member is similar to that seen in the Upper Carboniferous Otto Fiord Formation of the Sverdrup Basin (Beauchamp et al., 1987); interlaminated carbonate and sulfate are deposited in shallow water at the evaporite basin margins, and halite is deposited in deeper-water basin centers. Episodic closure of the Centralian Superbasin to the global ocean caused the deposition of evaporites.

The lower part of the Loves Creek Member (Units 1 and 2) was also deposited in a marine environment. Facies-independent secular change in seawater $\delta^{13}C_{carb}$ and low $^{87}Sr/^{86}Sr$ ratios are comparable to those in the upper Shaler Supergroup of Canada. Seawater $\delta^{34}S_{sulfate}$ values (Holser et al., 1988), low $\delta^{34}S_{pyrite}$, and evidence for algal biomarkers are also consistent with marine deposition. A minimum water depth of ~2 m is indicated by the synoptic relief of stromatolite biostromes. The shallow water depth and abundance of photosynthesizing cyanobacteria indicate that the water column was oxygenated. Below the sed-

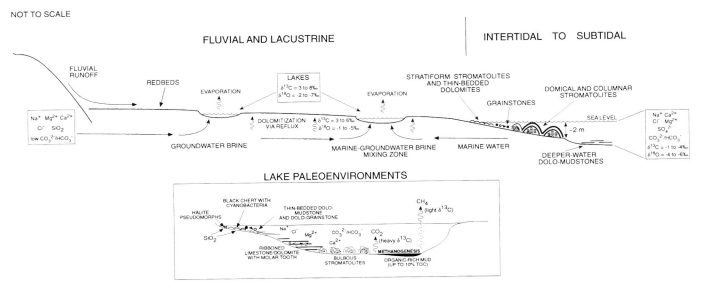

FIG. 8.—Paleoenvironmental reconstruction of the Loves Creek Member.

iment–water interface, depleted $\delta^{34}S$ in disseminated pyrite indicates the presence of bacterial sulfate reducers in an anaerobic environment. The extreme dominance of hopanes over steranes, and the abundance of monomethyl and dimethyl branched alkanes, are consistent with paleontological evidence that bacteria, including cyanobacteria, were the main contributors to organic matter, and algal input was minimal.

The upper part of the Loves Creek Member (Unit 3), and lower part of Unit 2, is nonmarine. Rarity of pyrite, heavy $\delta^{34}S_{pyrite}$, abundant irregularly branched C_{25} and C_{30} isoprenoids from methanogens, and abundant pseudomorphs after halite indicate carbonate precipitation in sulfate-poor hypersaline lakes. Heavy and variable $\delta^{13}C_{carb}$ and $\delta^{18}O$ indicate that continental groundwater brines, which were low in dissolved carbonate, drained into the lakes. Evaporation of the lake waters increased the concentration of dissolved carbonate, and increased still more the $\delta^{18}O$ values, and may have had a small effect on $\delta^{13}C_{carb}$. Dolomitization of the continental redbeds occurred by the evaporative reflux of groundwater. Cyanobacteria formed mats on the lake margins, where they were quickly silicified. Domical and irregular stromatolites formed within the lakes. The unexpected presence of the C_{30} desmethyl steranes and 4-methylsteranes suggests either that there were marine incursions in the lower parts of Unit 3 or that marine algae were transported to the lakes, possibly by winds. However, in the lakes there might have been nonmarine Neoproterozoic algae that synthesized these sterols.

The predominance of dolomite in the Bitter Springs Formation and the presence of bedded evaporites in the Gillen Member and evaporite pseudomorphs in the Loves Creek Member indicate an arid climate. The retention of original fabrics, carbon and oxygen isotopic separation between coexisting calcite and dolomite, and the preservation of increasingly heavy $\delta^{18}O$ with shallowing in lacustrine dolomite indicate that dolomitization took place soon after initial calcite precipitation.

ACKNOWLEDGMENTS

This project was supported by Australian Research Council (ARC) grants to Malcolm Walter and John Veevers as part of Ph.D. studies by Andrew Hill and Paul Gorjan, and post-doctoral research by Khaled Arouri. Isotopic analyses were completed at the Center of Isotope Studies (CIS), CSIRO, North Ryde. We are grateful to members of the CIS, in particular Andrew Todd and Steve Craven, for their guidance in isotope techniques, and Anita Andrew for valuable discussion. Leslie Dotter analyzed samples for trace elements at the CSIRO. Tom Bradley made all thin sections. We thank Martin Cardona for access to the Northern Territory Geological Survey core store in Alice Springs, and the Bureau of Resource Sciences for access to other cores in Canberra. Our work has benefited from discussions with Kaye Cotter, Tracy Frank, Linda Kah, and Guy Narbonne. John Veevers read an early draft of the manuscript, and we appreciate his thoughtful comments. Reviews by Ian Fairchild and Beverly Saylor greatly improved the manuscript.

REFERENCES

AITKEN, J. D., 1981, Stratigraphy and sedimentology of the Upper Proterozoic Little Dal Group, Mackenzie Mountains, Northwest Territories: Geological Survey of Canada, Paper 81–10, p. 47–71.

ALLAN, J. R., AND MATTHEWS, R. K., 1982, Isotope signatures associated with early meteoric diagenesis: Sedimentology, v. 29, p. 797–817.

ASMEROM, Y., JACOBSEN, S. B., KNOLL, A. H., BUTTERFIELD, N. J., AND SWETT, K., 1991, Strontium isotopic variations of Neoproterozoic seawater: implications for crustal evolution: Geochimica et Cosmochimica Acta, v. 55, p. 2883–2894.

BARGHOORN, E. S., AND SCHOPF, J. W., 1965, Microorganisms from the late Precambrian of central Australia: Science, v. 150, p. 337–339.

BEAUCHAMP, B., OLDERSHAW, A. E., AND KROUSE, H. R., 1987, Upper Carboniferous to upper Permian ^{13}C-enriched primary carbonates in the Sverdrup Basin, Canadian Arctic: Comparisons to coeval western North American ocean margins: Chemical Geology, v. 65, p. 391–413.

BERTRAND-SARFATI, J., AND MOUSSINE-POUCHKINE, A., 1988, Is cratonic sedimentation consistent with available models? An example from the Upper Proterozoic of the West African craton: Sedimentary Geology, v. 58, p. 255–276.

BRASSELL, S. C., EGLINTON, G., AND HOWELL, V. J., 1987, Palaeoenvironmental assessment of marine organic-rich sediments using molecular organic geochemistry, in Brooks, J., and Fleet, A. J., eds., Marine Petroleum Source Rocks: Geological Society of London, Special Publication 26, p. 79–98.

BRASSELL, S. C., WARDROPER, A. M. K., THOMSON, I. D., MAXWELL, J. R., AND EGLINTON, G., 1981, Specific acyclic isoprenoids as biological markers of methanogenic bacteria in marine sediments: Nature, v. 290, p. 693–696.

CALVER, C. R., AND BAILLIE, P. W., 1990, Early diagenetic concretions associated with intrasratal shrinkage cracks in an upper Proterozoic dolomite, Tasmania, Australia: Journal of Sedimentary Petrology, v. 60, p. 293–305.

CANFIELD, D. E., RAISWELL, R., WESTRICH, J. T., REAVES, C. M., AND BERNER, R. A., 1986, The use of chromium reduction in the analysis of reduced inorganic sulfur in sediments and shales: Chemical Geology, v. 54, p. 149–155.

CHEWINGS, C., 1914, Notes on the stratigraphy of Central Australia: Royal Society of South Australia, Transactions, v. 38, p. 41–52.

CLOUD, P. E., AND SEMIKHATOV, M. A., 1969, Proterozoic stromatolite zonation: American Journal of Science, v. 267, p. 1017–1061.

DERRY, L. A., KAUFMAN, A. J., AND JACOBSEN, S. B., 1992, Sedimentary cycling and environmental change in the Late Proterozoic: Evidence from stable and radiogenic isotopes: Geochimica et Cosmochimica Acta, v. 56, p. 1317–1329.

DERRY, L. A., KETO, L. S., JACOBSEN, S. B., KNOLL, A. H., AND SWETT, K., 1989, Sr isotopic variations in Upper Proterozoic carbonates from Svalbard and East Greenland: Geochimica et Cosmochimica Acta, v. 53, p. 2331–2339.

FAIRCHILD, I. J., AND SPIRO, B., 1987, Petrological and isotopic implications of some contrasting Late Precambrian carbonates, NE Spitsbergen: Sedimentology, v. 34, p. 973–989.

FAIRCHILD, I. J., EINSELE, G., AND SONG, T., 1997, Possible seismic origin of molar tooth structures in Neoproterozoic carbonate ramp deposits, north China: Sedimentology, v. 44, p. 611–636.

FANNING, M., 1986, $^{87}Sr/^{86}Sr$ of gypsum/anhydrite and carbonate samples: Australian Mineral Development Laboratories Report G 6696/86 (unpublished).

FERGUSON, J., AND SKYRING, G. W., 1995, Redbed-associated sabkhas and tidal flats at Shark Bay, Western Australia: Their significance for genetic models of stratiform Cu–(Pb–Zn) deposits: Australian Journal of Earth Sciences, v. 42, p. 321–333.

FOLK, R. L., AND LAND, L. S., 1975, Mg/Ca ratio and salinity: Two controls over crystallization of dolomite: American Association of Petroleum Geologists, Bulletin, v. 59, p. 60–68.

FRANCOIS, R., 1987, A study of sulfur enrichment in the humic fraction of marine sediments during early diagenesis: Geochimica et Cosmochimica Acta, v. 51, p. 17–27.

FRANK, T. D., LYONS, T. W., AND LOHMANN, K. C., 1997, Isotopic evidence for the palaeoenvironmental evolution of the Mesoproterozoic Helena Formation, Belt Supergroup, Montana, USA: Geochimica et Cosmochimica Acta, v. 61, p. 5023–5041.

FREEMAN, K. H., HAYES, J. M., TRENDEL, J. M., AND ALBRECHT, P., 1990, Evidence from carbon isotope measurements for diverse origins of sedimentary hydrocarbons: Nature, v. 343, p. 254–256.

FREIDMAN, I., AND O'NEIL, J. R., 1977, Data of Geochemistry: Compilation of stable isotope fractionation factors of geochemical interest: U.S. Geological Survey, Professional Paper 440-KK.

GAINES, A. M., 1968, An experimental investigation of the kinetics and mechanism of the formation of dolomite: unpublished Ph.D thesis, University of Chicago.

GAINES, A. M., 1980, Dolomitization kinetics: Recent experimental studies, in Zenger, D. H., Dunham, J. B., and Ethington, R. L., eds., Concepts and Models of Dolomitization: SEPM, Special Publication 28, p. 81–86.

GAMES, L. M., AND HAYES, J. M., 1976, On the mechanisms of CO$_2$ and CH$_4$ production in natural anaerobic environments, in Nriagu, J. O., ed., Environmental Biogeochemistry: Ann Arbor, Michigan, Ann Arbor Science, p. 51–73.

GAO, G., AND LAND, L. S., 1991, Early Ordovician Cool Creek Dolomite, Middle Arbuckle Group, Slick Hills, SW Oklahoma, USA: Origin and modification: Journal of Sedimentary Petrology, v. 61, p. 161–173.

GEBELEIN, C. D., AND HOFFMAN, P., 1973, Algal origin of dolomite laminations in stromatolitic limestone: Journal of Sedimentary Petrology, v. 43, p. 603–613.

GLAESSNER, M. F., PREISS, W. V., AND WALTER, M. R., 1969, Precambrian columnar stromatolites in Australia: Morphological and stratigraphic analysis: Science, v. 164, p. 1056–1058.

GOLDHABER, M. B., AND KAPLAN, I. R., 1974, The sulfur cycle, in Goldberg, E. D., ed., The Sea: Wiley-Interscience, p. 569–655.

GREGG, J. M., AND SHELTON, K. L., 1990, Dolomitization and dolomite neomorphism in the back reef facies of the Bonneterre and Davis Formations (Cambrian), southeastern Missouri: Journal of Sedimentary Petrology, v. 60, p. 549–562.

GROTZINGER, J. P., 1989, Facies and evolution of Precambrian carbonate depositional systems: Emergence of the modern platform archetype, in Crevello, P. D., Wilson, J. L., Sarg, J. F., and Read, J. F., eds., Controls on Carbonate Platform and Basin Development: SEPM, Special Publication 44, p. 79–106.

HARDIE, L. A., 1987, Dolomitization: A critical view of some current views: Journal of Sedimentary Petrology, v. 57, p. 166–83.

HAYES, J. M., 1983, Geochemical evidence bearing on the origin of aerobiosis, a speculative hypothesis, in Schopf, J. W., ed., Earth's Earliest Biosphere: Its Origin and Evolution: Princeton, New Jersey, Princeton University Press, p. 291–301.

HAYES, J. M., TAKIGIKU, R., OCAMPO, R., CALLOTH, H. J., AND ALBRECHT, P., 1987, Isotopic compositions and probable origins of organic molecules in the Eocene Messel Shale: Nature, v. 329, p. 48–51.

HOLLAND, H. D., 1984, The Chemical Evolution of the Atmosphere and Oceans: Princeton, New Jersey, Princeton University Press, 582 p.

HOLSER, W. T., SCHIDLOWSKI, M., MACKENZIE, F. T., AND MAYNARD, J. B., 1988, Geochemical cycles of carbon and sulfur, in Gregor, C. B., Garrels, R. M., MacKenzie, F. T., and Maynard, J. B., eds., Chemical Cycles in the Evolution of the Earth: New York, John Wiley & Sons, p. 105–174.

HOWCHIN, W., 1914, The occurrence of the genus Cryptozoon in the (?)Cambrian of Australia: Royal Society of South Australia, Transactions, v. 38, p. 1–10.

IRWIN, H., CURTIS, C., AND COLEMAN, M., 1977, Isotopic evidence for source of diagenetic carbonates formed during burial of organic-rich sediments: Nature, v. 269, p. 209–213.

KAUFMAN, A. J., AND KNOLL, A. H., 1995, Neoproterozoic variations in the C-isotopic composition of seawater: Stratigraphic and biogeochemical implications: Precambrian Research, v. 73, p. 27–49.

KENIG, F., SINNINGHE DAMSTE, J. P., KOCK–VAN DALEN, A. C., RIJPSTRA, W. I. C., HUC, A. Y., AND DE LEEUW, J. W., 1995, Occurrence and origin of mono-, di-, and trimethylalkanes in modern and Holocene cyanobacterial mats from Abu Dhabi, United Arab Emirates: Geochimica et Cosmochimica Acta, v. 59, p. 2999–3015.

KNOLL, A. H., 1981, Paleoecology of late Precambrian microbial assemblages, in Niklas, K. J., ed., Paleobotany, Paleoecology and Evolution v. 1: New York, Praeger, p. 17–54.

KNOLL, A. H., AND GOLUBIC, S., 1979, Anatomy and taphonomy of a Precambrian algal stromatolite: Precambrian Research, v. 10, p. 115–151.

KNOLL, A. H., AND SWETT, K., 1990, Carbonate deposition during the Late Proterozoic era: An example from Spitsbergen: American Journal of Science, v. 290-A, p. 104–132.

KRETZ, R., 1982, A model for the distribution of trace elements between calcite and dolomite: Geochimica et Cosmochimica Acta, v. 46, p. 1979–1981.

KUPECZ, J. A., AND LAND, L. S., 1991, Late-stage dolomitization of the lower Ordovician Ellenburger Group, West Texas: Journal of Sedimentary Petrology, v. 61, p. 551–574.

LAND, L. S., 1980, The isotopic and trace element geochemistry of dolomite: The state of the art, in Zenger, D. H., Dunham, J. B., and Ethington, R. L., eds., Concepts and Models of Dolomitization: SEPM, Special Publication 28, p. 87–110.

LAND, L. S., 1985, The origin of massive dolomite: Journal of Geological Education, v. 33, p. 112–125.

LAND, L. S., 1992, The dolomite problem: Stable and radiogenic isotope clues, in Clauer, N., and Chaudhuri, S., eds., Isotopic Signatures and Sedimentary Records: New York, Springer-Verlag, Lecture Notes in Earth Sciences 43, p. 49–68.

LINDSAY, J. F., 1987, Upper Proterozoic evaporites in the Amadeus Basin, central Australia, and their role in basin tectonics: Geological Society of America, Bulletin, v. 99, p. 852–865.

LOGAN, G. A., SUMMONS, R. E., AND HAYES, J. M., 1997, An isotopic biogeochemical study of Neoproterozoic and Early Cambrian sediments from the Centralian Superbasin, Australia: Geochimica et Cosmochimica Acta, v. 61, p. 1–17.

MACHEL, H. G., AND MOUNTJOY, E. W., 1986, Chemistry and environments of dolomite—A reappraisal: Earth-Science Reviews, v. 23, p. 175–222.

MACHEL, H. G., AND MOUNTJOY, E. W., 1987, General constraints on extensive pervasive dolomitization and their application to the Devonian carbonates of western Canada: Bulletin of Canadian Petroleum Geology, v. 35, p. 143–158.

MADIGAN, C. T., 1932a, The geology of the western MacDonnell Ranges, Central Australia: Geological Society of London, Quarterly Journal, v. 88, p. 672–711.

MADIGAN, C. T., 1932b, The geology of the eastern MacDonnell Ranges, Central Australia: Royal Society of South Australia, Transactions, v. 56, p. 71–117.

MADIGAN, C. T., 1935, The geology of the MacDonnell Ranges and neighbourhood, Central Australia: Report of the Australian and New Zealand Association of Advancements in Science, v. 21, p. 75–86.

MAWSON, D., AND MADIGAN, C. T., 1930, Pre-Ordovician rocks of the MacDonnell Ranges (Central Australia): Geological Society of London, Quarterly Journal, v. 86, p. 415–428.

MCKENZIE, J. A., HSÜ, K. J., AND SCHNEIDER, J. F., 1980, Movement of subsurface waters under the sabkha, Abu Dhabi, UAE, and its relation to evaporitic dolomite diagenesis, in Zenger, D. H., Dunham, J. B., and Ethington, R. L., eds., Concepts and Models of Dolomitization: SEPM, Special Publication 28, p. 11–30.

MCCREA, J. M., 1950, On the isotopic chemistry of carbonates and a paleotemperature scale: Journal of Chemical Physics, v. 18, p. 849–857.

MCKIRDY, D. M., 1976, Biochemical markers in stromatolites, in Walter, M. R., ed., Stromatolites: New York, Elsevier, p. 163–191.

MEYERS, W. J., LU, F. H., AND ZACHARIAH, J. K., 1997, Dolomitization by mixed evaporative brines and freshwater, upper Miocene carbonates, Nijar, Spain: Journal of Sedimentary Research, v. 67, p. 898–912.

MOLDOWAN, J. M., SEIFERT, W. K., AND GALLEGOS, E. J., 1985, Relationship between petroleum composition and depositional environment of petroleum source rocks: American Association of Petroleum Geologists, Bulletin, v. 69, p. 1255–1268.

MONTAÑEZ, I. P., AND READ, J. F., 1992, Fluid–rock interaction history during stabilization of early dolomites, upper Knox Group (Lower Ordovician), U.S. Appalachians: Journal of Sedimentary Petrology, v. 62, p. 753–778.

MORTON, J. G. G., 1997, Chapter 6: Lithostratigraphy and environments of deposition, in Morton, J. G. G., and Drexel, J. F., eds., Petroleum Geology of South Australia, Volume 3: Officer Basin: South Australian Department of Mines an Energy Resources Report Book 97/19.

MYCKE B., MICHAELIS W., AND DEGENS E. T., 1987, Biomarkers in sedimentary sulfides of Precambrian age, in Mattavelli, L., and Novelli, L., eds., Advances in Organic Geochemistry: Organic Geochemistry, v. 13, p. 619–625.

OEHLER, D. Z., 1976, Transmission electron microscopy of organic microfossils from the Late Precambrian Bitter Springs Formation of Australia, techniques and survey of preserved ultrastructure: Journal of Paleontology, v. 50, p. 90–106.

OEHLER, D. Z., 1977, Pyrenoid-like structures in Late Precambrian algae from the Bitter Springs Formation of Australia: Journal of Palaeontology, v. 51, p. 885–901.

OEHLER, D. Z., OEHLER, J. H., AND STEWART, A. J., 1979, Algal fossils from Late Precambrian hypersaline lagoon: Science, v. 205, p. 388–390.

PETERS, K. E., AND MOLDOWAN, J. M., 1993, The Biomarker Guide—Interpreting Molecular Fossils in Petroleum and Ancient Sediments: Princeton, New Jersey, Prentice-Hall, 363 p.

PYZIK, A. J., AND SOMMER, S. E., 1981, Sedimentary iron monosulfides: Kinetics and mechanism of formation: Geochimica et Cosmochimica Acta, v. 45, p. 687–698.

RADKE, M., AND WELTE, D. H., 1983, The methylphenanthrene index (MPI). A maturity parameter based on aromatic hydrocarbons, in Bjorøy, M., and

12 others, eds., Advances in Organic Geochemistry 1981: New York, John Wiley and Sons, p. 504–512.

ROSENBAUM, J., AND SHEPPARD, S. M. F., 1986, An isotopic study of siderites, dolomites and ankerites at high temperatures: Geochimica et Cosmochimica Acta, v. 50, p. 1147–1150.

SACKETT, W. M., AND CHUNG, H. M., 1979, Experimental confirmation of the lack of carbon isotope exchange between methane and carbon oxides at high temperatures: Geochimica et Cosmochimica Acta, v. 43, p. 273–276.

SARKAR, S., AND BOSE, P. K., 1992, Variations in Late Proterozoic stromatolites over a transition from basin to plain to nearshore subtidal zone: Precambrian Research, v. 56, p. 139–157.

SCHOPF, J. W., 1968, Microflora of the Bitter Springs Formation, Late Precambrian, Central Australia: Journal of Paleontology, v. 42, p. 651–688.

SCHOPF, J. W., AND BLACIC, J. M., 1971, New microorganisms from the Bitter Springs Formation (Late Precambrian) of the north-central Amadeus Basin, Australia: Journal of Paleontology, v. 45, p. 925–959.

SHEPPARD, S. M. F., AND SCHWARCZ, H. P., 1970, Fractionation of carbon and oxygen isotopes and magnesium between metamorphic calcite and dolomite: Contributions to Mineralogy and Petrology, v. 26, p. 161–198.

SIBLEY, D. F., AND GREGG, J. M., 1987, Classification of dolomite rock textures: Journal of Sedimentary Petrology, v. 57, p. 967–975.

SMITH, A. G., 1968, the origin and deformation of some molar-tooth structures in the Precambrian Belt–Purcell Supergroup: Journal of Geology, v. 76, p. 426–443.

SOUTHGATE, P. N., 1986, Depositional environment and mechanism of preservation of microfossils, upper Proterozoic Bitter Springs Formation, Australia: Geology, v. 14, p. 683–686.

SOUTHGATE, P. N., 1989, Relationships between cyclicity and stromatolite form in the Late Proterozoic Bitter Springs Formation, Australia: Sedimentology, v. 36, p. 323–339.

SOUTHGATE, P. N., 1991, A sedimentological model for the Loves Creek Member of the Bitter Springs Formation, northern Amadeus Basin, in Korsch, R. J., and Kennard, J. M., eds., Geological and Geophysical Studies in the Amadeus Basin, Central Australia: Australian Bureau of Mineral Resources, Geology and Geophysics Bulletin 236, p. 113–126.

STEWART, A. J., 1979, A barred basin marine evaporite in the Upper Proterozoic of the Amadeus Basin, central Australia: Sedimentology, v. 26, p. 33–62.

STILLER, M., ROUNICK, J. S., AND SHASHA, S., 1985, Extreme carbon-isotope enrichments in evaporating brines: Nature, v. 316, p. 434–435.

STRAUSS, H., DES MARAIS, D. J., HAYES, J. M., LAMBERT, I. B., AND SUMMONS, R. E., 1992, Procedures for whole rock and kerogen analysis, in Schopf, J. W., and Klein, C., eds., The Proterozoic Biosphere: A Multidisciplinary Study: Cambridge, U.K., Cambridge University Press, p. 669–707.

SUMMONS, R. E., 1992, Abundance and composition of extractable organic matter, in Schopf, J. W. and Klein, C., eds., The Proterozoic Biosphere: A Multidisciplinary Study: Cambridge, U.K., Cambridge University Press, p. 101–115.

SUMMONS, R. E., AND POWELL, T. G., 1991, Petroleum source rocks of the Amadeus Basin, in Korsch, R. J., and Kennard, J. M., eds., Geological and Geophysical Studies in the Amadeus Basin, Central Australia: Australian Bureau of Mineral Resources, Geology and Geophysics Bulletin 236, p. 511–524.

SUMMONS, R. E., AND STRAUSS, H., 1992a, Procedures for analysis of extractable organic matter, in Schopf, J. W., and Klein, C., eds., The Proterozoic Biosphere: A Multidisciplinary Study: Cambridge, U.K., Cambridge University Press, p. 799–809.

SUMMONS, R. E., AND STRAUSS, H., 1992b, Composition of extractable organic matter, in Schopf, J. W., and Klein, C., eds., The Proterozoic Biosphere: A Multidisciplinary Study: Cambridge, U.K., Cambridge University Press, p. 811–817.

SUMMONS, R. E., AND WALTER, M. R., 1990, Molecular fossils and microfossils of prokaryotes and protists from Proterozoic sediments: American Journal of Science, v. 290-A, p. 212–244.

SUN, S. Q., 1994, A reappraisal of dolomite abundance and occurrence in the Phanerozoic: Journal of Sedimentary Research, v. 64, p. 396–404.

TUCKER, M. E., 1983, Diagenesis, geochemistry, and origin of a Precambrian dolomite: The Beck Spring Dolomite of eastern California: Journal of Sedimentary Petrology, v. 53, p. 1097–1119.

TUTTLE, M. L., AND GOLDHABER, M. B., 1993, Sedimentary sulfur geochemistry of the Paleogene Green River Formation, western USA: Implications for interpreting depositional and diagenetic processes in saline alkaline lakes: Geochimica et Cosmochimica Acta, v. 57, p. 3023–3039.

VAHRENKAMP, V. C., AND SWART, P. K., 1990, New distribution coefficient for the incorporation of strontium into dolomite and its implications for the formation of ancient dolomites: Geology, v. 18, p. 387–391.

VEIZER, J., AND COMPSTON, W., 1976, $^{87}Sr/^{86}Sr$ in Precambrian carbonates as an index of crustal evolution: Geochimica et Cosmochimica Acta, v. 40, p. 905–914.

WALTER, M. R., 1972, Stromatolites and the biostratigraphy of the Australian Precambrian and Cambrian: Palaeontological Association [London], Special Paper 11, 190 p.

WALTER, M. R., AND VEEVERS, J. J., 1997, Australian Neoproterozoic palaeogeography, tectonics, and supercontinental connections: Australian Geological Survey Organization Journal of Australian Geology and Geophysics, v. 17, p. 73–92.

WALTER, M. R., KRYLOV, I. N., AND PREISS, W. V., 1979, Stromatolites from Adelaidean (Late Proterozoic) sequences in central and South Australia: Alcheringa, v. 3, p. 287–305.

WALTER, M. R., VEEVERS, J. J., CALVER, C. R., AND GREY, K., 1995, Neoproterozoic stratigraphy of the Centralian Superbasin, Australia: Precambrian Research, v. 73, p. 173–195.

WAPLES, D. W., HAUG, P., AND WELTE, D. H., 1974, Occurrence of a regular C_{25} isoprenoid hydrocarbon in Tertiary sediments representing a lagoonal-type, saline environment: Geochimica et Cosmochimica Acta, v. 38, p. 381–387.

WHITICAR, M. J., FABER, E., AND SCHOELL, M., 1986, Biogenic methane formation in marine and freshwater environments: Carbon dioxide reduction versus acetate fermentation—Isotopic evidence: Geochimica et Cosmochimica Acta, v. 50, p. 693–709.

WINGATE, M. T. D., CAMPBELL, I. H., COMPSTON, W., AND GIBSON, G. M., 1998, Ion microprobe U–Pb ages for Neoproterozoic basaltic magmatism in south-central Australia and implications for the breakup of Rodinia: Precambrian Research, v. 87, p. 135–159.

YOUNG, G. M., 1981, The Amundsen Embayment, N.W.T.: Relevance to the Upper Proterozoic evolution of North America: Geological Survey of Canada, Paper 81–10, p. 203–218.

ZANG, W., AND WALTER, M. R., 1992, Late Proterozoic and Cambrian Microfossils and Biostratigraphy, Amadeus Basin, Central Australia: Association of Australasian Palaeontologists, Memoir 12, 132 p.

ZEMPOLICH, W. G., WILKINSON, B. H., AND LOHMANN, K. C., 1988, Diagenesis of late Proterozoic carbonates: The Beck Spring Dolomite of eastern California: Journal of Sedimentary Petrology, v. 58, p. 656–672.

ZENGER, D. H., 1983, Burial dolomitization in the Lost Burro Formation (Devonian), east-central California, and the significance of late diagenetic dolomitization: Geology, v. 11, p. 519–522.

ZENGER, D. H., AND DUNHAM, J. B., 1988, Dolomitization of Siluro-Devonian limestones in a deep core (5,350 m), southeastern New Mexico, in Shukla, V., and Baker, P. A., eds., Sedimentology and Geochemistry of Dolostones: SEPM, Special Publication 43, p. 161–173.

ZHAO, J.-X., McCULLOCH, M. T., AND KORSCH, R. J., 1994, Characterisation of a plume-related 800 Ma magmatic event and its implications for basin formation in central-southern Australia: Earth and Planetary Science Letters, v. 121, p. 349–367.

DEPOSITIONAL δ18O SIGNATURES IN PROTEROZOIC DOLOSTONES: CONSTRAINTS ON SEAWATER CHEMISTRY AND EARLY DIAGENESIS

LINDA C. KAH

Department of Geological Sciences, University of Tennessee, Knoxville, Tennessee 37996, U.S.A.

ABSTRACT: The Mesoproterozoic Society Cliffs Formation consists of approximately 700 meters of cyclic, peritidal dolostones that were deposited on an extensive shallow-marine platform. Stratigraphic analysis allows the reconstruction of broad hydrologic and paleoenvironmental conditions on the platform (Kah, in press), and sedimentological and paleobiological information help constrain such aspects of the depositional environment as the origin of precipitated carbonate, degree of evaporation, temperature, and timing and environment of early diagenesis. Together, these observations provide an independent framework within which to examine the geochemical record of carbonate deposition and early diagenesis.

During evolution of the Society Cliffs platform, shoaling and subaerial exposure of a mid-ramp intraclastic/oolitic grainstone shoal restricted circulation of marine waters within an areally extensive microbial flat. Evaporation during periods of restriction resulted in widespread precipitation of abiotic, seafloor carbonate precipitates and marine sulfates. Early dolomitization of these primary phases is evidenced by a close correspondence of petrographic fabrics preserved in dolomite and early diagenetic chert, and by excellent fabric retention during dolomitization of highly-soluble evaporite phases.

Dolomitic rocks of the Society Cliffs Formation retain a pattern of oxygen isotopic variation that reflects regional depositional environments. Whereas mid-ramp dolostones record the isotopically lightest values (δ18O ~ −6‰), inner ramp dolostones vary from −5‰ to −3‰, values consistent with the isotopic enrichment of marine waters during periods of restriction and evaporation. An additional 2–3‰ enrichment of δ18O in subaerially exposed cycle caps (to −3‰ in mid-ramp facies and −1‰ in inner ramp facies) suggests a continued evaporative influence during widespread exposure of the platform. Data require that depositional, as well as diagenetic, variation be accounted for when interpreting the sedimentary record of δ18O. Furthermore, evidence that significant primary paleoenvironmental variation in δ18O can be retained in Proterozoic dolostones suggests first, that isotopic compositions were imparted during early dolomitization, and second, that samples containing the most enriched 18O abundances cannot *a priori* be presumed to record "least-altered" isotopic signatures. Therefore, despite a recognized propensity for alteration, when evaluated within an independently derived depositional framework, oxygen isotopic compositions of shallow marine dolostone facies may provide important constraints on both the geochemical evolution of marine systems and processes of early diagenesis.

INTRODUCTION

The ratio of 18O to 16O in modern marine waters can vary by several permil and is therefore of great value to oceanographers in tracing the movement of water masses in the oceans. Isotopic variation arises from fractionation that occurs during processes of evaporation and condensation, and results in marine surface waters whose isotopic composition is controlled primarily by the distribution of evaporation and precipitation over the surface ocean, and mixing with isotopically depleted river water in coastal areas (Anderson and Arthur, 1983). In modern systems, these hydrologic effects are easily recognized. For example, restricted marine basins with high rates of evaporation, such as the Mediterranean Sea (Thunell *et al.*, 1987) and the Persian Gulf (McKenzie *et al.*, 1980), show distinct 18O enrichment trends, whereas basins with excess precipitation, such as the Baltic Sea, commonly contain isotopically depleted waters (Hudson and Anderson, 1989).

Such hydrologic trends should have occurred in ancient marine basins as well. For example, geochemical mapping of Messinian carbonates in Sicily (McKenzie, 1985) and Permian deposits in Poland (Peryt and Scholle, 1997) have revealed distinct fresh-water signatures near basin margins and increasingly enriched oxygen isotopic values toward basin depocenters that preserve extensive gypsum and halite deposits. Oxygen isotopic variation, however, can result not only from the compositional variation of the water from which minerals precipitate, but also from the temperature of precipitation and from diagenetic overprinting. In ancient sedimentary successions, problems with interpretation are further compounded by ongoing controversy regarding the constancy of marine isotopic compositions through time. Several researchers suggest that marine isotopic compositions have been buffered to approximately 0‰ throughout Earth history (e.g. Gregory, 1991), yet the isotopic record of marine sedimentary minerals indicate that

Pre-Devonian marine isotopic compositions may have been significantly depleted with respect to 18O (e.g. Lohmann and Walker, 1989; Veizer *et al.*, 1997).

A variety of explanations have been offered to account for isotopically light values of pre-Devonian sedimentary minerals, including the temporal evolution of marine waters (Perry and Tan, 1972; Lohmann and Walker, 1989; Burdett *et al.*, 1990; Carpenter *et al.*, 1991; Veizer *et al.*, 1997); depositional (Zempolich *et al.*, 1988; Knauth and Roberts, 1991), early diagenetic (Kenny and Knauth, 1992) or post-depositional equilibration (Degens and Epstein, 1962) with isotopically light fluids; or precipitation of sedimentary minerals at elevated temperatures (Knauth and Epstein, 1976; Karhu and Epstein, 1986). Few studies, however, have interpreted isotopic values in the context of regional depositional patterns. Most have focused on the isotopic composition of thermodynamically stable biogenic components (Popp *et al.*, 1986; Veizer *et al.*, 1997) or the isotopic variation preserved in successive paragenetic stages during diagenesis (Fairchild and Spiro, 1987; Zempolich *et al.*, 1988; Carpenter *et al.*, 1991). These studies, while invaluable in resolving the geochemical effects of diagenesis, typically do not evaluate possible compositional variation within primary marine waters. Broad correlation between isotopic composition of carbonate rocks and depositional environment (Burdett *et al.*, 1990), suggests that further study is necessary to recognize the extent of primary δ18O variation preserved in ancient successions.

This paper examines oxygen isotopic variation observed in the Mesoproterozoic Society Cliffs Formation. Within the Society Cliffs Formation, depositional environments and the extent and conditions of diagenesis can be independently constrained from stratigraphic, sedimentologic, and paleobiologic observations. Because evaporitic trends in δ18O are well established in modern environments (Sofer and Gat, 1975; Gat and Bowser, 1991), the analysis of facies inferred to have precipitated from evaporatively modified seawater, rather than pre-

Carbonate Sedimentation and Diagenesis in the Evolving Precambrian World
Copyright © 2000, SEPM (Society for Sedimentary Geology) Special Publication 67, ISBN 1-56576-072-7

cluding their use as geochemical indicators, provides an additional constraint for the estimation of primary marine isotopic values. If systematic variation in oxygen isotopic compositions can be demonstrated to correlate with changes in depositional environments, observed patterns of isotopic variation may lead not only to a greater understanding of the isotopic evolution of marine waters, but may provide important constraints on the nature of early diagenesis.

REGIONAL GEOLOGIC SETTING

The Society Cliffs Formation is the lowermost carbonate unit in the Bylot Supergroup, a thick package (>6000 meters) of siliciclastic and carbonate rocks exposed within the fault-bounded Borden Basins of northernmost Baffin and Bylot islands (Fig. 1). Together, paleomagnetic (Fahrig *et al.*, 1981), radiometric (Le Cheminant and Heaman, 1989; Heaman *et al.*, 1992), chemostratigraphic (Kah *et al.*, 1999), and biostratigraphic (Hofmann and Jackson, 1994) constraints suggest that Bylot Supergroup sedimentation occurred between approximately 1270 and 1000 Ma. The extent and paleogeographic setting of the basin, however, remain unresolved. Sedimentary rocks of the Bylot Supergroup may record a complex history of rifting (Jackson *et al.*, 1980; Jackson and Iannelli, 1981), localized tectonic uplift (Jackson *et al.*, 1978; Ianelli, 1979), tectonically (?) induced sea level fluctuations (Narbonne and

James, 1996), and periods of regional stability (Geldsetzer, 1973a; Knight and Jackson, 1994).

The Society Cliffs Formation comprises ~700 meters of peritidal carbonate and subordinate siliciclastic strata exposed in two linear, east-west trending belts. Strata dip shallowly to the northeast and remain essentially undeformed. Karst breccias and other dissolutional structures associated with post-depositional Pb-Zn mineralization occur locally in the western Borden Basin (Geldsetzer, 1973b; Clayton and Thorpe, 1982; Olson, 1984) but do not affect strata within the study region. Stratigraphic interpretations were compiled from 16 measured sections distributed along the axis of the eastern Borden Basin (Fig. 1), as well as from published stratigraphic sections (Jackson *et al.*, 1975) and cross-sections (Geldsetzer, 1973a).

Two stratigraphically distinct carbonate ramps occur in the Society Cliffs Formation (Kah, in press). The lower ramp records the incursion of marine waters over the Society Cliffs basal unconformity and the initiation of carbonate deposition. Deposition of gypsiferous facies in both inner (Jackson and Cumming, 1981) and mid-ramp (Geldsetzer, 1973a; Olson, 1984) environments indicates restricted conditions across the platform. The upper Society Cliffs ramp formed in response to an increase in overall water depth. Platform flooding resulted in an abrupt eastward retreat of terrigenous siliciclastic facies and concurrent development intraclastic/oolitic facies in mid-ramp regions. Samples for isotopic and trace elemental analysis

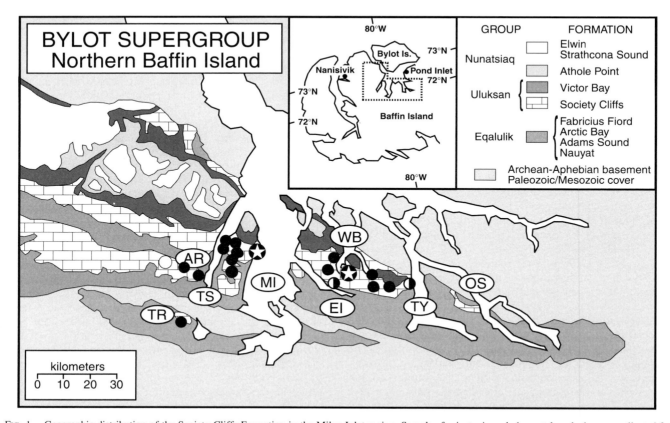

FIG. 1.—Geographic distribution of the Society Cliffs Formation in the Milne Inlet region. Samples for isotopic and elemental analysis were collected from measured sections at Milne Inlet and White Bay (marked with stars). Closed circles are locations of measured stratigraphic sections used for paleoenvironmental analysis; split circles are sections measured by Jackson et al. (1975); open circles are reconnoitered sections only. Reference localities Oliver Sound (OS), Tay Sound (TY), White Bay (WB), Eskimo Inlet (EI), Milne Inlet (MI), Tremblay Sound (TS), Tremblay Plateau (TR), and Alpha River (AR).

were collected from two measured sections of the upper ramp sequence at Milne Inlet and White Bay (Fig. 1). Additional geochemical data from the Nanisivik region (Ghazban et al., 1992), 200 km to the west of Milne Inlet, provides information on the isotopic composition of late-stage diagenetic fluids associated with ore mineralization.

PALEOENVIRONMENTAL EVOLUTION

Stratigraphic Evolution

The Society Cliffs upper ramp preserves two distinct scales of cyclicity; one in mid-ramp environments, and a second in inner ramp environments (Fig. 2). Detailed descriptions of lithologies are tabulated by Kah (in press). Mid-ramp cycles are typically thin (1–20 m, averaging 3.5 m), contain microbially laminated dolostone, oolitic and intraclastic grains, and abundant bedded micrite. Cycles are capped by a distinctive interval of fenestral grainstones, intraformational breccias, and tepee cracks indicating prolonged periods of exposure. Inner ramp cycles are considerably thicker (10–50 m), are largely devoid of grainstone facies, and consist dominantly of microbially laminated dolomicrospar. An increasing abundance of isopachously laminated carbonate, interpreted as seafloor cements (Kah and Knoll, 1996), and gypsum upward in shoaling cycles and eastward toward the inferred shoreline (Iannelli, 1979) indicate extensive evaporation and environmental restriction.

The observed disparity in cycle thicknesses between mid- and inner ramp facies are best explained by variable rates of sediment production and accumulation along the platform (Kah, in press). Sediment production and accumulation were highest in the mid-ramp regions and resulted in a large number of thin cycles that record short-term sea level variation (Fig. 2). During periods of high relative sea level, grainstone shoals built rapidly upwards while microbial facies occupied the low-energy, partially restricted regions landward of the shoal region (Fig. 3a). Deposition of inner ramp carbonates continued during periods of low relative sea level when subaerial exposure of mid-ramp grainstone shoals effectively cut off marine circulation to landward microbial facies. Extensive evaporation during environmental restriction led to widespread deposition of seafloor precipitates and evaporite minerals (Fig. 3b). Complete shoaling and exposure of inner ramp cycles occurred only during extended periods of restriction.

Temporal variations in sea level and sediment accumulation rates resulted in three distinct cycle stacking patterns and associated facies distributions: (1) Extended periods of subaerial exposure in mid-ramp facies resulted in long intervals of restriction. Inner ramp waters reached significantly elevated salinities resulting in widespread gypsum deposition (Fig. 2a). (2) Low-amplitude sea level oscillation near the platform surface is evidenced by numerous thin mid-ramp cycles (Fig. 2b). Widespread deposition of seafloor precipitates indicates regionally evaporative conditions, although episodic freshening of inner ramp waters impeded gypsum deposition. (3) Incomplete shoaling of inner ramp facies is marked by abrupt termination of carbonate deposition resulting from sea level falls that exposed the entire platform surface (Fig. 2c).

Sedimentology and Petrography

Society Cliffs facies sampled for geochemical analysis include micrite, coated grains, microbial laminated carbonate, and synsedimentary seafloor precipitates. All depositional components have been dolomitized. Micritic lithologies, here described as uniform, finely crystalline (<15 μm) anhedral dolomite (Fig. 4a), typically occur as thin beds and reworked intraclastic grains in mid-ramp environments and are restricted to individual laminae in inner ramp environments. Rapid cementation of micritic lithologies in mid-ramp environments is inferred from the reworking of micrite as intraclastic grains and is further evidenced by isopachous cement rims (25–300 μm

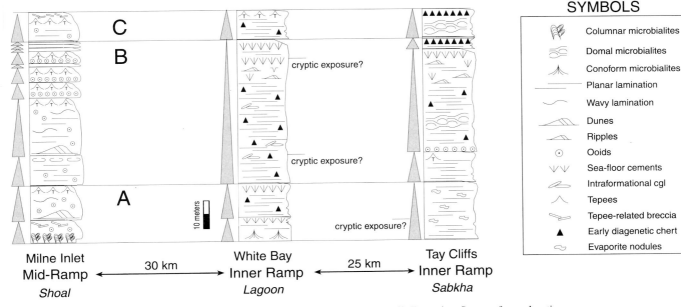

FIG. 2.—Two distinct scales of cyclicity in the Society Cliffs Formation. See text for explanation.

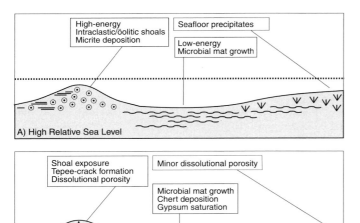

FIG. 3.—Summary of Society Cliffs Formation depositional environments. See Figure 2 for explanation of symbols.

thick) and abundance of composite reworked grains (Figs. 4*b*, *c*). Within zones of subaerial exposure intraclasts can exhibit a wider range of grain-size (<5–30 μm), finely crystalline rims with more coarsely crystalline centers, and dissolution of grain interiors, suggesting modification of primary fabrics during dolomitization. Micritic intraclasts and composite grains also occur as nuclei of coated grains with fine concentric laminae (<30 μm thick; Fig. 4*c*).

Microbial laminated carbonate in inner ramp environments typically consists of micritic to microsparitic (here described as 25–50 μm) anhedral dolomite. Laminations are defined by a decrease in average crystal size corresponding with the presence of laminae containing abundant remnant organic matter (Fig. 4*d*). Comparison of petrographic fabrics preserved within dolomite and early diagenetic chert allows detailed evaluation of the genesis of microbial dolomites. Early diagenetic chert is abundant as thin beds and nodules within inner ramp microbially laminated carbonates. Silicified fabrics contain a wide variety of microbial remains (Hofmann and Jackson, 1991), and are dominated by filamentous sheathes attributable to the cyanobacteria genera *Siphonophycus* and *Eomicrocoleus* (Fig. 4*e*; Kah and Knoll, 1996). Overall, the assemblage is strikingly similar to those found in modern, moderately-saline to hypersaline flats (Horodyski et al., 1977; Javor, 1983). Filaments mats are densely woven; direct contact between adjacent microbial sheathes suggests that little carbonate was originally bound within the mats, and that lithification proceeded by carbonate precipitation *in situ* with a microbial matrix, perhaps under the influence of hypersaline conditions. Carbonate precipitation during mat degradation (cf. Chafetz and Buczynski, 1992) is inferred from the morphological similarity between compacted and partially degraded organic-rich laminae preserved in cherts and dolostones, and is supported by carbon isotopic evidence of organic remineralization (Kah *et al.*, 1999). Similar microbial fabrics collected from mid-ramp environments contain a wider range in grain sizes and occasionally grade into coarse-grained dolomites (to 250 μm) that show sub-

hedral and euhedrally zoned crystals which obliterate depositional fabrics (Fig. 4*f*) and indicate substantial modification during dolomitization or later recrystallization. Fabric obliterative dolomite also is present within micritic and oolitic lithofacies. Samples containing such fabrics are denoted by asterisks in Table 1.

Synsedimentary seafloor precipitates are abundant within inner ramp facies of the Society Cliffs Formation (Kah and Knoll, 1996; Kah, in press). Seafloor precipitates occur in both early diagenetic chert and dolomite. In chert, precipitated fabrics are defined by organic staining that define elongate rays or botryoidal fans extending from the substrate, and micrometer to submicrometer-scale lamination (Fig 5*a*). Occasional preservation of cross-sections and square crystal terminations indicate primary aragonitic compositions. When preserved in carbonate, precipitates are represented by linear arrays of dolomite crystals (crystals typically 10–25 μm × 50–125 μm) elongate along inferred precursor crystal axes (Fig. 5*b*).

In addition to carbonate phases, the Society Cliffs Formation contains abundant evaporites (primarily gypsum), silicified evaporites, and dolomitized evaporite fabrics. Evaporite fabrics are variable. Preserved gypsum occurs as nodules and beds up to 3 m thick, with an estimated aggregate thickness exceeding 45 m, and occasionally contains silica-replaced halite cubes (Fig. 5*c*). Crystal rosettes preserved in chert (Fig. 5*d*) are morphologically identical to early stage cultured gypsum growth (Beales and Hardy, 1980, p. 200) and are interpreted as silicified gypsum. Dolomitized spindle-shaped crystals preserved in laminated fine-grained sediments (Fig. 5*e*) and nodules within microbially laminated dolostone (Fig. 5*f*) are similarly interpreted as replaced evaporites.

Implications for Early Diagenesis

Sedimentologic and petrographic relationships demonstrate that carbonate precipitation in the Society Cliffs Formation occurred within the water column (micrite, ooids, coated grains), at the sediment-water interface (seafloor precipitates), and within the shallow substrate (microbially laminated carbonate). Rapid lithification in all environments is evidenced by abundance of primary cement fabrics and reworked grains. Detailed fabric preservation of primary microbial, evaporite, and carbonate phases in chert indicates that silicification occurred very early in the diagenetic history of the Society Cliffs Formation. The high quality of microfossil preservation (cf. Hofmann and Jackson, 1991; Kah and Knoll, 1996) indicates silicification within weeks to months of deposition (Bartley, 1996). The occurrence of both fine-scale replacement of evaporite phases and silicification of halite in the presence of pristine gypsum suggests that earliest diagenetic silicification proceeded under a range of marine(?) to hypersaline conditions. Similarly fine-scale petrographic detail preserved in dolomitic lithologies and the close correspondence between dolomitized and silicified fabrics suggest that dolomitization occurred early in the diagenetic history of these strata. Excellent fabric retention of highly-soluble evaporite phases during dolomitization indicates that dolomitization occurred under hypersaline conditions as well.

Geochemical Predictions

Society Cliffs carbonates are interpreted to have been precipitated from, and to have been deposited within, a range of

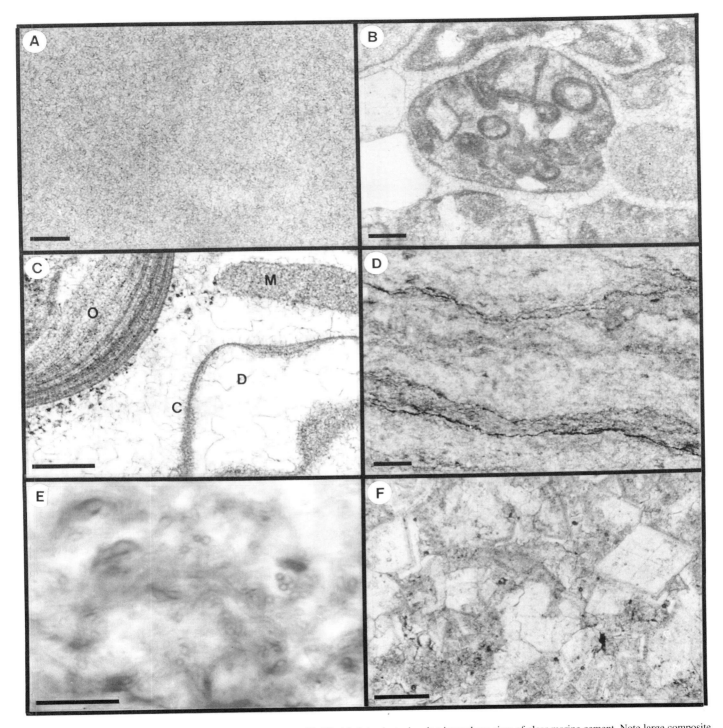

FIG. 4.—Society Cliffs microfacies. A) Equant dolomicrospar. B) Micritic intraclasts showing isopachous rims of clear marine cement. Note large composite grain. Clear grains are quartz. C) Oolitic/intraclastic grainstone from zone of subaerial exposure. Note concentrically laminated coated grain (O), recrystallization textures of micritic intraclast (M), isopachous cement rims (C), and evidence for dissolution of primary grains (D). D) Microbially laminated dolostone with organic sapropels. E) Excellent preservation of microbial filaments in early diagenetic chert. F) Dolomite obliterating primary depositional fabrics. Scale bar is 100 μm in A, B, E, 200 μm in C, D, F.

TABLE 1.—ISOTOPIC AND ELEMENTAL RESULTS, MID-RAMP FACIES

Sample	Environ. & phase[a]	Height (m)	$\delta^{13}C$	$\delta^{18}O$	Mg/Ca	Sr/Ca	Fe	Mn	Sr
			(‰PDB)				(ppm)		
MI-01	□	68	3.4	−5.0	0.29	0.00031	1022	147	79
MI-02	□	72	3.8	−4.0	0.34	0.00034	1034	124	77
MI-03a	⊡	83	3.9	−3.9	0.34	0.00031	911	77	69
MI-03b	⊿	83	4.0	−2.7	0.34	0.00031	805	127	72
MI-04	▾	93	4.0	−4.4	0.35	0.00026	783	95	51
MI-05	▾	106	4.0	−4.9	0.35	0.00026	872	76	56
MI-06	⊿	114	4.1	−2.2	0.52	0.00021	1394	30	38
MI-07	△	121	4.0	−3.0	0.50	0.00020	1082	63	36
MI-08	○	131	3.9	−7.3	0.56	0.00014	1203	51	25
MI-09	⊡	140	3.5	−5.8	0.56	0.00018	1057	107	32
MI-10	□	150	3.5	−4.2	0.55	0.00022	1070	49	43
MI-11	△	171	3.8	−3.1	0.57	0.00025	1135	38	45
MI-12	⊙	181	3.6	−6.2	0.53	0.00080	1075	57	143
MI-14	⊙*	202	3.7	−8.0	0.75	0.00018	200	24	14
MI-15	□	216	3.6	−3.9	0.33	0.00031	1031	106	76
MI-16	△	224	3.4	−3.7	0.37	0.00049	1875	78	90
MI-17	○*	236	3.2	−9.0	0.33	0.00040	1464	104	71
MI-18	○*	244	3.3	−12.4	0.40	0.00044	2487	96	83
MI-19	○*	253	3.5	−9.8	0.45	0.00012	460	64	24
MI-20	⊙	260	3.6	−6.9	0.47	0.00015	302	36	28
MI-21	▾	271	3.6	−5.6	0.50	0.00024	395	30	44
MI-22	□	284	3.2	−5.8	0.56	0.00019	71	39	24
MI-23	△	291	3.5	−3.8	0.49	0.00021	390	43	41
MI-24	○	300	3.6	−6.2	0.51	0.00021	359	67	37
MI-25	⊙*	310	3.5	−6.8	0.52	0.00017	385	64	30
MI-26	⊿	322	3.3	−3.4	0.49	0.00020	488	71	41
MI-27	○*	331	3.5	−7.6	0.50	0.00014	480	62	27
MI-28	▾	340	3.4	−5.6	0.49	0.00016	471	70	30
MI-29	⊿	356	3.6	−3.2	0.50	0.00023	465	81	41
MI-30	□	362	3.4	−5.1	0.48	0.00019	479	49	37
MI-31	⊿	372	3.5	−3.6	0.48	0.00022	489	40	42
MI-32	○*	382	3.4	−8.4	0.36	0.00010	400	76	29
MI-33	○*	392	3.1	−5.7	0.48	0.00016	492	79	31
MI-35	⊿	410	3.4	−3.8	0.51	0.00018	333	78	36
MI-36	⊿	434	3.2	−2.7	0.48	0.00020	512	76	39
MI-37	○	443	3.2	−6.2	0.49	0.00018	524	130	37
MI-38	△	451	3.7	−2.4	0.45	0.00035	500	37	69
MI-39	△	463	3.2	−3.8	0.46	0.00023	451	78	46
MI-40a	⊿	471	3.2	−2.1	0.46	0.00024	526	60	53
MI-40b	⊡	471	3.1	−6.1	0.47	0.00025	421	80	46
MI-41	⊿	483	2.9	−2.8	0.42	0.00024	446	43	46

[a] Samples are coded with respect to both exposed (△), interidal (□), and subtidal (○) depositional environments, as well as microsampled phases. Microsamples include ooids (●), microparitic microbial laminae (open symbols), and micritic laminae, matrix, and intraclasts (▾). Primry components typically show mimetic dolomite replacement; asterisks (*) denote coarse-grained euhedral, zoned dolomite.

[b] Dolomites are corrected for phosphoric acid fractionation at 90°C

marine (mid-ramp) to evaporative marine (inner ramp) waters. The timing and environmental conditions of dolomitization can be estimated from stratigraphic, sedimentologic, and paleobiologic observations. If primary $\delta^{18}O$ variation related to progressive evaporation of restricted marine waters is preserved, the following predictions can be made: (1) Marine seawater compositions are most likely to be preserved in the mid-ramp facies, where high energy conditions retain well mixed, unrestricted environments. (2) Inner ramp facies may show increased enrichment in ^{18}O with restriction and evaporation. Evaporation to gypsum salinities in modern and ancient environments rarely results in ^{18}O enrichment of greater than 6‰ (Sofer and Gat, 1975; McKenzie, 1985). A corollary to this is that mid-ramp facies should record relatively light isotopic compositions compared to inner ramp facies. (3) Supratidal and/or subaerially exposed facies, particularly those with evidence of dissolution, should show *either* isotopically light values indicative of fresh-water diagenesis, isotopically heavy values recording continued evaporation and upwards percolation of underlying pore waters (McKenzie et al., 1980), or values reflecting a combination of these processes.

GEOCHEMICAL PROCEDURES

Prior to microsampling, paired thin sections and polished thick sections were examined via standard petrographic and cathodoluminescence techniques to assess the diagenetic history of the samples and to ascertain the textural preservation of individual components. Least altered phases (ooids, seafloor precipitates, microbial laminae, micritic intraclasts, and micrite) larger than 1 mm were then drilled from polished thick sections using a 1 mm diamond drill bit. Resulting sample powder was collected and splits (2–5 mg) prepared for elemental and isotopic analysis. Preparation techniques are summarized in Kah et al. (1999) and reviewed in detail by Kaufman et al. (1991) and Kaufman and Knoll (1995).

Elemental concentrations of Ca, Mg, Mn, Fe, and Sr were measured via inductively-coupled plasma mass spectroscopy (ICP-MS). Analytical precisions, better than $\pm 5\%$, were determined using a combination of gravimetric standards and a 1 ppb Indium spike added to all sample solutions. Remaining splits were reacted off-line at 90°C with anhydrous phosphoric acid (H_3PO_4 $\rho \geq 1.89$ g/ml) and cryogenically distilled to re-

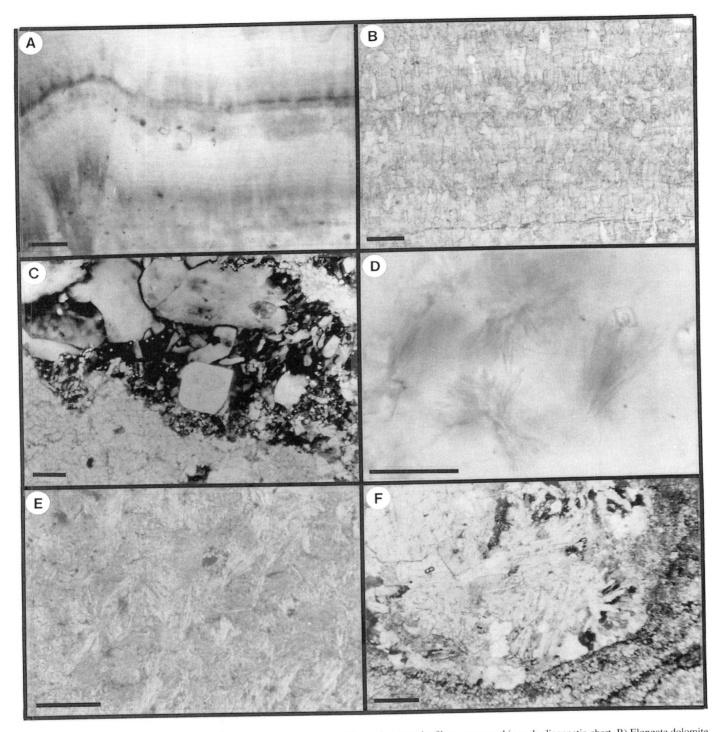

FIG. 5.—Society Cliffs microfacies. A) Seafloor precipitates composed of formerly aragonite fibers, preserved in early diagenetic chert. B) Elongate dolomite crystals replacing formerly aragonitic seafloor precipitates. C) Silicified halite cube preserved in primary gypsum. D) Silicified gypsum rosette. E) Lath-like crystal form of dolomite after gypsum (?). F) Partially dolomitized gypsum nodule within laminated microbial dolostone. Scale bar is 100 μm in A-F.

cover CO_2. Isotopic compositions were determined on a VG Isogas PRISM mass spectrometer and are expressed in δ-notation relative to a PDB standard. Precisions, ±0.1‰ for carbon and ±0.3‰ for oxygen, were based on multiple analyses of an internal laboratory standard.

Isotopic analyses were also performed on four whole-rock chert samples. Cherts were examined petrographically to assure primary fabric preservation, and samples chosen that contained uncompacted and compacted microbial populations, silicified seafloor precipitates, and silicified evaporites. Rock chips were etched in weak HNO_3–HCl to remove carbonate, rinsed, dried, and powdered. Samples powders were then baked at 850°C for 24 hours to oxidize the organic fraction (0.3–1.9 mg C/g sample), and 10–20 mg were analyzed by total oxygen extraction techniques and measured against Standard Mean Ocean Water (SMOW). Oxygen isotopic abundances for chert are precise to ±0.2‰.

RESULTS

Results of geochemical analyses are provided in Tables 1 and 2, and summarized in Table 3. Figure 6 illustrates isotopic data for both mid-ramp and inner ramp sample suites. Samples were collected at 10–15 m intervals from measured stratigraphic sections through both mid-ramp and inner ramp environments (Fig. 6a). This stratigraphic sampling did not permit detailed analysis of trends within a single depositional cycle. Rather, samples were labeled as subtidal, intertidal, or exposed based on dominant lithologic character and stratigraphic position of the samples within shoaling cycles (Fig. 6b). Data, therefore, collectively represent the range of isotopic compositions within specific environments sampled over successive cycles.

Evaluation of isotopic data from within a stratigraphic and depositional framework emphasizes several observations. First, minor variability in carbon isotopes is observed. Carbon isotopic compositions from mid-ramp environments are nearly invariant, with values averaging 3.5 ± 0.3‰PDB (Fig. 6a). These values are consistent with isotopic data recorded from late Mesoproterozoic successions worldwide and are interpreted as recording the carbon isotopic compositions of late Mesoproterozoic oceans (Kah et al., 1999). Carbon isotopic values of inner ramp facies, however, show variable depletion with respect to ^{13}C, averaging 2.9 ± 0.4‰. Variation of $\delta^{13}C$ in microbial components likely results from differential input of isotopically light organic carbon from degrading mat products during carbonate precipitation (Kah et al., 1999).

In contrast to the relatively uniform carbon isotopic compositions, $\delta^{18}O$ records a much broader range of isotopic compositions (Fig. 6b). Broad ranges of isotopic variation are commonly attributed to post-depositional diagenesis (see discussion below; Banner and Hanson, 1990; Marshall, 1992). That data reveal strong stratigraphic and paleogeographic facies dependency, however, suggests retention of at least some primary isotopic variation. Mid-ramp subtidal environments show the greatest range of isotopic compositions, ranging from −12.4‰ to −5.7‰. Subtidal samples are depleted in ^{18}O with respect to intertidal samples, and samples that show evidence of subaerial exposure are consistently enriched by up to 3‰ over subtidal and intertidal facies in the same stratigraphic succession. This pattern is apparent in both mid-ramp and inner ramp successions and is repeated in successive depositional cycles. A similar relationship occurs between mid- and inner ramp facies; inner ramp intertidal and exposed facies are typically enriched by 2‰ over comparable mid-ramp depositional environments.

Society Cliffs dolostones retain a pattern of oxygen isotopic variation that appears to mimic patterns predicted from stratigraphic and paleogeographic data. Values are therefore interpreted as reflecting primary differences in the isotopic composition of source waters, controlled by evaporation during the hydrological evolution of platform cycles. In this hypothesis, mid-ramp subtidal and intertidal facies reflect the least restricted depositional environments, while inner ramp subtidal and intertidal facies record a continuum of evaporitic states produced during episodic environmental restriction. Further enrichment recorded in exposed facies suggests continued evaporation of pore fluids during subaerial exposure of the platform (cf. McKenzie et al., 1980), and is consistent with the interpretation that arid conditions prevailed throughout platform evolution. Analytical results from four early diagenetic cherts, which preserve petrographic evidence of hypersaline conditions, reveal a range of oxygen isotopic values (−1.6 ± 0.7‰) consistent with their deposition under restricted, evaporative conditions. A single chert sample (TY-20245) containing replaced carbonate precipitates reveals isotopic values significantly lighter (−2.6‰) than carbonate values from similar facies (−1.2 ± 0.6‰) and may record a mixture of primary and secondary silica phases in that sample.

DIAGENETIC VERSUS PRIMARY MARINE ISOTOPIC COMPOSITIONS

Dolomitic rocks of the Society Cliffs formation preserve a wide range of oxygen isotopic compositions. Whereas preserved oxygen isotopes appear to mimic primary depositional variation, the actual isotopic values, with the exception of "most restricted" samples, are significantly lighter than modern marine compositions. Depleted oxygen isotopic values may record dolomitization either during burial diagenesis, or in the presence of isotopically light waters (fresh, meteoric, or mixed) during earliest diagenesis. If isotopic values record dolomitization from seawater or seawater-derived brines, depleted values may reflect either elevated temperature of precipitation, or precipitation from isotopically light marine waters.

Post-Depositional Alteration

Late-stage diagenetic alteration of oxygen isotopic values, resulting from the large-scale convection of marine, meteoric, or hydrothermal waters during burial, has been proposed as a possible explanation for the isotopically light values of Society Cliffs dolostones. Ghazban et al. (1992) proposed that light oxygen isotopic values resulted from large scale circulation of normal salinity marine waters through the Society Cliffs Formation during burial. Elevated temperatures and thermally driven circulation were presumed to have resulted from anomalously high geothermal gradients associated with Pb-Zn mineralization in the Nanisivik region. Alternatively, Geldsetzer (1973b) suggested that dolomitization of the Society Cliffs Formation occurred with the eastward migration of either meteoric waters or meteoric-derived brines through the platform during uplift, exposure, and karsting of the western basin.

It is unlikely that large-scale convection of either marine or meteoric fluids can account for the alteration of Society Cliffs carbonates. In the case of meteoric fluid migration, extensive preservation of sedimentary gypsum on Bylot Island and in the eastern Borden Basin precludes late-stage alteration by fluids not saturated with respect to gypsum. Meteoric waters would actively promote dissolution of gypsum within the formation and meteoric-derived brines, saturated from gypsum dissolution (i.e. high Ca^{2+}, low CO_3^{2-}), would be incapable of dolomitization. In the case of convecting marine fluids, although lateral

TABLE 2.—ISOTOPIC AND ELEMENTAL RESULTS, INNER RAMP FACIES

Sample	Environ. & phase[a]	Height (m)	δ13C	δ18O[b]	Mg/Ca	Sr/Ca	Fe	Mn	Sr
			(‰PDB)				(ppm)		
WB-1	□	186	3.7	−3.3	0.55	0.00027	824	104	43
WB-2	○	199	3.5	−4.5	0.54	0.00034	950	95	56
WB-3	□	208	3.3	−2.4	0.55	0.00038	1039	67	64
WB-4	▽	215	2.8	−2.4	0.57	0.00038	1000	62	67
WB-5	△	223	2.6	−1.0	0.59	0.00021	1125	192	38
WB-6	○	232	3.0	−4.6	0.55	0.00026	1042	170	47
WB-8	○	267	3.7	−5.0	0.56	0.00026	885	115	41
WB-9	□	278	2.9	−3.8	0.57	0.00018	1093	244	31
WB-10	▽	303	2.7	−2.4	0.53	0.00030	938	219	49
WB-11	⊙	321	2.4	−3.3	0.54	0.00027	1081	241	48
WB-12a	▽	331	2.6	−3.5	0.55	0.00022	667	179	26
WB-12b	□	331	2.7	−3.4	0.58	0.00021	1243	461	61
WB-13	□	344	2.0	−3.1	0.58	0.00013	1226	277	35
WB-14	△	345	2.7	−0.7	0.56	0.00023	1143	339	39
WB-15	△	372	2.9	−1.8	0.58	0.00038	1288	140	69
WB-16	▽	403	2.9	−2.8	0.58	0.00037	1417	545	66
WB-17	□	422	3.0	−3.0	0.57	0.00030	3250	471	50
TY-20245	chert (●)	—	—	−2.6	—	—	—	—	—
WB-18034	chert ( )	—	—	−1.9	—	—	—	—	—
WB-8675	chert (gypsum)	—	—	−1.0	—	—	—	—	—
WB-5	chert ( )	—	—	−1.0	—	—	—	—	—

[a]Samples are coded with respect to both exposed (△), interidal (□), and subtidal (○) depositional environments, as well as microsampled phases. Microsamples include mimetically replaced sea-floor precipitates (●), microparitic microbial laminae (open symbols), and micritic laminae, matrix, and intraclasts (▼).
[b]Dolomites are corrected for phosphoric acid fractionation at 90°C

TABLE 3.—SUMMARY OF ISOTOPIC RESULTS

	Mid-Ramp mean compositions		Inner Ramp mean compositions	n	‰Δ
Isotopic Data (‰PDB)					
δ12C all	3.5 ± 0.3	41	2.9 ± 0.4	17	0.6
δ18O all	−5.2 ± 2.2	41	3.0 ± 1.2	17	2.2
δ18O sub/intertidal	−6.3 ± 2.0	26	−3.4 ± 0.8	14	2.9
δ18O subtidal	−7.7 ± 1.9	13	−4.4 ± 0.7	4	3.3
δ18O subtidal	−7.7 ± 1.9	13	−4.4 ± 0.7	4	3.3
δ18O intertidal	−4.9 ± 0.8	13	−3.0 ± 0.5	10	1.9
δ18O exposed	−3.1 ± 0.6	15	−1.2 ± 0.6	3	1.9
δ18O chert (‰ PDB)	—		−1.6 ± 0.7	4	
(‰ SMOW)			29.2 ± 0.7		

cooling of convective fluids in regions distant from the thermal source could result in distinctly heavier isotopic values in the inner ramp, it cannot account for the stratigraphic variability of observed δ18O.

The degree of alteration associated with post-depositional fluid flow reflects the extent of water-rock interaction (Banner and Hanson, 1990). Because the extent of water-rock interaction is not strongly affected by porosity (between 0–75% porosity; Banner and Hanson, 1990), and because both water and carbonate rock reservoirs contain a similar mole fraction of oxygen, complete re-equilibration and homogenization of oxygen isotopic values occurs at low water-rock ratios. Dolomitization, which requires relatively high water-rock ratios in order to supply adequate Mg, should therefore result in complete re-equilibration of oxygen isotopic signatures. That isotopic compositions within the Society Cliffs Formation appear to reflect primary depositional variation supports an interpretation of early diagenetic dolomitization, occurring within primary depositional environments, via interaction with near-coeval seawater or seawater-derived fluids.

Early Dolomitization

If dolomitization occurred during early diagenesis of the Society Cliffs Formation, diagnostic alteration trends, calculated via iterative mass balances to simulate the rates at which various geochemical systems are altered during carbonate recrystallization processes (Banner et al., 1988; Banner and Hanson, 1990), can help constrain the composition of diagenetic fluids. Sr/Ca elemental ratios and Mn concentrations provide a sensitive indication of diagenesis because, during exchange with diagenetic fluids, Mn is commonly incorporated into sedimentary carbonates while Sr is flushed from the carbonate lattice (Brand and Veizer, 1980; Veizer, 1983). Interaction of a marine carbonate with fresh, meteoric, mixed waters, or seawater-derived evaporitic brines will therefore result in a rapid drop in Sr/Ca followed by an increase in Mn abundance (Arrow A, Fig. 7).

Strontium concentrations in Society Cliffs dolostones range from 24 to 143 ppm and Sr/Ca ratios are, with the exception of a single sample, less than 0.5×10^{-3}; ratios well below that of modern seawater (0.86×10^{-2}). The low ratios preserved in Society Cliffs dolostones are ambiguous and might indicate that dolomitization occurred in the presence of a Sr-depleted fluid (e.g. fresh or meteoric waters), that Sr was preferentially excluded from the dolomite phase during dissolution-reprecipitation reactions (Pierson, 1981; Sathyanarayan et al., 1987), or that Sr/Ca ratios of the initial carbonate were low. Low initial Sr/Ca ratios may have resulted from increased temperature of precipitation (Kinsman and Holland, 1969), rapid precipitation rate (Carpenter et al., 1991; DeViliers et al., 1994), or precipitation from marine waters depleted in Sr/Ca via increased Ca input from active spreading ridges (Graham et al., 1982).

Mn abundances in mid-ramp dolostones are tightly clustered between 21 and 147 ppm (Fig. 7), indicating little interaction with Mn-rich diagenetic fluids. That mid-ramp exposed dolo-

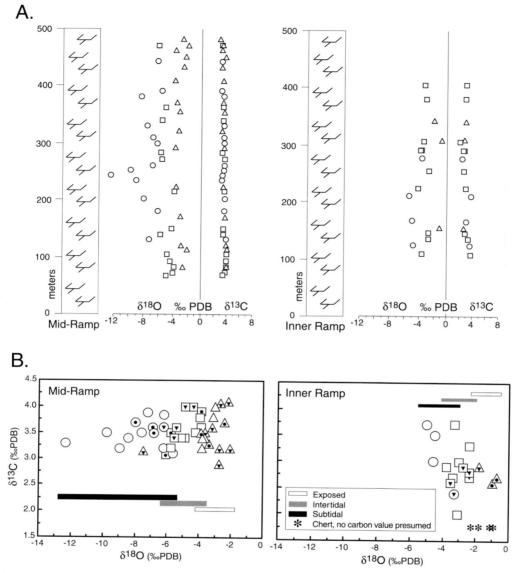

FIG. 6.—Society Cliffs Formation isotopic data. A) Stratigraphic distribution of isotopic data for mid-ramp and inner-ramp measured sections. Samples are assigned to depositional facies on the basis of lithology and stratigraphic position within 10–50 m shoaling cycles. B) δ¹³C vs δ¹⁸O for the Society Cliffs Formation. Whereas individual microdrilled components reveal no isotopic pattern, subtidal, intertidal, and exposed depositional environments record distinct oxygen-isotope compositions. Subaerially exposed facies are 2–3‰ heavier than mean subtidal and intertidal facies, and inner ramp facies are 2–3‰ heavier than those in equivalent mid-ramp facies. See Table 1 for symbol legend.

stones, which preserved enriched ¹⁸O values, have relatively low Mn concentrations suggests either that dolomitization occurred under very low water-rock ratios (i.e. effectively isolated from ambient diagenetic pore fluids), or that dolomitization originated from dominantly oxic marine waters. In contrast, inner ramp dolostones show Mn enrichment ranging from 62 to 545 ppm. Elevated Mn concentration may result from either interaction with non-marine (reducing) dolomitizing fluids or *in situ* microbial Mn reduction of organic matter (Hendry, 1993) within inner ramp environments; a possibility supported by petrographic evidence that inner ramp carbonate precipitation was intimately linked to degrading cyanobacterial mats.

Although Sr/Ca ratios and Mn abundances provide ambiguous information regarding the composition of diagenetic fluids, evaluation of oxygen isotopic trends and ⁸⁷Sr/⁸⁶Sr ratios gives additional constraints. When Mn concentration is compared to oxygen isotopic composition, a pattern contrary to that expected from fresh, meteoric, or mixed-water diagenesis emerges. Dolomitic stabilization via fresh, meteoric, or mixed-water diagenesis should result in a rapid decrease in oxygen isotopic composition followed by increasing Mn as diagenesis progresses (Arrow A, Fig. 8), providing reducing conditions and an available source for Mn. Society Cliffs data clearly do not fall along this trend. Rather, the observed trend of oxygen iso-

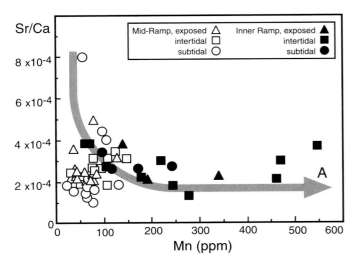

FIG. 7.—Sr/Ca vs. Mn elemental ratios. All Society Cliffs dolostones show low Sr/Ca ratios. Mid-ramp facies contain only low concentrations of Mn, whereas some inner-ramp facies are significantly enriched. Arrow indicates direction of alteration during increased interaction with nonmarine fluids (fresh, meteoric, mixed-water, or evaporitic brines).

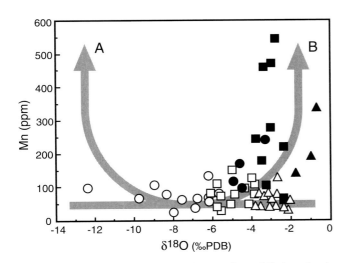

FIG. 8.—Mn vs. $\delta^{18}O$. Society Cliffs dolostones do not fall along the alteration trend (arrow A) indicating increased interaction with fresh, meteoric, or mixed-waters. Data are better explained by an initial isotopically light phase interacting with increasingly evaporitic brines (Arrow B). See Figure 9 for legend.

topic data is best explained by dolomitic stabilization via interaction with an evaporative brine (Arrow B, Figure 8). Microbial reduction of Mn in inner ramp facies during brine formation would supply Mn necessary for the observed concentrations. Overall depletion of oxygen isotopic compositions must then reflect a carbonate precursor that precipitated (1) from an isotopically depleted initial fluid, (2) from a range of fluid compositions, or (3) at elevated temperatures.

A marine composition of the initial fluid is supported by the $^{87}Sr/^{86}Sr$ ratios of Bylot Supergroup limestones and dolostones. Assuming a modern marine isotopic values of $-1‰$ and fresh and/or meteoric values of $-10‰$, over 50% of the solution

must be contributed from non-marine sources to produce an isotopic composition of $-6.3‰$ (mean value of sub/intertidal mid-ramp facies). Such a large contribution from non-marine waters would likely supply elevated $^{87}Sr/^{86}Sr$ ratios resulting from the geochemical alteration of crustal materials (Derry *et al.*, 1992). A single analysis of Society Cliffs dolostone reveals a $^{87}Sr/^{86}Sr$ ratios of 0.706270 (Rb/Sr = 2.2×10^{-3}). Whereas this value is slightly more radiogenic than those obtained from overlying shelf and slope limestones (0.70518, Rb/Sr = 1.2×10^{-5}; 0.70549, Rb/Sr = 2.4×10^{-4}; 0.70564, Rb/Sr = 3.7×10^{-4}; Kah, unpublished data), these values correspond closely to the non-radiogenic strontium signatures that appear to characterize Mesoproterozoic oceans (Hall and Veizer, 1996; Semikhatov *et al.*, 1998; J. Bartley, pers. comm., 1998) and suggest that Society Cliffs carbonate rocks preserve dominantly marine compositions.

Estimation of Primary Marine Carbonate Compositions

Isotopic and trace element data suggest that Society Cliffs dolostones precipitated dominantly from marine and evaporatively modified marine waters. The oxygen isotopic composition of fractures and pore fillings associated with Pb-Zn mineralization ($-12‰$ to $-14‰$; Ghazban *et al.*, 1992) provides a possible composition of a late-stage diagenetic end member. The poor petrographic preservation and isotopically light values ($-6.8‰$ and $-12.4‰$) of several mid-ramp samples (cf. Table 1) suggest secondary alteration by these late-diagenetic fluids. Excluding these samples, primary marine dolostone compositions are best estimated to be $-6.4‰$, the average composition of petrographically well preserved mid-ramp, subtidal samples. If equilibrium fractionation factors between limestone and dolomite are taken to be 3–4‰ (Land, 1980), primary marine limestone compositions would be between $-9.4‰$ and $-10.4‰$. These values correspond closely to estimates of $-9.75‰$ for Paleoproterozoic limestones (Burdett *et al.*, 1980), yet are lighter than estimates of $-6.1‰$ for limestones of the Mesoproterozoic Helena Formation (Frank and Lyons, this volume). Approximately 3‰ variation between best-estimates from the Society Cliffs and Helena formations may reflect either an underestimation of Society Cliffs values, or environmental restriction in the upper Helena (Frank *et al.*, 1997) and subsequent overestimation of primary (non-restricted) marine compositions (Frank and Lyons, this volume).

Evaluation of Depositional Temperatures

Given an estimate of $-6.4‰$ for primary marine dolostone values, isotopically light values must reflect either seawater significantly depleted from present marine compositions, or carbonate precipitation at elevated temperatures. The expression for dolomite fractionation (Sheppard and Schwartz, 1970) is problematic in that it corresponds to a 5–7‰ enrichment of ^{18}O in dolomite over calcite at surface temperatures, whereas empirical evidence suggests a wide range (1.5–7‰) of possible enrichment factor (Humphrey, 1998).

Figure 9 has been modified from Sheppard and Schwarcz (1970) to reflect an average 3–4‰ enrichment (Land, 1980) of the dolomite phase over coeval calcite. This value is comparable to the equilibrium enrichment of silica over limestone at low temperatures (Knauth and Epstein, 1976) and can therefore be used for presentation of both chert and dolomite data. Esti-

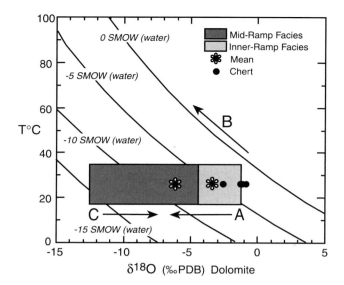

FIG. 9.—Equilibrium diagram for dolomite and chert precipitation, constructed from empirically derived calcite equilibrium equations (Friedman et al., 1977) shifted 3–4‰ heavier to account for calcite–dolomite fractionation. Variation in oxygen-isotope composition can result from dilution of formation waters and/or postdepositional exchange with isotopically depleted waters (A), increasing temperature of precipitation and/or equilibration (B), or evaporative enrichment of isotopically light formation waters (C). If precipitated from marine waters ($\delta^{18}O$ = 0‰ SMOW), estimated marine carbonate components ($\delta^{18}O$ = −6.4‰ PDB) would require depositional temperatures >65°C. Alternatively, precipitation at temperatures <35°C would require formation waters isotopically depleted with respect to ^{18}O ($\delta^{18}O$ = −5‰ to −7‰ SMOW).

mated dolomite compositions of −6.4‰ would require precipitation temperatures in excess of 65°C if marine waters were of similar composition to today's oceans (0‰SMOW; Fig. 9). Chert data, which are commonly thought to be less susceptible to postdepositional alteration, would only require temperatures near 40°C. However, evaporite fabrics preserved in this chert, however, require deposition under evaporatively modified seawater. Correction for isotopic enrichment associated with evaporation would imply significantly higher temperatures.

Isotopically depleted chert and dolomite values preserved in Precambrian rocks have been used to suggest that Proterozoic oceans were anomalously warm (Knauth and Epstein, 1976). Although upper temperature limits for prokaryotic photoautotrophs (72–74°C; Bauld and Brock, 1973) are above the limit defined above (65°C), only a handful of cyanobacterial species can metabolize and reproduce efficiently at these temperatures. Nowhere at elevated temperatures is a large diversity of cyanobacteria observed in modern environments. It therefore seems unlikely that the Society Cliffs Formation, which is characterized throughout by cyanobacterial populations containing more than 30 morphospecies (Hofmann and Jackson, 1991), is representative of elevated depositional temperatures.

A final constraint on depositional temperatures in the Society Cliffs formation comes from the occurrence of a probable multicellular, eukaryotic red alga preserved in early diagenetic chert (Kah and Knoll, 1996). Similar alga have been described from laterally equivalent Hunting (Butterfield et al., 1990) and Narssârssuk (Enzien, 1990) formations and have been ascribed to the extant genus *Bangia* (Butterfield et al., 1990). Modern *Ban-*

gia is one of the most environmentally tolerant genera of the red algae (Dawson, 1966). It occurs predominantly in upper intertidal environments, from boreal latitudes to the tropics, where its increasing importance in the algal community reflects wide salinity and temperature tolerances. Although modern *Bangia* can survive up to several days desiccated in air temperatures ~40°C, submergence for 24 hours in water temperatures of 35°C is lethal (Dawson, 1966). Bangiophytic red alga preserved in the Society Cliffs Formation can therefore tentatively constrain surface seawater temperatures to <35°C; temperatures similar to those recorded in the modern Persian Gulf (Emery, 1956).

ESTIMATED COMPOSITION OF MESOPROTEROZOIC SEAWATER

If estimates of maximum surface water temperature (~35°C) and composition of primary marine carbonate phases ($\delta^{18}O$ ~ −6.4‰) are correct, Society Cliffs carbonates would have had to precipitate in equilibrium with marine waters significantly depleted (−5‰ to −7‰SMOW; Fig. 9) with respect to modern seawater. These values are inconsistent with ophiolite data that suggests the isotopic composition of marine waters has remained buffered to near 0‰ throughout Earth history (Muehlenbachs and Clayton, 1976; Muehlenbachs, 1986). These estimates are, however, comparable to those inferred from a wide suite of well-constrained Phanerozoic (Lohmann and Walker, 1989; Carpenter et al., 1991; Veizer et al., 1997) and Proterozoic (Burdett et al., 1990; Frank and Lyons, this volume) carbonates. The origin of this apparent divergence between sedimentary and igneous datasets is unresolved, but may include (1) imbalances in alteration estimates of oceanic and continental crust (Barret and Friedrichsen, 1989; Walker and Lohmann, 1989), (2) alkalinity effects on carbonate isotopic composition (Spero et al., 1997), or compositional decoupling of deep oceans from surface waters (via saline circulation; Railsback, 1990) or epeiric seas (via long-term crustal interaction; Holmden and Muehlenbachs, 1998).

IMPLICATIONS FOR EARLY DIAGENESIS

Despite ambiguity regarding the genesis of isotopically light seawater, isotopic variation recorded in the Society Cliffs Formation has several implications for the environment, timing, and mechanism of early diagenesis. The facies dependency of isotopic values observed in the Society Cliffs Formation necessitates that careful environmental, as well as diagenetic studies accompany interpretation of the sedimentary record of oxygen isotopes. Isotopic samples that retain the most enriched ^{18}O abundances cannot *a priori* be presumed to be "least-altered" with respect to their oxygen isotopes, rather, they may reflect primary variation in water composition. As a corollary, the relatively enriched isotopic values typically preserved in Proterozoic early diagenetic cherts (this study; Knauth and Epstein, 1976; Kenny and Knauth, 1992), rather than recording more accurate seawater values, may result from silica precipitation under primarily evaporitic environmental conditions (Maliva et al., 1989). Furthermore, preservation of primary (depositional) isotopic differences in water composition within dolomitic lithologies requires either that Society Cliffs carbonates were dolomitized without isotopic exchange of oxygen (i.e. closed system behavior where geochemical characteristics of the dolomite are inherited from precursor limestone), or that dolomitization was near-penecontemporaneous and proceeded via interaction with both seawater and evaporatively modified seawater.

Two distinct environments of dolomitization must be accounted for in the Society Cliffs Formation: (1) dissolution and dolomitization of subaerially exposed intervals containing the most ^{18}O enriched isotopic values, and (2) dolomitization of Society Cliffs carbonates which retain isotopic values reflecting their depositional environment. The pattern of preserved isotopic variation may help constrain mechanisms of dolomitization. Significantly enriched $\delta^{18}O$ values within zones of subaerial exposure are consistent with dolomitization driven by evaporative processes. Evaporitic pumping mechanisms (Hsu and Siegenthaler, 1969) require an upward movement of marine-derived groundwater to replace pore fluids lost through evaporation and should result in isotopic enrichment of local ground waters through evaporation. Although criticized as inefficient (Machel and Mountjoy, 1986), evaporative pumping may have been a powerful hydrologic effect within laterally extensive environments thought to have been subject to subaerial exposure on many ancient shelves (McKenzie, 1991).

Evaporative pumping, however, cannot account for dolomitization of subtidal and intertidal facies. Sedimentological and geochemical evidence of episodic, platform-wide hypersalinity suggests that reflux of hypersaline brines (Adams and Rhodes, 1960) may be a plausible mechanism for circulation of dolomitizing fluids. However, density driven brines, formed during basin restriction, should migrate sub-vertically through sedimentary strata and affect underlying facies. That refluxing brines did not impart enriched oxygen isotopic signatures on underlying intertidal and subtidal strata implies either (1) that refluxing brines were not the dolomitizing agent, or (2) that dolomitic stabilization may have been near completion at the time of brine reflux. Alternative models calling for active circulation of dolomitizing fluids (i.e. a hydrologic pump; Hardie, 1987 for review) can similarly be called into question by the observed stratigraphic and paleogeographic pattern of isotopic variation.

Reconciliation of isotopic data requires dolomitization to have been penecontemporaneous, originating from coeval marine and evaporative marine waters, and to have proceeded at or near the sediment-water interface. Under such restrictions, local hydrologic conditions may have played an important role in dolomitization. When broad expanses of platform are cut off from freely circulating marine waters, the exchange of dissolved species between freely circulating marine waters and restricted waters is greatly reduced. Both diffusional processes at air-water and/or sediment-water interfaces (i.e. evaporation, microbial growth and degradation) and processes occurring within the water column (i.e. carbonate precipitation) will become increasingly important in determining the chemical composition of the local water column (Fig. 10). The aerial extent of inner ramp environments therefore suggests that the Society Cliffs Formation, as a whole, should have had a high dolomitizing potential. Extensive evaporation in inner ramp regions led to deposition of marine sulfates, and abundant carbonate was precipitated as seafloor precipitates, microspar within microbial mats, oolitic grains, and micrite. Evaporation and carbonate precipitation would have acted in concert to raise Mg/

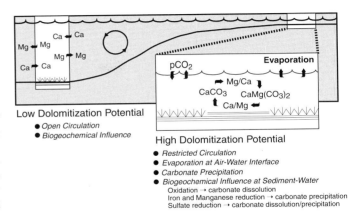

Fig. 10.—Dolomitizing potential of platform carbonates. In a shallow, restricted water column, restricted circulation, evaporation, carbonate ($\pm$gypsum) precipitation, and biogeochemical reactions lead to greater dolomitizing potential. In a deeper, less-restricted water column, biogeochemical influences within benthic microbial mats may become increasingly important for early dolomitization to occur.

Ca ratios within the water column well above primary seawater values and into a zone conducive to dolomite formation. Microbial processes acting at the sediment-water interface may have also acted to modify pore-waters and further facilitate dolomite precipitation. Microbial mats may have provided active nucleation sites and, during degradation, may have released Mg into local pore waters (Ferris et al., 1989). Anoxic heterotrophic bacteria (Fe, Mn, and S reducers) within degrading mats may have further promoted dolomitization by increasing local alkalinity (Hendry, 1993) or by reducing potential kinetic inhibitors to dolomitization (Vasconcelos and McKenzie, 1997).

In contrast to shallow marine environments, dolomitizing potential should have been significantly lower in deeper/open-water settings. In these environments, dolomite-promoting effects of evaporation and/or carbonate precipitation will essentially be negated by volumetric considerations or the active dispersal of ions with increased circulation. Microbial activity, however, may still be important in influencing pore waters within organic-rich substrates (e.g. organogenic dolomite formation). In many ancient successions, subtidal carbonates commonly remain limestone even when supratidal sediments are dolomitized (e.g. Knoll and Swett, 1990; Montañez and Read, 1992; Mutti and Simo, 1994; Sherman et al., this volume). In the Society Cliffs Formation, lower dolomitization potential of mid-ramp environments may be reflected in the geochemical overprinting of subtidal carbonates by secondary diagenetic events. The relative stability of dolomite suggests samples with initially incomplete dolomitization may have been more susceptible to secondary alteration events.

CONCLUSIONS

The Society Cliffs Formation retains a pattern of oxygen isotopic variation that reflects carbonate deposition and early diagenesis in a variety of marine to evaporitic marine conditions. Society Cliffs samples show little evidence for post-depositional alteration or precipitation at elevated temperatures, and isotopic values may reflect equilibrium precipitation from isotopically light marine waters. Reasonable estimates for depositional temperature ($<35°C$) and primary composition of marine phases (dolomite: $-6.4‰$, calcite: $-9.4‰$ to $-10.4‰$) require seawater values significantly depleted ($-5‰$ to $-7‰$) over modern marine values. These estimates are consistent with those from little-altered shallow-marine sediments in Proterozoic and early Paleozoic successions worldwide, and imply that ancient surface oceans may have been isotopically depleted with respect to modern oceans. Although the origin of this apparent isotopic depletion is currently unresolved, the pattern of isotopic variation recorded in the Society Cliffs Formation has several broad implications for the environment, timing, and mechanisms of early diagenesis.

First, the range of isotopic values observed in the Society Cliffs Formation emphasizes the necessity for careful environmental, as well as diagenetic, studies when evaluating the sedimentary record of oxygen isotopes. Isotopic samples that retain the most enriched isotopic abundances cannot *a priori* be presumed to be "least-altered"; rather, they may reflect primary variation in water compositions. Second, the pattern of isotopic variation recorded in the Society Cliffs Formation implies that stabilization of oxygen isotopic compositions occurred during dolomitization of Society Cliffs sediments, and that dolomitization occurred within inferred primary depositional environments. Whereas evaporative pumping of seawater is consistent with the sedimentology, fabric preservation, and isotopic signatures within exposed cycle caps, dolomitization of intertidal and subtidal facies is more consistent with penecontemporaneous, diffusion-driven dolomitization in which geochemical modification of surface and shallow subsurface pore waters resulted in conditions favorable to dolomite formation. Because exact mechanisms of dolomitization are difficult to determine, an approach which identifies a variety of depositional conditions that act in concert can help to define environments with high dolomitization potential. Such an approach is sensitive to 1) the hydrologic environment associated with specific platform geometries, 2) the dynamics of the carbonate factory, and 3) the structure of benthic biological communities, and may provide a means for evaluating both spatial and temporal patterns of early diagenetic dolomitization.

ACKNOWLEDGMENTS

Laboratory work supported in part by grants from NASA (to A.H. Knoll) and the National Geographic Society (Kah). Field logistical support provided by the Polar Continental Shelf Project, Natural Resources Canada. Thanks to J. Sullivan for field assistance and M. Emmons, B. McDonough, J. Kaufman, J. Bartley, and Geochron Laboratories for analytical assistance. This manuscript benefited from discussions with A. Knoll, J. Bartley, J. Kaufman, T. Lyons, T. Frank, and B. Foucke; as well as comments and reviews from N. James, B. Meyers, B. Pratt, and M. Coniglio.

REFERENCES

ADAMS, J. E., AND RHODES, M. L., 1960, Dolomitization by seepage refluxion: AAPG Bulletin, v. 44, p. 1912–1921.

ANDERSON, T. F., AND ARTHUR, M. A., 1983, Stable isotopes of oxygen and carbon and their application to sedimentologic and environmental problems, *in* Stable Isotopes in Sedimentary Geology: Tulsa, OK, SEPM Short Course Notes, v. 10, p. 1–151.

BANNER, J. L., HANSON, G. N., AND MEYERS, W. J., 1988, Water-rock interaction history of regionally extensive dolomites of the Burlington-Keokuk Formation (Mississippian): isotopic evidence, *in* Shukla, V., and Baker, P., eds., Sedimentology and Geochemistry of Dolostones: SEPM Special Publication, v. 43, p. 97–114.

BANNER, J. L., AND HANSON, G. N., 1990, Calculation of simultaneous isotopic and trace element variations during water-rock interaction with applications to carbonate diagenesis: Geochimica et Cosmochimica Acta, v. 54, p. 3123–3137.

BARRETT, T. J., AND FRIEDRICHSEN, H., 1989, Stable isotopic compositions of atypical ophiolite rocks from east Liguria, Italy: Chemical Geology, v. 80, p. 71–84.

BARTLEY, J. K., 1996, Actualistic taphonomy of cyanobacteria; implications for the Precambrian fossil record: Palaios, v. 11, p. 571–586.

BAULD, J., AND BROCK, T. D., 1973, Ecological studies of *Chloroflexus*, a gliding photosynthetic bacterium: Archiv für Mikrobiologie, v. 92, p. 267–284.

BEALES, F. W., AND HARDY, J. L., 1980, Criteria for the recognition of diverse dolomite types with an emphasis on studies on host rocks for Mississippi Valley-type ore deposits, *in* Zenger, D. H., Dunham, J. B. and Ethington, R. L., eds., Concepts and Models of Dolomitization: Tulsa, Oklahoma, SEPM Special Publication, v. 28, p. 87–110.

BRAND, U., AND VEIZER, J., 1980, Chemical diagenesis of a multicomponent carbonate system—1) Trace elements: Journel of Sedimentary Petrology, v. 50, p. 1219–1236.

BURDETT, J. W., GROTZINGER, J. P., AND ARTHUR, M. A., 1990, Did major changes in the stable isotopic composition of Proterozoic seawater occur?: Geology, v. 18, p. 227–230.

BUTTERFIELD, N. J., KNOLL, A. H., AND SWETT, K., 1990, A bangiophyte red alga from the Proterozoic of Arctic Canada: Science, v. 250, p. 104–107.

CARPENTER, S. J., LOHMANN, K. C., HOLDEN, P., WALTER, L. M., HUSTON, T. J., AND HALLIDAY, A. N., 1991, $\delta^{18}O$ values, $^{87}Sr/^{86}Sr$ and Sr/Mg ratios of Late Devonian marine calcite: Implications for the composition of ancient seawater: Geochemica et Cosmochimica Acta, v. 55, p. 1991–2010.

CHAFETZ, H. S., AND BUCZYNSKI, C., 1992, Bacterially induced lithification of microbial mats: Palaios, v. 7, p. 277–293.

CLAYTON, R. H., AND THORPE, L., 1982, Geology of the Nanisivik zinc-lead deposit: Geological Association of Canada Special Paper, v. 25, p. 739–758.

DAWSON, E. Y., 1966, Marine Botany: New York, Holt Rinehart and Winston, Inc., 371 p.

DE VILIERS, S., SHEN, G. T., AND NELSON, B. K., 1994, The Sr/Ca-temperature relationship in corraline aragonite; influence of variability in Sr/Caseawater and skeletal growth parameters: Geochimica et Cosmochimica Acta, v. 58, p. 197–208.

DEGENS, E. T., AND EPSTEIN, S., 1962, Relationship between O^{18}/O^{16} ratios in coexisting carbonates, cherts, and diatomites: Americal Association of Petroleum Geologists Bulletin, v. 46, p. 534–542.

DERRY, L. A., KAUFMAN, A. J., AND JACOBSEN, S. B., 1992, Sedimentary cycling and environmental change in the late Proterozoic: evidence from stable and radiogenic isotopes: Geochimica et Cosmochimica Acta, v. 56, p. 1317–1329.

EMERY, K. O., 1956, Sediments and water of the Persian Gulf: AAPG Bulletin, v. 40, p. 2354–2383.

ENZIEN, M. V., 1990, Cyanobacteria or Rhodophyta? Interpretation of a Precambrian microfossil: BioSystems, v. 24, p. 245–251.

FAHRIG, W. F., CHRISTIE, K. W., AND JONES, D. L., 1981, Paleomagnetism of the Bylot Basins: evidence for Mackenzie continental tensional tectonics, in Campbell, F. H. A., ed., Proterozoic Basins of Canada: Geological Survey of Canada, Paper 81-10, p. 303–312.

FERRIS, F. G., SHOTYK, W., AND FYFE, W. S., 1989, Mineral formation and decomposition by microorganisms, *in* Beveridge, T.J. and Doyle, R. J., eds., Metal ions and bacteria: Guelph, Ontario, University of Guelph, p. 413–441.

FRANK, T. D., LYONS, T. W., AND LOHMANN, K. C., 1997, Isotopic evidence for the paleoenvironmental evolution of the Mesoproterozoic Helena Formation, Belt Supergroup, Montana: Geochimica et Cosmochimica Acta, v. 61, p. 5023–5041.

FRANK, T. D., AND LYONS, T. W., The integrity of $\delta^{18}O$ records in Precambrian carbonates: a Mesoproterozoic case study, *this volume*.

FRIEDMAN, L., O'NEILL, J. R., AND FLEISHER, M., 1977, Compilation of stable isotope fractionation factors of geochemical interest: U.S. Geological Survey, Professional Paper 440-KK, p. 1–12.

GAT, J. R., AND BOWSER, C., 1991, The heavy isotope enrichment of water in coupled evaporative systems: Geochemical Society, Special Publication 3, p. 159–168.

GELDSETZER, H., 1973a, The tectono-sedimentary development of an algal-dominated Helikian succession on Northern Baffin Island, N.W.T.: Geological Association of Canada, Memoir, v. 19, p. 99–126.

GELDSETZER, H., 1973b, Syngenetic dolomitization and sulfide mineralization, *in* Amstutz, G. C. and Bernard, A. J., eds., Ores in Sediments: New York, Springer Verlag, p. 115–127.

GHAZBAN, F., SCHWARCZ, H. P., AND FORD, D. C., 1992, Multistage dolomitization in the Society Cliffs Formation, northern Baffin Island, Northwest Territories, Canada: Canadian Journal of Earth Sciences, v. 29, p. 1459–1473.

GRAHAM, D. W., BENDER, M. L., WILLIAMS, D. F., AND KEIGHWIN, L. D., 1982, Strontium to calcium ratios in Cenozoic planktonic foraminifera: Geochimica et Cosmochimica Acta, v. 46, p. 1281–1292.

GREGORY, R. T., 1991, Oxygen isotope history of seawater revisited: timescales for boundary event changes in the oxygen isotope composition of seawater: The Geochemical Society Special Publication, v. 3, p. 65–76.

HALL, S. M., AND VEIZER, J., 1996, Geochemistry of Precambrian Carbonates: VII. Belt Supergroup, Montana and Idaho, USA: Geochimica et Cosmochimica Acta, v. 60, p. 667–677.

HARDIE, L. A., 1987, Perspectives on dolomitization: a critical view of some current views: Journal of Sedimentary Petrology, v. 57, p. 166–183.

HEAMAN, L. M., LECHEMINANT, A. N., AND RAINBIRD, R. H., 1992, Nature and timing of Franklin igneous events, Canada: Implications for a late Proterozoic mantle plume and the break-up of Laurentia: Earth and Planetary Science Letters, v. 109, p. 117–131.

HENDRY, J. P., 1993, Calcite cementation during bacterial manganese, iron, and sulphate reduction in Jurassic shallow marine carbonates: Sedimentology, v. 40, p. 87–106.

HOFMANN, H. J., AND JACKSON, G. D., 1991, Shelf-facies microfossils from the Uluksan Group (Proterozoic Bylot Supergroup), Baffin Island, Canada: Journal of Paleontology, v. 65, p. 361–382.

HOFMANN, H. J., AND JACKSON, G. D., 1994, Shale-facies microfossils from the Proterozoic Bylot Supergroup, Baffin Island, Canada: Paleontological Society Memoir, v. 37, p. 1–39.

HOLMDEN, C., CREASER, R. A., MUEHLENBACHS, K., LESLIE, S. A., AND BERGSTROM, S. M., 1998, Isotopic evidence for geochemical decoupling between ancient epeiric seas and bordering oceans; implications for secular curves: Geology, v. 26, p. 567–570.

HORODYSKI, R. J., BLOESER, B., AND VONDER HAAR, S., 1977, Laminated algal mats from a coastal lagoon, Laguna Mormona, Baja California, Mexico: Journal of Sedimentary Petrology, v. 47, p. 680–696.

HSÜ, K. J., AND SIEGENTHALER, C., 1969, Preliminary experiments on hydrodynamic movements induced by evaporation and their bearing on the dolomite problem: Sedimentology, v. 12, p. 11–25.

HUDSON, J. D., AND ANDERSON, T. F., 1989, Ocean temperatures and isotopic compositions through time: Transactions of the Royal Society of Edinburgh, v. 80, p. 183–192.

HUMPHREY, J. D., 1998, Applicaiton of dolomite oxygen isotope fractionation to the problems of dolomitization: Geological Society of America, Abstracts with Programs, v. 30, p. A-196.

IANNELLI, T. R., 1979, Stratigraphy and depositional history of some Upper Proterozoic sedimentary rocks on Northwestern Baffin Island, District of Franklin: Geological Survey of Canada, Paper 79-1A, p. 45–56.

JACKSON, G. D., DAVIDSON, A., AND MORGAN, W. C., 1975, Geology of the Pond Inlet map-area, Baffin Island, District of Franklin: Geological survey of Canada, Paper 74-25, p. 1–33.

JACKSON, G. D., IANNELLI, T. R., NARBONNE, G. M., AND WALLACE, P. J., 1978, Upper Proterozoic sedimentary and volcanic rocks of northwestern Baffin Island: Geological Survey of Canada, Paper 78-14, p. 1–15.

JACKSON, G. D., IANELLI, T. R., AND TILLEY, B. J., 1980, Rift related Late Proterozoic sedimentation and volcanism on North Baffin and Bylot Islands: Geological survey of Canada, Paper 80-1A, p. 319–328.

JACKSON, G. D., AND CUMMING, L. M., 1981, Evaporites and folding in the Neohelikian Society Cliffs Formation, Northeastern Bylot Island, Arctic Canada: Geological Survey of Canada, Paper 81-1C, p. 35–44.

JACKSON, G. D., AND IANNELLI, T. R., 1981, Rift-related cyclic sedimentation in the Neohelikian Borden Basin, northern Baffin Island: Geological Survey of Canada, Paper 81-10, p. 269–302.

JAVOR, B. J., 1983, Planktonic standing crop and nutrients in a saltern ecosystem: Limnology and Oceanography, v. 28, p. 153–159.

KAH, L. C., AND KNOLL, A. H., 1996, Microbenthic distribution in Proterozoic tidal flats: Environmental and taphonomic considerations: Geology, v. 24, p. 79–82.

KAH, L. C., SHERMAN, A. B., NARBONNE, G. M., KAUFMAN, A. J., KNOLL, A. H., AND JAMES, N. P., 1999, δ¹³C Isotope Stratigraphy of the Mesoproterozoic Bylot Supergroup, Northern Baffin Island: Implications for regional lithostratigraphic correlations: Canadian Journal of Earth Sciences, v. 36, p. 313–332.

KARHU, J., AND EPSTEIN, S., 1986, The implication of the oxygen isotope records in coexisting cherts and phosphates: Geochimica et Cosmochimica Acta, v. 50, p. 1745–1756.

KAUFMAN, A. J., HAYES, J. M., KNOLL, A. H., AND GERMS, G. J. B., 1991, Isotopic compositions of carbonates and organic carbon from upper Proterozoic successions in Namibia: stratigraphic variation and the effects of diagenesis and metamorphism: Precambrian Research, v. 49, p. 301–327.

KAUFMAN, A. J., AND KNOLL, A. H., 1995, Neoproterozoic variations in the C-isotopic composition of seawater: stratigraphic and biogeochemical implications: Precambrian Research, v. 73, p. 27–49.

KENNY, R., AND KNAUTH, L. P., 1992, Continental paleoclimates from dD and δ¹⁸O of secondary silica in paleokarst chert lags: Geology, v. 20, p. 219–222.

KINSMAN, D. J. J., 1969, The co-precipitation of cations with CaCO₃—IV. The co-precipitation of Sr²⁺ with aragonite between 16° and 96°C: Geochimica et Cosmochimica Acta, v. 33, p. 1–17.

KNAUTH, L. P., AND EPSTEIN, S., 1976, Hydrogen and oxygen isotope ratios in nodular and bedded cherts: Geochimica et Cosmochimica Acta, v. 40, p. 1095–1108.

KNAUTH, L. P., AND ROBERTS, S. K., 1991, The hydrogen and oxygen isotope history of the Silurian-Permian hydrosphere as determined by the direct measurement of fossil water, *in* Taylor, H. P., Jr., O'Neil, J. R. and Kaplan, I. R., eds., Stable Isotope Geochemistry: A Tribute to Samuel Epstein: The Geochemical Society, p. 91–104.

KNIGHT, R. D., AND JACKSON, G. D., 1994, Sedimentology and Stratigraphy of the Mesoproterozoic Elwin Subgroup (Aqigilik and Sinasiuvik Formations), uppermost Bylot Supergroup, Borden Rift Basin, northern Baffin Island: Geological Survey of Canada, Bulletin 455, p. 1–43.

KNOLL, A. H., AND SWETT, K., 1990, Carbonate deposition during the late Proterozoic era: an example from Spitsbergen: American Journal of Science, v. 290-A, p. 104–132.

LAND, L. S., 1980, The isotopic and trace element geochemistry of dolomite: the state of the art., *in* Zenger, D. H., Dunham, J. B. and Ethington, R. L., eds., Concepts and Models of Dolomitization: Tulsa, Oklahoma, SEPM Special Publication, v.28, p. 87–110.

LECHEMINANT, A. N., AND HEAMAN, L. M., 1989, Mackenzie igneous events, Canada: Middle Proterozoic hotspot magmatism associated with ocean opening: Earth and Planetary Science Letters, v. 96, p. 38–48.

LOHMANN, K. C., AND WALKER, J. C. G., 1989, The δ¹⁸O record of Phanerozoic Abiotic marine calcite cements: Geophysical Research Letters, v. 16, p. 319–322.

MACHEL, H. G., AND MOUNTJOY, E. W., 1986, Chemistry and environments of dolomite—a reappraisal: Earth Science Reviews, v. 23, p. 175–222.

MALIVA, R. G., KNOLL, A. H., AND SIEVER, R., 1989, Secular change in chert distribution: a reflection of evolving biological participation in the silica cycle: Palaios, v. 4, p. 519–532.

MARSHALL, J. D., 1992, Climatic and oceanographic signals from the carbonate rock record and their preservation: Geological Magazine, v. 129, p. 143–160.

MCKENZIE, J. A., 1985, Stable-isotope mapping in Messinian evaporative carbonates of central Italy: Geology, v. 13, p. 851–854.

MCKENZIE, J. A., 1991, The dolomite problem: An outstanding controversy, *in* Müller, D. W., McKenzie, J. A., and Weissert, H., eds., Controversies in Modern Geology: London, Academic Press, p. 37–54.

MCKENZIE, J. A., HSÜ, K. J., AND SCHNEIDER, J. F., 1980, Movement of subsurface waters under the sabkha, Abu Dhabi, UAE, and its relation to evaporative dolomite genesis, *in* Zenger, D. H., Dunham, J. B. and Ethington, R. L., eds., Concepts and Models of Dolomitization: Tulsa, OK, SEPM Special Publication, v. 28, p. 11–30.

MONTAÑEZ, I. P., AND READ, J. F., 1992, Eustatic control on early dolomitization of cyclic peritidal carbonates: Evidence from the Early Ordovician Upper Knox Group, Appalachians: Geological Society of America Bulletin, v. 104, p. 872–886.

MUEHLENBACHS, K., 1986, Alteration of the oceanic crust and the ¹⁸O history of seawater: Reviews in Mineralogy, v. 16, p. 425–444.

MUEHLENBACHS, K., AND CLAYTON, R.N., 1976, Oxygen isotope composition of the oceanic crust and its bearing on seawater: Journal of Geophysical Research, v. 81, p. 4365–4369.

MUTTI, M., AND SIMO, J. A., 1994, Distribution, petrography, and geochemistry of early dolomite in cyclic shelf facies, Yates Formation (Guadelupian), Capitol Reef Complex, USA, *in* Purser, B. H., Tucker, M. E. and Zenger, D. H., eds., Dolomites: Oxford, Blackwell Scientific, p. 91–107.

NARBONNE, G. M., AND JAMES, N. P., 1996, Mesoproterozoic deep-water reefs from Borden Peninsula, Arctic Canada: Sedimentology, v. 43, p. 827–848.

OLSON, R. A., 1984, Genesis of paleokarst and stratabound Zn-Pb sulfide deposits in a Proterozoic dolostone, Northern Baffin Island, Canada: Economic Geology, v. 79, p. 1056–1103.

PERRY, E. C., AND TAN, F. C., 1972, Significance of oxygen and carbon isotopic variation in Early Precambrian cherts and carbonate rocks of South Africa: Geological Society of American Bulletin, v. 83, p. 647–664.

PERYT, T. M., AND SCHOLLE, P. A., 1996, Regional setting and role of meteoric water in dolomite formation and diagenesis in an evaporite basin: studies in the Zechstein (Permian) deposits of Poland: Sedimentology, v. 43, p. 1005–1023.

PIERSON, B. J., 1981, The control of cathodoluminescence in dolomite by iron and manganese: Sedimentology, v. 28, p. 601–610.

POPP, B. N., ANDERSON, T. F., AND SANDBERG, P. A., 1986, Brachiopods as indicators of original isotopic compositions in some Paleozoic limestones: Geological Society of America Bulletin, v. 97, p. 1262–1269.

RAILSBACK, L. B., 1990, Influence of changing deep ocean circulation on the Phanerozoic oxygen isotopic record: Geochimica et Cosmochinica Acta, v. 54, p. 1501–1509.

SATHYANARAYAN, S., ARNETH, J. D., AND SCHIDLOWSKI, M., 1987, Stable isotope geochemistry of sedimentary carbonates from the Proterozoic Kaladagi, Badami and Bhima groups, Karnataka, India: Precambrian Research, v. 37, p. 147–156.

SEMIKHATOV, M. A., GOROKHOV, I. M., KUZNETSOV, A. B., MEL'NIKOV, N. N., PODKOVYROV, V. N., AND KISLOVA, I.V., 1998, The strontium isotopic composition in early Late Riphean seawater: limestones of the Lakhanda Group, the Uchur-Maya region, Siberia: Doklady Earth Sciences, v. 360, p. 488–492.

SHEPPARD, S. M. F., AND SCHWARTZ, H. P., 1970, Fractionation of carbon and oxygen isotopes and magnesium between coexisting metamorphic calcite and dolomite: Contributions to Mineralogy and Petrology, v. 26, p. 161–198.

SHERMAN, A. G., JAMES, N. P., AND NARBONNE, G. M., Sedimentology of a late Mesoproerozoic muddy carbonate ramp, northern Baffin Island, Arctic Canada, *this volume*.

SOFER, Z., AND GAT, J. R., 1975, The isotope composition of evaporating brines: Effect of the isotopic activity ratio in saline solutions: Earth and Planetary Science Letters, v. 26, p. 179–186.

SPERO, H. J., BIJMA, J., LEA, D. W., AND BEMIS, B. E., 1997, Effect of seawater carbonate concentration on foraminiferal carbon and oxygen isotopes: Nature, v. 390, p. 497–500.

THUNELL, R. C., WILLIAMS, D. F., AND HOWELL, M., 1987, Atlantic-Mediterranean water exchange during the late Neogene: Paleoceanography, v. 2, p. 661–678.

TUCKER, M. E., 1992, The Precambrian-Cambrian boundary: Seawater chemistry, ocean circulation, and nutrient supply in metazoan evolution, extinction, and biomineralization: Journal of the Geological Society of London, v. 149, p. 655–668.

VASCONCELOS, C. O., AND MCKENZIE, J. A., 1997, Microbial mediation of modern dolomite precipitation and diagenesis under anoxic conditions (Lagoa Vermelha, Rie de Janeiro, Brazil): Journal of Sedimentary Research, v. 67, p. 378–390.

VEIZER, J., 1983, Trace elements and isotopes in sedimentary carbonates: Reviews in Mineralogy, v. 11, p. 265–300.

VEIZER, J., BRUCKSCHEN, P., PAWALLEK, F., DIENER, A., PODLAHA, O. G., CARDEN, G. A. F., JASPER, T., KORTE, C., STRAUSS, H., AZMY, K., AND ALA, D., 1997, Oxygen isotope evolution of Phanerozoic seawater: Palaeogeography, Palaeoclimatology, Palaeoecology, v. 132, p. 159–172.

WALKER, J. C. G., AND LOHMANN, K. C., 1989, Why the oxygen isotopic composition of sea water changes with time: Geophysical Research Letters, v. 16, p. 323–326.

ZEMPOLICH, W. G., WILKINSON, B. H., AND LOHMANN, K. C., 1988, Diagenesis of Late Proterozoic carbonates: the Beck Springs Dolomite of Eastern California: Journal of Sedimentary Petrology, v. 58, p. 656–672.

SUBJECT INDEX

SUBJECT INDEX